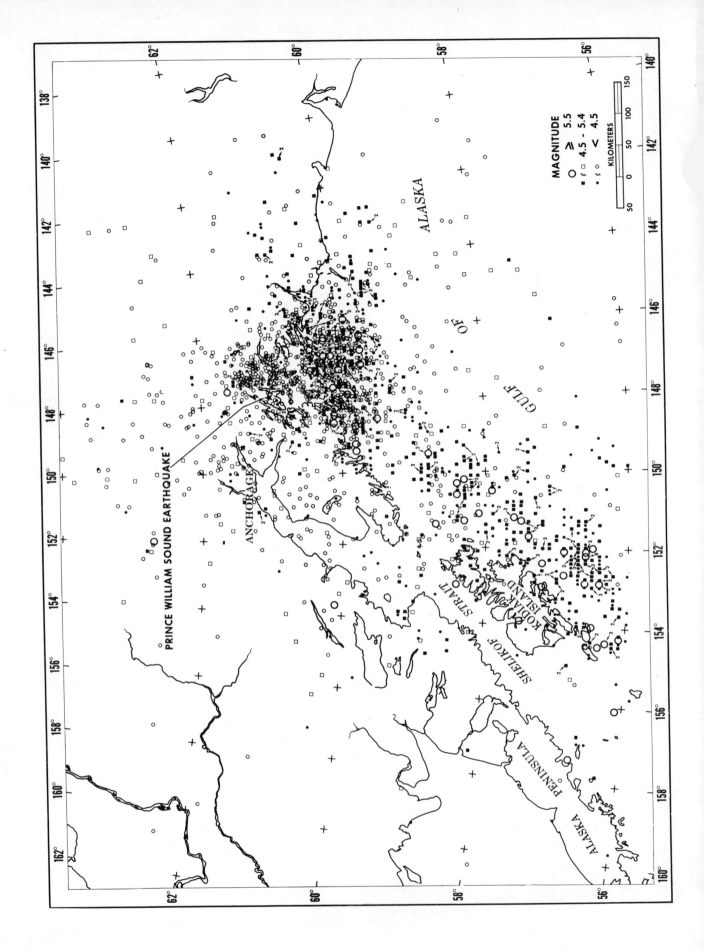

MAGNITUDE

○ ≥ 5.5
■ 4.5 – 5.4
• < 4.5

KILOMETERS

PRINCE WILLIAM SOUND EARTHQUAKE

ANCHORAGE

ALASKA

GULF OF

KODIAK ISLAND

SHELIKOF STRAIT

ALASKA PENINSULA

The Great Alaska Earthquake of 1964

⌐ᵛ·2⌐

COMMITTEE ON THE ALASKA EARTHQUAKE
OF THE
DIVISION OF EARTH SCIENCES
NATIONAL RESEARCH COUNCIL
ⁱⁱ

SEISMOLOGY AND GEODESY

NATIONAL ACADEMY OF SCIENCES
WASHINGTON, D.C.
1972

THE GREAT ALASKA EARTHQUAKE OF 1964

Geology

Seismology and Geodesy

Hydrology

Biology

Oceanography and Coastal Engineering

Engineering

Human Ecology

Summary and Recommendations

Available from
Printing and Publishing Office
National Academy of Sciences
2101 Constitution Avenue
Washington, D.C. 20418

ISBN 0–309–01602–9

Library of Congress Catalog Card Number 68–60037

Printed in the United States of America

FRONTISPIECE   All epicenters located between March 28, 1964, and December 31, 1965. The small open squares and circles are aftershocks located with data from the temporary-station network. All other shocks were located using teleseismic data. (U.S. Coast & Geodetic Survey)

Foreword

Soon after the Alaska earthquake of March 27, 1964, President Lyndon B. Johnson wrote to Donald F. Hornig, his Special Assistant for Science and Technology:

> It is important we learn as many lessons as possible from the disastrous Alaskan earthquake. A scientific understanding of the events that occurred may make it possible to anticipate future earthquakes, there and elsewhere, so as to cope with them more adequately.
>
> I, therefore, request that your office undertake to assemble a comprehensive scientific and technical account of the Alaskan earthquake and its effects. . . .
>
> In defining the scientific and technical questions involved and the related informational requirements for collection and assessment, I hope that you will be able to enlist the aid of the National Academy of Sciences. . . .

In discussions that followed, the Academy was requested by Dr. Hornig to establish the Committee on the Alaska Earthquake, to be charged with three principal tasks—to evaluate efforts being made to gather scientific and engineering information about the earthquake and its effects, to encourage the filling of gaps in the record, and to compile and publish a comprehensive report on the earthquake.

Under the chairmanship of Konrad B. Krauskopf of Stanford University, a twelve-man committee was formed of specialists from related scientific and technical disciplines. Their first meeting was held on June 15, 1964.

The resulting documents, prepared by the Committee and its seven specialized panels, constitute perhaps the most comprehensive and detailed account of an earthquake yet compiled. The Committee has attempted to compile from the available information and analysis a useful resource for present and future scholars in this field. As a result of the present study, much that is new and useful has been learned about earthquakes as well as about natural disasters in general.

In addition to the membership of the central committee, the work of several hundred scientists and engineers is represented in the Committee's report. Many of these are staff members of government agencies that have gathered facts and data about the earthquake and its effects; others are from universities and nongovernmental scientific organizations with an interest in earthquake-related research. Their help and cooperation in making this report possible is deeply appreciated.

PHILIP HANDLER
President
National Academy of Sciences

Preface

South central Alaska (Figure 1), including Prince William Sound and the Aleutian area, is one of the world's most active seismic regions. On March 27, 1964, at about 5:36 p.m. local time (0336, or 3:36 a.m. GMT, March 28), an earthquake of unusual severity struck the Prince William Sound area. Seismologists record earthquake occurrences in Greenwich mean time (GMT). The U.S. Coast and Geodetic Survey, therefore, uses 03h 36m 14.0 ± 0.2s GMT, March 28, 1964, as the time of the earthquake. The coordinates of the epicenter of the main shock have been calculated as lat. $61.04° ± 0.05°$N and long. $147.73° ± 0.07°$W, and the focus was within a few tens of kilometers of the surface. Not only was this earthquake of large magnitude (between 8.3 and 8.6 on the Richter scale, on which the greatest known earthquake is 8.9), but its duration (3 to 4 minutes) and the area of its damage zone (50,000 mi²) were extraordinary. Probably twice as much energy was released by the Alaska earthquake as by the one that rocked San Francisco in 1906.

The shock was felt over 500,000 mi². A tsunami (a train of long waves impulsively generated, in this case by movement of the sea floor) or "tidal wave" swept from the Gulf of Alaska across the length of the Pacific and lapped against Antarctica. Water levels in wells as far away as South Africa jumped abruptly, and shock-induced waves were generated in the Gulf of Mexico. An atmospheric pressure wave caused by the earthquake was recorded at La Jolla, California, more than 2,000 mi away. Seismic surface waves, with periods of many seconds, moved the ground surface of most of the North American continent by as much as 2 in.

The magnitude of the earthquake can be calculated only from teleseismic records, and its duration can be estimated only from eyewitness accounts, because no seismic instruments capable of recording strong ground motion were in Alaska at the time. The range of uncertainty in the magnitude calculations (8.3–8.6) is far greater in terms of energy release than the figures suggest; from the most generally accepted relation of magnitude to energy release, it can be calculated that magnitude 8.6 represents approximately twice the energy release of magnitude 8.3.

Measured crustal deformation was more extensive than the deformation related to any known previous earthquake. Areas of uplift and subsidence were separated by a line of zero land-level change trending both southwestward and eastward from the vicinity of the epicenter, about 80 mi east-southeast of Anchorage; this line parallels the major tectonic features of the region. Areas north and northwest of the zero line subsided as much as 7.5 ft; areas south and southeast rose, over wide areas, as much as 6 ft. Locally the uplift was much greater: 38 ft on Montague Island and more than 50 ft on the sea floor southwest of the island. The zone of uplift was along the continental margin of the Aleutian Trench. Not only was the earth's crust displaced vertically, but horizontal movements of tens of feet took place, in which the landmass moved southeastward relative to the ocean floor. The area of crustal deformation was more than 100,000 mi².

The mechanism of the earthquake remains to some extent uncertain. Fault-plane solutions for the main shock and the principal aftershocks, of which there were 10 of magnitudes greater than 6.0 within 24 hr after the initial shock, are consistent either with thrusting of the continent over the ocean floor along a plane dipping 5°–15° north or northwest, or with downward slip of the continent along a near-vertical plane; in either case the strike of the fault is northeast in the vicinity of Kodiak Island to east in Prince William Sound, parallel to the dominant tectonic trend. Although the fault-plane solutions do not permit an unambiguous decision between the two possible planes, several other lines of evidence strongly favor the low-angle thrust alternative.

The strong ground motion induced many snowslides, rockfalls, and landslides, both subaerial and submarine. The submarine landslides created local sea waves or tsunamis, which, together with the major tsunami generated by the crustal deformation, smashed port and harbor facilities,

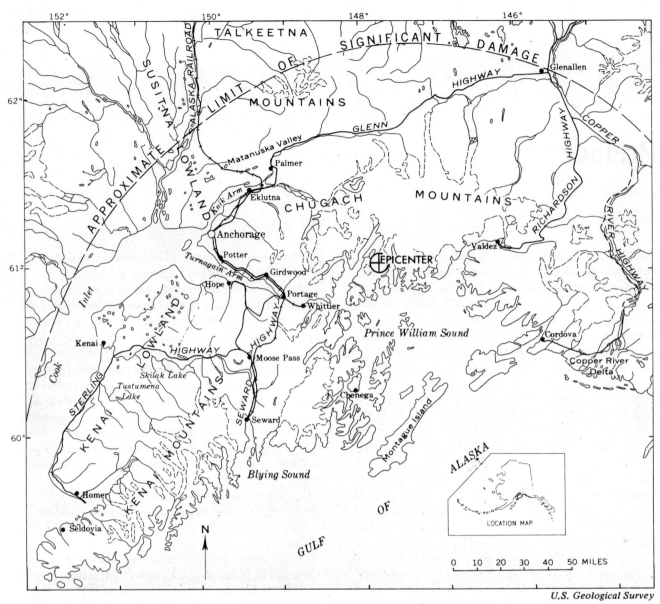

FIGURE 1 Map of south central Alaska.

covered sessile organisms and salmon-spawning beds with silt, disturbed and killed salmon fry, leveled forests, and caused saltwater invasion of many coastal freshwater lakes.

The tectonic elevation and depression caused extensive damage to the biota of coastal forests, migratory-bird nesting grounds, salmon-spawning waters and gravels, as well as shellfish habitats, and initiated long-term changes in littoral and stream morphology. Clams, barnacles, algae, and many other marine and littoral organisms perished in areas of uplift. Spawning beds, trees, and other vegetation were destroyed in areas of depression.

Except for the major tsunami, which caused extensive damage in British Columbia and took 16 lives in Oregon

and California, violence to man and his structures was restricted to the area of tectonic land-level change. Tsunamis, major and local, took the most lives. Landslides caused the most damage.

The number of lives lost in Alaska, 115, was very small for an earthquake of this magnitude. Factors that contributed to the light loss of life were the sparse population, the fortuitous timing of the earthquake, a low tide, the absence of fire in residential and business areas, the generally clement weather, and the fact that the earthquake occurred during the off-season for fishing. The earthquake came on the evening of a holiday, when the schools were empty and most offices deserted, but when most people were still wearing their warm clothing. The low tide and the absence of fishermen and cannery workers mitigated the destruction and loss of life from tsunamis.

Public and private property loss was over $300 million. Hundreds of homes were destroyed. A multistory apartment building (fortunately not occupied), a department store, and other buildings in Anchorage collapsed. Oil storage tanks at Valdez, Seward, and Whittier ruptured and burned. Many other structures were destroyed or damaged. Most of downtown Kodiak was inundated by the major tsunami.

Damage to surface transportation facilities was extensive. The Alaska Railroad lost its port facility at Whittier, its docks at Seward, and numerous bridges on the Kenai Peninsula. Many highway bridges, especially on the Seward and Copper River highways, were damaged. Many port and harbor facilities, especially at Seward, Valdez, Kodiak, Whittier, Cordova, and Homer, were destroyed.

The earthquake crippled Alaska's economy because nearly half the people of the state live within the damage area and because the land- and sea-transport facilities on which the economy depends were knocked out.

Relief came quickly. The extensive military establishment proved a great source of strength in implementing emergency measures designed to reduce the loss of life, to ease immediate suffering, and to restore needed services promptly. Financial assistance for relief purposes was provided immediately by the Office of Emergency Planning under provisions of the Federal Disaster Act.

Recovery was rapid. Of major importance in the reconstruction effort was a congressional program to provide additional federal aid not possible under existing authority. This program was recommended by the Federal Reconstruction and Development Planning Commission for Alaska, a unique body appointed by President Lyndon B. Johnson on April 2, 1964. The additional aid included transitional grants to maintain essential public services; an increase in the federal share of highway reconstruction costs; a decrease in the local share of urban renewal projects; debt adjustments on existing federal loans; federal purchase of state bonds; and grants for a state mortgage-forgiveness program. An estimated $330 million of government and private funds financed Alaska's recovery from the earthquake.

The Alaska earthquake is the best documented and most thoroughly studied earthquake in history. Attempts have been made to draw lessons from both the physical event and the human experience. Strong-motion seismographs and accelerographs were installed in Alaska shortly after the earthquake, providing a basis for study of the stronger aftershocks. The tsunami warning system for the North Pacific was greatly improved within a few months, mainly by establishment of three new seismograph stations in south central Alaska as the basic elements in the system. Risk maps for Anchorage, Homer, Seward, and Valdez, based upon exten-

sive geological studies, were prepared by the Scientific and Engineering Task Force of the Reconstruction Commission and were used discriminatingly as a basis for federal aid to reconstruction and as guides to future builders. The entire town of Valdez was relocated. Communities and state and professional organizations in seismic areas outside Alaska reexamined codes and programs related to earthquake hazard in light of the Alaska experience. Finally, the Alaska earthquake turned the nation's attention again, and sharply, to the problems of improving the elements of a national natural-disaster policy: zoning and construction codes; prediction and warning systems; rescue and relief organizations; disaster-data collection and analysis; and disaster insurance and reconstruction aids.

Thus the earthquake had many facets. It was a natural scientific experiment on a grand scale, providing data on a variety of long-standing problems regarding the mechanism and effects of earthquakes. It served as a test of man-made structures under extreme conditions, and as a guide to improvements in the location and design of such structures to make them better able to withstand seismic shocks. It was an object lesson in human response to disaster, pointing the way to increased effectiveness of warning systems, of emergency measures during disasters, and of relief and recovery operations.

The charge to the Committee on the Alaska Earthquake was made to ensure that as much technical and scientific information as possible would be wrung from the earthquake experience and that the results would be assembled into a comprehensive report. At its first meeting the Committee decided that its initial task of evaluating and encouraging efforts to gather scientific and technical information could best be carried out by panels representing the major disciplines involved in the data-gathering: engineering, geography (human ecology), geology, hydrology, oceanography, and seismology. Biology, at first included within oceanography, was later made the basis of a separate panel.

As information for a comprehensive report accumulated, it became clear that the report itself could most appropriately follow the panel structure. Accordingly, this report appears in eight volumes, seven put together by the separate panels and a summary volume prepared by the full Committee.

In the early meetings of the Committee, and especially as it became apparent that many of the physical-science and some of the engineering aspects of the earthquake would be treated comprehensively in government publications and individual studies, there was considerable discussion of the appropriate content of the Committee's final report.

The Committee finally decided that the advantages of having available, under one cover and in one place in a library, a truly comprehensive report on the earthquake would justify the expense of duplicating some material already published. In addition, the Committee agreed, a complete report would provide a better basis for the inclusion of cross-disciplinary papers, for pointing out lessons learned from the Alaska experience, and for making recommendations designed to reduce the loss of life and property in subsequent major earthquakes.

As a model for its work, the Committee could look back to the classic report on the 1906 San Francisco earthquake, published by the Carnegie Institution in 1908. To emulate the comprehensiveness of this magnificent report seemed possible, but not the unity and coherence that it gained from the encyclopedic knowledge of its editor and principal author, A. C. Lawson. The breadth and depth of scientific interest in earthquakes have increased so greatly since 1906 that no one man can hope to master, as Lawson did, a great part of existing technical knowledge on all aspects of earthquakes. A report today must necessarily have many authors and must reflect in its length and diversity the extraordinary development of disciplines and instruments over the past half century.

Despite the Committee's attempt to make the report broadly comprehensive, there are unfortunate and obvious gaps in the record, mainly in those subject-matter fields not included in the work of government agencies. Such gaps are identified in the appropriate volumes of the report.

Apart from these gaps, the report covers a wide variety of subjects in engineering, natural science, and social science. Ranging from seismology to human ecology, it sets forth what is known about the structure of the earth's crust in south central Alaska, especially in relation to possible earthquake mechanisms and to tsunami generation; describes the effects of the earthquake on geologic processes, rocks, and soils; outlines the seismic history of Alaska and gives the seismic parameters of the earthquake; presents the results of energy-release, strain-release, and focal-mechanism studies of the main shock and aftershocks; describes the effects of the earthquake on groundwater and surface-water bodies and on glaciers and snowfields; discusses the generation, propagation, and effects of earthquake-induced tsunamis; describes immediate as well as long-term effects on plants and animals of abrupt land elevation and depression and of slides and tsunamis; sets forth in detail, with analyses, the response of man-made structures to the earthquake; chronicles in narrative form both the physical and human events of the earthquake; describes the impact of the earthquake on individuals, communities, and organizations; and puts forward recommendations that range from geologic mapping for hazard zoning, through methods of assuring site-suited earthquake-resistant construction, to means of improving the human response to disaster.

This volume, one of the eight into which the report is divided, describes the results of studies on the mechanisms

of the earthquake and on the land displacements that it produced. Quite apart from its destructive aspects, the earthquake can be viewed as a natural scientific experiment on a huge scale, and the papers herein are a record of data obtained and conclusions drawn from the experiment.

As a scientific experiment, an earthquake has the disadvantage that its time and exact place of occurrence cannot be predicted, so that adequate preparations are hard to make. This difficulty is especially serious for a major seismic event like the Alaska earthquake, in that most seismographs are not adapted for recording violent ground movement. In Alaska every instrument within a radius of several hundred kilometers was thrown off scale shortly after the first shock. Details of the ground motion, important both for scientific study of the earthquake mechanism and for engineering evaluation of building response, were thus impossible to obtain. Hence, the insistent and repeated recommendation in the papers of this volume that the number of strong-motion instruments in seismically active areas be greatly increased so that records of ground movement in future large earthquakes will not be lost.

Among the scientific conclusions recorded in these papers, several represent new contributions to seismologic knowledge or a marshaling of evidence for older ideas more complete than has been heretofore obtained. Especially notable is the strong support for a model in which the earthquake resulted from movement along a low-angle thrust fault dipping northwestward under the mainland, a kind of movement consistent with current ideas about the behavior of crustal blocks at continental margins around the Pacific. The thrust-fault hypothesis is not yet established beyond all doubt, as is shown by two papers favoring the alternative vertical-fault idea, but the papers providing many-sided evidence for thrust movement build a case that is difficult to refute. The indication from P-wave first motions that the earthquake was a multiple-fracture event—that is, rock breakage spreading from the hypocenter in two directions by a series of fractures—is similar to conjectures from previous earthquakes, but the evidence has never before been so complete. Unusually good evidence is also presented in two papers for the excitation of free oscillations of the earth by the earthquake. Atmospheric waves coupled with surface waves in the ground have been noted for other earthquakes, but the Alaska event is the first for which seismic air waves set up near the epicenter and traveling long distances in the atmosphere have been identified. Also for the first time earthquake-generated disturbances of the ionosphere were noted, disturbances similar to those that have been described from nuclear explosions. In the papers on geodesy the evidence is particularly striking for relatively enormous horizontal displacements of the land surface, greater than those measured for any previous earthquake, in addition to the more obvious elevation and subsidence of large areas.

Besides these major conclusions from the seismologic and geodetic investigations, the papers in this volume suggest other more tentative conclusions that will need verification by comparison of the data compiled here with data from future earthquakes. Like any successful large-scale scientific experiment, the Alaska earthquake has thus provided a number of new generalizations, abundant confirmation of older ideas, and hints of further generalizations that must be tested in the future.

Some topics ordinarily treated in the seismologic literature are not fully covered here, but appear in other volumes of the report. Many aspects of the Pacific-wide tsunami generated by the earthquake are described in the Oceanography and Coastal Engineering volume, as well as seaquakes and *T*-phases. Seiches that affected surface waters in lakes, rivers, and bays even at great distances from the epicenter, changes in level of underground water observed on well-level recorders in many parts of the world, and avalanches precipitated by the earthquake, are included in the Hydrology volume. The Engineering volume, although focused on the behavior of man-made structures, contains data on the response of soils and rocks to vibration and sliding. And the Geology volume has descriptions of the spectacular damage caused by subaerial and submarine landslides triggered by the earth tremors, as well as information on the tectonic elevations and depressions of the land surface that supplements material contained in the present volume.

The Committee has tried to bring together here the more important papers that have been written on the seismologic phenomena and geodetic measurements associated with one of the strongest earthquakes ever recorded in North America. For details not reproduced here, numerous references and an annotated bibliography provide a guide to other sources.

KONRAD B. KRAUSKOPF
Stanford University

EDITORIAL NOTE

Although the Committee has used Donald J. Orth's 1967 *Dictionary of Alaska Place Names*, U.S. Geological Survey Professional Paper 567, to standardize the spelling of place names in its report, the reader may still detect alternate spellings, such as Ouzinkie in one place and Uzinki in another. Such differences result largely from our decision to reproduce a sizable portion of this volume directly from the pages of the original publications in which they appeared. Changes in the articles were made for the purpose of clarification.

Seismologists use a universal time, such as Greenwich Mean Time (GMT), or Universal Time (UT), to record the onset of earthquakes and the arrival of the various shock waves around the world. Because GMT is 10 hours later than Alaska Standard Time (AST), the Alaska earthquake, which to most people occurred at about 5:36 p.m. (AST), March 27, 1964, is recorded by seismologists at about 3:36 a.m. (GMT), March 28, 1964.

Acknowledgments

The Committee on the Alaska Earthquake and the Panel on Seismology are particularly indebted to the National Science Foundation, the former U.S. Coast and Geodetic Survey, the U.S. Geological Survey, the Office of Emergency Preparedness, the Army Research Office, the Atomic Energy Commission, the Advanced Research Projects Agency, the Office of Naval Research, the Office of Civil Defense, and the Department of Transportation for support of the Committee under Contract NSF C-310, Task Order 89; to the Department of Housing and Urban Development for similar support under Contract H-1229; to the Department of the Interior for special support; and to the National Science Foundation for publication support under Contract NSF C-310, Task Order 208; and also to those agencies with projects that culminated in papers appearing in this volume.

The Committee and Panel greatly appreciate the time and effort provided by Bruce A. Bolt, Benjamin F. Howell, Jr., and Jack Oliver and his colleagues for their comments and suggestions as reviewers for the Division of Earth Sciences.

They are also grateful to the American Association for the Advancement of Science, the American Geophysical Union, MacMillan (Journals) Ltd., the North-Holland Publishing Co., the Seismological Society of America, Sylvania Electric Products, Inc., the University of Hawaii, the University of Hawaii Press, the former U.S. Coast and Geodetic Survey, and the U.S. Geological Survey for the use of their previously published professional papers, journal articles, and previously unpublished materials.

The Panel thanks the various government and private organizations that made available the time of the authors whose works make up the volume. Special recognition is due the former U.S. Environmental Science Services Administration, the former U.S. Coast and Geodetic Survey, the University of Alaska, the California Institute of Technology, Sylvania Electric Products, Inc., and Saint Louis University for making it possible for some of their personnel to serve as Panel members, authors, and reviewers. Similarly, the Panel expresses its appreciation to Stanford University, the California Institute of Technology, Texas A&M University, the University of Hawaii, the U.S. Geological Survey, The Geological Society of America, The Ohio State University, the University of Colorado, the former U.S. Bureau of Commercial Fisheries, the University of Southern California, Clark University, the University of California, and the former U.S. Environmental Science Services Administration for making available their personnel for service on the parent Committee; and also to the Office of Science and Technology, the National Science Foundation, the Department of Defense, the former U.S. Coast and Geodetic Survey, the U.S. Geological Survey, the Office of Emergency Preparedness, and the Atomic Energy Commission for the time and assistance provided by their liaison representatives to the Committee.

The Panel is grateful to the University of Idaho, the U.S. Geological Survey, and Emory University for making the services of editors and indexers available; to the former U.S. Coast and Geodetic Survey, the U.S. Geological Survey, and the U.S. Army Corps of Engineers for assistance with maps and illustrations; to the U.S. Army and the U.S. Air Force for transportation to the affected areas; and to the University of Nevada, the former U.S. Environmental Science Services Administration, and the University of Arizona for furnishing meeting places for the Panel on Seismology.

Since 1964, reorganizations within federal agencies and departments have involved several of the Committee's supporting agencies. On July 13, 1965, the U.S. Coast and Geodetic Survey (USC&GS) and other component agencies were combined to form the Environmental Science Services Administration (ESSA), under the Department of Commerce. On October 3, 1970, ESSA together with several other organizations, including elements of the Department of the Interior's U.S. Bureau of Commercial Fisheries (BCF), became the National Oceanic and Atmospheric Administration (NOAA), also under the Department of Commerce. Although the USC&GS, ESSA, and BCF no longer exist as organizations, their names are used for historical accuracy, as is that of the Office of Emergency Planning, which was renamed the Office of Emergency Preparedness on October 21, 1968.

Contents

IV. RELATED GEOPHYSICAL EFFECTS

V. SUMMARY AND CONCLUSIONS

[xvii]

General Introduction: Tectonics and Seismic Effects of the Alaska Earthquake and the Seismicity of Alaska

The 1964 Alaska earthquake resulted from a major dislocation in the rock in, and possibly also beneath, the earth's crust. Movement began abruptly some distance below the earth's surface in the region north of Prince William Sound. Initially the rupture progressed in various directions from the starting point, but the principal advance, and that of longest duration, was in a southwesterly direction toward, and perhaps beyond, Kodiak Island. The progression of rupture was fitful, so that seismograms of great complexity were written by seismographs of magnification low enough that they were not driven completely off scale by the initial elastic waves. Gross distortions of the surface of the earth can be seen in the silent testimony of the shorelines of south central Alaska, here depressed, here uplifted, with permanent vertical movements amounting to more than 10 m in some places and to several meters over wide areas. Careful geodetic observations have revealed horizontal displacements of the land amounting to as much as 20 m.

In addition to producing elastic waves of unusual amplitude and complexity in the solid earth, the earthquake set up gravity waves in the waters in and adjacent to Prince William Sound that crossed the Pacific Ocean. The earthquake also caused acoustic-gravity waves in the atmosphere, which propagated to great distances after being launched as high as the ionosphere from the earth's surface near the epicenter. Examples of seldom-described effects were widespread and numerous, and the opportunities for the advancement of knowledge were great in several fields ordinarily not greatly concerned with seismic phenomena. Thus the complete report of the Committee on the Alaska Earthquake includes entire volumes devoted to studies in hydrology, biology, oceanography, and human ecology—disciplines that are represented in reports of lesser seismic events by a few paragraphs, if indeed they are mentioned at all.

The seismographic record of this earthquake is woefully incomplete, particularly with regard to the measurement of the amplitudes and periods of the elastic waves in the macroseismic region. On March 28, 1964, there were no strong-motion seismographs operating anywhere in the state of Alaska; all existing seismographs of any description within hundreds of kilometers of Prince William Sound were driven off scale within seconds of the arrival of the first impulses of the earthquake. As a result, accurate information on the motions of the ground at destructive levels—information important both to the engineers responsible for improving the structural design of buildings in earthquake-prone regions and to the seismologists attempting to study the physical mechanism operative in the vicinity of the focus of the shock—is not available from this major event. Once again, seismologists and earthquake engineers jointly lament the missing of a rare opportunity to improve human knowledge in a vital area because of the lack of a comparatively small number of inexpensive strong-motion instruments. The seismologists and engineers most directly concerned with studies employing strong-motion information have learned and relearned the obvious lesson in many previous earthquakes. They cannot correct the situation, however, without the sympathetic understanding of officials of the executive and legislative branches of government, who must approve the appropriations necessary for what has historically been regarded as a prosaic program.

[1]

THE WORK OF THE PANEL
ON SEISMOLOGY

The earliest seismological studies of the 1964 Alaska earthquake, although preliminary in nature, had already appeared in print (U.S. Coast and Geodetic Survey, 1964) before the first meeting of the Committee on the Alaska Earthquake in Washington, D.C. (June 15, 1964), and it was by then obvious that many scientists in the United States and other countries would be making investigations of a number of the myriad effects of this major tectonic event. A Seismology Working Group was convened at Anchorage, Alaska, as an adjunct to the second meeting of the Committee, August 28–30, 1964. The Working Group was asked to outline the scope of the seismological studies that should be included in the Committee's report of the earthquake, to identify gaps in the overall program of seismic studies, and to suggest ways in which those gaps might be closed. The working group was composed of four future members of the Panel on Seismology and one of the Panel on Geology: Don Tocher, *Chairman*; S. T. Algermissen; Clarence R. Allen; Eduard Berg; and James Brune. Their report to the Committee served as the basis for the later work of the Panel on Seismology and also as a guide to the selection of members of that Panel. In the division of responsibilities among the various panels, the parent Committee initially assigned responsibility for geodetic studies to the Panel on Geology. By December 1964, selection of members of the Panel on Seismology was completed and tentative areas of responsibility assigned:

Don Tocher, Earthquake Mechanism Laboratory, U.S. Coast and Geodetic Survey (now Environmental Research Laboratories, National Oceanic and Atmospheric Administration), *Chairman*, earthquake mechanisms

S. T. Algermissen, U.S. Coast and Geodetic Survey (now Earth Science Laboratories, Environmental Research Laboratories, NOAA), aftershocks, engineering seismology

Eduard Berg, The University of Alaska, crust-mantle structure

James N. Brune, California Institute of Technology (now with the University of California, San Diego), main-shock parameters, tsunamis

Stewart W. Smith, California Institute of Technology (now with the University of Washington), magnitude, related geophysical effects

William V. Stauder, Saint Louis University, main-shock parameters

Colin O. Hines, The University of Chicago, atmospheric and ionospheric waves. Late in 1965, Dr. Hines resigned from the Panel, and was succeeded by:

Ronald V. Row, Sylvania Electronics Systems, atmospheric and ionospheric waves

The organization of the Panel and assignment of individual

responsibilities was accomplished at its first meeting in Albuquerque, New Mexico, on January 14, 1965. At this meeting, great emphasis was placed on the need for close coordination of the Panel's efforts with those of other panels, especially those on Geology and Engineering, so that unnecessary duplication of coverage would be avoided in the Committee's final report and so that topics that might fall between the areas of responsibility of two or more panels would not be neglected.

Efforts were made, after the Anchorage meeting of the Seismology Working Group, to stimulate the making of a reversed seismic refraction profile from Anchorage to the Gulf of Alaska to provide information on the seismic structure of the earth's crust in the aftershock region. These attempts were abandoned when it became evident that the study could not command sufficient financial support within the normal procedures of any of the federal agencies that support research projects relevant to their respective missions.

In view of the dim prospects for such a profile, the Panel recommended to the parent Committee that a substitute program of seismic calibration be carried out, and that this be done before the scheduled mid-1965 dismantling of the temporary network of seismographs being operated in southern Alaska by the U.S. Coast and Geodetic Survey. The Committee endorsed this recommendation on February 12, 1965. However, despite all efforts, sufficient support could not be generated for the desired seismic calibration program; as a result, a considerable gap still exists in our knowledge of the seismic structure of the earth's crust and upper mantle in the region of the epicenter of the main shock of March 28, 1964, and its aftershocks.

Most questions regarding topical coverage by the several panels, and the handling of overlapping of material, were resolved during the Panel's first year of life, largely through a series of joint meetings of the Panel Chairman with other panels and their chairmen. During the first half of the Panel's existence, concern was expressed several times that the results of geodetic resurveys in south central Alaska should be published in the same volume of the Committee's report as papers describing field observations of the gross movements of the earth's surface. By mutual agreement between the chairmen of the Panels on Geology and Seismology, Committee Chairman Krauskopf in the autumn of 1967 reassigned responsibility for geodetic studies from the Panel on Geology to the Panel on Seismology. With this reassignment of responsibilities, the Panel volume's subtitle was changed to Seismology and Geodesy, and the Panel gained an additional member:

Charles A. Whitten, U.S. Coast and Geodetic Survey, now Office of National Geodetic Survey, NOAA, geodesy

Scientific articles in the seismological literature, which touch in one way or another on the Alaska earthquake of

March 28, 1964, by now number several hundred. In making its selection of this volume's contents, the Panel has excluded articles of only marginal relevance to this shock; in a few instances, studies that included information on other shocks as well as the Alaska earthquake were revised or rewritten at the Panel's request, especially for inclusion in this volume. With these exceptions, and with the further exception of the section introductions contributed by Panel members, much of the material in this volume has previously appeared elsewhere, albeit in some instances with Panel stimulation. Other related articles are referenced in the Annotated Bibliography.

SEISMOGRAMS OF THE MAIN SHOCK

The *Atlas of Maps and Seismograms Accompanying the Report of the State Earthquake Investigation Commission upon the California Earthquake of April 18, 1906,* published by the Carnegie Institution of Washington in 1908 (and reprinted in 1969), was an especially valuable adjunct to the classic report on that earthquake. In describing the collection and reproduction of the seismograms of the 1906 earthquake, Professor Harry Fielding Reid remarked that "The intensity of the shock was so great that practically all seismographs, situated in any part of the world, recorded it." Even at that relatively early date in the history of seismometry, Fielding Reid was able to obtain data from 96 seismographic stations around the world and included reproductions of seismograms in the *Atlas,* those from 71 in their original size. Although all types of seismographs represented in the *Atlas* were primitive by 1964 standards, many of those records contain a great deal of useful information on the 1906 earthquake; except for stations near the epicenter, relatively few of the seismograms reproduced by Fielding Reid were off scale. On those that were off scale, generally only the maxima of the long-period surface waves were too large to be successfully recorded.

Great advances were made in the field of seismometry in the years between the California Earthquake of 1906 and the Alaska Earthquake of 1964, both in the numbers of active stations and in the magnification of the instruments in general use around the world. In describing seismograms of the earthquake of March 28, 1964, that most of the Panel members had seen by the time of the first meeting of the Panel in January 1965, it would be a fair paraphrase of Fielding Reid's statement to say that the intensity of the shock was so great that practically all seismographs, situated in any part of the world, went off scale shortly after the first preliminary waves arrived. For this reason, there was general agreement at that meeting that the final report of the Committee on the Alaska Earthquake should not include a section of reproductions of seismograms as long as most apparently carried little useful information beyond the times of arrival of the first preliminary waves. It later became apparent, however, that important

studies had been done that made use of other information gleaned from seismograms of the Alaska earthquake. In particular, Wyss and Brune (1967, and this volume) used seismograms from low-magnification instruments at 70 stations in their analysis of the complexity of the failure mechanism that was operative in the source region. A subpanel was therefore appointed at the Panel's sixth meeting, December 1967, to make the necessary selection from available collections of seismograms, to annotate the selected records, and to assemble and edit such necessary ancillary information as on magnification and timing, for a group of seismograms to be reproduced as an appendix to this volume. It has not, however, proved economically feasible to reproduce meaningful numbers of useful records at full scale. Instead, the assemblage of low-magnification seismograms collected by Wyss and Brune at the California Institute of Technology has been archived at the U.S. National Geophysical Data Center. High quality photographic copies of these records, of records from the cooperating stations of the World-Wide Network of Standard Seismographs, and of additional seismograms from low-magnification instruments available from the permanent collection of the National Oceanic and Atmospheric Administration, can be obtained at nominal cost from:

> Data Archives and Distribution (DS624)
> NOAA, EDS, National Geophysical Data Center
> Seismological Data Division
> Federal Building
> Asheville, North Carolina 28801

Information on seismograms available and on prices of copies on 35-mm and 70-mm film chips or on full size photographic copies can be obtained from the above address.

CONTRIBUTIONS TO SEISMOLOGIC KNOWLEDGE IN RELATED VOLUMES

Some topics ordinarily treated in the seismological literature are not covered fully in the present volume, but are discussed at length in other volumes of *The Great Alaska Earthquake of 1964.* Thus, many aspects of the Pacific-wide tsunami generated by the Alaska earthquake are described in the Oceanography volume; the same volume contains information on seaquakes, seiches, and T-phases. Ground movements associated with the earthquake affected underground and surface waters in many parts of the world. Seiches disturbed surface waters in lakes, rivers, and bays, and changes in level, both oscillatory and permanent, were observed on well-level recorders in many wells distributed widely around the world; descriptions of these effects, as well as of the remarkable avalanches precipitated by the earthquake, are to be found in the Hydrology volume. The Geology volume includes descriptions of the spectacular damage caused by landslides, both submarine and subaerial, triggered by the earth tremors, and also contains considerable information on the tectonic elevations and depressions of the land surface in addition to that to be found in the present volume.

THE SEISMICITY OF ALASKA

The earliest extant reports of earthquakes in Alaska are fragmentary and noninstrumental in character. In the distribution of their origins, these early reports closely reflect the distribution of nonindigenous settlers of the Aleutian Islands and coastal Alaska. The earliest permanent settlements were established by the Russians on Kodiak Island in 1783, and on Cook Inlet in 1788; the oldest report we have of an earthquake is associated with an eruption of Pavlof Volcano on the Alaska Peninsula in 1786. Most earthquake reports for the next 50 years are of earthquakes associated with volcanic eruptions on the Alaska Peninsula and the Aleutian Islands. Thus, rather than giving us a clear picture of the distribution of earthquakes throughout the entire area now included in the State of Alaska, these early reports merely reflect the fact that the early Russian settlers, and the indigenous Alaskans with whom they did business, confined their activities to the places where fish and fur-bearing mammals were to be had most easily.

The pattern of settlement established by the Russians—widely scattered villages on the islands and inlets of the southern coast and the inner Aleutian Islands, followed by a few villages on Norton Sound and along the Yukon River—remained largely unchanged for a quarter of a century following the purchase of Alaska from Russia by the United States in 1867. After gold was discovered in the Klondike in the 1890's, the pattern of settlement changed to one of filling in the gaps, at least in the southern half of mainland Alaska. As the trend of population growth turned inland, the number of felt earthquakes reported increased sharply. Even today, however, large segments of northern Alaska and the Aleutian Islands are inhabited so sparsely that only a very distorted picture of the seismicity of Alaska can be obtained from consideration of reports of felt earthquakes. Tabulations and summaries of felt earthquakes and damage reports from Alaska earthquakes and attendant tsunamis are readily available in publications by Eppley (1965, p. 86–98) and, in more extended form, by the U.S. Coast and Geodetic Survey (1966, p. 11–73).

In terms of energy release, most of Alaska's seismic activity is associated with the Aleutian–Alaskan Arc. The Arc extends from the Commander Islands near Kamchatka, eastward across the northern edge of the Pacific Ocean to the Alaska Peninsula, and into southern Alaska. The Aleutian–Alaskan Arc exhibits most of the distinguishing features of typical Pacific arcuate structures. In the classification given by

Richter (1958), these features are, from south to north: (a) the deep oceanic trench or foredeep; (b) the belt of negative gravity anomalies and epicenters of shallow earthquakes and the nonvolcanic anticline, which in the western part of the Arc appears typically as a bench between the trench and the main arc of islands, but in the east begins to emerge above sea level as islands south of the main arc; (c) a belt of positive gravity anomalies and intermediate depth earthquakes; (d) the main arc of islands, punctuated with numerous active and dormant volcanoes, with earthquakes beneath the line of volcanoes at depths typically 60–100 km. The deeper earthquakes characterizing features (e) and (f) of the Pacific-type arc structure have not been detected in Alaska to date.

The relation of earthquake hypocenters to these arcuate features near the eastern end of the Arc have been investigated recently in some detail by Tobin and Sykes (1966). They made careful redeterminations of hypocentral coordinates of about 300 earthquakes in mainland Alaska, the Alaska Peninsula, and adjacent offshore areas during the decade immediately preceding the 1964 earthquake.

Intermediate-depth earthquakes, occurring at depths of from 70 km to no greater than 170 km, constituted about 20 percent of the events investigated by Tobin and Sykes (1966). A narrow zone of intermediate-depth earthquakes was traced from the Aleutians to the Alaska Peninsula and into central Alaska beneath the Alaska Range and Cook Inlet lowlands. The northern boundary of the zone of intermediate-depth shocks coincides approximately with the Denali fault zone. The Aleutian Range volcanoes are located over the intermediate-depth earthquakes, but these earthquakes extend some 250 km beyond the northern limits of present volcanism. The remaining earthquakes in the Tobin and Sykes (1966) study were assigned depths of less than 70 km. Their epicenters are concentrated in a belt extending from the Alaska Peninsula and adjacent offshore areas into central Alaska. This zone of shallow activity seems to be distinct from the shallow earthquake activity of southeast Alaska. A few earthquakes were located on the Seward Peninsula, but no events were detected anywhere in Alaska north of lat. 68°N.

The panhandle of southeast Alaska is characterized by block tectonics, with none of the arc features described above.

The great Yakutat Bay earthquakes of September 1899 apparently had hypocenters near the junction of the Aleutian-Alaskan Arc and the block tectonic zone of southeast Alaska. These shocks were the earliest in Alaska for which instrumental determinations of hypocenters were possible. In all probability, no great earthquakes (M > 7.7) since 1899 are missing from the available tabulations of earthquakes in Alaska (Gutenberg and Richter, 1954; Richter, 1958; Rothé, 1969). Table 1 includes all identified Alaska earthquakes with surface-wave magnitude (M) greater than 7.7 from 1899 through 1965, and all identified Alaska shocks with M ≥ 7

TABLE 1 Instrumentally Determined Epicenters of Large Earthquakes in Alaska

Date	Origin Time GMT hr min sec	Location		Depth km	M	Date	Origin Time GMT hr min sec	Location		Depth km	M
Great Earthquakes (M > 7.7), 1899–1917						Major Earthquakes (M ≥ 7.0), 1918–1965					
1899 Sept. 4	00:22	60N	142W		8.3	1944 July 27	00:04:23	54N	165½W	70	7.1
1899 Sept. 10	17:04	60N	140W		7.8	1944 Dec. 12	04:17:10	51½N	179½E		7.0
1899 Sept. 10	21:41	60N	140W		8.6	1946 Jan. 12	20:25:37	59¼N	147¼W	50	7.2
1900 Oct. 9	12:28	60N	142W		8.3	1946 Apr. 1	12:28:54	52¾N	163½W		7.4
1901 Dec. 31	09:02	52N	177W		7.8	1946 Nov. 1	11:14:24	51½N	174½W	40	7.0
1902 Jan. 1	05:20	55N	165W		7.8	1947 Oct. 16	02:09:47	64½N	147½W		7
1904 Aug. 27	21:56.1	64N	151W		8.3	1948 May 14	22:31:43	54½N	161W		7.5
1905 Feb. 14	08:46.6	53N	178W		7.9	1949 Feb. 2	17:41:29	53N	173W	220	7.0
1906 Aug. 17	00:10.7	51N	179E		8.0	1949 Sept. 27	15:30:45	59¾N	149W	50	7.0
1907 Sept. 2	16:01.5	52N	173E		7¾	1951 Feb. 13	22:12:57	56N	156W		7.1
						1953 Jan. 5	07:48:18	54.0N	170.5E	n*	7.1
						1955 Mar. 14	13:12:14	52.5N	173.5W	75	7.0
Major Earthquakes (M ≥ 7.0), 1918–1965						1957 Jan. 2	03:48:50	53.0N	168.0W	n	7.0
						1957 Mar. 9	14:22:28	51.3N	175.8W	n	8.2
1923 May 4	16:26:39	55½N	156½W		7.1	1957 Mar. 9	20:39:18	52.8N	169.6W	n	7.1
1925 Aug. 19	12:07:27	55¼N	168E		7.2	1957 Mar. 11	09:58:44	53.0N	169.3W	n	7.0
1926 Oct. 13	19:08:07	52N	176W		7.1	1957 Mar. 11	14:55:19	51.5N	178.7W	n	7.2
1927 Oct. 24	15:59:55	57½N	137W		7.1	1957 Mar. 12	11:44:54	51.4N	176.9W	n	7.3
1928 June 21	16:27:13	60N	146½W		7.0	1957 Mar. 14	14:47:45	51.3N	176.4W	n	7.2
1929 Mar. 7	01:34:39	51N	170W	50	8.6	1957 Mar. 16	02:34:15	52.0N	179.0W	n	7.2
1929 July 5	14:19:02	51N	178W		7.0	1957 Mar. 22	14:21:10	53.7N	165.2W	20	7.0
1929 July 7	21:23:12	52N	178W		7.3	1957 Apr. 10	11:30:00	56.0N	153.9W	0	7.1
1929 Dec. 17	10:58:30	52½N	171½E		7.6	1957 Apr. 19	22:19:30	52.2N	166.3W	50	7.3
1933 Apr. 27	02:36:04	61½N	150¾W		7.0	1957 June 13	10:40:41	51.5N	175.1W	n	7.0
1934 May 4	04:36:07	61¼N	147½W	80	7.2	1958 Apr. 7	15:30:40	66.0N	156.6W	0	7.3
1937 July 22	17:09:29	64¾N	146¾W		7.3	1958 July 10	06:15:56	58.3N	136.5W	n	7.9
1937 Sept. 3	18:48:12	52½N	177½W	80	7.3	1960 July 3	20:20:46	50.5N	177.0W	n	7.0
1938 Nov. 10	20:18:43	55½N	158W		8.7	1960 Nov. 13	09:20:32.3	51.4N	168.8W	32	7.0
1938 Nov. 17	03:54:34	55½N	158½W		7.2	1964 Feb. 6	13:07:20.9	55.8N	155.9W	0	7.1
1940 Feb. 7	17:16:02	51½N	175E	70	7	1964 Mar. 28	03:36:13	61.1N	147.6W	20	8.5
1940 Apr. 16	06:07:43	52N	173½E		7.1	1965 Feb. 4	05:01:21.8	51.3N	178.6E	40	7.9
1940 Apr. 16	06:43:07	52N	173½E		7.2	1965 Feb. 4	08:40:40.9	51.3N	179.5E	40	7.1
1940 July 14	05:52:53	51.8N	177.5E	80	7.8	1965 Mar. 30	02:27:07.2	50.6N	177.9E	51	7.5
1940 Aug. 22	03:27:18	53N	165½W		7.1	1965 July 2	20:58:40.0	53.1N	167.7W	59	7.1
1942 Sept. 9	01:25:26	53N	164½W	80	7.0	1965 July 29	08:29:22.1	51.2N	171.3W	23	7.0
1943 Nov. 3	14:32:17	61¾N	151W		7.3	1965 Sept. 4	14:32:47.9	58.2N	152.6W	19	7.0

*n = normal depth.

for the interval 1918–1965. The foregoing descriptions of the tectonic features of Alaska are supported by the geographic distribution of the tabulated earthquakes (Figure 1).

The temporal distribution is also worthy of comment. A number of writers have remarked on the high level of worldwide seismic activity around the beginning of the present century; a significant decrease in the rate of energy release since 1907 has been demonstrated by Duda (1965). This feature is especially evident in Alaska from a consideration of the 17 great Alaska earthquakes (M > 7.7) that have occurred beginning with the Yakutat Bay earthquakes. Of those 17, ten occurred in the first 8 years of the 7-decade in-

terval. Although the frequency of the largest earthquakes in Alaska in recent years does not approach that of the years 1899–1907, it seems clear that in this region the pace has quickened in the years since 1957. Rothé (1969) has remarked on the three extraordinary series of earthquakes in 1957, 1964, and 1965 that have affected successively three different parts of the Aleutian-Alaskan Arc.

The central part of the Arc was active in 1957 over a distance of 1,000 km, between long. 160°W and 180°; in 1964, the most activity occurred in the eastern part, between 142° and 156°W; in 1965, activity was greatest in the western part, between long. 165°E and 180°.

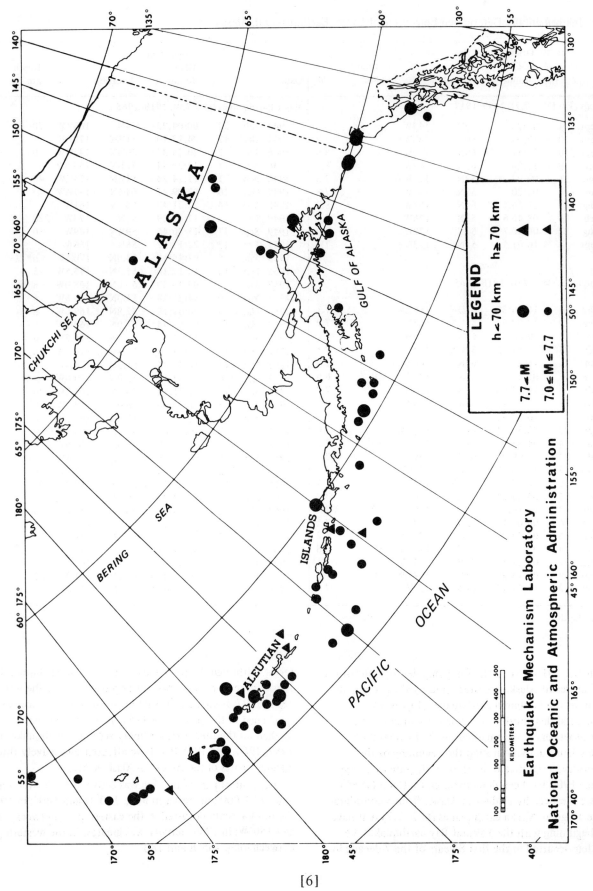

FIGURE 1 Earthquakes in Alaska with magnitude greater than 7.7 during the period 1899–1970 and with magnitude 7.0 or greater during the period 1918–1965.

The earthquake statistics of Gutenberg and Richter (1954) have led several writers to the conclusion that for the interval 1904–1952, seismic activity of Alaska, including the Aleutians, accounts for 5 or 6 percent of world seismicity. In the statistics of Rothé (1969), it appears that Alaska played a much more important role in the seismicity of the earth during the years 1953–1965, when approximately 17 percent of worldwide seismic energy release took place in the Aleutian–Alaskan Arc and interior Alaska.

DON TOCHER
Earthquake Mechanism Laboratory
Environmental Research Laboratories
National Oceanic and Atmospheric
Administration (NOAA)

REFERENCES

Duda, S. J., 1965. Secular seismic energy release in the circum-Pacific Belt. *Tectonophysics*, 2 (No. 5), 409–452.

Eppley, R. A., 1965. Earthquake history of the United States, Part I: Stronger earthquakes of the United States (exclusive of California and western Nevada). U.S. Coast and Geodetic Survey. Washington: Government Printing Office. 120 p.

Gutenberg, B., and Charles F. Richter, 1954. Seismicity of the earth and associated phenomena. Princeton: Princeton University Press. 322 p.

Richter, Charles F., 1958. Elementary seismology. San Francisco: W. H. Freeman and Company. 768 p.

Rothé, J. P., 1969. The seismicity of the earth 1953–1965. Paris: United Nations Educational, Scientific and Cultural Organization. 336 p.

Tobin, Don G., and Lynn R. Sykes, 1966. Relationship of hypocenters of earthquakes to the geology of Alaska. *Journal of Geophysical Research*, 71 (March 15), 1659–1667.

U.S. Coast and Geodetic Survey, 1964. Preliminary report–Prince William Sound, Alaskan earthquakes March–April 1964 (second printing). Seismology Division Report. Washington: U.S. Coast and Geodetic Survey. 101 p.

U.S. Coast and Geodetic Survey, 1966. The Prince William Sound, Alaska, earthquake of 1964 and aftershocks. Fergus J. Wood, editor. Volume I: Operational phases of the Coast and Geodetic Survey program in Alaska for the period March 27 to December 31, 1964. Washington: Government Printing Office. 263 p.

Wyss, Max, and James N. Brune, 1967. The Alaska earthquake of 28 March 1964: A complex multiple rupture. *Bulletin of the Seismological Society of America*, 57 (October), 1017–1023. Also *in* The Great Alaska Earthquake of 1964: Seismology and Geodesy. NAS Pub. 1602. Washington: National Academy of Sciences, 1972.

EDUARD BERG

GEOPHYSICAL INSTITUTE, UNIVERSITY OF ALASKA

Crustal Structure
in Alaska

ABSTRACT: Knowledge of the crustal structure is still fragmentary, despite the stimulus to geophysical work provided by the earthquake of March 28, 1964 (GMT), the underground nuclear explosion LONGSHOT, and the June 1967 series of earthquakes in the Fairbanks area. The most reliable information about structure has come from a combination of seismic–refraction profiles, gravity surveys, and magnetic surveys. This report is a summary of recent investigations, but the results are not adequate to permit unambiguous generalizations about crustal structure.

The major tectonic elements in the crustal structure of Alaska are (from north to south and from east to west) the Arctic Slope, the Brooks Range, the Alaska Range, the Aleutian Arc and Aleutian Range, the Talkeetna and Wrangell mountains, the Chugach Mountains, the Continental Shelf, and the Aleutian Trench. Roughly parallel with the mountain ranges are the major faults: the Denali fault, following the bend of the Alaska Range from the Bering Sea into southeastern Alaska (St.-Amand, 1957); farther south the Lake Clark fault zone, and through part of the Alaska Peninsula and along Cook Inlet the Bruin Bay fault; and a large fault or system of faults that must be assumed through Kodiak Island and Prince William Sound in the aftershock area of the March 1964 earthquake. The greatest seismic activity, as shown by an energy-release map (Berg, 1965), is in south central Alaska where the structural trend changes abruptly from southwest–northeast (Aleutian Arc structure) to northwest–southeast (eastern Pacific mountain ranges). Evidence for this structural transition is shown also by differences in chemical composition of lavas, by the stress system deduced from fault–plane solutions of the aftershocks of the March 1964 earthquake and interior earthquakes (Gedney and Berg, 1969a,b), and by the sharp directional change of iso-Bouguer-anomaly lines near Prince William Sound. P-wave residuals recorded from the underground nuclear detonation LONGSHOT or from the 1964 earthquake also show steep gradients through this transitional area (Carder and others, 1967; Sherburne and others, 1969, and this volume), but are possibly associated with other structural elements such as a dipping tectonic plate (Davies and Berg, unpublished data).

Investigations of crustal structure by seismic, gravity, or magnetic methods are relatively recent in Alaska. Whereas transcontinental seismic and gravity profiles are well interpreted in the "lower 48," such profiles are almost nonexistent for Alaska. The original effort by Tatel and Tuve (1955, 1956) to obtain a long seismic-refraction profile from a shot point at Prince William Sound along existing roads to the north toward Fairbanks is still the longest unreversed seismic profile in the south–north direction. The original data have been later interpreted by Woollard and others (1960) and by Hales and Asada (1966). The longest distance covered in the west–east direction by a single shot is that obtained from the underground nuclear detonation LONGSHOT in the Aleutians (Carder and others, 1967). The shot point was so far from mainland Alaska, however, that the only structural indications obtained are in the form of *P*-wave travel-time residuals. Station residuals from earthquake sources were also studied after the 1964 Alaska earthquake by Sherburne and others (1969, and this volume). More recently apparent *P*-wave velocities have been determined throughout the interior by Davies and Berg (unpublished data).

Seismic-refraction studies off the coast have been reported by Shor (1962) and gravity and magnetic data have been included in an offshore study by Peter and others (1965). A map of regional variations of the depth to the Mohorovicic (M) discontinuity (Moho) is given by Woollard and Strange (1962).

Structural studies inland are not abundant and, except for the Tatel and Tuve expedition, the nuclear explosion LONGSHOT, and the Davies–Berg study, they cover rather small areas. Because the scope of this summary is limited, results of those studies are included only for the area south of the Tanana Valley flats where the earthquake was still strongly felt. Matumoto and Page (1969, and this volume) give structures for the Prince William Sound–Kenai Peninsula area determined from microearthquakes, an area also covered by the Tatel and Tuve shot data. Berg, Kubota, and Kienle (1967) give preliminary crustal structure interpretation from seismic and gravity data for parts of the Alaska Peninsula around the Katmai National Monument. Finally, the interpretation of an unreversed refraction profile from the Alaska Range through the Tanana Valley and the Fairbanks area has been completed (Hanson and others, 1968).

Results of these studies are described in the following sections: first, those from offshore; then those in the coastal area; and finally those to the north.

OFFSHORE AREA

For this area Woollard and others (1960) have given depths to the Mohorovicic discontinuity based on regional Bouguer anomalies, and Shor (1962) has presented extensive seismic-refraction studies. Shor's three refraction profiles are located on the shelf northeast of Kodiak, on the shelf southeast of Kodiak, and south of Kodiak, slightly to the northwest of the axis of the Aleutian Trench. The third profile is a reversed profile along the axis of the trench and the second is a compound station on the shelf. Shor (1962, p. 52) writes of the general Kodiak section:

Under the station northeast of Kodiak are 3 km of material with velocity of 4 km/sec or less overlying 6 km/sec material which probably corresponds to the intrusive rocks of Kodiak Island. A few points on the travel-time plots indicate the possible presence of a layer with a velocity of 7 km/sec, equivalent to the oceanic layer, only 6 km below sea level. This may be the remaining trace of an old oceanic ridge between the two branches of the Aleutian Trench that were proposed by Menard and Dietz (1951, p. 1277).

Southeast of Kodiak the oceanic layer could not be found. The low-velocity sedimentary material thins closer to the edge of the shelf, but the layer of more lithified material with velocity 4 km/sec thickens somewhat, and an additional intermediate layer 6 km thick with velocity 5.5 km/sec is present. If the oceanic layer is present, it is masked by a layer with continental crust velocity and lies at least 15 km below sea level. The Mohorovicic discontinuity, neglecting a possible masked oceanic layer, is 20 km below sea level.

The Aleutian Trench at Kodiak has a sedimentary layer at least 1.5 km thick; the base of this was inferred from reflection data, and a "second layer" with the same velocity as that found beneath the adjacent shelf has been introduced beneath. If the second layer is not present, or if the reflector is not present, or if the reflector is only a thin volcanic flow, the sedimentary layer may be as much as 2 km thick. Beneath the inferred second layer is a crust with a velocity of 6.6 km/sec, which approaches normal oceanic value, and normal mantle (8.2 km/sec) at a depth of 15 km below sea level.

Shor's results are condensed in Figure 1 from his paper. Additional geophysical data have been obtained for this area by Peter and others (1965). Combination of magnetic

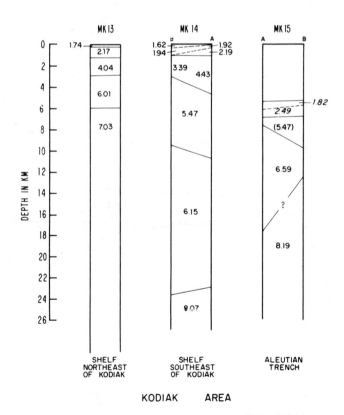

FIGURE 1 Columnar sections, Kodiak area (from Shor, 1962).

and gravity surveys with the refraction profiles of Shor (1962) leads these investigators to the cross section of crustal structure shown in Figure 2. This section runs across the Aleutian Trench some 300 km southwest of Kodiak Island, from a point approximately 53.1°N, 156.9°W to 54.9°N, 157.5°W. The detailed discussion by Peter and others (1965, p. 362) of the gravity and magnetic data, possible errors, and the existing theories of trenches, concludes at one point:

The most significant result is the positive magnetic anomaly trend near the axis of the trench. This anomaly is interpreted as a fissure in the crust (20 km wide, 300 km long) filled with basic igneous rock material. This interpretation is also supported by the gravity anomalies which indicate the concentration of higher-density rocks in the area.

When the seismic refraction profiles for the center of the trench (Shor, 1962) were plotted on a detailed USC&GS bathymetric map (Gibson, 1960), it was found that their location is slightly north of the axis of the trench. Since the location of the inferred central fissure in

the trench is south of its deepest part, this may be why the seismic profile did not record its presence. The mantle is shown at a depth of 12 km on [Shor's third] profile; according to free-air anomaly calculations, it is at 10 km in the centre of the trench.

For the section between Kodiak Island and the Katmai volcanic chain, Berg, Kubota, and Kienle (1967) obtained from earthquake recordings a preliminary structure with a 12-km-thick layer (P-wave velocity of 5.5 km/sec) and a 20-km-thick layer (6.5 km/sec) above the Mohorovicic discontinuity (8.1 km/sec below).

COASTAL AREA

For the coastal area, data and interpretations exist from several authors, who have used different techniques. Tatel and

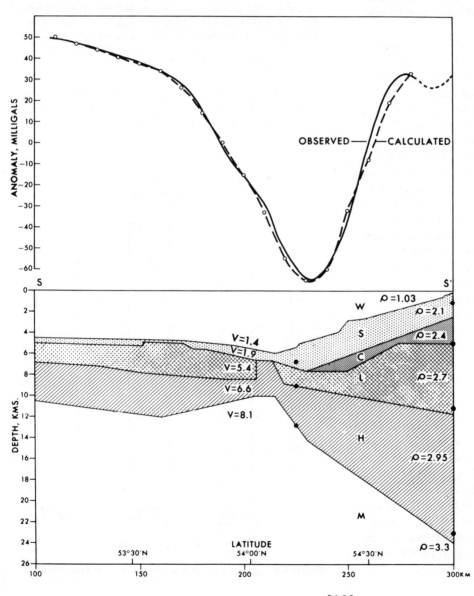

FIGURE 2 Crustal structure derived from the gravity, seismic, and magnetic data, showing observed and calculated free-air anomaly curves over a section across the Aleutian Trench southwest of Kodiak Island (from Peter and others, 1965).

Tuve's original data (1955, 1956) have been reinterpreted by Woollard and others (1960) and Hales and Asada (1966). Figure 3 (from Hales and Asada, 1966) shows the shot point in College Fiord (Prince William Sound) and the recording points in the Kenai Peninsula and toward interior Alaska. The interpretation is based on unreversed profiles. Matumoto and Page (1969, and this volume) used two tripartite networks to determine a smoothed model of crustal velocities applicable to the eastern part of the Kenai Peninsula; for the Katmai region, Berg, Kubota, and Kienle (1967) elaborate a preliminary crustal model based on earthquake and gravity data.

Woollard and others (1960) give an interpretation of the Prince William Sound shot data on a profile extending west and southwest on the Kenai Peninsula: a surface layer (excluding sediments) in which the P-wave has a velocity of 5.6–5.7 km/sec, two intermediate layers with P-wave velocities of 6.5–6.7 km/sec and 7.3 km/sec, and a layer below the Moho

with a P-wave velocity of 8.3 km/sec, reaching to a total depth of 47 km (Figure 4). Time offsets are interpreted to originate from displacements of the layers along faults on the travel path. Hales and Asada (using the same original Tatel and Tuve records) find that the Pn velocity is not well determined. The seismic stations at the end of the recording line through the Kenai Peninsula run parallel to the strike of a rapidly changing Bouguer gravity anomaly. Hales and Asada also find evidence for more systematic deviations in the Kenai Peninsula than in other areas for which the same shot data were used. Travel times as interpreted by Hales and Asada (Figure 5) result in a depth of 35.1 km for the Moho. An independent determination of the crustal model was achieved with two tripartite networks by Matumoto and Page (1969, and this volume). They calculated two crustal models, A and B (see Figure 6), where model A represents the best fit with the data; model B was used to investigate errors. These data

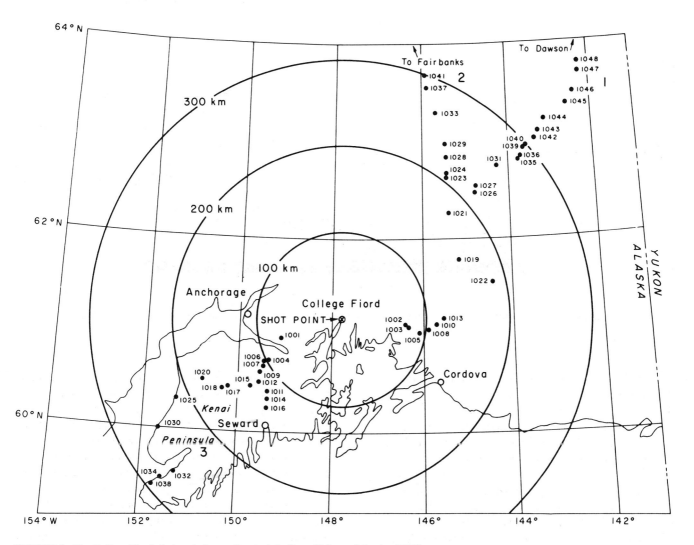

FIGURE 3 The College Fiord shot and observation points (from Hales and Asada, 1966).

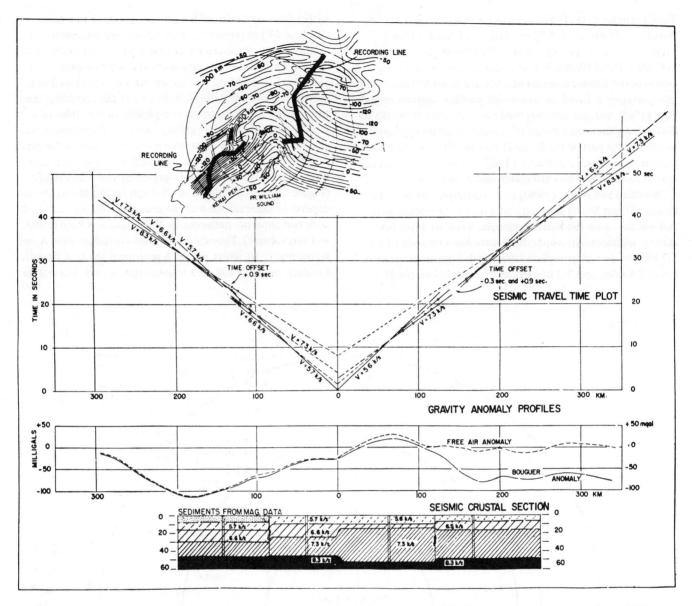

FIGURE 4 Relation of Bouguer gravity anomalies to seismic layout, observed travel-time data, and derived crustal structure in Prince William Sound area, Alaska (from Woollard and others, 1960).

were obtained from microaftershock recordings. Location of foci and origin time were obtained by conventional methods. The small tripartite net directly above the earthquake then was used to determine the average velocity (distance of focus to network, divided by travel time) as a function of depth. This information then leads to the calculation of the velocity as a function of depth, with Poisson's ratio held constant. The Matumoto–Page model A yields near-surface velocities from 5.2 to 5.5 km/sec, somewhat lower than the surface velocities found by Woollard and his associates (5.6–5.7 km/sec) or Hales and Asada (6.0 km/sec). It also presents a rapid velocity increase beneath depths from 10 to 30 km and velocities in the range 7.5–8 km/sec at depths from 30 to 50 km. A com-

parison of the Matumoto–Page models A and B and the findings of Woollard and his associates are shown in Figure 6.

A preliminary determination of crustal structure in the coastal volcanic chain of the Katmai National Monument has been obtained by Berg, Kubota, and Kienle (1967). They used earthquake recordings from a temporary network of stations and a gravity survey to determine that a depth to the Moho of 34 and 38 km is most probable. It was emphasized that Poisson's ratio is near 0.3 in that area near the Moho and is not a constant. This fact indicates the possible presence of magma pockets, which have been found by the screening and differential-attenuation effect of shear waves (Kubota and Berg, 1967).

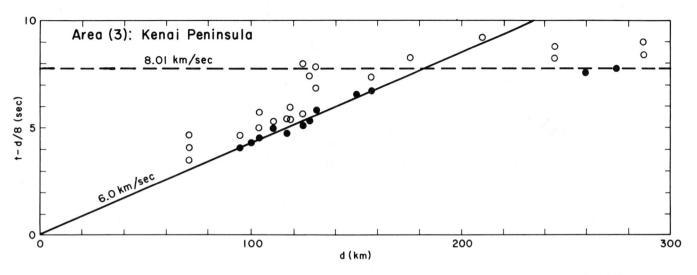

FIGURE 5   Reduced travel times for the Kenai Peninsula observations from the College Fiord shot point (from Hales and Asada, 1966).

INTERIOR ALASKA

For interior Alaska several unreversed seismic profiles and gravity data are available. Structure determinations along lines from College Fiord to Dawson and Fairbanks (Figure 3) were attempted by Tatel and Tuve (1956), and their data were later reinterpreted by Woollard and others (1960) and by Hales and Asada (1966). The University of Alaska group (Hanson and others, 1968) recently obtained an unreversed refraction profile from the Alaska Range to the north through the Tanana Valley and Fairbanks area, as well as other data for the Fairbanks area (Gedney and Berg, 1969a).

Interpretation by Woollard and his associates of the seismic and gravity data and the local geology is summarized in Figures 4 and 7. The same crustal P-wave velocities of 5.6, 6.5,

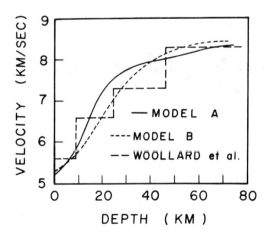

FIGURE 6   Velocity distribution of P-waves with depth for the eastern part of the Kenai Peninsula (from Matumoto and Page, 1969).

7.3 km/sec and the sub-Moho velocity of 8.3 km/sec appear along this recording line. The seismic thickness of the crust varies from 53 km over the intrusive east of the shot point in Prince William Sound to 49 km further to the northeast. These thicknesses differ from the thickness calculated from the Bouguer anomalies, presumably because of varying crustal densities over the area.

Hales and Asada's reinterpretation of the same seismic data (Figure 8) yields P-wave velocities of 6.79, 6.98, and 8.07 km/sec. Depth of the crust to the Moho is not greatly changed by two different assumptions regarding the surficial-layer velocity or by a model with 1 or 2 intermediate layers. Extreme values are 53.0 km, under the assumption of a surficial velocity of 5.84 km/sec derived from the arrival at the first recording station, and 48.6 km, with an assumed velocity of 3.0 km/sec. The crustal velocities of approximately 6.8 and 7.0 km/sec are markedly different, however, from those obtained by Woollard and others (1960). Hales and Asada summarize their four possible interpretations (Table 1). Flat-layered models are used.

An uncertainty exists in the interpretation of the first arrivals at Pn distances. In reporting large amplitudes for the first arrivals Hales and Asada discuss the possibility that they are actually missing Pn and conclude that such an amplitude must have been very small if it was missed. I believe that such a possibility exists. Within the new telemeter network of the University of Alaska, I have observed very high amplitude ratios between the second and Pn arrivals at similar distances across the Alaska Range (Berg, Sperlich, and Feetham, 1967). This high amplitude ratio makes a proper location of epicenters very difficult when Pn (at distances over 250 km) cannot be recognized and the first arrival is of large amplitude (Richter magnitude range 1.5–2.5) on the records.

Further details of crustal structure have been added by

[13]

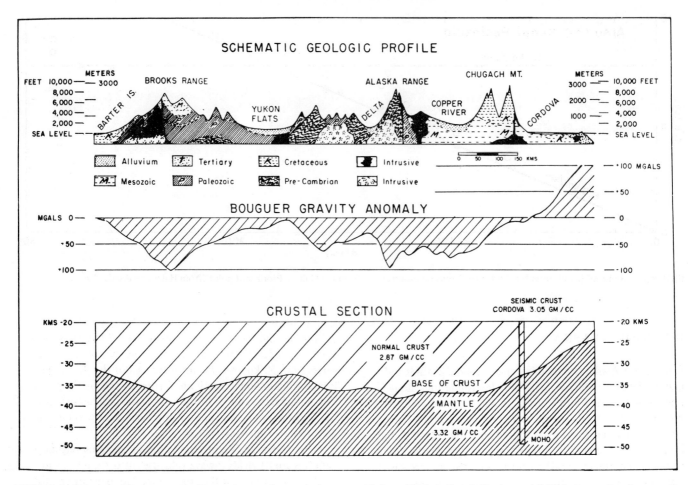

FIGURE 7 Relation of Bouguer anomalies, geology, and topography across Alaska, with derived variation in crustal thickness; section from north (Barter Island) to south (Cordova) between 146° and 145° W (from Woollard and others, 1960).

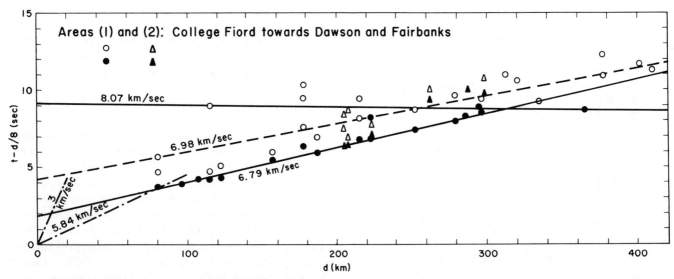

FIGURE 8 Reduced travel times for the observations toward Dawson and Fairbanks from the College Fiord shot point (from Hales and Asada, 1966).

[14]

TABLE 1 Crustal Thickness and Seismic Velocities along Line from College Fiord toward Dawson (Hales and Asada, 1966)

	Sedimentary Velocity 5.84 km/sec			Sedimentary Velocity 3.0 km/sec		
	Velocity (km/sec)	Thickness (km)	Depth to Interface (km)	Velocity (km/sec)	Thickness (km)	Depth to Interface (km)
Two intermediate layers assumed						
Superficial layer	5.84	10.2	10.2	3.0	3.0	3.0
Layer 1	6.79	33.3	43.5	6.79	35.1	38.1
Layer 2	6.98	9.5	53.0	6.98	11.5	49.6
Sub-Moho	8.07			8.07		
One intermediate layer assumed						
Superficial layer	5.84	10.2	10.2	3.0	3.0	3.0
Layer 1	6.79	41.9	52.1	6.79	45.6	48.6
Sub-Moho	8.07			8.07		

recent work of the University of Alaska group (Hanson and others, 1968). During the winter of 1966–1967 an unreversed seismic-refraction profile was obtained utilizing chemical blasts at the point "origin" of Figure 9. The profile stretches northward across the Tanana River flats in central interior Alaska for a distance of 217 km. Eleven permanent and temporary stations were used to record the blasts. A four-layer crustal model has been proposed to explain the first and later prominent arrivals (see also Figures 10 and 11):

Layer	V_P (km/sec)	V_S (km/sec)	Thickness (km)	V_P/V_S
1	3.67	2.31	2.6	1.59
2	5.27	3.27	4.5	1.61
3	5.80	3.45	9.6	1.68
4	6.60	3.66	–	1.80
Mantle	8.83	4.78	–	1.85

A thickness for the fourth layer is not shown, for it appears certain that the Mohorovicic discontinuity dips toward the south under the Alaska Range. Because the profile is unreversed, accurate values for velocities in the mantle cannot be obtained, although they are certainly less than the apparent velocity of 8.83 km/sec and probably in the neighborhood of 8 km/sec. If the latter velocity is assumed for the upper part of the mantle, the depth to the Moho beneath the shot point is calculated to be about 48 km, which, assuming a plane sloping interface, would produce a computed depth beneath Fairbanks of about 31 km.

Geologic considerations and the fact that the values for V_P/V_S in the first two layers seem to be somewhat low suggest that these layers are dipping slightly to the north.

A recent generalized simple Bouguer gravity map (Barnes, 1967) also suggests a general increase in depth to the M discontinuity from the Fairbanks area (Bouguer anomaly near –10 mgal) toward the shot point and the Alaska Range (–50 to –60 mgals).

OTHER STRUCTURAL INDICATIONS

Other structural indications may be obtained from study of the *P*-wave arrival residuals. Such studies have been carried out by Carder and others (1967) from the nuclear explosion LONGSHOT in the Aleutian Islands and by Sherburne and others (1969, and this volume) from aftershocks in the Prince William Sound area recorded at College.

Carder and others (1967) examined *P*-wave residuals by using different travel-time curves and a dense temporary network of stations through Alaska. Although the maps of residuals from different travel-time curves differ in details, they indicate much the same structural trend and the same steep anomaly gradients. Carder and others (1967) write

The structural pattern along a curve extending from the Aleutian Arc east of Adak, through the Alaska Peninsula, and northward through central Alaska and then westward along the Arctic including Nome, is indicated by positive residuals. A near-parallel pattern which may possibly include the trench, but which does include Kodiak, Cook Inlet, Anchorage, and points northeast, is indicated by negative residuals. Available Bering Sea data indicate residuals likewise negative. The average travel-time difference between the positive and negative areas is about two seconds: and the extreme difference between Port Heiden and Kodiak, which are on the same great circle, is four seconds. Kodiak is anomalously early.

Although in detail we may use different references and may contour the maps differently, the primary features would remain. The steep gradient along the continuation of the Aleutian Arc from central Alaska toward the southeast appears to be a reality and to point to a steep structural anomaly in the upper mantle.

[15]

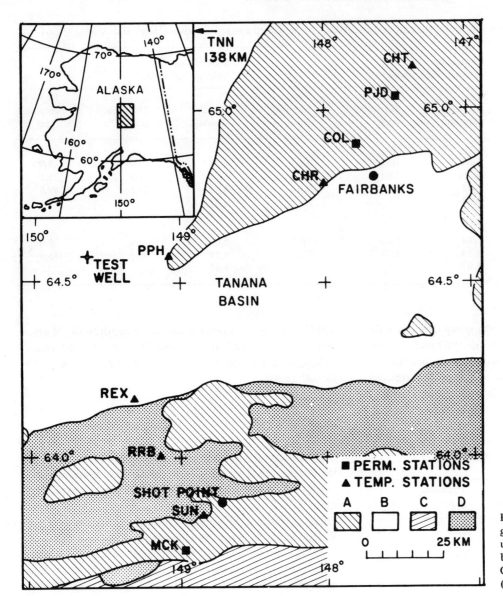

FIGURE 9 Profile stations and general geology in central interior Alaska. Map units: A—Paleozoic and Precambrian basement rocks, B—Quaternary deposits, C—Mesozoic rocks, D—Tertiary rocks (from Hanson and others, 1968).

Sherburne and his associates, on the other hand, analysed *P*-wave residuals at the College, Alaska, station of the World-Wide Network of Standard Seismographs (WWNSS) from aftershocks of the earthquake in order to obtain a better epicenter and focal depth for the main event. These residuals decreased linearly from +2.0 to −3.0 seconds with increased distance south from College. The 5-second change occurs over a distance of 270 km in the range from 400 to 670 km from College. The authors suggest, "The sharp change in *P(O-C)* residuals with distance from College suggests anomalous crustal or upper mantle velocities in the vicinity of Prince William Sound or beneath the Chugach Mountains." They

give two possible crustal sections for the area, either of which can possibly explain the observed residuals; one represents a thickening of the crust (with *P*-wave velocity of 6.1 km/sec) by some 20 km under the Chugach Mountains, and the other shows a segment of anomalously high mantle velocity (8.8 km/sec) over the distance for which the variation of the residuals at College takes place. The crustal velocities are given as 6.1 km/sec for the first and 5.8 km/sec for the second case, with the crust assumed to be a single layer over the Mohorovicic discontinuity.

Between 1967 and 1969, the University of Alaska's seismic group investigated the *Pn* velocities and seismicity of interior Alaska. Indications are that the Moho in the southern part is dipping toward the Alaska Range, and *Pn* velocities there are above 8 km/sec. Probably the most interesting result shows that the earthquake zone in the north–northeasterly extension of Cook Inlet dips steeply west–northwestward, indicating the continuation of the Aleutian Arc structure into central Alaska.

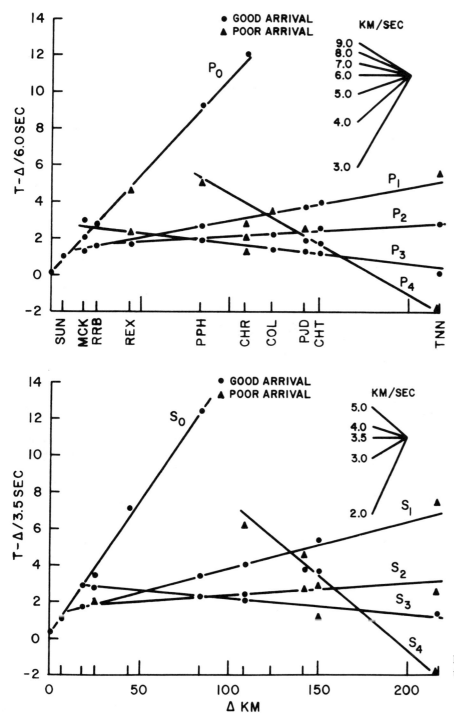

FIGURE 10 Composite *P* and *S* reduced travel-time curves (from Hanson and others, 1968).

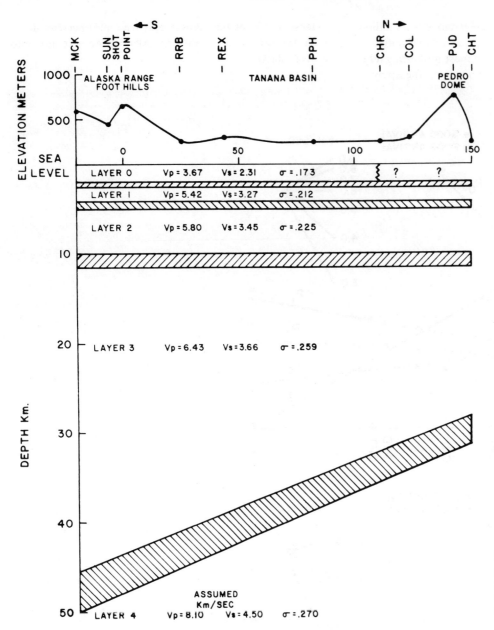

FIGURE 11 North–south section of crust–mantle model adopted. Shaded areas present difference between *P* and *S* wave interpretation (from Hanson and others, 1968).

REFERENCES

Barnes, David F., 1967. Four preliminary gravity maps of parts of Alaska. U.S. Geological Survey Open-File Report. Menlo Park: U.S. Geological Survey.

Berg, Eduard, 1965. The Alaska earthquake, its location and seismic setting in Science in Alaska, 1964: Proceedings Fifteenth Alaskan Science Conference, College, Alaska, August 31 to September 4, 1964. College: Alaska Division American Association for the Advancement of Science, March 15. p. 218–232.

Berg, Eduard, Susumu Kubota, and Jürgen Kienle, 1967. Preliminary determination of crustal structure in the Katmai National Monument, Alaska. Bulletin of the Seismological Society of America, 57 (December), 1367–1392.

Berg, Eduard, Norbert Sperlich, and William Feetham, 1967. Large aperture seismic telemetering system for central Alaska. Scientific Report UAG R-188. College: University of Alaska, Geophysical Institute, May. 43 p.

Carder, D. S., Don Tocher, Charles Bufe, S. W. Stewart, Joseph Eisler, and Eduard Berg, 1967. Seismic wave arrivals from Longshot, 0° to 27°. Bulletin of the Seismological Society of America. 57 (August), 573–590.

Gedney, Larry, and Eduard Berg, 1969a. The Fairbanks earthquake of June 21, 1967; aftershock distribution, focal mechanism and crustal parameters. Bulletin of the Seismological Society of America, 59 (February), 73–100.

Gedney, Larry, and Eduard Berg, 1969b. Some characteristics of tectonic stress pattern in Alaska. Geophysical Journal, 17 (April), 293–304.

Gibson, William M., 1960. Submarine topography in the Gulf of Alaska. Geological Society of America Bulletin, 71 (July), 1087–1108.

Hales, A. L., and T. Asada, 1966. Crustal structure in coastal Alaska in The earth beneath the continents. Geophysical Monograph No. 10. John S. Steinhart and T. Jefferson Smith, editors. Washington: American Geophysical Union. p. 420–432.

Hanson, Kenneth, Eduard Berg, and Larry Gedney, 1968. A seismic refraction profile and crustal structure in central interior Alaska. Bulletin of the Seismological Society of America, 58 (October) 1657–1665.

Kubota, Susumu, and Eduard Berg, 1967. Evidence for magma in the Katmai volcanic range. Bulletin Volcanologique, Tome XXXI, p. 175–214.

Matumoto, Tosimatu, and Robert A. Page, Jr., 1969. Microaftershocks following the Alaska earthquake of March 28, 1964: Determination of hypocenters and crustal velocities in the Kenai Peninsula-Prince William Sound area in Volume II-B,C: The Prince William Sound, Alaska, earthquake of 1964 and aftershocks. Environmental Science Services Administration, U.S. Coast and Geodetic Survey. Washington: Government Printing Office. p. 157–173. Also in The Great Alaska Earthquake of 1964: Seismology and Geodesy. NAS Pub. 1602. Washington: National Academy of Sciences, 1972.

Menard, H. W., and R. S. Dietz, 1951. Submarine geology of the Gulf of Alaska. Geological Society of America Bulletin, 62 (October), 1263–1285.

Peter, G., D. Elvers, and M. Yellin, 1965. Geological structure of the Aleutian Trench southwest of Kodiak. Journal of Geophysical Research, 70 (January 15), 353–366.

Sherburne, R. W., S. T. Algermissen, and Samuel T. Harding, 1969. The hypocenter, origin time, and magnitude of the Prince William Sound earthquake of March 28, 1964 in Volume II-B,C: The Prince William Sound, Alaska, earthquake of 1964 and aftershocks. Environmental Science Services Administration, U.S. Coast and Geodetic Survey. Washington: Government Printing Office. p. 49–69. Also in The Great Alaska Earthquake of 1964: Seismology and Geodesy. NAS Pub. 1602. Washington: National Academy of Sciences, 1972.

Shor, George G., Jr., 1962. Seismic refraction studies off the coast of Alaska: 1956–1957. Bulletin of the Seismological Society of America, 52 (January), 37–57.

St.-Amand, Pierre, 1957. Geological and geophysical synthesis of the tectonics of portions of British Columbia, the Yukon Territory and Alaska. Geological Society of America Bulletin, 68 (October), 1343–1370.

Tatel, Howard E., and Merle A. Tuve, 1955. Seismic explorations of a continental crust in Crust of the earth. A. Poldervaart, editor. Geological Society of America Special Papers 62. New York: The Geological Society of America. p. 35–50.

Tatel, Howard E., and Merle A. Tuve, 1956. Seismic crustal measurements in Alaska (Abstract). Transactions, American Geophysical Union, 37 (June), 360.

Woollard, George P., and William E. Strange, 1962. Gravity anomalies and the crust of the earth in the Pacific Basin in The crust of the Pacific Basin. Geophysical Monograph No. 6. Gordon A. MacDonald and Hisashi Kuno, editors. Washington: American Geophysical Union. p. 60–80.

Woollard, George P., Ned A. Ostenso, E. C. Thiel, and W. E. Bonini, 1960. Gravity anomalies, crustal structure, and geology in Alaska. Journal of Geophysical Research, 65 (March), 1021–1037.

I
PARAMETERS
OF THE
MAIN SHOCK

Introduction

The parameters of an earthquake are the determinable physical quantities that specify its initial point of origin as well as the character and extent of the entire motion that follows. The quantities include focal coordinates, orientation of the plane of faulting, direction of motion, source dimensions, velocity of rupture propagation, stress field causative of the earthquake, residual strains, intensity, magnitude, moment, and energy release.

As a term applied to the measures of earthquake motion, *parameter* has been introduced only recently into the nomenclature of seismology. This circumstance reflects the rapid progress of recent years in understanding and determining earthquake-source phenomena from observational data. It reflects as well something of the character of the quantities determined. True to the connotation of the word, earthquake parameters usually are not uniquely determined; ranges of values are usually possible, arising from the imperfections of the data and subject to coherence of the various parameters among themselves. Consequently, families of "solutions" (or conclusions) often may be generated as the value of this or that particular parameter is varied. To obtain a better knowledge of the source, and of the limitations on our knowledge of the source, we must consider all reasonable variants.

The determination themselves of the parameters of an earthquake, usually the combined result of the efforts of several different investigators, is a two-stage process. First, there are the efforts to acquire initial information about the source: epicenter coordinates, origin time, focal depth, spatial and temporal distribution of aftershocks, the character of the radiation patterns. To this end, traditional techniques are usually applied. One enters upon these phases of the study more-or-less blind as to what might be the special significance of this particular earthquake.

Second, there are the evidences an investigator begins to note in the data with which he is working: anomalies in travel time of seismic waves; or peculiarities in the character of seismic signature, which may suggest opportunity to identify phases or effects predicted by theoretical studies or already verified in the small by model studies. These evidences turn the investigator back toward the data themselves and toward the properties of the source or of the medium whose impress on the waveform he has noted. It is from this stage of the study that there come the discoveries about our earth and its structure, or about seismic source phenomena, that make the study of the earthquake an occasion of significant contribution to knowledge.

Some major advance of this nature is forthcoming from the study of almost every large earthquake. Thus the Kamchatka earthquake of November 2, 1952, was followed by important studies of the spatial and temporal distribution of aftershocks and of the strain-energy-release regime of the main shock and its aftershock sequence. The same earthquake occasioned the first tentative identification of the free oscillations of the earth. The Alaska earthquake of July 10, 1958, afforded opportunity to apply phase-equalization methods from surface-wave data of many stations to determine the phase at the source. The great Chilean earthquake of May 21, 1960, excited free oscillations of the earth, which for the first time were positively and conclusively identified, thereby achieving a breakthrough in the techniques for the study of the deep interior of the earth and initiating the science of terrestrial spectroscopy. The same earthquake provided, for the first time, the evidence for determining the length of faulting and velocity of fault propagation from the spectra of surface waves.

The final geophysical significance of the Alaska earthquake of 1964 is not necessarily known at the time of writing. But in any case, conclusions of primary importance will be those pertaining to the initiation and propagation of the fracture, those pertaining to the nature and orientation of the fault motion, and those pertaining to permanent strain fields at large distances from the source. Contributions selected for this section are key papers in the development of these three aspects of the seismological study of the earthquake.

INITIATION AND PROPAGATION OF THE FRACTURE

The first report of the focal coordinates of the Alaska earthquake was the March 30, 1964, Special Preliminary Determination of Epicenters (PDE) card issued by the Seismology Division of the U.S. Coast and Geodetic Survey (1964a). The USC&GS Preliminary Report (U.S. Coast and Geodetic Survey, 1964b)—published April 17, 1964, which reported epicenters of the main shock and aftershocks through April 13—also provided information on the seismic history of Alaska, the geology of the source area, the alert by the Seismic Sea-Wave Warning System (now Tsunami Warning System), and various reconnaissance reports. The regular PDE card pertaining to the Alaska earthquake, dated April 27, 1964, gave the hypocenter as 61.1°N, 147.6°W, at a depth of 20 km; origin time as $03^h 36^m 12.7^s$ (U.S. Coast and Geodetic Survey, 1964c).

In the months following the earthquake, as revised readings and records from Standard Stations and others became available, a careful examination of the hypocenter was made. The resulting paper was produced by Sherburne and others (this section); who used the best data available and carefully devised different ways of grouping them. Two distinct computer programs and several variants of the P-wave travel-time curve were used. In all, ten epicenters were computed. A remarkable feature of the multiple epicenters is their close agreement; all are located within a circle of radius 3.5 km. The most satisfactory hypocenter and origin time are $61.04 \pm 0.05°N$, $147.73 \pm 0.07°W$, $O = 03^h 36^m 14.0^s$ (GMT), h (depth of focus) = 33 km (restrained). This is in good agreement with the first preliminary determination.

Attention may appropriately be called to the discussion by Sherburne and others of residuals in the arrival time of P at College, Alaska, the station nearest to the epicenter. This portion of their paper is a good example of how, in the course of directly determining focal parameters, an effect is noted that, by way of bonus, as it were, leads to evidence of heterogeneity in earth structure—in this case, the presence of a low-velocity zone, crustal thickening, or both, beneath the Chugach Mountains.

While latitude and longitude of the earthquake are probably determined with an accuracy greater than normal, little or no precise information is available concerning depth of focus. Sherburne and others discuss the problems related to determining focal depth. Chief of these arise from the fact that no station was located closer than 436 km to the epicenter and from the circumstance that most seismograms were off scale a few seconds after the initial P; it was impossible to use reflected or secondary phases as aids to determine focal depth. Depth of aftershocks, amplitude of surface waves, and information from the earthquake history of the epicentral region indicate a probable depth of focus less than 60 km.

The focus may reasonably be restrained to any normal focal depth (that is, $h < 60$ km).

Note also the relation of focal depth of the main shock to the discussion concerning focal mechanism. The uncertainty of the depth parameter removes from consideration one type of evidence that might be diagnostic of vertical as against thrust faulting.

Sherburne and others describe a further characteristic of the initial P portion of the seismograms of this earthquake. While the onset of the P wave is impulsive and of large amplitude on records from long-period instruments, the P arrival is emergent and of small amplitude, marked by apparent successive P arrivals, on the short-period records. This circumstance is almost the rule in large earthquakes. Because m_b, the magnitude routinely determined by the USC&GS, is dependent on the largest amplitude of the first few cycles of the P wave recorded on short-period Benioff instruments, the emergent character of the P wave resulted in values of m_b two magnitudes lower than the surface-wave magnitude (M_s) of the earthquakes.

The *magnitude* of an earthquake is an instrumentally determined quantity, which is a single value characterizing a given earthquake. Of the routinely determined conventional parameters, it is the one most closely connected with the energy released in the event. The paper by Dillinger and Algermissen reports on this aspect; the Sherburne and others paper also describes the difficulties associated with making this determination.

The paper by Wyss and Brune demonstrates the significance of the emergent character of the short-period P waves. They interpret the initial portion of the short-period record in this earthquake as arising from a multiple-event source mechanism, as the propagating rupture triggers larger distinct events. Signals from the multiple sources record as separate events on the short-period records, whereas long-period instruments respond only to the integrated, and hence impulsive (relative to the periods concerned), long-period earth motion of the longer-period portion of the spectrum. Though the trace, even on short-period Benioffs, is off scale after a few seconds (10 or 15 seconds at most), Wyss and Brune had at their disposal seismograms of low magnification from 70 stations distributed azimuthally at large distances from the source. On these records the authors succeed in correlating six events, corresponding to six distinct episodes of rupture with origin times up to 72 seconds after that of the initial fracture and distant as much as 250 km from the initial epicenter.

While indications of multiple-source mechanisms have been noted in previous earthquakes, including the San Francisco earthquake of 1906 (Reid, 1910; Gupta, 1964), the exceptional documentation of this interpretation of the data by Wyss and Brune may be singled out as *one of the major contributions toward understanding earthquake origins that have resulted from study of the Alaska earthquake.* The phenomenon is important not only for its contribution to knowledge of the time-history of fault propagation, but also for its relation to theoretical and model studies of the properties of materials, such as those of Savage and Hasegawa (1964) or of Savage (1965), which have indicated the existence of stopping and break-out phases, or those of Mansinha (1964), who has demonstrated momentary crack cessation and bifurcation when cracking in rock materials reaches a limiting velocity.

Difficulties noted in this section by Sherburne and others and by Wyss and Brune, as well as elsewhere in this volume, on the interpretation of seismic data from the Alaska earthquake emphasize an essential deficiency in the present instrumentation of seismographic stations. With few exceptions, existing instruments are simply not suitable for adequate recording of major earthquakes: The ground motion is so large that recordings are off scale. It is unfortunate that in the most significant of earthquakes little seismic information can be decoded beyond the initial direction of onset of the *P* wave.

From the engineering point of view, as well as for an appreciation of the effect of the earthquake on the works of man and of nature, another significant parameter is the *intensity*. The whole of the Engineering volume of this report is relevant to this quantity. *Intensity* is seismologically significant in indicating the dimensions of the area of disturbance, the effect of different media on wave propagation, and directional characteristics of the earth motion. The paper by Cloud and Scott summarizes these aspects of the field studies. The U.S. Geological Survey (1965–1970) has published a series of six Professional Papers that present further graphic accounts of the regional and local effects of the 1964 earthquake in south central Alaska. Portions of these appear in the Geology and Hydrology volumes of this series.

As opposed to *magnitude*, which is computed from seismograms, *intensity* is based on field evidences of the degree of shaking, which varies from point to point. Tocher (1964) provides a more detailed explanation of the meanings of the terms *magnitude* and *intensity* and the differences between them.

Not all the energy stored in the strained rock of the earth is released in the major shock. Of comparable importance, perhaps of even greater importance for understanding the processes involved, is the energy released in the aftershocks and the rate of this release. This aspect of the Alaska earthquake is reported on in the section on foreshocks and aftershocks in this volume.

NATURE AND ORIENTATION OF THE FAULT MOTION

A second area of major seismological significance of the Alaska earthquake concerns the focal mechanism. The topic is the more interesting in that it involves a difference of opinion in the interpretation of the source mechanism or fault motion in the major earthquake: Was the faulting reverse in character on a steeply dipping fault extending deep into the earth or was it instead an overthrust on a thrust plane dipping gently under the continent? Either interpretation is consistent with the single, well-determined nodal plane of *P*-wave first motion with strike 62°–72°E and dip 82°–90°SE. A second nodal plane, though not determined by the *P*-wave data, is restricted to a relatively gentle or moderate dip to the north or northwest. The question has been much debated and has only gradually reached resolution.

The papers on focal mechanisms set forth, somewhat in the historical, expanding order of their disclosure, the elements of evidence on which the discussion of mechanism is based. The basic interpretations—reverse faulting as opposed to thrust faulting—are displayed respectively in the papers by Press and Jackson and by Plafker in this section and in Plafker (1965). The remaining papers in this section examine specific phases of the question. The conclusions drawn may favor one interpretation over the other, but in each case their inferences are couched in terms that show the authors' awareness of the ambiguity involved.

Points of evidence that guide the thought of the investigator and that must be mutually reconciled include observable crustal deformation, seismic data from *P* and *S* waves and from surface waves, tsunami generation, and auxiliary investigations such as aftershock studies, profiles by seismic-echo soundings of the ocean bottom, and geodetic measurements.

The area of observable surface deformation in the Alaska earthquake is truly remarkable—"larger than any such area known to be associated with a single earthquake in historic time" (Plafker, 1965). The area of deformation is divided into a region of subsidence and one of uplift, clearly separated by a line of zero change. Press and Jackson correlate the residual displacement field with displacements calculated from displacement theory to infer, as mentioned above, that the primary fault is vertical. The exceptionally large distances extending either side of the zero line, and over which uplift or subsidence is measurable, require the fault to extend 100–200 km into the earth. This interpretation is consistent with a determination of fault length and vertical orientation of the fault plane from the spectra of surface waves (Toksöz and others, 1965), and with far-field displacements recorded on a strain seismograph in Hawaii.

As the reader weighs for himself the evidence presented here and in the following papers for the varying interpretations of focal mechanism, it may be well to call attention to a comment in the contribution by Savage and Hastie. Though Press and Jackson remark, and Press repeats, that the surface-wave solution uniquely determines a near-vertical fault plane, Savage and Hastie rightly point out that the double-couple fault representation does not distinguish between the fault plane and the auxiliary plane. While in some instances the surface-wave directivity function has this power, in the present case rupture propagation is approximately along the null axis. In this circumstance it is unlikely that even the directivity function can distinguish between the fault plane and the auxiliary plane.

Plafker, on the basis of exceptionally well-documented field studies of the various aspects of geological evidence in the region of subsidence and uplift, postulates thrust faulting along a fault or zone of faulting that dips to the northwest from the Aleutian Trench beneath the Aleutian Arc. He supports his position by correlation with the seismic data, especially the areal distribution and focal depth of aftershocks.

Savage and Hastie renew the examination of the surface deformation from the viewpoint of the displacement theory of Maruyama (1964). The vertical displacements, they show, can be explained either by the vertical-fault or by the thrust hypothesis, though the model that they prefer agrees with the fault motion proposed by Plafker.

Harding and Algermissen use data from body waves to study the focal mechanism of the main shock, two preshocks and eight aftershocks (six within the first 17 hours). For the main shock, in addition to the P-wave polarity at 122 stations, they were able to determine the angle of polarization of the S wave from seismograms of low-magnification instruments at 17 stations. The focal mechanism they propose as most likely corresponds to right-lateral strike-slip motion on a nearly vertical plane, with a significant dip-slip component of motion. This mechanism is incompatible with the thrust hypothesis, but in general agreement with the results reported by Press and Jackson.

Stauder and Bollinger also present a study of the focal mechanism of the main shock and those of the larger aftershocks from the data of P and S waves. For the main shock they find a single, steeply dipping, nodal plane of P, nearly identical to that of Harding and Algermissen. But by comparing it with the P- and S-wave solutions of 28 of the larger aftershocks of the entire earthquake sequence, they conclude that this single plane is more likely not the fault plane but rather the auxiliary plane of the main shock, that is, a plane normal to the motion on the fault. This conclusion is in agreement with Plafker's.

These last two papers illustrate the inadequacy of the available seismic data for an understanding of this important earthquake. Conventional recorders were simply over-driven, precluding for the most part the use of any part of the seismic signature beyond the initial onset. Very likely a satisfactory mechanism solution will never be forthcoming based on the seismic body wave data alone. The conflicting interpretations thereby highlight the deficiency remarked above: The present instrumentation of seismic stations is not suitable for adequate recording of major earthquakes.

Over and above limitations of the data, there are factors that may explain, in part, differences in results. For the main shock the S-wave data of Harding and Algermissen are from instruments with free periods of about 5 seconds. The work of Wyss and Brune documents an episodic character to the motion in the main shock. It may be that the results of Harding and Algermissen pertain to the motion at or near the very initiation of the shock. Half-periods of 25–30 seconds in the initial P motion recorded on long-period records imply an integrated effect over a region of large volume. It is this overall motion that is of more central interest. Harding and Algermissen also rely on short-period P-wave data in their study of aftershocks of the first 17 hours after the main shock. Recently Bolt and others (1968) and Akasché and Berckhemer (1970), among others, have documented the fact that long-period and short-period P waves are not uncommonly of opposite polarity. They have also demonstrated that notably different, good-quality mechanism solutions are obtained as one uses short-period or long-period first motion.

Individually, the mechanism of the aftershocks studied by Stauder and Bollinger are subject to the same ambiguity of interpretation as that of the main shock. Only when they are taken together and correlated with other evidence is an overall interpretation of the total fault motion presented that is more consistent with the thrust hypothesis.

Further evidence of the general character of the earth motion is presented in the papers by Pararas-Carayannis, who correlated the rupture area with tsunami generation and travel time, and by Furumoto, who applied the spectral ratio of direct and return Rayleigh waves (directivity function) to examine the character of the fracture propagation. Others, too, have applied this technique (e.g., Toksöz and others, 1965). The paper of Furumoto illustrates the method. While the surface wave data in this earthquake are difficult to interpret because of the large amplitudes of the displacements and because of asymmetries in the Love and Rayleigh wave data, Furumoto found that the rupture propagated in a direction S 30°W from its point of origin and that the length of faulting was 800 km.

In the years since the Alaska earthquake, Kanamori (1970) has developed an entirely new approach to the use of surface wave data. Surface waves are synthesized by a superposition of normal modes; the synthesized waves are then compared with the observed Love or Rayleigh signals. Applied to the Alaska earthquake, Kanamori's later paper (this section) notes that the asymmetry of the Rayleigh waves at azimuths perpendicular to the steeply dipping nodal plane of P makes it impossible that these waves could have been generated by any motion on this plane. The asymmetry of both the Love and Rayleigh waves indicates that the motion took place on a low angle thrust fault (dip 20°, dip direction N 24°W), that the motion was reverse dip-slip, and that the direction of rupture propagation (S 25°W) was somewhat oblique to the strike of the fault.

Despite the large surface deformations, notable surface faulting was observed only on Montague Island. This faulting is described in the paper by Plafker and more amply documented in the Geology volume. The faulting on Montague Island is generally considered to be secondary. The paper by von Huene presents an excellent examination of the southwestward extension of this faulting, or of preexisting fault zones coincident with the extension of the Alaska earthquake aftershock region. Marine seismic profiles map steeply dipping discontinuous faults parallel to the zone. The author's discussion of the implication of his studies regarding the mechanism of the earthquake affords a good example of restraint in not drawing conclusions beyond the evidence of his data.

In concluding this discussion of focal mechanism, there remains the important evidence from the data of geodetic measurements. Vertical displacements have been determined by precise leveling and are presented in the paper by Small and Wharton in the section on Geodesy and Photogrammetry. The geodetic measurements support and confirm the extensive evidence of vertical changes manifested in shorelines and by tide gages. By themselves, however, the vertical measurements are not a sufficient criterion to distinguish high-angle reverse faulting from thrust faulting.

Crucial evidence concerning the mechanism hangs on the horizontal displacements that are presented in the paper by Parkin (this volume). Figure 4 of his paper is a summary of these measurements. The horizontal displacements—up to 70 ft south-southeastward—are among the largest ever detected. Part of this motion may possibly have occurred as creep in the period of several years between the first survey and the earthquake or during the months between the earthquake and the second survey; as Parkin observes in his conclusion, part of the indicated motion may be the result of regional tilting, which would give rise to differential horizontal movement between sea level and the elevations of the triangulation stations. While either vertical or thrust faulting would cause notable horizontal motion at the earth's surface, the horizontal displacements from the thrust-fault models hypothesized would be two to three times greater than those from vertical-fault models. Subject to these uncertainties, displacements of the order of magnitude and of the directions shown in Parkin's Figure 4 are consistent only with the thrust hypothesis.

To summarize this discussion, the paper by Kanamori may truly be said to culminate the studies of the mechanism of the Alaska earthquake. Together with the work of Plafker, of Savage and Hastie, and of Stauder and Bollinger, and the agreement with the geodetic data, it can be established beyond reasonable doubt that the motion in this earthquake occurred along a low angle thrust fault, representing an underthrust of the continental margin by an oceanic plate.

This conclusion, that the Alaska earthquake took place along a low angle thrust, is in keeping with the theory of plate tectonics (Isacks and others, 1968). Indeed, this interpretation of the earthquake motion plays a supporting role in the confirmation of the theory, for the underthrusting of the oceanic plate is evidence of the sink mechanism required for the spreading of the ocean floor. The theory of plate tectonics itself is one that has been proposed since the occurrence of the earthquake and is the most significant development in geology and in geophysics of the solid earth in recent years. Thus the establishment of the mechanism of the Alaska earthquake as a low angle thrust is certainly *another of the major contributions that has resulted from the study of this earthquake.*

The consideration of focal mechanism, however, should not permit one to lose sight of other significant parameters of the earthquake source. The areal extent of deformation and of the aftershock region indicates how extensive was the whole fault region. The papers by Press and Jackson, by Savage and Hastie, by Stauder and Bollinger, by Furumoto, and especially that by Kanamori, discuss at length determinations of fault dimensions and velocity of rupture propagation.

PERMANENT STRAINS IN THE FAR FIELD

No less remarkable than the areal extent of permanent deformation of the earth in the focal region is the existence of permanent strains and tilts at large epicentral distances. The article by Press discusses the magnitude of the effect to be expected at large distances from the source on the surface of a half-space. He shows that modern instruments are sufficient to detect the strains and tilts in question. Though the theory used by Press is not entirely adequate to account for the distortion on the surface of a spherical body (Ben-Menahem and others, 1969), future large earthquakes will undoubtedly result in precise measurements of this sort. Already, special instruments for this purpose, including some with radical innovations, are being designed and tested.

Press interprets a step offset on the record from a strain seismometer in Hawaii as evidence of such permanent strain in the Alaska earthquake. The offset occurs on the record of a single instrument operating at the time. This circumstance, plus the added circumstance that similar offsets were not observed on strain records at other sites, leaves some doubt concerning the correlation between the record and actual change in strain in the earth. In this and examples cited in other earthquakes, it is not certain that the recorded offset is not the effect of a shift within the instrument. Evidence is beginning to cumulate, however, showing that at least in some instances the offsets noted on records of near or very large distant earthquakes do in fact correspond to permanent changes in the strain field. It is not unlikely that a major seismological contribution resulting from observations recorded in the next major earthquake will be the documentation of changes in the strain field.

WILLIAM STAUDER
Saint Louis University

REFERENCES

Akasche, B., and H. Berckhemer, 1970. Focal mechanism of deep and shallow earthquakes as derived from short and long-period seismograms. Proceedings of the Tenth Assembly of the European Seismological Commission, Leningrad, September 3-11, 1968, Volume II. Moscow: Academy of Sciences of the USSR. p. 334-359.

Ben-Menahem, Ari, Sarva Jit Singh, and Faïza Solomon, 1969. Static deformation of a spherical earth model by internal dislocations. *Bulletin of the Seismological Society of America*, 59 (April), 813-853.

Bolt, B. A., C. Lomnitz, and T. V. McEvilly, 1968. Seismological evidence on the tectonics of central and northern California and the Mendocino escarpment. *Bulletin of the Seismological Society of America*, 58 (December), 1725-1767.

Gupta, Indra N., 1964. A note on the Alaska earthquake of July 10, 1958. *Bulletin of the Seismological Society of America*, 54 (December), 2081-2083.

Isacks, Bryan, Jack Oliver, and Lynn R. Sykes, 1968. Seismology and the new global tectonics. *Journal of Geophysical Research*, 73 (September 15), 5855-5899.

Kanamori, Hiroo, 1970. Synthesis of long-period surface waves and its application to earthquake source studies—Kurile Islands earthquake of October 13, 1963. *Journal of Geophysical Research*, 75 (September 10), 5011-5027.

Mansinha, L., 1964. The velocity of shear fracture. *Bulletin of the Seismological Society of America*, 54 (February), 369-376.

Maruyama, T., 1964. Statical elastic dislocations in an infinite and semi-infinite medium. *Bulletin of the Earthquake Research Institute*, University of Tokyo, 42 (June), 289-368.

Plafker, George, 1965. Tectonic deformation associated with the 1964 Alaska earthquake. *Science*, 148 (June 25), 1675-1687.

Reid, Harry Fielding, 1910. The time and origin of the shock *in* The mechanics of the earthquake, Volume II: The California earthquake of April 18, 1906. Report of the State Earthquake Investigation Commission. Washington: Carnegie Institution. p. 3-15. (Reprinted, 1969).

Savage, J. C., 1965. The stopping phase on seismograms. *Bulletin of the Seismological Society of America*, 55 (February), 47-58.

Savage, J. C., and H. S. Hasegawa, 1964. Some properties of tensile fractures inferred from elastic wave radiation. *Journal of Geophysical Research*, 69 (May 15), 2091-2100.

Tocher, Don, 1964. Earthquakes and rating scales. *Geotimes*, 8 (May-June), 15-20.

Toksöz, M. Nafi, Ari Ben-Menahem, and David G. Harkrider, 1965. Source mechanism of Alaska earthquake from long period seismic surface waves (Abstract). *Transactions, American Geophysical Union*, 46 (March), 154.

U.S. Coast and Geodetic Survey, 1964a. Special Preliminary Determination of Epicenters card, Alaska earthquakes of March 28-30, 1964, issued March 30, 1964. Washington: U.S. Coast and Geodetic Survey. 1 p.

U.S. Coast and Geodetic Survey, 1964b. Preliminary Determination of Epicenters card, Prince William Sound, Alaska earthquake and after aftershocks, March 28, 1964, issued April 27, 1964. Washington: U.S. Coast and Geodetic Survey. 1 p.

U.S. Coast and Geodetic Survey, 1964c. Preliminary report—Prince William Sound, Alaskan earthquakes March-April 1964 (second printing). Seismology Division Report. Washington: U.S. Coast and Geodetic Survey. 101 p.

U.S. Geological Survey, 1965-1970. The Alaska earthquake, March 27, 1964. A series of six Professional Papers with the following subtitles: PP 541, Field investigations and reconstruction effort; PP 542 A-G, Effects on communities; PP 543 A-J, Regional effects; PP 544 A-E, Effects on the hydrologic regimen; PP 545 A-D, Effects on transportation, communications, and utilities; PP 546, Lessons and conclusions. Washington: Government Printing Office.

R. W. SHERBURNE*
S. T. ALGERMISSEN
SAMUEL T. HARDING
U.S. COAST AND GEODETIC SURVEY†

Reprinted with minor changes from
U.S. Coast and Geodetic Survey Volume II-B,C: Seismology and Marine Geology,
"The Hypocenter, Origin Time, and Magnitude of the
Prince William Sound Earthquake of March 28, 1964"

Hypocenter, Origin Time, and Magnitude

ABSTRACT

Ten separate epicenter computations were made using various data sets, computer programs, and traveltime curves. The preferred epicenter, using 46 stations paired in distance and azimuth, Jeffreys-Bullen [1958] traveltime curves, and the epicenter computer program of the Coast and Geodetic Survey has coordinates latitude 61.04 N., longitude 147.73W., origin time 03:36:14.0. The focal depth was fixed at 33 kilometers. Indications of possible surface faulting were found 38 kilometers N. 31°E. of the instrumental epicenter. A study of $P(O-C)$ time residuals at the College, Alaska, station shows a crustal thickening beneath the Chugach Mountains or possibly higher than normal mantle velocities beneath Prince William Sound. The mean value of M_s was 8.3±.33 magnitude units using 37 observations.

INTRODUCTION

Immediately following the Prince William Sound Earthquake of March 28, 1964 (G.M.T.), the United States Coast and Geodetic Survey published a *Preliminary Determination of Epicenters* (PDE) card entitled "SPECIAL", giving the location and magnitude of the earthquake based on provisional data available. Subsequently, slight revisions of the epicenter were published by the Seismology Division, Coast and Geodetic Survey [1964] and by von Hake and Cloud [1966]. Because of the importance of the earthquake and to obtain from the available data the best possible hypocenter and magnitude, a special study of seismograms from 169 stations and readings obtained from 79 additional stations were analyzed.

Several factors contributed significantly to the problem of determining the hypocenter, origin time, and magnitude of this earthquake. Many of the first motions recorded on short-period seismographs throughout the world were emergent. Consequently, arrival times of P at stations operating at low magnification were questionable, and emergent phases recorded at high-magnification stations were difficult to correlate accurately. Few phases other than P could be used to locate the shock, to establish the origin time, or to compute the magnitude because nearly all seismograms throughout the world were off scale within a few seconds after the

*Now at Pennsylvania State University.
†Now in part Earth Sciences Laboratories, National Oceanic and Atmospheric Administration.

first motion. The determination of focal depth was a special problem, for the nearest station to the epicentral area was at a distance of approximately 436 kilometers.

MATERIALS USED

The primary source of data for calculating the hypocenter was the seismograms recorded by the Worldwide Network of Standard Seismograph Stations (WWNSS) maintained by the United States Coast and Geodetic Survey. Seismograms from other United States Coast and Geodetic Survey stations, cooperative stations, and independent stations throughout the world, however, were also used in various hypocenter solutions. When possible, the arrival times were read from the seismograms by the authors; but when seismograms could not be obtained, readings from some stations read by other investigators were included in the computations. In general, data from seismograms not read by the authors were used only when the reading was from a station known to have good time control, a history of reliable reporting of arrival times, and the first motion was reported as impulsive. Arrival times from the seismograms read by the authors were used in the computations only when independent readings made by investigators agreed within 0.2 second. All readings with residuals greater than 4.0 seconds were rejected from the final computations.

The first motions recorded on seismograms were classified as being of four general types:

(1) Very clear, impulsive first motion followed by waves of increasing amplitude with no clearly discernible large-amplitude phase within 5 seconds;

(2) Very clear, impulsive first motion followed within 5 seconds by a large-amplitude phase;

(3) Emergent first motion followed within 5 seconds by a large-amplitude second phase; and

(4) Emergent first motion followed within 5 seconds by waves of gradually increasing amplitude with no clearly discernible large-amplitude phase.

Figures 1 and 2 show typical examples of long- and short-period seismograms displaying the types of motion discussed above. All long-period seismograms shown in figure 1 are examples of first motions, type 1. In figure 2, seismograms from Blacksburg (BLA) and New Delhi (NDI) are considered to show typical first motions, type 2; Rapid City (RCD) and Honiara (HNR) first motions are considered characteristic of types 3 and 4, respectively. [Seismograph stations abbre-

viations are listed alphabetically in the appendix to this paper.]

EPICENTER COMPUTATIONS

The epicenter solutions were computed by using two different digital computer programs and various sets of data. For 9 of the 10 computations, the focal depth was constrained at a depth of 33 kilometers. Although the depth of 33 kilometers is somewhat arbitrary, it is considered to be a reasonably accurate estimate of the depth of this earthquake. The determination of focal depth is discussed in more detail in a later section of this paper. Of the computations, seven epicenters were computed by using the United States Coast and Geodetic Survey digital computer program described by Engdahl and Gunst [1966]. The three other epicenters computed at the Seismic Data Laboratory (SDL) of Teledyne Incorporated, Alexandria, Va., used the computer program described by Flinn [1965]. Although the programs differ slightly in computational technique, they basically used the same least-squares procedure of Geiger [1910], but different traveltime tables. The United States Coast and Geodetic Survey computer program used the Jeffreys-Bullen traveltime tables [1958], and the Seismic Data Laboratory program used the traveltime tables developed by Herrin [1961]. Herrin's curves utilized data from nuclear explosions in the Pacific and in Nevada.

The epicenter calculations are classified as follows:

(1) Computations using only data from stations paired in distance and azimuth with respect to the epicenter;

(2) Computations using all reliable data;

(3) Computations using only data from stations at distances greater than $25°$ from the epicenter; or

(4) Computations using special sets of data, such as first motions recorded on long-period seismograms or secondary phases recorded on short-period seismograms.

All results are summarized and listed by number in table 1. The various computations will be discussed, using the identification numbers for each computation listed in table 1.

Computations 1 and 2. The traveltimes of seismic waves along great-circle paths to North America and Europe are heavily weighted in least-squares epicentral calculations, because of the relatively large number of seismograph stations in these areas.

An attempt was made to correct, at least partially, for this effect by selecting data from stations paired in azi-

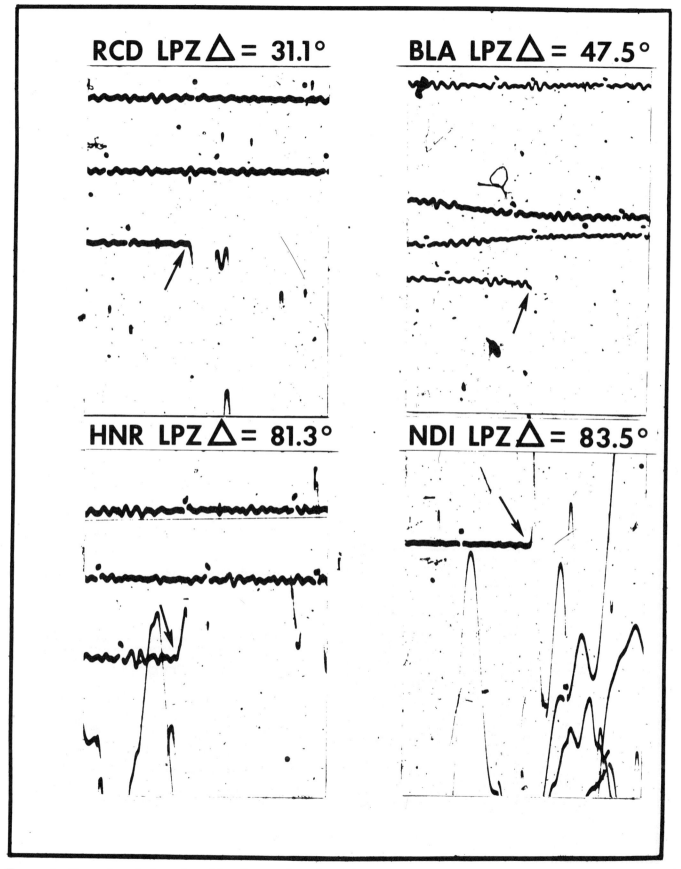

FIGURE 1.—Examples of clear, impulsive first motions (type 1, see text) recorded by long-period vertical seismographs at various stations of the Worldwide Network.

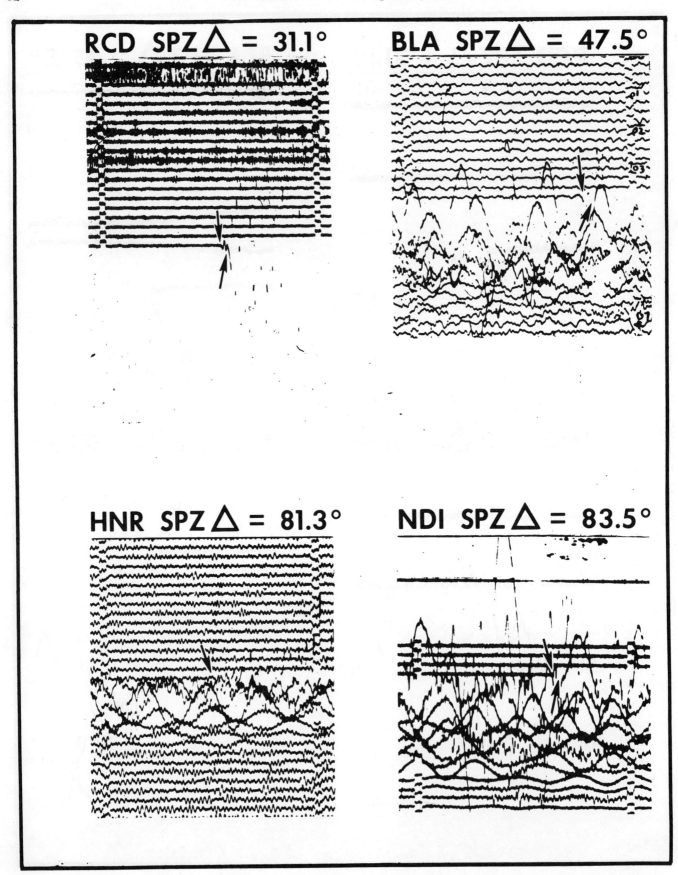

FIGURE 2.—Examples of types 2, 3, and 4 (see text) first motions recorded on short-period vertical seismographs at various stations of the Worldwide Network.

muth and distance from the epicentral region. Data were selected in the following manner for computation 1 in table 1: (1) Only data recorded at epicentral distances greater than 25° were used, and (2) stations in oppo-site directions from the epicenter were paired; so each pair of stations was at approximately the same distance from the epicenter within ±5° and at opposite azimuths from the epicenter within ±5°.

TABLE 1.—*Summary of location computations*

Computations [1]		Type of computation	Origin time (G.M.T.)			Standard error	Latitude N.	Standard error	Longitude W.	Standard error	Depth [2]	Standard error	Number of stations	Station distribution numbers
No.	By		Hr.	Min.	Sec.	Sec.	Degrees	Degrees	Degrees	Degrees	Km.	Km.		
1	C&GS	Stations paired in distance and azimuth.	03	36	14.0	±0.2	61.04	±0.05	147.73	±0.07	33		46	
2	C&GS	Station corrections applied to data of computation 1.	03	36	14.4	±0.2	60.98	±0.04	147.63	±0.06	33		46	
3	C&GS	All reliable data............	03	36	14.4	±0.1	61.03	±0.02	147.69	±0.03	33		181	
4	SDL	All reliable data............	03	36	14.4	±0.1	60.99	±0.02	147.79	±0.06	33		181	.259
5	SDL	All reliable data............	03	36	13.6	±1.5	60.99	±0.02	147.80	±0.07	27.6	±9.7	181	.259
6	C&GS	Epicentral distance greater than 25°.	03	36	14.4	±0.1	61.01	±0.02	147.74	±0.03	33		168	
7	SDL	Epicentral distance greater than 25°.	03	36	14.4	±0.1	60.98	±0.02	147.82	±0.06	33		168	.269
8	C&GS	Short-period first motion.....	03	36	14.4	±0.2	61.08	±0.04	147.68	±0.07	33		45	
9	C&GS	Large-amplitude second arrival.	03	36	16.8	±0.3	61.09	±0.05	147.75	±0.09	33		45	
10	C&GS	Long-period first motion.....	03	36	15.4	±0.2	61.01	±0.04	147.71	±0.07	33		45	

[1] The abbreviation SDL refers to the Seismic Data Laboratory, Teledyne, Inc., Alexandria, Va.
[2] The depth of focus was fixed at 33 kilometers, except for computation 5, in which the depth was computed.

Initially, readings from 248 stations were analyzed, and from these stations, 181 were selected as having the largest set of data to be used in any of the 10 epicenter calculations. The arrival times of *P* for each of the 181 stations are shown in table 2 with the traveltime residuals for the 10 computations summarized in table 1. Readings from 46 stations, the largest number of stations that could be paired in distance and azimuth (as described above) were used in computations 1 and 2. The distribution of the 46 stations is shown in figure 3. No station corrections (other than ellipticity corrections) were used in computation 1.

To make use of recent work on seismic traveltimes and possibly to improve the epicentral location of the earthquake, the azimuth solution was rerun, using the station traveltime corrections given by Hales and Cleary [1966]; however, corrections were estimated for stations not considered by them. Their work is based on an analysis of the traveltimes of 25 earthquakes and on data from earlier studies of Pacific nuclear explosion traveltimes. The epicenter computed (computation 2) is given in table 1. Figures 4 and 5 show the $P(O-C)$ residuals with distances and azimuths for computations 1 and 2.

The epicenter computed, using station corrections given by Hales and Cleary [1966], is 5.5 kilometers

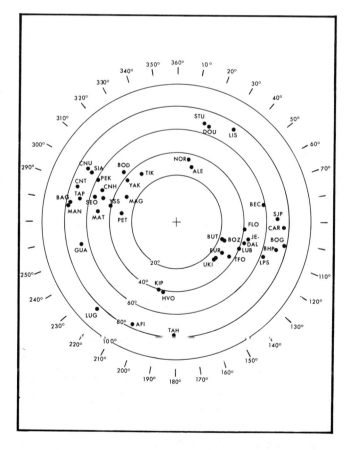

FIGURE 3.—Polar plot of stations used in computations 1 and 2 (see table 1).

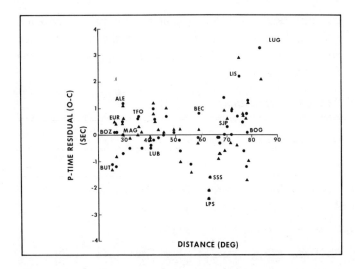

FIGURE 4.—$P(O-C)$ residuals, with epicentral distances for computations 1 and 2, are indicated by circles and triangles, respectively (see table 1).

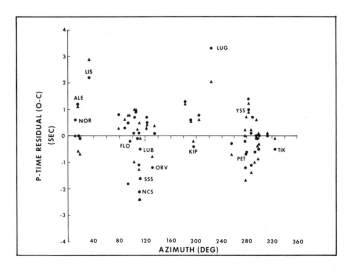

FIGURE 5.—$P(O-C)$ residuals, with azimuths for computations 1 and 2, are indicated by circles and triangles, respectively (see table 1).

southeast of the computation without station corrections (fig. 6).

Computations 3, 4, and 5. Three epicenters were computed using readings from the 181 stations listed in table 2. For computation 3, the depth of focus was constrained at 33 kilometers, because in trial computations with the same data, the depth of focus took on negative values, *i.e.,* above the mean sphere.

Figure 7 is a polar plot that shows the distribution of the 181 stations from which data were used. Figure 8 shows the $P(O-C)$ residuals with distances, and figure

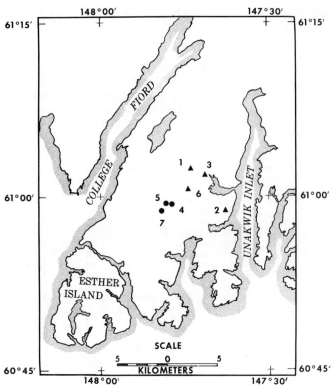

FIGURE 6.—Epicenters computed by using arrival times from short-period seismograms. The numbers refer to the sets of data listed in table 1.

9 shows the residuals with azimuths for computation 3. For computation 5, the Seismic Data Laboratory program was used, and the focal depth was not restricted. A focal depth of 27.6 kilometers was computed. The Seismic Data Laboratory program was rerun with the depth of focus restricted to 33 kilometers, simply to compare computation 5 with computation 3.

The Seismic Data Laboratory computer program also calculates statistical parameters known as confidence regions; these have been described by Flinn [1965]. Figure 10 is a map showing the epicenters resulting from computations 3 and 4. The 99 and 75 percent confidence regions are shown for computation 4. The areas of the 99 and 75 percent confidence regions are 173.0 and 52.2 square kilometers, respectively.

Computations 6 and 7. Two epicenters were computed, using only data from 168 stations at distances greater than 25° from the epicentral area in order to eliminate, to some extent, traveltime anomalies in the crust and upper mantle. The data used were the same as that used for computations 3, 4, and 5, except that data from 13 stations located at distances less than 25° were excluded. The focal depth was set at 33 kilometers for both com-

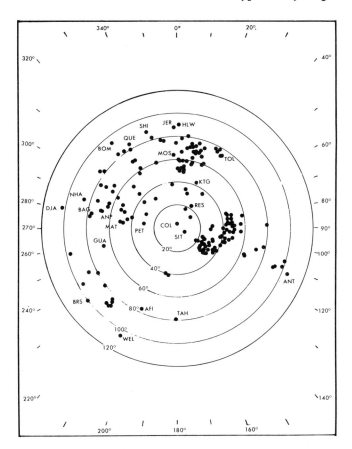

FIGURE 7.—Polar plot of stations used in computation 3 (see table 1).

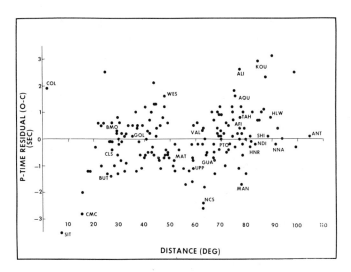

FIGURE 8.—$P(O-C)$ residuals with distances from computation 3.

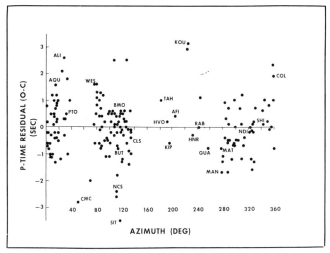

FIGURE 9.—$P(O-C)$ residuals with azimuths from computation 3.

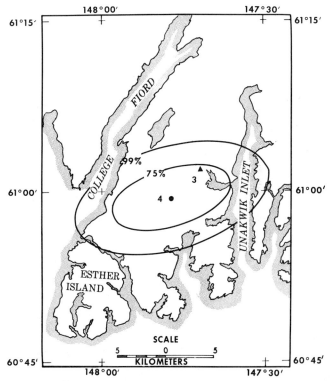

FIGURE 10.—Epicenters resulting from computations 3 and 4 (see table 1). The 99- and 75-percent confidence regions are shown for computation 4.

putations. The United States Coast and Geodetic Survey computer program and Jeffreys-Bullen traveltime curves were used for computation 6. The Seismic Data Laboratory computer program and Herrin's [1961] traveltime curves were used for computation 7. The epicenters shown in table 1 are nearly the same as the epicenters developed in computations 3, 4, and 5. This is probably due to the small number of readings available from stations at close distances, rather than the possible lack of crustal and upper mantle velocity anomalies. The areas of the 99- and 75-percent confidence regions resulting from computation 7 are 176.6 and 53.2 square kilometers, respectively. The areas of both confidence regions are slightly larger than for computation 5; this reflects poorer azimuthal distribution of stations in computation 7 when comparing with computation 5.

Computations 8, 9, and 10. Three special epicenter computations were run, using 45 selected Worldwide Network of Standard Seismograph Stations. All of the short-period seismograms from the 45 stations selected exhibited motion described previously as type 2, *i.e.*, a very clear, impulsive first motion followed within 5 seconds by a large-amplitude phase. All of the first motions recorded on the long-period seismograms were impulsive. The following epicenter computations were run, using data from the 45 stations: (1) Computation 8 used short-period first motions, (2) computation 9 used the large-amplitude second phase on the short-period seismograms, and (3) computation 10 used the first motion recorded on long-period seismograms.

The purpose of the calculations was to find out whether all of the phases were generated from the same epicentral location within the accuracy of the locations. The three epicenters are shown in figure 11. All three of the epicenters fall within a circle with a radius of 2.5 kilometers. The stations used, their associated traveltime residuals, and the arrival times of the phases are given in table 2.

It is concluded that of the waves considered—that is, the first arrival and later the large-amplitude phase

recorded on short-period seismograms and the large impulsive first arrival recorded on long-period seismograms—all originated in essentially the same focal region.

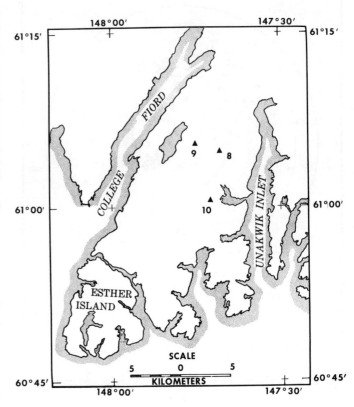

FIGURE 11.—Epicenter computed by using the arrival times of short-period first motions (8), large-amplitude, short-period secondary phases (9), and long-period first motions (10).

TABLE 2.—*Summary of arrival times of* P *and selected other phases and* P(O−C) *residuals for ten hypocenter computations*

Station	Code [1]	Distance [2]	Azimuth [2]	Phase [3]	Arrival time (G.M.T.)			Residual [4]									
					Hr.	Min.	Sec.	1	2	3	4	5	6	7	8	9	10
		°	°					Sec.	Sec.	Sec.	Sec.	Sec.	Sec.	Sec.	Sec.	Sec.	Sec.
College Outpost, Alaska____	COL [5]	3.92	359.42	*iP*	03	37	15.2			1.9	3.5	3.7					
Sitka, Alaska_____	SIT [5]	7.51	116.31	*eP*	03	38	00.8			−3.5	−0.4	−0.2					
Copper Mine, Canada_____	CMC [5]	15.49	49.98	*iP*	03	39	48.6			−2.8	−1.8	−1.7			−2.4		
				*i*ᵃ	03	39	51.4									−2.1	
				iP ᵇ	03	39	49.6										−3.0
Yellow Knife, Canada_____	YKC [5]	15.71	70.08	*iP*	03	39	51.5			−2.0	−1.1	−1.0					
Mould Bay, Canada_____	MBC [5]	18.10	21.48	*iP*	03	40	23.0			−1.2	−1.8	−1.7					
North Pole, Canada_____	NP-	18.11	21.42	*iP*	03	40	23.0			−1.2	−1.9	−1.8					
Victoria, Canada_____	VIC	18.63	121.14	*eP*	03	40	30.0			−1.2	−1.6	−1.5					
Longmire, Wash._____	LON [5]	20.70	121.83	*iP*	03	40	53.8			−0.3	−0.5	−0.4					
Corvallis, Oreg._____	COR [5]	21.87	127.61	*iP*	03	41	06.5			0.6	0.5	0.5			0.3		
				*i*ᵃ	03	41	09.0									0.1	
				iP ᵇ	03	41	07.4										0.6
Hungry Horse, Mont._____	HHM [5]	22.92	108.22	*eP*	03	41	16.7			0.5	0.2	0.2					
Resolute, Canada_____	RES [5]	23.06	32.72	*eP*	03	41	16.0			−1.0	−1.4	−1.4					

See footnotes at end of table.

TABLE 2.—*Summary of arrival times of P and selected other phases and P(O−C) residuals for ten hypocenter computations*—Continued

Station	Code [1]	Distance [2]	Azimuth [2]	Phase [3]	Arrival tme (G.M.T.) Hr.	Min.	Sec.	Residual [4] 1	2	3	4	5	6	7	8	9	10
		°	°					Sec.	Sec.	Sec.	Sec.	Sec.	Sec.	Sec.	Sec.	Sec.	Sec.
Blue Mountains, Oreg_____	BMO [5]	24.11	118.24	eP	03	41	28.5			0.6	0.4	0.4					
Klamath Falls, Oreg_____	KFO	24.44	128.27	eP	03	41	34.2			2.5	2.4	2.5					
Butte, Mont_____	BUT [5]	25.32	110.28	eP	03	41	38.2	−1.1	−1.3	−1.3	−1.5	−1.5	−1.5	−1.6			
Bozeman, Mont_____	BOZ [5]	26.05	109.77	iP	03	41	46.3	0.1	0.5	−0.1	−0.3	−0.3	−0.3	−0.4	−0.3		
				eᵃ	03	41	48.6									−0.7	
				iP ᵇ	03	41	47.6										0.2
Ukiah, Calif_____	UKI [5]	26.64	134.03	eP	03	41	51.7	0.1	0.4	−0.1	−0.2	−0.1	−0.1	−0.1			
Oroville, Calif_____	ORV [5]	26.89	130.99	eP	03	41	52.7	−1.2	−0.8	−1.4	−1.4	−1.4	−1.4	−1.4			
Calistoga, Calif_____	CLS [5]	27.31	133.57	eP	03	41	57.5			−0.4	−0.5	−0.5	−0.4	−0.5			
Crown Mine, Nev_____	CMN	27.34	123.83	iP	03	41	58.9			0.6	0.4	0.4	0.5	0.4			
Reno, Nev_____	REN [5]	27.53	128.52	eP	03	42	00.0			−0.1	−0.2	−0.2	−0.1	−0.2			
Byerly, Calif_____	BKS [5]	28.11	133.77	eP	03	42	04.2			−1.0	−1.0	−1.0	−1.0	−1.0			
Eureka, Nev_____	EUR [5]	29.10	123.18	iP	03	42	14.5	0.5	0.4	0.3	0.2	0.2	0.2	0.2			
Mina, Nev_____	MN-	29.13	127.28	iP	03	42	14.6			0.2	0.1	0.1	0.1	0.1			
Alert, Canada_____	ALE [5]	29.44	15.49	iP	03	42	17.0	1.2	1.1	0.8	0.4	0.5	0.6	0.3			
Petropavlovsk, U.S.S.R.__	PET	29.50	278.83	iP	03	42	16.0	−0.7	0.0	−1.3	−0.8	−0.7	−1.1	−0.7			
Magadan, U.S.S.R._____	MAG	29.55	294.83	iP	03	42	17.0	0.0	0.6	−0.6	−0.3	−0.2	−0.5	−0.1			
Salt Lake City, Utah_____	SLC [5]	29.77	116.38	iP	03	42	20.1			0.0	−0.1	−0.1	0.0	−0.1			
Paraiso, Calif_____	PRS [5]	29.80	133.89	eP	03	42	20.0			−0.2	−0.2	−0.2	−0.2	−0.2			
Tonopah, Nev_____	TNP [5]	29.80	126.35	iP	03	42	20.4			0.0	−0.1	−0.1	0.0	−0.1			
Dugway, Utah_____	DUG [5]	29.82	118.25	iP	03	42	20.3			−0.2	−0.4	−0.4	−0.3	−0.4			
Priest, Calif_____	PRI [5]	30.22	133.03	eP	03	42	24.7			0.6	0.6	0.6	0.6	0.6			
Flaming Gorge, Utah_____	FGU [5]	30.73	113.18	iP	03	42	27.9			−0.8	−0.9	−0.9	−0.9	−0.9			
Red Lake, Canada_____	RK-	31.05	84.26	eP	03	42	30.9			−0.1	−0.3	−0.3	−0.3	−0.5			
Rapid City, S. Dak_____	RCD [5]	31.14	102.41	iP	03	42	32.3			0.2	0.0	0.0	0.1	0.0	0.1		
				iᵃ	03	42	35.4									0.6	
				iP ᵇ	03	42	34.0										0.9
Uinta Basin, Utah_____	UBO [5]	31.14	114.09	eP	03	42	32.4			0.2	0.1	0.1	0.1	0.1			
Laramie, Wyo_____	LAR	32.16	108.34	iP	03	42	41.0			0.1	0.0	0.0	0.0	0.0			
Tiksi, U.S.S.R._____	TIK	32.24	323.81	iP	03	42	40.0	−0.5	−0.1	−1.2	−0.9	−0.9	−1.1	−0.9			
Boulder City, Nev_____	BCN	32.57	125.14	iP	03	42	44.9			0.2	0.3	0.0	0.2	0.3			
Pasadena, Calif_____	PAS [5]	32.91	131.20	iP	03	42	46.7			−0.9	−0.8	−0.8	−0.9	−0.8			
Golden, Colo_____	GOL [5]	33.54	109.90	iP	03	42	53.7			0.5	0.4	0.4	0.4	0.4			
Nord, Greenland_____	NOR [5]	35.24	11.08	iP	03	43	07.0	0.6	0.0	0.1	0.1	0.1	0.0	0.0			
Minneapolis, Minn_____	MNN [5]	35.37	91.71	iP	03	43	08.9			0.5	0.4	0.4	0.3	0.3	0.5		
				iᵃ	03	43	10.5									−0.6	
				iP ᵇ	03	43	09.0										−0.5
Tonto Forest, Ariz_____	TFO	35.48	122.10	iP	p3	43	10.4	0.7	0.3	0.5	0.6	0.6	0.5	0.6			
Godhavn, Greenland_____	GDH [5]	36.56	36.64	iP	03	43	19.0			1.0	0.8	0.8	0.7	0.7			
Yakutsk, U.S.S.R._____	YAK	36.90	308.83	iP	03	43	20.0	−0.5	0.1	−1.2	−0.7	−0.6	−1.1	−0.6			
Albuquerque, N. Mex_____	ALQ [5]	36.97	115.78	iP	03	43	22.9			0.4	0.5	0.5	0.4	0.5			
Tucson, Ariz_____	TUC [5]	37.40	123.13	eP	03	43	26.5			0.5	0.7	0.7	0.5	0.7	0.3		
				iᵃ	03	43	28.6									−0.2	
				iP ᵇ	03	43	26.5										−0.4
Kheis, U.S.S.R._____	KHE	37.88	353.33	iP	03	43	29.0			−0.1	0.1	0.1	−0.2	0.0			
Manhattan, Kans_____	MHT [5]	38.06	101.14	iP	03	43	30.6			−0.6	−0.5	−0.6	−0.8	−0.6	−0.7		
				iᵃ	03	43	33.2									−0.7	
				iP ᵇ	03	43	33.0										0.7
Lawrence, Kans_____	LAW	38.89	100.07	eP	03	43	37.0			−1.1	−1.0	−1.0	−1.2	−1.1			
Las Cruces, N. Mex_____	LC-	39.08	118.09	iP	03	43	40.5			0.5	0.7	0.7	0.5	0.7			
Lubbock, Tex_____	LUB [5]	40.16	111.81	iP	03	43	48.0	−0.5	−0.1	−0.7	−0.5	−0.5	−0.8	−0.5			
Kipapa, Hawaii_____	KIP [5]	40.20	104.08	eP	03	43	48.7	0.3	0.2	0.6	0.3	0.3	0.4	0.5	1.0		
				iᵃ	03	43	50.9									−1.2	
				iP ᵇ	03	43	50.8										0.7
Chicago-Loyola, Ill_____	CHI	40.31	90.10	iP	03	43	51.0			1.2	1.3	1.3	1.0	1.2			
Wichita Mountains, Okla_	WMO [5]	40.72	107.35	iP	03	43	53.4			0.0	0.2	0.2	−0.1	0.2			
Yuzno-Sakhalinsk,U.S.S.R.	YSS	41.14	282.91	iP	03	43	57.0	1.0	1.2	0.3	1.3	1.3	0.5	1.4			
Florissant, Mo_____	FLO [5]	41.37	95.58	iP	03	43	58.1	−0.2	0.8	−0.5	−0.2	−0.3	−0.6	−0.3			
Hawaiian Volcano Observatory, Hawaii____	HVO	41.88	190.77	iP	03	44	03.6	0.6	0.5	0.2	1.2	1.2	0.5	1.4			
Ann Arbor, Mich_____	AAM [5]	41.95	86.29	iP	03	44	04.0			0.7	1.0	0.9	0.5	0.8			
London, Canada_____	LND [5]	42.59	83.53	eP	03	44	09.6			1.0	1.3	1.3	0.9	1.2	1.1		
				iᵃ	03	44	12.1									1.0	
				iP ᵇ	03	44	10.5										0.9

See footnotes at end of table.

TABLE 2.—*Summary of arrival times of* P *and selected other phases and* P(O−C) *residuals for ten hypocenter computations*—Continued

Station	Code[1]	Distance[2]	Azimuth[2]	Phase[3]	Hr.	Min.	Sec.	1	2	3	4	5	6	7	8	9	10
		°	°				Sec.	Sec.	Sec.	Sec.	Sec.	Sec.	Sec.	Sec.	Sec.	Sec.	Sec.
Bloomington, Ind	BLO[5]	42.94	91.71	iP	03	44	11.0			-0.5	-0.2	-0.2	-0.7	-0.3	-0.5		
				i[a]	03	44	12.2									-1.9	
				iP[b]	03	44	12.8										0.2
Dallas, Tex	DAL[5]	43.11	107.05	iP	03	44	12.7	-0.1	0.2	-0.3	0.1	0.1	-0.4	0.1			
Ottawa, Canada	OTT[5]	43.46	76.94	eP	03	44	15.0			-0.6	-0.3	-0.3	-0.8	-0.4			
Kap Tobin, Greenland	KTG[5]	43.43	23.46	iP	03	44	17.0			2.1	2.4	2.4	1.9	2.3	2.5		
				i[a]	03	44	19.0									2.2	
				iP[b]	03	44	17.0										+1.0
Cleveland, Ohio	CLE	43.59	85.30	iP	03	44	18.0			1.3	1.6	1.6	1.1	1.5			
Rochester, N.Y	ROC	44.26	80.57	iP	03	44	25.3			1.3	1.7	1.6	1.1	1.5			
Montreal, Canada	MNT	44.37	75.26	eP	03	44	23.0			0.1	0.4	0.4	-0.1	0.3			
Bodaybo, U.S.S.R	BOD	45.48	312.06	eP	03	44	31.0			-0.7	0.3	0.4	-0.6	0.4			
Morgantown, W. Va	MRG[5]	45.79	85.66	iP	03	44	33.6			-0.8	-0.3	-0.3	-0.9	-0.4			
State College, Pa	SCP[5]	45.89	82.90	eP	03	44	35.5			0.4	0.8	0.8	0.2	0.7	0.4		
				i[a]	03	44	37.2									-0.5	
				iP[b]	03	44	35.9										-0.3
Cumberland Plateau, Tenn	CPO[5]	46.24	94.00	eP	03	44	36.8			-1.1	-0.6	-0.6	-1.3	-0.7			
Jena, La	JE-	46.24	103.11	eP	03	44	38.5	0.7	1.0	0.5	1.1	1.1	0.4	1.0			
Ogdensburg, N.J	OGD[5]	47.26	80.06	eP	03	44	46.5			0.8	1.2	1.2	0.6	1.1			
Blacksburg, Va	BLA[5]	47.46	88.12	iP	03	44	46.9			-0.7	-0.1	-0.1	-0.8	-0.2	-0.6		
				i[a]	03	44	49.1									-1.0	
				iP[b]	03	44	47.6										-1.0
Palisades, N.Y	PAL[5]	47.65	79.55	eP	03	44	50.5			1.6	2.2	2.2	1.4	2.1			
Georgetown (Wash., D.C.)	GEO[5]	47.76	83.89	eP	03	44	49.2			-0.6	0.0	-0.1	-0.8	-0.2			
Fordham, N.Y	FOR[5]	47.77	79.65	eP	03	44	51.0			1.2	1.7	1.7	1.0	1.6			
Weston, Mass	WES[5]	47.82	76.35	iP	03	44	51.8			1.6	2.2	2.2	1.4	2.1	1.7		
				i[a]	03	44	53.7									1.1	
				iP[b]	03	44	53.8										2.5
Atlanta, Ga	ATL[5]	48.58	94.60	iP	03	44	55.9			-0.4	0.2	0.2	-0.5	0.1	-0.4		
				i[a]	03	44	59.7									0.8	
				iP[b]	03	44	56.7										-0.6
Spring Hill, Ala	SHA[5]	48.99	100.20	eP	03	45	00.1			0.6	1.3	1.3	0.5	1.2	0.6		
				i[a]	03	45	02.4									0.3	
				iP[b]	03	45	01.3										0.8
Vladivostok, U.S.S.R	VLA	49.14	287.33	eP	03	45	00.0	0.1	0.2	-0.5	0.8	0.8	-0.3	0.9			
Tromsoe, Norway	TRO	49.31	6.13	iP	03	45	00.6			-0.6	0.1	0.1	-0.8	0.0			
Kevo, Finland	KEV[5]	49.48	2.42	iP	03	45	01.9			-0.7	0.1	0.1	-0.8	0.0	-0.3		
				i[a]	03	45	03.3									-1.1	
				iP[b]	03	45	03.3										-0.4
Kiruna, Sweden	KIR[5]	51.17	5.76	iP	03	45	14.5			-1.0	-0.2	-0.2	-1.1	-0.3	-0.6		
				i[a]	03	45	16.2									-1.2	
				iP[b]	03	45	15.8										-0.8
Matsushiro, Japan	MAT	51.30	277.08	iP	03	45	16.3	-0.2	0.2	-0.8	0.6	0.6	-0.6	0.7			
Changchun, China	CNH	51.60	292.75	iP	03	45	18.0	-0.6	-1.0	-1.2	0.1	0.1	-1.1	0.2			
Apatity, U.S.S.R	APA	51.75	359.50	iP	03	45	19.0			-0.8	0.0	0.0	-1.0	-0.1			
Sodankylä, Finland	SOD	51.86	2.79	iP	03	45	20.5			-0.2	0.6	0.6	-0.3	0.5			
Irkutsk, U.S.S.R	IRK	53.39	313.27	eP	03	45	32.0			-0.4	0.8	0.8	-0.3	0.8			
Umea, Sweden	UME[5]	55.17	6.49	eP	03	45	44.0			-1.1	-0.4	-0.4	-1.3	-0.5	-0.8		
				i[a]	03	45	46.6									-0.4	
				iP[b]	03	45	48.2										2.0
Seoul, South Korea	SEO[5]	55.83	286.82	iP	03	45	48.8	-1.1	-1.4	-1.7	-0.4	-0.3	-1.5	-0.2	-1.6		
				e[a]	03	45	50.2									-2.2	
				iP[b]	03	45	50.3										-1.1
Oslo, Norway	OO-	58.15	12.45	iP	03	45	58.4			-1.2	-0.4	-0.4	-1.3	-0.5			
Eltsovka, U.S.S.R	ELT	58.27	325.10	iP	03	46	06.0			-1.6	-0.6	-0.6	-1.5	-0.6			
Kongsberg, Norway	KON[5]	58.41	13.28	iP	03	46	08.1			-0.2	0.6	0.6	-0.3	0.5	0.1		
				i[a]	03	46	11.3									1.1	
				iP[b]	03	46	09.2										-0.2
Nurmijärvi, Finland	NUR[5]	58.68	4.42	iP	03	46	09.3			-0.8	-0.1	-0.1	-0.9	-0.2	-0.5		
				e[a]	03	46	12.9									-0.9	
				iP[b]	03	46	09.9										-1.3
Peking, China	PEK	58.69	296.69	iP	03	46	10.0	-0.1	-0.3	-0.7	0.4	0.4	-0.6	0.5			
Uppsala, Sweden	UPP[5]	58.94	8.58	iP	03	46	10.9			-1.1	-0.4	-0.4	-1.2	-0.5			

See footnotes at end of table.

TABLE 2.—*Summary of arrival times of* P *and selected other phases and* P(O−C) *residuals for ten hypocenter computations*—Continued

Station	Code[1]	Distance[2]	Azimuth[2]	Phase[3]	Arrival time (G.M.T.) Hr.	Min.	Sec.	Residual[4] 1	2	3	4	5	6	7	8	9	10
		°	°					Sec.	Sec.	Sec.	Sec.	Sec.	Sec.	Sec.	Sec.	Sec.	Sec.
Bermuda—Columbia, Bermuda	BEC[5]	58.97	78.56	eP	03	46	13.1	0.8	0.2	0.5	1.0	1.0	0.3	0.9	0.6		
				iª	03	46	14.9									−0.2	
				ePᵇ	03	46	13.1										−0.6
Sverdlovsk, U.S.S.R.	SVE	60.44	342.53	eP	03	46	23.0			0.6	1.4	1.4	0.6	1.4			
Eskdalemuir, Scotland	ESK[5]	60.68	22.38	eP	03	46	23.8			−0.2	0.3	0.3	−0.3	0.2	0.1		
				eª	03	46	26.2									0.2	
				iPᵇ	03	46	25.4										0.3
Valentia, Ireland	VAL[5]	62.39	28.20	eP	03	46	35.8			0.3	0.6	0.6	0.2	0.5	0.6		
				iª	03	46	39.6									2.1	
				iPᵇ	03	46	37.1										0.5
Semipalatinsk, U.S.S.R.	SEM	62.48	327.60	iP	03	46	36.0			−0.2	0.5	0.5	−0.2	0.5			
LaPalma, El Salvador	LPS[5]	62.56	111.29	eP	03	46	34.8	−2.4	−2.4	−2.6	−2.3	−2.3	−2.7	−2.3	−2.7		
				eª	03	46	37.8									−2.3	
				iPᵇ	03	46	36.9										−1.5
Copenhagen, Denmark	COP[5]	62.61	12.52	iP	03	46	37.3			0.4	0.8	0.8	0.3	0.7			
Nueva Concepción, El Salvador	NCS	62.72	111.41	eP	03	46	36.0	−2.1	−2.1	−2.4	−2.0	−2.0	−2.4	−2.0			
San Salvador, El Salvador	SSS[5]	63.08	111.65	eP	03	46	39.0	−1.6	−1.6	−1.8	−1.5	−1.5	−1.9	−1.5			
Moscow, U.S.S.R.	MOS	63.53	356.64	eP	03	46	43.0			0.0	0.4	0.4	0.0	0.3			
Zose, China	ZSC	63.85	287.17	iP	03	46	45.0			−0.6	0.1	0.2	−0.4	0.3			
Nanking, China	NAN	64.16	289.67	iP	03	46	47.0			−0.5	0.2	0.2	−0.4	0.3			
Uccle, Belgium	UCC	66.32	18.95	eP	03	47	02.0			1.0	0.9	0.9	0.9	0.8			
Sian, China	SIA	66.69	298.66	eP	03	47	03.0	−0.1	−0.9	−0.7	−0.4	−0.4	−0.6	−0.4			
Colmberg, Leipzig, Germany	CLL	66.98	13.02	iP	03	47	04.9			−0.2	−0.4	−0.4	−0.4	−0.5			
Dourbes, Belgium	DOU	67.04	18.98	eP	03	47	05.0	−0.1	−0.7	−0.5	−0.7	−0.8	−0.6	−0.8			
Jena, Germany	JEN	67.17	14.05	eP	03	47	07.0			0.7	0.5	0.4	0.5	0.4			
Lanchow, China	LAN	67.26	303.55	iP	03	47	07.0			−0.5	−0.3	−0.3	−0.4	−0.2			
Guam, Mariana Islands	GUA[5]	67.34	256.64	eP	03	47	07.3	−0.3	−0.7	−0.8	−0.5	−0.5	−0.6	−0.3			
Moxa, Germany	MOX	67.47	14.09	eP	03	47	07.0			−1.3	−1.5	−1.6	−1.4	−1.6			
Heidelberg, Germany	HEI	68.33	16.33	eP	03	47	13.9			0.2	−0.1	−0.1	0.1	−0.2			
Praha, Czechoslovakia	PRA	68.35	12.28	iP	03	47	14.8			1.0	0.7	0.7	0.9	0.6			
Gräfenberg, Germany	GG-	68.36	14.56	eP	03	47	14.3			0.4	0.1	0.1	0.3	0.0			
Anpu, Taiwan	ANP[5]	68.69	283.47	eP	03	47	16.6			0.1	0.2	0.2	0.3	0.4	0.2		
				eª	03	47	18.9									0.4	
				iPᵇ	03	47	17.5										+0.1
Taipei, Taiwan	TAP	68.81	283.39	eP	03	47	18.0	1.4	0.9	0.9	1.0	1.0	1.0	1.1			
Stuttgart, Germany	STU[5]	69.02	16.09	eP	03	47	17.5	0.0	−0.6	−0.4	−0.8	−0.9	−0.5	−0.9	−0.1		
				eª	03	47										0.8	
				iPᵇ	03	47	18.8										−0.2
Tübingen, Germany	TUB	69.23	16.29	iP	03	47	20.4			1.2	0.8	0.7	1.1	0.7			
Feldberg, Germany	FEL	69.72	17.17	eP	03	47	22.7			0.3	−0.2	−0.2	0.2	−0.3			
Alma-Ata, U.S.S.R.	AAB	69.82	326.56	eP	03	47	23.0			0.1	−0.1	−0.2	0.1	−0.1			
Ravensberg, Germany	RAV	70.03	16.07	iP	03	47	25.0			0.9	0.4	0.3	0.8	0.3			
San Juan, Puerto Rico	SJG[5]	70.04	88.09	eP	03	47	24.6	0.3	0.6	0.0	−0.6	−0.7	−0.1	−0.7			
Uzhgorod Ungvar, U.S.S.R.	UZH	70.42	7.02	eP	03	47	27.0			0.5	0.0	0.0	0.4	0.0			
Frunze, U.S.S.R.	FRU	70.95	328.40	iP	03	47	30.0			0.2	−0.1	−0.2	0.2	−0.1			
Budapest, Hungary	BUD	71.34	9.46	eP	03	47	31.0			−1.0	−1.5	−1.6	−1.1	−1.6			
Balboa Heights, C.Z.	BHP[5]	71.68	105.01	eP	03	47	35.2	0.9	1.0	0.6	−0.1	−0.1	0.6	−0.1			
Chengtu, China	CNU	71.86	300.58	iP	03	47	35.0	0.0	−0.3	−0.5	−0.8	−0.8	−0.4	−0.7			
Trieste, Italy	TRI[5]	72.59	13.50	iP	03	47	39.0			−0.4	−1.1	−1.1	−0.5	−1.2			
Zagreb, Yugoslavia	ZAG	72.72	11.00	eP	03	47	40.7			0.5	0.1	0.2	0.4	−0.2			
Porto (Serra do Pilar), Portugal	PTO[5]	72.90	31.16	iP	03	47	41.8			0.5	−0.3	−0.3	0.3	−0.4	0.7		
				eª	03	47	45.2									1.8	
				iPᵇ	03	47	44.0										1.6
Isola, France	ISO	73.18	18.70	iP	03	47	42.9			−0.2	−0.9	−0.9	−0.3	−0.9			
Beograd, Yugoslavia	BEO	74.10	8.74	iP	03	47	49.5			1.2	0.5	0.5	1.1	0.4			
Canton, China	CNT	74.30	289.12	iP	03	47	50.0	0.7	−0.4	0.1	−0.2	−0.2	0.2	−0.1			
Simferopol, U.S.S.R.	SIM	74.40	358.66	iP	03	47	51.0			1.0	0.3	0.3	0.9	0.2			
Hong Kong	HKC[5]	74.59	288.02	eP	03	47	52.3			0.7	0.3	0.3	0.8	0.4			

See footnotes at end of table.

TABLE 2.—*Summary of arrival times of* P *and selected other phases and* P(O−C) *residuals for ten hypocenter computations*—Continued

Station	Code [1]	Distance [2]	Azimuth [2]	Phase [3]	Hr.	Min.	Sec.	1	2	3	4	5	6	7	8	9	10
		°	°					Sec.	Sec.	Sec.	Sec.	Sec.	Sec.	Sec.	Sec.	Sec.	Sec.
Lisbon, Portugal	LIS	75.04	32.41	eP	03	47	55.6	2.2	2.9	1.8	1.0	0.9	1.7	0.9			
Toledo, Spain	TOL [5]	75.19	28.15	iP	03	47	54.4			−0.3	−1.1	−1.2	−0.4	−1.2	−0.1	0.0	1.1
				i a	03	47	56.8										
				iP b	03	47	56.9										
Aquila, Italy	AQU [5]	75.86	14.33	iP	03	48	00.1			1.6	0.8	0.8	1.5	0.7			
Caracas, Venezuela	CAR [5]	76.40	92.92	iP	03	48	02.4	0.5	0.8	0.2	−0.7	−0.8	0.1	−0.8	0.2	1.4	−0.8
				e a	03	48	06.2										
				iP b	03	48	02.4										
Baguio City, Philippine Islands	BAG [5]	76.64	279.58	iP	03	48	02.5	−0.6	0.7	−1.1	−1.5	−1.5	−1.0	−1.4	−1.1	−2.1	−2.1
				i a	03	48	03.6										
				iP b	03	48	02.5										
Afiamalu, Samoa Islands	AFI [5]	77.09	203.98	iP	03	48	06.5	0.8	0.6	0.4	0.0	0.0	0.6	0.2	0.2	2.7	0.9
				e a	03	48	11.3										
				iP b	03	48	07.8										
Bakuriani, U.S.S.R.	BKR	77.21	351.41	iP	03	48	07.0			0.8	0.2	0.2	0.8	0.1			
Kunming, China	KUN	77.24	298.86	eP	03	48	07.0			0.0	−0.4	−0.4	0.1	−0.3			
Alicante, Spain	ALI	77.44	25.86	iP	03	48	10.0			2.6	1.8	1.7	2.5	1.7			
Manila, Philippine Islands	MAN [5]	77.90	278.26	eP	03	48	08.7	−1.2	−1.7	−1.7	−2.1	−2.1	−1.5	−2.0	−1.7	−1.5	−0.5
				i a	03	48	11.0										
				iP b	03	48	10.8										
Lhasa, Tibet	LHA	77.91	310.44	iP	03	48	12.0			1.2	0.6	0.6	1.2	0.7			
Kirovabad, U.S.S.R.	KRV	78.06	349.13	iP	03	48	11.0			0.2	−0.5	−0.6	0.1	−0.6			
Bogotá, Colombia	BOG [5]	78.07	102.17	eP	03	48	11.6	0.1	−1.0	−0.2	−1.1	−1.2	−0.2	−1.2	−0.2	−0.8	−1.1
				e a	03	48	13.5										
				iP b	03	48	11.7										
Istanbul-Kandilli, Turkey	ISK	78.26	2.50	eP	03	48	12.1			0.2	−0.6	−0.6	0.2	−0.6			
Istanbul, Turkey	IST [5]	78.28	2.56	eP	03	48	11.4			−0.6	−1.4	−1.4	−0.6	−1.4	−0.3	0.0	−0.2
				i a	03	48	13.9										
				iP b	03	48	12.8										
Tahiti, Tahiti	TAH	78.47	181.56	iP	03	48	14.5	1.3	1.2	1.0	0.3	0.3	1.1	0.5			
Trinidad, West Indies	TRN [5]	78.97	88.01	eP	03	48	16.7			0.4	−0.6	−0.6	0.3	−0.6	0.4	4.2	−0.1
				i a	03	48	23.0										
				iP b	03	48	17.2										
Rabaul, New Britain	RAB [5]	79.71	241.52	iP	03	48	20.4			0.0	−0.5	−0.5	0.2	−0.3	0.1	2.9	−0.9
				i a	03	48	25.6										
				iP b	03	48	20.4										
Warsak, Pakistan	WRS	79.96	327.90	eP	03	48	20.0			−1.3	−2.0	−2.0	−1.3	−2.0			
Athens, Greece	ATH [5]	81.13	6.86	eP	03	48	27.1			−0.3	−1.1	−1.2	−0.4	−1.2	0.0	0.4	0.2
				i a	03	48	29.8										
				iP b	03	48	28.6										
Shillong, India	SHL [5]	81.26	308.00	iP	03	48	28.7			0.1	−0.5	−0.5	0.2	−0.4			
Honiara, Solomon Islands	HNR [5]	81.28	232.22	iP	03	48	28.4			−0.3	−0.8	−0.8	−0.1	−0.7			
Lahore, Pakistan	LAH [5]	81.62	324.70	iP	03	48	30.0			−0.1	−0.8	−0.8	−0.1	−0.8			
Teheran, Iran	TEH	82.35	344.43	eP	03	48	35.0			1.0	0.3	0.2	1.0	0.2			
New Delhi, India	NDI [5]	83.47	321.36	iP	03	48	39.4			−0.2	−0.9	−1.0	−0.2	−0.9	0.1	0.4	−0.1
				i a	03	48	41.2										
				iP b	03	48	40.5										
Chittagong, Pakistan	CHT	84.19	306.68	eP	03	48	44.0			0.7	0.1	0.0	0.7	0.1			
Luganville, New Hebrides	LUG	84.32	223.40	iP	03	48	47.0	3.3	2.1	2.9	2.3	2.3	3.1	2.4			
Quetta, Pakistan	QUE [5]	84.85	330.38	iP	03	48	47.5			0.7	0.0	0.0	0.7	0.0	0.9	−0.2	1.3
				i a	03	48	48.6										
				iP b	03	48	49.1										
Nhatrang, South Viet-Nam	NHA [5]	85.66	287.25	iP	03	48	51.8			1.0	0.4	0.4	1.1	0.5			
Port Moresby, New Guinea	PMG [5]	86.54	243.76	eP	03	48	56.2			1.1	0.5	0.5	1.2	0.6	0.9	0.9	0.8
				e a	03	48	58.4										
				iP b	03	48	56.8										
Jerusalem, Israel	JER [5]	87.54	357.53	iP	03	49	02.0			2.3	1.5	1.4	2.2	1.4			
Shiraz, Iran	SHI [5]	88.19	342.48	eP	03	49	03.2			0.1	−0.6	−0.6	0.1	−0.6	0.3	−0.6	1.2
				i a	03	49	04.5										
				iP b	03	49	04.3										
Helwan, Egypt	HLW	89.47	0.83	iP	03	49	09.7			0.8	0.0	−0.1	0.7	−0.1	1.0	−0.2	0.6
				i a	03	49	10.7										
				iP b	03	49	10.6										

See footnotes at end of table.

TABLE 2.—*Summary of arrival times of* P *and selected other phases and* P(O−C) *residuals for ten hypocenter computations*—Continued

Station	Code [1]	Dis-tance [2]	Azi-muth [2]	Phase [3]	Arrival time (G.M.T.) Hr.	Min.	Sec.	Residual [4] 1	2	3	4	5	6	7	8	9	10
		°	°					Sec.	Sec.	Sec.	Sec.	Sec.	Sec.	Sec.	Sec.	Sec.	Sec.
Koumac, New Caledonia___	KOU	89.97	224.15	iP	03	49	14.5			3.1	2.5	2.5	3.3	2.7			
Nana, Peru_____	NNA [5]	91.37	112.39	iP	03	49	17.8			-0.2	-1.3	-1.3	-0.3	-1.3	-0.3		
				e [a]	03	49	18.6									-2.0	
				iP [b]	03	49	17.8										-1.2
Huancayo, Peru_____	HUA	92.10	111.09	iP	03	49	22.3			0.4	-0.6	-0.7	0.4	-0.6			
Bombay, India_____	BOM	93.99	321.93	iP	03	49	30.0			0.0	-0.6	-0.6	-0.1	-0.6			
LaPaz, Bolivia_____	LPB [5]	99.36	107.03	eP	03	49	54.5			-0.3	-1.3	-1.4	-0.3	-1.3			
LaPaz, Bolivia_____	LZ-	98.95	107.22	eP	03	49	55.5			2.5	1.4	1.4	2.5	1.4			
Antofagasta, Chile_____	ANT [5]	104.52	112.53	iP	03	50	17.3			0.1	-0.9	-1.0	0.1	-0.9			

[1] Code obtained from *Seismograph Station Abbreviations*, U.S. Department of Commerce, Coast and Geodetic Survey, Rockville, Md., 46 pp., February 1965.
[2] Distance and azimuth are those obtained from computation 1 in table 1, which utilized 46 stations beyond 25° epicentral distance and where paired in distance and azimuth.
[3] Phases noted with [a] or [b] have the following meaning:
    [a]: The large-amplitude second arrival observed on short-period seismograms.
    [b]: First arrival observed on long-period seismograms.
[4] Residuals listed are the observed minus the computed traveltime. Coast and Geodetic Survey computations determine the computed traveltime from the Jeffreys-Bullen *Seismological Tables* (1958) and the Seismic Data Laboratory use the traveltime curves developed by Herrin (1961). Column numbers refer to modes of computation listed in table 1.
[5] Seismograms read by the authors.

The origin time for the solution computed, using the second large-amplitude arrivals on short-period seismograms (computation 9), was 2.4 seconds later than the origin time obtained by using short-period first-motion data (computation 8). The origin time for the epicenter computed, using the first motions from long-period seismograms (computation 10), was only 1.0 second later than the origin time obtained by using the short-period first motions. Thus, we may conclude that the long-period motion originated at approximately the same time and from approximately the same focal region as the short-period waves. The secondary, large-amplitude short-period waves seem to have originated at the same location as the short-period and long-period first motions. The secondary, large-amplitude short-period wave is either a reflected phase that follows a different path to the stations than the short- and long-period first motions or a phase that originates at a later time than the short- and long-period first motions.

SUMMARY OF EPICENTER COMPUTATIONS

All of the epicenters discussed above are in close agreement and lie within a circle having a radius of 3.5 kilometers (fig. 6). The close grouping of the epicenters computed by using different data sets, computer programs, and traveltime curves does not guarantee the correct location of the earthquake. It is well known that nuclear explosions whose locations and times of detonation are accurately known have been poorly located when using conventional hypocenter location techniques and stand-ard traveltime curves; an example is the underground nuclear explosion, Longshot, detonated on Amchitka Island in the Aleutian Islands on October 29, 1965. The location of this explosion was 51.44° N., 179.18° E., depth 0.66 kilometer, and origin time 21:00:00.1 (G.M.T.). The location of the explosion, obtained using the United States Coast and Geodetic Survey hypocenter program, the Jeffreys-Bullen traveltime curves, and the data from 242 stations was 51.67° ± 0.01° N., 179.18° ± 0.01° E.; depth, 40 kilometers ± 3.6 kilometers; and origin time 21:00:03.0 ± 0.4 second. Thus, the errors in epicentral location, depth, and origin time were 25.6 kilometers, 39.34 kilometers, and 3.0 seconds, respectively.

The epicenter with coordinates 61.04° ± 0.05° N., 147.73° ± 0.07° W. and origin time 03:36:14.0 (computation 1, table 1) was obtained by using 46 stations with relatively good azimuthal distribution; it is considered the best epicentral location on the basis of the information presently available. This epicenter was computed using the standard Jeffreys-Bullen traveltime curves, and it can be compared easily with the locations of many other earthquakes located by using the same curves. The epicenter computed (computation 2) by using station corrections of Hales and Cleary [1966] is difficult to evaluate, since the station corrections were only recently published and, consequently, have not been tested extensively. It should also be emphasized that epicenters computed with and without station corrections (computations 1 and 2) differ by only 6.5 kilometers.

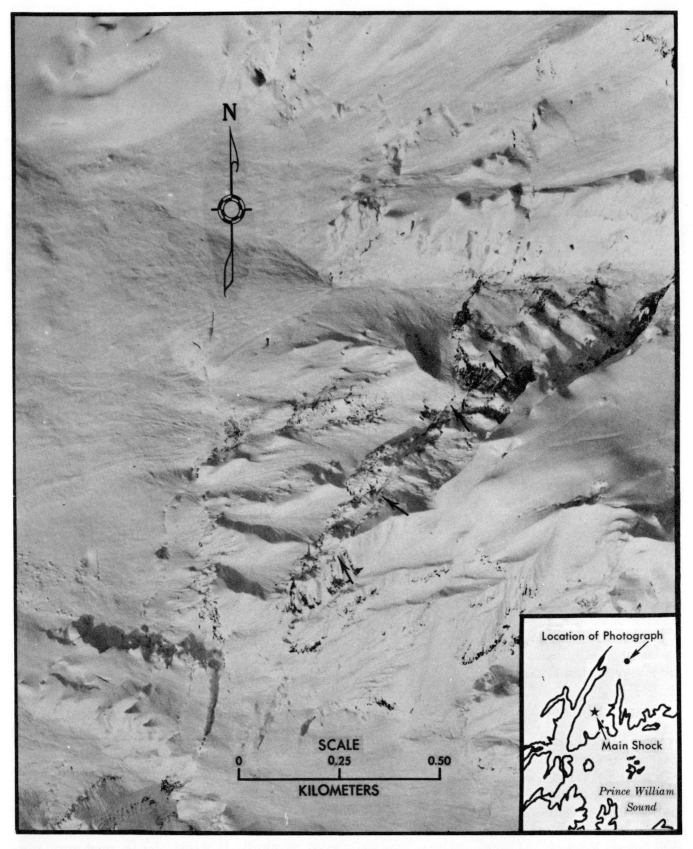

FIGURE 12.—This portion of Coast and Geodetic Survey aerial photograph (No. 64W6891) shows possible faulting 38 kilometers N. 31° E. of the preferred instrumental epicenter.

The epicenter of the Prince William Sound Earthquake lies about 15 kilometers inland from the north shore of Prince William Sound on the narrow peninsula between College Fiord and Unakwik Inlet. The peninsula is largely glacier covered. No positive evidence of surface faulting could be found on United States Coast and Geodetic Survey aerial photographs of the peninsula. Some evidence of possible faulting, however, can be seen on the portion of the C&GS air photo number 64W6891, shown as figure 12. This photograph was taken at an elevation of 12,000 feet on April 19, 1964. Subsequent snowfall prevented further study of the area. The possible surface breakage, shown by arrows in figure 12, has a strike of N. 42° E.

FOCAL DEPTH

The depth of focus of the main shock is uncertain for the following reasons:

(1) The complicated nature of the first motion recorded from the earthquake made depth phases—such as pP and sP— difficult to identify with certainty, even though seismograms from earthquakes occurring in this part of Alaska commonly show clear depth phases;

(2) Many of the first motions recorded were emergent. Consequently, any depth phase recorded would theoretically have a small amplitude and would be difficult to identify;

(3) Many of the seismograms recorded were off scale within a few seconds after the first motion; and

(4) The closest station to the epicentral area was College, Alaska, a distance of approximately 436 kilometers. Focal depths computed, using conventional least-squares hypocenter programs such as those discussed in the previous section, may be considerably in error when no data are available from stations at epicentral distances closer than the depth of focus.

Epicenter computations 1 through 7 are summarized in table 1; they yielded depths less than 50 kilometers or negative depths, i.e., above the mean sphere, whenever the depth parameter was not restricted to some arbitrary focal depth before the calculation of the hypocenter. The indication is, therefore, that the earthquake had a shallow focus. The focal depth was set at 33 kilometers for most of the computations in table 1; thus the various epicenters can be compared.

An attempt was made to identify depth phases—such as pP and sP—on seismograms. The majority of seismograms throughout the world were off scale a few seconds

after the first motion was recorded. For seismograms that remained on scale, no consistent phases identifiable as pP or sP could be found on the seismograms available for study.

The $P(O-C)$ time residuals for College, Alaska, are large and positive, ranging from 1.9 to 3.7 seconds for the epicenter computations summarized in table 1. Since it had been observed that $P(O-C)$ time residuals at College for many aftershocks of the March 28 earthquake were commonly negative, a further analysis of the residuals at College for aftershocks in Prince William Sound was made in the hope that something might be learned about the depth of the main shock. A plot was first made of $P(O-C)$ residuals for College (COL) versus magnitude (m_b) for 102 aftershocks located in Prince William Sound to ascertain whether the time residuals were related in a systematic manner to magnitude. The results (fig. 13) indicate that there is no

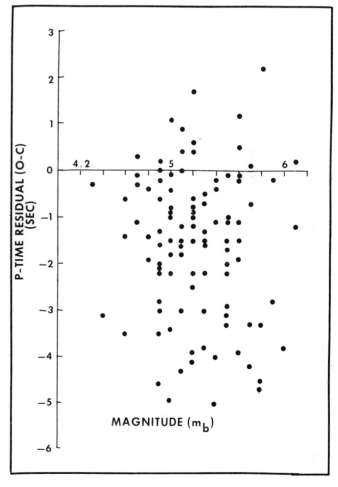

FIGURE 13.—$P(O-C)$ time residuals of aftershocks computed for the College, Alaska, station versus magnitude m_b (C&GS). The aftershocks are all within 400 to 670 kilometers south of College.

apparent relationship between the time residuals at College and magnitude. Of the 102 aftershocks initially selected for study, the focal depths of 29 could be reasonably well determined. The epicenter of each of these 29 aftershocks was computed by using teleseismic data, but readings from College were excluded from the computations. Focal depths were determined by using data from temporary seismograph stations, installed after the earthquake, that were within 100 kilometers of the epicenters, from *pP* or *sP* phases observed at teleseismic distance or both. The range of focal depths for the sample of 29 earthquakes was from 4 to 47 kilometers. Figure 14 shows the

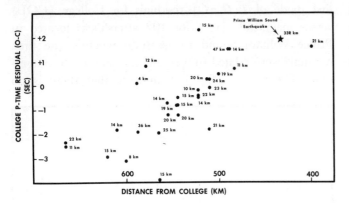

FIGURE 14.—$P(O-C)$ time residuals at College, Alaska, for 29 aftershocks as a function of focal depth and distance from College Outpost, Alaska, station.

$P(O-C)$ time residuals that were computed for College as a function of focal depth and distance from College. Some interesting observations are possible from figure 14. There appears to be no relationship between residual and focal depth for earthquakes with focal depths in the range of 4 to 47 kilometers. The $P(O-C)$ time residuals for College decrease linearly from $+2.0$ to -3.0 seconds, with increased distance south from College. The 5-second change in average residual occurs in distance, ranging from 400 to 670 kilometers south of College.

The sharp change in $P(O-C)$ residuals with distance from College suggests anomalous crustal or upper mantle velocities in the vicinity of Prince William Sound or beneath the Chugach Mountains. Figure 15 illustrates two possible crustal configurations that account for the observed residual. The thickening of the crust beneath the Chugach Mountains, as shown in the upper portion of figure 15, is somewhat similar to a crustal section derived by Woollard, Ostenso, Thiel, and Bonini [1960], mostly on the basis of gravity data.

There is additional evidence not illustrated in figure 15 for the existence of a crustal thickening and/or a low-velocity zone beneath the Chugach Mountains. The residuals for College were examined for 13 earthquakes, routinely located by the Coast and Geodetic Survey during 1963 through 1965, that occurred between the Chugach Mountains and College. The focal depths ranged

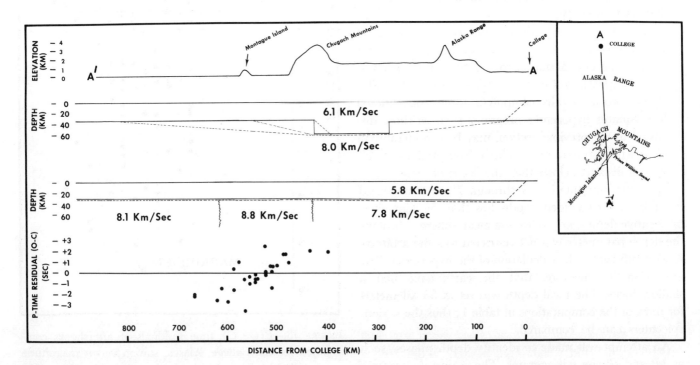

FIGURE 15.—Possible crustal structure and *P*-wave velocities. $P(O-C)$ residuals at College versus distances **are those** shown at a larger scale in figure 14.

from 7 to 113 kilometers. The residuals at College varied from +1.6 to −0.7 seconds. The mean of the residuals was zero. All of the earthquakes were located north of the Chugach Mountains and closer to College than the earthquakes whose residuals are shown in figures 14 and 15. The grouping of the residuals near zero is interpreted as evidence that these 13 earthquakes occurred north of the "root" or the low-velocity zone that is thought to lie beneath the Chugach Mountains.

The increase of mantle velocity beneath Prince William Sound shown in the lower portion of figure 15 is only an idealized representation of one of many anomalous velocity distributions that could produce the observed traveltime residuals at College. It is known from gravity surveys of the Coast and Geodetic Survey [Algermissen, 1964] and the U. S. Geological Survey [Case, Barnes, Plafker, and Robbins, 1966] that a band of large, positive Bouguer gravity anomalies exists in an arcuate pattern from south of Knight Island in Prince William Sound, north and eastward to the Ellamar Peninsula. Case, Barnes, Plafker, and Robbins [1966] have interpreted the positive 60-milligal Bouguer anomaly centered over Knight Island as a wedge of greenstone, with a width (in an east-west direction) of 40,000 feet at the surface and a depth of 40,000 feet. While the anomalous mass causing the gravity anomaly would probably propagate seismic waves at somewhat higher velocities than the adjacent material, the mass and the probable increase in seismic wave velocity associated with the mass are considered insufficient to cause the observed $P(O-C)$ residual pattern at College.

The problem of the depth of focus of the March 28, 1964, earthquake cannot be completely resolved with the data available. The distribution of $P(O-C)$ residuals from College, as a function of focal depth and distance from College, indicates anomalous velocities and/or crustal thicknesses—either beneath Prince William Sound or the Chugach Mountains or beneath both. The focus of the earthquake is believed to be shallower than 60 kilometers for three reasons:

(1) None of the aftershocks in the vicinity of the main shock, for which focal depths could be reasonably well determined, had focal depths greater than 50 kilometers;

(2) The large-amplitude surface waves generated by this earthquake indicate a normal depth focus; and

(3) Earthquakes with focal depths slightly greater than normal and which were located in the general vicinity of, and north of, the main shock during the

years 1963-65 do not have, on the average, positive residuals at College.

MAGNITUDE

The magnitude m_b routinely reported by the Coast and Geodetic Survey for earthquakes throughout the world proved unsatisfactory for the study of the Prince William Sound Earthquake. The general procedure for determining m_b has been discussed by Engdahl and Gunst [1966]. Two m_b values, 5.5 and 6.2, were calculated, using 15 stations. The first magnitude, 5.5, was computed by using the amplitude of the first cycle of the first motion recorded at each station. The second magnitude, 6.2, was based on the average amplitude of several cycles of the large-amplitude second arrivals that were recorded on most short-period seismograms, 2 to 5 seconds after the first motion. Both m_b values were significantly lower than the magnitude derived from surface-wave data.

The magnitude M_s was computed for the earthquake, using the amplitudes of surface waves of approximately 20-second periods. The method is described by Guten-

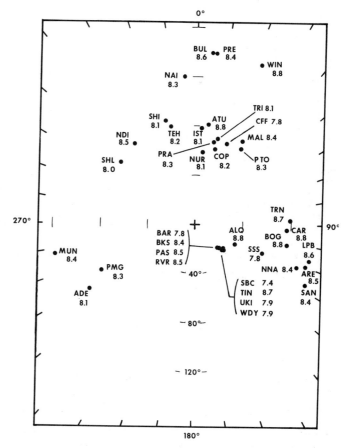

FIGURE 16.—Distribution in distance and azimuth of data used in the M_s magnitude calculations.

berg [1945]. Data from 37 stations were used. The stations and magnitudes are listed in table 3, and the geographic distribution of the stations is shown in figure 16. The mean value of M_s from 37 observations is 8.3, with a standard deviation of ±0.33 magnitude unit. The distribution is nearly normal, with 64.9 percent of the data points falling within one standard deviation of the mean. The magnitude $M_s = 8.3 \pm 0.33$ is somewhat lower than the preliminary magnitudes reported for this earthquake. If all magnitude values outside one standard deviation are discarded, the new mean M_s magnitude remains 8.3.

TABLE 3—*Summary of* M_s *magnitude calculations*

Station	Code [1]	Distance	Azimuth	Instrument [2]	Time	$A \times 10^3$	M_s	Remarks
		Degrees	*Degrees*		*Seconds*	*Microns*		
Ukiah, Calif	UKI	26.64	134.03	Mc-R	23	4.23	7.9	One component
Byerly, Calif	BKS	28.11	133.77	W-A	18	13.20	8.4	
Tinemaha, Calif	TIN	30.31	128.74	W-A	18	23.80	8.7	
Woody, Calif	WDY	31.27	130.83	W-A	19	14.90	7.9	One component
Santa Barbara, Calif	SBC	32.08	133.10	W-A	20	1.20	7.4	
Pasadena, Calif	PAS	32.91	131.20	W-A	20	9.90	8.5	
Riverside, Calif	RVR	33.34	130.24	W-A	20	12.00	8.5	
Barrett, Calif	BAR	34.77	130.34	W-A	21	1.90	7.8	One component
Albuquerque, N. Mex	ALQ	36.97	115.78	W-A	21	24.90	8.8	One component
Nurmijärvi, Finland	NUR	58.68	4.42	SPBH	19	1.79	8.1	One component
Copenhagen, Denmark	COP	62.61	12.52	SPBH	20	2.32	8.2	
San Salvador, El Salvador	SSS	63.08	111.65	W	18	1.06	7.8	Magnification questionable
Paraiso, Calif	PRS	68.35	12.38	W	20	2.50	8.3	
Clermont-Ferrand, France	CFF	70.99	21.17		20	0.69	7.8	
Trieste, Italy	TRI	72.59	13.50	SPBH	19	1.31	8.1	
Porto, Portugal	PTO	72.90	31.16	SPBH	19	2.18	8.3	
Caracas, Venezuela	CAR	76.40	93.92	SPBH	22	6.12	8.8	
Bogotá, Colombia	BOG	78.07	102.17	SPBH	20	7.30	8.8	
Málaga, Spain	MAL	78.11	29.39	SPBH	23	2.87	8.4	
Istanbul, Turkey	IST	78.28	2.56	SPBH	19	1.40	8.1	
Trinidad, West Indies	TRN	78.97	88.01	SPBH	20	5.22	8.7	
Athens University, Greece	ATU	81.13	6.86	SPBH	20	7.00	8.8	One component
Shillong, India	SHL	81.26	308.00	SPBH	20	1.03	8.0	
Teheran, Iran	TEH	82.35	344.43	M-S	25	1.50	8.2	
New Delhi, India	NDI	83.47	321.36	SPBH	20	3.08	8.5	
Port Moresby, New Guinea	PMG	86.54	243.76	W-A	23	1.78	8.3	
Shiraz, Iran	SHI	88.19	342.48	SPBH	18	1.07	8.1	
Nana, Peru	NNA	91.37	112.39	SPBH	21	1.97	8.4	
Arequipa, Peru	ARE	97.73	109.88	SPBH	20	2.32	8.5	
La Paz, Bolivia	LPB	99.36	107.03	SPBH	21	3.04	8.6	
Adelaide, Australia	ADE	112.65	238.62	SPBH	19	6.69	8.1	
Santiago, Chile	SAN	112.81	117.89	SPBH	19	1.46	8.4	
Mundaring, Australia	MUN	120.27	258.10	SPBH	21	1.40	8.4	
Nairobi, Kenya	NAI	120.33	354.78	SPBH	20	1.08	8.3	One component
Bulawayo, Rhodesia	BUL	139.10	5.29	SPBH	19	1.60	8.6	
Windhoek, South Africa	WIN	140.16	22.23	SPBH	19	2.90	8.8	
Pretoria, South Africa	PRE	144.65	6.32	SPBH	18	1.08	8.4	

[1] Code obtained from *Seismograph Station Abbreviations*, U.S. Department of Commerce, Coast and Geodetic Survey, Rockville, Md., 46 pp., February 1965.
[2] Type: Mc-R ═ McComb-Romberg seismometer.
W-A ═ Wood-Anderson seismometer.
W ═ Wiechert.
SBPH ═ Standard short-period Benioff horizontal.
M-S ═ Milne-Shaw seismometer.

CONCLUSIONS

The most satisfactory hypocenter and origin time computed for the Prince William Sound Earthquake are latitude: 61.04° ± 0.05° N.; longitude: 147.73° ± 0.07° W.; origin time: 03:36:14.0 (G.M.T.); and depth: normal (<60 kilometers). Ten epicenters were computed, using various data sets, computer programs, and traveltime curves. All of the epicenters fell within a circle having a radius of 3.5 kilometers. The preferred epicenter that was computed used data from 46 stations paired in distance and azimuth, Jeffreys-Bullen [1958] traveltime curves, and the epicenter computer program of the Coast and Geodetic Survey. The epicenter was located on a narrow peninsula between College Fiord and Unakwik Inlet. The area is, for the most part, covered with glaciers. No positive evidence of surface faulting could be found on Coast and Geodetic Survey photographs of the immediate epicenter region. Some evidence, however, of possible faulting was found on an aerial photo taken 39 kilometers N. 31° E. of the instrumental epicenter.

The focal depth of the earthquake is believed to be normal, *i.e.*, <60 kilometers. No depth sensitive phases, such as pP and sP, could be identified on the relatively few complete seismograms available for the earthquake. The conclusion that the earthquake occurred at normal depth is based on: (1) An analysis of focal depths of aftershocks and earthquakes occurring in the general vicinity of the main shock from 1963 through 1965, and (2) the large-amplitude surface waves generated by the earthquake.

A study of $P(O-C)$ time residuals at the College, Alaska, station for earthquakes between the Gulf of Alaska and College, Alaska, indicates the presence of a low-velocity zone and/or crustal thickening beneath the Chugach Mountains and possibly higher than normal mantle velocities beneath Prince William Sound.

The m_b magnitude, as computed by the Coast and Geodetic Survey, yielded a value 2 magnitude units lower than the M_s (surface-wave magnitude) for the earthquake. The mean value of M_s, using 37 observations, is 8.3 ± 0.33 magnitude unit.

REFERENCES

Algermissen, S. T., "Seismological Investigations of the Prince William Sound Earthquake and Aftershocks," (abstract), *Transactions of the American Geophysical Union*, vol. 45, p. 633, 1964.

Case, J. E., Barnes, D. F., Plafker, G., and Robbins, S. L., "Gravity Survey and Regional Geology of the Prince William Sound Epicentral Region, Alaska," *Geological Survey Professional Paper 543–C*, 12 pp., 1966.

Engdahl, E. R. and Gunst, R. H., "Use of a High Speed Computer for the Preliminary Determination of Earthquake Hypocenters," *Bulletin of the Seismological Society of America*, vol. 56, pp. 325–336, 1966.

Flinn, E. A., "Confidence Regions and Error Determinations for Seismic Event Location," *Reviews of Geophysics*, vol. 3, pp. 157–185, 1965.

Geiger, L., "Herdbestimmung bei Erdbeben aus den Ankunftszeiten," *Nachrichten der Königlichen Gesellschaft der Wissenschaften zu Göttingen, Mathematisch-physikalische Klasse*, vol. 4, pp. 331–349, 1910.

Gutenberg, B., "Amplitudes of Surface Waves and Magnitudes of Shallow Earthquakes," *Bulletin of the Seismological Society of America*, vol. 35, pp. 3–12, 1945.

Hales, Anton, L. and Cleary, John, "An Analysis of the Travel Times of P Waves to North American Stations, in the Distance Range 32° to 100°," *Bulletin of the Seismological Society of America*, vol. 56, pp. 467–489, 1966.

Herrin, E., *Report on Revision of Hypo Travel-Time and Time-Derivative Tables*, Dallas Seismological Observatory, Southern Methodist University, Dallas, Texas, 1961.

Jeffreys, H. and Bullen, K. E., *Seismological Tables*, British Association for Advancement of Science, Gray Milne Trust, London, England, 1958.

U.S. Department of Commerce, Coast and Geodetic Survey, *Preliminary Report, Prince William Sound, Alaskan Earthquakes March–April 1964*, 83 pp. (plus photos), Washington, D. C., April 17, 1964.

von Hake, C., and Cloud, W. K., *United States Earthquakes, 1964*, U.S. Department of Commerce, Environmental Science Services Administration, Coast and Geodetic Survey, Washington, D. C., 91 pp., 1966.

Woollard, G. P., Ostenso, N. A., Thiel, E., and Bonini, W. E., "Gravity Anomalies Crustal Structure, and Geology in Alaska," *Journal of Geophysical Research*, vol. 65, pp. 1021–1037, 1960.

APPENDIX

Seismograph Station Abbreviation (Code)

Code	Station	Region
AAB	Alma-Ata	U.S.S.R.
AAM	Ann Arbor	Michigan
ADE	Adelaide	Australia
AFI	Afiamalu	Samoa Islands
ALE	Alert	Canada
ALI	Alicante	Spain
ALQ	Albuquerque	New Mexico
ANP	Anpu	Taiwan
ANT	Antofagasta	Chile
APA	Apatity	U.S.S.R.
AQU	Aquila	Italy
ARE	Arequipa	Peru
ATH	Athens Observatory	Greece
ATL	Atlanta	Georgia
ATU	Athens University	Greece
BAG	Baguio City	Philippines
BAR	Barrett	California
BCN	Boulder City	Nevada
BEC	Bermuda-Columbia	Bermuda
BEO	Beograd (Belgrade)	Yugoslavia
BHP	Balboa Heights	Canal Zone
BKR	Bakuriani	Georgia S.S.R.
BKS	Byerly	California
BLA	Blacksburg	Virginia

SEISMOGRAPH STATION ABBREVIATION (CODE)—
Continued

SEISMOGRAPH STATION ABBREVIATION (CODE)—
Continued

Code	Station	Region	Code	Station	Region
BLO	Bloomington	Indiana	HNR	Honiara	Solomon Islands
BMO	Blue Mountains	Oregon	HUA	Huancayo	Peru
BOD	Bodaybo	U.S.S.R.	HVO	Hawaiian Volcano Obser.	Hawaii
BOG	Bogotá	Colombia	IRK	Irkutsk	U.S.S.R.
BOM	Bombay (Colaba)	India	ISK	Istanbul-Kandilli	Turkey
BOZ	Bozeman	Montana	ISO	Isola	France
BUD	Budapest	Hungary	IST	Istanbul	Turkey
BUL	Bulawayo	Rhodesia	JE-	Jena	Louisiana
BUT	Butte	Montana	JEN	Jena	Germany
CAR	Caracas	Venezuela	JER	Jerusalem	Israel
CFF	Clermont-Ferrand	France	KEV	Kevo	Finland
CHI	Chicago-Loyola	Illinois	KFO	Klamath Falls	Oregon
CHT	Chittagong	Pakistan	KHE	Kheis	U.S.S.R.
CLE	Cleveland	Ohio	KIP	Kipapa	Hawaii
CLL	Colmberg (near Leipzig)	Germany	KIR	Kiruna	Sweden
CLS	Calistoga	California	KON	Kongsberg	Norway
CMC	Copper Mine	Canada	KOU	Koumac	New Caledonia
CMN	Crown Mine	Nevada	KRV	Kirovabad	U.S.S.R.
CNH	Changchun	China	KTG	Kap Tobin	Greenland
CNT	Canton	China	KUN	Kunming	China
CNU	Chengtu	China	LAH	Lahore	Pakistan
COL	College Outpost	Alaska	LAN	Lanchow	China
COP	Copenhagen	Denmark	LAR	Laramie	Wyoming
COR	Corvallis	Oregon	LAW	Lawrence	Kansas
CPO	Cumberland Plateau	Tennessee	LC-	Las Cruces	New Mexico
DAL	Dallas	Texas	LHA	Lhasa	Tibet
DOU	Dourbes	Belgium	LIS	Lisbon	Portugal
DUG	Dugway	Utah	LND	London	Canada
ELT	Eltsovka	U.S.S.R.	LON	Longmire	Washington
ESK	Eskdalemuir	Scotland	LPB	La Paz	Bolivia
EUR	Eureka	Nevada	LPS	La Palma	El Salvador
FEL	Feldberg in Schwarzwald	Germany	LUB	Lubbock	Texas
FGU	Flaming Gorge	Utah	LUG	Luganville	New Hebrides
FLO	Florissant	Missouri	LZ-	La Paz	Bolivia
FOR	Fordham	New York	MAG	Magadan	U.S.S.R.
FRU	Frunze	Kirghiz S.S.R	MAL	Málaga	Spain
GDH	Godhavn	Greenland	MAN	Manila (Diliman)	Philippines
GEO	Georgetown	Washington, D.C.	MAT	Matsushiro	Japan
GG-	Gräfenberg	Germany	MBC	Mould Bay	Canada
GOL	Golden	Colorado	MHT	Manhattan	Kansas
GUA	Guam	Mariana Islands	MN-	Mina	Nevada
HEI	Heidelberg (Konigstuhl)	Germany	MNN	Minneapolis	Minnesota
HHM	Hungry Horse	Montana	MNT	Montreal	Canada
HKC	Hong Kong	Hong Kong	MOS	Moscow	U.S.S.R.
HLW	Helwan	Egypt	MOX	Moxa	Germany

SEISMOGRAPH STATION ABBREVIATION (CODE)—
Continued

SEISMOGRAPH STATION ABBREVIATION (CODE)—
Continued

Code	Station	Region
MRG	Morgantown	West Virginia
MUN	Mundaring	Australia
NAI	Nairobi	Kenya
NAN	Nanking	China
NCS	Nueva Concepción	El Salvador
NDI	New Delhi	India
NHA	Nhatrang	South Viet-Nam
NNA	Nana	Peru
NOR	Nord	Greenland
NP-	North Pole	Canada
NUR	Nurmijärvi	Finland
OGD	Ogdensburg	New Jersey
OO-	Oslo	Norway
ORV	Oroville	California
OTT	Ottawa	Canada
PAL	Palisades	New York
PAS	Pasadena	California
PEK	Peking (Chiufeng)	China
PMG	Port Moresby	New Guinea
PRA	Praha (Prague)	Czechoslovakia
PRE	Pretoria	South Africa
PRI	Priest	California
PRS	Paraiso	California
PTO	Porto (Serra do Pilar)	Portugal
QUE	Quetta	Pakistan
RAB	Rabaul	New Britain
RAV	Ravensburg	Germany
RCD	Rapid City	South Dakota
REN	Reno	Nevada
RES	Resolute	Canada
RK-	Red Lake	Canada
ROC	Rochester	New York
RVR	Riverside	California
SAN	Santiago	Chile
SBC	Santa Barbara	California
SCP	State College	Pennsylvania
SEM	Semipalatinsk	U.S.S.R.
SEO	Seoul (Keizyo, Keijo)	Korea
SHA	Spring Hiil	Alabama
SHI	Shiraz	Iran
SHL	Shillong	India

Code	Station	Region
SIA	Sian	China
SIM	Simferopol	U.S.S.R.
SIT	Sitka	Alaska
SJG	San Juan	Puerto Rico
SLC	Salt Lake City	Utah
SOD	Sodankylä	Finland
SSS	San Salvador	El Salvador
STU	Stuttgart	Germany
SVE	Sverdlovsk	U.S.S.R.
TAH	Tahiti	Tahiti
TAP	Taipei	Taiwan
TEH	Teheran	Iran
TFO	Tonto Forest	Arizona
TIK	Tiksi	Yakutsk S.S.R.
TIN	Tinemaha	California
TNP	Tonopah	Nevada
TOL	Toledo	Spain
TRI	Trieste (Grotta Gigante)	Italy
TRN	Trinidad	West Indies
TRO	Tromsoe	Norway
TUB	Tübingen	Germany
TUC	Tucson	Arizona
UBO	Uinta Basin	Utah
UCC	Uccle	Belgium
UKI	Ukiah	California
UME	Umea	Sweden
UPP	Uppsala	Sweden
UZH	Uzhgorod Ungvar	Ukrainian S.S.R.
VAL	Valentia	Ireland
VIC	Victoria	Canada
VLA	Vladivostok	U.S.S.R.
WDY	Woody	California
WES	Weston	Massachusetts
WIN	Windhoek	South Africa
WMO	Wichita Mountains	Oklahoma
WRS	Warsak	Pakistan
YAK	Yakutsk	U.S.S.R.
YKC	Yellow Knife	Canada
YSS	Yuzno-Sakhalinsk	U.S.S.R.
ZAG	Zagreb (Agram)	Yugoslavia
ZSC	Zose	China

WILLIAM H. DILLINGER, JR.
S. T. ALGERMISSEN
U. S. COAST AND GEODETIC SURVEY*

Reprinted with minor changes from
U.S. Coast and Geodetic Survey Volume II-B,C: Seismology and Marine Geology,
"Magnitude Studies of Alaska Earthquakes"

Magnitude Studies

ABSTRACT

Comparisons of M_L, M_s, and m_b are presented for the main shock and aftershocks of the Prince William Sound Earthquake of March 28, 1964 (G.M.T.), and for other selected south-central Alaskan and Aleutian Island earthquakes. Earthquakes with m_b magnitudes between 5 and 6 have corresponding surface-wave magnitudes in the range of 4 to 7. Least-squares straight-line equations are given for all comparisons.

INTRODUCTION

During the Coast and Geodetic Survey (C&GS) investigation of the Prince William Sound Earthquake, it was observed that the magnitude m_b routinely computed by the C&GS was normally lower than the surface-wave magnitude M_s computed for the main shock and for the larger aftershocks. An extreme example of the difference between m_b as computed by the C&GS and checked by the authors and M_s as computed by the authors is provided by the computations from the main shock of March 28, 1964 (G.M.T.). The magnitude m_b computed by the authors using data from 28 world-wide seismic network stations was 6.4. The surface-wave magnitude M_s computed using data from 37 worldwide seismic network stations was 8.3 [Sherburne, et al., 1968]. A study of the relationship between m_b computed by the C&GS and magnitudes computed using other methods was undertaken to gain a better understanding of the relationship between the various magnitudes and the general energy release in the Prince William Sound Earthquake aftershock area during 1964–1965.

Since 1963, the C&GS has routinely reported m_b. The historical background for the magnitude scale and a description of several magnitudes computed and reported by various investigators have been given by Richter [1958, 1964].

TECHNIQUES USED

Various magnitudes were compared for 188 earthquakes in south-central Alaska and in the Aleutian Islands. The earthquakes studied are loosely grouped into three sets: (1) The main shock and aftershocks of the Prince William Sound Earthquake; (2) the 24 Aleutian Islands earthquakes previously studied by Liebermann, et al., [1966]; and (3) a selected number of other large magnitude shocks in south-central Alaska and

---

*Now in part Earth Sciences Laboratories, National Oceanic and Atmospheric Administration.

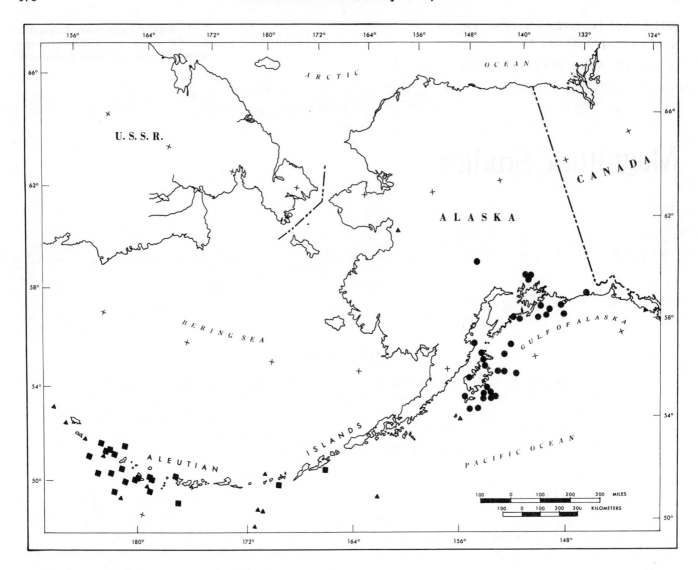

FIGURE 1.—Epicentral location of selective earthquakes considered. The circles indicate some aftershocks of the Prince William Sound Earthquake of March 28, 1964 (G.M.T.) ; the triangles, other selected south-central Alaskan and Aleutian Island earthquakes chosen for this paper; and the squares, the 24 Aleutian Island earthquakes studied by Liebermann, *et al.,* [1966].

in the Aleutian Islands. Some of the epicenters of earthquakes considered in this paper are shown in figure 1; all are listed with their hypocenter and magnitude data in table 1, with the exception of those studied by Liebermann, *et al.,* which are not listed.

The following magnitudes were computed.

TABLE 1.—*Hypocenter and magnitude data for earthquakes compared in this paper*

No.	Date			Description	Origin time G.M.T.			Epicenter		$*M_L$	$*M_{sh}$	$*M_{sz}$	$\dagger M_b$
	Yr.	Mo.	Day					Latitude North	Longitude West				
					Hr.	Min.	Sec.	Degrees	Degrees				
1	58	07	10	Lituya Bay	06	15	51.0	58.6	137.1				6.3
2	64	02	06	Kodiak Island	13	07	25.2	55.7	155.8		6.80(6) §	6.76(4) §	5.6
3	64	03	28	P.W.S. Main shock‡	03	36	14.2	61.0	147.8		8.3(37)		6.4
4	64	03	28	P.W.S. Aftershock	20	29	08.6	59.8	148.7		6.22(7)	6.19(6)	5.8
5	64	03	29	P.W.S. Aftershock	06	04	44.5	56.1	154.3		5.81(7)	5.86(6)	5.6

See footnotes at end of table.

TABLE 1.—*Hypocenter and magnitude data for earthquakes compared in this paper*—Continued

No.	Date			Description	Origin time G.M.T.			Epicenter		$*M_L$	$*M_{sh}$	$*M_{sz}$	$†M_b$
	Yr.	Mo.	Day		Hr.	Min.	Sec.	Latitude North	Longitude West				
								Degrees	Degrees				
6	64	03	29	P.W.S. Aftershock	16	40	57.9	59.7	147.0		5.85(5)	5.88(5)	5.6
7	64	03	30	P.W.S. Aftershock	02	18	06.3	56.6	152.9		6.56(9)	6.51(8)	5.8
8	64	03	30	P.W.S. Aftershock	07	09	34.0	59.9	145.7		6.27(7)	6.35(6)	5.6
9	64	03	30	P.W.S. Aftershock	13	03	34.9	56.5	152.7		5.30(8)	5.28(6)	5.3
10	64	03	30	P.W.S. Aftershock	16	09	28.4	56.6	152.1		5.69(9)	5.46(7)	5.5
11	64	04	03	P.W.S. Aftershock	22	33	42.2	61.6	147.6		5.68(4)	5.63(3)	5.7
12	64	04	04	P.W.S. Aftershock	04	54	01.7	60.1	146.7		5.71(3)	5.81(3)	5.6
13	64	04	04	P.W.S. Aftershock	08	40	29.8	56.5	152.6		5.98(1)	6.07(1)	5.3
14	64	04	04	P.W.S. Aftershock	09	10	55.1	56.9	152.7		5.81(1)	5.95(1)	5.9
15	64	04	05	P.W.S. Aftershock	19	28	18.1	60.2	146.7		5.19(2)	4.88(2)	5.8
16	64	04	09	P.W.S. Aftershock	05	43	24.0	60.0	148.2	4.3			4.1
17	64	04	09	P.W.S. Aftershock	12	33	23.9	59.5	148.9	4.5			4.7
18	64	04	09	P.W.S. Aftershock	13	06	15.2	59.6	146.1	5.4			5.1
19	64	04	10	P.W.S. Aftershock	00	29	46.2	60.3	147.1	4.6			4.0
20	64	04	10	P.W.S. Aftershock	07	04	11.3	60.2	147.0	4.3			4.0
21	64	04	10	P.W.S. Aftershock	19	05	52.6	59.7	148.2	5.2			5.2
22	64	04	10	P.W.S. Aftershock	21	44	06.7	60.1	153.7	6.0			5.6
23	64	04	11	P.W.S. Aftershock	07	33	52.2	59.6	144.8	4.1			4.4
24	64	04	11	P.W.S. Aftershock	08	23	29.1	59.8	147.6	4.1			3.9
25	64	04	11	P.W.S. Aftershock	10	20	39.5	60.8	143.5	4.2			4.2
26	64	04	11	P.W.S. Aftershock	11	36	00.5	60.4	146.4	5.1			4.8
27	64	04	11	P.W.S. Aftershock	22	02	38.2	60.2	146.9	4.5			4.5
28	64	04	11	P.W.S. Aftershock	23	11	22.8	60.1	146.5	4.6			4.6
29	64	04	12	P.W.S. Aftershock	01	24	31.2	56.6	152.2		6.01(4)	5.99(4)	5.6
30	64	04	13	P.W.S. Aftershock	07	06	39.6	59.7	147.4	4.3			3.9
31	64	04	13	P.W.S. Aftershock	07	28	35.5	58.9	149.8	3.3			4.0
32	64	04	13	P.W.S. Aftershock	08	41	53.9	58.4	151.2	4.4			4.8
33	64	04	13	P.W.S. Aftershock	12	25	36.0	59.4	143.9	5.8			4.9
34	64	04	13	P.W.S. Aftershock	14	05	00.0	57.6	151.2	5.2	4.90(1)	4.65(1)	5.5
35	64	04	13	P.W.S. Aftershock	21	25	33.0	57.5	153.9		5.02(2)	4.97(2)	5.5
36	64	04	13	P.W.S. Aftershock	21	43	16.5	59.4	143.1	4.8			5.1
37	64	04	13	P.W.S. Aftershock	23	48	52.7	61.0	149.3	4.5			4.1
38	64	04	14	P.W.S. Aftershock	10	58	11.2	59.9	146.8	4.1			4.1
39	64	04	14	P.W.S. Aftershock	15	55	10.9	61.3	147.3	5.3	5.78(1)	5.83(1)	5.4
40	64	04	14	P.W.S. Aftershock	16	05	46.1	59.9	146.0	4.4			4.4
41	64	04	14	P.W.S. Aftershock	16	59	30.1	61.4	150.8	5.0			5.1
42	64	04	14	P.W.S. Aftershock	21	33	37.3	61.0	147.3	4.5			4.2
43	64	04	14	P.W.S. Aftershock	22	29	31.1	59.9	145.6	4.5			4.5
44	64	04	14	P.W.S. Aftershock	22	55	31.3	58.0	152.6	5.8	5.4(3)	5.36(3)	5.4
45	64	04	15	P.W.S. Aftershock	09	24	11.1	60.0	148.6	4.2			3.7
46	64	04	15	P.W.S. Aftershock	15	30	47.1	56.5	154.4	6.3	5.76(3)	5.78(3)	5.5
47	64	04	16	P.W.S. Aftershock	03	19	34.8	57.2	151.4	4.9			5.0
48	64	04	16	P.W.S. Aftershock	07	37	35.8	59.6	146.9	4.0			4.3
49	64	04	16	P.W.S. Aftershock	11	56	04.5	58.3	150.7	4.8			4.4
50	64	04	16	P.W.S. Aftershock	12	11	15.7	58.2	152.7	5.2			4.5
51	64	04	16	P.W.S. Aftershock	14	31	16.3	61.4	149.2	4.7			4.6
52	64	04	16	P.W.S. Aftershock	19	26	57.4	56.4	152.9	5.7	6.28(4)	6.20(4)	5.5
53	64	04	17	P.W.S. Aftershock	04	03	55.9	59.6	144.7	4.7			4.9
54	64	04	17	P.W.S. Aftershock	04	16	59.4	59.6	144.7	4.2			4.9
55	64	04	17	P.W.S. Aftershock	07	26	39.0	61.1	149.4	4.3			4.4
56	64	04	17	P.W.S. Aftershock	09	09	07.8	57.7	151.4	5.2	5.59(4)	5.64(4)	5.4
57	64	04	17	P.W.S. Aftershock	09	59	52.4	60.4	145.9	4.9			4.9
58	64	04	17	P.W.S. Aftershock	12	05	59.9	60.4	145.0	3.8			3.8
59	64	04	18	P.W.S. Aftershock	03	06	43.5	56.7	148.9	4.4			4.5
60	64	04	18	P.W.S. Aftershock	07	10	58.5	60.8	145.2	4.6			4.2
61	64	04	18	P.W.S. Aftershock	07	44	03.4	60.2	147.6	4.1			3.9
62	64	04	18	P.W.S. Aftershock	20	16	16.3	56.1	153.7		5.81(1)	5.77(1)	4.9
63	64	04	18	P.W.S. Aftershock	23	38	03.4	59.3	147.5	4.3			5.1
64	64	04	19	P.W.S. Aftershock	06	34	14.4	60.6	147.4	4.3			4.1
65	64	04	19	P.W.S. Aftershock	18	51	10.9	60.2	148.6	4.5			4.7
66	64	04	20	P.W.S. Aftershock	03	34	45.1	59.7	144.6	4.5			4.7
67	64	04	20	P.W.S. Aftershock	08	07	54.8	60.2	147.0	4.3			4.3
68	64	04	20	P.W.S. Aftershock	11	56	41.6	61.4	147.3	5.6	5.92(7)	5.95(6)	5.7
69	64	04	20	P.W.S. Aftershock	16	18	26.4	60.7	145.3	4.9			4.9
70	64	04	20	P.W.S. Aftershock	16	39	30.0	59.9	145.1	4.5			4.1

See footnotes at end of table.

Table 1.—*Hypocenter and magnitude data for earthquakes compared in this paper*—Continued

No.	Date			Description	Origin time G.M.T.			Epicenter		$*M_L$	$*M_{sh}$	$*M_{sz}$	$\dagger M_b$
	Yr.	Mo.	Day		Hr.	Min.	Sec.	Latitude North	Longitude West				
								Degrees	Degrees				
71	64	04	20	P.W.S. Aftershock	16	49	41.8	61.4	147.3	4.5			4.2
72	64	04	21	P.W.S. Aftershock	05	01	35.7	61.5	147.4	4.9	5.29(5)	5.36(5)	5.4
73	64	04	22	P.W.S. Aftershock	20	29	20.3	58.6	150.0	5.0	4.41(1)	4.63(1)	5.1
74	64	04	23	P.W.S. Aftershock	03	13	55.7	60.9	144.3	4.7			4.2
75	64	04	23	P.W.S. Aftershock	14	56	30.9	57.3	151.9	5.2			5.3
76	64	04	23	P.W.S. Aftershock	15	47	15.1	59.9	147.5	4.3			4.1
77	64	04	24	P.W.S. Aftershock	03	51	05.0	59.5	144.5		4.95(4)	4.96(3)	5.2
78	64	04	24	P.W.S. Aftershock	08	57	09.8	58.7	149.5	3.8			4.5
79	64	04	25	P.W.S. Aftershock	00	17	56.1	60.3	147.0	3.9			3.9
80	64	04	25	P.W.S. Aftershock	00	51	08.0	59.9	147.1	4.5			4.1
81	64	04	25	P.W.S. Aftershock	01	59	14.4	60.0	145.1	3.7			4.0
82	64	04	25	P.W.S. Aftershock	07	01	19.7	59.8	145.3	3.9			3.8
83	64	04	25	P.W.S. Aftershock	09	43	30.7	59.9	144.9	4.7	5.13(1)		5.0
84	64	04	25	P.W.S. Aftershock	18	11	24.4	60.7	145.3	4.1			3.7
85	64	04	28	P.W.S. Aftershock	13	34	10.4	57.6	150.0	4.4			4.4
86	64	04	30	P.W.S. Aftershock	17	26	29.9	60.1	142.2	4.9	5.45(6)		4.9
87	64	05	01	P.W.S. Aftershock	03	13	03.5	57.4	150.0	4.4	4.17(1)		5.3
88	64	05	02	P.W.S. Aftershock	17	08	57.6	59.7	147.0	4.6			4.8
89	64	05	03	P.W.S. Aftershock	21	31	53.2	59.0	148.5	4.0			4.4
90	64	05	03	P.W.S. Aftershock	21	39	30.4	61.0	145.8	4.2			3.9
91	64	05	04	P.W.S. Aftershock	12	04	46.1	58.2	152.3	4.8			5.3
92	64	05	05	P.W.S. Aftershock	02	04	17.9	57.4	149.5	4.0			4.4
93	64	05	05	P.W.S. Aftershock	02	32	42.3	60.4	147.1	4.5			4.4
94	64	05	05	P.W.S. Aftershock	04	05	08.3	59.7	148.9	4.4			4.6
95	64	05	05	P.W.S. Aftershock	22	41	07.1	61.8	156.7	4.7			4.7
96	64	05	07	P.W.S. Aftershock	00	15	48.9	60.1	147.4	4.2			4.2
97	64	05	07	P.W.S. Aftershock	19	12	37.8	60.4	144.8	4.3			4.3
98	64	05	08	P.W.S. Aftershock	05	56	13.7	55.2	153.9	5.4			4.4
99	64	05	08	P.W.S. Aftershock	09	23	33.1	59.4	145.4	4.6			4.5
100	64	05	08	P.W.S. Aftershock	21	34	40.6	60.8	143.6	5.6			5.4
101	64	05	09	P.W.S. Aftershock	18	53	25.8	59.9	147.9	4.1			3.9
102	64	05	09	P.W.S. Aftershock	21	06	12.2	61.7	152.0	5.5			5.0
103	64	05	10	P.W.S. Aftershock	02	00	27.5	59.9	146.5	4.1			3.6
104	64	05	10	P.W.S. Aftershock	12	01	23.8	60.7	148.4	3.9			3.7
105	64	05	10	P.W.S. Aftershock	14	46	15.3	59.9	147.1	4.7			4.5
106	64	05	10	P.W.S. Aftershock	15	40	53.3	60.1	146.3	4.2			4.3
107	64	05	11	P.W.S. Aftershock	03	31	38.7	60.2	147.2	4.6			3.9
108	64	05	11	P.W.S. Aftershock	20	10	36.5	60.3	146.1	5.4			4.0
109	64	05	12	P.W.S. Aftershock	11	47	32.2	60.1	147.0	5.0			4.7
110	64	05	14	P.W.S. Aftershock	11	55	28.2	62.8	152.3	4.3			4.6
111	64	05	14	P.W.S. Aftershock	14	19	05.1	59.7	144.4	4.2			4.5
112	64	05	16	P.W.S. Aftershock	14	44	54.3	57.6	151.0	5.7			5.4
113	64	05	19	P.W.S. Aftershock	02	23	45.2	59.4	145.2	4.8			4.3
114	64	05	19	P.W.S. Aftershock	13	19	20.7	59.7	152.3	4.1			4.2
115	64	05	20	P.W.S. Aftershock	05	32	13.7	58.0	149.6	4.4			4.9
116	64	05	20	P.W.S. Aftershock	09	28	38.5	60.2	147.4	4.3			4.4
117	64	05	21	P.W.S. Aftershock	01	11	23.4	60.4	145.9	5.1			4.6
118	64	05	21	P.W.S. Aftershock	13	31	50.9	60.2	147.2	4.6			4.2
119	64	05	21	P.W.S. Aftershock	15	36	01.5	59.0	153.5	6.2			5.3
120	64	05	23	P.W.S. Aftershock	06	29	24.4	57.3	150.7	4.6			4.5
121	64	05	24	P.W.S. Aftershock	00	40	21.9	60.2	148.0	4.9			4.9
122	64	05	24	P.W.S. Aftershock	10	16	21.5	59.9	145.5	4.6			4.3
123	64	05	26	P.W.S. Aftershock	05	33	44.6	60.3	145.5	4.5			4.3
124	64	05	26	P.W.S. Aftershock	21	58	34.1	60.1	147.0	4.2			4.1
125	64	05	28	P.W.S. Aftershock	14	06	58.2	60.2	147.7	3.8			3.7
126	64	05	28	P.W.S. Aftershock	16	18	04.2	58.3	150.6	5.1	4.43(1)	4.47(1)	5.4
127	64	06	02	P.W.S. Aftershock	16	29	41.5	59.7	144.2	4.3			4.8
128	64	06	22	P.W.S. Aftershock	08	32	02.1	62.1	148.5	3.1			4.1
129	64	06	22	P.W.S. Aftershock	12	11	09.4	60.0	146.7	3.8			4.0
130	64	06	23	P.W.S. Aftershock	08	42	52.7	60.5	144.9	3.9			3.9
131	64	06	25	P.W.S. Aftershock	11	23	00.6	60.3	149.1	4.8			4.6
132	64	06	29	P.W.S. Aftershock	07	21	32.8	62.7	152.0	5.8	4.93(2)	5.00(2)	5.6
133	64	06	29	P.W.S. Aftershock	19	04	49.9	61.0	143.7	4.2			4.5
134	64	07	05	P.W.S. Aftershock	03	14	33.3	60.8	144.9	4.9			4.9
135	64	07	05	P.W.S. Aftershock	17	58	59.7	60.2	146.2	4.4			4.9

See footnotes at end of table.

TABLE 1.—*Hypocenter and magnitude data for earthquakes compared in this paper*—Continued

No.	Date Yr.	Mo.	Day	Description	Origin time G.M.T. Hr.	Min.	Sec.	Epicenter Latitude North Degrees	Longitude West Degrees	*M_L	*M_{sh}	*M_{sz}	†M_b
136	64	07	09	P.W.S. Aftershock	00	21	17.7	59.8	150.0	4.4			4.3
137	64	07	11	P.W.S. Aftershock	09	44	18.7	59.7	146.1	4.1	4.80(1)		5.3
138	64	07	11	P.W.S. Aftershock	20	25	40.3	59.7	146.2	4.2	5.34(4)	5.30(3)	5.6
139	64	07	11	P.W.S. Aftershock	21	05	49.9	59.7	146.5	3.7			4.9
140	64	07	12	P.W.S. Aftershock	09	00	39.9	60.1	146.1	4.0			3.8
141	64	07	14	P.W.S. Aftershock	05	22	20.0	60.4	142.9	3.9			4.8
142	64	07	23	P.W.S. Aftershock	07	11	28.5	60.7	147.9	3.8			3.9
143	64	07	23	P.W.S. Aftershock	15	56	27.6	59.7	145.8	3.2			4.7
144	64	07	23	P.W.S. Aftershock	19	08	06.6	59.9	149.2	5.2	4.70(1)	4.89(1)	5.4
145	64	07	24	P.W.S. Aftershock	13	40	45.3	60.3	148.3	3.9			3.9
146	64	07	24	P.W.S. Aftershock	19	06	54.3	60.0	146.2	3.8			3.9
147	64	07	26	P.W.S. Aftershock	18	36	02.5	60.2	147.0	3.8			4.2
148	64	07	27	P.W.S. Aftershock	23	20	56.2	60.9	148.0	4.2			4.2
149	64	07	31	P.W.S. Aftershock	09	25	51.6	59.7	145.0	3.8			4.4
150	64	09	03	P.W.S. Aftershock	18	59	06.8	59.8	149.7	5.1			4.1
151	65	02	02	Aleutian Islands	12	06	04.3	52.6	172.1=				5.8
152	65	02	04	Rat Island Main shock	05	01	21.8	51.3	178.6=				6.0
153	65	02	04	Rat Island Aftershock	08	40	40.9	51.3	179.5=				6.4
154	65	02	04	Aleutian Islands	14	18	27.9	53.0	171.0=				5.7
155	65	02	04	Aleutian Islands	15	51	25.5	53.1	170.8=				5.7
156	65	02	05	Aleutian Islands	09	32	09.3	52.3	174.3=				5.9
157	65	02	06	Aleutian Islands	04	02	53.0	52.1	175.7=				5.9
158	65	02	06	Aleutian Islands	16	50	29.0	53.3	161.8				6.1
159	65	04	04	Alaskan Earthquake	23	22	18.6	64.7	160.1		5.73(4)	5.65(4)	
160	65	06	23	Kodiak Island Region	11	09	15.7	56.5	152.8		6.07(5)	6.03(5)	5.7
161	65	07	29	Aleutian Islands	08	29	22.1	51.2	171.3		6.6 (3)		6.4
162	65	08	07	Aleutian Islands	02	13	05.1	50.6	171.3				6.5
163	65	09	04	Kodiak Island Region	14	32	47.9	58.2	152.6		6.79(6)	6.67(6)	6.1
164	65	12	22	Kodiak Island Region	19	41	23.0	58.4	153.0		5.63(6)	5.72(6)	6.5

*Magnitude computed by authors.
†Magnitude reported by the U.S.C.&GS.
‡Prince William Sound Earthquake of March 28, 1964 (G.M.T.).
§Number of stations used in the determination of magnitude is in parentheses.
=Longitude in degrees East.

1. Computation of m_b. The magnitude m_b as reported by the C&GS is based on the amplitude of short-period P-waves. The formula is given as

$$m_b = \log \frac{A}{T} + Q + S,$$

where

A = maximum ground amplitude of the first several cycles of the compressional (P) wave recorded on vertical-component short-period seismographs;

T = period of the observed short-period waves;

Q = parameter which depends on the epicentral distance (Δ) and the focal depth (h); and

S = ground correction characteristics of the station. This last symbol is taken as zero or an average station ground condition.

Not all values of the amplitude and of the period used in the determination of the final magnitude for a particular earthquake are scaled by C&GS personnel. Many values are reported by cooperating stations, presumably using the method described below. The method used to obtain a final magnitude value is described in the C&GS Earthquake Data Report [1967] as follows:

The magnitude is an average of the individual station magnitudes. Prior to October 31, 1966, the magnitude was the logarithm of the average of the $A/T \times 10^Q$ values where Q is the distance-depth factor as defined by Gutenberg and Richter, A is the P-wave amplitude in microns, and T is the period in seconds. Amplitude values stated in this report are in millimicrons. Values which deviate from the average by the equivalent of 0.7 unit of magnitude at any point in the computation, or which are associated with P readings having residuals greater than 10 seconds, are not used in the average and are marked with an asterisk.

All of the earthquakes included in this paper occurred before October 31, 1966. Consequently, C&GS magnitudes routinely computed and discussed in this paper are the logarithm of the average of the $A/T \times 10^Q$ values determined, which are the antilog of the individual station magnitudes. In practice, the above method of averaging the individual magnitude values results in a slightly higher final magnitude than would result from an average value of the individual magnitudes. Those m_b values computed by the authors are averages of the individual magnitudes. Further details of computation of m_b by the C&GS are given in a compilation by Båth [1967].

2. Computation of M_s. There are two techniques in common use for the determination of magnitude from surface waves. Both are based on the following formula:

$$M_s = \log A_{20} + B$$

where

$A_{20} =$ ground amplitude of the 20-second surface wave, and

$B =$ parameter which depends on the epicentral distance. The magnitude M_{sh} derived from the amplitudes of the horizontal components of surface waves with periods near 20 seconds (a summary of the method is given by Richter) [1958]. The magnitude M_{sz} is derived from the amplitude of the vertical component of surface waves with periods near 20 seconds [Båth, 1952]. In this paper, only surface waves between periods of 17 and 23 seconds were used for the computation of M_{sh} and M_{sz}. Båth's [1952] path corrections were not used in the computation of M_{sz}.

3. Computation of M_L. The original magnitude as defined by Richter [1935] was computed for aftershocks of the Prince William Sound Earthquake, using data from the standard Wood-Anderson torsion seismometers installed in 1964 at Kodiak, Middleton Island, Seward, and Valdez (fig. 2). For a more complete description of these temporary seismograph stations, see Volume I, pages 75–87, of this publication. The distance corrections $(-\log A_0)$ given by Richter [1958] were used to compute the magnitudes.

RESULTS

The least-squares straight-line relationships between the various magnitudes compared are summarized in table 2 and illustrated in figures 3 through 7. Figure 3 is a comparison between m_b and M_L computed for 128 aftershocks of the Prince William Sound Earthquake. Using the least-squares relationship shown in table 2, m_b is equal to M_L at 4.5; for earthquakes less than 4.5, m_b is larger than M_L; and for earthquakes greater than 4.5, m_b is smaller than M_L. There is considerable scatter of the data over the whole range of magnitudes available. Part of the scatter results because data were available from only one Wood-Anderson torsion seismometer for many of the earthquakes studied. Figure 4 shows a comparison between m_b (computed by the authors) and M_{sz} computed for 34 aftershocks of the Prince William Sound Earthquake. The data scatter in figure 4 is considerably less than for the comparison between average m_b and M_L shown in figure 3. Figure 5 is a comparison between m_b

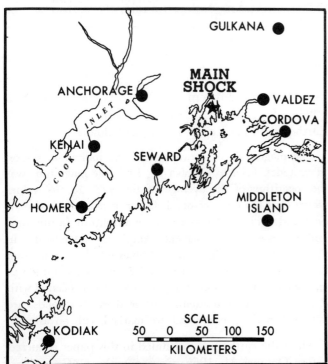

FIGURE 2.—Location of the seismometers from which data were taken. Standard Wood-Anderson torsion seismometers were installed temporarily at Kodiak, Middleton Island, Seward, and Valdez in 1964.

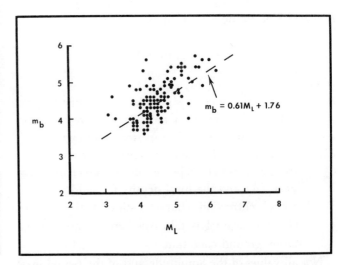

FIGURE 3.—Average m_b versus M_L for 128 aftershocks of the Prince William Sound Earthquake. Certain dots overlap because the m_b and M_L coincide.

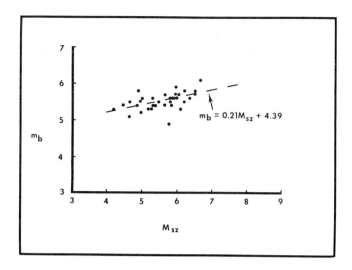

FIGURE 4.—Average m_b versus M_{sz} for 34 aftershocks of the Prince William Sound Earthquake.

(computed routinely by the C&GS) and M_{sh} computed for the same set of aftershocks shown in figure 4, with the addition of the main shock and 4 other aftershocks of the Prince William Sound Earthquake. There is excellent agreement between M_{sh} and M_{sz} computed for 34 aftershocks of the Prince William Sound Earthquake. The comparison is shown in figure 6. The same set of aftershocks were compared in figures 4 and 6.

To supplement the data available from Prince William Sound Earthquake aftershocks, magnitude data on 24 earthquakes studied by Liebermann, *et al.,* [1966] were used. Data from earthquakes numbered 1, 4, 5, 10, and 13 in this paper by Lieberman, *et al.,* were not used because these earthquakes in our judgment were considered to be too far west of the Aleutian Islands. Data were assembled for 13 other south-central Alaskan and Aleutian Island earthquakes in an attempt to improve the dis-

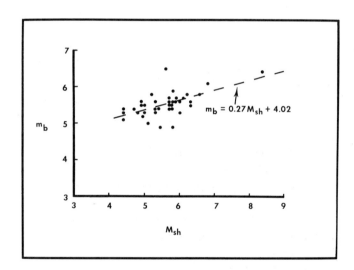

FIGURE 5.—Average m_b versus M_{sh} for the main shock and 38 aftershocks of the Prince William Sound Earthquake.

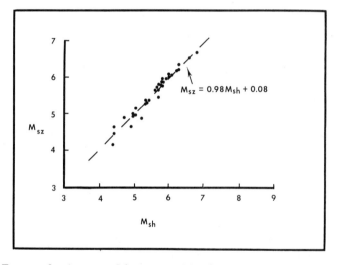

FIGURE 6.—Average M_{sz} versus M_{sh} for 34 aftershocks of the Prince William Sound Earthquake.

TABLE 2.—*Summary of magnitude comparisons*

Earthquakes	Least-squares relationship	Variance σ^2	Remarks
128 aftershocks of the Prince William Sound Earthquake*	$m_b = 0.61 M_L + 1.76$	.154	Data plotted in figure 3
34 aftershocks of the Prince William Sound Earthquake	$m_b = 0.21 M_{sz} + 4.39$	.069	Data plotted in figure 4
38 aftershocks and main shock of the Prince William Sound Earthquake	$m_b = 0.27 M_{sh} + 4.02$	.075	Data plotted in figure 5
34 aftershocks of the Prince William Sound Earthquake	$M_{sz} = 0.98 M_{sh} + 0.08$	.014	Data plotted in figure 6
38 aftershocks of the Prince William Sound Earthquake; 13 selected south-central Alaskan and Aleutian Island earthquakes; and 24 earthquakes studied by Liebermann, *et al.,* [1966]	$m_b = 0.32 M_s + 3.82$ $m_b = 0.34 M_s + 3.73$ (3 largest earthquakes excluded)	.084 .080	Data plotted in figure 7

*Earthquake of March 28, 1964 (G.M.T.).

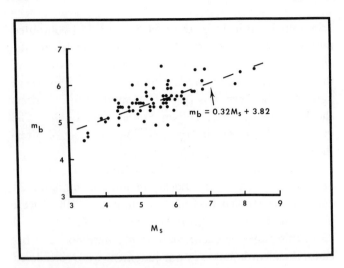

FIGURE 7.—Average m_b versus M_s (M_{sh} and M_{sz}) for 75 south-central Alaskan and Aleutian Island earthquakes. Certain dots overlap because the m_b and M_s coincide.

tribution of magnitudes available for a comparison of M_s and m_b. The magnitude M_s refers to magnitudes obtained from the amplitudes of surface waves with periods near 20 seconds, either by combining the horizontal-component amplitudes (M_{sh}) or by using the amplitude of the vertical component (M_{sz}). Results from all sources have been combined and are shown in figure 7. It is worth noting that in the last least-squares relationship solution of table 2, the three largest earthquakes are removed, but this removal makes very little difference in the solution obtained.

DISCUSSION AND CONCLUSIONS

Comparisons of m_b as computed by the C&GS, the original magnitude quantity M_L defined by Richter [1935], and M_s have been presented for south-central Alaskan and Aleutian Island earthquakes. The agreement between the two common techniques of M_s computed using the amplitude of the vertical component of surface waves with periods between 17 and 23 seconds (M_{sz}) and using the vector sum of the amplitudes of the horizontal components of surface waves with periods between 17 and 23 seconds (M_{sh}) was excellent. For earthquakes distributed over a wider geographical area, Texas Instruments, Inc. [1967] found more scatter in a comparison of M_{sh} and M_{sz}.

The comparison of M_s and m_b indicates a least-squares relationship of the form $m_b = 0.32 M_s + 3.82$. Although more data on large earthquakes are needed to confirm this relationship, it is significantly different from the least-squares relationship established by Gutenberg and

Richter between m from body waves and M from surface waves [Richter, 1958]. To a certain extent, this difference might be expected because Gutenberg and Richter, in general, used the amplitude/period ratio of other phases, such as PP and S in addition to P, in their determination of m from body waves. Figure 7 shows that m_b, routinely computed by the C&GS, is a relatively insensitive measure of energy for the south-central Alaskan and Aleutian Island earthquakes considered in this paper when compared with magnitude values derived from surface waves. For example, shocks which have magnitude m_b values between 5 and 6 represent those with surface-wave magnitudes between 4 and 7. No systematic investigation of the variance of m_b or M_s values was made in this paper. If the variance associated with values of m_b and M_s are assumed to be the same order of magnitude, errors in m_b result in much larger errors in the estimates of strain energy than the corresponding errors in M_s. This relationship between m_b and M_s must be taken into account in any study made of the energy release of earthquakes in the area considered.

More data are necessary to establish the reliability of the relationship. In particular, more data are needed in the magnitude range M_s of 7 to 8.

REFERENCES

Båth, Markus, "Earthquake Magnitude Determination from the Vertical Component of Surface Wave," *Transactions American Geophysical Union,* vol. 33, pp. 81–90, 1952.

——, compiler, *Handbook on Earthquake Magnitude Determinations,* Seismological Institute, Uppsala, Sweden, 114 pp., 1967.

Liebermann, Robert C., King, Chi-Yu, Brune, James N., and Pomeroy, Paul W., "Excitation of Surface Waves by the Underground Nuclear Explosion Long Shot," *Journal of Geophysical Research,* vol. 71, pp. 4333–4339, 1966.

Richter, Charles F., "An Instrumental Earthquake Magnitude Scale," *Bulletin of the Seismological Society of America,* vol. 25, pp. 1–32, 1935.

——, "History and Applications of the Magnitude Scale," *Publications du Bureau Central Séismologique International, série A, Travaux Scientifiques,* fascicule 17, pp. 217–224, 1950.

——, *Elementary Seismology,* W. H. Freeman and Co., Inc., San Francisco, Calif., 768 pp., 1958.

——, "Historical Background of the Magnitude Scale," *Proceedings of the Vesiac Conference on Seismic Event Magnitude Determination,* Acoustics and Seismics Laboratory [Vesiac = VELA Seismic Information Analysis Center], VESIAC Report 4410–71–X, Institute of Science and

Technology, Univ. of Michigan, Ann Arbor, Mich., pp. 1–12, 1964.

Sherburne, Roger W., Algermissen, S. T., and Harding, Samuel T., "The Hypocenter, Origin Time and Magnitude of the Prince William Sound, Alaska, Earthquake of March 28, 1964," this volume.

Texas Instruments, Inc., Fisher, Ray L., project manager, *Worldwide Collection and Evaluation of Earthquake Data,* ARPA Project no. 6207, Dallas, Tex., 1965–1966.

Three semiannual technical reports prepared for U.S. Department of Commerce, ESSA, Coast and Geodetic Survey.

U.S. Department of Commerce, ESSA, Coast and Geodetic Survey, *Earthquake Data Report,* EDR no. 45–67, 50 pp., 1967.

———, Wood, F. J., editor, *The Prince William Sound, Alaska, Earthquake of 1964 and Aftershocks,* vol. II, part A, 392 pp., 1967.

MAX WYSS*
JAMES N. BRUNE†
CALIFORNIA INSTITUTE OF TECHNOLOGY

Reprinted with minor changes from
Bulletin of the Seismological Society of America, Vol. 57, No. 5
"The Alaska Earthquake of 28 March 1964: A Complex Multiple Rupture"

A Complex Multiple Rupture

The region of energy release during large shallow earthquakes, as determined from the distribution of aftershocks, surface rupture, and long-period surface-wave radiation, is of the order of 500–1,000 km in length. However, the nature of energy release that occurs in this zone is not well understood. Surface-wave radiation suggests that the gross pattern of energy release is like that of a propagating source (Benioff, 1955; Benioff and others, 1961; Ben-Menahem, 1961; Ben-Menahem and Toksöz, 1962, 1963; Press and others, 1961) with velocity of about 3 km/sec, but the long wavelengths used lack the resolution to determine the details of the release, in particular whether it is smooth or erratic. Body waves from large earthquakes often suggest a complicated pattern of energy release (Vesanen, 1942; Usami, 1956; Richter, 1958; Miyamura and others, 1965; Båth, 1965). In this paper the P-wave portion of seismograms from the Alaska earthquake of March 28, 1964, is studied in detail and interpreted in terms of a multiple source, to better understand the nature of energy release during large earthquakes.

DATA

Seismograms from low-magnification instruments at 70 stations were collected. The instrument types were Wiechert, JMA 59, World-Wide Network of Standard Seismographs (WWNSS), Milne-Shaw, and Galitzin. The stations covered a wide range of azimuths and distances ranging from 40° to 90°. The azimuth distribution, however, was uneven because stations are concentrated in Europe, North and South America, and Japan. Figure 1 shows records from stations in Europe, Mexico, and Japan. Arrows point out six of the most outstanding phases. These phases do not correspond to any of the phases predicted by standard travel-time curves. The amplitude of the first arrival is much smaller than that of the following phases. The average magnitude (all magnitudes are m_b), corresponding to the very first P pulse determined from WWNSS stations, is 6.6. Phases with successively larger ampli-

ABSTRACT: The seismograms of the Alaska earthquake of March 28, 1964 (GMT), are characterized by multiple P phases not predicted by travel-time curves. Seismograms with low magnifications from 70 stations covering distances from 40° to 90° and a wide range of azimuths were analyzed. The character of the P-wave portion of the seismograms is interpreted in terms of an approximate multiple-event source mechanism where the propagating rupture triggers larger distinct events. Six events were located using the Gutenberg sine-curve method. The times after the initial origin time were 9, 19, 28, 29, 44, and 72 seconds, respectively, and the events were located 35, 66, 89, 93, 165, and 250 km away from the initial epicenter. Dividing the distance by the delay-time gives an average rupture velocity of 3.5 km/sec.

*Now with Lamont-Doherty Geological Observatory.
†Now with University of California, San Diego.

tudes follow the first event. The magnitude determined for the largest amplitudes in the *P*-wave train, occurring about 60 seconds after the first arrival, is 7.8. This value agrees approximately with the corresponding magnitudes determined from surface waves (7.8) and *S* waves (8.1) using the conversion formula between surface-wave magnitude and body-wave magnitude given by Richter (1958). The character of the first 2 minutes of the seismograms cannot be explained by either second arrivals of a simple point source or a simple, smoothly propagating rupture. Therefore, a more complex source is necessary and the records suggest that the source might be approximated by a series of point sources distributed in space and time.

ANALYSIS

To establish the distribution of events for the multiple point-source approximation, all outstanding phases in the first 2 minutes of the seismograms were read. For each station a list of time lags with respect to the first arrival resulted. The criteria for picking a time lag were a sudden substantial increase in amplitude and an abrupt change in phase. The stations were ordered in azimuth for comparison of their time-lag sequences. The largest and most obvious pulse, event C on Figure 1, could be identified and correlated between the stations of different azimuth without difficulty. The other pulses were harder to correlate. The time lag with which they appear on the records is a function not only of source-time and position differences, but also of the azimuth and distance of the stations. To aid in further correlation, a model of a propagating rupture spreading out in a horizontal plane with a velocity of 3.3 km/sec was assumed. A tentative correlation was

then made by computing the approximate distance from the initial epicenter under these assumptions. The approximate distance is given by:

$$\Delta_i = \frac{t_i}{\dfrac{1}{\beta} + \cos(\theta - \phi)\dfrac{dp}{d\Delta}}$$

t_i = seconds after first arrival, read from the seismograms,

β = propagating velocity of rupture, assumed,

$\dfrac{dp}{d\Delta}$ = slope of travel-time curve,

θ = azimuth from the initial epicenter to station,

ϕ = azimuth from the event to initial epicenter, parameter.

The distances Δ_i were computed from the time lags of several stations at different azimuths and distances, under variation of the parameter ϕ, the propagation direction. For different ϕ, different combinations of time lags could give more or less concordant results for the distance Δ_i. For combinations of time lags that were concordant, relocation of the epicenters of the corresponding events using the Gutenberg sine-curve method, was carried out with all available readings. In Figure 2 the distance residues for the location of event C are plotted as a function of azimuth. The reliability of certain combinations of time lags is indicated by the scattering of the residues of the Gutenberg sine-curve method. Incorrect combinations made it impossible to fit a sine curve.

After detailed analysis of the records by the above procedures, 6 events denoted by A, B, C, X, Y, and Z were identified. Epicenters for the events A, B, and C are well-established for the following reasons: (a) the standard deviation for the sine-curve fit is small; (b) these events are represented by conspicuous pulses on 90–95 percent of the analyzed records; (c) their locations lie within the zone of aftershocks; and (d) the delay times from the initial epicenter give quite reasonable rupture velocities, about 3.5 km/sec.

The events X, Y, and Z are presented here somewhat less confidently as possible additional events. They could be identified on 60–75 percent of the records analyzed. Because of very high amplitudes and complexity of the signal, no further events could be established beyond 80 seconds after the first arrival, although they very probably occurred.

DISCUSSION

The preceding analysis has indicated that the energy release during the Alaska earthquake was characterized by more or less distinct high-amplitude bursts or events, possibly superimposed on a smaller continuous level of energy release associated with a propagating wave or rupture or both. This

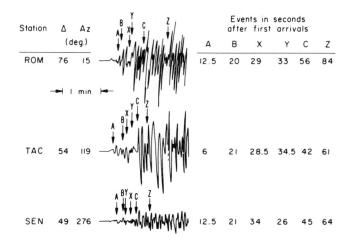

FIGURE 1 *P*-wave portion of seismograms from Europe, Mexico, and Japan. Arrows point out the phases attributed to the six determined events. The table on the right gives the time-lags of the phases with respect to the first arrivals.

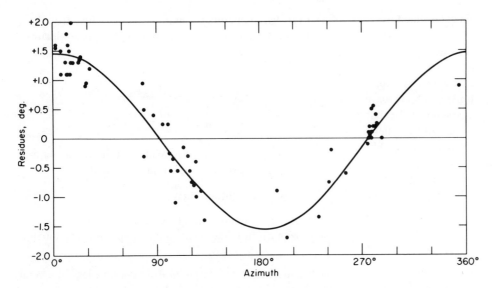

FIGURE 2   Sine-curve plot for the location of event C. Standard deviation 22 km.

interpretation is consistent with Haskell's (1964) conclusion that large earthquakes must have erratic source-time functions because a simple moving source does not radiate as much short-period energy as is observed. The events could represent consecutive bifurcation points caused by the rupture velocity accelerating to a limiting value as suggested by Mansinha (1964). If his calculations are applicable for the Alaska earthquake, the velocity of transverse waves in the source region would be obtained by dividing the rupture velocity of 3.5 km/sec by a factor of about 0.7. The resulting transverse-wave velocity of 5.0 km/sec would indicate that the source region is to be placed in the upper mantle rather than the crust.

The evidence as to whether this mechanism is applicable is not conclusive because opposed to such an interpretation is the fact that aftershocks occurred at an average depth of 22 km, a depth consistent with the thrust-fault models of Plafker (1965) and Savage and Hastie (1966, and this volume). The strongest event of the described series, event C, is located only 40 km from the zone of maximum uplift in model 3 given by Savage and Hastie. This raised the question as to whether event C represents a breakout phase (Savage, 1965).

A fault plane dipping 9° northwest and having a depth of about 22 km at the original epicenter would intersect the surface in the region of event C. The resulting difference in depth of event C with respect to the original epicenter, 20 km, leads to a decrease of the time delay as determined from the time lags on the seismic records. Because the distance from the original epicenter remains in first order the same, the rupture velocity deduced from event C is then increased to about 4 km/sec. Alternatively, event C may be a stopping phase representing the end of the southward rupture.

The sequence of events started out from the initial epicenter location. During the first 44 seconds, events apparently occurred at various azimuths. Event Y perhaps represents a stopping phase for the northerly direction of propagation.

After event C the sequence continued 60 km in a southwesterly direction to the south tip of Kodiak Island. The last event that could be identified, event Z, lies 250 km from the initial rupture and occurred 72 seconds later (Figure 3). Still later events probably occurred southwest of the event Z, but could not be identified because of the complexity of the seismograms.

The standard deviation of the distance residues for the Gutenberg sine-curve location of the epicenters was 0.2° (22 km). Considering the complexity of the analyzed records, this standard deviation is quite satisfactory. The locations and time lags give velocities between 3.1 and 3.9 km/sec for a disturbance radiating from the origin and triggering events (Table 1). The average southwesterly component of the propagation velocity is about 3.2 km/sec and thus the velocities determined in this manner agree approximately with those determined from the directivity of the surface-wave radiation pattern for this earthquake (Furumoto, 1965). The values of the rupture velocity can be varied somewhat if variations in depth relative to the first shock are allowed.

The pulses representing events A, B, and C on the records are compared to the initial pulse in the average 6, 12, and 30 times larger, respectively, corresponding to a magnitude increase from approximately 6.6 to 7.8. In Figure 3 it appears that the events are not surrounded by aftershocks in their immediate vicinity. This suggests that the strain was released in the vicinity of the events so that there was no strain-energy left for aftershocks.

CONCLUSIONS

1. The Alaska earthquake of March 28, 1964 (GMT), ruptured in a series of events. Many other large earthquakes may have a source mechanism of this type.

[62]

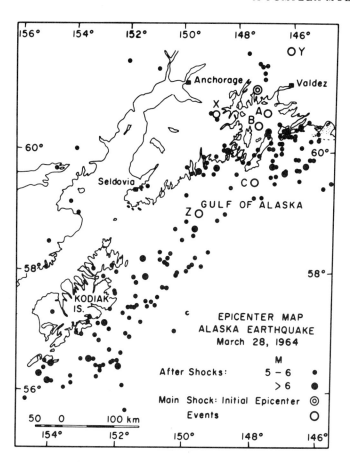

FIGURE 3 Epicenter map showing locations of six events A, B, C, X, Y, and Z. Aftershocks according to Algermissen (1966).

4. The amount of energy represented by discrete events is much greater than the energy that can be attributed to continuous radiation.

ACKNOWLEDGMENTS

This study was supported by National Science Foundation Grant GP 2806.

We wish to thank all those who cooperated by sending seismograms of the Alaska earthquake.

REFERENCES

Algermissen, S. T., 1966. Seismic studies in Alaska *in* ESSA Symposium on Earthquake Prediction. U.S. Dept. of Commerce, Environmental Science Services Administration. Washington: Government Printing Office. p. 48–52.

Båth, Markus, 1965. *Seismological Bulletin* (Uppsala, Sweden) (February 4), 3.

Benioff, Hugo, 1955. Mechanism and strain characteristics of the White Wolf Fault as indicated by the aftershock sequence. *California Division of Mines Bulletin*, 171 (November), 199–202.

Benioff, Hugo, Frank Press, and S. Smith, 1961. Excitation of the free oscillations of the earth by earthquakes. *Journal of Geophysical Research*, 66 (February), 605–619.

Ben-Menahem, Ari, 1961. Radiation of seismic surface-waves from finite moving sources. *Bulletin of the Seismological Society of America*, 51 (July), 401–435.

Ben-Menahem, Ari, and M. Nafi Toksöz, 1962. Source-mechanism from spectra of long-period seismic surface waves, 1, The Mongolian earthquake of December 4, 1957. *Journal of Geophysical Research*, 67 (May), 1943–1955.

Ben-Menahem, Ari, and M. Nafi Toksöz, 1963. Source-mechanism from spectra of long-period seismic surface waves, 3, The Alaska earthquake of July 10, 1958. *Bulletin of the Seismological Society of America*, 53 (October), 905–919.

Furumoto, Augustine S., 1965. Analysis of Rayleigh wave, Part II *in* Source mechanism study of the Alaska earthquake and tsunami of 27 March 1964. Report HIG-65-17. Honolulu: University of Hawaii, Institute of Geophysics, December. p. 31–42.

Haskell, N. A., 1964. Total energy and energy spectral density of elastic wave radiation from propagating faults. *Bulletin of the Seismological Society of America*, 54 (December), 1811–1841.

Mansinha, L., 1964. The velocity of shear fracture. *Bulletin of the Seismological Society of America*, 54 (February), 369–376.

Miyamura, S., S. Omote, R. Teisseyre, and E. Vesanen, 1965. Multiple shocks and earthquake series pattern. *Bulletin of the International Institute of Seismology and Earthquake Engineering* (Tokyo), 2, 71–92.

Plafker, George, 1965. Tectonic deformation associated with the 1964 Alaska earthquake. *Science*, 148 (June 25), 1675–1687.

Press, Frank, Ari Ben-Menahem, and M. Nafi Toksöz, 1961. Experimental determination of earthquake fault length and rupture velocity. *Journal of Geophysical Research*, 66 (October), 3471–3485.

Richter, Charles F., 1958. Elementary seismology. San Francisco: W. H. Freeman and Company. 768 p.

Savage, J. C., 1965. The stopping phase on seismograms. *Bulletin of the Seismological Society of America*, 55 (February), 47–58.

2. The rupture propagated initially in various azimuthal directions but after about 44 seconds continued only in a southwesterly direction.

3. The average propagation velocity obtained by dividing the distances of the event-epicenters from the original epicenter by the corresponding time delays was 3.5 km/sec.

TABLE 1   Rupture Propagation Velocity

Event	Time Lag (sec)	Distance to Initial Event (km)	V^a (km/sec)
A	9	35	3.9
B	19	66	3.5
C	44	165	3.8
X	28	89	3.1
Y	29	93	3.2
Z	72	250	3.5

[a] Average propagation velocity, V = 3.5 km/sec.

Savage, J. C., and L. M. Hastie, 1966. Surface deformation associated with dip-slip faulting. *Journal of Geophysical Research*, 71 (October 15), 4897–4904. Also *in* The Great Alaska Earthquake of 1964: Seismology and Geodesy. NAS Pub. 1602. Washington: National Academy of Sciences, 1972.

Usami, T., 1956. Seismometrical study of Boso-Oki earthquake of November 27, 1953. *Quarterly Journal of Seismology*, 21 (August), 1–13.

Vesanen, Eijo, 1942. Über die Typenanalytische Auswertung der Seismogramme. Annales Academiae Scientiarum Fennicae, AIII, 5. Helsinki: Suomalainen Tiedeakatemia. p. 214–229.

WILLIAM K. CLOUD*
NINA H. SCOTT
U.S. COAST AND GEODETIC SURVEY†

Reprinted from
U.S. Coast and Geodetic Survey Volume II-B,C: Seismology and Marine Geology,
"Distribution of Intensity, Prince William Sound Earthquake of 1964"

Distribution of Intensity

ABSTRACT

Effects of the Prince William Sound Earthquake of 1964 are described in terms of eye-witness reports, and the effects evaluated from these and many other reports are summarized numerically on a map to roughly indicate distribution of intensity. From the map, the felt area of the earthquake is estimated approximately at 700,000 square miles and the damage area, exclusive of distant areas affected by tsunami and seiche action, about 80,000 square miles.

INTRODUCTION

Earthquake intensity is a subjective evaluation of the effects of an earthquake on people, on manmade structures, and on the earth. Evaluation is guided by grouping typical effects into classes ranging from not felt to total damage. Numbering of the classes makes it possible to assign general ratings in a concise form on a map.

---

*Now with the University of California at Berkeley.
†Now in part Earth Sciences Laboratories, National Oceanic and Atmospheric Administration.

The advantages of such a map is that it provides an overall view of effects within the felt area of an earthquake. However, such a map never can replace fully detailed descriptions of observed effects.

The best evaluation is obtained from an intensity scale based on typical effects observed during the particular earthquake being rated. However, to improve comparison between earthquakes, the practice for many years has been to use a scale based on effects of one or more earthquakes to rate all earthquakes.

MODIFIED MERCALLI INTENSITY SCALE OF 1931

In the United States, the U. S. Coast and Geodetic Survey, for example, has used the Modified Mercalli Intensity Scale of 1931 for 37 years. In abridged form, grouping of effects on this scale is as follows:

I. Not felt except by a very few under specially favorable circumstances.

II. Felt only by a few persons at rest, especially on upper floors of buildings. Delicately suspended objects may swing.

III. Felt quite noticeably indoors, especially on upper floors of buildings, but many people do not recognize it as an earthquake. Standing motorcars may rock slightly. Vibration like passing truck. Duration estimated.

IV. During the day felt indoors by many, outdoors by few. At night some awakened. Dishes, windows, and doors disturbed; walls make creaking sound. Sensation like heavy truck striking building. Standing motorcars rocked noticeably.

V. Felt by nearly everyone, many awakened. Some dishes, windows, etc., broken; a few instances of cracked plaster; unstable objects overturned. Disturbance of trees, poles, and other tall objects sometimes noticed. Pendulum clocks may stop.

VI. Felt by all, many frightened and run outdoors. Some heavy furniture moved; a few instances of fallen plaster or damaged chimneys. Damage slight.

VII. Everyone runs outdoors. Damage negligible in buildings of good design and construction; considerable in poorly built or badly designed structures. Some chimneys broken. Noticed by persons driving motorcars.

VIII. Damage slight in specially designed structures; considerable in ordinary substantial buildings, with partial collapse; great in poorly built struc-

tures. Panel walls thrown out of frame structures. Fall of chimneys, factory stacks, columns, monuments, walls. Heavy furniture overturned. Sand and mud ejected in small amounts. Changes in well water. Persons driving motorcars disturbed.

IX. Damage considerable in specially designed structures; well-designed frame structures thrown out of plumb; great in substantial buildings, with partial collapse. Buildings shifted off foundations. Ground cracked conspicuously. Underground pipes broken.

X. Some well-built wooden structures destroyed; most masonry and frame structures destroyed with foundations; ground badly cracked. Rails bent. Landslides considerable from river banks and steep slopes. Shifted sand and mud. Water splashed (slopped) over banks.

XI. Few, if any, (masonry) structures remain standing. Bridges destroyed. Broad fissures in ground. Underground pipelines completely out of service. Earth slumps and land slips in soft ground. Rails bent greatly.

XII. Damage total. Waves seen on ground surfaces. Lines of sight and level distorted. Objects thrown upward into the air.

USE OF THE SCALE

Before attempting to use the Modified Mercalli Scale of 1931 or similar scales, a decision should be made regarding the meaning of intensity. If the dictionary definition—degree of strength, force, energy, etc., is used, then observed effects must be normalized to some parameter of motion; but this is not practical since all of the factors contributing to what happens during an earthquake are seldom, if ever, fully known. This is illustrated by Hershberger's study in 1956. He compared maximum accelerations recorded on 108 strong-motion records obtained during 50 earthquakes with intensity ratings assigned to the places where the records were obtained. For a given rating, intensity V, he found the highest maximum acceleration to be 50 times the lowest.

Since the literal meaning of intensity poses a problem, a more practical connotation, and the one used by the U.S. Coast annd Geodetic Survey, is seriousness of effects regardless of cause.

This connotation of intensity solves one problem in use of the scale, but there are other problems. First, the scale brings together long-period and short-period effects. Second, certain of the effects listed in the scale are not well defined.

The results of bringing together long- and short-period effects are not serious when attempting to rate moderate earthquakes. However, results are striking when attempting to rate major events, such as the Prince William Sound Earthquake, due to the greatly increased proportion of long-period effects to short-period effects. Effects in Anchorage, Alaska, offer a classic example. Here, there was serious damage to taller buildings and to slide-prone areas, but homes and other small structures, even those adjacent to the taller buildings and slide areas, suffered comparatively little damage. The U.S. Coast and Geodetic Survey's solution to this problem was to assign a range of intensities rather than a single intensity.

The poorly defined effects result in possible confusion when comparing earthquakes. Such phrases in the scale as "building of good design, well-built ordinary buildings, specially designed structures," etc., have meanings that change with time. Aside from updating the scale, perhaps as suggested by Richter [1958], there is no solution for this problem. For the Prince William Sound Earthquake, ratings were based on existing construction. Whether or not the construction compared in quality with construction that Wood and Neumann [1931] had in mind when they prepared the intensity scale is not known.

INTENSITY MAP

Information on observed effects for use in evaluating intensity during the Prince William Sound Earthquake was obtained from reconnaissance flights made immediately after the earthquake over the higher intensity areas; field inspections in the Anchorage, Valdez, Seward, Kodiak, Cordova, and intermediate locations; reports by other organizations and news media; and from over 450 reports received from 1,000 questionnaire forms sent out to locations in Alaska and Canada.

As might be expected there was a wealth of data from centers of population, but very little data from the vast, sparsely settled outlying regions—so little data, in fact, that drawing of lines to indicate isoseismal zones, as usually done, was of doubtful value. Thus, the intensity map, figure 1, zones only the macroseismic area and the approximate limits of the felt area. This map is but one of several intensity maps prepared for the Prince William Sound Earthquake. Each map differs slightly from the others, since the subjective evaluation

of different people was involved. However, the differences are not such as to cause serious confusion.

From figure 1, estimates indicate that the earthquake was felt within an area of approximately 700,000 square miles, and caused serious damage within an area of approximately 80,000 square miles. Additionally, but not shown on the map, serious tsunami and seiche effects were observed great distances from the epicenter.

For reasons stated previously, intensity ratings on the map simply indicate that observed effects were considered approximately equal in seriousness to criteria of the scale. Knowledge of what the effects of the Prince William Sound Earthquake actually were can be obtained only from thorough study of the many volumes of descriptive and pictorial reports.

The descriptive section that follows is but a sample, based as near as possible on eyewitness reports of what occurred in various places during the earthquake.

REFERENCES

Wood, Harry O. and Neumann, Frank, "Modified Mercalli Intensity Scale of 1931," *Bulletin of the Seismological Society of America,* vol. 21, no. 4, December 1931.

Hershberger, John, "A Comparison of Earthquake Acceleration With Intensity Ratings," *Bulletin of the Seismological Society of America,* vol. 46, no. 4, October 1956.

Richter, Charles F., *Elementary Seismology,* W. H. Freeman and Company, San Francisco, 1958, 137 pp.

OBSERVED EFFECTS

(Excerpts From Earthquake Reports)

UNITED STATES

Alaska

ANCHORAGE

Turnagain Heights (Robert B. Atwood, Editor and Publisher of the *Anchorage Daily Times; Daily Alaska Empire,* Juneau).—I had just started to practice playing the trumpet when the earthquake occurred. In a few short moments it was obvious that this earthquake was no minor one: the chandelier made from a ship's wheel swayed too much. Things were falling that had never fallen before. I headed for the door. At the door I saw walls weaving. On the driveway I turned and watched my house squirm and groan. Tall trees were falling in

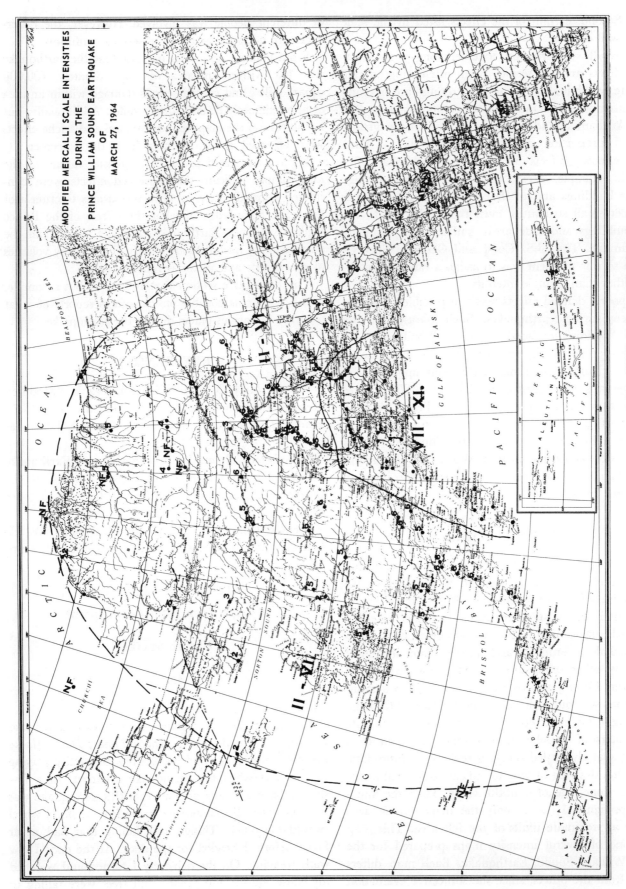

FIGURE 1.—Distribution of intensities during the Prince William Sound Earthquake.

FIGURE 2.—Soil slumpage in the Turnagain Heights area of Anchorage, Alaska. Cook Inlet is visible in the background.

our yard. I moved to a spot where I thought it would be safe, but, as I moved, I saw cracks appear in the earth. Pieces of ground in jigsaw-puzzle shapes moved up and down, tilted at all angles. I tried to move away, but more appeared in every direction. I noticed that my house was moving away from me, fast. As I started to climb the fence to my neighbor's yard, the fence disappeared. Trees were falling in crazy patterns. Deep chasms opened up. Table-top pieces of earth moved upward, standing like toadstools with great overhangs, some were turned at crazy angles. A chasm opened beneath me. I tumbled down. I was quickly on the verge of being buried. I ducked pieces of trees, fence posts, mailboxes, and other odds and ends. Then my neighbor's house collapsed and slid into the chasm. For

a time it threatened to come down on top of me, but the earth was still moving, and the chasm opened to receive the house. When the earth movement stopped, I climbed to the top of the chasm. I found angular landscape in every direction (fig. 2). I found my neighbor carrying his young daughter. We found his wife atop one of the high mushroom-like promontories. She was standing alone with her auto, marooned. We climbed up and down chasm walls and under dangerous overhanging pieces of frozen ground to safety. Helicopters were overhead, but they couldn't land near us—the ground was too topsy-turvy. After what seemed to be an endless time, rescuers came and helped the party out of the quagmire that had once been a home (fig. 3).

FIGURE 3.—Partial view of Turnagain Heights slide area, Anchorage, Alaska.

Downtown Anchorage (Spotlight, publication of Universal Services, Inc., Connie Casey).—My husband and I were in the Chart Room at the Westward Hotel. We had just sat down at the table when things started to move. By the time we reached the front door, people were pouring out of buildings into the street. As we got outside, the plate glass windows of an office building across the street popped out. All the ground was weaving like an ocean wave. It really seemed like trying to balance yourself on a ball. We could see pavement breaks. All the glass was out of the Northern Commercial Building. There was debris all over. We looked down Fifth Avenue and could not believe the crazy angle of the J. C. Penney Store (fig. 4). It was almost like we were in a daze, and couldn't believe the things we saw. A new, 2-story office building had sunk into

the ground. We got home and changed into warm clothing, not even realizing we were wet from falling and sitting in the snow. We were very lucky; no damage to our house except a few broken dishes and a few scratches.

(Bert Londerville).—I had just arrived at the Hofbrau and was sitting in the cocktail lounge when the shock hit. The entire back section of the Hofbrau started to shake. We ran into the parking lot and by the time we got there, sections of the lot had already fallen in, and the cars were rolling back and forth, with cracks opening all around. I happened to be looking toward the Anchorage Hardware store when it fell. Then the building adjoining the Hofbrau started falling, and I could hear the kitchen and bar of the Hofbrau falling, although the back wall stood up. The next thing I can

FIGURE 4.—J. C. Penney store in Anchorage, Alaska. Note undamaged buildings in foreground.

remember is looking toward the Westward Hotel, seeing it sway, and wondering what kept it from falling down. I will probably always remember the screams of the people on the top floors of the hotel. It seemed as though the ground was moving in all directions—sideways, in circles, and up and down.

(Jimmie Doss).—At the start of the quake, we were across the street from the 1200 L Street apartment building. After a few seconds, we knew this was something worse than we had ever experienced. Dishes were thrown from the shelves, and pictures fell from the walls. We had to have our feet planted 2 to 3 feet apart to keep from falling. The windows [1200 L Street apartment building] were all popping out, and the concrete was falling like snowflakes to the ground (fig. 5). Our house came through without a scratch—inside and out—

but we lost most of our glassware.

(Don Usher).—I had just entered my apartment when I noticed a slight shake; then the shake intensified until everything—furniture, dishes, clothes, lamps, and papers—was flying in all directions. After 4 to 5 minutes of this violent shaking, rolling, swaying, and heaving, the 32-apartment building finally settled down, and I went outside to take a look around. The four apartments at the far end had broken off the building and fallen into a crevasse which was previously B Street. All the cars in the building had been thrown through their respective doors and were piled in a huddle in the parkway covered with debris. Those who had run out of the building were thrown on the ice-covered sidewalks.

Hillside Apartments, corner 16th and H Sts. (John R. Williams, geologist).—I was sitting on a couch in

FIGURE 5.—1200 L Apartment Building, Anchorage, Alaska. Note the broken windows and fractured pier in the second story. *U.S. Bureau of Land Management photograph.*

the living room of Apartment W–35. At first we noticed a rattling of the building. The initial shaking lasted perhaps 5 to 10 seconds. The first shaking motion was followed without any noticeable quiet period by a strong rolling motion which appeared to move from the east toward the west. The strong rolling motion swung the closet door, and started plaster dust falling. After a few seconds of the strong rolling motion, I took my son to the door leading to the hall, opened the door to prevent jamming, and stood in doorway. Watched deformation of street entrance door and glass blocks bordering door. Glass in door broke, and blocks began breaking. Looked in hallway and back in apartment and noticed blocks working against one another in interior walls and saw some fall into the street and into apartment and hall. Took son and ran to parked car. Looked at the building which was swaying in east-west direction. Blocks were

toppling, ground heaving, trees and poles were swaying strongly. The Hillside apartment building is a total loss (fig. 6). Our apartment was one of the least damaged. It was next to the apartment on the west end of the building on the south side, two floors above the ground, and one below the street. The light day-beds were in position; drum table was in place; and table lamp about 12-inches high (quite unstable) was upright on the table. Papers on this table (north side of living room) were in place. A portable TV on a wheeled stand was upright; pictures looked normal; plaster cast of the child's hand on wall was in place. Metal shelving on the north-facing wall of hall fell so that it was oriented about N. 70° E., but its fall may have been controlled by position of walls. A wooden bookcase, 4 feet high, located on the west-facing wall of the living room, did not fall, but books spilled out. The stove did not move, but the icebox slid perhaps 1½ feet southeast from its position on the east-facing wall. Kitchen cupboards did not come open, and no glassware or dishes were broken, although we did not inspect all cabinets for damage. Unstable knickknacks on the windowsill fell, but others did not. Only one or two boxes in an unstable heap on top shelf of living room closet fell to floor. Heavy, wooden clothes locker, 8 feet high, remained upright. Before dark on the 27th and again on the 28th, I made an inspection of the grounds of the apartment building (but not downhill) and of adjacent homes along the bluff and on H Street for cracks that would indicate potential danger from landslides. I saw no cracks of any kind, except those in the street which were winter contraction cracks which may have been opened by the earthquake. No cracks were

FIGURE 6. — Hillside Manor Apartments in Anchorage, Alaska. *Frank McClure photograph.*

seen in the snow cover. Also on the 28th, I inspected and interviewed the occupants of a house at 733–16th Avenue, located on the north side of 16th Avenue, directly across from the east end of the apartment house and approximately 100 feet to the north. It was of frame construction and had large, 5- to 8-foot long thermopane windows along the south, west, and east walls. The basement was of cinder block on dry gravel. Although the motion was violent enough to make standing difficult and caused damage to dishes by opening cupboards with magnetic locks, toppled the TV, etc., no windows were broken, and the chimney and block basement were intact and uncracked. I inspected the frame house (poured concrete basement) at 1555 H Street, on east side of street, three houses north of intersection of 16th and H Streets. Although the occupants of this house were severely shaken, lamps toppled, cupboards opened, the only apparent damage was a small crack in the south wall of the basement.

1200 L Street Apartments (W. G. Binkley).—I was in my apartment on the 12th floor, northwest corner, when the most violent lateral motion was felt. There was a definite vertical movement. The motion was so violent that I was thrown to the floor and was unable to regain my feet until it stopped. There was a period of 20 to 30 seconds of relatively gentle shaking before the main shock, which seemed to last 2 to 3 minutes.

Apartment Building (Dorothy L. Sturm).—When the earthquake started, I picked up my baby so she would not be frightened. Had I not picked her up then, I would never have been able to get to her. I tried to reach the front door, about seven steps away, but when I reached for the doorknob, I was thrown onto the sofa. Lucky for me, because if I had gotten the door open my baby and I would have been thrown over the rail of the balcony. We were on the third floor of the apartment building.

Government Hill, 744 Sunset Drive (John S. Iubon(?)). —The ground appeared to vibrate in a waving motion. Vertical motion was appreciable; in the horizontal direction, it seemed to be east-west, lasting for 2 to 3 minutes, then it changed to north south and was stronger for perhaps the last minute. The bluff west of our house slid out, and the Government Hill School dropped down 15 to 20 feet into the slide. Figure 7 displays the damage that the Government Hill School sustained during the Prince William Sound Earthquake. Cracks spread east of the slide.

Federal Building (U.S. Weather Bureau).—Although I was standing, presumably erect, on the sidewalk, it

FIGURE 7.—Government Hill School, Anchorage, Alaska.

was almost impossible for me to determine the direction of the major movement. Fortunately, we have a record of the sequence of earth movements by the manner in which our files were displaced in the data file room at this office. A large, single section, open-shelf file against the west wall was thrown violently eastward, emptying all contents on the floor. A similar shelving of double files along the south wall also had contents completely emptied on the floor. However, the contents from the file on the west were found on the bottom of the heap, while the material on the shelving along the south wall was found on top. This sequence of earth movements is also substantiated by the fact that the vertical file on the west wall broke loose and was leaning against the end of the double file which later, moving in a north-south direction, made a rather deep scar in the west end of the double file at a distance of about 6 feet above the floor level. In other words, the violent north-south movement of the double file occurred after the file on the west wall had been tipped over against the double file.

1306 E. Fourth Avenue (M. K. Weaver).—The ground rolled for a minute or so, then broke open, and worked up and down. The shock picked up speed in the first minute or so, then held it. It seemed to stop all at once. It was very still when it was over. Damage slight.

1040 D Street (R. Schmidt).—When I returned to my house, books and bookcases had fallen from east-west walls but not from north-south walls. Dishes did not fall out of cupboards; no breakage. House has 8-inch, poured concrete basement. Tenants suffered no damage;

one cup broken. Only very poorly placed objects fell in basement (skis on east-west wall but not heavy objects, such as canned foods).

2809 67th Avenue (Thomas W. Gregory).—Appeared to rock north-south with rolling motion. Very slight damage to my house. No visible fissures in ground around or near house. Dishes and standing lamp broken.

2006 W. Northern Lights Boulevard, Spenard District (L. J. Lantz).—Main shock waves felt like very short, sharp, and up-and-down movements, ending almost instantaneously. Had no apparent damage to my own trailer and furnishings. No visible damage to trailers and small wooden houses at trailer court right after shock. Several fuel drums fell or contents spilled. Propane tanks and electric and utility lines undamaged.

CHENEGA

Tsunami destroyed every building in this fishing village, except a school on a hill behind the village.

CHITINA AND VICINITY

(Mrs. Ray Stalder).—Chitina received severe shocks. One side of the mountain directly west of town caved off as we watched. The ground split as our children ran three ways. The splits closed, sending dirt into the air. Ground cracked in business and residential areas. Huge boulders rolled onto road 1 mile south of town.

(Howard Knutson).—The drugstore leaned towards south during shock. A safe, which took eight men to move on skids, overturned to south. A warehouse, with welded railroad rails for foundation, collapsed. Chitina Hotel leaned towards north and also pushed us towards north. Could not stand up straight. About 7 miles north of here, on the Copper River, large riverbank slide. Considerable damage to warehouse, grocery, and hotel supplies.

(*Cordova Times,* 4–9–64).—At Long Lake near Chitina, salmon spawning beds were badly shaken up and faulted.

COOPER LANDING

(Betty J. Fuller, U.S. Geological Survey).—Landslides; cracks 18 inches wide and 6 to 8 feet deep in ice, mud, and pavement.

COPPER CENTER AREA AND RICHARDSON HIGHWAY SOUTH OF COPPER CENTER

(Ralph B. Lane, Maintenance Foreman, Ernestine Camp).—I was on my way to Copper Center with my family. While driving, the earthquake hit us at Milepost 83. The road began to roll, and cracks were visible in several places. We did not know at first just what was happening. After it was over, we proceeded on our way past Wolf Homestead, where everyone was in the yard and seemed to be all right. We went on to Copper Center and upon arriving at our home, found that the power was off. I immediately went to Copper River Cash Store to use the telephone and try to get in contact with Glennallen or the Ernestine Maintenance Camp; the phone was out of order. When we returned to Ernestine Camp, the radio transmitter and receiving units were on the floor. The following is my personal view of damage done to the Richardson Highway: Tonsina Hill slipped down as much as 18 to 24 inches in places, leaving one-way traffic; large cracks across road; great quantities of water pushed up through the ground. Little Tonsina Bridge damaged and impassable; bridge pushed together, causing the deck to rise above the pavement and pushing the pavement 3 to 4 feet in the air. Traffic was maintained by breaking down the deck and building an earth bridge over the top. Little Tonsina and Squirrel Creek Campgrounds appeared to be all right. At Kendall Cache, damage to the building appeared slight; merchandise was all over the floor. At Milepost 29, large heave; between Mileposts 37 to 64, very minor damage; at Mileposts 38, 39, 42, snowslides; at Milepost 40, Tonsina River blocked off and water backed up to a depth of 10 feet. Water worked its way through the slide. These slides closed the road for 6 hours. Milepost 44, rockslide; at Milepost 50, the extra amount of water coming down the Tiekel River had been blocked off by a large snowslide. A channel through the snow, 12 feet deep and 70 feet long, had to be blasted through the snow to let the water through. Great numbers of cracks opened between Mileposts 64 and 85, some were as large as 8 inches wide. Many parts were raised on one side and dropped on the other, with a difference of as much as 6 to 8 inches; Milepost 67, road heaved and cracked in many places; at Milepost 74, broken ice on the Little Tonsina River, caused a jam; at Mileposts 76 and 77, water flowed down roadway and washed fill. Milepost 78½, ice jams on Tonsina River caused water to back up very close to road level.

Copper Center (J. M. Goddard).—Fireplace cracked; furniture broken. Our warehouse is 140 by 40 feet and full of automotive parts and Standard Oil products— all the stock was thrown to the floor. Damage slight.

Copper Center (G. M. Goble).—Ground cracked.

Milepost 101.5 (Joy Morgan).—Small cracks in highway; ground cracked. Considerable shelf damage in store. One bookcase (facing north) torn from wall, spilling contents. No damage to basement or attic; no damage to sewers, gas line, or water line.

Milepost 89, 12 miles south of Copper Center (Mrs. Roy Hooper).—Knickknacks and books fell. Ground cracked. Damage slight.

Milepost 83½, Pippin Lake (Paul E. Wolf).—Knickknacks and books fell; dishes broken; trees shook violently. Ground cracked. No damage to wood or concrete. I was clearing timber with a Caterpillar over soil and marshy ground about 50 yards from Pippin Lake shore; the earth had rolling wave motion, like water waves.

Milepost 82½, Pippin Lake (J. Williams).— Knickknacks, books, and pictures fell; dishes broken. Ground cracked. Damage slight. Ice shattered and water and mud pumped on the east side of lake. Full-length fissure, running north-south, on west side of lake, also on a small lake 1 mile east. Roads cracked on both the Richardson and Edgewater Highways. Spring in Bernard Creek area lost water (very old spring used by Signal Corps and highway camp).

Kenny Lake School (Frances Kibble).—Furniture overturned; books and pictures fell. Damage slight.

(From letter to Dr. Carl Benson, Geophysical Institute, College, from Jack Wilson, Wilson Air Service, Glennallen).—I finally got up to Mt. Wrangell at a time when it was clear, April 11. There was so much vapor rising out of the cone that I could never see down into it at all. There was much more activity than before, and it seemed unlikely that atmospheric conditions could have caused it all. The fissures around the rim of the Big Basin appeared to be very active too. One noticeable thing was the amount of bare ground over on the northeast side where the higher peaks and jagged cliffs are. The ash there had melted so much snow. There was a lot of bare ground on the sides. There are a few new cracks which run sort of crosswise to the older crevasses, but none of them are more than a few inches wide. Other than that, the old mountain held up very well. There is a small tributary glacier which runs into Sherman Glacier near Cordova. (Sherman Glacier is in the Chugach Mountains between the Copper River delta and the town of Cordova.) This side glacier, which comes in from the south, slid down its valley out over Sherman Glacier, and ended up almost at the terminal of Sherman, a slothful receding glacier.

CORDOVA AND COPPER RIVER HIGHWAY

(Luther M. Brown, Weather Bureau).—Slight tremors were felt for about 20 seconds, then they increased steadily for another 20 seconds, finally becoming abruptly violent. Violent shaking continued for several minutes and was accompanied by noise similar to that of distant cannon booms. The entire sequence of motion seemed to increase and decrease in a smooth wave-type motion. The city of Cordova and vicinity was not damaged, even though badly shaken. Substantial buildings were unaffected; fissures did not appear in the ground; and no personal injuries occurred. Some merchandise was lost, even in some of the newly constructed stores, when toppled from shelves to the floor. About midnight, following the earthquake, the first of three tsunamis assaulted the city (the Airport Station was not affected). During the surges, water rose to a level of 10 feet above the highest recorded high tide. Cordova tides appear (April 6) to be running 6 feet below normal. *Copper River Highway.*—The area to the east of the city (from Milepost 6 through Milepost 50) was more severely affected. Numerous ground fissures were observed up to 4 feet wide and 50 feet long. All of the newly built (1960-61) concrete and steel bridges were damaged, with more than 10 rendered impassable. Glaciers were moved as much as a quarter of a mile in the area. The Weather Bureau Airport Station, located at Milepost 13, received some damage. The airport runway had minor damage. The newly built FAA–WB control building settled somewhat, causing doors to stick and the concrete-slab floor to crack along the walls. Plumbing facilities were disrupted, since nearly all of the underground pipes were broken. The underground power cable to the ceiling light was severed, but Weather Bureau instruments were undamaged. The Weather Bureau apartment building settled somewhat, causing doors to stick, but there was no significant damage.

(*Cordova Times*, 4–2–64).—In Cordova, there was no damage to water mains, sewer lines, telephone or power installations, and no cracks in the streets. The old wooden water pipe from Meals Lake, now used only as a fire reserve water supply, was destroyed. There was little or no damage to any of the old frame houses which are built on the sides of the hills around the bay. Murcheson Falls, the main water source, had been only a trickle, and the city was being supplied from the deep well. When the shock occurred, Murcheson Falls opened up and filled the main with a sizeable creek from the overflow. It was not until early morning that the water waves came. The first came with a roar into the small boat harbor, tearing loose pilings already loosened by the shock. This wave was hardly higher than a large tide. The second wave was about 10 feet higher, and this wave caused most of the damage in Cordova, floating away homes and boat houses along the shore. Many boats were left aground. Canneries, boat yards, and clam beds were left high and dry by the massive uplift of the earth.

EAGLE RIVER

(Lucille M. Fly, Postmaster; from USGS report).—Several cracks in the pavement and other materials, with average length of 30 feet and width of 1 inch. Water level rose in well; several wells in vicinity went dry.

(R. L. Tedrow).—Chimneys cracked; dishes broken; furniture overturned. Damage slight.

Post Office; (Martha E. Hall).—Walls cracked. Damage slight to masonry. Furniture overturned; dishes broken.

EAGLE RIVER VALLEY

From *Spotlight,* publication of Universal Services, Inc., Vol. 4, No. 1, May 1964 (Edna Zaccaro).—I was almost to my home in Eagle River Valley when the shock occurred. Since going over our pioneer access road always feels as though one were in an earthquake, I did not get to experience much of the shock. However, the quake did trigger many avalanches in the valley, and there was a terrible roar plus high winds. The glacier that my husband was standing on at the time started cracking beneath him, and he ran for the nearest tree and hung on. Our mountain A-frame house came through without a scratch.

EKLUTNA (near)

(*Anchorage Daily Times,* 4–6–64).—Huge concrete pier set deep in the bed of the Knik River, offset about 8 inches at the new highway section near Eklutna. Only other damage at the construction site was to a temporary wooden work bridge which had damaged piling and a broken deck.

GIRDWOOD—PORTAGE AREA

(*Anchorage Daily Times,* 4–2–64).—The most severe damage to the Chugach Electric Association facilities occurred to the Cooper Lake Line and the Knik Arm Steam Plant on Ship Creek. Approximately 200 poles down in the area. Three structures damaged at the Silvertip section of the line.

GLENNALLEN AND VICINITY

(Maxine M. Millard, Acting Postmaster; from USGS report).—One long crack 200 feet long and 4 inches wide. Healthy trees as large as 8 inches in diameter broken. Three wells in area ceased to flow.

(Gilbert Monroe).—Hundreds of earth cracks in the area, some 12 inches wide. Water gushed from many fissures but stopped within 24 hours. One of the 100-foot-deep wells ceased to flow; other deep wells were unaffected.

Air Traffic Control Station, 6 miles east of Glennallen (Francis G. Brown).—Small ground cracks in east-west direction directly outside of building. Water main running east-west broke about 5 feet below surface.

ACS Building (Russell C. Forson).—Ground cracked. Plaster cracked and fell; furniture overturned and broken. Damage considerable.

Copper Valley School (Bridget D. Condon).—Slight damage to some buildings; considerable damage to one building. Six-foot cross on dome bent. Corners out of one 2-story cement-block building. One water main broken. Ground cracked; landslides.

(H. C. Prater).—Well casing broken. Furniture broken. About 16-inch-wide ground cracks.

(James E. Gore, RCA).—Moved 50- by 10-foot trailer off blocks about 1 foot.

Tazlina, 7 miles south of Glennallen (Leonard Brenwick).—When shock started I was inside our house. After about 1 minute I went outside into the yard, and by then it was difficult to walk. I hung onto a tree which was shaking very strongly. Looking west, the shock waves seemed to be coming from that direction and looked to be about 6 to 8 inches high, and traveling so rapidly that they seemed to be only about 20 feet from the crest to the low. Although the waves looked to be traveling east, several objects, which could fall in any direction, fell north-south. Heavy objects moved; furniture overturned.

Milepost 111, Richardson Highway (Joseph F. Dimonde).—Ground cracked. Damage slight to concrete. Furniture overturned; dishes and windows broken.

Milepost 111½, Richardson Highway (W. Dittman).—Ground cracked. Furnishings shifted; pictures fell; dishes broken.

GLENN HIGHWAY AREA

Sutton, about 20 miles northeast of Palmer (Grace F. Boulder; from USGS report).—Many cracks, some one-eighth mile long and 18 inches wide. One area of the highway, about one-fourth mile long, subsided about 3 feet. Water level in well fell.

Snowshoe Lake, Milepost 147 (Rick Houston).—Chimneys cracked slightly. Minor cracks in roadway. Lake ice upheaved. Pressure ridges to 2½ feet high generally follow shoreline, but many farther out in lake. Cracks 6 to 8 inches wide to depth of ice. Mud and ice thrown through cracks in more shallow areas of lake 3 to 5 feet, and water in areas of over 10 feet deep.

South shore of lake appears to have settled 6 to 8 inches, and this is shore, not just ice. Very difficult to walk or stand during shock. No great alarm. At Milepost 158.8 (Al Lee home), the lake shore settled 3 to 5 feet. Ice pulled out from under airplane tied down by shore, leaving plane in water. Entire site of 3 acres (Lee property) is so cut up by cracks and crevasses that there is no area large enough on which to rebuild his house. Wood-frame house damaged severely.

Chickaloon, east of Milepost 95 (Wallace Bays).— A mountain a short distance away had a large slide during and after the shock. It is Strelshla Mountain at the east end of Anthracite Ridge, just west of Sheep Mountain on the Glenn Highway.

Milepost 42 (Frank Reale).—Water completely disappeared from our 18-foot-deep well. Basement walls and floor cracked.

Milepost 55.5 (R. W. Wade).—Plaster, windows, walls, chimneys, and ground cracked; plaster and chimneys fell. Furniture overturned and broken.

Milepost 72 (L. G. Bunnell).—Furniture overturned; dishes and glass broken. No ground cracks. Violent up-and-down motion. I had just left home and was traveling north on Glenn Highway. Car almost turned over from heaving motion. All trees, poles, and land in strong up-and-down motion.

Milepost 95 (Daniel M. Parmenter).—Ground cracked. Asbestos chimney fell. Damage slight to concrete (slight crack). Furniture overturned; dishes broken. (Wallace Bays).—Furnishings shifted; knickknacks and books fell. Dishes broken.

Milepost 113, Sheep Mountain Lodge (Oscar F. Jurgilet (?)).—Ground cracked. Windows and dishes broken. Damage considerable to windows, toilet bowls; one underground water pipe. Furniture overturned.

Milepost 127, Eureka (David C. Vigdahl).—Everything seemed to move several feet back and forth. Every pavement joint showed some effect. Barrel of water on back porch emptied; lamps and dishes fell to floor.

Milepost 94 (Harry R. Fowler).—Furnishings shifted; knickknacks fell. Ground cracked.

HOMER AND VICINITY

Anchor Point (Clarence D. Smith from USGS report).—Across road from Anchor Point to Homer, 70 to 100 cracks. One observer reported hearing loud noises like gunshots as the cracks in the road closed. Water level in wells fell.

Kachemak Bay, head of (R. W. Rainwater).— Ground cracked. Furniture overturned; dishes broken.

Huge landslide on bluffs near the bay. Some of these will impound spring runoff in canyons. Road to beach blocked by slide of much earth, trees, etc. Large cracks, 3 to 18 inches wide, all over the ridge and flats.

Kachemak Bay, 14½ miles east of Homer (Lester A. Dufour).—Ground cracked. Dishes broken. Large dirt or rock slide along Grewingk Glacier across the bay from me. Looks to be about one-fourth mile wide.

Homer (Albert E. Greer from USGS report).—Many ground cracks, some 6 inches wide. Mole tracks or pressure ridges. One landslide 800 by 1,500 feet occurred 6 miles east of Homer. Approximately 5 square miles of ground subsided as much as 6 feet. Water spouts, some 10 feet high, formed several craters in a line. Water level in wells fell; some wells went dry and did not come back immediately. Water level in nearby lake dropped 5 feet.

Homer (James R. Heay, Weather Bureau).—Roads cracked; landslides on cliffs adjacent to Homer. Several buildings in the Homer area were badly damaged and were unusable. In general, damage was reported as moderate; few walls cracked; little plaster damage; some chimneys cracked; some foundations cracked, a few beyond repair. One underground control cable (52-pair, lead covered, armored), running north-south, ruined. All objects in houses not fastened down were knocked to floor, including some heavy objects. Most objects seemed to fall in north-south direction. Some grocery stores suffered very heavy losses to stock. Tide approximately 6 feet higher than normal.

Homer, Diamond Ridge (Evelyn Lofgreen).—Pipeline broke; chickenhouse foundation damaged. Freezer shifted; dishes broke. After the shock, I heard noises at frequent intervals which sounded like blasting or big guns firing. We have several hairline cracks in the snow near the building.

Homer (Mrs. Don Judd).—The front part of our house is an old log cabin with concrete floor. The shock started slowly. At first I didn't feel it, but my husband (sitting) did. My husband, five girls, and myself reached the front door more or less in a group when the full impact hit. My 3- and 6-year-old girls were thrown off their feet into the snow. I was thrown back quite hard against the south side of the door jamb. The trees were heavy with wet spring snow, and I noticed the snow being thrown straight up and landing on the branches again before being shaken off. My husband had returned to the house to turn off the stoves. I thought I heard him yell and hurried into the house. The floor seemed to come up and meet me one minute and drop away from my feet the next, causing me to stagger. My plates were being dealt out of the cupboard like cards. Cupboards are on the north side of house.

HOPE AND VICINITY

(K. L. Wilkins; from USGS report).—Many cracks, most only a few feet long. One crack one-half mile long and 6 inches wide. Entire town evidently sank 4 to 6 feet. Water spouts formed, the highest 8 feet and lasted 4 to 5 seconds. Water level in wells rose, and water became somewhat salty during high tides. New springs formed, and other springs increased in flow.

(Vera S. Specking).—Plaster, windows, chimneys, and ground cracked; windows broke; chimneys fell. Damage great to chimneys. The first extreme high tide was 7:00 a.m., Easter Sunday. This was when we first suspected the land had subsided. Tide was on schedule, not a wave, and continued on schedule. About one-half of the Hope townsite must be abandoned to the tide because of land subsidence.

KENAI AND VICINITY

Clam Gulch, about 10 miles south of Kasilof (Postmaster, from USGS report).—Many cracks in all areas. Few water spouts. Water level in one well fell.

Kasilof, about 6 miles south of Kenai (Mr. and Mrs. Ira L. Miller).—Many cracks, several feet in length and 1 inch wide in mud, sand, tundra, and ice. Mole track, or pressure ridges. One landslide, 300 by 100 feet, on north bank of Kasliof River. One area, approximately 100 feet wide, subsided 1 inch to 4 feet. Water level in wells fell; new springs formed; streams decreased in flow.

Cohoe, few miles south of Kasilof (Elfreda Lewis, from USGS report).—No tsunami was noticed. Tide levels in the area 1½ feet higher.

Kenai (J. R. Lietzke).—Cars facing north rolled; cars facing west-east rocked and bounded.

Kenai (Allan L. Peterson).—Furnishings shifted; knickknacks, books, and pictures fell; dishes broke. Damage slight.

Kenai (F. Torkilsen).—Some small objects and furnishings shifted; lamps overturned; knickknacks fell. Damage slight.

Wildwood Station, about 6 miles north of Kenai (Charles H. McCrary, Chief, Communications Branch). —Generally, walls cracked in line with joints. Quite a few cracked vertically. Building No. 16 was partially damaged by water from fallen wooden water tower; concrete POL station was also damaged by falling tower.

Water tower seemed to be on rubber legs and appeared to dance, then it split and collapsed; seemed to come straight down. Telephone cable cut by falling tower. Some damage to water mains at several points on the station. Fire extinguishers fell off mounts; cabinets and other nonstationary items shifted on floors. Plaster cracked in numerous places.

MOOSE PASS AND VICINITY

(Mrs. Delbert L. Wolfe).—Our piano (upright, full size) on east-west wall shifted 2½ feet to south. Stove and oil heater (west wall) shifted 6 to 8 inches northeast. Three chests of drawers on north wall fell to floor. Open shelves standing about 34 inches high on east and south walls (covered with potted plants) lost only four plants, and none of contents came out, but potted plants on bookshelves on north wall were buried under books. Four-foot open shelves in bathroom (north wall) emptied of contents. Deep freeze (21 cubic feet) against west wall rocked back and forth; 500-gallon oil barrel on 5-foot rack (end of barrel east-west) rocked north-south but did not go over 2 by 4 inch chocks. Lock boxes at post office (over east-west counter) shifted 14 to 15 inches to south but did not fall. Desk, file case, and stove in post office shifted slightly (frame building 12 by 16 feet and about 18 inches off ground on four blocks). We saw an avalanche of snow come down mountain to west of Seward-Anchorage Highway about one-half mile west of Moose Pass. Could hear roar but still so dazed by shock, can't say how loud. We ran from house and clung to car to keep from being thrown to the ground.

(Mrs. Delbert L. Wolfe from USGS report).—Many ground cracks up to 50 feet long with an average width of 1 inch in the vicinity of home. Water level in well rose; streams in the vicinity decreased in flow. Several landslides 8 miles north of Moose Pass. Six miles south of Moose Pass, house and building almost sank out of sight. Kenai Lake Ranger Station was extensively damaged by wave and ice blocks.

(Clayton Mortiboy).—Chimneys fell. Loosened foundation bricks; cracked 2 two by fours of house frame; small wall crack. Refrigerator and dressers fell; oil cook stove shifted and stovepipe knocked down. Deep freeze and heavy bed moved. Hot water tank shifted a few inches; few leaking water pipes. Ground heaved and rolled.

Milepost 27½, Seward Highway (B. Shaffer).—Plaster, walls, and chimneys cracked. Dishes broke.

FIGURE 8.—Portage, Alaska, after the Prince William Sound Earthquake. Note large cracks parallel to the secondary road. Large fissures cross the Anchorage-Seward Highway; the small bridge has been damaged. *U.S. Army photograph.*

PORTAGE

(Mary L. Redmond).—Walls fell; chimneys, columns and monuments twisted and fell. Furniture broke. Damage great. Large cracks appeared in the Seward-Anchorage Highway in the Portage, Alaska, area. [In figure 8, note the surface cracking adjacent to the highway, the damaged bridge, and the cracking paralleling a secondary road into Portage.]

(*Anchorage Daily Times,* 4–6–64).—The community of Portage now consists of an old log lodge called "Diamond Jim's," according to a report by a team of Army Engineers who spent 4 days opening a temporary road into the stricken area. As the only building not condemned by civil defense inspectors, the lodge is community center, hospital, kitchen and bedroom for the 35 persons remaining in Portage. Portage is "almost a total loss."

PORT WELLS AREA

(From report by Ralph G. Migliaccio, District Geologist, Valdez, to R. G. Sherman, Chief Geologist, College).—I made two flights by helicopter over the reported epicenter of the shock and in one instance landed on the western side of Port Wells at the site of the Granite Mine. Wooden buildings at this point are damaged but are generally intact. Waves in this area rose 6 to 8 feet above normal high-tide level.

FIGURE 9.—Port facilities at Seward, Alaska.

SEWARD

(*Fairbanks Daily News-Miner,* 4–2–64).—Residential area of Seward escaped, but everything on the waterfront was wiped out—docks, cargo handling facilities, warehouses, railroad terminal, and the shrimp processing plant. Everything on the waterfront will have to be rebuilt. [Figures 9 and 10 show damage to waterfront buildings in the Seward, Alaska, area. Most of this damage was due to the tsunami generated by the earthquake.]

(From *Safety Bulletin,* April 1964, California Shipping Company; H. Solabakke, Master, *Alaska Standard*).—The MS *Alaska Standard* was moored at the dock at Seward. The first shock was followed shortly by a series of violent quakes. Almost immediately fire broke out on shoreside. A seismic wave heeled the ship to starboard, suddenly and dangerously. The vessel rose to such a height that hoses and lines either broke or took shore risers and part of pipelines and mooring piles with them. All this happened within about 1 minute. What the quake had not destroyed along the shoreline, the seismic wave demolished and obliterated. We were underway within an estimated 5 minutes after the first quake was felt. We were practically surrounded by fire on the surface of the water, and it was getting closer to us by the second. After we got clear of the fire and turned the vessel about to head out the bay, we noticed a large circular area in the middle of the bay where the water looked muddy and was rolling and boiling.

FIGURE 10.—Docking area at Seward, Alaska.

It is miraculous that we and the vessel were able to escape.

(Arreta L. Howell).—Several buildings had wall cracks; several concrete-block buildings cracked; several foundations cracked outside of town. Heavy damage to water mains, rails, bridges, structural foundations, cables, on edge of town. Objects such as chimneys, etc., fell north-south. Store lost all goods on shelves. Shock broke the pipes on the big oil storage tanks; tanks blew up and caught fire. [Figures 11 and 12 show the damage to petroleum storage tanks and railroad facilities in the Seward waterfront area. Note that the railroad freight cars were thrown about and the occurrence of large surface cracks.] All boxcars on the railroad and docks were burned. Tsunamis, 13 to 30 feet high, in about 20 minutes after the shock; others later.

Metcalf's Grocery Store, Milepost 5½, Seward Highway).—Ground cracks all around and in all directions. Small landslides. Railroad rails broken in front of place. Damage slight to building: walls cracked generally under windows and by doors. Powerlines out, causing loss of heat and lights. Trees whipped like whipping a buggy whip.

(*Alaska Shop; Mrs. O. T. Blair*).—We were in a 1-story, concrete building at the time. Glass was falling all around us, and I couldn't stand up alone. When the power went off, we ran to the middle of a wide street. Parked cars were rolling and bouncing. At our

FIGURE 11.—Petroleum tank farm at Seward, Alaska. Note large surface cracking and scatter of railway freight cars. *U.S. Army photograph.*

home, a frame building, the chimney and the electric hot water heater were damaged. We lost dishes, pottery, etc.

234 Second Avenue (Melba Torvanger).—Wood joists and basement ceiling cracked; dishes broke. Furniture overturned.

430 Third Avenue (Mary L. Stainbrook).—Bedroom ceiling light torn loose. China cup on kitchen cupboard not disturbed. No ground cracks.

Hospital, west section (Constance d'Albert).—Floors cracked. Tables, bed stands, trays rolled in all directions.

Grocery store in central section (Leo Kunnuk).— Grocery stock displaced. Pendulum clock stopped.

SOLDATNA

(Eleanor M. Fad(?), from USGS report).—Many cracks in gravel and pavement. Water level in well fell; streams increased in flow.

STERLING

(Mrs. Ray McNutt from USGS report).—Two cracks, average length 20 to 40 feet and average width ½ to 2 inches. Pressure ridges along margins of lake, where ice was piled 6 to 10 feet high. Trees in the area whipped back and forth but did not break. Water level in well fell; streams decreased in flow. Slight damage to frame houses. Dishes broke.

VALDEZ AND VICINITY

Tatitluk, south of Valdez (Anne Jackson from USGS report).—Three tsunamis noticed.

(From report by Ralph G. Migliaccio, District Geologist, Valdez, to R. G. Sherman, Chief Geologist, Col-

FIGURE 12.—Oblique view of Seward, Alaska, waterfront. Note the overturned petroleum tank and fires still burning several days after the tsunami. *U.S. Army photograph.*

lege).—Since I was not in Valdez at the time of the quake, I have gathered the following information from the most reliable witnesses available:

The ground surface was heaving in much the same manner as a swell in the open ocean, except that the swells were much more rapid and frequent. These waves or heaves have been literally frozen in places in the highway east of Valdez. Large cracks, opening and closing all over the area, were accompanied by water and silt which spurted from cracks and reached as high as 4 to 5 feet into the air. Trees were pitching in much the same manner as they do in a strong wind. This was also the case with buildings as they rode the ground waves. Sewer lines were breaking and sewage was flowing on the surface, and in some cases, into houses. Water mains were breaking and sending large amounts

of water into the streets. During this period, the principal damage was to masonry and cinder-block buildings. Merchandise was thrown from shelves; dishes fell from cupboards in houses.

Two structures, the Gibson Building and the Alaskan Hotel, were severely damaged. The front walls of both structures broke away from the remainder of the buildings. The west wall of the Gibson Building leaned without collapsing, but the east wall of the Alaskan Hotel collapsed, leaving upstairs rooms exposed (fig. 13). Other walls of the latter structure are cinder-block and were badly fractured. Several buildings, namely the Peterson Garage, Stitch Motors, Port Valdez Motel (fig. 14), and Dieringer's Chevron Service, were of similar construction and were nearly demolished. They have not collapsed but are still settling and are so badly

FIGURE 13.—Alaskan Hotel in Valdez, Alaska, illustrating damage resulting from the Prince William Sound Earthquake of 1964.

fractured that they could fall at any time. Most wooden structures in Valdez survived the tremors; that is, they are still standing. Most have suffered at least one or two of the following: Moved off foundations; broke in two pieces; wallboard buckled; walls warped; walls cracked; building settled differentially; foundations cracked; building broken by crevice extending under the building. It is remarkable to note that some of the buildings (houses only) show no damage whatsoever. Indeed, had matters been confined to a shaking of the ground, property losses in Valdez would have been considerably less.

Within seconds of the initial tremors, it was apparent to eyewitnesses that something violent was occurring in the area of the Valdez waterfront. The most obvious (at first) and noticeable action involved the steamer *Chena*. This vessel is approximately 400 feet long and was pitched around like a cork. It rose some 20 to 30 feet, then dropped, pitched, bottomed, shot forward, bottomed again, and was lifted clear. This happened so rapidly that it is difficult to obtain a reliable account. Whatever occurred was extremely violent, and it is nothing short of a miracle that the ship survived. Men on the ship claim it heeled over to the 50° mark and was righted by the waves. Witnesses state the bow rose until it could be seen well above the dock warehouses. Then, the bow fell, and the stern rose, exposing the ship's propellers. Two men on the ship were killed

FIGURE 14.—Damage to Valdez Motel in Valdez, Alaska.

by falling cargo, and another died of a heart attack. Almost simultaneously the Valdez dock was in violent movement. Within seconds of the first tremors the dock broke in two; the warehouses flipped forward; and all disappeared into the sea, which was extremely turbulent at this point. Men, women, and children were seen staggering around the dock, looking for something to hold onto. None had time to escape, since the failure was so sudden and violent. Some 300 feet of dock disappeared. Almost immediately a large wave rose up, smashing everything in its path. Buildings were reduced to kindling wood, semitrailers were thrown all over the waterfront, and cars and trucks were smashed into twisted masses of metal. Several people stated, the wave was 30 to 40 feet high, or more. At any rate it was truly massive. This wave crossed the waterfront and, in some areas, reached beyond McKinley Street. Other areas were not affected. It should be kept in mind that all these events took less than 2 to 3 minutes. Approximately 10 minutes after the initial wave receded, a second wave or surge crossed the waterfront carrying large amounts of wreckage, etc. This wave was high enough to place 18 inches of water in the Valdez Hotel on McKinley Street. Other areas were untouched. Indeed, many people did not even notice this wave. There followed a lull of approximately 5 to 6 hours during which time search parties were able to search the waterfront area for possible survivors. There were none. Individuals state that many boats, including the cruise ship *Gypsy*, had been deposited on the beach along with tons of tangled wreckage. Between 11:00 p.m. and midnight, a third wave rose over the water-

front. This wave carried debris as far as the U.S. Post Office on Hobart Street. Water was approximately 2.5 feet deep in the Valdez Hotel. As the third wave was beginning to recede, a fourth wave moved in. This occurred at approximately 1:45 a.m. This wave, adequately described as a tidal bore, moved inland until water was 5 to 6 feet deep in most of the buildings on McKinley Street. Water was even deeper on Front Street, and was 2 feet deep on Hobart Street. The wave or surge did not have a high velocity, as people were able to run out of or away from it. This particular wave was responsible for the majority of property damage losses in downtown Valdez. Discounting, of course, breakage due to tremors. Almost every store in downtown Valdez lost all merchandise in this wave. Large quantities of silt were left behind when the water finally receded, and this ruined what the water and quake did not. It would appear that some of the wood structures in Valdez actually floated. It should be kept in mind that the wave which struck the waterfront during the quake was the one with fantastic destructive force. It should also be noted that the last wave, when receding, must have had a strong undertow, since large amounts of wreckage as well as large boats were carried out to sea and have not been seen since.

A fishing boat was anchored just outside the Valdez Narrows (about 10 miles west of Valdez) when the tremors began. The owner backed away from the beach and turned the boat toward Valdez. Shortly thereafter, a huge wave came into the Narrows moving out to sea. The witness informed me that the wave looked like it was 35 to 60 feet high while confined in the Narrows. Upon emerging from this obstruction, the wave spread laterally with subsequent lowering and the boat was able to ride over the top. This description is confirmed by the fact that the upper part of a lighthouse, located in the center of the Valdez Narrows, was swept away. I estimate that this would require a wave at least 20 to 25 feet high. In addition, watermarks were noted which were considerably higher but have not yet been measured. This wave was moving very rapidly and was undoubtedly a true tsunami.

A group of fishermen was in Unakwik Inlet when the quake struck. The men stated that their boat seemed to run aground, but a check of the fathometer showed there was over 300 feet of water beneath the keel. The boat was severely rocked even in this depth of water. A large wave inundated the beaches almost immediately. In addition, these men observed large numbers of dead fish while returning to Valdez, particularly in the Valdez

Narrows. These fish were principally bottom dwellers in an area where there is some 600 to 800 feet of water. It is apparent that waves or tremors caused severe disturbance at depth in the Valdez Arm. Glaciers in College Fiord and Unakwik Inlet have calved small icebergs, and lake ice was shattered. The Columbia Glacier showed no effects from the earthquake, and icebergs were entirely absent in Glacier Bay.

At this time (April 10), tide fluctuation in the Valdez area appears normal. However, normal high tides are inundating areas which were previously high and dry. Since tides are not exceptionally high at this date, it would appear that the Valdez waterfront has settled between 4 to 6 feet.

(From report by Charles H. Clark, Geologist, State of Alaska, Department of Highways).—I was in Valdez at the time of the quake, and the following is an attempt to describe the earthquake as it occurred: The first tremors were hard enough to stop a moving person, and shock waves were immediately noticeable on the surface of the ground. These shock waves continued with a long frequency which gave the observer an impression of a rolling feeling rather than abrupt hard jolts. After about 1 minute, the amplitude or strength of the shock waves increased in intensity and failures in buildings as well as the frozen ground surface began to occur. Cracks in the roadway surface opened and closed again as the trough and crests passed the failure. These cracks opened as much as 3 feet, but the most frequent failures were only opened several inches. As these cracks closed due to passing of a shock wave trough, water from both ground-water sources and broken sewers and water pipes squirted in a spray about 20 feet into the air. These occurred at intervals of several seconds between sprays, but no other timing of the waves was attempted by me. The amplitude of the waves was estimated by observance of my son standing about 410 feet away. He is 6 feet tall and was in plain sight during most of the earthquake. As a crest passed him, he would appear in full sight with one depression between himself and me. As he entered a trough, he would appear to sink out of sight up to about 1 foot below belt line.

Failure in buildings became apparent and power poles began going down after about 2 to 2½ minutes. After about 3½ minutes, the severe shock waves ended, and people began to react as could be expected. Buildings of wooden frame construction swayed and rocked as if on a high sea. The frame structures evidently were flexible enough to give and sway with very little structural damage. Damage to foundations occurred under these structures, but in general, they held together very well for a shock of this intensity and duration. Structures of concrete block or other masonry construction suffered severe damage to both bearing walls and foundations. Glass breakage was very limited. Also, it should be noted that the cracks mentioned previously extended under almost every building in town, causing damage to plumbing and foundations.

Northeast Section (Steve J. Guest, Highway Engineering Technician).—Snow and rock slides occurred on mountains north of town and on the Richardson Highway. My home, a 2-story apartment building, swayed back and forth about 2 feet. Slight damage to building. Refrigerator, beds, dressers, range, etc., moved generally north-south. Slight damage to personal property in apartment. All were alarmed; only a few were panic stricken at the immediate time of the shock. I saw only a few women in our immediate neighborhood who were panicky.

(Mrs. Alice Horton).—Almost impossible to stand. Earth opened up and dirt shot up high as houses. I saw this three times. Waves of water came up fast; had to run to get away from it. After three blocks of running, I got in a car and went for higher ground at 7 Mile.

608 Broadway (Warren G. Hoyt).—Dishes, windows, and furniture broken. Damage slight to my house (old house; very flexible).

(Raymond O'Toole).—Lived in Vista Apartments. Very flexible buildings (three separate buildings). Water waves did most of the damage to furniture and personal property on ground floor level.

WHITTIER AND VICINITY

(From report by USC&GSS *Surveyor*).—Deep fissures found in bottom of marginal wharf. Large concentration of heavy debris noted, consisting of timbers bolted together, with lengths up to 30 feet. Logs, 2 feet in diameter, 20 to 30 feet long, disappeared on outgoing tide. A 24-hour tide gage record indicated mean sea level had risen, with respect to land area, about 6½ feet. Steel pier blocked by sunken barge along its side. No wave reported during major earthquake, but water rose rapidly, with recession more violent and damaging than the inrush of water.

(*Fairbanks Daily News-Miner*, 4–2–64).—Buildings adjacent to docks and piers destroyed. Thousands of gallons of fuel oil burned. State civil defense officials reported the Buckner Composite Building and the 14-story Hodge Building came through in good shape.

Officials also reported the Alaska Railroad tunnel between Whittier and Portage sustained no major damage.

(Mrs. Hazel Covington, on third floor of 12-story apartment building).—Walls cracked. Furniture overturned and broken. Ground cracked.

(Joyce McDonough, on second floor of concrete and steel building).—Plaster and walls cracked. Furnishings shifted; pictures fell; dishes broken.

WINGHAM AND KAYAK ISLANDS

Wingham Island (Cordova Times, 4–2–64).—One vessel found herself high and dry in the deep sheltered anchorage in the lee of Wingham Island during the terrific ebb of the tsunami. Clam diggers at Copper Sands reported sand spouting up higher than their heads. Their skiff began to sink in the sand and then was heaved back up.

Kayak Island, Cape St. Elias (Alaska Daily Empire, 2–29–64).—The U.S. Coast Guard reported three tsunamis. One coast guardsman was washed out to sea.

(From USGS report, Circular 491).—One rockslide at the south tip of Kayak Island, approximately 135 miles southeast of the epicenter, killed a coast guardsman stationed at the Cape St. Elias lighthouse.

CAPE YAKATAGA AND VICINITY

(Mrs. Edna M. Watson, from USGS report).—Many cracks, some several hundred feet long. One area, approximately 1 mile square, sank 2 to 3 feet. The Kaliak River delta area was checkered with cracks and appeared to have been lowered slightly. Quite a large landslide on Ducktooth Mountain.

FAA Station.—Plaster, windows, walls, chimneys, and ground cracked; plaster fell, dishes and windows broken. Highline wires, running east-west, swung, causing breakers to drop out on engine generators.

(Doyle W. Shaw).—Ground cracked. Small objects and furnishings shifted; vases, small objects overturned; knickknacks, books, and pictures fell. Dishes broken.

(Mrs. Edna M. Watson).—Our house is located a few feet above high tide mark. Couple of items fell. Neighbors farther inland had items fall from shelves and walls.

GAKONA AND VICINITY

FAA Station.—Ground cracks in highway and runway. A 2-foot hill of dirt was thrown up north of runway. Water main broken. Furniture overturned.

Gakona Lodge (A. Schnader).—Plaster cracked at some places. Knickknacks and books fell; dishes fell and broke.

Tok Cutoff at Milepost 6 (Roy E. Hooper).—I had to stop the car. Thought it was a flat tire. Trees and telephone wires swung as in a strong wind. Small cracks opened in road.

KODIAK ISLAND AND VICINITY

Afognak Island, north of Kodiak (Anchorage Daily Times, 4–13–64).—The native village of Afognak had 15 homes, the village store, post office, and community hall destroyed, but all 170 residents reached safety on the mountain behind the village before the tsunami hit the community which lines a beach on the southern shore of the island. Since the village has settled several feet lower in the sea, preparations are underway to relocate this village in Settler Cove in Kizhuyak Bay on the northern shore of Kodiak Island.

Afognak Island (Martha Nelson; from USGS report).—Tsunami in the area first occurred at 6:30 p.m., about 1 hour after the earthquake. It was followed by 4 or 5 other waves of unknown height. Nearly all the houses were damaged. The community hall and two houses were washed out to sea. A bridge was washed out, and creeks were changed. Tides in the area are higher by an unknown number of feet.

Kodiak Island (U.S. Fleet Weather Central).—Moderate to severe earthquake. Sustained earthquake ceased at 1740 hours. Electrical equipment in tower out of commission. Power O.K. Tide station inoperative due to earthquake damage. FAA circuits inoperative. At 1810 hours, Cape Chiniak reported a 30-foot tsunami. Tsunami warning broadcast. People evacuated to higher ground. At 2300 hours, preliminary inspection revealed tide station inundated. Record lost. GMD building inundated repeatedly. All equipment on first deck washed away or damaged and immersed. At 2316 hours, water crested 30 feet above staff zero. Heights were referred to staff zero in the following manner: After each crest, a pencil mark was made at the resultant waterline in a building very near the water. When it was impossible to make a pencil mark, the water level referred to the nearest identifying feature on the building was noted and marked in pencil after the water had ebbed enough to permit this. The highest mark was then measured in reference to tide staff at the tide gage, and the heights of all other wave heights in the building where pencil marks were made were subtracted from this height. The building mentioned was not in the immediate vicinity of the tide gage. Other high watermarks on cliffs and buildings were measured along a 3-mile area from Nyman Peninsula to about one-half mile northeast of the mouth of Buskin River. All were

FIGURE 15.—Kodiak, Alaska, showing of commercial district damage due to tsunami generation of the Prince William Sound Earthquake.

within 2 feet of the highest watermark at the tide gage. The tide gage is located on Marginal Pier, Nyman Peninsula, U.S. Naval Station, Kodiak, and is in Womens Bay.

(*Fairbanks Daily News-Miner,* 4–6–64).—Latest figures on losses to the fishing fleet, show at least 57 vessels destroyed or missing and 50 others damaged. Thirty-one of the lost boats were from the fisheries at Shearwater Bay. The cannery was destroyed, and boats stored on the beach were tossed into the sea. Continuing high tides caused speculation as to whether the canneries which came through the shock would be able to operate this season.

(*Anchorage Daily Times,* 4–13–64).—Only a few Kodiak businesses have been able to reopen at their former locations. Nearly 70 firms had their places of business and most of their inventories destroyed. [Figure 15 displays a Kodiak street near the waterfront. Note the damaged sidewalk and watermarks on the buildings.] The tsunami destroyed 157 living units in downtown Kodiak. [Typical tsunami damage to the Kodiak waterfront residential area may be seen in figure 16.] Reports on boat damage showed 17 fishing boats registered out of Kodiak missing; 10 with major damage; considerable damage to 15; and slight damage to 20. Another 35 were either sunk or put aground (fig. 17). Another 42 boats were lost in the Kodiak area outside of the city.

(From Bureau of Naval Personnel publication entitled *All Hands,* July 1964; Naval Station, D. D.

FIGURE 16.—Near waterfront of Kodiak, Alaska, with residential area shown in background.

Hendricks).—I was cinching up my tie when the world began to shake. When I realized what was happening—that we were experiencing a full-scale earthquake—I knew I had to get out of the building and into the open. The building sounded like a wooden matchbox being crushed underfoot. Every joint and brace was creaking and groaning. Light globes fell from the ceiling; bottles fell from shelves and dressers; mirrors crashed from walls. Fortunately the building stood up as we all ran outside.

(W. E. Stepp).—It was difficult to walk or even stand. Buildings seemed to swing and jump up and down. Light poles swayed like saplings in a breeze; chimneys toppled. Landslides kicked up dust from the sides of the surrounding hills. Cars and trucks bounced around as though they were on a trampoline.

Aircraft bounced, with all three wheels leaving the ground. A large paved ramp around the hangars cracked and buckled; at one place water spouted 10 feet into the air. The Naval Station at Kodiak experienced 7-foot waves. Waterfront facilities were washed with sea water. Powerplants were flooded. Ruptured fuel lines left sticky-coated floatsam littering the flooded station runway. Damage to three aircraft hangars. The major blow to the base was the temporary loss of power. The powerplant was flooded repeatedly as tides remained 6 to 8 feet above normal. The road to the nearby communications station was washed out. Station cargo docks were partially floated loose, and their approaches swept away.

Naval Station (Cmdr. A. L. Dodson).—Moderate damage to light structural parts, such as chimneys, etc.;

FIGURE 17.—Kodiak waterfront showing ships carried inland by the tsunami resulting from the Prince William Sound Earthquake.

cinderblock walls cracked, but not poured concrete. Chimneys, etc., fell in all directions. All movable objects moved. Very obvious visible swaying of buildings and trees. Remarkable little breakage in 2-story residence. Son bathing in basement of home (tub oriented northeast-southwest) was thrown back and forth lengthwise; water (85 percent) sloshed from tub.

Kodiak, central section (Neil Sutherland).—I stood on sidewalk holding onto parking sign. Landslides at slide area between town and Naval Base. Slight damage to buildings in most cases; no severe damage. Minor cracks in one block building; few windows broken; chimneys fell; few foundation cracks (actual damage slight). Water rose slowly in all cases where observed

in downtown area. On slight incline, people could walk ahead of it.

Kodiak, directly uphill from boat harbor, about 200 feet up on Pillar Mountain (William R. Gregory).—I was outside standing and kneeling during most of the shock. Small slide cracks in soil. Landslide on east face of Old Womens Mountain. Moderate damage to concrete-block buildings; slight damage to frame buildings; very few chimneys collapsed. Though it seems unreasonable to me, I have the impression that I saw transverse waves in a vertical plane, perhaps 2-foot amplitude, moving through Pillar Mountain from southeast-northwest during initial disturbance. Shock occurred near time of low tide. Immediately following, sea level dropped an additional 4 to 7 feet, exposing rocks and reefs that had never been seen before, even at lowest normal tide levels. Water began to rise again in about 30 minutes (about 6:30 p.m.). Water rose gently but swiftly to a level of perhaps 3 to 4 feet higher than ever observed at highest tide. After about another 30 minutes, water receded again, lower than before, and then rose to a higher level. Fluctuation continued throughout the night, seeming to rise higher with each cycle until about midnight. Two spruce trees (10-inch diameter) swayed an estimated 20 to 25° each side of vertical. House rocked and swayed.

Kodiak, central section (Dr. Bruce Keers).—I was standing outside the front entrance of hospital holding onto cartop luggage rack. Only noticed flagpole swaying. In clinic, corners of rooms had tiny cracks (ground floor of 3-story frame building). No cracks in hospital or home. A fairly large number of persons went up on Pillar Mountain, due to tsunami warning.

Kodiak Island, Larsen Bay (Marian K. Howe, from USGS report).—There was tsunami damage but not substantial. Tides are now about 2 feet higher than normal. (Weather Bureau report). Shock felt at Larsen Bay.

Kodiak Island (*Karluk*), (Laurie James(?)).—A total of four tsunamis noticed, all of them about 1½ feet high, the first one commencing 1½ hours after the main shock. Tides in the area are now 1½ feet higher.

Sitkinak Island, about 25 miles south of Kaguyak (U. S. Coast Guard Station (William J. Morgan)).—Prestressed concrete beams cracked; plaster fell. Dishes and equipment broken. Cattle fell down. Ground cracked. Station flagpole whipped 4 feet from side to side; trucks bounced up and down, sometimes clearing the ground. Buildings and heavy objects shifted. Damage great. (Stephen C. Grove; U. S. Coast Guard Station), —Heavy meters and power supplies, weighing 8 tons, shifted more than 1 foot in an easterly direction, also Caterpillars and trucks. Road, airstrips, etc., cracked. Barracks condemned by engineers.

Spruce Cape, about 3 miles northeast of Kodiak (Thurston Jackson). Furniture overturned; dishes broke. No shock damage, but tsunami damage. The loudest noise was caused by the ice breaking on the lakes, about 500 feet away, and this noise became even louder when the ocean broke into the lakes. This noise lasted about 5 minutes, then stopped suddenly. I stayed near my home on a cliff near the bay (about 20 feet in elevation).

Spruce Island, Ouzinkie (John Pestnikoff, from USGS report).—First tsunami was at 5:47 p.m., about 10 minutes after the main shock. The wave was 5 feet high. This was followed by seven more waves of heights 5, 10, 20, 30, 20, 10, and 5 feet. The water came inland 200 yards and about a maximum of 30 feet above sea level. A salmon cannery, two docks, three homes, and four fishing boats were demolished. Several homes and fishing boats were severely damaged. Tides are now 5 feet higher than formerly.

Old Harbor; Post Office (Sophia Simeonoff).—House cracked in half; walls fell; chimneys on four homes twisted and fell; windows cracked. All homes greatly damaged and total loss. Stoves, etc., shifted; stoves overturned.

Old Harbor (*Anchorage Daily Times*, 4–17–64).—The 225 Old Harbor villagers, sheltered at Anchorage since the tsunamis swept away their community, are expected to return to Old Harbor and re-establish their community.

*Kaguyak, about 30 miles south of Old Harbor.—*Tsunamis completely obliterated the village.

PALMER AND VICINITY

(Keth O. McCavit(?)).—Plaster, windows, chimneys, and ground cracked; lake ice cracked. Dishes, windows, and plumbing broke. Furniture overturned.

(Merritt C. Long).—Furniture overturned.

Fishhook Road (Samuel A. Boyd).—Plaster, chimneys, and ground cracked. Dishes and furniture broke. Strong enough to pull out stationary washtubs and break them all to pieces.

(Beatrice A. John).—TV nearly tipped over; bookcase in basement overturned. Water splashed out of water closet and toilet bowl. Furnace smokepipe detached from chimney. Crack in stairway landing leading to basement.

Baldy Hill (W. O. Sharp).—Chimneys and ground cracked. Dishes broke. Furniture overturned.

Independence Mine (Julius H. Moon(?)).—Plaster cracked. Knickknacks, books, and pictures fell.

SELDOVIA AND VICINITY

(Susan English, from USGS report).—Tsunami, 23 feet high, came in about 8 hours after the main shock. There were three waves between 2:00 a.m. and 4:40 a.m. Several buildings and the dock in the area were damaged. Tides in the area are now about 3 feet higher.

(Chas. S. Hendrix).—Walls fell; chimneys, columns, and monuments twisted. Some plaster, windows, walls, chimneys, and ground cracked. Not too much breakage to dishes.

(Harry D. Schwartz).—Furniture overturned. Dishes broke. Tsunami destroyed small boat harbor.

(Jack R. English).—Small objects overturned; knick-knacks fell; dishes broke.

(Dick Inglima(?)).—Small objects shifted and over-turned. Trees, bushes shaken strongly. The tsunami damage was much worse than the shock. Tides rose at least 12 feet and are still not normal. We are very worried about these tides.

(Otto Miller).—House creaked. Trees, bushes shaken strongly. Nothing sifted or overturned in the house; no damage.

Port Graham, about 10 miles southwest of Seldovia (Verne Rimling, from USGS report).—A minor tsunami was noticed about 9 minutes after the main shock. Tides in the area are now 2 feet higher than normal.

SKWENTNA AND VICINITY

(Marjorie C. Collins).—Muskeg around area cracked, and small cracks in runway. Alarms set off due to par-tial power outage; fuses blown out on powerline. Oil storage tanks spilled over to north. Minute cracks in corners and around ceilings and doors, mostly on north side of building. Drill press, etc., in garage fell; solvent, etc., in containers spilled. On March 28, we flew over the area and noticed all rivers and creeks had many cracks—some huge; also, many lakes had sunk 2 to 3 feet. Saw cracks on side of Mt. Yenlo and through the general area in swamps and muskeg.

(Belie Shellabarger; from USGS report).—Many cracks, some as wide as 3 feet. Mole tracks or pressure ridges as high as 5 feet. Water spouts, 10 feet high, in creek in front of house, forming a crater 3 feet in diam-eter.

SUSTINA RIVER VALLEY

Across from Cook Inlet (*Fairbanks Daily News-Miner*, 4-1-64).—Spider-web patterns of cracks and fissures in the lower Sustina River Valley across from Cook Inlet.

WASILLA

(May C. Carter, from USGS report).—Pressure ridges in ice along banks of lake. Five or six healthy trees, as large as 8 inches in diameter, broken; crowns fell mainly in southerly direction. Water level in some wells in the area rose; in some, water level fell. Dishes broke. Slight damage to wood frame houses.

CHRISTOCHINA

(Douglas W. Neeley).—Ground cracks. Furnishings shifted.

CHUGIAK AREA

Birchwood, about 20 miles northeast of Anchorage (Marilyn Lassalin(?)).—Trees, bushes shaken strongly. Knickknacks and books fell; one wall plaque broken.

BIRCH CREEK

About 6 miles from Circle City and about 12 miles downstream from the Steese Highway crossing of the Birch (Patricia Oakes).—Two trappers said they felt motion for more than a minute. Trees swayed and whipped back and forth; tent sagged and bagged. They saw the ice on Birch Creek wave and buckle. The ice broke and fell to water level, causing some backup and water over ice and fouling of some beaver traps. They quickly felt seasick and had to sit down until things quieted down.

CENTRAL AND CIRCLE HOT SPRINGS

(Patricia Oakes).—At Central and Circle Hot Springs, jolts seemed to have been sharper than we felt at Circle. At Central, dishes were broken; one well lost water immediately. This may have been caused by a cracked pipe, but more likely from a slight change in water table; wells of that depth usually "go out" between late February and early April. No noted change in water flow at Circle Hot Springs.

(Roy O. Riddle).—Felt by all at home. Visible sway-ing of buildings and trees. We were riding in truck at the time, between Miller house and Central. Did not know of it until heard on radio at 7:00 p.m.

COLLEGE AND VICINITY

(John A. Shuster).—Foundation shift caused walls to crack slightly. Our dogs lying at rest did not detect the motion; however, they fiercely challenged the pinata, which hangs from the roof, when it suddenly came to life.

(Ralph R. Stefano).—Small objects overturned. Pen-dulum clock stopped. Felt by observer riding in auto-mobile.

West College, Agricultural Experiment Station (Franz Maier).—Suspended signs, shelves, lamps, etc., swayed in changing directions. Some people frightened, but most not especially concerned.

College Road, 4 Mile (Nita Balvin).—TV antenna on TV swung around.

DELTA JUNCTION

(Mrs. R. L. Johnson).—Plaster cracked. Knickknacks and pictures fell.

(Edwin A. Fredeen).—Dishes and jars of baby food broken.

DENALI LAKES

10 miles south of McKinley Park (William J. Nancarrow).—There was a definite movement of rocks—could be heard. Trees swayed in all directions. Three boxes shifted 4 inches. Felt here as a heavy, swell-like motion. No rattling of dishes or creaking of ice in lake.

EGEGIK

(Simmy Shuravloff).—Ground cracked.

(J. F. Preston).—The motion here was a rather slow, steady, smooth rocking motion. Ice in river broke and some ice cakes bobbed up and down. Small cracks, about one-half inch wide; one large crack, about 2½ inches wide and 100 yards long, on the mud flats.

(F. W. Timm).—Doors rattled and swung; frame creaked.

FAIRBANKS AND VICINITY

International Airport, 4 miles west of Fairbanks; Weather Bureau Airport Station (Millard A. Landers).—Strong, visible swaying of buildings, trees, and ground. Few items fell off shelves. Most objects that could swing did so rather sharply. Many doors flew open. I would say that the ground movement in swaying was at least 5 to 6 inches, moving sidewise north-south and that the ground rose at least 2 to 3 inches up and down during the 4 minutes the shock lasted.

(From report of MTAIC, Weather Bureau Airport Station to Regional Administrator, WBRAO, Anchorage).—The earthquake was felt in Fairbanks as a rather severe and prolonged shock. Many people were alarmed and evacuated their homes and public buildings, but no major damage was suffered in the Fairbanks area.

(*Fairbanks Daily News-Miner*, 3–28–64).—Some residents became dizzy. Earth seemed to roll and toss without hard jerks. Police department flooded with calls. Tall radio towers on top of the Northward and Lathrop Buildings swayed. Ground almost seemed to ripple; ice almost went out in the Chena River. Slight damage was reported at the Eielsen Air Force Base. A market reported one small jar fell from shelf and broke. Everyone was jolted but unharmed.

(John C. Brinsmade).—I was in the waiting room at the International Airport, standing at the corner near the newsstand, when an unexpected, rolling motion, like on shipboard with a moderately rough sea, indicated that we were having one of our periodic earthquakes, somewhat more severe than any we had experienced recently. The most conspicuous effect was a wide swinging back and forth of electric signs suspended by wires from the ceiling, sometimes mostly north-south and

sometimes east-west. I saw a waitress, hurrying through the kitchen door, stop as if to restore her balance and then hurry on. People stopped momentarily with surprised smiles on their faces, some laughed, and then resumed what they were doing. The suspended signs continued swinging. My immediate reaction was to hurry home, but after going outside and noting that there was no indication of damage, I returned to the waiting room to look at the clock. The time was then 5:43 p.m. The suspended signs were still swinging, and I noted that the motion was then essentially rotary and clockwise. At my home, wife reported no damage and no fallen objects, though she had caught a tall floor lamp as it swayed and threatened to fall. We have received no reports of local damage.

Milepost 4½, Steese Highway (Harry A. Parmick).—Trees, bushes shaken strongly; doors, etc., swung. Small objects shifted.

FORT YUKON

(Oliva Negron(?)).—Plaster, wood, windows, walls, chimneys, and ground cracked. Small objects and furnishings shifted.

(Virginia Toussaint, from USGS report).—Many cracks in the area.

(Mike Churkin and Bill Brosge, from USGS report).—One crack, 1 inch wide, and broken pipeline discovered in the area some time after the shock near Post Office but not certainly related to earthquake. Birdcage (true pendulum) swung about east-west.

(Walter W. Hannum).—Small objects and furnishings shifted. I felt the building sway and thought the wall or roof might come down. Water sloshed in barrels.

(Donald J. Rollins).—Shock made a couple of doors swing and now they fit better.

HEALY FORK

(Ferne Hollis).—I dashed out the door. Seemed like I was having a bad dizzy spell. Steady rolling motion from south-north. Telephone wires attached to house swung furiously. Timbers in small, unattached shop squeaked, but no noise in our strongly built frame house. Neighbor said her cement basement was cracked.

(Philip and Margaret Hertz).—Felt shock while walking outdoors.

HURRICANE

Trees, bushes shaken strongly. Small objects shifted.

JUNEAU AND VICINITY

Douglas (*Daily Alaska Empire*, 3–30–64).—Plane flipped over and sank at Kenny Loken's float.

Municipal Airport, Weather Bureau Airport Station (John J. Rissa).—Five rolling shocks at close intervals. The first shock was so strong it nearly knocked me off my feet (leaning against cabinet). I became quite dizzy, almost to the point of being sick. Ground cracked at west-central section of runway. Door (on tracks) at City Shop thrown off tracks. Visible swaying of trees, houses, and light fixtures. Tide was 4 to 6 feet higher than normal.

(From report to Regional Administrator, WBRAO, Anchorage, from Meteorologist in Charge, WBAS, Juneau).—The earthquake was felt principally in the Gastineau Channel area, with the heaviest rolling shocks apparently concentrated in the Mendenhall Valley. Shocks were felt in other parts of the channel, but they were lighter, and in some areas, no discernible shock was felt. Numerous cracks, up to one-half inch wide, in the airport runway, most of them oriented along the axis of the valley. The airport tower was abandoned for a time. Several of the valley residents reported moderate tremors which displaced and moved objects. Perhaps the most alarming effect was the long-time communications blackout which immediately followed the shock.

Mendenhall Valley, 1½ miles south of Mendenhall Glacier face (Carol J. Winton).—Visible swaying of trees, light poles, and houses. Wall clock tilted; mantel swayed; water in fish tank agitated. Objects on north-south walls displaced the most.

(Corrine J. Kenway).—Five distinct shocks were felt in about 5 minutes or less. The second, third, and fourth shocks would not have been noticed except that attention was called by the first. Only the last (fifth) shock, which was the strongest, was felt by other members of the family, who by then were alerted. Next door neighbors also felt the shock, but in other parts of this community it was not felt at all.

At store near airport (Elna Barrington).—Felt by several; frightened few.

East side of Douglas Island, across from Juneau (James A. von Heydt).—Dishes rattled. Trees and bushes shaken slightly.

(Catherine D. Nordale).—Tremors were felt here in Juneau in varying degrees, depending upon the location within the area. The effect of the earthquake here was very slight.

KANDIK RIVER AREA

At Charlie Creek, 1 mile up the Kandik from the Yukon (Gordon Bertoson).—Cabin creaked so loudly man was frightened and went outside; staggered when leaving cabin. Dogs bristly, alert.

KING SALMON

Weather Bureau Airport Station (Gary N. Allen).—Slight damage to one building. Crack in concrete floor of newly constructed King Salmon store. Visible swaying of telephone poles. Weighs on all clocks swung violently. Many people went outdoors.

MCGRATH

Weather Bureau Airport Station (James M. Fair).—Visible swaying of trees, antennas, etc. Slight damage to buildings. Slight movement of chimneys, etc.; movement of water in all filled water vessels; all suspended objects swayed; pendulum clock stopped (pendulum moving north-south).

FAA Station (Dorothy E. Bryant).—Trees, bushes shaken strongly. Hanging objects swung east-west. Plants at home shifted 6 inches on shelf.

MIDDLETON ISLAND

FAA Station (Mrs. Philip M. Ahlstedt).—Our island has evidently risen several feet. Towers swayed. Knickknacks fell.

(Dwight D. Meeks).—Walls cracked. Dishes broke. Damage slight.

(John Nasworthy).—Small objects and furnishings shifted; small objects overturned.

MINTO

(Gordon Olson, from USGS report).—Many cracks in ice on sloughs and on Tanana River. Mud and moss forced to the surface on most of the cracks.

MOUNT MCKINLEY NATIONAL PARK

(Donald M. McLane).—Plaster, snow and ice cracked. Small objects shifted. Trees and bushes shaken strongly. Pendulum clock started.

Mount McKinley Park Hotel (Gary A. Crabb).—Block wall cracked. Small objects shifted. Pendulum clock facing north started. Living room swing, 9 feet long, swung about 3½ feet north-south.

Mount McKinley National Park Headquarters (W. Watson, Park Naturalist).—Cupboard doors swung; light cords swung. Building creaked moderately; trees and bushes shook moderately. Virtually no damage was observed.

NAKNEK AND VICINITY

(F. A. Davey, from USGS report).—Many cracks. Water level in wells fell. Mr. Davey also reported to USC&GS: Walls creaked. Frightened few. Deep wells muddied but soon cleared.

South Naknek (Cardel Simin, from USGS report).—Several cracks, some as long as 100 feet and 3 inches wide. Water level in well fell.

NENANA AND VICINITY

(Rev. Wallace M. Olson).—Ground cracked. Small objects shifted. It was very noticeable by the swaying of trees and poles. Packed ice and snow on the streets could be heard cracking. House settled slightly; doors now stick a little when opened.

FAA Station.—Visible swaying of buildings and trees (rocking like ocean waves). Disturbed objects observed by many. Pendulum clock stopped. Few panic stricken.

(Virgil Patterson).—Ground cracked.

Eight miles south of Nenana on new highway (Mrs. Glenn Maulding).—Walking the 24 feet to the door was like walking on the deck of a boat. My daughters, age 13 and 15, and I had to shift from one foot to the other in order to keep our balance. The quonset is just 4 inches off solid ground. Birdcage swung with a rather paced motion.

Four miles north of Nenana (Mrs. Glenn Maulding). —My husband was in the root cellar, 10 feet underground, and did not feel the shock.

NODALTON

(Roy Gronning).—Felt by all. Pressure crack piled ice upon lake in ridge about 3 feet high.

PAXON AND VICINITY

Paxon Lodge (Stanley F. Brown).—Slight damage to buildings. Walls cracked. Damage to light structural parts such as chimneys, etc. General alarm.

Paxon Lake, Milepost 179, Richardson Highway (L. L. Hufman).—Trees and bushes shaken strongly. Pendulum clock facing north stopped. Small objects shifted. Few cracks, running east-west, on ice of Paxon Lake.

PILOT POINT

(Stella O. Griechen, from USGS report).—Many cracks in the area. Some water spouts. Water level in wells fell.

(Guilbert G. Thompson).—Ground cracked. Pendulum clock stopped. Trees and bushes shaken strongly. People walked as though in drunken staggers.

(Aleck V. Griechen).—Ground cracked; ice on ponds cracked. Small objects shifted.

(Earl Mollohan).—The lakes used for drinking water were considerably stirred up. Gun rack fell.

PORT ALSWORTH

(Mary A. Alsworth).—One window cracked; slight crack in chimney. Buildings and trees swayed visibly back and forth.

RICHARDSON HIGHWAY

Milepost 218, Trim's Camp, Delta River Valley (Mr. and Mrs. H. A. Tatro).—Slight damage to buildings; vertical cracks in walls. Road cracked on the Richardson Highway from Milepost 218 to 177. Expansion joints on bridges spread north-south. Visible swaying of trees, buildings, and machinery; trees almost touched the ground. Bed jumped up and down.

Milepost 195 (Mr. and Mrs. H. A. Tatro).—Pressure ridges on south and east banks of Summit Lake due to water moving back and forth.

Milepost 150 (F. Chmielowski).—Small objects shifted and overturned; knickknacks, books, and pictures fell; dishes broke. Trees and bushes shaken strongly.

SHAGELUK

(David Benz, from USGS report).—Cracks up to one-half inch wide and 6 inches deep.

SINONA CREEK

(Mrs. I. S. Poston).—Many ground and surface cracks, with water seeping up through some; large north-south crack, about one-half mile long, across Christochina River. Snow slid off mountains; mountains were black and bare for few days. Damage slight to concrete. People fell down; dogs fell off dog houses.

SLANA AND VICINITY

(D. M. Duffy).—Damage slight. Ground cracked. Earth waves, about 18 inches high and 50 to 60 feet apart, were observed moving across yard. Buildings rocked like a boat.

(Fred Bronniche(?)).—Ground cracked. Books fell. Trees and bushes shaken strongly.

Cobb Lake, few miles west of Slana (C. M. Corkle).— Pictures jumped up and down. Trees and bushes shaken strongly. Often I heard hollow cracking and booming noises during the shock.

SUMMIT

(Henry L. Olsen).—Ground cracked; mouldings cracked. Trees and bushes shaken moderately.

FAA Station (Jesse H. Jones).—Plaster cracked. Knickknacks fell. Pendulum clock facing east stopped.

(James Mulholland).—Felt by all (observers outdoors active).

TALKEETNA

(Frank Moenniske(?)).—Log and frame buildings intact, except for one frame and one log house which had concrete in chimneys and cellars cracked. Trees and bushes shaken strongly. Knickknacks and books fell; dishes broke.

(Kenneth J. Lobdell).—Small objects shifted. Trees and bushes shaken strongly.

TANANA

(H. A. Peters, from USGS report).—Five cracks, mostly in ice and mud. Average length 50 feet; average width one-fourth inch.

(James H. Simons).—Felt like I was intoxicated, dizzy, unable to walk.

(Fred B. Anderson).—Trees and bushes shaken moderately (faint noise from moving trees). Pendulum clock facing north stopped. Arm on phonograph shifted.

TETLIN

(From USGS report).—Slight damage to log buildings. Few cracks in the area, some as wide as 3 inches.

TOK

(Herbert W. Morgan).—Wells at depth to 90 feet (gravel to total depth) muddied, but most cleared within a few hours. Small objects shifted. Trees and bushes shaken strongly.

(Wm. Craig).—Walls cracked. Trees and bushes shaken moderately.

(Lawrence A. Stoll).—Water in well discolored for about 15 hours. Doors swung. Trees and bushes shaken moderately.

(Mrs. Mildred J. Sanford).—Pendulum clock facing east stopped. Car rolled gently back and forth a few inches. Shock came on so gradually that at first I had a feeling of nausea until aware of the actual movement.

WILLOW

(Robert A. Douglas).—Ground and windows cracked. Books, pictures, and pendulum clock fell; dishes broke.

(Zoa Hazel).—Ground and windows cracked. Small objects and furnishings shifted. Trees and bushes shaken strongly.

(Clarence A. Lammers).—Small objects shifted; vases overturned. Trees and bushes shaken moderately to strongly.

YAKUTAT

(Albert T. Gorman, Weather Bureau).—Visible swaying of buildings and trees. Pictures, books, and curios fell. Doors opened and closed; water spilled. Tide fluctuated in 10-minute cycles. Loud sounds, like cannon shots, heard by many for 20 minutes after the shock. The sounds, about 20 in number, were heard by people at the airfield, the Loran Station, and in town. Everyone agreed they came from Khantaack Island. Examination of the island by plane the next morning showed some slumping of a beach near Point Turner on the bay side and considerable debris, mainly kelp, in all bays and lagoons, with water extremely dirty looking.

(Martha Totland).—Felt by all. Small objects and furnishings shifted slightly.

ALEKNAGIK

(Roland Moody).—Felt by most persons. There were two waves on the lake about 1 foot high and 150 feet apart. This was observed in the open water (near mouth of lake) which was not frozen.

BETHEL

(Maxwell L. Tancher).—Plaster cracked slightly. No structural damage here. I was in school (wood building on steel beams) talking to janitors. We all felt dizzy and could hear the building creak.

(Mrs. Ben R. Wilkins).—Everyone with whom I have spoken had the same feeling of dizziness, as if one were about to faint. I would not have realized it was an earthquake had I not noticed the drapery pull cord swaying.

(J. Hont, Fish and Wildlife).—Felt by many. Some experienced feeling of nausea.

Three miles southwest of Bethel at airport (Ernesto J. Salas, Weather Bureau).—Felt by many.

CANTWELL

(Anna E. Herman).—Felt by all. Small objects shifted.

(John B. Agwiah).—Felt by all. I was in Cantwell visiting friends. We were riding in car when it happened. Only time we knew of shock was when we stopped in front of our friend's house. We all felt movement for about 4 minutes or more.

CHIGNIK

(Myrtle Lamond).—Frightened all. Small objects and furnishings shifted.

(Mrs. William R. Filtee, Jr.).—Tsunami at about midnight. About a 10-foot swell came at low tide, causing water to go up about 1 to 2 feet beyond normal high watermark.

(Arthur G. Skoreberg, from USGS report).—A tsunami or unusually high tide occurred 2 hours after the main shock. There were 12 waves 10 feet high. Tides in the area are now lower than normal by about 2 feet.

Chignik Lagoon (Mrs. Viola E. Grunner, from USGS report).—Tsunami reported 3 hours after the main shock. Height of wave about 3 feet. Tides in the area are now lower by about 2 feet.

Perryville, about 35 miles southwest of Chignik (Angelina M. Shongin, from USGS report).—Area affected by high tides or tsunami approximately 4½ hours after the main shock. There were 3 or 4 waves

10 feet high. Tides in the area are now lower than usual by about 2 feet.

CHISANA

(D. J. Folger).—Small objects overturned. Jeep rocked north-south. Pendulum clock facing east stopped. The Chisana Glacier, about 6 air miles southwest of the townsite, roared and rumbled for 30 minutes after the shock.

CIRCLE CITY

(Patricia Oakes).—Houses along and parallel to the Yukon felt the shock more sharply than we did at the school located inland from the riverbank and airfield. Lanterns swung parallel to the river; dishes didn't fall. Children bringing up water from the river left the ice at once as they were frightened by the cracking noises and the fact that the water splashed up over the rim of the ice hole. School flagpole swayed at right angles to riverbank.

(Mike Churkin and Bill Brosge, from USGS report).—Hanging planter box swung north-south. Tremor not felt, but nausea experienced.

CURRY

Milepost 248.5, Alaska Railroad (Mrs. James R. Brown).—Frightened all in home. Small objects shifted; knickknacks fell.

DILLINGHAM

(Lillian E. Ingram).—Felt by all.

EAGLE

(Anton Merly).—Pendulum clock facing east stopped.

(Mike Churkin and Bill Brosge, from USGS report).—Hanging lamps swung north-south. Very gentle ground roll.

FARWELL

FAA Station (Raymond F. Harvey).—Felt by all; frightened many. Sounds from ice and snow cracking. Trees and bushes shaken moderately.

GOLD CREEK

About 150 miles north of Anchorage (John Callaham).—Felt by all. Small objects shifted and overturned; knickknacks fell. Trees and bushes shaken strongly.

ILIAMNA LAKE

Intricate Bay (Grant Vannoy, Weather Bureau).—Sudden and unusually severe onset. Objects hanging on wall swung back and forth; trees swayed in east-west direction. Felt by all adults in the immediate vicinity; some children playing in cabin didn't notice the tremors.

KAKRINES

(Harry Titus).—Felt by all. Trees and bushes shaken moderately.

KOTZEBUE

(Percy Ipalook(?)).—Small objects shifted. Ice cracked. Frightened few.

(Robert K. Baker).—Felt by all. Hanging objects swung east-west. A few large cracks in the ice on Kobuk Lake were caused by the shock. The cracks run east-west generally. I have seen no cracks in the sea ice that I would identify as caused by wave action.

Airport housing area (Charles H. Edwards and Dawaine A. Shoemaker, Weather Bureau office and home).—Slight visible sway of buildings and trees. Few persons disturbed. Ice a short distance offshore on Kotzebue Sound was cracked.

(Ray Hendricks).—Light swung. Tape in oil tank (900,000-gallon capacity, 60 feet in diameter) going up and down from 22-foot mark to 25-foot mark.

RUBY

(Rev. Russell W. Arnold).—Felt by all in home. Pictures on wall moved; antenna wire swung some.

(Frank Stanyer).—Trees and bushes shaken moderately. Hanging objects swung east-west.

SAL LAKE

(Lawrence G. Sible).—Felt by all. While standing on the lake ice, I felt it move very slightly and crack. Also, there was a sound as if a chain were being dragged over concrete.

SKAGWAY

10th and State Streets (A. J. Nore).—Felt by all; frightened all in home. Plaster cracked slightly. Hanging objects swung east-west. Trees and bushes shaken moderately.

(James W. Burton).—Felt by all; frightened few in home. Hanging objects swung north-south. Trees and bushes shaken strongly.

11th and Main Streets (Orrin R. Edwards).—Felt by many. Frame creaked slightly.

(Judd Lee, from USGS report).—Tsunami 17 feet high occurred approximately 10:30 p.m., 3½ hours after the main shock. There were three more waves, the highest of which was 5 feet. The water came inland as much as 30 feet and was about 10 feet above ocean level. No damage.

SLEETMUTE

(Nellie E. Osborn).—Felt outdoors by observer and others active; frightened many in community. Trees and bushes shaken moderately.

(F. Sahateirra(?)).—Felt by all; frightened all in home. Trees and bushes shaken strongly.

TOGIAK

(Julius Pleasant).—Felt by all. Doors swung slightly in north direction; hanging objects and window shades swung for 45 seconds.

UMIAT

(At bush camp; Richard L. Martin).—Felt by and frightened all. Ground cracked. Small objects shifted and overturned; books fell.

UNALAKLEET

(Leonard J. Davis).—Small objects shifted. Trees and bushes shaken moderately. Hanging objects swung north-south.

(Mrs. John A. Moore).—Felt by many; frightened few.

(Nick Riley).—Only very few persons felt the shock. Some experienced a feeling of nausea. Some heard river ice cracking.

BARTER ISLAND

(Robert J. Braen(?)).—Felt by observer active in strongly built steel frame building. Walls creaked. Hanging lamps swung.

(Ben Hopson).—I was alone in the new school building. I went into bunkhouse and I heard a big bang, like someone hit the side of the house. I went outside to check but did not see anything, so I went back inside. About a minute later, I heard this big bang on the house again, and so again I went outside because this was unusual. This time I went around the house and stopped on a big snowbank and heard squeaking under the snow, so I said to myself that it was an earthquake. I forgot all about it and went inside. At 9:30 p.m., I turned on the radio and heard about Anchorage. Next morning, there was a crack on the ground running south-north or north-south. This crack is 20 feet from my bunkhouse and was probably the big bang I heard. No damage of any kind was found at this place.

CANYON VILLAGE AREA

(Report from Weather Bureau).—A visit to the Canyon Village area in May revealed that a wide split, running some 500 feet down the main channel, occurred in the ice on the Porcupine River. Both sides of this cleavage immediately separated a distance of approximately 3 inches. The ice layer on the river was approximately 5 feet thick. The observer, hearing the terrible noise resulting from this fracture, ran out on the river, but had barely reached the fracture when water began rising very rapidly through the fracture to a depth of 8 to 10 inches, overflowing all the ice in the general area. Although snow cover hampered a careful view of open water areas south of the Porcupine River country, we saw no evidence of cracks of this nature in either lakes or rivers in the area to the southward. Lake Chandalar experienced a number of fractures of the ice surface, which was about 4 feet thick, causing a series of sharp cracking sounds, like rifle shots in rapid succession.

COLD BAY

Weather Bureau Airport Station (Frederick H. Day).—Felt by majority of people; many felt seasick. Building swayed gently, moved about 6 to 8 inches; hanging lamps swayed about 6 to 8 inches; water in aquarium oscillated. Three distinct waving motions were felt by observer, the second and third had greater magnitude than initial wave, and the third had greater magnitude than the first or second. No tremors were felt after third wave subsided. No tsunami disturbances noted.

(Report from Weather Bureau Airport Station to Regional Administrator, Anchorage).—All equipment and facilities at Cold Bay are normal. We felt the shock, but no damage was done to any buildings or equipment. Shemya advised that no damage was done by either earth tremors or water activity. Their operation is normal. King Salmon and Bethel also advised that they are in normal operation and that neither station suffered damage.

GARNER

(Carl Lindquist).—Dishes rattled. Trees and bushes shaken slightly.

HOONAH AND VICINITY

(C. M. Thompson).—Felt by many. Windows, doors, and dishes rattled. The tide came in several feet higher a few minutes after the shock was felt. Reports from logging camps up the bay from here are that the water level rose several times in the hours after the shock.

(C. M. Thompson, from USGS report).—The tsunami came about 8 p.m., 20 minutes after the earthquake. There was some damage to a logging camp near town.

(B. F. Thompson).—Felt by several; some outdoors quiet. There was water action at the floats in the harbor. A few boat mooring lines were broken, causing slight damage.

(Mrs. J. C. Van Valkentura(?)).—Hanging objects swung. Water in bay receded rapidly and was disturbed most of the night. I know of no damage. We made a trip up Glacier Bay nearly to the end of Muir Inlet on April 5, and saw no visible damage or floating icebergs.

Elfin Cove, northwest of Hoonah (Elliott S. Fleming, from USGS report).—Tides in the area are now lower than usual. Evidently these measurements were taken on bedrock. Two tsunamis, 6 to 7 feet high, reported at 9:00 and 11:00 p.m. No damage.

Pelican, southwest of Hoonah (Oscar R. Haynes, from USGS report).—The first tsunami, 5 feet high, was at 7:40 p.m. It was followed by seven or eight more waves, the highest of which was 5 feet. Water damage extensive to several homes.

Pelican (Daily Alaska Empire, 3-30-64).—One home flooded; two scows drifted loose; boardwalk warped. People went to higher ground.

Yakobi Island, west of Pelican (press report).—Shock not felt by observers, but tremendous roaring noise heard. Suddenly we heard a tremendous roaring sound, somewhat like a jet plane flying overhead. I immediately rushed outside to see what happened but saw nothing unusual, though I pinpointed the noise as coming from a northerly direction, more or less in line with Yakobi Mountain. Then I rushed inside to turn on the radio, but neither the Sitka nor the Juneau stations reported anything unusual. The great noise continued and appeared to be coming from the sky. This sound, as near as I can describe it now, would have been pretty much like the noise from a great blast of steam or vapor from a volcano which had erupted violently. We noticed that the water in our back channel, where we keep our boat float, was beginning to race madly back and forth, then it rushed out of the bay, leaving our float down in the mud at the bottom of the bay. While this was taking place the roaring sound from the sky seemed to more or less come to a stop, and a new sound, like that of the explosions of anti-aircraft shells, took its place. This lasted for nearly 25 minutes. By this time we heard that an earthquake had occurred. We found out later that our shoreline had been pushed up 2 feet, and there's little doubt that the entire coastline to both the north and south of us has been raised as well.

LAKE CHANDALAR

(Wayne Adney).—Felt by three persons. The shock was heard more than felt. The noise was similar to two rather distant dynamite explosions with some rumbling of the ice in the lake. Lake ice had numerous cracks. A gold miner, 10 miles east of here, thought someone had fired two dynamite blasts rather close to his cabin.

MANLEY HOT SPRINGS

(Gus A. Benson).—Strongly built log cabin rocked and rolled mildly. Objects swung around inside cabin.

STEESE HIGHWAY

Milepost 66 (Mike Churkin and Bill Brosge, from USGS report).—Lamp in roadhouse swung approximately northwest-southeast.

TANACROSS

(Rev. Alfred H. Smith, Jr.).—Felt by many. Ice on river below village cracked, exposing open water. Buildings creaked; loose objects rattled.

UNIMAK ISLAND

Scotch Cap USCG Station.—Felt by all at station; frightened few. Windows, doors, and dishes rattled. Pictures swung. At the Loran Station, on northwest end of island, effects were very slight, with but a few of the 50 or so men in the area noticing any movement at all.

WILD LAKE

67.5° North, 151.6° West (Frederick Meade).—No tremor was felt on land, but lake ice, approximately 2 feet 10 inches thick, heaved and cracked for approximately 20 minutes. Water in ice hole, 1 foot 2 inches by 1 foot 8 inches, rose and fell with a maximum variation of 4 inches. This measurement was taken about 12 to 15 minutes after the ice began to heave.

CHUKCHI SEA

69°10′ North, 171°40′ West (Stephen L. Der Hartog (?)).—No motion felt, but geodetic gravity meter was impossible to read. Motion with period of 3 to 4 seconds. Natural frequency of meter unknown to me. We were on the ice for 10 minutes only. Slight motion also noticed on meter at Point Lay (69°44′ N., 163°00′ W.) at 05:55 G.C.T. on 28th. No noticeable ice breakup the following day between Point Lay and 69°30′ N., 178°00′ W.

DIME LANDING

(Oscar Swanson).—Felt by observer.

GAMBELL

(John Agangalook(?)).—Felt slightly by only a few persons.

HAINES

(Florence Lammers).—Rocking motion felt while walking in house. Tides observed in small boat harbor. Tide came in and out about four times from midnight to 0000 hours.

(Retha M. Young, from USGS report).—Unusually high tide occurred at 1:15 a.m., about 5¾ hours after the main shock. It was 19 feet high. This tide was followed by five more waves or high tides about 1 hour apart. These were a maximum of 17 feet high.

HOLY CROSS

(William Newman).—A few persons said they felt the earthquake. It was very light.

LIVENGOOD

(Fred Blixt).—Felt by several.

NOME

(Robert Forstman).—Slight tremor felt by few; frightened one.

PETERSBURG

(Mrs. Glenn Reid).—Felt by several. Hanging objects swung.

(Richard Brennan).—I was sitting in an easy chair at home having coffee about 7:40 p.m. Felt a very slight jiggle—chair arm jiggled slightly east-west. It was so slight I was not sure it was an earthquake so did not mention it to the family present. About 4 minutes later, I felt another jiggle, slightly stronger. Mentioned this to family. They did not believe me. I saw a faint motion of coffee in cup. Went out to see if any heavy equipment had passed. Equipment would have transmitted a much stronger motion through the muskeg, if within 50 yards. House is about 400 yards from waterfront and about 60 to 70 feet higher. It is on piling driven through 4 to 5 feet of muskeg to blue clay or gravel. There was a slight surge in the harbor, enough to break lines on one or two boats, apparently about 7:40 p.m. Subsequently, I watched the tide and could not see that it had been altered by an inch or a minute.

(Richard Brennan, from USGS report).—Tide levels in the area are now lower by about 1½ feet. (Judging from a fairly detailed report supplied by Mr. Brennan, these figures seem to be reasonably plausible and correct.)

(Kesten L. Dotts).—Felt slightly. Trees and bushes shaken slightly.

PRINCE OF WALES ISLAND AND ANNETTE ISLAND

Craig (Norma Anderson, from USGS report).—Tsunami, 14 feet high, reported about midnight. No damage.

Klawack (Herbert K. Smarl).—One wave, 10 feet high, occurred about 9:00 p.m. It was followed by two more about midnight, and these were 15 feet high. The water came 50 feet inland, destroying three frame dwellings on the city dock. Tides in the area reportedly 2 feet lower than normal.

Annette, south of Ketchikan (Virginia L. Simords, from USGS report).—A tsunami, 3 to 4 feet high, was noticed 9 hours after the main shock, at 4:40 a.m. No damage; no change in tide level. Earthquake not felt (USC&GS).

SITKA AND VICINITY

Pulp Mill (J. E. Downes).—I was sitting at table on 5- to 6-story level. Sway seemed to be 2 to 3 inches, causing a dizzy sensation. Upon getting up and walking the motion seemed to stop but continued when I sat down. Lasted 5 to 6 minutes. Felt by several.

(*Seattle Daily Times*, 3–28–64).—The Coast Guard reported that a dock collapsed at Sitka.

(*Daily Alaska Empire*, 3–30–64).—Little damage at Sitka. Two floats broke loose from their moorings.

Baranof, few miles northeast of Sitka (Mrs. William Short, from USGS report).—Tsunami 15–20 feet high reported about 7:35 p.m. It was followed by four or five other waves. Minor damage to float and boats in the area.

WAINWRIGHT

(G. Ray Bane, from USGS report).—This is a community about 100 miles southwest of Barrow on the North Slope. Mr. Bane, a BIA schoolteacher, reported that he felt the earthquake and said that cracks as large as 2 inches in width occurred in the area. (USGS report): Tides are higher than usual.

ADAK, ANGOON (NORTHEAST OF SITKA), ARCTIC VILLAGE, COOPER LAKE, MAY CREEK, PUNTILLA, AND UGANIK

(Weather Bureau reports).—No details but reported felt. At May Creek, strongly felt.

REPORTED NOT FELT

Auke Bay (Lena Cove, 17½ miles north of Juneau on Glacier Highway), Barrow, Bettles Field (near Bettles), Japonski Island (few miles offshore, west of Sitka), Kaktovik, Ketchikan, Mount Edgecumbe (tidal changes only), Nolan Creek (northeast of Bettles Field, mouth of Smith Creek), North River (Unalekeet area), Saint George Island (Pribilof Islands), Thane and Milepost 5 on Thane Highway, Umiat (Schrader Bluff), and Wiseman.

Washington

SEATTLE

(*Seattle Times*, 3–28–64).—Chandeliers swung and startled people in church; fixtures swung at Northgate. Motion was reported as barely perceptible at the Space Needle Restaurant. The manager likened the sway to motion of a very strong wind. He was in the center of the restaurant and noticed it, but patrons on the turntable didn't notice it at all.

CANADA

Yukon Territory

SNAG

(G. Dobson).—Ground cracking during the tremors. Severe vibration of buildings. Tremors lasted 10 minutes.

DOT Barracks (G. Sidoroff).—Felt by all. Small objects shifted. I was sitting in my room tuning across Ham bands. Felt moderate rocking of wooden chair. Small instruments shook; curtains swung. Heard muffled thuds from overhead and thought someone was on the roof. When I realized it was an earthquake, I went outside and saw poles and vertical antennas whipping strongly back and forth. Creaking of buildings was loud and other noises were audible. Operator on duty at air operator's position reported radio panel rack (heavy metal) raked and fluorescent light fixtures swung. Teletype circuit was temporarily out of service.

DOT Barracks (K. De Bruyn(?)).—Felt by many. Crackling of snow heard. Windows rattled; walls creaked. Trees and bushes shaken moderately. Hanging objects swung.

WHITE RIVER
White River at Alaska Highway (G. Dobson).—Wells were polluted for many hours. A resident reported this tremor was worse than the one in 1958.

BURWASH LANDING
(G. Dobson).—Felt by all; frightened few. Moderate cracking noises made by ground frost. House creaked as it swayed northeast-southwest. Trees and bushes shaken moderately.

DESTRUCTION BAY
(Douglas Smith).—Felt by all; frightened few. Hanging objects swung. Rocking chair facing northwest rocked.

Milepost 1083 (D. Swenson).—Hanging objects swung north. Ice on lake cracked.

DONJEK RIVER
Donjek River at Alaska Highway (G. Dobson).—Effects similar to those at Burwash Landing.

MAYO
(M. Baker).—Felt by all; frightened all in home. Hanging objects swung east. Trees and bushes shaken moderately.

(F. Kunze).—Hanging objects swung east-west. Trees and bushes shaken slightly.

(John H. Boyce).—Windows and dishes rattled. Hanging objects swung north-south and east-west. Trees and bushes shaken moderately.

WHITEHORSE
(E. G. Hartman).—Felt by all; frightened few. One cement and brick basement wall cracked. Damage slight.

(C. Marlens).—Trees and bushes shaken slightly.

(N. B. Keobke).—Felt by all in home. Dishes rattled slightly. Hanging objects swung north.

(G. H. Mead).—Felt by several. Direction north-south. Trees and bushes shaken moderately.

(Vern Flinhauy(?)).—Hanging objects swung. Trees and bushes shaken slightly.

DAWSON
(E. M. Lintick).—Felt by several. Windows, doors, and dishes rattled; house creaked. Hanging objects swung.

(T. A. Letulluck(?)).—Very slight motion. Felt by several. Dishes rattled; walls creaked.

(Donald Shailer).—The only evidence of anything unusual was a slight movement of a door about 1 inch east-west. Nothing was actually felt.

MINTO
Mayo Highway, Milepost 142.4, Midway Lodge (Mrs. Hazel Remonde).—Felt by several. House creaked. Trees and bushes shaken slightly.

British Columbia

FRANCOIS LAKE
Central British Columbia, about 10 miles south of Burns Lake (*The Province*, 3–30–64).—Church bells rang.

EAST KOOTENAYS
Southeastern British Columbia (*Seattle Times*, 3–28–64).—Tremors felt.

FORT ST. JOHN
Northeastern British Columbia (*Seattle Times*, 3–28–64).—Tremors felt.

NORTH VANCOUVER
(*Seattle Times*, 3–28–64).—Some apartment house dwellers in North Vancouver felt the shock. Vancouver and Victoria were generally unaware of the earthquake.

PRINCE GEORGE
Central section of British Columbia (*Seattle Times*, 3–28–64).—Tremors felt.

PRINCE RUPERT
Eighty miles south of Ketchikan, Alaska (*Seattle Times*, 3–28–64).—Tremors felt.

Northwest Territories

FORT MCPHERSON
Reported not felt.

TSUNAMI, SEICHE, AND LONG-PERIOD WAVE EFFECTS OUTSIDE OF ALASKA

CANADA

British Columbia

Kaslo, southeastern British Columbia.—On Kootenay Lake water sloshed up the beach several times for a distance of 3 feet in normally placid Kaslo Bay.

VANCOUVER ISLAND

Alberni and Port Alberni (Seattle Times, 3–28–64).—The concentrated fury of tsunamis from Alaska's death-dealing earthquake funneled up a narrow inlet and into the heart of this Vancouver Island community. The 25,000 residents of the twin cities, Alberni and Port Alberni, had 10 minutes' warning before each wave struck. The waves took 10 minutes to surge up the channel from the Bamfield Lighthouse at the mouth of the inlet. Most inhabitants were asleep when the lightkeeper sent his first warning. No loss of life was reported, but there were minor injuries. The waves took a twisting course 40 miles inland through Alberni Inlet. They sloshed through Port Alberni's logging industry complex and into the city center. One person reported: "I was standing in a foot of water after the first wave hit. Suddenly the second one surged up into the street. I heard people screaming and men running back and forth across the street in front of the wave. It covered cars, crashed into stores and buildings. By then I was running too—to get away. I was amazed to see two big houses, 30 feet by 50 feet and two stories high, floating out in the Somass River. They gradually broke up and sank. The second wave was like a surge. One minute the river surface was rippling, the next minute it was over the bank. I could see it hit a row of about six auto cabins on the riverbank. It lifted them all simultaneously." With the impact of the first wave, the Japanese freighter *Meishusan Maru* broke away from the pier and landed on the mud flats. When she floated on the second wave, crew members managed to get the vessel clear and anchor her back in the inlet. The second wave was the most severe. The third was much reduced in strength, and the fourth was neutralized by low tide. The first wave struck shortly after midnight, and the third swept in at 2:35 a.m. At least two fires broke out, due to escaping gas. Service stations in downtown areas were flooded; water seeped into storage tanks and sent gasoline flowing into the streets. Two logging-boom boats were hurled into downtown streets; a 50-foot log was balanced atop a car. Five MacMillan-Bloedal operations were knocked out, including a pulp and paper mill, sawmill, planer mill, and plywood plant. The B. C. Packers Company wharf was heavily damaged. The Port Alberni Engineering Works and the 70-foot Barclay Hotel were severely flooded. Water rose 25 to 30 feet inside the engineering works, covering machinery. The skipper of the Port Alberni pilot boat, *Riley II*, said: "We had just tied up the boat at 12:30 a.m. when the first wave hit. The floating dock came completely above the 20 to 25 foot pilings and stayed there about 15 minutes."

Port Alice.—Like Port Alberni at the end of a fiordlike inlet leading in from the open Pacific, waves ripped away boat and seaplane moorings and flooded some buildings. At least 20 boats were washed into the bay. Thousands of feet of lumber and pulpmill logs were tumbled along the waterfront. Lumber barges were high and dry, where they were tossed ashore by the surges. Police reported more than a dozen homes were pushed off foundations in an area of 300 homes in the River Road District. Debris blocked all roads hereabouts.

Hot Springs Cove.—An Indian village, near the northern tip of Vancouver Island, 18 homes were damaged.

Alberni (The Province, 3–30–64).—Area Commander of Civil Defense reported: "Apart from the fact that the first wave gave people some warning before the second and more severe one arrived, I am unable to account for the lack of casualties." The first wave struck at 12:10 a.m., and caused minor flooding in the low-lying areas. There was no sudden surge of water. Quietly the sea came up, gurgling into basements, and oozing over floorboards. The noise awakened people. The water receded, but at 1:20 a.m. the second wave struck, and for 10 minutes the water rose a foot a minute. In the area of River Road, Beaver Creek Road, Heaslip Road, and Alexander Road, 60 homes in the immediate area were heavily damaged, and perhaps 200 more were evacuated. Cars, runaway boats, houses, and log booms floated idly about. A small church floated to the center of a recreation ground. Other small coast communities were hit by the waves, but none suffered as seriously as the Alberni Valley. At Port McNeill, a $25,000 tug was smashed against a broken boom and sank. At a settlement at the mouth of the Sarita River, all houses were damaged.

Port Alberni Area about 7½ miles off the coast, (Nature, 4–25–64, vol. 202).—The waves caused a break in the Commonwealth telephone cable connecting Canada with Australia and New Zealand, at a point about 7½ miles off the coast near Port Alberni.

GRAHAM ISLAND

Masset (W. H. Perlstrom, Regal Air Service, Ltd.).—The earthquake was not felt here in Masset by me, but there were three distinct surges of water, about 45 minutes apart, the highest one about 6 feet. Prior to the surge, the suction lifted 2-ton concrete anchors out of the mud in which they were buried and then broke the cables holding my aircraft floats. When the surge came back, it washed my floats up on the beach. This was the only damage done in this community. (R. A. Rottluff).—At approximately 7:50 p.m. the tide started to rise and fall quite rapidly. All boats tied to the floats were pitched back and forth, but no damage resulted. The tide rose approximately 6 feet at the highest surge.

UNITED STATES

Alabama

BREWTON

(Rev. Louis J. Eisele, S. M., Spring Hill College).—One mile south of Brewton an underground cable was pulled apart at a splice. This occurred close to 2200 C.S.T. The cable runs east-west at the location of the break.

MOBILE

(Rev. Louis J. Eisele, S. M., Spring Hill College).—A frame dwelling, about 100 feet from the Physics Building, began "sounding off" at about 2200 C.S.T. Doors thumped so loudly one of the Fathers checked all around because he thought someone was trying to break in. I could experience no motion at all during all this, but when I closed my eyes I distinctly experienced a dizzy sensation. In Mobile, a rather poorly constructed church (basement and one upper floor constructed of cement block without metal reinforcing strips between courses and already showing settling cracks) was found, on Easter Sunday, to have developed entirely new and different kinds of cracks. These new cracks were not vertical, as were the settling cracks, but diagonal. The new cracks go through the blocks, not just along the mortar.

Arkansas

BONANZA

(*Stone County Republican, Missouri, 4–2–64*).—The Weather Bureau reported that at Bonanza, water level rose 3 feet after the earthquake.

California

BOLINAS BAY

Tsunami swept man to his death.

CRESCENT CITY

(From report of San Francisco Regional Officer, U. S. Coast and Geodetic Survey, after visit to Crescent City).—The alert was received at Crescent City at 11:08 p.m. P.S.T. that there would be a seismic sea wave. The surges began rolling in at midnight. At first with minor damage, but the one recorded at 1:00 a.m. was higher; then at 1:40 a.m. came in a destructive giant that gushed through the downtown section; then on top of that came another that leveled some buildings, moved others, and tossed cars and trucks around like so many matchsticks. The water reached as high as 8 feet in the surges. More than 300 buildings were destroyed or knocked askew by the 5 to 8 foot water surges. Short circuits contributed to fires at two bulk gasoline plants and five storage tanks exploded. An estimated 20 commercial fishing vessels were demolished or missing. Waves shattered buildings and wharves, uprooted trees, and giant debris logs were tossed about like driftwood during the peak of the disaster. The breakwaters seemed to have stood up quite well.

FORT BRAGG

(*San Francisco News Call Bulletin, 3–28–64*).—Fort Bragg reported "a number of boats—probably more than half a dozen—sank." Hundreds of volunteers worked from midnight to dawn in efforts to save the city's fishing fleet.

HUMBOLDT BAY

(Professor James A. Gast, Humboldt State College).—From water lines observed on pilings and dock structures in the interior portions of the bay, maximum water level range was estimated at 14 feet.

KLAMATH

(Press).—Man drowned by tsunami while eel fishing in the Klamath River.

SAN FRANCISCO BAY AREA

(*San Francisco News Call Bulletin, 3–28–64*).—Extensive damage to pleasure boats in Sausalito and San Rafael. Inside San Francisco Bay, erratic tides, swelling and ebbing furiously, shattered a number of boats. A number of boats broke loose and sank. The boat channel into San Rafael was clogged with wreckage and debris. At San Francisco, several yachts broke their moorings in the St. Francis Yacht Harbor but were recovered without damage. The huge 66-year-old ferry *Berkeley,* now a floating gift shop, snapped her moorings and smashed into the pier in Sausalito. The pier was severely damaged but the ferry was not badly damaged. In San Francisco, the Holland-American Line freighter *Amsteldyk* snapped a steel bowline. At Fisherman's Wharf, scores of boats bobbed like corks as the tide receded and then charged forward again. In yacht harbors, water receded so far at times that tall-masted yachts settled into the sand, only to be jerked upright as the water again hissed under their hulls.

SANTA CRUZ

(*San Francisco News Call Bulletin*, 3–28–64).—A huge dredging barge broke loose in the new yacht harbor in Santa Cruz.

SOUTHERN CALIFORNIA

(*Los Angeles Times*, 3–29–64).—Hardest hit were the Marina del Rey, between Venice and Playa del Rey, and the Fellows and Stewart boat harbor in Cerritos Channel, between Terminal Island and the mainland. At Marina del Rey, a surge of seawater ripped out 450 feet of docking facilities operated by the Union Oil Company and shoved it half a mile up the channel. Nearly half a dozen floats of the Caballo del Mar facility were torn loose and banged about. A barge loaded with 600 tons of breakwater stone broke loose in the marina. At the Terminal Island harbor, tidelike surges of 5 to 10 feet heaved through the narrow Cerritos Channel, ripping out walkways and dock floats and tearing scores of boats from their moorings. Observers reported the water movement was both inward and outward, with a swift rising or lowering of levels and swift, erratic currents. At Marina del Rey, the rise was measured at 52 inches in the harbor and 5 feet at the entrance. At Santa Barbara, a newly built rock wall was credited with saving 500 boats in the city yacht harbor. One 47-foot ketch was smashed against a piling. In Ventura, the water level of the small-boat harbor dropped 8 feet in 25 minutes, but no serious damage occurred. Farther north, residents of low areas of Cambria, Cayucos, Morro Bay, Avila, Shell Beach, Pismo Beach, and Oceano were evacuated. The first wave surged into Morro Bay tearing boats from moorings and ripping out and sinking the harbor's floating yacht club. The owner of Graham's Landing said he saw the club barge go floating by as the mass of water moved back out to sea. "It was like someone pulled a plug in the bay." In San Diego Harbor, a 60-foot schooner broke loose, smashing into pier pilings and a boat. There was some damage to shore installations on Shelter Island. A wave that came in at 4 a.m. ripped a U. S. Navy floating pier from its 5,000-pound anchors,

dragging one of the anchors 100 yards. No damage was reported at Santa Catalina Island, where Avalon Bay and the isthmus anchorage lie on the sheltered side.

Delaware

SEAFORD

(Weather Bureau).—Man reported water in his indoor swimming pool and others in the neighborhood, oscillated in a noth-south direction with a period of about 2 seconds. The water in the center of the pool rose and fell about 1½ inches above and below the normal level.

Florida

TALLAHASSEE

(*Tallahassee Democrat*, 3–31–64).—Fluctuation in artesian well noted at the Florida State University campus.

WOODINVILLE

(*Tallahassee Democrat*, 3–31–64).—Well water muddied.

Georgia

BRUNSWICK

(*Tallahassee Democrat*, 3–31–64).—Artesian wells rose 3½ feet above normal and fell the same amount below normal. It was reported that where float recorders were in use, no readings were obtained due to cables being knocked off their wheels by the sudden fluctuations.

Hawaii

(Department of Civil Defense).—Principal damage occurred in the Wailuku District, County of Maui, and was estimated at approximately $52,490.00. At Hilo, damage was estimated at about $15,000, and was caused by flooding of three restaurants, one home, and slight damage to the Wailoa River Bridge. Wave heights did not exceed 10 feet. There were no casualties.

Kentucky

(*Louisville Courier-Journal*, 3–31–64).—Seiches were observed on Harrington Lake and Lake Cumberland.

Louisiana

SOUTHERN LOUISIANA AREA

(*Baton Rouge Advocate*, 3–28–64).—A wide area of southern Louisiana reported shocks and minor tsunamis or water disturbances. Nervous residents of Baton Rouge, Geismar, along Bayou Lafourche, the Amite River, and Pontchartrain telephoned police and weather bureau and newspaper offices after witnessing strange water actions between 10:00 and 11:00 p.m. C.S.T.

At Baton Rouge, water sloshed more than 6 inches over a 50-foot-long pool; at the Capitol House, in the center of town, the swimming pool on the fourth floor was reported "boiling." Near Baton Rouge, a man reported he was looking down at the placid Amite River when "all of a sudden, water came in waves 4 feet high." Further down the Amite, a man at Denham Springs observed the waves tear apart boathouses and ramps at a fishing camp. People standing on a fishing wharf where the water was 4 to 5 feet deep reported that "they looked down and suddenly there was no water—they were looking at the riverbed. Then the water came rushing back in. I saw that wave tear up a wharf . . . it broke an 8-inch piling." At Riverview Park, off the Hoo-Shoo-Too Road, the Amite River was suddenly disturbed by 4-foot-high waves which lasted about 20 minutes. Man reported a floating boatstore on the Mississippi River moved down the river about 10 feet and about 5 feet toward midstream. Boats bounced at moorings on Lake Pontchartrain. Police at Opelousas reported Bayou Cortableau rose some 4 feet between 10:00 and 11:00 p.m. The bayou churned with tremendous waves. A watchman at the New Orleans Industrial Canal reported water suddenly rose 6 feet above normal. "It was one of the wildest scenes I've seen in a long time. The water was rolling; barges began to move in and out, and the lines began to turn and break." An 83-foot Coast Guard vessel was torn loose from its mooring.

LAKE CHARLES

(*Shreveport Times*, 3–29–64).—Waves jumped as high as 4 feet in Calcasieu River near Lake Charles. At City Service Docks, workers said the river "quivered and sloshed," causing a large tanker tied up at the docks to move sharply. Several barges almost broke loose from their tows.

MADISONVILLE, COVINGTON

(*St. Tammany Farmer*, 4–3–64).—At Madisonville, water was backed up in Tchefuncte River for several miles, and some persons reported hearing ripples along the breakwaters. At St. Tammany Parish Drainage District No. 2, at Slidell, it was reported new levees and canals were damaged or their structures were changed. The bottom of one or more canals raised about 2 feet and· did not settle again. In Washington Parish, stock ponds rose and spilled debris above normal water line.

OPELOUSAS AREA

(*Opelousas Daily World*, 3–29–64).—A series of large waves swept Bayou Cortableau, the Atchafalaya River and smaller streams—even ponds—some time after 10:00 p.m., various residents of the Opelousas area reported. Witnesses said the waves in the Bayou Cortableau were "like a great big boat went by." In Darbonne Bay, waves ranged up to 4 feet high. One Lawtell area farmer reported water from his two stock ponds spilled out over nearby fields. At a fishing camp on Darbonne Bay, just inside the West Atchafalaya spillway, boats knocked together and floated away; chain was broken on large raft by the first wave which was about 4 feet high; ropes on four or five other boats broke. "The waves washed all kinds of debris up on the bank, and we saw logs, shaken up from the bottom of the water, floating away. The disturbance lasted for about 45 minutes."

PLAQUEMINE AREA

(*Greater Plaquemine Post*, 4–2–64).—There were major disturbances in the waters of Bayou Plaquemine, Bayou Grosse Tete and Grand River, similar to those reported in the Amite and Comite Rivers. No major damage was reported, but boatowners found their crafts overturned, moved downstream, resting upon land, or broken away from their moorings. Several boat sheds were damaged. At Plaquemine, it was reported a 20-ton boat broke loose and was washed up on land. The impact of water broke a $3/8$-inch galvanized cable. A cottonwood water-soaked log, 7 feet in diameter and 125 feet long, to which the boat was moored, was moved downstream about 120 feet.

(*Plaquemine Iberville South*, 4–2–64).—At Lake Long (back of Bayou Goula), waves 3 feet high splashed against a wharf. Bateau bounced wildly up and down for 10 minutes; nearby houseboat bounced up and down.

ST. FRANCISVILLE

(*St. Francisville Democrat*, 4–2–64).—The only effect noted in the area was on the Mississippi River where a rapid rise on the west bank of between 2 to 3 feet was observed by ferry personnel.

THIBODAUX LAFOURCHE PARISH

(*Thibodaux Lafourche Parish Press*, 3–31–64).—The destructive force of the earthquake was apparently felt only in the sea level area of the parish and only in a limited area from upper Golden Meadow to the vicinity of the Falgout Funeral Home at Galliano. It was reported water rose out of the bayou in different areas. It was not a solid wave from Golden Meadow to Galliano. Water remained perfectly calm for stretches of a half mile to a mile and then areas of a quarter mile were found where water had broken over the bayou banks. Minor damage was reported to the Alidor Terrebonne net shop in Golden Meadow, and three small skiffs, oil drums, and much debris were thrown up on the highway. A small barge was sunk in the bayou and a fishing boat broke loose from its mooring lines and damaged pilings at Golden Meadow.

Mississippi

(*Vicksburg Evening Post,* 3–29–64).—In the Yazoo Canal, mooring lines were pulled from the showboat *Sprague,* and the wave motion caused the vessel to bob up and down and move sideways. The steel walkway was bent at a 30° angle.

Missouri

(*Stone County Republic,* 4–2–64).—A man fishing at Table Rock late Friday night reported he had shoved his boat part way into the bank at Flat Creek and the James River off Cape Fair when the water began rolling and pulled his boat back into the lake. He said there was a whirling current where there should not have been any, and there was physical evidence all up and down the lake that the water had risen and then receded.

Oregon

CANNON BEACH

(*Seattle Times,* 3–28–64).—Utility poles knocked down and a two-story house was washed into Elk Creek.

DEPOE BAY

(*Seattle Times,* 3–28–64).—A family of six were sleeping in sleeping bags on the shore of Beverly State Park when the wave came in. Four children were washed out to sea and drowned.

SEASIDE

(*Seattle Times,* 3–28–64).—A bridge was seriously damaged, a house demolished, and automobiles in the city parking lot were washed into the river.

South Carolina

CHARLESTON

(Charles F. Mercer, Columbia Seismograph Station).— A man in Charleston reported he noticed a curious "jump" in the water of his swimming pool at 22:45 E.S.T.

LAKE MURRAY, CENTRAL SOUTH CAROLINA

(Charles F. Mercer).—At Snelgrove's Landing, a man reported he noticed a synchronous rise and fall of the lake level at about 22:45 E.S.T. There were no boats on the lake, and no wind, but the lake rose and fell with an amplitude of 2 inches every 30 seconds on full cycle for some time.

Texas

(*The Houston Post,* 3–29–64).—The strongest effects of the wave were felt in the Beaumont and Port Arthur areas where waters of the Sabine-Neches Ship Channel were churned violently. The Sabine Pass U. S. Coast Guard reported the tsunami came through the pass and pushed the tide 3 feet higher than normal at 10:00 p.m., E.S.T. Fishing boats and other small craft were torn from their moorings from Beaumont to Port Arthur, a U. S. Coast Guard spokesman reported, and the marine dock at the foot of Cypress Street in Beaumont was damaged to the extent of several thousand dollars. Mooring lines on two of the U. S. Coast Guard's 40-foot launches, tied up at Sabine Pass, were broken. As the wave ranged down the Texas coast, with diminishing effects, little damage was reported until it reached the Matagorda Peninsula area. The wave reached Freeport about midnight, sending tides about a foot higher, but causing no damage. Shortly before 1:00 a.m. Saturday [March 28], the tides surged up the Colorado River at Matagorda, causing a rapid rise and fall of the water level and thousands of dollars damage to boats and piers. Owner of a fishing camp on the Colorado River between Matagorda and the Gulf reported an estimated several thousand dollars in damage to piers and boats along a 4¼-mile area. Several boats moored along the river were sunk and several unmanned boats were observed drifting downstream toward the gulf. The wave reached the Corpus Christi area at 1:20 a.m. Saturday [March 28], with little noticeable effects, pushing the tide only about a foot higher than normal. The Tropicana Swimming Club reported a 2-foot wave splashed over the edge of the pool, causing the loss of 25,000 gallons of water.

(*The Houston Chronicle,* 3–29–64).—Three vessels broke loose from their moorings in the Houston Ship Channel, four boats sank in the Colorado River, and two U. S. Coast Guard motor launches slipped their lines and were pushed around a bit. Damage was negligible except along the Colorado. Water at the Anchor Bait Camp on the Colorado rose about 4½ feet, then "went up and down like a yo-yo". The owner of the camp said he checked along 5 miles of the river and reported three sport boats and one shrimp boat were sunk. At least $5,000 in damage to private docks and piers was reported; damage to boats was about $2,000. Farther down the river, a swishing and sucking sound of the water was heard and a woman reported she saw 25 feet of river bottom as the water "got real high in the middle." Fish jumped out of the water. A 4-foot rise in water was reported at the Intracoastal Canal drawbridge, but no damage occurred. In the Ship Channel, two freighters and the Port of Houston inspection boat broke their moorings. A 3-foot wave rolled from the Sabine area up the Neches and Sabine Rivers toward Beaumont and Orange. At Beaumont, two old boats were splintered, three steel barges broke loose from their moorings, but damage at Beaumont was slight. The U. S. Coast Guard at Galveston reported the wave caused 1½-foot tides. A 22-foot skiff and a 16-foot skiff broke loose from their moorings and sank off Bolivar Peninsula. At Caddo Lake (18 miles northwest of Marshal, in eastern Texas), the owner of a lake house on Big Cypress Bayou, which runs into Caddo Lake from the west, reported the bayou rose 2 feet and then fell more than 2 feet, with logs and trash boiling up from the bottom of the bayou.

Washington

ABERDEEN

(*Fairbanks Daily News Miner*, 3–30–64).—The water hit the beach area north of Aberdeen, slamming at trailers, knocking out two highway bridges, and piling logs and debris on the beaches. A park ranger at Ocean City reported: "It came over the dunes shooting 5 to 6 feet high, tossing logs around like matchsticks. Man stopped in the middle of the Copalis River Bridge watching driftwood piling up when suddenly the bridge gave way and his auto plunged down."

BELFAIR

Hood Canal (*Seattle Times*, 3–28–64).—A fire department spokesman said tides of about 3 feet higher than normal struck shortly after midnight, but no damage was reported. Water went over the highway at Beard's Corner, and brush and trees were floating in the canal.

FRIDAY HARBOR

(Seattle Regional Office, USC&GS).—Observer reported waves up to 2 feet high.

LONG BEACH

(*Seattle Times*, 3–28–64).—Four boys were routed from their tent. Their automobile was washed away.

NEAH BAY

(*Seattle Times*, 3–28–64).—Neah Bay showed a tide of about 4 feet above normal on the 27th at 11:30 p.m. It oscillated in and out three times in a short period early in the morning of the 28th. No damage was reported.

OCEAN SHORES

(*Seattle Times*, 3–28–64).—Guests were evacuated from Ocean Shores about 11:30 p.m. The water ran up an access road from the beach into the office and motel area to a depth of about 2 feet, but no damage occurred.

OLYMPIA

(*Fairbanks Daily News-Miner*, 3–30–64).—Woman at Olympia was suddenly awakened by water rocking her trailer. She stepped from trailer into waist-deep rushing water. An area resort owner said the water swept nearly half a mile beyond its normal tidelines, carrying some trailers more than 100 feet. "There was more than 4 feet of water down there," he reported. "I hauled out 10 trailers."

POINT GREENVILLE, NEAR TAHOLA, NORTH OF LONG BEACH

(*Seattle Times*, 3–28–64).—Camping party routed from tent. Automobile and camping gear damaged.

SEATTLE

(Reported by Seattle Regional Office, USC&GS).—Water disturbance in Lake Union snapped a mooring line on the *Lester Jones* and caused minor damage to the gangway on the *Patton*. After replacing the line, the security watch on the *Lester Jones* logged the event as occurring at 7:41 p.m., P.S.T. The marigram at the Seattle tide station showed fluctuations beginning about 6 hours after the major shock. These increased to an amplitude of about 1.5 feet about 2 hours later, then diminished for 3 hours until a smooth curve was restored.

(*Seattle Times*, 3–28–64).—Houseboat dwellers were "jolted" three times, beginning about 7:45 p.m., as the waters of Lake Union "seemed to move with the surface remaining calm." Houseboats broke loose from their moorings and water supply pipes were broken. It was reported the most severe action on the houseboats was to those moored closest to shore. One man reported: "My houseboat is out near the end of our pier at 2035 Fairview Avenue E. We did not get much motion, but a much larger houseboat right next to the shore broke loose and banged against the wall." A neighbor said the whole pier moved in the first tremor which rose from the lake bottom. The second and third tremors, each milder than the preceding tremor, left the lake calm but moved the houseboats. Five houseboats at the 2331–2339 Fairview Avenue E. moorage snapped their moorings and water supply lines.

The most severe damage was across Lake Union at the Four Winds Restaurant, a former ferry boat, moored at 900 Westlake Avenue N. About 55 patrons were evacuated when the north mooring line pulled a pile from the lake bottom. "We had a steel cable spring line which held when we started to swing away." Some dishes were broken when they slid to the floor. Whole back of wall torn off. The boat rocked for about 10 minutes. Nearby, at Kim's Restaurant, the manager said the restaurant rocked, but there was no damage. "It felt like logs were hitting against the pilings." At the Aqua Barn, the place rocked enough to let dancers know something was happening. At the Puget Sound Marina, several logs were torn loose from their moorings, but no damage was reported to the boats. Harbor police reported that several large boats strained at their moorings in the Lake Washington Ship Canal, but no damage was reported. At Ray's Boathouse, on Shilshoe Bay, no effects of the tremor were felt.

SOUTH BEND

Bone River, 10 miles south of South Bend (Seattle Times, 3–28–64).—An empty beach house, on pilings, was picked up by wave and jammed against a bridge. The bridge was heavily damaged.

TACOMA

(*The Sunday Star* [*Washington, D.C.*], 3–29–64.— At Point Defiance Park Zoo, the birds and animals created a deafening din. "I was on our porch overlooking the zoo around 7:30 p.m. when suddenly there was a tremendous uproar in the zoo. First it was the ducks and geese, then the lions, coyotes, and all the rest joined in."

JAPAN

(*San Francisco News Call Bulletin,* 3–28–64).—A series of waves, 3 to 10 inches higher than normal, hit the shores of Japan. There were no reports of damage.

FRANK PRESS*
DAVID JACKSON†
CALIFORNIA INSTITUTE OF TECHNOLOGY

Reprinted from *Science*, Vol. 147,
"Alaskan Earthquake, 27 March 1964:
Vertical Extent of Faulting and Elastic Strain Energy Release"

Vertical Extent of Faulting and Elastic Strain Energy Release

Abstract. *The residual displacement field indicates that the primary fault responsible for the great Alaskan earthquake extended to depths of 100 to 200 kilometers and came to within 15 kilometers of the surface. The vertical extent is an order of magnitude greater than reported for all other earthquakes. Approximately 10^{25} ergs of elastic strain energy was released. About 12,000 aftershocks ($M_L \gtrsim 3.5$) probably occurred in a 69-day period after the main shock. One-half the strain rebound occurred the first day with the main shock contributing one-fourth of the total.*

It has become possible to determine several important properties of faults associated with major earthquakes, such as initial slip direction, orientation and horizontal extent of the fault plane, and rupture velocity. The vertical extent of faulting and the elastic strain energy release are parameters which have been estimated, but dilemmas arise in connection with the results. The vertical extent can be deduced from the rate of decrease of the residual displacement or the seismic energy with distance. When the data from the San Francisco earthquake (1906) were applied to the San Andreas fault, fault depths of 2 to 10 km were obtained (1, 2). It is difficult to reconcile these small values with the 436-km length of the fault break. Estimates of strain energy release depend on the extent of faulting, and they also are in doubt.

The Alaskan earthquake (27 March 1964) produced residual vertical displacements which could be measured to distances of 200 km on the basis of tide gauge records and shoreline changes (3). These data are unmatched in extent and precision and offer an excellent opportunity for estimating the vertical extent of faulting and the elastic strain energy release.

The length of the primary fault is approximately 800 km as estimated from the extent of the belt of aftershocks. The distribution of polarity of first motion is consistent with a nearly vertical fault plane (4). Fault length determined from the spectra of surface waves is about 650 km, and a near-vertical fault plane is uniquely indicated (5). The residual vertical changes projected on a section normal to the strike of the fault are shown in Fig. 1. Locally on Montague Island, uplift exceeded 10 m. These points are not plotted since they are apparently secondary features, subsidiary to the regional uplift and associated with the zone of maximum flexure. Striking features of the residual displacement profile are (i) the occurrence of a zone of zero elevation change rather than a scarp separating the region of uplift and subsidence; (ii) zones of maximum elevation change and greatest flexure which roughly define the width of the belt of epicenters; (iii) gradual decrease in residual displacement to distances of 150 to 250 km;

*Now with Massachusetts Institute of Technology.
†Now with University of California, Los Angeles.

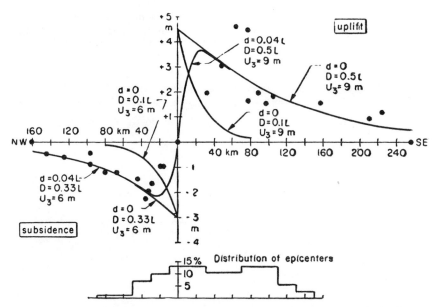

Fig. 1. Residual vertical displacements projected on a section normal to and bisecting the fault. Parameters for theoretical curves are d, depth to top of fault; D, depth to bottom of fault; L, half-length of fault (400 km); U_3 vertical slip; index of seismicity, shown at bottom, is percentage of aftershocks in zone 20 km wide in the 3 days after main shock.

and (iv) asymmetry in the curves of uplift and subsidence.

The last feature may be due to slight dip in the fault plane. An approximate interpretation of the first three features can be made representing the fault as a vertical, rectangular dislocation sheet in a half-space. The displacement fields for such a source can readily be computed (2, 6) and fitted to the observed displacements with the vertical extent of faulting as an adjustment parameter. Two types of theoretical curves are drawn through the data in Fig. 1. The curves with $d = 0$ correspond to a fault reaching the surface and show the expected scarp. The curves with $d = .04\,L \sim$ 16 km (L being the fault half-length) show zero displacement above the fault and a zone of flexure separating the uplifted and down-dropped blocks. The two curves are indistinguishable at distances greater than 30 km in the direction normal to the fault. At these larger distances the curves are sensitive to the depth of the lower boundary of the fault, as can be seen by comparing the cases $D = 0.1\,L \sim 40$ km with $D = 0.33\,L \sim 130$ km and $D = 0.5\,L \sim 200$ km. The last two cases fit

the data in the down-dropped and uplifted blocks respectively, the first case showing much too rapid a decrease in displacement with distance. We conclude that the primary fault came to within 15 to 20 km of the surface and extend to depths of 100 to 200 km.

A large depth of faulting is also required to explain the residual strain of 10^{-8} observed in Hawaii (Fig. 2). If the dislocation representation is used and the strike-slip is 5 to 6 m (7), strains in the range 10^{-9} to 10^{-8} are computed for Hawaii when $D \sim 1.0\,L$, whereas 10^{-10} to 10^{-9} are found when $D = 0.1\,L$ (8).

An estimate of the elastic strain energy released by the Alaskan earthquake can be made by evaluating the volume integral of the strain energy density function or computing the energy required to produce the dislocation. If the rigidity is 5×10^{11} dynes/cm², fault dimensions are 800 by 200 km, and horizontal and vertical slips are 6 m, we find stresses of 10^7 dynes/cm² adjacent to the fault and an energy release of 10^{25} ergs. Presumably this is an upper bound for the energy released as seismic waves. With

the Gutenberg-Richter relation between magnitude and energy, $\log E = 11.8 + 1.5\,M$, and the value $M = 8.4$ found from surface waves, a value of 3×10^{24} ergs is indicated for the energy in seismic waves. A line distribution of 100 underground nuclear explosions totaling 100 megatons each would correspond in seismic energy to such a source. It may be compared to the value 10^{28} ergs which represents the energy reaching the earth's surface annually as heat from the interior.

Thirteen days after the main shock we installed standard Wood-Anderson seismographs in Seward and on Middleton Island (9). We have used these instruments to estimate some aftershock statistics as follows: In a 57-day period beginning 9 April, N earthquakes were indicated per 0.1 unit in magnitude M_L, where $\log N = a - bM_L$, $a = 6.6$, and $b = 1.1$. A correction for radius of perceptibility was used on the assumption that the seismic release was constant over the fault. Approximately 800 shocks were actually recorded in the magnitude range $M_L \cong$ 3.5. The coefficient b was found to be independent of time. For the period

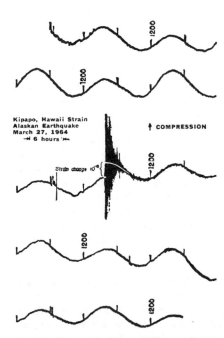

Fig. 2. Residual strain of 10^{-8} recorded at Kipapa, Oahu, on strain seismograph. Several days of recording before and after earthquake show strains associated with tidal loading only.

[110]

28 March to 9 April, the U.S. Coast and Geodetic Survey reported 103 earthquakes with $M_L \gtreqqless 5.3$ (10). With these data to determine an appropriate value of a, the number of shocks in the range $3.5 \lesseqqgtr M_L \lesseqqgtr 5.3$ could be inferred. For the 69-day period following the earthquake, 12,000 shocks are estimated to have occurred with $M_L \gtreqqless 3.5$.

The characteristics of the cumulative strain release for these 12,000 shocks are summarized in Fig. 3. The ordinate is $E^{\frac{1}{2}}$, which is proportional to strain (11) and is computed from the magnitude-energy relationship $\log E = 9.9 + 1.9 M_L - 0.024 M_L^2$. We see that the total seismic energy released in the 69-day period was about 5×10^{25} ergs. Approximately half the strain rebound occurred in the first day, with the main shock contributing one-fourth the total. It is unusual that no aftershock with $M > 7$ occurred, the aftershock strain release occurring mainly from the large number of smaller shocks.

The vertical extent found for the Alaskan earthquake fault exceeds by one or two orders of magnitude the values found for other earthquakes. This difference may be associated with the larger magnitude reported for the Alaskan fault. In the case of the San Francisco earthquake, this explanation

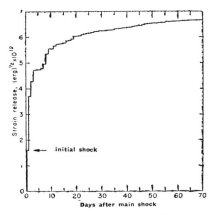

Fig. 3. Cumulative strain release for 69-day period for Alaskan earthquake and aftershock sequence. Ordinate is square root of energy computed from magnitudes, and is proportional to strain change. Except for main shock, daily values represent sums of strain release.

does not suffice since the magnitude difference between the two events is small. Most displacement observations fell within 5 km of the San Andreas fault, and anomalously low rigidities in the fault zone (12) could have resulted in a misleading displacement-distance relationship.

FRANK PRESS
DAVID JACKSON
Seismological Laboratory, California Institute of Technology, Pasadena

References and Notes

1. P. Byerly and J. DeNoyer, *Contrib. Geophys.* **1**, 17 (1958); L. Knopoff, *Geophys. J.* **1**, 44 (1958).
2. M. A. Chinnery, *Bull. Seismol. Soc. Am.* **51**, 355 (1961).
3. G. Plafker, in preparation. I thank Mr. Plafker for letting me see his data in advance of publication.
4. S. T. Algermissen, in *Program of the Annual Meeting Geological Society of America*, Miami, Florida, 19–21 November 1964, abstr., p. 2.
5. A. Ben-Menahem and M. N. Toksoz, personal communication, 20 December 1964.
6. T. Maruyama, *Bull. Earthquake Res. Inst. Tokyo Univ.* **42**, 289 (1964).
7. Results from geodetic resurveying show horizontal movement between Montague and Latouche islands amounting to 5 to 6 m, as reported by C. A. Whitten, in *Program of the Annual Meeting of the Geological Society of America*, Miami, Florida, 19–21 November 1964, abstr., p. 222.
8. F. Press, *J. Geophys. Res.*, in press.
9. We thank S. T. Algermissen and his colleagues of the U.S. Coast and Geodetic Survey for arranging for the operation and maintenance of the instruments.
10. Actually the U.S. Coast and Geodetic Survey reported magnitudes based on surface waves which we converted to M_L.
11. H. Benioff, *Bull. Seismol. Soc. Am.* **41**, 31 (1951).
12. ———, in *Continental Drift*, S. K. Runcorn, Ed. (Academic Press, New York, 1962).
13. Contribution 1312, Division of Geological Sciences, California Institute of Technology. This work was supported by NSF grant No. GP-2806.

Former sea floor at Cape Cleare, Montague Island, Prince William Sound, exposed by 26 feet of tectonic uplift. The surf-cut surface, which slopes gently from the base of the sea cliffs to the water, is about a quarter of a mile wide. The white coating on the rocky surface consists mainly of the desiccated remains of calcareous algae and bryozoans. Photograph taken at about zero tide stage, May 30, 1964.

GEORGE PLAFKER
U.S. GEOLOGICAL SURVEY

Reprinted with minor changes from
U.S. Geological Survey Professional Paper 543-I,
"Tectonics of the March 27, 1964, Alaska Earthquake"

Tectonics

ABSTRACT

The March 27, 1964, earthquake was accompanied by crustal deformation—including warping, horizontal distortion, and faulting—over probably more than 110,000 square miles of land and sea bottom in south-central Alaska. Regional uplift and subsidence occurred mainly in two nearly parallel elongate zones, together about 600 miles long and as much as 250 miles wide, that lie along the continental margin. From the earthquake epicenter in northern Prince William Sound, the deformation extends eastward 190 miles almost to long 142° and southwestward slightly more than 400 miles to about long 155°. It extends across the two zones from the chain of active volcanoes in the Aleutian Range and Wrangell Mountains probably to the Aleutian Trench axis.

Uplift that averages 6 feet over broad areas occurred mainly along the coast of the Gulf of Alaska, on the adjacent Continental Shelf, and probably on the continental slope. This uplift attained a measured maximum on land of 38 feet in a northwest-trending narrow belt less than 10 miles wide that is exposed on Montague Island in southwestern Prince William Sound. Two earthquake faults exposed on Montague Island are subsidiary northwest-dipping reverse faults along which the northwest blocks were relatively displaced a maximum of 26 feet, and both blocks were upthrown relative to sea level. From Montague Island, the faults and related belt of maximum uplift may extend southwestward on the Continental Shelf to the vicinity of the Kodiak group of islands. To the north and northwest of the zone of uplift, subsidence forms a broad asymmetrical downwarp centered over the Kodiak-Kenai-Chugach Mountains that averages 2½ feet and attains a measured maximum of 7½ feet along the southwest coast of the Kenai Peninsula. Maximum indicated uplift in the Alaska and Aleutian Ranges to the north of the zone of subsidence was 1½ feet. Re-triangulation over roughly 25,000 square miles of the deformed region in and around Prince William Sound shows that vertical movements there were accompanied by horizontal distortion, involving systematic shifts of about 64 feet in a relative seaward direction. Comparable horizontal movements are presumed to have affected those parts of the major zones of uplift and subsidence for which retriangulation data are unavailable.

Regional vertical deformation generated a train of destructive long-period seismic sea waves in the Gulf of Alaska as well as unique atmospheric and ionospheric disturbances that were recorded at points far distant from Alaska. Warping resulted in permanent tilt of larger lake basins and temporary reductions in discharge of some major rivers. Uplift and subsidence relative to sea level caused profound modifications in shoreline morphology with attendant catastrophic effects on the nearshore biota and costly damage to coastal installations. Systematic horizontal movements of the land relative to bodies of confined or semiconfined water may have caused unexplained short-period waves—some of which were highly destructive—observed during or immediately after the earthquake at certain coastal localities and in Kenai Lake. Porosity increases, probably related to horizontal displacements in the zone of subsidence, were reflected in lowered well-water levels and in losses of surface water.

The primary fault, or zone of faults, along which the earthquake occurred is not exposed at the surface on land. Focal mechanism studies, when considered in conjunction with the pattern of deformation and seismicity, suggest that it was a complex thrust fault (megathrust) dipping at a gentle angle beneath the continental margin from the vicinity of the Aleutian Trench. Movement on the megathrust was accompanied by subsidiary reverse faulting, and perhaps wrench faulting, within the upper plate. Aftershock distribution suggests movement on a segment of the megathrust, some 550–600 miles long and 110–180 miles wide, that underlies most of the major zone of uplift and the seaward part of the major zone of subsidence.

According to the postulated model, the observed and inferred tectonic displacements that accompanied the earthquake resulted primarily from (1) relative seaward displacement and uplift of the seaward part of the block by movement along the dipping megathrust and subsidiary faults that break through the upper plate to the surface, and (2) simultaneous elastic horizontal extension and vertical attenuation (subsidence) of the crustal slab behind the upper plate. Slight uplift inland from the major zones of deformation presumably was related to elastic strain changes resulting from the overthrusting; however, the data are insufficient to permit conclusions regarding its cause.

The belt of seismic activity and major zones of tectonic deformation associated with the 1964 earthquake, to a large extent, lie between and parallel to the Aleutian Volcanic Arc and the Aleutian Trench, and are probably genetically related to the arc. Geologic data indicate that the earthquake-related tectonic movements were but the most recent pulse in an episode of deformation that probably began in late Pliocene time and has continued intermittently to the present. Evidence for progressive coastal submergence in the deformed region for several centuries preceding the earthquake, in combination with transverse horizontal shortening indicated by the retriangulation data, suggests pre-earthquake strain directed at a gentle angle downward beneath the arc. The duration of strain accumulation in the epicentral region, as interpreted from the time interval during which the coastal submergence occurred, probably is 930–1,360 years.

INTRODUCTION

Among the most notable aspects of the 1964 Alaska earthquake was the great areal extent and amount of the tectonic movements that accompanied it. From the epicenter in northern Prince William Sound, the region affected by tectonic deformation parallels the trends of the Aleutian Volcanic Arc, the Aleutian Trench, and the Gulf of Alaska coast for about 600 miles (fig. 1). In south-central Alaska, where the northeastern end of the arc intersects the continent at an oblique angle, the pattern of deformation can be observed in an exceptionally complete profile extending more than 200 miles northward from the seaward edge of the Continental Shelf across the northeastern end of the volcanic arc. Within this region, tectonic displacements on land include absolute vertical movements ranging from as much as 38 feet of uplift to 7½ feet of subsidence, relative horizontal movements of about 64 feet, and dip-slip offset on reverse faults of as much as 26 feet. Furthermore, the available data indicate that these movements extended over a large segment of the adjacent offshore area where they may have been as large, or larger, than those measured on land.

This report substantially enlarges upon a preliminary summary and interpretation of the tectonic movements that accompanied the 1964 earthquake (Plafker, 1965). It presents the available data on the distribution and nature of the earthquake-related displacements and of the manifold, often disastrous, effects of these movements. Geologic, geodetic, and seismologic data pertinent to the tectonics that were available to the writer prior to

completion of this report in July 1967 are summarized. Implications of the data for the earthquake mechanism are reviewed, and a tentative qualitative model is outlined, which attempts to explain most of the observations.

ACKNOWLEDGMENTS

Field mapping of the vertical shoreline displacements and surface faults was accomplished by a party headed by the writer from mid-May through August 1964 and during 1 month in 1965. Geological Survey personnel included L. R. Mayo, J. E. Case, S. L. Robbins, and William Bastian during 1964, and Mayo and M. G. Bonilla during 1965. An especially large part of the fieldwork and data compilation were carried out by L. R. Mayo during both field seasons. G Dallas Hanna, marine biologist of the California Academy of Sciences, spent 3 weeks with the party in Prince William Sound in 1964, during which time he studied effects of the earthquake on the ecology of the intertidal fauna and flora and provided invaluable advice on the use of sessile marine organisms for determining changes in land level.

The U.S. Geological Survey research vessel, *Don J. Miller*, was used as a base of operations for work in Prince William Sound and Resurrection Bay during the 1964 season. Helicopters and fixed-wing aircraft were used during both field seasons for work along shorelines elsewhere. Outstanding logistical support of the field investigations was provided—often under difficult circumstances—by the crew of the *Don J. Miller*, which consisted of Capt. John Stacey and cook-seaman John

Muttart of the U.S. Geological Survey, and by bush pilots Jim Osborne, Glenn Wheeler, "Stinky" Myers, Al Cratty, Bob Leonard, Oren Hudson, and Bob Barnett.

R. L. Detterman, Reuben Kachadoorian, T. N. V. Karlstrom, G. W. Moore, and B. L. Reed, all of the Geological Survey, contributed data on changes in land level as determined by coastal residents of Cook Inlet and the Kodiak group of islands. Many residents of Alaska gave helpful information on earthquake effects, including tectonic changes, in about 150 interviews with the writer and on numerous form questionnaires.

Virtually all the seismologic, geodetic, and marine data incorporated in this report were obtained by the U.S. Coast and Geodetic Survey as part of their massive investigations of this major seismic event. I am especially indebted to the numerous individuals in the U.S. Coast and Geodetic Survey who freely made available unpublished data and have discussed their interpretations of these data with the writer on many occasions. Among these, special thanks for assistance are due S. T. Algermissen of the Seismology Division, W. D. Barbee, R. J. Malloy, and E. W. Richards of the Office of Oceanography, and C. A. Whitten, E. J. Parkin and J. B. Small of the Geodesy Division.

Postearthquake vertical aerial photographs were provided through the courtesy of Col. M. L. Fallwell, U.S. Army, Fort Richardson, and H. R. Cravat of the Photogrammetry Division, U.S. Coast and Geodetic Survey. R. A. Page, Jr., of the Lamont Geological Observatory furnished a computer plot of the larger magnitude

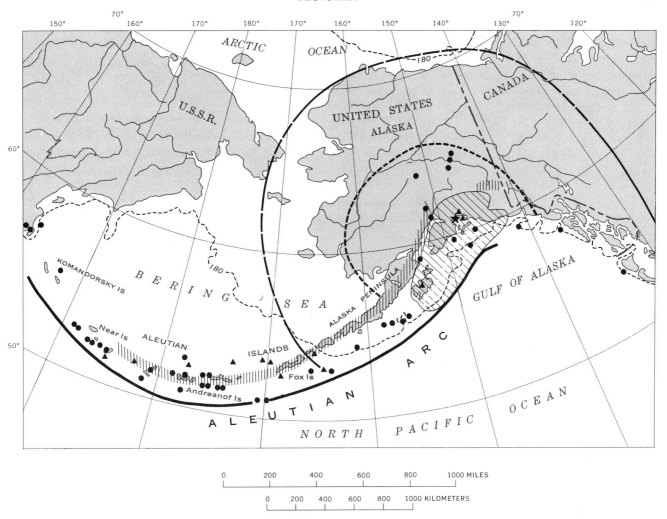

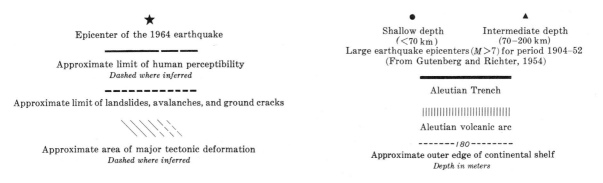

EXPLANATION

★

Epicenter of the 1964 earthquake

——————————

Approximate limit of human perceptibility
Dashed where inferred

— — — — — — — — —

Approximate limit of landslides, avalanches, and ground cracks

/ / / / / / /

Approximate area of major tectonic deformation
Dashed where inferred

●   ▲

Shallow depth   Intermediate depth
(<70 km)   (70–200 km)
Large earthquake epicenters ($M > 7$) for period 1904–52
(From Gutenberg and Richter, 1954)

Aleutian Trench

||||||||||||||||||||||||||||

Aleutian volcanic arc

- - - - - - -*180*- - - - - - -

Approximate outer edge of continental shelf
Depth in meters

1.—Map of Alaska and adjacent areas showing the location of the 1964 earthquake, the area affected by the earthquake, epicenters of previous major earthquakes, belts of active volcanism, and the Aleutian Trench.

aftershock epicenters. William Stauder, S. J., provided data on focal mechanisms of the earthquake and its aftershock sequence in advance of his own publication. D. F. Barnes and Roland von Huene of the Geological Survey made available unpublished results of submarine geophysical and geological studies carried out in south-central Alaska after the earthquake.

I am grateful to colleagues in the Geological Survey for very helpful discussions of the various tectonic aspects of the earthquake during which many of the ideas incorporated in this report were generated. The manuscript has been improved through critical reviews by E. B. Eckel and G. D. Eberlein and reviews of portions by D. F. Barnes, R. R. Coats, R. O. Burford, and C. B. Raleigh. Vector shifts for the readjustment of triangulation data were calculated by J. T. Minta and C. R. Lloyd of the Geological Survey's Topographic Division.

SEISMICITY

THE MAIN SHOCK

The 1964 earthquake was centered in a sparsely inhabited, mountainous area of northern Prince William Sound in south-central Alaska near the eastern end of the Aleutian Arc (fig. 1). Its epicenter was located by the U.S. Coast and Geodetic Survey (Wood, 1966, p. 62) at lat 61.06° N., long 147.44° W. and its origin time was at about 5:36 p.m., Friday, March 27, 1964, A.s.t. (03:36: 13.5, Saturday, March 28, 1964, G.m.t.). The hypocenter, or focus, could not be determined more closely than between 12 and 31 miles (20–50 km) in depth.

Magnitude of the earthquake, based upon surface-wave amplitudes (M_s) is estimated to have been about 8.4 (Pasadena seismograph station). Earthquake vibrations were felt over an area in excess of a million square miles in Alaska and adjacent parts of Canada (fig. 1), and they caused widespread damage throughout an area of about 50,000 square miles in south-central Alaska. The manifold effects of the shaking, which have been described in numerous reports are concisely summarized by Hansen and Eckel (1966) in the previous paper of this series of reports.

Rupture along a fault of considerable length is suggested from (1) the exceptionally long duration of strong ground motion, (2) the character of the radiated seismic surface and body waves, and (3) the extensive belt over which aftershocks were distributed.

Eyewitness accounts indicate that both the amplitude and duration of ground motion definitely tended to be largest in areas of relatively unconsolidated saturated deposits and least in areas of crystalline or metamorphic rocks. Within the immediate area affected by the earthquake, the only known instrumental records of the duration of shaking were made on several automatic recording charts in a steam powerplant built on bedrock at Whittier. On the clearest of these records, trace vibrations lasted for nearly 4 minutes. At other bedrock sites on Kodiak Island and on the Kenai Peninsula, where the motion was timed by observers with pocket watches or clocks, it was 2½–5 minutes. Anomalously s h o r t durations, ranging from only 15 seconds to 1½ minutes, were reported by residents at Seldovia and in two nearby localities in areas underlain by metamorphic rock at the southwestern tip of the Kenai Mountains (Plafker, Kachadoorian, Eckel, and Mayo, 1969).

According to most eyewitness accounts, the earthquake started without prior warning as a gentle rolling motion that lasted for a period of 20 seconds to 1 minute, shook hard for as much as 4 minutes, and then gradually subsided. There were no foreshocks perceptible to observers such as are known to immediately precede many great earthquakes. A few observers heard premonitory low rumbling sounds several seconds before the earthquake was felt. The ground motion was variously described as a rolling wavelike motion, a strong horizontal acceleration, or a hard jarring motion. A few individuals noted that the ground motion during the earthquake periodically eased up for a short period and then resumed with increased violence.

Reports of the directions of vibrations vary widely, and at some places, prevailing vibration directions reportedly changed during the earthquake. The majority of the reports indicate a tendency for ground oscillation to be grouped in the quadrants between northwest-southeast and northeast-southwest although it also was reported from all other quadrants. A westward propagation of vibrations between Anchorage and Kenai is indicated by the fact that power failure due to shaking in the Anchorage area caused an overload of the circuits at the interconnected Bernice Lake powerplant near Kenai, 53 miles farther from the epicenter, some 15–20 seconds before the plant superintendent felt the tremors.

On the basis of a study of seismic surface waves, Toksöz, Ben-Menahem, and Harkrider (1965, p. 154) determined that the rupture propagated S. 50° W. from the epicenter of the main shock for a distance of about 370 miles (600 km) at an average velocity of 3 km per sec. Furumoto (1967) found from analysis of Rayleigh waves recorded by the Kipapa, Hawaii, strain seismometer that the rupture more probably propagated S. 30 ± 5° W. for 500 miles (800 km) at this same velocity. A detailed study of *P*-phases by Wyss and Brune (1967) suggests that the rupture actually broke in a complex series of events at an average propagation velocity of 3.5 km per sec and that each event was characterized by more or less distinct high-amplitude bursts or events. Their data further indicate that, although the rupture propagated initially in various azimuthal directions, after an elapsed time of 44 seconds it continued only in a southwesterward direction.

THE AFTERSHOCKS

The epicenters and depth distributions of 598 aftershocks with Richter magnitudes equal to or greater than 4.4 recorded through December 31, 1964, are shown on figure 2. Of these, the largest shock had a magnitude of 6.7, six were larger than 6.0, 127 were between 5.0 and 6.0, and the remainder were less than 5.0 (U.S. Coast and Geodetic Survey, Preliminary Determination of Epicenter cards). During this same period of time, thousands of smaller aftershocks were also recorded.

The aftershock sequence diminished rapidly in frequency and intensity. All aftershocks with magnitudes larger than 6.0 recorded teleseismically by the U.S. Coast and Geodetic Survey, occurred within the first several hours and most of those that were strongly felt occurred within 3 weeks of the main event. Daily frequency of all shocks dropped rapidly from a high of about 120 the first day after the earthquake to 30 in 5 days, 15 in 10 days, and a steadily decreasing number thereafter (Jordan, Lander, and Black, 1965, p. 1324). As noted by Jordan and associates, the number of aftershocks at the beginning of the series may be much larger than indicated, because the first aftershocks are commonly masked by the train of large amplitude waves generated by the main shock and these waves may have a duration of several hours at distant stations.

The larger aftershocks ($M \geqq 4.4$) were concentrated mainly in an arcuate belt 600 miles long by as much as 200 miles wide that roughly parallels the continental margin. From the epicenter of the main shock it extends 425 miles southwestward to the vicinity of the Trinity Islands and about 175 miles eastward nearly to long 142° W. (fig. 2). Most of the largest aftershocks in this belt ($M \geqq 5.0$) were situated over that part of the belt lying seaward from the zero isobase between the major zones of uplift and subsidence. Smaller aftershocks ($M \geqq 4.4$) were spread over a larger area that extends inland from the zero isobase beneath the coastal mountains that border the Gulf of Alaska, and the smallest aftershocks ($M < 4.4$) were scattered over an even larger area. There was a distinct concentration of activity within the aftershock belt on the Continental Shelf at the southwestern end and in the area southeast of Prince William Sound

near the northeastern end. Burk (1965, p. 150) noted that the fairly sharp southwestern limit of the aftershock belt approximately coincides with a transverse structural boundary on the Alaska Peninsula, and he suggested the possibility that a transverse fault marks the southwestern margin of the crustal block involved in the 1964 earthquake. Only about 3 percent of the aftershocks with magnitudes of 4.4 or more were outside the main belt of activity along the continental margin. Their epicenters were widely scattered, mainly in the Shelikof Strait-Cook Inlet areas and on the ocean floor seaward from the Aleutian Trench axis. Significantly, none of the aftershocks were centered as far inland as the chain of active volcanoes in the Aleutian Range, southern Alaska Range, and the Wrangell Mountains. The possibility that they were directly related to vulcanism is thus ruled out.

Depth distribution of the aftershocks is less perfectly defined than their epicentral positions because of (1) inherent errors in the determination of hypocenters in areas of uncertain crustal structure and seismic velocity, and (2) the wide spacing of the seismographs on which the shocks were recorded. Algermissen (1965) found that hypocenters of aftershocks with magnitudes greater than 5.0 were at depths between 3 and 25 miles (5–40 km) and they average about 12 miles (20 km). Only 25 of the earthquakes with magnitudes of 4.4 or more were deeper than 22 miles (35 km), the deepest ones being less than 56 miles (90 km). According to Page (1967; also unpub. data), the microaftershocks—which had a spatial distribution similar to that of the aftershocks—were at depths of 22 miles (35 km) or less. He

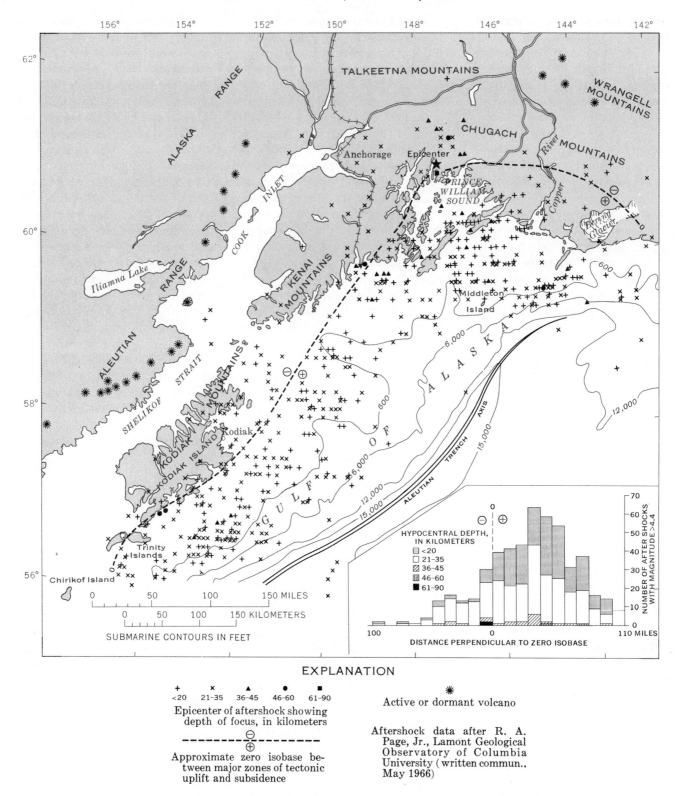

EXPLANATION

+	×	▲	●	■
<20	21–35	36–45	46–60	61–90

Epicenter of aftershock showing
depth of focus, in kilometers

⊖
– – – – – – – – – – – –
⊕

Approximate zero isobase between major zones of tectonic
uplift and subsidence

✳ Active or dormant volcano

Aftershock data after R. A.
Page, Jr., Lamont Geological
Observatory of Columbia
University (written commun.,
May 1966)

2.—Distribution and depth of aftershocks (4.4≦M≧6.7) from March 27, to December 31, 1964.

suggests that subcrustal earthquakes in and near the aftershock region may have represented the normal seismicity of the region. Aftershock hypocenters do not fall into any well-defined planar zone although there is a vague tendency towards a slight deepening of their lower limit beneath the continent. The proportion of hypocenters deeper than 12 miles relative to those shallower than 12 miles also shows an increase in the same direction (fig. 2).

Large earthquakes at shallow and intermediate depths are thought by most geologists and geophysicists to result from sudden rupture, or faulting, in strained rocks. Aftershocks which follow large earthquakes presumably represent continuous adjustments of the strained volume of rock, or focal region, within which faulting occurred (Benioff, 1951). According to this model, therefore, faulting associated with the 1964 earthquake was largely confined to the part of the continental margin extending roughly 150–200 miles northward from the axis of the Aleutian Trench, it was limited in depth to the crust, or perhaps the uppermost part of the mantle, and its lower limit may deepen slightly beneath the arc.

FOCAL MECHANISM STUDIES

Mechanism studies of the main shock, of a number of larger aftershocks, and of one preshock that occurred about 7 weeks prior to the earthquake provide data relevant to the fault orientation and sense of displacement at the earthquake foci. Body-wave solutions define a pair of orthogonal planes at the focus, one of which presumably contains the active fault surface. Inherent in the focal mechanism studies are the basic assumptions of an elastic-rebound

source and initial displacements at the earthquake foci that approximately reflect the regional stress field.

Focal mechanism studies of P-waves for the main shock yield one well-defined nodal plane that strikes between N. 61° and 66° E. and dips 82°–85° SE. (Stauder and Bollinger, 1966. Algermissen, 1965; written commun., March 19, 1965). The alternative low-angle plane is restricted by the data to a plane that dips towards the northwest; Algermissen's solution suggests an inclination of about 8°. If the well-defined nodal plane is regarded as the fault plane, its strike was N. 61°–66° E. and the motion was predominantly dip-slip on a steep reverse fault with the southeast side relatively upthrown. Alternatively, if the steep nodal plane is considered to be normal to the motion, the fault would be a northwest-dipping thrust. Focal mechanism studies of the main shock alone cannot distinguish which of these two planes is the fault plane. Surface-wave studies that define the direction of rupture may permit distinction between the fault and auxiliary planes in cases where the strikes of the two planes differ significantly. However, as noted by Savage and Hastie (1966, p. 4900), surface waves do not permit a unique solution for the 1964 earthquake because the direction of rupture propagation is essentially the same for either plane.

Stauder and Bollinger (1966) determined focal mechanisms, based on combined P-wave first-motion and S-wave polarization data, for a preshock and 25 aftershocks in the Kodiak Island and Prince William Sound areas. Most of these solutions have one near-vertical nodal plane that resembles the well-defined nodal plane for the main shock; the other dips

5°–15° to the northwest or north. Strike of the steep plane is between N. 50° and 72° E. to the southwest of Prince William Sound; it is variable in the Prince William Sound area and nearly east-west to the east of the sound. This systematic variation in orientation of the steep nodal plane tends to follow a change in trend of tectonic features along the coastal belt. Four aftershock solutions in the Prince William Sound area and one located seaward from the Aleutian Trench off Kodiak Island, however, are anomalous in that they do not correspond to this general pattern.

The preshock and all the aftershock fault-plane solutions are subject to the same ambiguity of interpretation as the main shock. Thus, on the basis of all the individual solutions (except for the five apparently anomalous ones) the motion at the source of the earthquake and the related pre- and aftershocks may be (1) almost entirely dip-slip on a steeply dipping reverse fault along which the seaward side is relatively upthrown or (2) dip-slip on a northward-dipping thrust fault along which the landward block overrides the seaward block in an average S. 25° E. direction to the southwest of Prince William Sound and in a S. 10°–15° W. direction to the east of Prince William Sound (Stauder and Bollinger, 1966, p. 5295). In considering the solutions in relation to one another, Stauder and Bollinger observe that in the first alternative the faulting may consist of en echelon segments that follow a sinuous path roughly paralleling the curving trend of both the aftershock belt and the zero isobase between the major zones of earthquake-related vertical tectonic deformation (fig. 2). In the second alternative the thrust plane has a dip of less than 14° beneath the continent, displacement of the upper plate is relatively seaward, and the direction of motion is roughly normal to the trend of the aftershock belt and the zones of tectonic deformation.

The steep plane in solutions of the main shock, the preshock, and most aftershocks differs in strike from the tectonic trends of the region, the orientation of the earthquake focal region, and the pattern of vertical displacements associated with the earthquake.

These differences suggest to Stauder and Bollinger (1966, p. 5293–5294) that the steep plane corresponds to the auxiliary plane rather than the fault plane. They also interpret the spatial distribution of foci for which mechanism studies were made and the nature of the inferred motions as being more compatible with thrusting on the shallowly dipping plane than to movement on the steep plane.

Solutions for the main shock and most of the other shocks sug-

gest a maximum-stress axis at the foci of these earthquakes oriented approximately normal, or at a small oblique angle, to major structural elements within the focal region. Within the limitations of the data, this orientation is in reasonably good agreement with geodetic and geologic data cited in subsequent sections (p. I 49) that suggest dominantly tangential compressive stress on land within the region affected by tectonic movements during the earthquake.

DEFORMATION

Crustal deformation, including both vertical and horizontal movements, associated with the 1964 Alaska earthquake was more extensive than any known to have been related to a single tectonic event. Vertical movements occurred over an arcuate region that roughly parallels the continental margin for almost 600 miles from the southwestern tip of the Kodiak group of islands northeastward through Prince William Sound and thence eastward to about long 142° W. (fig. 3). In a northwest to southeast direction, the deformation extends at least 200 miles from the west shore of Cook Inlet to Middleton Island at the seaward edge of the Continental Shelf. In addition, crustal warping appears to extend inland as far as the Alaska Range and it may extend seaward to the axis of the Aleutian Trench.

Observable tectonic deformation involved (1) regional crustal warping, including both uplift and subsidence relative to sea level, in broad zones that roughly parallel the trend of the continental margin, (2) systematic regional horizontal extension and shortening in

a direction approximately transverse to that of the zones of warping, (3) displacement across longitudinal reverse faults exposed on land and on the sea floor, and (4) possible displacement on at least one wrench fault. Evidence for these various movements, their manifold effects, and their tectonic significance are discussed below.

REGIONAL VERTICAL DISPLACEMENTS

Notable tectonic changes in land level during the 1964 earthquake occurred over an area of at least 70,000 square miles, and probably more than 110,000 square miles, of south-central Alaska. The areal distribution and approximate amount of the vertical displacements are summarized on figure 3. Plates 1 and 2 show data points where quantitative measurements of vertical displacement were made, as well as the method used and year of measurement. Also shown on the figure and plates are isobase contours, or lines of equal vertical displacement based on these data, and the approximate axes of the major upwarped and downwarped zones. The deforma-

tion includes two broad major zones of warping, each about 600 miles long and as much as 130 miles wide. The seaward zone is one of uplift that includes a fringe of coast along the Gulf of Alaska, the adjacent Continental Shelf, and perhaps the continental slope; it is bordered to the northwest and west by a zone of subsidence. Slight uplift also occurred in at least three areas extending inland from the major zone of subsidence as far northward as the Alaska Range.

METHODS OF MEASUREMENT

Quantitative information on vertical displacements along the coast (pls. 1, 2) comes mainly from (1) comparison of pre- and post-earthquake tide gage readings, (2) the position of the upper growth limit of certain sessile intertidal organisms relative to sea level, (3) differences in the pre- and post-earthquake positions of the upper growth limits of sessile intertidal organisms or the lower growth limit of terrestrial vegetation, (4) differences in the heights of pre- and postearthquake storm beaches, (5) estimates or measurements of changes in the position of shoreline

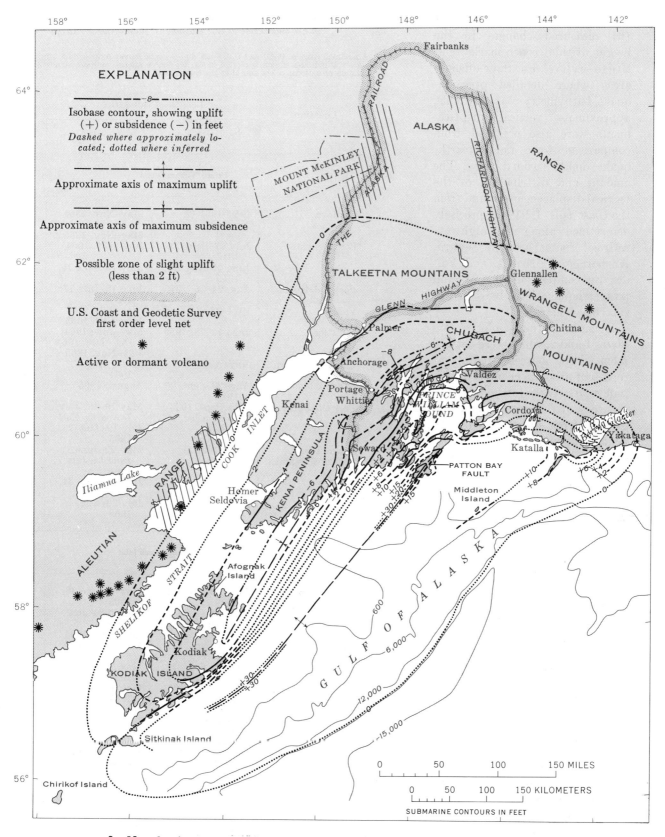

3.—Map showing the distribution of tectonic uplift and subsidence in south-central Alaska.

markers by local residents, and (6) measured changes in the height of tidal bench marks relative to sea level. For those offshore areas where detailed preearthquake bathymetry was available, approximate vertical displacements were also obtained from comparison of pre- and postearthquake depth s o u n d i n g s. The amount and distribution of the vertical displacements inland from the coast (pls. 1, 2) was precisely determined along the highway-railroad routes between Seward, Anchorage, Fairbanks, and Valdez by comparison of pre- and postearthquake level lines tied to tidal bench marks.

Isobase contours plotted on plates 1 and 2, which were derived from all the sources listed above, represent absolute changes in altitude related to the earthquake. The accuracy of the contouring varies greatly from place to place depending upon the type and amount of data, but, because it is essentially an averaging process, the contouring tends to be most accurate in areas where many data points are available, and least accurate in areas where data are sparse. In general, contours shown as solid or dashed lines are estimated to be accurate at least to within ±1 contour interval; at most places they are probably accurate to within half an interval.

The various techniques used for determining vertical displacement, estimates of their relative precision, and sources of data are outlined below.

COMPARISON OF PRE- AND POSTEARTHQUAKE TIDE-GAGE READINGS

The directions and relative amounts of vertical displacement were determined from coupled pre- and postearthquake tide-gage readings made by the U.S. Coast and Geodetic Survey at two

TABLE 1.—*Land-level changes based on comparison of pre- and postearthquake tide series at tide stations in south-central Alaska*

[After Small (1966, p. 19-22) and U.S. Coast and Geodetic Survey (unpub. data, April 22, 1966). Asterisk indicates station is plotted in fig. 10; double asterisk indicates standard tide-gage station operational before and after the earthquake]

Location	Length of tide series		Land movement (feet)
	Preearthquake	Postearthquake	
Prince William Sound			
*Cordova_____	1950–1951 (2 years)	May–Nov. 1964	+6. 2
*Port Gravina_____	July 17–Sept. 26, 1913	May–Nov. 1965	+6. 2
		July 3–31, 1964	+4. 5
Port Fidalgo_____	June 15–Aug. 19, 1915	May 16–June 16, 1965	+4. 2
	Aug. 24–26, 1915	June 18–July 17, 1965	+2. 4
Valdez_____	1924–26 (3 years)	May–July 1964	−. 9
		July–Nov. 1965	[1] −3. 5
*Whittier_____	June 12–29, 1956	May–June 1964; Oct.–Dec. 1964	−5. 4
		July–Nov. 1965	[1] −5. 7
*Chenega Island___	July–Aug. 1957	July 7–Aug. 4, 1964	+4. 8
Green Island_____	Aug. 23–Sept. 20, 1911	August, 1965	+6. 6
*Port Chalmers____	July–Sept. 1933 (3 months)	May 19–30; July 7–Aug. 6, 1964	+10. 5
		July 19–Aug. 23, 1965	+10. 5
*Sawmill Bay, Evans Island__	May, 1927 (1 month)	May 20–June 1; June 14–July 7, 1964	+7. 2
		July 29–Aug. 31, 1965	+7. 2
Hogg Bay_____	June 15–July 21, 1927	July 20–Aug. 16, 1965	+5. 8
Kenai Peninsula and Cook Inlet			
Day Harbor_____	May 20–July 13, 1928	May 7–June 30, 1965	−. 5
**Seward_____	1926–38 (13 years)	June 1964–Jan. 1965	−3. 6
		Jan.–Sept. 1965	−3. 6
Aialik Bay_____	July 6–Sept. 21, 1912	May–June 1965	−4. 5
*Two Arm Bay____	July 20–Sept. 18, 1928	May 14–June 30, 1965	−5. 4
Chance Cove_____	May 14–July 25, 1930	May 15–June 30, 1965	−6. 6
Shelter Cove_____	June–Aug. 1927 (3 months)	July 1965	−5. 4
*Port Dick_____	Aug. 1–Sept. 26, 1930	May 21–June 30, 1965	−6. 2
**Homer_____	Oct. 3–Nov. 17, 1962	June–Dec. 1964; Sept.–Nov. 1965	−5. 4
			[1] −5. 8
*Port Chatham____		May 22–June 4, 1965	−4. 6
*Seldovia_____	April 30–Oct. 8, 1908	June–Oct. 1964	−3. 9
	May 8–Sept. 29, 1910	April–July 1965	−3. 8
Nikiski_____		June 18–July 31, 1964	−. 9

See footnote at end of table.

TABLE 1.—*Land-level changes based on comparsion of pre- and postearthquake tide series at tide stations in south-central Alaska*—Continued

Location	Length of tide series		Land move-ment (feet)
	Preearthquake	Postearthquake	
Kenai Peninsula and Cook Inlet—Continued			
Anchorage	June–Sept. 1910; June–Oct., Dec. 1922; May–Nov. 1923; May–Sept. 1924; May–Oct. 1925	May–Oct. 1964	−2. 6
		April–Oct. 1965	−2. 3
Kodiak group of islands			
Carry Inlet	July 1931	July 8–Aug. 7, 1965	−3. 2
Redfox Bay	July–Aug. 1926	July 1–Aug. 8, 1965	−3. 4
*Tonki Bay	Aug. 23–31, 1932	July 10–Aug. 7, 1965	−5. 2
Nachalni Island	July 30–Sept. 8, 1941	June 14–July 10, 1965	−3. 9
Dolphin Point	Sept. 10–Oct. 1, 1941	June 7–July 8, 1965	−2. 9
St. Paul Harbor		June–Oct. 1964	−5. 5
		May–Nov. 1965	−5. 0
*Ugak Bay	August 1932	June 12–July 10, 1965	−4. 2
Port Hobron	June 1–Sept. 19, 1928	July 26–Aug. 27, 1965	−. 7
Jap Bay	July 1931	July 28–Aug. 24, 1965	. 0
*Lazy Bay	May 16–Sept. 29, 1929	June 11–30, July 1–Aug. 14, 1964	−. 4
	June 1–Sept. 30, 1930	July 28–Aug. 15, Aug. 20–24, 1965	−. 2
*Larsen Bay	Aug. 19–22, 1929	June 13–Aug. 31, 1964	−2. 5
		July 18–Aug. 17, 1965	−2. 4
Uyak Bay	July 14–30, 1908	July 22–Aug. 17, 1965	−1. 9
*Port O'Brien	June 22–July 30, 1929	July Aug. 1964	−3. 6
		June 8–July 19, 1965	−3. 6
**Women's Bay	1950–59 (10 years)	April–July 1964	−5. 6
Alaska Peninsula			
**Kukak Bay	July–Aug. 1949 (2 months)	July 17–Aug. 16, 1965	−. 5

[1] Change between 1964 and 1965 possibly due to surficial compaction.

operative standard stations, and 34 temporary stations within the region affected by tectonic movements during the earthquake (table 1). Such measurements were made at localities where a series of pre-earthquake tidal observations had been made and where tidal bench marks had been established that were not destroyed during or before the earthquake.

The Seward and Womens Bay (Kodiak) stations were equipped with standard automatic tide gages; readings could therefore be compared for series taken immediately before and after the earthquake. These determinations of vertical displacement are probably accurate to within a few tenths of a foot. The only other standard station in the region, at Homer Spit in Kachemak Bay, could not be used directly to measure vertical tectonic displacement because it was inoperative at the time of the earthquake, and the tectonic subsidence was augmented by pronounced surficial settlement of the unconsolidated deposits that made up the spit. Because the amount of surficial settling was known from level lines to areas of relatively firm ground (Waller, 1966a, p. D13), net tectonic subsidence could be obtained by subtracting the surficial effect from total subsidence relative to sea level at the gage. This difference amounted to about 2.9 feet.

Accuracy of the changes determined at the temporary stations depends largely on the length of the preearthquake series of observations, some of which were as short as 4 days, and also on the time interval between the pre- and postearthquake series, which at one station is 54 years and at many is more than 30 years (table 1). Positions of the preearthquake tidal datum planes at these stations may not have been precisely determined originally, and (or) they may have changed from their original values because of relative land-level changes in the time interval between tide observations. At most of the temporary stations such errors are believed to be small because, where other sources of data such as estimates by local residents or measured differences between pre- and postearthquake shoreline features are available in the immediate vicinity, they tend to agree with the tide data within 0.5 foot or less. An exception is the 7.0-foot uplift of the Sawmill Bay station on Evans Island, Prince William Sound, derived from the tidal observations(table 1). It is about 2 feet too low when compared with (1) the 9.0-foot estimated uplift of shoreline features whose preearthquake heights were precisely known to residents of the area and (2) the 8.9 feet of uplift indicated by differences in the pre- and postearthquake upper growth limit of barnacles (pl. 2). The preearthquake tidal observations at this particular station consist of a 1-month series taken in 1927, 37 years before the postearthquake series with which it was compared. Therefore, either about 2 feet of uplift occurred in the area during the 37 years prior to the earthquake or the tidal measurements are in error. Because Sawmill Bay had been continuously inhabited during this time interval and because there was no indication of preearthquake changes in land level, it appears probable that the latter alternative is the correct one.

THE UPPER GROWTH LIMIT OF SESSILE INTERTIDAL ORGANISMS RELATIVE TO SEA LEVEL

Vertical displacements in coastal areas were determined mainly from more than 800 measurements of the upper growth limits of intertidal sessile marine organisms relative to sea level along the long, intricately embayed rocky coast. In Prince William Sound and Resurrection Bay, where we used outboard-motor-powered skiffs for studying these changes during 1964, measurements were made continuously along the shore at spacings of about 1–5 miles except in those places where cliffs, heavy surf, or floe ice in fiords prevented

boat landings or where the upper growth limits were not well-defined. During both the 1964 and 1965 seasons, measurements of vertical displacement were also made at localities shown on plates 1 and 2 that were accessible by light plane or helicopter along the ocean coast, on the offshore islands, and around the shores of the Kodiak group of islands.

In measuring land-level change from the displacement of sessile marine organisms relative to sea level, the zonation of plants and animals between tide marks was used—a zonation that has long been recognized by marine ecologists. The intertidal zone along the predominantly steep and rocky coastline of south-central Alaska is inhabited by certain species of organisms—notably barnacles, mussels, and algae—whose vertical growth limits are usually well defined (pl. 3A, facing p. I 16; fig. 4). The zonation of intertidal organisms in the Prince William Sound region was studied in detail by a party headed by G Dallas Hanna of the California Academy of Sciences in 1965. To the writer's knowledge, there were no published preearthquake data on the intertidal ecology for any part of the Gulf of Alaska coast.

In particular, the common acorn barnacle, *Balanus balanoides* (Linnaeus), and closely similar forms such as *B. glandula* are widely distributed on rocky shores and form a conspicuous band with a sharply defined, readily recognizable upper limit (figs. 5–7) The common olive-green rockweed (*Fucus distichus*), which has an upper growth limit near that of the barnacles, served as a useful datum for measuring land-level changes along shores where barnacles were absent or poorly developed (pl. 3B, facing p. I14). The upper limit of this zone, re-

ferred to as the "barnacle line," corresponds roughly to the top of the Balanoid or Midlittoral Zone of Stephenson and Stephenson (1949); to Zone 2, the High Tide Region, or the Upper Horizon of Ricketts and Calvin (1962); and the Upper Intertidal Zone of Rigg and Miller (1949). The barnacle line usually, but not always, approximates the lower growth limit of the dark-gray-to-black encrusting lichen (*Verrucaria*) which commonly forms a black band in the splash zone immediately above the barnacles and *Fucus* (pl. 3A, facing p. I16; fig. 4).

The upper limit of all intertidal organisms depends mainly on the ability of immature individuals to survive prolonged exposure to air and on the tidal characteristics at any given locality (Kaye, 1964, p. 591–592). In referring to the survival ability of barnacles, Kaye has termed this maximum exposure interval the "lethal limit." He found experimentally that it was close to 150 hours for yearling barnacles and ranged to an absolute maximum of 192 hours for mature barnacles. *Fucus*, which has a nearly identical upper growth range, must have approximately the same "lethal limit." To a lesser extent the upper growth limit of barnacles and *Fucus* depends upon a number of other factors which, in parts of Prince William Sound, locally cause the barnacle line to deviate as much as 0.6 foot from its average height at any given locality. Wave action during the lowest annual neap tides and protection from desiccation by shady locations tend to elevate the upper growth limit; exposure to fresh water near large streams or tidewater glaciers tends to depress it. Annual variations in sea level may cause further slight upward or downward shifts of the organisms' upper growth limits.

4.—Characteristic parallel bands formed by zoned intertidal marine organisms along uplifted west shore of Knight Island, Prince William Sound. Encrusting lichens form the upper dark band and brown laminarians form the lower one; light-colored barnacle zone is between the two. Photograph taken at about 2-foot tide stage, May 20, 1964.

5.—Measuring height of the barnacle line at Port Bainbridge in an area of the Kenai Peninsula uplifted 5.7 feet. Photograph taken at 4.4-foot tide stage, June 21, 1964.

6.—Barnacle line clearly marked by upper limit of light-gray barnacles and desiccated rockweed in dark patches and by the lower growth limit of dark-gray encrusting lichens of the splash zone. Uplift of 3.2 feet in Whale Bay, western Prince William Sound. Photograph taken at 3.0-foot tide stage, June 22, 1964.

7.—Barnacle line on hull of S.S. *Coldbrook*, Middleton Island. The upper growth limit of the dark band of barnacles on this vertical surface is clearly defined and at a uniform level, even though it is in a locality that was exposed to open-coast surf conditions prior to the earthquake. Indicated uplift is 11.7 feet. Photograph taken at 6.5-foot tide stage, July 26, 1965.

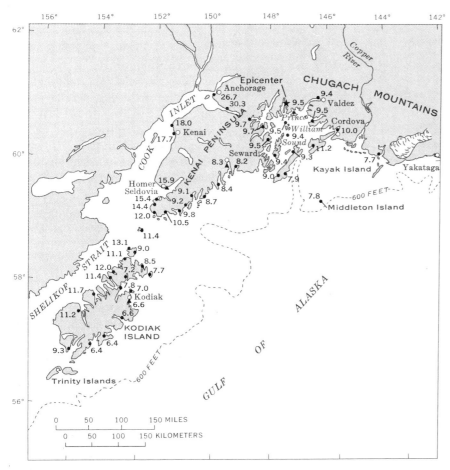

8.—Variations of mean tide range in areas of south-central Alaska where tide levels were used as a datum in measuring vertical displacement of the coast. Triangles show locations of permanent tide gages prior to the earthquake. Data from U.S. Coast and Geodetic Survey (1964).

Specific data on the normal upper growth limit of barnacles and *Fucus* relative to tide levels were unavailable for the part of coastal south-central Alaska that was affected by vertical tectonic displacements associated with the earthquake at the time this study was made. However, elsewhere on the Pacific Coast of North America and in other areas of the world the height of the barnacle line roughly approximates annual mean high water along shores with a small or moderate tidal range. In the region where measurements of vertical displacements were made during this study, tidal range, and hence the height of the barnacle line, differs from place to place along the coast. For exam-

ple, the mean tide range (that is the difference in height between mean high and mean low water) varies from a minimum of 6.4 feet along the ocean coast of the Kodiak group of islands to a maximum of 15.9 feet at Homer near the entrance to Cook Inlet (fig. 8). Even higher tides—as high as 30.3 feet—prevail within Cook Inlet. However, the exceptionally large tidal range, in combination with a general lack of stable rocky shores and an increasingly impoverished marine fauna toward the head of the inlet precluded use of marine organisms for measuring vertical displacement.

On figure 9 are shown the variations in the 1964 positions of six of the important sea-level datum

planes corresponding to mean tide ranges of 6.4 feet to 15.9 feet in south-central Alaska.[1] Kaye (1964) has reviewed the definition of these tidal planes, the way in which they are derived from tide-gage records, and the control they exert on the zonation of intertidal organisms.

Field procedure for determining land-level changes by the barnacle-line method was to measure the height of the upper limit of barnacle or *Fucus* growth above or below water level at any stage of tide. On smooth steep rocky slopes sheltered from heavy surf, this line is sharply defined and can be readily determined to within 0.2 foot or less. On sloping shores or shores exposed to heavy surf it tends to be less regular, although even under such conditions it generally can be determined with confidence to within 0.5 foot. At most places where the barnacle line was above water, its height was measured with a hand level or surveyor's level and stadia rod. Where the barnacle line was visible under water, its depth below the surface was measured directly with the stadia rod.

Stage of tide at the time of measurement was then determined from the U.S. Coast and Geodetic Survey table of predicted tides for

[1] Extreme high and low water are the highest and lowest predicted annual tides; the extreme high-water line is also the approximate lower limit for growth of terrestrial vegetation along shores sheltered from wave splash. Because tides in south-central Alaska are of the semidiurnal type, the levels of the two daily high and low tides differ, varying between a maximum (spring tides) and a minimum (neap tides), depending on the interactions of the tide-producing forces. Thus, mean high water (MHW) and mean low water (MLW) are the average heights of all high and low tides within the period of measurement. Mean lower low water (MLLW), the mean of the spring tides, is the tidal datum plane commonly used as the zero datum by the U.S. Coast and Geodetic Survey. Mean tide level (MTL) is the exact midpoint of the range MHW–MLW. It differs by a few tenths of a foot from mean sea level, because the average of all hourly tide readings over a given period, because the tidal curve is not a simple sine curve, but rather is compounded of a number of simple sine curves, some of which have fixed phase relationships with respect to each other (Marmer, 1951, p. 70).

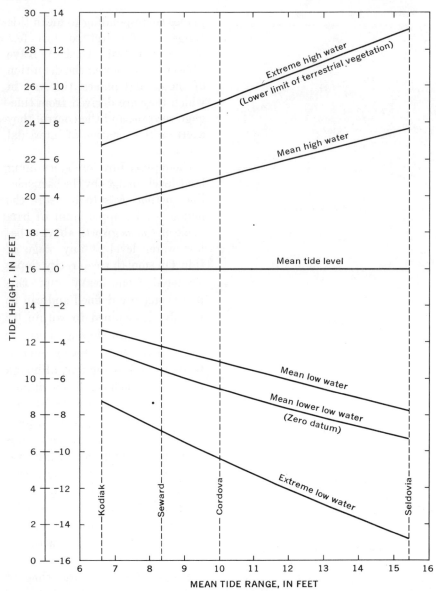

9.—Tidal parameters in areas of south-central Alaska where tide levels were used as a datum in measuring vertical displacement of the coast. Data from U.S. Coast and Geodetic Survey (1964).

the closest reference station, and, finally, the position of the barnacle line relative to the mean lower low water (MLLW) datum was calculated. For measurements made close to the 16 U.S. Coast and Geodetic Survey tide gages that were installed in the area immediately following the earthquake, we later made corrections to the actual, rather than the predicted, tides. During the period of field-work, it was found that few tides deviated by as much as 1.5 feet

from predictions; most were within a few tenths of a foot of predicted values.

Differences in the height of the barnacle line in local areas of similar tide range provided a powerful tool for determining relative changes in land level along the coast even where the absolute change was not known. Absolute uplift or subsidence relative to sea level at any given locality was taken as the difference in height between the measured elevation of

the barnacle line and the "normal" preearthquake upper growth limit for the barnacles and *Fucus* as indicated in figure 10.

The "normal" preearthquake upper growth limit of barnacles and *Fucus* relative to MLLW was determined empirically at the 17 localities listed on figure 10 where the amount of vertical displacement was known from Coast and Geodetic Survey tide gage readings. Its position at these localities was taken as the measured height relative to MLLW corrected for the amount of tectonic uplift or subsidence indicated by the tide-gage readings. On figure 10 these heights are plotted against the mean tide range at the station. The least-square curve through these points represents the average preearthquake height of the barnacle line for mean tides ranging from 6.4 to 15.9 feet in the study area. The curve suggests that the preearthquake barnacle line was close to mean high water for the lowest mean tides and that it lowered progressively relative to MHW with an increase in mean tide range. For the lower tides of 6.4–10.0 feet which prevail along most of the Gulf of Alaska and in Prince William Sound, it ranged from MHW to 0.6 foot below MHW level; for the higher mean tides of as much as 15.4 feet at Seldovia in lower Cook Inlet and Shelikof Strait, the barnacle line dropped to 1.7 feet below MHW.

The derived curve for the approximate height of the barnacle line is only a crude approximation to the actual position of the barnacle line. In addition to uncertainties in measurement of the position of the postearthquake barnacle line relative to sea level, it incorporates inherent errors in the determination of land-level change at the temporary tide-gage stations as discussed previously (p. I 11).

EFFECTS OF THE EARTHQUAKE ON INTERTIDAL ORGANISMS

A (right).—Sharply zoned intertidal marine organisms along west shore of Port Bainbridge. The barnacle line, uplifted 6.1 feet, is at the contact between the upper black band of encrusting lichens and the light-gray band of barnacles. Greenish material in the lower part of the rock face is marine algae; its upper limit marks the approximate position of the postearthquake barnacle line. Photograph taken at 3.1-foot tide stage, June 18, 1964.

This photograph is printed in color in the USGS original.

B (left).—Barnacle line defined by upper growth limit of olive-brown rockweed and lower limit of dark-gray encrusting lichens. Shoreline shown (Malina Bay, Afognak Island) subsided about 3 feet during the earthquake. Photograph taken at 6.5-foot tide stage, July 20, 1964.

This photograph is printed in color in the USGS original.

C (right).—Postearthquake yearling barnacles (light gray) among preearthquake barnacles (yellow). Within 4 months after the earthquake the new crop of barnacles had base diameters of as much as 0.3 inch. Large divisions in upper scale are inches. Photograph taken August 2, 1964.

This photograph is printed in color in the USGS original.

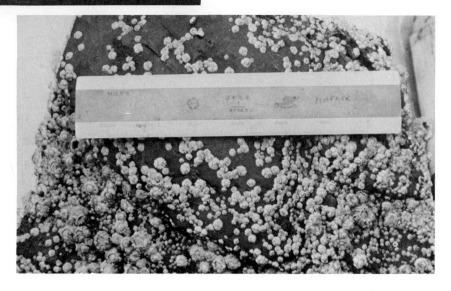

EFFECTS OF THE EARTHQUAKE ON SHORELINE FEATURES

A.—Living (olive-green) and desiccated (dark-brown) *Fucus* along the shore of Glacier Island, Prince William Sound. The top of the band of desiccated algae was near the preearthquake barnacle line and the top of the band of living algae was near the postearthquake barnacle line. The 3.0-foot difference between their elevations was a measure of the tectonic uplift in this area. Photograph taken at 8.8-foot tide stage, June 13, 1964.

This photograph is printed in color in the USGS original.

B.—Extensive area of brown terrestrial vegetation at Kiliuda Bay, Kodiak Island, killed by salt-water immersion after about 4 feet of tectonic subsidence and an unknown amount of surficial subsidence. Dikelike gray ridge of beach gravel was built up in adjustment to the new higher base level. The area behind this beach ridge may eventually become a shallow lagoon. Photograph taken July 17, 1964.

This photograph is printed in color in the USGS original.

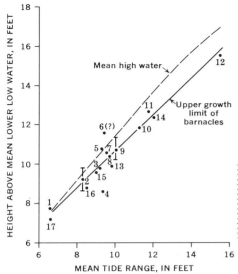

Data Points

1. Womens Bay, Kodiak Island
2. Seward, Kenai Peninsula (average of 2 measurements, range indicated by vertical bar)
3. Chenega Island, Prince William Sound
4. Lazy Bay, Kodiak Island
5. Port Chalmers, Montague Island, Prince William Sound
6. Sawmill Bay, Evans Island, Prince William Sound
7. Port Gravina, Prince William Sound
8. Whittier, Prince William Sound
9. Cordova, Prince William Sound (average of 28 measurements; range indicated by vertical bar)
10. Larsen Bay, Kodiak Island
11. Port O'Brien, Kodiak Island
12. Seldovia, Kenai Peninsula
13. Port Dick, Kenai Peninsula
14. Port Chatham, Kenai Peninsula
15. Two Arm Bay, Kenai Peninsula
16. Tonki Bay, Afognak Island
17. Ugak Bay, Kodiak Island

10.—Height of upper growth limit of barnacles above mean lower low water for mean tide ranges of 6.4–15.9 feet in south-central Alaska. The least-square curve for the upper growth limit of barnacles is based on measurements made at 17 stations (dots) where the vertical displacement was determined independently by the U.S. Coast and Geodetic Survey (Small, 1966) from tide-gage observations. Standard deviation is 0.627 foot.

However, the validity of using the empirically determined barnacle line was generally confirmed by our observations in late 1964 and in 1965 that the upper growth limits of new postearthquake barnacles and *Fucus* were generally within about ±1 foot of this line.

The precision of the land-level changes determined by the barnacle-line method varies within wide limits because of the numerous variables involved in making the measurements and the assumptions inherent in the presumed preearthquake position of the barnacle line. The measurements are generally within 1 foot of changes estimated by local residents or found by means of other techniques. Under the least favorable combination of circumstances, such as along segments of the coast exposed to heavy surf or swells or in areas of high and erratic tides in Cook Inlet and Shelikof Strait, measurements may locally be in error by as much as 2½ feet. In such areas, however, more reliance was placed on changes indicated

by those techniques that do not require use of tide level as a datum.

DIFFERENCES IN THE EXTREME PRE- AND POSTEARTHQUAKE GROWTH LIMITS OF SESSILE INTERTIDAL ORGANISMS AND TERRESTRIAL VEGETATION

Throughout the region affected by tectonic land-level movements, postearthquake changes in the upper growth limit of barnacles and *Fucus* or in the lower growth limit of terrestrial vegetation provided direct indications of the direction and approximate amount of movement. Thus, along uplifted shores a band of dead barnacles, *Fucus*, and other sessile organisms developed within 2 months after the earthquake. The height of this band reflected the amount of uplift (pl. 4A). By July of 1964 a new postearthquake line of young barnacles, and in some places *Fucus*, was well established on most shores. The height of this line above or below the preearthquake line furnished a direct measure of the amount of uplift or subsidence (pl. 3C; fig. 11). Similarly, at many places, the amount

of subsidence could be clearly determined within 2 months after the earthquake from certain ephemeral features such as the elevation to which the highest spring tides inundated terrestrial vegetation (fig. 12). By the 1965 field season, land plants had become sufficiently well established over much of the uplifted shore that the approximate amount of uplift could be determined from differences in the pre- and postearthquake lower growth limits (fig. 13). This method was particularly useful in areas of uplift such as Middleton Island where, for some unknown reason, barnacles and *Fucus* had not become established in the intertidal zone even a year after the earthquake.

Land-level changes determined from differences in pre- and postearthquake positions of the barnacle line or of the lower limits of terrestrial vegetation provide reasonably precise values for the tectonic movements where the postearthquake growth limits have had time to reach a position in equilibrium with the local tides and where the earthquake-related displacements have not caused significant changes in the tidal characteristics. Such measurements are thought to represent the actual vertical change at least to within 1.0 foot, and probably to within 0.5 foot in most places.

DIFFERENCES IN THE HEIGHTS OF PRE- AND POSTEARTHQUAKE STORM BEACHES

Along uplifted sandy shores on Montague Island in Prince William Sound and along the linear stretch of coast east of Kayak Island, the amount of uplift could be approximated in 1965 from the relative positions of pre- and postearthquake storm beaches (fig. 14). The accuracy of such measurements is difficult to evaluate, although where they could be

11.—Conspicuous white band of postearthquake barnacles along the shore of Kizhuyak Bay, Kodiak Island. The difference in elevation between the upper growth limit of the yearling barnacles in the photograph and the preearthquake barnacles, which were at water level, indicates at least 3 feet of tectonic subsidence. Photograph taken July 20, 1964.

12.—Drowned brush and trees along shore of Harriman Fiord, Prince William Sound. The color change (arrow) between the dead brown foliage (light gray) below and the green foliage (darker gray) reflects the position of the postearthquake extreme high-tide line. The difference in elevation between the lower growth limit of terrestrial vegetation and the new extreme high-tide line provided a measure of tectonic subsidence, which was 7.2 feet at this locality. Photograph taken at 0.9-foot tide stage, June 10, 1964.

13.—Wild flowers and grass growing among dead barnacles (white) on shore of Middleton Island uplifted about 11 feet. The differences in the lower growth limits of pre- and postearthquake terrestrial vegetation provided a direct indication of the approximate amount of uplift. Photograph taken July 26, 1965.

14.—Coast at Cape Suckling uplifted about 13 feet during the earthquake. The difference in elevation between the postearthquake storm beach (marked by band of light-colored driftwood) and the preearthquake storm beach, which was above the base of the sea cliff, provided a crude measure of the uplift. The smooth area between the upper limits of driftwood and the sea cliff is now a marine terrace, and the former island in the foreground is a stack on its surface. The flat surface on the stack is probably an older marine terrace. Photograph taken at about zero tide stage, July 24, 1965.

compared with changes at nearby rocky shores, they appear to give results consistent, within about 3 feet, with those obtained from barnacle lines. The measurements between Kayak Island and Yakataga (pl. 1) are particularly uncertain because the shore there consists of active sand dunes that had partially concealed the old storm-beach line by the time measurements were made in 1965. This method was used only where no other means was available for measuring vertical displacement.

ESTIMATES OR MEASUREMENTS BY LOCAL RESIDENTS

Where possible, data on local land-level changes were obtained from local residents in interviews and on form questionnaires. The amount of these changes and the confidence limits expressed by observers are shown on plates 1 and 2. Most of the estimates were made by fishermen, mariners, loggers, and other coastal residents who had long experience in observing the levels of local tides relative to familiar shoreline features. Consequently, most of their estimates or measurements of the vertical displacements are probably correct to within a foot or less.

HEIGHT OF TIDAL BENCH MARKS RELATIVE TO SEA LEVEL

At a few localities in Prince William Sound, changes in land level were determined by leveling from the water surface to U.S. Coast and Geodetic Survey tidal bench marks of known preearthquake elevation. The accuracy of these determinations, which depends mainly upon the precision of leveling and the degree to which the actual tides at the time of measurement correspond with predicted tides, is believed to be within 0.5 foot.

COMPARISON OF PRE- AND POSTEARTHQUAKE DEPTH SOUNDINGS

Submarine control for the offshore uplift indicated southwest of Montague Island is provided by comparisons of detailed bottom soundings taken by the U.S. Coast and Geodetic Survey in 1927 and after the earthquake in 1964 (Malloy, 1964, p. 1048–1049; 1965, p. 22–26). Because of the technical problems involved in carrying out such surveys, however, the inferred submarine displacements could locally be in error by 10 feet or more.

COMPARISON OF PRE- AND POSTEARTHQUAKE LEVELINGS

The amount and distribution of the vertical tectonic movements inland from the coast were defined by the U.S. Coast and Geodetic Survey's prompt releveling of 722 miles of previously surveyed first-order level lines connecting the cities of Seward, Anchorage, Valdez and Fairbanks (pl. 1; fig. 3). Details of the methods used in these surveys were presented by Small (1966); changes in elevation between successive levelings at bench marks along these routes have been tabulated by Wood (1966, p. 124–130). The changes indicated by this method are probably accurate to within a few tenths of a foot.

Small (1966, p. 2) has cautioned that observed divergences in the results of the original leveling dating from 1923 and the postearthquake leveling in 1964 and 1965 may not be due entirely to movement associated with the earthquake because there is evidence for minor gradual regional movement along some lines where repeated levelings were made prior to 1964. At a few bench marks along these routes, which were located on unconsolidated deposits, the indicated subsidence

was anomalously large. Such anomalous measurements obviously represented changes caused by accidental displacement of the bench marks or by local phenomena such as frost heaving, surficial settling, or thawing of permafrost rather than to tectonic movements; they are not shown on plate 1.

DISTRIBUTION OF LAND-LEVEL CHANGES

Figure 3 summarizes the known and inferred areal distribution of land-level changes. The deformation extends for almost 600 miles along the Gulf of Alaska coast from the southwest tip of the Kodiak group of islands through the Prince William Sound region and eastward to the vicinity of Yakataka where it seems to die out. The deformed region consists essentially of (1) a broad zone of subsidence centered along the axis of the Kodiak-Kenai-Chugach Mountains, (2) a major zone of uplift that borders it on the seaward side and extends from the coast onto the sea floor, and (3) a zone of slight uplift that borders it on the landward side and extends northward into the Alaska and Aleutian Ranges. The distribution of subsidence and uplift in these three zones is described below.

THE ZONE OF SUBSIDENCE

The zone of tectonic subsidence includes almost all of the Kodiak group of islands, most of the Kenai Peninsula, the northern and western parts of Prince William Sound, and probably the western segment of the Chugach Mountains (pls. 1, 2; fig. 3). Areas of subsidence in most rocky embayed coastal areas are clearly defined by the various criteria outlined in the preceding section or by qualitative indicators of shoreline submergence. In sheltered embayments the

changes may be noticeable where the subsidence is as little as 1 foot. Such effects were most pronounced in areas of lowest mean annual tide range (fig. 8), inasmuch as both the frequency and duration of shoreline immersion for a given amount of subsidence vary inversely with the tidal range.

Along coasts with large tidal ranges and nonrocky shores, such as the part of Cook Inlet north of Homer, the subsidence is known only from tide gage readings near Kenai and at Anchorage, from a few observations by local residents, and from leveling along the coast near the head of the inlet. In this area, and along Shelikof Strait, the northwestern limit of the zone of subsidence is poorly defined. It seems to be close to the west side of the inlet from Redoubt Bay southwestward to Kamishak Bay and probably extends inland between the south side of that bay and the general area of Katmai Bay.

Control on the distribution and absolute amount of subsidence inland from the coast is provided by the Coast and Geodetic Survey's releveling of the first-order net shown on figure 3. Subsidence was indicated on all these lines south of the approximate southern margin of the Alaska Range except in the immediate vicinity of Valdez where a few bench marks were uplifted less than 0.2 foot (pl. 2). The leveling clearly demonstrates that the subsidence extends as a broad warp without abrupt changes of level across the Kenai Mountains northward from Seward and across the Chugach Mountains north of Valdez (pl. 1). Within the Chugach Mountains, subsidence of about half a foot extends eastward at least to Chitina. The northern limits of the zone are approximately defined by the leveling along The Alaska Railroad and Richardson Highway. Because of the small measured land-level changes on those lines, errors of as little as 0.5 foot could cause shifts of as much as 30 miles in the position of the northern boundary of the zone.

MAJOR ZONE OF UPLIFT

The main zone of uplift on land, as determined from shoreline changes, includes (1) a narrow fringe of points, capes, and small islands along the seaward side of the Kodiak group of islands, (2) all but the extreme northwestern and northern parts of the Prince William Sound region, and (3) the coastal belt extending about 120 miles east of the sound. Direct indications of uplift of parts of the contiguous Continental Shelf are afforded by emergence of all the offshore islands and reefs, including Middleton Island near the edge of the Continental Shelf (pl. 1, 2; fig. 1).

The extreme southwestern limit of the zone is believed to lie between Sitkinak Island, which was uplifted about 1½ feet according to a local resident (Mr. Hall Nelson), and Chirikof Island, where there apparently was no change in level (Neal Hoisington, written commun., 1965). Its eastern limit is probably at, or just west of, Yakataga.

The trend of the isobase contours in the northeastern part of the zone of uplift (fig. 3) and the distribution of aftershocks (fig. 2) seem to justify the inference that uplift also occurred over much of the submarine part of the continental margin in a broad zone extending southwestward at least to the latitude of southern Kodiak Island. Seaward projection of the trend of the isobase contours from the area between Yakataga and Middleton Island also suggests that uplift occurred over much of the continental slope and could have extended to the toe of the

continental slope, as is shown in figure 3 and on plate 1.

Independent evidence for uplift over a large segment of the Continental Shelf and slope comes from the seismic sea waves (tsunami) generated by the submarine movements. Because seismic sea waves are gravity waves set up in the ocean mainly by vertical disturbances of the sea bottom, the sense of displacement in the generative area can be determined under favorable conditions from the initial water motion at suitably situated tide stations. Tidegage records outside the immediate area affected by the earthquake show an initial rise that indicates a positive wave resulting from upward motion of the sea bottom (Van Dorn, 1964, p. 166). The initial direction of water movement along the coast of the Gulf of Alaska within the area affected by the earthquake is less clear, however, because there were no operative tide gages, and in many localities the water movements reported by eyewitnesses were complicated by (1) changes of land level along the coast, (2) local waves generated mainly by submarine landslides, and (3) seiches, or other water disturbances related to horizontal tectonic displacement.

The shape of the source area within which the train of seismic sea waves was generated can be approximated from an envelope of imaginary wave fronts projected back toward the wave source from observation stations along the shore at which arrival times are known. Distances traveled by the waves can be determined if both the wave velocity along the propagation path and the travel time are known. Because of their long wavelengths, seismic sea waves move as shallow water waves even in the deepest ocean,

and their approximate velocity is given by La Grange's equation (in Lamb, 1932, p. 257):

$$V = \sqrt{gh}$$

were g is the gravitational constant, and h is the water depth along the travel path (as determined from nautical charts). Travel time is taken as the elapsed time between the main shock and the arrival of the first wave crest at shore stations. The distribution of tide gage stations outside the seismic sea-wave generative area precludes precise delineation of the source by this method. However, its general position as derived by Van Dorn (1964, fig. 8), Pararas-Carayannis (1967), and M.G. Spaeth (oral commun., Sept. 1964) is consistent with uplift in the broad zone that lies roughly between the Aleutian Trench axis and the coast and extends from the general area offshore from Yakataga southwestward to about the latitude of Kodiak.

The position of the axis of the wave source shown on figure 15 was inferred from the arrival times of the initial wave crest along the adjacent coast, the general distribution of wave damage, and the reported movement directions of the initial wave. Approximate travel times to shore stations, sense of initial water motion, and the data sources are given in table 2. These data suggest that the wave crest was generated along one or more line sources within an elongate belt that extends about 350 miles from the vicinity of Montague Island in Prince William Sound to the area offshore from Sitkalidak Island in the Kodiak group. This inference is supported by the fact that at the northeast end of this axis on Montague Island warping and faulting have resulted in uplift of 38 feet in a

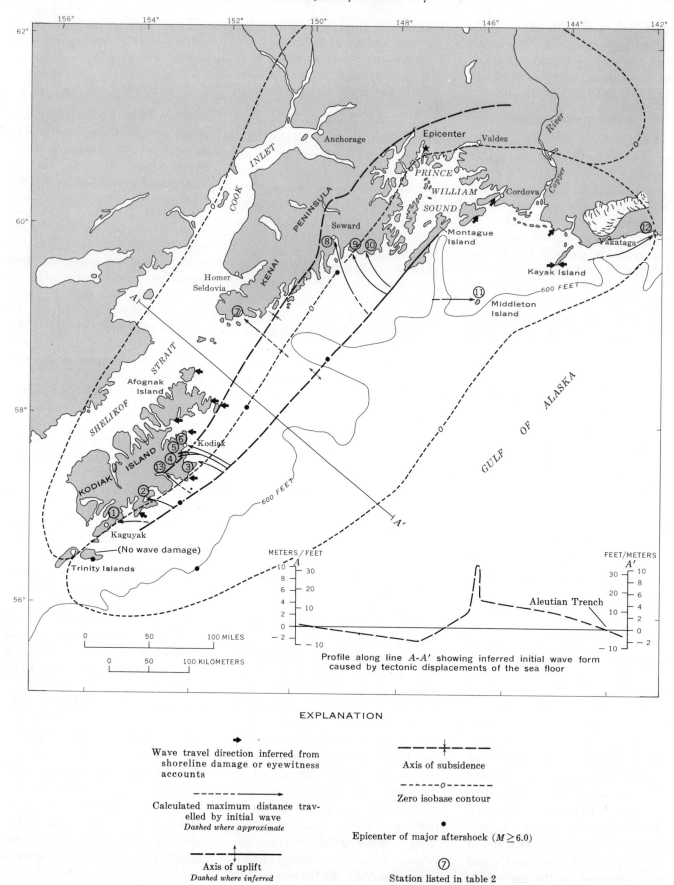

Profile along line A-A' showing inferred initial wave form caused by tectonic displacements of the sea floor

EXPLANATION

→   Wave travel direction inferred from shoreline damage or eyewitness accounts

– – – – –   Calculated maximum distance travelled by initial wave
Dashed where approximate

– ·· – ·· –   Axis of uplift
Dashed where inferred

— · — · —   Axis of subsidence

– – – –0– – – –   Zero isobase contour

●   Epicenter of major aftershock (M ≥ 6.0)

⑦   Station listed in table 2

15.—Submarine extension of the zone of maximum uplift and faulting on Montague Island as inferred from movement directions and calculated travel distances of seismic sea waves generated by the tectonic displacements.

TABLE 2.—*Travel times of seismic sea-wave crest to near-source observation stations*

[Locations shown on figure 15. Travel time from start of the earthquake (5:36 p.m., A.s.t.)]

Station		Travel time (minutes)	Reported sense of first motion	Data source
No. (fig. 15)	Name			
1	Kaguyak	38±5	?	Larry Matfay (radioed message received at Old Harbor).
2	Old Harbor	48	Up	Larry Matfay.
3	Cape Chiniak	38	Up	Fleet Weather Central, Kodiak Naval Station.
4	Kalsin Bay	70	?	U.S. Geological Survey stream gage.
5	Kodiak Naval Station.	63	Up	Fleet Weather Central, Kodiak Naval Station.
6	Kodiak	45±3	Down	Jerry Tilley.
7	Rocky Bay	¹ 30	Down	Guy Branson.
8	Seward	30±5	Up	Scottie McRae.
9	Whidbey Bay	19½±½	Up	Bill Sweeney.
10	Puget Bay	20±2	Up	Sam Hatfield.
11	Middleton Island	¹ 20	Down	Dwight Meeks
12	Cape Yakataga.	60±1	Down	Charlie Bilderback.
13	Saltery Cove	¹ 30	?	Ron Hurst.

¹ Approximate.

belt about 6 miles wide (Plafker, 1968), and comparable displacements are known to have occurred on the adjacent sea floor (Malloy, 1964). Similarities in maximum wave-runup heights along physiographically comparable segments of coast, both on the Kenai Peninsula opposite Montague Island and on the ocean coast of Kodiak Island, suggest that the vertical sea-floor displacements that generated the waves in these two areas could be of the same order of magnitude. If so, the initial wave form resulting from sea-floor displacement had the approximate shape shown by profile *A–A'*, figure 15. Other factors, however, such as rate of uplift, initial slope at the wave source, and energy loss along the propagation path preclude direct correlation of runup heights with displacement at the source.

PROBABLE ZONE OF SLIGHT UPLIFT

Minor uplift, probably associated with the earthquake, has

been detected in three areas adjacent to, and inland from, the zone of subsidence (fig. 3). The distribution of uplift in these three areas strongly suggests the possibility that they may be part of a continuous zone, roughly 100 miles wide, that parallels the major zones of subsidence and uplift.

Slight uplift in the Alaska Range is indicated by U.S. Coast and Geodetic Survey releveling along both the Richardson Highway and The Alaska Railroad (Small, 1966, fig. 9). Comparison of the 1964 leveling with a line run in 1952 shows general uplift along the Richardson Highway in a zone from about 25 miles north of Glennallen to within 50 miles of Fairbanks (fig. 3). Maximum uplift recorded on this line was 0.89 foot near the center of the zone, with irregular but generally progressive decreases toward the north and south. Land-level changes indicated by comparison of 1922 and 1964 levelings along The Alaska Railroad are less con-

sistent but they are predominantly positive and are as much as 0.36 foot in a zone where the line crosses the Alaska Range. The relatively large amount of change (0.89 ft) in only 12 years between the successive surveys on the Richardson Highway strongly suggests that at least the major part of the measured changes were probably associated with the earthquake. Furthermore, the fairly systematic rise and fall in the amounts of uplift across the Alaska Range suggest that uplift is not due to surveying errors or errors inherent in tying the level lines to tidal datum planes. Thus, it is tentatively concluded that the uplift along these two lines represents earthquake-related uplift over a broad zone centered in the general area of the Alaska Range.

Residents along the Iliamna, Chinitna, and Tuxedni Bays on the northwest shore of Cook Inlet (pl. 1; fig. 3) report a decrease in the height of tides after the earthquake that suggests shoreline uplift of 1–2 feet. There is little doubt about the validity of these estimates, particularly in Iliamna and Tuxedni Bays, where reference marks existed whose pre-earthquake relationship to tide levels were precisely known. Between 1963 and 1965 a slight uplift, presumably related to the earthquake, occurred also on the west side of Augustine Island (R. L. Detterman, oral commun., 1965) where beach berms have been lowered ½–1½ feet. The observed changes along the northwest side of Cook Inlet strongly suggest slight tectonic uplift of the shoreline during the earthquake. They cannot be explained by changes in the tidal characteristics due to regional subsidence of the entrance to Cook Inlet, inasmuch as deepening of the entrance would be expected to increase, rather than decrease, the height of the tides by facilitating diurnal movement of the tidal prism.

GEOMETRY OF THE DEFORMATION

The pattern of absolute vertical deformation associated with the earthquake is indicated by the isobase contours and profiles of plates 1 and 2 and is shown at a smaller scale in figure 3. The isobase contours may be pictured as the amounts of vertical displacement of an imaginary surface that was horizontal before the earthquake. The resulting map, therefore, is a special form of structure-contour map showing the configuration of the deformed surface. The maps and profiles indicate that the deformation occurred in three broad elongate warps, each of which is from 100 to 130 miles wide and has axes that roughly parallel the trend of the continental margin. Subsidence occurred in the middle warp and uplift in the adjacent warps on the seaward and landward sides. The zero isobases between the zone of subsidence and the adjacent zones of uplift are axes of tilt across which the sense of vertical displacement relative to the preearthquake position changes gradually. No abrupt changes of level have been found between the adjacent zones that would indicate vertical fault displacement between them.

ZONE OF SUBSIDENCE

The zone of subsidence is a synclinal downwarp whose axis is situated roughly along the crest of the coastal mountain ranges. The axis of subsidence plunges gently northeastward from the Kodiak Mountains and southwestward from the Chugach Mountains to a low of 7½ feet on the south coast of the Kenai Peninsula. In cross section the down-warp is strongly asymmetrical with an average tilt in the middle part of the deformed region of about 1 foot per 14 miles from the landward side towards the axis and a much steeper average tilt of 1 foot per 2–3½ miles on the seaward side. The prevailing simple synclinal form of the downwarp is broken only by the slight warping of the tilted surface near the axis of subsidence immediately north of Seward in an area where both triangulation and geologic data suggest the possibility of minor earthquake-related movement on a conspicuous north-south-trending lineament.

Apparent reduction in crustal volume within the zone of subsidence, as calculated by summing the average volumes included between successive isobase contours on plate 1, is about 29 cubic miles. Total area of the zone affected by subsidence is about 48,000 square miles, and the average amount of subsidence within it is roughly 2½ feet.

MAJOR ZONE OF UPLIFT

The major zone of uplift along the continental margin is a broad upwarp with a maximum amplitude of 15 feet, upon which is superimposed a narrow belt, less than 10 miles wide, in which there has been strong uplift associated with displacement on reverse faults. The axis of the uplifted zone trends southwestward from Montague Island, presumably to the area offshore from Sitkalidak Island in the Kodiak group. Maximum uplift along this axis on Montague Island is 38 feet and it may be as much as 50 feet on the sea floor.

The position of the axis of uplift to the northeast of Montague Island is uncertain; it may continue offshore from Hinchinbrook Island and the Copper River Delta to intersect the coast at Cape Suck-ling where 13 feet of uplift was measured. Because of the scarcity of data points in the Cape Suckling area, the shape of the deformed surface there cannot be closely defined and the possibility cannot be ruled out that the large amount of uplift there may reflect local warping or faulting.

The part of the upwarp available for observation in Prince William Sound has an irregular shape that suggests combined tilting and warping. As indicated by profiles A–A' and B–B' on plate 1, the landward slope outside the narrow belt of extreme uplift averages 1 foot per 2.1 miles northwest of Montague Island and only 1 foot per 7.4 miles north of Hinchinbrook Island. Local tilts as high as 1 foot in 185 feet occur within the belt of extreme uplift and surface faulting in southern Montague Island. The isobases in the central and southeastern part of Prince William Sound reflect a broad undulating platform 4–8 feet above its preearthquake position. In at least two areas of western Prince William Sound, local flattening or even reversals of slope are indicated.

Data on the configuration of the upwarped surface in the Kodiak Island area, although less conclusive, suggest northwestward tilting that is as steep as 1 foot per mile at Narrow Cape.

Little is known about the shape of that part of the upwarped zone that is seaward from the axis of uplift because only a few points are available for observation. The slope between the most southeasterly capes of Montague Island and Middleton Island 50 miles to the southeast averages 1 foot per 11 miles, but the shape of the surface in the water-covered area between these points is conjectural. Nor is it known whether the uplift seaward from Middleton Island dies out gradually toward the toe of the continental slope, as inferred on the profiles on plate 1, or whether it terminates abruptly in one or more faults or flexures on the slope.

The apparent increase in crustal volume within the major zone of uplift is much less certain than that involved in subsidence, because the distribution of uplift in extensive submarine areas must be inferred from the trend of isobase contours in the northeastern part of the zone and a few offshore control points. If the deformation has the general form shown by the profiles on plate 1, the volume increase would be approximately 89 cubic miles, or roughly three times the decrease in the zone of subsidence. Total area of the uplifted zone is inferred to be roughly 60,000 square miles. Average amount of uplift is about 6 feet, except in the narrow axial belt of uplift and faulting extending southwestward from Montague Island, where it is probably 30 feet or more.

PROBABLE ZONE OF SLIGHT UPLIFT

Where the broad slight upwarp landward from the zone of subsidence is crossed by level lines, its axis seems to be centered along the crest of the Alaska Range and its maximum indicated uplift is 0.89 foot on the Richardson Highway line and 0.35 foot on The Alaska Railroad line. The upwarp crossed by these two lines of leveling may be part of a continuous zone that extends into the Aleutian Range of the Alaska Peninsula where uplift of as much as 1.5 feet has been reported at several places in the Kamishak Bay-Tuxedni Bay area. A rough estimate of the apparent increase in crustal volume in the zone of slight uplift, based on an average uplift of 0.3 foot and an area of 24,000 square miles is about 1.0 cubic miles.

EARTHQUAKE FAULTS

Faults on land associated with the 1964 earthquake were found only at two localities on southwestern Montague Island in Prince William Sound and on the subsea continuation of one of these faults southwest of the island. Comparable faults entirely on the sea floor may have gone undetected. As far as could be determined no definite movement occurred along any other faults on land, although faulting at depth is suspected in some areas of unconsolidated surficial deposits characterized by linear zones of landslides or surficial cracks.

MONTAGUE ISLAND FAULTS

The location of, and displacement across, the earthquake faults on and near Montague Island are shown on plate 1. Their surface characteristics and tectonic significance are briefly summarized in the following paragraphs. In a separate volume of the Geological Survey's series of papers on the Alaska earthquake, they are described in more detail (Plafker, 1967b).

The longer of the two faults, the Patton Bay fault, is represented by a complex system, 22 miles long, of en echelon reverse faults and associated flexures with an average N. 37° E. strike. Surface dip of the fault is northwest at about 85° near its southern end and 50°–75° elsewhere along the scarp. Displacement on the fault is almost entirely dip slip—the northwest side upthrown relative to the southeast side. The maximum measured vertical component of slip is 20–23 feet, and maximum indicated dip slip is about 26 feet. A left-lateral displacement component of less than 2 feet near the southern end of the fault is probably a local phenomenon related to

a change in strike of the fault that causes it to trend at an oblique angle to the N. 53° W. principal horizontal stress direction.

The Patton Bay fault system was traced by the U.S. Coast and Geodetic Survey (Malloy, 1964) for at least 17 miles on the sea floor southwest of Montague Island. Indirect evidence, from the distribution of large aftershocks associated with the earthquake and from the distribution of submarine scarps, suggests that the faulting on and near Montague Island occurred at the northeastern end of a reactivated submarine fault system. This system approximately coincides with the axis of uplift inferred from seismic sea waves between the southeast coast of Kodiak Island and Montague Island (fig. 15). The fault apparently dies out on its northwestern end, although the possibility cannot be ruled out that it is offset en echelon towards the southeast (in a righthanded sense) and continues northeastward offshore from Montague Island at least as far as Hinchinbrook Island.

The shorter of the two faults, the Hanning Bay fault, is a virtually continuous reverse fault with an average strike of N. 47° E. and a total length of about 4 miles. Dip of the fault is 52°–75° NW. at the surface. Displacement is dip slip except for a left-lateral strike-component of about a third of a foot near the southern limit of the exposure. The maximum measured vertical component of slip is $16\frac{1}{3}$ feet near the middle of the fault, the indicated dip slip at that locality being about 20 feet.

The two reverse faults on Montague Island and the postulated submarine extension of the Patton Bay fault constitute a zone within which crustal attenuation and maximum known uplift occurred during the earthquake. Nevertheless, there are no significant lithologic differences in the rock sequences across them to suggest that these faults form major tectonic boundaries. Furthermore, their spatial distribution relative to the regional zone of tectonic uplift associated with the earthquake, to the earthquake focal region, and to the epicenter of the main shock suggests that they are probably subsidiary features, rather than the primary faults along which the earthquake originated.

OTHER POSSIBLE EARTHQUAKE FAULTS ON LAND

As far as could be determined, there are no other surface faults on land along which movement occurred during the earthquake. A careful search for renewed movement on known preexisting faults did not reveal any detectable surface displacements. Nor were any anomalous abrupt changes found in amounts of vertical movement along the coast or along level lines inland from the coast that would suggest significant displacement on concealed faults. All reports of suspected faulting that were checked in the field proved to be landslides or surficial cracks in unconsolidated deposits. It is reasonably certain that if additional faulting did indeed occur, its surface expression is far more subtle than that on Montague Island.

Some of the linear belts of concentrated surficial cracking and landsliding may reflect displacements on concealed faults. Foster and Karlstrom (1967, p. F24) suggested that movement on a concealed fault may have produced a northeast-trending linear belt of conspicuous surface fissures on the Kenai Lowland in the western part of the Kenai Peninsula. However, no evidence has been found for ver-

tical displacements where the belt crosses the U.S. Coast and Geodetic Survey level line south of Anchorage, and there is a notable absence of aftershock activity along the postulated fault.

A second possible line of fault movement lies along the broad north-south-trending topographic depression, referred to here as the "Kenai lineament," that extends northward from Resurrection Bay through the valley containing the eastern arm of Kenai Lake (pl. 1). Faulting is suggested (1) by local concentrations of fissures seemingly unrelated to seismic shaking along The Alaska Railroad (D. S. McCulloch, oral commun., October 1967), (2) by reported angular changes between points on either side of the lineament as indicated by comparison of pre- and postearthquake triangulation surveys, and (3) by a distinct change in trend of isobase contours across the lineament (pl. 1). The geodetic data have been interpreted as suggesting left-lateral displacement of as much as 5 feet between stations about 4 miles apart on either side of the lineament (Wood, 1966, p. 122). These data, if correct, could indicate either slight movement on a north-south-trending concealed fault or crustal warping localized along the lineament.

HORIZONTAL DISPLACEMENTS

Although the vertical displacements that occurred during the earthquake are unusually large, they appear to be secondary to the horizontal displacements indicated by retriangulation over much of the deformed region. During 1964–65, the U.S. Coast and Geodetic Survey carried out revisional triangulations in the area shown in figure 16. The resurvey includes an area of about 25,000 square miles

bounded on the west by the Seward-Anchorage highway, on the north by the Glenn Highway, and on the east by the Richardson Highway and the east coast of Prince William Sound. To the south, the resurvey extends to stations on the Gulf of Alaska coast and on Middleton Island 50 miles offshore from the coast. A tellurometer traverse was also run around the south coast of the Kenai Peninsula from Seward to Homer and from Homer to Moose Pass (at Kenai Lake) via Kenai. Because the precision of station locations obtained by the tellurometer traverse is probably too low to yield meaningful data on earthquake-related horizontal displacements, the stations are not shown in figure 16 and the indicated shifts of these stations are not considered here.

METHODS OF MEASUREMENT

Parkin (1966, p. 2–5) has described the procedures used in adjusting the pre- and postearthquake surveys. The preearthquake net consisted of: (1) a primary arc extending along the highway route from Anchorage northeastward to Valdez via Glennallen, surveyed in 1941 and 1944, (2) a second-order arc across the north shore of Prince William Sound from Valdez to Perry Island, surveyed in 1947–48, (3) a third-order arc surveyed from Perry Island to Anchorage between 1910 and 1914, (4) third-order triangulation between 1900 and 1961 for chart control across Prince William Sound and extending south to Middleton Island and westward along the southern Kenai Peninsula to Seward, and (5) a double arc from Seward north to connections at Turnagain Arm, surveyed by the U.S. Army Corps of Engineers in 1941–42. All these observations were combined into a single composite network and a

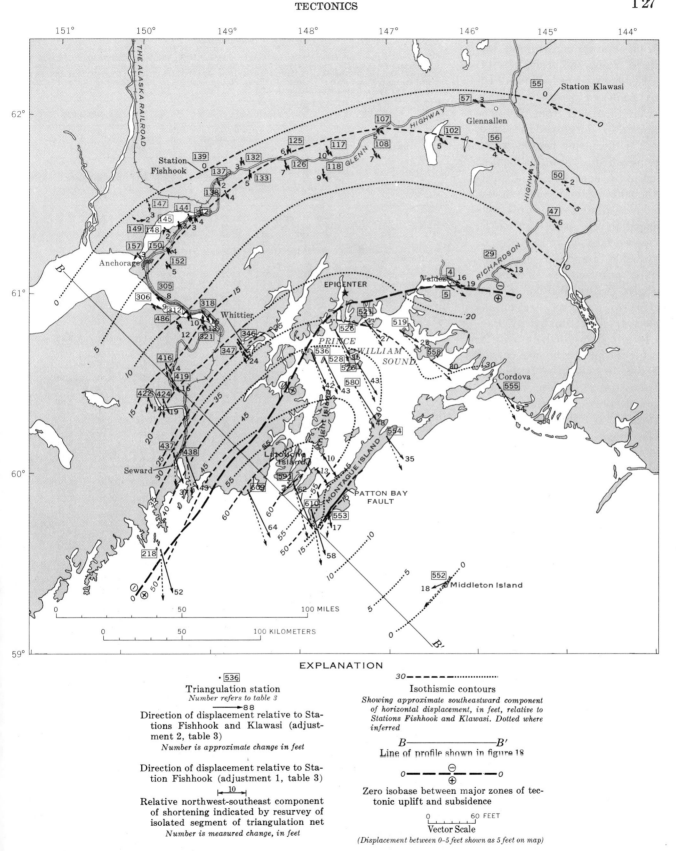

EXPLANATION

• 536
Triangulation station
Number refers to table 3

88
Direction of displacement relative to Stations Fishhook and Klawasi (adjustment 2, table 3)
Number is approximate change in feet

Direction of displacement relative to Station Fishhook (adjustment 1, table 3)

10
Relative northwest-southeast component of shortening indicated by resurvey of isolated segment of triangulation net
Number is measured change, in feet

30
Isothismic contours
Showing approximate southeastward component of horizontal displacement, in feet, relative to Stations Fishhook and Klawasi. Dotted where inferred

B ———————— B'
Line of profile shown in figure 18

0 —⊖— ⊕ —— 0
Zero isobase between major zones of tectonic uplift and subsidence

0   60 FEET
Vector Scale
(Displacement between 0–5 feet shown as 5 feet on map)

16.—**Map showing horizontal tectonic displacements in the Prince William Sound region and nearby areas. Horizontal displacements based on triangulation surveys by U.S. Coast and Geodetic Survey (Parkin, 1966, table 1).**

free adjustment (an adjustment with no external constraints) was made in which one position—Station Fishhook—was held fixed. Internal scale and orientation for the net were furnished from 5 Laplace azimuths, 15 short taped base lines, and 1 tellurometer length, which were included in the adjustment as observation equations. The postearthquake triangulation survey, which was all first-order work, was adjusted in the same way as the earlier work.

Probable errors in the geographic positions of stations in southern Prince William Sound relative to the fixed station, as conservatively estimated by Parkin from the residuals, are 15–20 feet for the preearthquake survey and 6–8 feet for the postearthquake survey. These probable errors decrease progressively for stations closer to the fixed station.

The horizontal shift of recovered stations relative to Station Fishhook between the pre- and postearthquake surveys, as computed by Parkin, are listed in table 3 as adjustment 1 and are shown graphically as displacement vectors (dashed) in figure 16. Because the postearthquake net was not carried northward to an area of stability, changes shown are relative rather than absolute. However, small angular shifts in the northern part of the net, as compared with those farther south, suggest that the northern part of the resurveyed net probably approaches an area that was not strongly affected by horizontal distortion during the earthquake. Anomalous aspects of the adjustment are (1) a gradual increase in displacement along the Glenn Highway arc east of Station Fishhook to almost 13 feet at Station Klawasi, and (2) an apparent 32-foot shift of Middleton Island southwestward in a direction al-

TABLE 3.—*Pre- and postearthquake differences in triangulation station plane coordinates*

[Data after U.S. Coast and Geodetic Survey (Parkin, 1966, and B. K. Meade, written commun., June 24, 1966). Adjustment 1: station 139 (Fishhook) held fixed; orientation and scale from azimuths and baselines of preearthquake net (Parkin, 1966, table 1). Adjustment 2: stations 139 (Fishhook) and 55 (Klawasi) held fixed for additional orientation and scale of preearthquake net. Station locations are shown in figure 16 except for stations 180, 184, 186, 188, and 218. Azimuth: north=0°.]

| Station | Adjustment 1 | | | | Adjustment 2 | | | |
| | Position shifts (feet) | | Resultant vector | | Position shifts (feet) | | Resultant vector | |
	ΔX (east (+)-west (−))	ΔY (north (−)-south (+))	Length (feet)	Azimuth	ΔX (east (+)-west (−))	ΔY (north (−)-south (+))	Length (feet)	Azimuth
4	+18.74	−13.73	23.23	125°	+15.51	−4.65	16.18	117°
5	+21.66	−11.50	24.52	120°	+18.60	−2.32	18.72	97°
29	+17.32	−15.39	23.17	130°	+12.37	−5.23	13.43	113°
47	+11.17	−14.32	18.16	140°	+4.17	−4.73	6.30	139°
50	+8.45	−11.84	14.55	145°	+1.96	−0.54	2.03	105°
55 (Klawasi)	+10.06	−7.82	12.74	130°	0	0	0	-------
56	+10.08	−10.47	14.53	135°	+2.23	−3.29	3.97	146°
57	+10.74	−6.82	12.72	120°	+2.25	−1.23	2.56	119°
102	−10.05	−9.03	13.51	130°	+3.34	−3.60	4.91	137°
107	+8.47	−7.73	11.47	130°	+2.99	−4.16	5.12	144°
108	+8.01	−10.23	12.99	140°	+3.14	−6.13	7.05	154°
117	+5.26	−8.88	10.32	150°	+1.57	−6.20	6.40	166°
118	+4.64	−12.48	13.31	160°	+1.62	−9.30	9.44	170°
125	+3.83	−7.09	8.06	150°	+1.10	−5.41	5.52	169°
126	+3.88	−9.23	10.01	155°	+1.54	−7.29	7.45	168°
132	+1.46	−3.91	4.17	160°	+0.17	−3.12	3.12	177°
133	+1.45	−6.61	6.77	170°	+0.23	−5.40	5.40	178°
137	+0.83	−2.37	2.51	160°	+0.81	−1.81	1.97	157°
138	+1.55	−4.74	4.99	160°	+1.42	−3.75	4.01	159°
139 (Fishhook)	0	0	0	-------	0	0	0	-------
142	+0.58	−4.71	4.75	175°	+1.93	−3.76	4.22	153°
144	+0.40	−3.68	3.70	175°	+1.82	−2.90	3.42	148°
145	−0.49	−3.41	3.45	190°	+1.35	−2.70	3.02	153°
147	−1.84	+3.15	3.65	330°	+0.37	−2.61	2.64	172°
148	−0.51	−2.04	2.10	195°	+1.88	−1.53	2.42	129°
149	−2.46	+2.06	3.21	310°	+0.42	+1.68	1.73	76°
150	−0.07	−4.38	4.38	180°	+2.70	−3.27	4.24	140°
152	+0.58	−5.56	5.59	175°	+3.70	−4.18	5.25	143°
157	−1.54	−2.43	2.88	210°	+2.19	−1.95	2.93	132°
218	+5.08	−58.20	58.42	175°	+15.34	−49.67	51.98	163°
305	+2.77	−4.83	5.57	150°	+6.99	−2.80	7.55	112°
306	+3.29	−5.50	6.41	150°	+7.79	−3.40	8.50	114°
312	−2.96	−10.69	11.09	165°	+6.80	−7.51	10.11	138°
318	+3.26	−15.58	15.92	170°	+6.66	−12.07	15.81	140°
321	+3.94	−14.22	14.76	165°	+7.58	−10.51	12.96	144°
346	+9.68	−21.89	23.93	155°	+12.96	−16.78	21.20	142°
347	+10.72	−24.23	26.50	155°	+14.12	−19.00	23.67	143°
416	+2.63	−14.85	15.08	170°	+8.26	−10.89	13.67	143°
419	+2.64	−18.23	18.42	170°	+8.46	−13.89	16.26	149°
422	−1.08	−17.25	17.28	185°	+5.88	−12.91	14.19	156°
424	+1.85	−21.59	21.67	175°	+8.35	−16.88	18.83	154°
437	+5.34	−41.20	41.54	175°	+12.88	−34.86	37.16	160°
438	+8.84	−46.34	47.18	170°	+16.26	−39.65	42.85	158°
486	+4.09	−11.98	12.66	160°	+8.41	−8.89	12.24	137°
519	+22.13	−22.78	31.76	135°	+21.22	−13.76	25.29	123°
521	+19.46	−28.40	34.43	145°	+18.18	−20.46	27.37	138°
526	+18.01	−37.17	41.30	155°	+18.70	−29.84	35.22	148°
528	+18.19	−45.85	49.33	160°	+19.76	−38.18	42.99	153°
536	+16.68	−44.77	47.78	160°	+18.67	−37.72	42.09	154°
552	−21.56	−22.61	31.24	225°	−17.02	−6.32	18.16	250°
553	−3.14	−28.77	28.94	185°	+2.34	−17.05	17.31	172°
554	+18.63	−39.50	43.67	155°	+20.81	−28.26	35.09	144°
555	+20.85	−41.30	46.26	155°	+19.35	−28.32	34.29	146°
558	+25.94	−23.87	35.25	135°	+25.18	−13.30	29.45	118°
576	+22.24	−45.30	50.46	155°	+23.51	−36.48	43.40	147°
580	+23.59	−48.63	54.05	155°	+25.25	−39.43	47.82	147°
591	+18.60	−67.40	69.92	165°	+23.88	−57.59	62.34	157°
609	+22.06	−66.56	70.19	160°	+28.91	−57.49	64.34	153°
610	+11.30	−66.35	67.30	170°	+17.12	−55.23	57.82	163°

most normal to that of stations along the coast.

The first of these anomalies is eliminated, and the second considerably reduced, by an alternative preferred adjustment of the data in which two stations, Fishhook and Klawasi spaced 140 miles apart, are held fixed to provide additional orientation and scale of the postearthquake net (fig. 17).

The assumption that the base line remained relatively stable in length and azimuth is justified on the basis of its position in the seismically inactive part of the net where there was only slight vertical displacement and by its orientation roughly parallel to the trend of isobase contours and normal to the trend of the horizontal shifts. The revised adjustment involves a

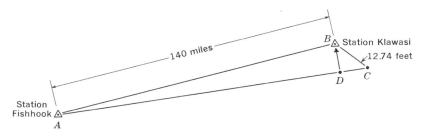

17.—Schematic diagram illustrating the method of deriving triangulation adjustment 2 from adjustment 1. According to adjustment 1, the postearthquake position of line *AB* is given by *AC*; point *B* shifted 12.74 feet S. 50° E. to point *C*. For adjustment 2, which assumes no change in distance or azimuth between *A* and *B*, the postearthquake net was rotated counterclockwise 0.0000124277 radians (angle *BAC*) and reduced in scale by the amount *DC*, or a factor of 0.9999881256 (the ratio of *AB/AC*).

counterclockwise rotation of the earthquake net of 0.0000124277 radians and a decrease in scale by a factor of 0.9999881256—changes probably well within the limits of error of these surveys. The resulting horizontal shifts, which appear to be more consistent with the vertical displacements, are given in table 3 as adjustment 2 and are plotted vectorially in figure 16 as solid lines. Unless otherwise specified, horizontal displacements referred to in the following sections are those of adjustment 2.

AMOUNT AND DISTRIBUTION OF THE DISPLACEMENTS

Absolute magnitudes and precise directions of the horizontal changes cannot be determined because the preearthquake triangulation net consisted mainly of third-order surveys and because the postquake survey, all of which was precise first-order work, was not carried northward to an area unaffected by the earthquake. Nevertheless, most of the changes are so large and systematic that there can be little doubt that they are in the general direction and are of the order of magnitude indicated by comparison of the two surveys. The true orientation and amount of displacement of the stations on the southeast shore of Montague Island (553) and on Middleton Island (552) are especially un-

certain. This uncertainty exists because (1) both stations are in a part of the net where large differential earthquake-related vertical movements may have caused significant horizontal shifts in their positions, (2) the preearthquake triangulation involving these stations was only third order and the stations were tied to the net in Prince William Sound through several figures that are geometrically weak, and (3) the stations are situated near the extremity of the net where errors in displacement relative to the fixed stations are likely to be at a maximum. As a consequence, errors inherent in the adjustments could equal or exceed the observed displacements of these two stations in either of the two alternative adjustments.

The pattern of horizontal displacements relative to stations Fishhook and Klawasi during the time between the surveys is brought out by the displacement vectors (solid) in figure 16. Except for Middleton Island (552), they show relative seaward movements that are predominantly toward the south-southeast in the western part of the area, almost due southeast in the central part, and east-southeast in the eastern part. Over the central part of the net, the magnitude of the displacements relative to the base

line increases progressively from the base line to a maximum of 64 feet at station 609 on the mainland immediately west of Prince William Sound, after which it decreases towards the southeast. In the western and eastern parts of the net, displacements show a progressive increase in magnitude to the most seaward stations amounting to as much as 52 feet south-southwest from Seward (218) and 34 feet near Cordova (555). In addition, resurveys of small isolated triangulation nets spanning the straits from Latouche and Knight Islands to Montague Island indicate relative shortening of 10–13 feet in a northwest-southeast direction (fig. 16).

The overall pattern of movement relative to the fixed stations is emphasized by the isothismic contours (lines of equal horizontal movement) in figure 16 which show the approximate component of horizontal displacement in a S. 45° E. direction, or nearly parallel to the average trend of the vectors in the same area. Contours are based on the displacement vectors (adjustment 2, table 3) and on relative horizontal movements within an isolated segment of the triangulation net between Montague, Latouche, and Knight Islands (Parkin, 1966, p. 9; C. A. Whitten, written commun., 1965).

Isothismic contours in figure 16 indicate that the entire area from the northern arc of the net to southwestern Prince William Sound showed a relative extension in a seaward direction, whereas the part of the net southeast of the Knight Island-Latouche Island area showed a relative shortening in a northwest-southeast direction. In other words, the position of Middleton Island, and perhaps the area southeast of the

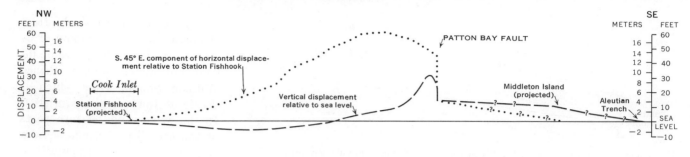

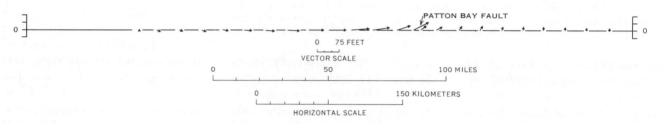

18.—Profile showing measured and inferred tectonic displacements (above) and vectorial sum of the horizontal and vertical movements (below) along section B–B' of plate 1 and figure 16.

island, remained essentially fixed relative to the base line, whereas the intervening area was displaced in a relative seaward direction, the amount of displacement attaining a maximum in the Latouche-Knight Island area.

Triangulation data indicating shortening across M o n t a g u e Island agree well with the observed imbrication on reverse faults in this area (Plafker, 1967b, p. G40–G41). However, the exact amount of shortening is uncertain because the geographic positions of the stations on the seaward side of Montague Island (553) and on Middleton Island (552) are subject to large errors that may equal or exceed the indicated amounts of displacement at these stations. If the S. 45° W. component of displacement dies out at Middleton Island, as inferred in figure 16, the average contraction between that point and the 60-foot isothismic contour is 60 feet. That this amount of contraction may not be unreasonable is indicated by (1) the 10- to 13-foot shortening in a northwest-southeast d i r e c t i o n indicated by reobservation of the

small isolated triangulation net spanning M o n t a g u e Strait between Montague Island and Latouche and Knight Islands, (2) the horizontal shortening of at least 9.3 feet, and possibly as much as 19 feet, across the Patton Bay fault that is indicated by surface mapping, and (3) the pronounced crustal warping that occurred on and near Montague Island.

RELATIONSHIP TO REGIONAL VERTICAL DISPLACEMENTS AND SURFACE FAULTS

A genetic relationship between the horizontal and vertical regional displacements is strongly suggested by the orientation of the horizontal displacement vectors in a direction roughly normal to the trend of the isobases and by approximate coincidence of the maximum vertical displacements with areas of maximum transverse extension or contraction. This relationship is brought out by the profiles in figure 18 which show magnitudes of the horizontal displace-

ments in a relative S. 45° E. direction and the vertical displacements relative to sea level along line B–B' of figure 16. Also shown in figure 18 are the vectorial sums of the horizontal and vertical displacements along the line of profile, that is, the direction and relative amount of movement of points on the ground surface along this line.

The horizontal displacement data indicate that the zone of subsidence extended tranversely by an average of 1.1×10^{-4}, or 1.1 parts in 10,000, and reached a maximum of about 3×10^{-4} slightly seaward from the axis of the subsided zone. By contrast, at least part of the zone of uplift seems to be one of net transverse shortening resulting from crustal warping and reverse faulting. Average contraction across the uplifted zone as far seaward as Middleton Island is about 10^{-4} and it averages as much as 8×10^{-4} across the narrow belt of maximum uplift on Montague Island. Presumably, a comparable relationship exists between horizontal displacements and the earthquake-related vertical move-

[144]

ments that ocurred outside the re-triangulated area. Extension of the retriangulation net over this area could provide a definitive test of this assumption.

In a general way, the displacement vectors on either side of the Patton Bay fault (stations 610 and 553) are consistent with the field observations that the fault has undergone reverse movement with resultant crustal shortening by imbrication in the dip direction. In detail, however, there is an unresolved discrepancy between the observed dip-slip movement on the Patton Bay fault and the apparent left-lateral strike-slip shift of triangulation stations on either side of it (Plafker, 1967b, fig. 35). The discrepancy was reduced by the readjustment (adjustment 2, table 3) used here, but not altogether eliminated. Absence of an observable component of lateral slip on the fault suggests either that the displacement was taken up largely by horizontal distortion between the fault and the two triangulation stations or, more probably, that an error has been introduced into this part of the triangulation adjustment through a slight clockwise rotation of displacement vectors.

It is significant that, regardless of the details of the horizontal displacements, the triangulation data suggest rebound of a broad segment of the continental margin that had been elastically compressed and shortened by at least 64 feet prior to the earthquake. The vectors in figure 16 show the general sense and amount of the rebound within the retriangulated area. This indicated rebound implies preearthquake regional compression oriented parallel to the trend of the vectors, or roughly normal to the continental margin and trend of the eastern end of the Aleutian Arc.

TIME AND RATE OF THE DEFORMATION

Instrumental records of the time and rate of tectonic movements in the deformed area are nonexistent. Three standard tide gages at Seward, Kodiak, and Homer were located where they might have been able to record the vertical land movements relative to sea level had they been operative during the earthquake. However, the Seward gage was destroyed in a submarine landslide at the time of the earthquake, the Kodiak gage with the marigram for the month of March was lost when it was washed away by seismic sea waves half an hour after the earthquake, and the Homer gage was made inoperative by the shaking. There were no accelerographs in the affected region to record the horizontal movements. As a consequence, the time and rate of the movements can only be inferred from the reports of eyewitnesses, from photographs taken after the earthquake, and from the water and atmospheric disturbances generated by the movements.

EARTHQUAKE-RELATED MOVEMENTS

Numerous eyewitness reports of immediate withdrawals of water from uplifted coastal areas indicate that much, if not all, of the deformation occurred during the 1½–5 minutes of violent tremors. In most places, however, immediate water disturbances resulting from submarine slides or other causes precluded estimates of relative changes in level for several hours or days after the earthquake. In an area uplifted 6.3 feet, one eyewitness (Gordon McMahon, oral commun., 1964), thought that the displacements were perceptible as a series of distinct upward accelerations during the earthquake. Another eyewit-

ness (Guy Branson, oral commun., 1964), from an area that subsided 5 feet, described a definite dropping or sinking sensation toward the end of the strong ground motion "as when a plane hits an air pocket." No other observers reported perceptible accelerations in the direction of the tectonic displacements.

All of the uplift and surface faulting at the southwest tip of Montague Island occurred prior to March 30th. On this date the uplifted platform at Cape Cleare and a part of the Patton Bay fault were photographed during a reconnaissance flight (fig. 20). Jim Osborne, a bush pilot who knows the Prince William Sound area intimately and is an exceptionally perceptive observer, informed me that all of the shoreline displacements took place prior to the morning of March 28—the day he first flew over the area after the earthquake. According to Osborne, there were no noticeable shoreline changes after the 28th. His evaluation is corroborated by residents along the coast in all areas affected by the tectonic displacements. Movement along strongly uplifted shores occurred at least fast enough to trap many mobile marine animals such as small fish, starfish, and snails above the tide level (fig. 24; p. I 36).

That a substantial fraction of the net vertical displacement occurred very rapidly is also suggested by the pattern of seismic air and sea waves. The peaks between compression and rarefaction on the La Jolla microbarograph record (Van Dorn, 1964, fig. 5) were 7 minutes apart, a difference which suggests a peak-to-peak separation at the origin of about 83 miles; this figure is in close agreement with the observed spacing between the axes of uplift and subsidence. As noted by Van Dorn, the recorded disturbance could only have been produced by vertical motions over a very large area, and in a time interval of the order of that required for an acoustic wave to propagate across the dimensions of the generator. The elapsed time between the earthquake and the arrival of the initial wave crest along the ocean coast of the Kenai Peninsula further suggests that the initiating disturbance along the submarine extension of the axis of maximum uplift southwest of Montague Island (fig. 15) occurred during, or within a few minutes after, the earthquake.

There is no direct evidence as to when the horizontal displacements, which in some inhabited localities were as much as 60 feet, occurred. No observers reported strong systematic horizontal movements at any time during the main shock, nor could such movements be inferred with confidence from the incomplete data on the directions in which objects or structures fell. Nevertheless, as suggested on page I39, horizontal displacements probably occurred during the earthquake, and at a rate fast enough to cause waves in some bodies of surface water. Accelerations due to the permanent displacements probably were undetected by observers because they were masked by the strong ground motions resulting from the transient elastic seismic waves.

PREEARTHQUAKE MOVEMENTS

Vertical changes in the position of the shore relative to sea level have been noted within a period of hours prior to some major earthquakes in Japan (Imamura, 1930, p. 141). These changes, which have been termed "acute" tiltings or deformations by Japanese scientists, have been a subject of special interest because of their obvious

potential importance in earthquake prediction.

During the field investigation of the 1964 Alaska earthquake, an effort was made to ascertain whether any premonitory changes of level were noted by residents in coastal areas or were recorded on operative tide gages. The only suggestion of preseismic changes was an observation made by an officer of Fleet Weather Central at the Kodiak Naval Station to the effect that tides in the area were at least 1½, and possibly 2½, feet lower than normal a few days before the earthquake and that the low tides were apparently unrelated to atmospheric conditions (Lt. C. R. Barney, oral commun., 1964). However, the loss of the March marigram prevented documentation of the reported low tides. The Seward and Homer marigrams for the time preceding the earthquake do not show evidence of preseismic changes, nor have such changes been reported elsewhere by coastal residents.

POSTEARTHQUAKE MOVEMENTS

Relevelings, tidal observations, and gravity readings suggest either no postearthquake vertical changes or, perhaps, slight changes in the earthquake-affected region.

The most convincing indication of continued postearthquake movement comes from releveling in May–June and in October 1964 of a line 22 miles long extending northwestward from Portage on Turnagain Arm and a third releveling from Portage to Anchorage in the summer of 1965. Between the preearthquake leveling and the initial postearthquake leveling, Portage subsided 5.6 feet, the area 22 miles to the northwest subsided about 4.9 feet, and Anchorage subsided about 2.3 feet (pl. 1). Comparison of the two

1964 relevelings shows a progressive increase in divergence from northwest to southeast, which suggests additional relative subsidence of about 0.16 foot at Portage in the period between surveys (Small, 1966, p. 13). Comparison of the May–June 1964 and the 1965 leveling suggests relative postearthquake subsidence of 0.36 foot at Anchorage and 0.52 foot at Portage during this interval (Small, 1966, p. 17). Unfortunately, neither the October 1964 line nor the 1965 line was tied to tidal bench marks, so the absolute postearthquake displacements are uncertain. Furthermore, because both Anchorage and Portage are situated in areas of extensive thick unconsolidated deposits, the possibility cannot be ruled out with the data available that some or all of the indicated subsidence may be due to continued consolidation of soft sediments.

Small (1966, p. 18) also reports a gravity increase of about 0.18 mgal on Middleton Island relative to an Anchorage base station. This increase occurred between the time of a postearthquake 1964 measurement and one made in 1965 which would indicate about 2 feet of additional uplift between surveys. However, the possibility that this large difference in the successive gravity readings may be due to meter drift in one or both surveys is suggested by the fact that residents of the island did not notice changes in relative tide levels during this same interval. Two feet of uplift at Middleton Island should have been readily detectable along the shore.

A comparison of tidal observations made in 1964 and 1965 provides data on the postearthquake land-level changes at 14 of the stations listed in table 1. However, it is difficult to separate purely tectonic movements from meteorological effects and the effects of surficial compaction at gages situated on soft sediments. Tidal observations in the zone of uplift at Cordova, Port Chalmers, and Sawmill Bay showed no detectable change suggestive of continued tectonic movements, but one station, Port Gravina, apparently subsided 0.3 foot between 1964 and 1965. In the zone of subsidence, gages at Seward and Port O'Brien had no detectable change in mean sea level; five gages at bedrock sites showed slight rises ranging from 0.1 to 0.5 foot, possibly suggestive of postearthquake tectonic uplift. Comparisons of 1964 and 1965 tidal observations at Valdez, Whittier, and Homer, in the zone of subsidence, indicated apparent continued subsidence ranging from 2.6 feet at Valdez to 0.3 foot at Whittier. The postearthquake subsidence at Valdez is definitely related to seaward extension and subsidence of the thick prism of deltaic deposits on which the tide gage is situated; much or all of the subsidence at the other two sites, both of which are on thick deposits of unconsolidated sediment, could also have resulted from surficial effects.

The available data on postearthquake changes outlined above are internally inconsistent and inconclusive with reference to postearthquake vertical movements. Disregarding the Valdez, Whittier, and Homer stations, where superficial subsidence of unconsolidated deposits is known or suspected to be large, the repeated postearthquake tidal observations indicate either recovery (by uplift) of as much as 0.5 foot or no change in the subsided zone. However, the repeated levelings on the Portage-Anchorage line and repeated gravity readings at Anchorage have been interpreted as indicating either continued subsidence or sta-

bility in that part of the zone of subsidence. On the other hand, tidal observations in the zone that was uplifted during the earthquake suggests either postearthquake subsidence of as much as 0.3 foot or stability, whereas the pair of gravity measurements at Middleton Island in this zone suggest additional uplift of about 2 feet. Repeated tidal observations, levelings, and gravity readings over a longer time period will be required before definite conclusions may be drawn concerning the postearthquake pattern of adjustments in the deformed region. It is abundantly clear, from available data, however, that there was no large rapid postearthquake recovery of vertical displacement comparable to the recoveries reported after some major earthquakes along the coasts of Japan and South America.

EFFECTS OF THE TECTONIC DISPLACEMENTS

Regional vertical tectonic displacements, both upward and downward, have caused profound modifications in shoreline morphology and attendant widespread effects on the biota. Changes in the position of the shorelines relative to sea level directly affected numerous coastal installations, shipping, and the fishing and shellfish industries. A major indirect effect of the vertical movements was the generation of a train of destructive seismic sea waves that were responsible for 35 of the 115 fatalities and for much of the property damage attributable to the earthquake. The movements also appear to have generated atmospheric and ionospheric disturbances that were detectable at several places in the conterminous United States.

The systematic regional horizontal displacements may have caused waves in certain confined and semiconfined bodies of surface water, and related porosity changes may have caused temporary water losses from surface streams and lakes as well as drops in water levels of some wells that tap confined aquifers.

Because the displacements were along faults that are under water and in uninhabited places on land they did not damage any works of man. Had they occurred in inhabited areas, however, these displacements surely would have caused extensive damage to structures built across them. It is also reasonably certain that phenomena related to the reverse faulting, such as the landsliding, extension cracking, and severe warping that occurred in a belt as much as 3,000 feet wide adjacent to the fault traces (Plafker, 1967b), would have been a definite hazard for engineering works.

Most of the effects resulting from vertical movement of the shoreline have been known from other earthquakes in coastal areas throughout the world. Especially detailed descriptions have been given by Tarr and Martin (1912) of the various physiographic and biologic effects of uplift and subsidence associated with the great earthquakes of 1899, centered near Yakutat Bay along the Gulf of Alaska coast. Effects of such movements on the works of man have also been amply documented for numerous major earthquakes along the coasts of South America, New Zealand, India, Japan, and elsewhere, most of which have been summarized by Richter (1958). Although submarine tectonic movements have long been suspected as the most probable generative mechanism for seismic sea waves, the 1964 Alaska earthquake provides what is probably the clearest evidence for a cause-and-effect relationship between these two phenomena. Atmospheric disturbances of the type associated with the 1964 earthquake have been recorded previously after large volcanic explosions and nuclear detonations, but they have never before been observed in association with tectonic earthquakes. To the writer's knowledge, there are no published reports relating surface-water disturbances or ground-water changes to horizontal tectonic displacements during previous earthquakes.

PHYSIOGRAPHIC CHANGES

Tectonic subsidence, augmented locally by surficial subsidence of unconsolidated deposits, resulted in narrowing or, in extreme cases, complete submergence of beaches. Sea water inundated the lower reaches of some streams in subsided areas as much as 4,500 feet inland from the former mouths, and salt water encroached upon former beach-barred lakes at stream mouths or bay heads (Plafker and Kachadoorian, 1966, p. D27). Beach berms and deltas in subsided areas rapidly shifted landward and built up into equilibrium with the new, relatively higher sea levels (pl. 4B). Former reefs and low-lying islands along the coast were submerged, and some tombolo-tied points or capes became islands. Wave action at the higher sea levels caused rapid erosion of shorelines—especially those composed of poorly consolidated deposits that were brought within reach of the tides (fig. 19). An irreplaceable loss resulting from such accelerated erosion of these deposits was destruction of coastal archaeological sites at several places in the Kodiak Island group and on the southern Kenai Peninsula.

The major effect of tectonic uplift was to shift the extreme high-

19.—Spruce trees on a spit near the mouth of Resurrection Bay killed by salt-water immersion and undermined by erosion after the land subsided about 3 feet. Photograph taken at a 9-foot tide stage, July 10, 1964.

tide line seaward and thereby expose parts of the littoral and, at some places, the sublittoral zones (frontispiece; figs. 14, 20). In the areas of maximum uplift on southwestern Montague Island, the emergent sea floor is as much as 1,800 feet wide (Plafker, 1967b, pl. 1, 2). As a consequence, former beaches and sublittoral marine deposits were rapidly incised by streams that cut down through them to new, relatively lower base levels (fig. 21). In many places, beach-barred lakes were drained in varying degrees by incision of their outlet streams. About 8 or 9 feet of uplift at the outlet of shallow Bering Lake, which formerly was reached by high tides, caused the lake to be suddenly reduced in area by about 4 square miles to a third its preearthquake size. Beaches and deltas developed below, and seaward from, their previous positions (fig. 14). Along the uplifted shores, preearthquake beaches, sea cliffs, driftwood lines, sea caves, notches, stacks, and benches were elevated above their normal position relative to sea level. Similarly, in offshore areas,

uplift created new islands and exposed reefs at stages of tide when they formerly were under water.

TILTING OF LAKE BASINS

Regional tilting or warping of the land surface seems to have caused permanent shoreline changes at Kenai and Tustumena lakes on the Kenai Peninsula. It may have had comparable effects on other lakes for which observational data are unavailable.

Tilting of Kenai Lake, which is about 25 miles long, is indicated by changes in the relative position of the bench marks that had been established near its ends prior to the earthquake. Although the accuracy of some of the recovered bench mark positions is open to question, the postearthquake survey suggests that the western end of the lake sank 3.0 feet with respect to the east end, and that the dip of the tilted surface is N. 72° W. at 1 foot per 5.4 miles (McCulloch, 1966, p. A29). These data are corroborated by the fact that the west end of the lake is close to the axis of subsidence (pl. 1) and that residents report a relative lower-

20.—Rocky surf-cut platform a quarter of a mile wide at Cape Cleare, Montague Island, exposed by 26 feet of tectonic uplift. The white band on the upper part of the platform consists mainly of barnacles and calcareous worm tubes; brown algae, or "kelp," cover much of the surface below the barnacle zone. Photograph taken at about zero tide stage, March 31, 1964. Compare with frontispiece, taken 2 months later in same general area.

21.—Bay-head deposits in MacLeod Harbor, Montague Island, deeply incised by stream erosion following about 33 feet of uplift. Arrows indicate the positions of pre- and postearthquake high-tide shorelines. Photograph taken August 6, 1965.

ing of the lake level at the eastern end after the earthquake (McCulloch, 1966).

The long axis of the 20-mile-long Tustumena Lake and its outlet stream, the Kasilof River, are oriented northwest-southeast, or almost normal to the projected trend of isobase contours in the area (pl. 1). After the earthquake, water levels at the inlet end of the lake reportedly rose above the banks; about 2 feet of southeastward tilt of the lake basin is thus suggested (J. D. Reardon, oral commun., 1965). The amount of tilt across the basin, as indicated by reported relative changes in lake levels, is in good agreement with that suggested by the spacing of isobase contours projected from the coast into the Kenai Lowland area (pl. 1).

TILTING OF RIVER DRAINAGES

Regional tilting may also have temporarily reduced the flow of certain rivers, such as the Copper, Kenai, and Kasilof Rivers, whose flow directions were opposite to the regional tilt (pl. 1). The Kasilof River was reduced to a trickle the day after the earthquake (Alaska Dept. Fish and Game, 1965, p. 23) and the Copper River reportedly ceased flowing at its mouth for several days. Immediately after the earthquake the Kenai River for almost a mile below the Kenai Lake outlet temporarily reversed its direction and flowed back towards Kenai Lake (McCulloch, 1966, p. A28), but it is not clear to what extent this reversal was due to tilting and to what extent it was related to the seiching of the lake.

Because rivers and lakes were approximately at their lowest annual levels when the tilting occurred, slight changes in gradient caused disproportionately large changes in discharge. The changes probably were largely related to upstream tilting of the larger lake basins in the drainage systems with consequent reductions or reversals of discharge until the basins once again filled to the spillover point. To some extent, however, the reduced flow in the river channels may have resulted from the lowered gradient of the beds. The regional tilting averaged 1 foot per 4.8 miles in the lower Copper River drainage and 1 foot per 10 miles or less in the Kenai Lowland. Other causes, such as channel blockage by river ice or landslides, may also have contributed to the reported temporary declines in discharge.

BIOLOGIC CHANGES

Vertical displacements of the shoreline strongly affected both the fauna and the flora over a vast segment of coastal south-central Alaska. Some of these effects were apparent within days after the earthquake; others, which depend upon the complex interrelations of one organism to another and to their habitat, will not be known for a long time. G Dallas Hanna, who studied the biologic effects of the earthquake in the littoral zone, has given a graphic summary of these earthquake-related changes (Hanna, 1964). The results of detailed governmental and private studies of the effects of the earthquake on intertidal organisms, land plants, and fish are to be reported in the Biology Volume of the planned series of publications of the Committee on the Alaska Earthquake of the National Academy of Sciences (W. L. Petrie, oral commun., 1968).

The most conspicuous effect of subsidence was the fringe of terrestrial vegetation killed by salt-water inundation at periods of high tides (pl. 4B; figs. 12, 19).

22.—Spruce trees in Nuka Passage on the southern Kenai Peninsula killed by repeated inundation with salt water in an area of 6.3 feet of tectonic subsidence. Algae and animals of the upper littoral have encroached upward into the former terrestrial environment. Inset shows a barnacle (white) and numerous *Littorina* or "periwinkles" (gray) on the roots of a tree. Photograph taken July 22, 1965.

Virtually all noncliffed shorelines that subsided more than 3 feet clearly showed fringes of dead vegetation within 2 months after the earthquake. In some sheltered localities at which vegetation extended down to the extreme high-tide line, dead vegetation was noticeable even where subsidence was as little as 1 foot.

Trees, bushes, beach grass, and muskeg along many former beaches were killed and partially buried in gravel or sand. Extensive areas of coastal marshland and forest that formerly had provided winter forage for grazing animals or nesting grounds for migratory birds were inundated. In such places, marine organisms encroached upward into the new littoral zone and it was not uncommon to find barnacles, limpets, and algae living on or among the remains of land plants (fig. 22).

The effects of subsidence on sessile intertidal marine organisms submerged below their normal growth positions were not readily apparent. Undoubtedly, individuals near the lower depth range of the species were adversely affected by the changed conditions and were gradually replaced by other organisms better adjusted to the deeper water environment.

Effects of uplift on the biota of the littoral zone were more striking than those resulting from subsidence, because the uplift caused complete extermination of organisms that were permanently elevated above their normal ranges. The width of the resultant band of dead organisms depended, of course, on both the amount of uplift and the slope of the uplifted shore. In areas where uplift exceeded the local tide range, as on islands in southern Prince William Sound, on parts of the mainland coast to the east of the Sound, and on several offshore islands on the Continental Shelf, destruction of the sessile organisms was almost absolute. Even many of the mobile forms—including starfish, gastropods, and small fish—did not survive. Some of the effects of uplift

23.—Closeup view of surf-cut surface at Cape Cleare, Montague Island, shown in frontispiece. The white coating on the rocks consists primarily of desiccated calcareous algae and bryozoans; the dark ropelike objects are stipes of laminarians ("kelp"). Photograph taken June 1, 1964.

on organisms of the littoral zone are illustrated by plates 3A, 4A; figures 5, 23, and 24. The dramatic change with time in the appearance of the shore and sea floor after about 26 feet of uplift at the southwest end of Montague Island may best be appreciated by comparing the aerial photograph taken on March 30th, 3 days after the earthquake (fig. 20), with one taken 2 months later on May 30th (frontispiece).

By August 1964 a few land plants had encroached onto the fringe of shore reclaimed from the sea, and in the summer of 1965 scattered clumps of grasses and wildflowers grew everywhere, on raised beaches and deltas and in favorable localities on rock benches amid the dead and dried remains of marine organisms (fig. 13). In a few years the bleak aspect of these fringes of uplifted shore should become subdued by a luxuriant cover of brush and timber comparable to that growing on older uplifted marine terraces in the area. By July 1965,

land plants had covered much of the raised platform on Middleton Island and sea birds had already begun nesting in the former intertidal zone.

Throughout the uplifted areas in and near Prince William Sound, the mortality of all types

of shellfish—including commercially important razor clams—has been estimated to be as high as 90 percent by G Dallas Hanna (oral commun., 1965). At many places where uplift exceeds the normal tide range, the clam population was literally wiped out. In such areas, the populations of birds, fish, and other animals that normally feed on shellfish must eventually readjust downward to the reduced food supply.

The potential effect of the land-level changes on the important salmon runs in the affected areas cannot be fully evaluated until the matured 1964 hatch returns from the sea to spawn. Spawning areas for pink and chum salmon, which are intertidal spawners, received major damage due to changes in land level and seismic sea waves (Alaska Dept. Fish and Game, 1965, p. 3; Thorsteinson, 1965). Spawning areas of upstream migrants, including the red and silver salmon, where relatively unaffected by the earthquake.

Many low-lying coastal lakes that were important habitats for

24.—Mass of dead starfish in a depression on the uplifted platform shown on figure 23. Photograph taken May 31, 1964.

waterfowl and for fresh-water fish were damaged mainly by salt-water pollution related to subsidence or to draining in varying degrees resulting from uplift and incision of their outlet streams. A few of the uplifted lakes that formerly received salt water through their outlets during high tides become entirely fresh with consequent changes in the number and species of fish they can support.

GENERATION OF SEISMIC SEA WAVES

Most major earthquakes in coastal areas that involve vertical tectonic displacements beneath the sea are accompanied by seismic sea waves, and the 1964 earthquake generated one of the larger seismic sea waves of recent times (Grantz and others, 1964, p. 11–12; Van Dorn, 1964; Plafker and Mayo, 1965; Plafker and Kachadoorian, 1966; Pararas-Carayannis, 1967). Between the southern tip of Kodiak Island and Kayak Island, these waves took 20 lives and caused destruction all along the ocean coast. The waves were especially destructive along the ocean coast of the Kodiak group of islands and the Kenai Peninsula areas that had been lowered relative to sea level by tectonic subsidence or by the combination of tectonic subsidence and compaction of unconsolidated deposits during the earthquake. In addition, the waves, which were recorded on tide gages throughout the Pacific Ocean, caused 15 deaths and major damage in British Columbia, Oregon, and California.

The wave-source mechanism was initially investigated by Van Dorn (1964), who concluded that the waves were generated by a dipolar displacement of water resulting from regional tectonic warping. He inferred that the positive pole of this disturbance included much of the shallow Continental Shelf bordering the Gulf of Alaska within the major zone of uplift, and that the negative pole lay largely under land or beneath Cook Inlet and Shelikof Strait in the major zone of subsidence. From preliminary data on the amount and distribution of vertical displacements along the shore, Van Dorn (1964, p. 17) calculated that the total potential energy imparted to the positive part of the seismic sea wave by submarine uplift (assuming (1) vertical displacement of 6 feet that increases progressively from zero at the southwest end to 6 feet at the northwest end and (2) source dimensions of 240 miles by 100 miles), was 1.7×10^{14} ft-lbs (2.3×10^{21} ergs), or only about 0.1–0.05 percent of the approximately 10^{24} to 2×10^{24} ergs of seismic-wave energy released by the main shock. Pararas-Carayannis (1967), using source dimensions of 93 miles (150 km) by 435 miles (700 km) and the same average uplift as inferred by Van Dorn, arrived at a total water-wave energy of 5.88×10^{21} ergs.

The Geological Survey's subsequent studies of the vertical displacements on land and their probable extension beneath the sea provide additional data relevant to the probable configuration of the initial positive wave and its energy content. These data suggest that the initial wave form, due to vertical displacement of the sea floor on the Continental Shelf, probably had the general cross-sectional shape indicated by the profile in figure 15 and that the offshore areas involved in the uplift and the amounts of sea-floor displacement are considerably greater than was indicated by preliminary reconnaissance surveys. Thus, the general shape of the deformed surface on the Continental Shelf may be roughly approximated by a broad low-amplitude upwarp with minimum dimensions of 400 by about 75 miles, superimposed upon which is a narrow belt of maximum uplift about 6 miles wide that is inferred to extend some 350 miles southwestward from Montague Island. As indicated on profiles $A-A'$, $B-B'$ $C-C'$ plate 1, average uplift across the broad upwarp is roughly about 12 feet and that across the narrow zone is probably at least 30 feet. Because this highly simplified model does not consider the additional wave energy at the ends of the deformed region, where uplift gradually falls off to zero, or in that part lying seaward from the edge of the Continental Shelf where the deformation field is unknown, the calculated energy should be considered as a minimum.

If the initial wave form approximates that of the uplift, total potential energy transferred to the water, E_t was the sum of the energy in both the broad low-amplitude part of the wave (E_1) and in the narrow superimposed high-amplitude part (E_2). Total potential energy transferred to the water, E_t, derived by using Iida's equation (1963, p. 65), was

$$E_t = E_1 + E_2 = \frac{\rho g (h_1)^2 A_1}{2} + \frac{\rho g (h_2)^2 A_2}{2}$$

where ρ is the density of sea water, g is the gravitational acceleration, h is the average vertical displacement, and A is the area over which the deformation occurred. Therefore, by substitution,

$$E_1 = (1.1)(32)(15)^2(6)(350)(5,280)^2 = 4.6 \times 10^{14} \text{ ft-lbs } (6.2 \times 10^{21} \text{ ergs});$$

$$E_2 = (1.1)(32)(6)^2(75)(400)(5,280)^2 = 1.06 \times 10^{15} \text{ ft-lbs } (1.4 \times 10^{22} \text{ ergs});$$

and their sum,

$$E_t = 1.5 \times 10^{15} \text{ ft-lbs } (2 \times 10^{22} \text{ ergs}).$$

These figures suggest that the total potential energy in the positive part of the wave may be about an order of magnitude larger than that derived by Van Dorn, or 1.0–0.5 percent of the seismic wave energy release. According to the model used, roughly one-third of the energy was concentrated in the narrow high-amplitude part of the wave along the axis of maximum uplift and two-thirds was distributed over the low-amplitude part of the wave which has an area roughly 15 times larger. Thus, the relatively greater damage and higher wave runups along the outer coast of the Kodiak group of islands and the Kenai Peninsula, as compared to the ocean coast of Prince William Sound and the mainland east of the sound, appears to be a function of proximity to the narrow zone of high wave-energy concentration along the axis of maximum uplift.

ATMOSPHERIC EFFECTS

An atmospheric pressure wave that was the atmospheric counterpart of the seismic sea waves was recorded on microbarographs at the University of California at Berkeley and at the Scripps Institute of Oceanography at La Jolla, Calif. The wave traveled at the speed of sound in air (roughly 1,050 ft per sec in the lower atmosphere), reaching Berkeley, 1,950 miles from the epicenter, 2 hours and 40 minutes after start of the earthquake (Bolt, 1964, p. 1095) and La Jolla 39 minutes later (Van Dorn, 1964, fig. 5). Travel times to these stations correspond to an initiating disturbance in the epicentral region during the earthquake. The pressure wave's signature further suggests that it was caused by the vertical tectonic displacements of the land and sea surfaces that accompanied the earthquake.

The atmospheric pressure wave also seems to have caused a traveling ionospheric disturbance that was observed in Hawaii, Alaska, and the conterminous United States on high-frequency radio sounders (Row, 1966). The disturbance at Boulder, Colo., was characterized by an abrupt onset, speeds appropriate to sound waves above 100 km in altitude, an oscillatory long-period tail, and an initial negative doppler. Computations by Row indicate that the essential features of the observations may be reproduced by sudden vertical ground displacement of the type observed in the epicentral region below a plane isothermal gravitating atmosphere.

WATER DISTURBANCES POSSIBLY RELATED TO HORIZONTAL DISPLACEMENTS

Water disturbances that accompanied the earthquake in some lakes, fiords, and rivers may have been generated by inertial effects of the water bodies as the land mass was displaced horizontally beneath them. Horizontal movement of a deep steep-sided basin or fiord, if it occurred fast enough, would be expected to impart potential energy to a contained water mass by changing its surface configuration as illustrated diagrammatically by figure 25. Thus, because of its inertia, water would tend to pile up above its original level along shores on the side of the basin opposite to the direction of displacement, and it would simultaneously be lowered along shores in the direction of displacement. For a given amount and rate of displacement, the effect of horizontal movement on the water mass would be proportionally greatest where orientation of shores is normal to the direction of horizontal movement and relatively steep basin sides permitted the maximum energy to be

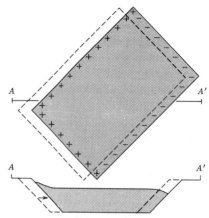

25.—Schematic diagram illustrating the postulated effect of a sudden horizontal displacement on water in an enclosed basin, the amount of displacement assumed to be small relative to the dimensions of the basin. Dashed lines indicate the original position of the basin, solid lines the position after displacement. Symbols along the basin margin in the plan view (above) indicate shores along which an initial rise (+) or drop (−) in water level would occur; profile A–A' shows a possible configuration of the water surface immediately after the displacement.

transferred from the basin to the contained water mass.

McCulloch (1966, p. A39) has reported uninodal and multinodal seiche waves in Kenai Lake with half-wave amplitudes of 5–6 feet and initial runup heights that were locally as much as 30 feet. He inferred that they were generated by a tectonic tilting of the lake basin that amounted to no more than 3 feet. A possible alternative explanation, however, is that the waves and seiche in Kenai Lake—a lake which lies in a long narrow steep-sided glacial valley—resulted mainly from the 15–25 feet of south-southeast horizontal translation of the lake basin that accompanied the earthquake in that area (fig. 16). Because of the irregular shape of the basin and uncertainties regarding the rate at which the horizontal displacements occurred, it is not possible to determine quantitatively whether the horizontal displacements alone or in combination with tectonic tilting could generate the waves recorded at Kenai Lake.

Sudden rises of water level during or immediately after the earthquake, observed at numerous coastal localities where there was no evidence for submarine sliding, strong tilting, or faulting could also have been caused by the horizontal displacements. Within Prince William Sound, where horizontal displacements in a south-to-southeast direction ranged from about 20 to 62 feet (fig. 16), local waves of unknown origin were responsible for the loss of at least 28 lives and caused extensive property damage at Chenega, Port Ashton, Port San Juan, Port Oceanic, Perry Island, and probably at Port Nellie Juan and Point Nowell (Plafker and others, 1969). Similar waves that did not cause damage also were reported at Port Wells, Unakwik Inlet, Tatitlek, Naked Island, and several other localities in Prince William Sound. Much of the damage from local waves was concentrated along east-west- to northeast-southwest-trending shores in semiconfined bays or along deep steep-sided fiords and straits. These waves, which appeared at widely separated localities in the sound within minutes after the earthquake was first felt, must have been generated locally and almost simultaneously. Most eyewitnesses observed a single large wave with runup as high as 70 feet (as at Chenega), preceded or followed by much smaller waves at intervals of a few minutes. The sudden onset, short period, and local distribution of the waves distinguish them from the train of long-period seismic sea waves generated in the Gulf of Alaska that did not reach the outer coast

of the Kenai Peninsula until about 20 minutes after the start of the earthquake. That the waves may have been generated by relative seaward movement of the land mass in Prince William Sound is suggested by (1) their appearance during the earthquake, (2) their occurrence in an area where there were large horizontal displacements, and by (3) the orientation and configuration of the affected shorelines.

Unexplained waves were also observed in widely scattered coastal areas of the Kenai Peninsula and Kodiak Islands, where retriangulation data are unavailable but where significant horizontal displacements probably occurred. For example, waves as high as 9 feet were reported by eyewitnesses in the Homer area during and immediately after the earthquake. Such waves could not be attributed to sliding, slumping, or other causes (Waller, 1966a, p. D3–D4). The curious breaking and surging of the waves on the tidal flats suggested to one observer that "the land was being shoved under the bay" (Waller, 1966a, p. D4). Rapid, calm rises in water level of 9 feet at Kodiak (Plafker and Kachadoorian, 1966, p. D30) and of about 26 feet at Whittier (Plafker and Mayo, 1965, p. 15) that cannot be readily ascribed to any other cause may also have been related to horizontal displacement of the land.

In summary, horizontal displacements of the magnitude indicated by retriangulation data, if they occurred fast enough, should theoretically generate waves in water bodies of suitable size and configuration. This movement may have been the cause, or a contributing cause, of some waves observed in certain localities during or immediately after the earthquake that cannot be directly re-

lated to vertical tectonic displacements, regional tilting, seismic shaking, or submarine landslides.

CHANGES IN ARTESIAN-WELL LEVELS

Systematic long-term drops in water levels of wells tapping confined aquifers in Pleistocene and late Tertiary strata were recorded at various widely spaced localities within the zone of tectonic subsidence (Waller, 1966a, p. D16–D18; 1966b, p. A18–A26). Records of seven representative artesian wells from Anchorage, Chugiak, and four communities on the Kenai Peninsula are shown in figure 26. The residual drops in well levels at the time of the earthquake range from about 7 to 25 feet, and none of the wells showed full recovery within a year after the earthquake.

Observed long-term changes in well levels suggest changes in the physical structure of the aquifers and a net increase in aquifer-pore space. Such changes could be caused by rearrangement of grains or fractures as a result of the horizontal extension (on the order of 2×10^{-4}) and (or) the elastic dilatation that is known or inferred to have affected the areas in which these wells are located.

A similar effect was looked for, but not found, in the oil wells of the Swanson River oil field located in the zone of tectonic subsidence near Kenai (R. I. Levorsen, written commun., 1966). Any small strain change that may have occurred probably was masked by changes in volume of the relatively compressible oil-water-gas mixture filling the pore space of the field reservoir.

The only artesian water wells in the zone of tectonic uplift are in a thick deposit of glacial drift at Cordova (Waller, 1966b, p. A20–A21). Because these wells did not have recorders installed in them, their response to the earth-

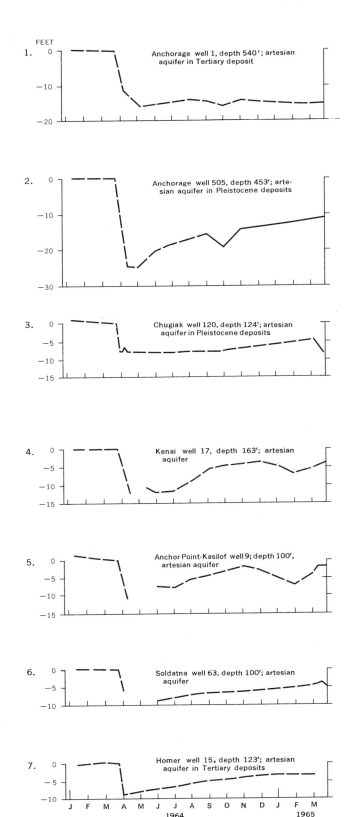

26.—Artesian well records from the zone of tectonic subsidence showing systematic drop in water levels at the time of the earthquake. After Waller (1966a, fig. 13; 1966b, figs. 14, 20, 22).

quake cannot be correlated with that of the wells in the zone that subsided. However, comparison of measurements in three wells made in July 1962 with measurements made 4 months after the earthquake showed about a 1-foot rise in water level, rather than the residual drop that characterized wells in the subsided zone.

STREAMFLOW, LAKE LEVELS, AND SHALLOW WELLS

Changes in the levels of many lakes, streams, and shallow wells in unconfined aquifers were observed at numerous localities within the zone of tectonic subsidence. In general, the reported changes involved temporary water losses (Waller, 1966b, p. A8–A11; Plafker and Kachadoorian, 1966, p. D23–D24). One of the more probable causes for such changes is an increase of intergranular or fracture porosity in the surrounding materials consequent upon horizontal extension and elastic dilatation across the subsided zone during the earthquake.

COASTAL FACILITIES AND SHIPPING

Regional land-level changes— including both subsidence and uplift—caused direct and costly damage to homes, canneries, transportation routes, airfields, docks, harbors, and other facilities throughout the affected areas (figs. 27, 28). Many facilities that had otherwise been unaffected either by the earthquake or the destructive water waves associated with it were damaged by land-level changes. Such changes had relatively few short-term beneficial effects on the works of man. Because the various forms of damage resulting from vertical tectonic movements have already been described in detail in the various reports of this series on effects to communities (U.S. Geol. Survey Professional Paper 542) and were

27.—Road along Womens Bay, Kodiak Island, in an area of about 5.5 feet of tectonic subsidence and an unknown, but probably substantial, amount of local settling of unconsolidated deposits. Since subsidence, the road has been flooded at high tide and subject to erosion by waves. Photograph taken at 4.0-foot tide stage, July 20, 1964.

28.—Canneries and fishermen's homes along Orca Inlet in Prince William Sound placed above the reach of most tides due to about 6 feet of uplift. Photograph was taken on July 27, 1964, at a 9-foot tide stage, which would have reached beneath the docks prior to the earthquake.

summarized by Hansen and Eckel (1966) and Eckel (1967), they need not be described here.

GRAVITY CHANGES

Vertical displacements were accompanied by measurable changes in gravity at several stations where comparative pre- and postearthquake gravity readings were made (D. F. Barnes, 1966; oral commun. 1966). The stations were distributed in both the zones of subsidence and the zones of uplift where

changes in elevation ranged from —5.8 feet at Portage to about +11 feet at Middleton Island. Corresponding gravity changes were between +0.5 milligals to —0.67 milligals. Barnes (1966, p. 455) noted that the gravity changes, at least in the uplifted area, tend to approximate the Bouguer, rather than the free-air, gradients. Although uncertainties in relocating some of the station positions preclude firm conclusions, the data suggest that there has been a redistribution of mass in at least those parts of the deformed region where the changes correspond to Bouguer gradients.

COMPARISON WITH OTHER EARTHQUAKES

In terms of areal extent of deformation and amount of residual horizontal and vertical displacement, the 1964 Alaska earthquake is one of the most impressive tectonic events ever recorded. This fact is brought out by table 4, which compares the deformation associated with the 1964 event with that of selected great earthquakes for which quantitative data are available.

The area of observable crustal deformation, or probable deformation, that accompanied the 1964 earthquake is larger than any such area known to have been associated with a single earthquake in historic times. Comparable tectonic deformations have probably occurred during other great historic earthquakes, but if so they were beneath the sea, along linear coast lines, or inland, where it generally is not possible to determine the areal extent of such features with any degree of confidence. For example, the area affected by vertical displacements during the great series of Chilean earthquakes in May and June of 1960 extended

TABLE 4.—*Comparative deformations of the 1964 Alaska earthquake and some other great earthquakes*

Earthquake	Date	Approximate Magnitude (Richter scale)	Probable area of surface warping (square miles)	Maximum vertical warping relative to sea level (feet)	Maximum relative horizontal distortion (feet)	Maximum relative fault displacement (feet) (H, horizontal; V, vertical)	Data source
1964 Alaska	March 27, 1964	8.4+	108,000 (major zones only).	+38, −7½	64	2H?; 20–23V	This paper.
Niigata, Japan	June 16, 1964	7.7	≈20,000	+4.9, −1.5	No data	Submarine only, displacement unknown.	Earthquake Research Institute (1964).
1960 Chile	May 22, 1960	8.3	17,000+	+10–13, −7.2	____do	No known surface faults.	Saint-Amand (1961).
Lituya Bay, Alaska	July 10, 1958	8.0	No data; fault rupture 115+ miles long.	None reported	____do	21.5H; 6V	Tocher (1960).
Gobi-Altai, Mongolia	December 4, 1957. (G.)	8.6	≈32,000 (area of faulting).	No data	____do	29H; 30V	Florensov and Solonenko (1963).
Nankaido, Japan	December 20. 1946.	8.5	20,000+	+2.9, −2.0	6.2	No known surface faults.	Inoue (1960, p. 84–85).
Hawkes Bay, New Zealand	February 3, 1931	7.9	2,000 (minimum)	+9, −2 to 3	No data	6–7H; 6–8V?	Henderson (1933).
Kwanto, Japan	September 1, 1923.	8.3	10.+	+6.6, −5.3	15	6.6V	Muto (1932); Inamura (1930).
San Francisco, Calif.	April 18, 1906	8.3	No data; fault rupture 270 miles long.	Minor	≈20	21H; 3V	Richter (1958, p. 476–486).
Yakutat Bay, Alaska	September 1899	8.5–8.6	1,300 (minimum)	+47, −7(?)	No data	8+H?; 8V (on subsidiary faults).	Tarr and Martin (1912).
Assam, India	June 12, 1897	8.7	2,000 (minimum)	No data	____do	0H?; 35V	Richter (1958, p. 49–50).

north-south some 420 miles along the Pacific Ocean coast, and at least 40 miles in an east-west direction at the Gulf of Ancud near the southern end of the affected area (Saint-Amand, 1961). If the inland extent of deformation to the north is comparable to that in the Gulf of Ancud, the minimum area of surface warping on land would be 17,000 square miles. The distribution of aftershocks and the source area of the destructive train of seismic sea waves associated with the earthquake suggest further that significant movements occurred over an extensive area of the sea floor adjacent to the deformed Pacific coast of Chile.

Other major earthquakes in which long sections of the west coast of South America reportedly changed elevation ocurred in 1751, 1822, 1835, 1837, and 1906 (Richter, 1958); data on the areal distribution of the changes, however, are scarce. Warping associated with one of these, the violent Chilean earthquake of 1822, gave rise to speculation that an area of some 100,000 square miles of coastal Chile had been uplifted (Lyell, 1874, p. 94), but there are few data to support this asser-

tion. Imamura (1930) lists 26 Japanese earthquakes that resulted in vertical displacements. Regional warping has accompanied some of the more recent Japanese earthquakes, notably the 1946 Nankaido earthquake (Inoue, 1960, p. 85) and the 1964 Niigata earthquake (Hatori, 1965, p. 133–136). Elsewhere in the circum-Pacific region, additional large-scale vertical tectonic deformation was reported following the major earthquakes of 1848, 1855, and 1931 in New Zealand, and 1762 in India and Burma. Known areas of deformation associated with all of these earthquakes, however, are but small fractions of that involved in the 1964 Alaska event.

The 38 feet of uplift on Montague Island during the 1964 earthquake is known to have been exceeded only by the 47.3 feet of uplift that occurred during the earthquakes of 1899 that were centered at Yakutat Bay, 185 miles to the east (Tarr and Martin, 1912, pl. 14). Reported submarine vertical displacement offshore from Montague Island, however, may equal or perhaps exceed the 1899 movements (Malloy, 1964, p. 1048).

Subsidences roughly equal to,

or slightly larger than, the 7½ feet that accompanied the 1964 earthquake have been recorded during previous seismic events, although at many places determination of the absolute amount has been complicated by surficial slumping or compaction effects in unconsolidated deposits. For example, the largest reported coastal subsidence, 17 feet, which accompanied the Great Cutch earthquake (Lyell, 1874, p. 98) was at the mouth of the Indus River in an area where significant surficial compaction of deltaic deposits was to be expected.

Following the 1923 Kwanto, Japan, earthquake, unusually large submarine displacements, involving as much as 825 feet of uplift and 1,320 feet of subsidence on the sea floor in Sagami Bay, were inferred from a comparison of pre- and postearthquake soundings (Richter, 1958, p. 570–571). However, because of (1) possible errors in the positioning of the preearthquake survey and (2) the effects of submarine sliding, these data are of doubtful value for inferring tectonic movement; consequently they are not included in table 4.

The regional horizontal displacements associated with the 1964 earthquake, which were about 64 feet, are significantly larger than any previously recorded. By contrast, regional displacements associated with the great 1923 Kwanto earthquake, as indicated by retriangulation, were less than 15 feet (Muto, 1932, fig. 6), and the maximum relative displacement resulting from combined distortion and fault offsets associated with the 1906 California earthquake was roughly 21 feet (Reid, 1911).

Measured vertical displacements across the two subsidiary earthquake faults on Montague Island—the Patton Bay fault (20–23 ft) and Hanning Bay fault (16⅓ ft)—are considerably larger than any others of definite reverse type previously described (Plafker, 1967b). A few normal or oblique-slip faults, however, have undergone larger vertical displacements. The largest of these was associated with the 1897 Indian earthquake and reportedly was as much as 35 feet (Richter, 1958, p. 51).

TECTONIC SETTING

In the following sections the 1964 earthquake is viewed from the perspective of its broad relationship to the Aleutian Arc and to other major structural elements of south-central Alaska. Emphasis is placed on the geological and geophysical evidence for late Cenozoic tectonic movements in the immediate region affected by the earthquake. Earlier tectonic features and events, and contemporaneous features and events outside the region affected by the earthquake, are not of primary interest here, although they are mentioned where necessary to provide the setting of the principal features and events that are treated.

Most of Alaska has been studied geologically in a reconnaissance manner, but detailed mapping is still relatively uncommon and is largely confined to a few mining districts and to outcrops of potentially petroliferous or coal-bearing rocks around the margins of sedimentary basins. Gross aspects of the lithology and structure in outcrop areas are reasonably well known, but present knowledge of the geologic record in most places is inadequate for a detailed interpretation of the tectonic history. Subsurface investigations in the vast terrestrial areas of sparse outcrops and in the submarine parts of the Continental Shelf and Aleutian Arc are in a state so rudimentary that geological interpretations based upon them must be considered as very tentative. The spatial distribution of earthquakes and the rapidly increasing number of available fault-plane solutions provide valuable indirect evidence for the orientation and nature of displacements that have given rise to the earthquakes. Recent improvements in locating hypocenters of Alaskan earthquakes should contribute substantially to resolving the precise relationship of the earthquakes to known structural features.

THE ALEUTIAN ARC

The 1964 earthquake occurred in the tectonically complex region where northeast-trending structural elements associated with the Aleutian Arc overlap and merge with arcuate structures of south-central Alaska. The belt of seismic activity and the major zones of tectonic deformation associated with the 1964 earthquake lie largely between and parallel to the chain of active volcanoes and the oceanic trench that constitute the arc and are presumably related genetically to it (fig. 1). Consequently, it is pertinent to review briefly the data and current hypotheses relevant to tectonic processes within the arc.

MAJOR FEATURES

The Aleutian Arc, which sweeps 1,800 miles (2,800 km) across the North Pacific Ocean from Kamchatka to southern Alaska, exhibits all of the striking features characteristic of the festoons of arcs that ring the Pacific basin. These are (1) an arcuate deep oceanic trench — the Aleutian Trench—which is convex toward the ocean basin except near its eastern end, (2) a subparallel volcanic chain on the concave, or inner, side, away from the ocean basin—the Aleutian volcanic arc, (3) an associated belt of active seismicity between the trench and volcanic chain in which the lower limit of hypocenters tends to deepen from the vicinity of the trench toward the arc, and (4) parallel zones of isostatic gravity lows over the trench bottom and gravity highs between the trench bottom and volcanic arc.

The Aleutian Arc differs from most other arcs in that it partly traverses and partly follows along the margin of the oceanic basin (fig. 1). In its western part the arc consists of the Aleutian Ridge, which is surmounted by a chain of volcanoes that comprise the Aleutian Islands, and the Aleutian Trench, which lies at a distance of less than 155 miles (250 km) on the convex (south) side of the ridge. As it approaches south-central Alaska, the distance between the volcanic arc and the trench gradually increases to more than 250 miles (400 km), the belt of seismic activity becomes broader and less well defined, and the trench gradually shallows to become indistinguishable from the floor of the North Pacific Ocean. It is in this eastern portion of the arc that the line of volcanoes and the belt of seismicity overlap and in part merge with preexisting structural elements that roughly parallel the margin of the Gulf of Alaska (fig. 29). The group of volcanoes in the Wrangell Mountains, which are separated from Mount Spurr, the most northerly volcano of the Aleutian Range, by a gap of 420 miles, are similar in age and composition to the Aleutian Arc volcanoes. These similarities, and their position near the eastern end of the Aleutian Trench and its associated belt of intermediate-depth earthquakes, suggest that the Wrangell Mountains volcanoes may also be genetically related to the arc.

The geology of the Aleutian Islands segment of the arc was summarized by Coats (1962), that of the Aleutian Range and nearby areas by Burk (1965). Both of these writers presented thorough reviews of available bathymetric, seismologic, and marine geophysical data as well as hypotheses concerning origin of the arc. Results of detailed marine geophysical surveys along the eastern end of the Aleutian Arc, carried out during 1964 and 1965 by the Scripps Institute of Oceanography and the U.S. Coast and Geodetic Survey,

had not been published at the time this report was completed.

SEISMICITY

Figures 1 and 30 indicate that, in plan, most of the belt of concentrated seismic activity is between the trench and the volcanic chain along the length of the arc; a small number of earthquakes occurred on the south wall of the Aleutian Trench and north of the volcanic chain. Shallow-depth (<70 km) earthquakes have occurred throughout the area included between the Aleutian Trench and the Aleutian volcanic arc, but most of the intermediate-depth earthquakes (70–170 km) were located in the northern part of this area or north of the volcanic chain. The most easterly intermediate-depth earthquakes have been along the coast of the North Pacific Ocean at long 145° W. in the vicinity of the Wrangell Mountains. In south-central Alaska the belt of seismicity associated with the Aleutian Arc bifurcates into a broad zone of shallow and intermediate depth shocks that sweeps northward into central Alaska and a belt of shallow-focus earthquakes that extends eastward along the continental margin. Comparison of figures 2 and 31 shows that the spatial distribution of the seismicity associated with the 1964 Alaska earthquake closely follows the pattern of previously recorded earthquakes along the arc and thereby implies a genetic relationship between them, as suggested by Arthur Grantz, shortly after the event (Grantz and others, 1964, p. 2).

From studies of earthquake distribution along the Aleutian Arc, Benioff (1954, p. 391) concluded that the hypocenters lie in a broad zone that dips northward from the vicinity of the Aleutian Trench at an average angle of 28°. Saint-

Amand (1957, p. 1348) interprets the same data as indicative of a zone dipping at an angle of about 45° between long 172° and 179° W. and at a "somewhat lower angle" in the eastern part of the arc. Detailed studies of seismicity associated with the 1964 earthquake suggest that some planes within the earthquake focal region dip beneath the arc at angles of less than 15°.

Benioff postulated that the dipping seismic zone marked the location of a complex "reverse" fault (termed a "megathrust" by Coats, 1962, p. 103) along which the arc relatively overrides the ocean basin. According to the sea floor spreading hypothesis advanced by Hess (1962, p. 617) and Dietz (1961), arc structures are sites of down-welling mantle-convection currents, and the planar seismic zones dipping beneath them mark the zone of shearing produced by downward-moving material thrust against a less mobile block of the crust and upper mantle. This hypothesis is in general consistent with other data suggestive of active spreading of the sea floor in a northwest-southeast direction away from the East Pacific Rise (Vine, 1966, p. 1412), and with active regional shoreline submergence suggestive of a downward-directed component of deformation near the eastern end of the arc (p. I 60).

Because of the scarcity of standard seismograph stations in Alaska as well as incomplete travel-time data for Alaska earthquakes prior to 1964, the horizontal and vertical distribution of earthquakes could not be defined precisely enough to resolve details of structure within the broad seismic zone either at depth or laterally along it. As a result, large uncertainties exist regarding the

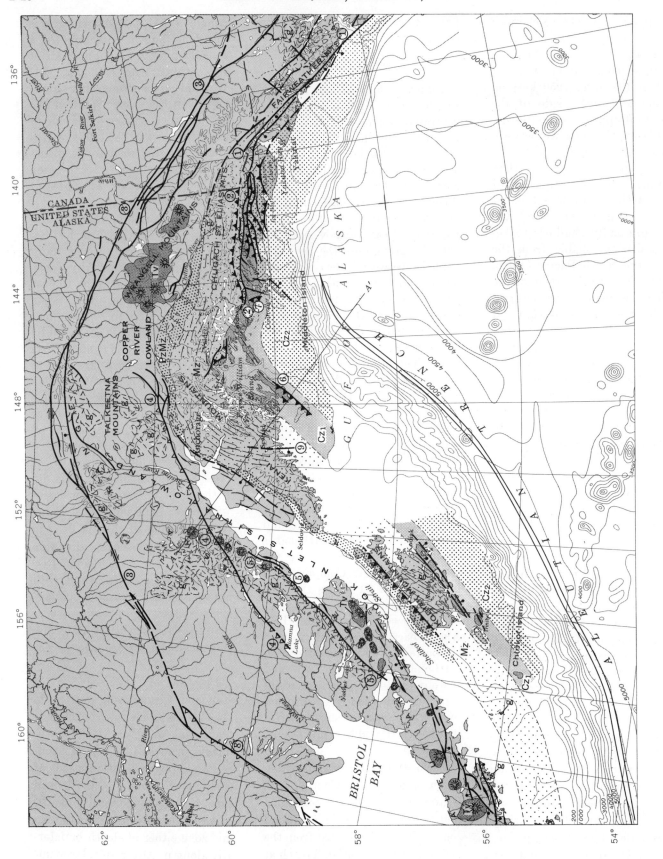

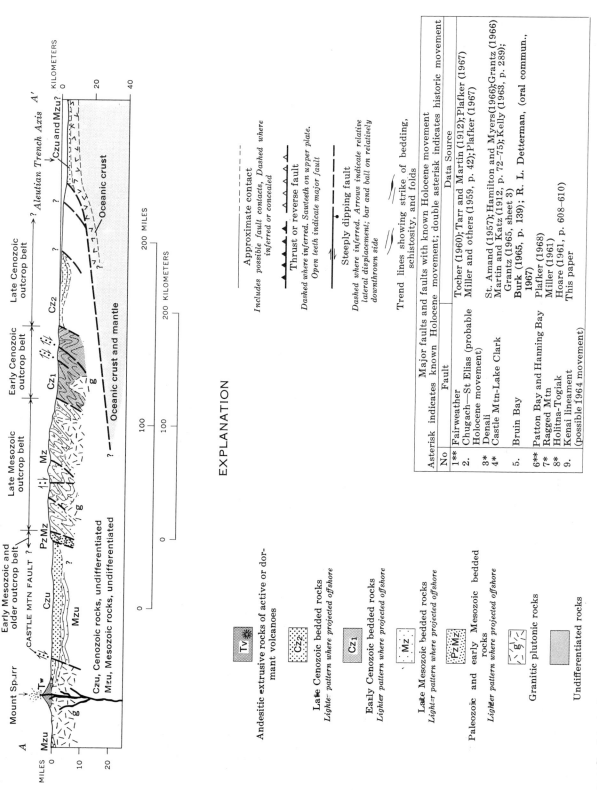

EXPLANATION

Tv ✳ Andesitic extrusive rocks of active or dormant volcanoes

Cz2 Late Cenozoic bedded rocks
Lighter pattern where projected offshore

Cz1 Early Cenozoic bedded rocks
Lighter pattern where projected offshore

Mz Late Mesozoic bedded rocks
Lighter pattern where projected offshore

PzMz Paleozoic and early Mesozoic bedded rocks
Lighter pattern where projected offshore

g Granitic plutonic rocks

Undifferentiated rocks

Czu, Cenozoic rocks, undifferentiated
Mzu, Mesozoic rocks, undifferentiated

Approximate contact
Includes possible fault contacts, Dashed where inferred or concealed

Thrust or reverse fault
Dashed where inferred. Sawteeth on upper plate. Open teeth indicate major fault

Steeply dipping fault
Dashed where inferred. Arrows indicate relative lateral displacement. Arrows indicate relative lateral displacement; bar and ball on relatively downthrown side

Trend lines showing strike of bedding, schistosity, and folds

Major faults and faults with known Holocene movement
Asterisk indicates known Holocene movement; double asterisk indicates historic movement

No	Fault	Data Source
1**	Fairweather	Tocher (1960);Tarr and Martin (1912);Plafker (1967)
2.	Chugach—St Elias (probable Holocene movement)	Miller and others (1959, p. 42);Plafker (1967)
3*	Denali	St. Amand (1957);Hamilton and Myers(1966);Grantz (1966)
4*	Castle Mtn-Lake Clark	Martin and Katz (1912, p. 72–75);Kelly (1963, p. 289); Grantz (1965, sheet 3)
5.	Bruin Bay	Burk (1965, p. 139); R. L. Detterman, (oral commun., 1967)
6**	Patton Bay and Hanning Bay	Plafker (1968)
7*	Ragged Mtn	Miller (1961)
8*	Holitna-Togiak	Hoare (1961, p. 608–610)
9.	Kenai lineament (possible 1964 movement)	This paper

29.—Generalized tectonic map and idealized vertical section showing selected rock units and structural features of south-central Alaska. Indicated displacement direction on faults is the net late Cenozoic movement only. Geology modified from a manuscript tectonic map of Alaska by P. B. King and from unpublished U.S. Geological Survey data; the thickness of crustal layers and the structure shown in the section are largely hypothetical.

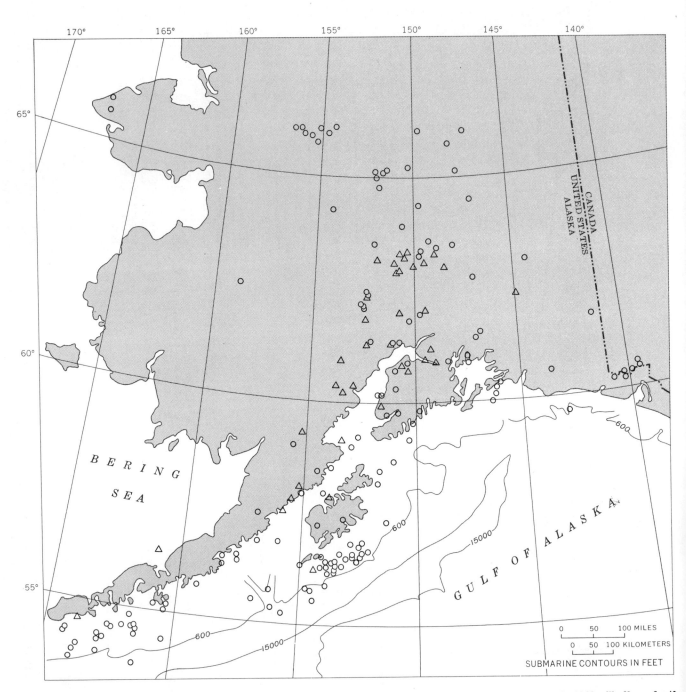

30.—Epicenters of earthquakes ($M \geq 4$) in central Alaska during the period January 1954 to March 1963. Shallow depth (≤ 70 km) earthquakes indicated by circles; intermediate depth (≥ 70 km) indicated by triangles. Data after Tobin and Sykes (1966).

precise orientation and lower depth limits of planes within the zone along which earthquakes originate. Nor is it known to what extent movement on subordinate faults within the upper plate contributes to the recorded seismicity.

Focal mechanism studies of arc earthquakes suggest that the pattern of faulting is extremely complex and that it changes significantly laterally along the arc. The small number of fault-plane solutions of arc earthquake sequences that are based on both P and S waves tend to group in pairs of dip-slip and strike-slip (Bollinger and Stauder, 1965; Stauder, 1967. p. 218–219); those based solely on P waves are almost entirely strike-slip (Hodgson, 1957, p. 641). The dip-slip solutions may be interpreted as representing northwestward-dipping planes that parallel the trend of the eastern part of the arc and are oblique to it in the central part. Coats (1962, p. 95) observed that solutions yielding predominantly strike-slip movement on steeply dipping planes may originate on transverse tear or wrench faults oriented at a large oblique angle to the arc trend. Coats further suggested that the positions of individual volcanoes may be localized by transverse fractures and that their regular position relative to the trench is determined by the distance at which tensional fractures can penetrate through the upper plate to tap eruptible material.

The predominance of transverse faults and other linear elements on land and offshore from the Aleutian Islands (Coats, 1962, fig. 2; Gates and Gibson, 1956, fig. 12) and relatively abrupt transverse boundaries for aftershock sequences of the February 1964 Rat Island earthquake (Jordan and others, 1965), the 1957 earthquake sequence in the Andreanof-Fox Island region (Brazee, 1965), and the 1964 earthquake (p. I 15), all lend support to the inference that transverse faults segment the plate above the megathrust into large tectonic blocks. Conversely, there is no seismological or geological evidence of systematic dextral strike-slip displacement parallel to the arc in support of the speculation that it marks the trace of a major fault along which the North Pacific Ocean basin is rotating counterclockwise relative to North America, as was suggested by Saint-Amand (1957, p. 1367).

INFERRED REGIONAL STRESS PATTERN

According to the sea-floor spreading hypothesis, compressive forces should be directed roughly normal to the arcs and the deepsea trenches would be interpreted as due to dragging down of the oceanic crust above a descending mantle convection current (Hess, 1955, 1957, 1962). In the Aleutian Arc, transverse compression landward from the trench axis is suggested by (1) the orientation of major stress axes derived from mechanism studies of most, but not all, previous arc earthquakes (Balakina and others, 1961; Lensen, 1961, fig. 4); (2) the orientation of the axes of folded late Cenozoic rocks in the Aleutians, on the Alaska Peninsula and around the Gulf of Alaska roughly parallel to the arc trend (Coats, 1962, p. 93; Burk, 1965, p. 3; fig. 29); and (3) the distribution and nature of the seismicity, surface faulting, and warping associated with the 1964 earthquake. Both the pattern of residual displacements in 1964 (fig. 3), and the late Cenozoic fold-fault pattern (fig. 29) near the eastern end of the arc suggest that regional compressional deformation extends across it, from at least the outer edge of the Continental Shelf to the vicinity of the volcanic arc.

On the other hand, reconnaissance marine-geophysical studies across the Aleutian Trench and along the north wall of the trench have revealed an apparent lack of features indicating transverse compression or the existence of a megathrust intersecting the sea floor. From interpretations of gravity and magnetic data over the Aleutian Trench and outer margin of the arc southwest of Kodiak Island, Peter, Elvers, and Yellin (1965, p. 366) concluded that there probably exists "crustal tension, rather than compression, underthrust, or downbuckle." Marine reflection-refraction data suggest that the trench, with its relatively undeformed veneer of acoustically transparent sediments, reflects an origin by tension or vertical movements of the crust (Shor, 1966, p. 221; Ewing and others, 1965, p. 4599; Von Huene and others, 1966, p. 176).

It should be emphasized, however, that the geophysical investigations, particularly along the north wall of the trench, have provided direct information only on the approximate geometry and properties of the crust; they do not permit unambiguous conclusions regarding the deformations or the nature of the causative forces. More data, including a knowledge of the lithology and internal structure of the crustal rock in these areas, are required to determine whether features that seem to indicate absence of compression actually reflect the regional stress pattern. The seismic and geologic evidence in the eastern part of the Aleutian Arc suggests to me that any regional stress, other than transverse compression, must be largely limited to the part of the arc that lies seaward from the edge of the Continental Shelf.

SUMMARY OF THE PRE-HOLOCENE (RECENT) TECTONIC HISTORY OF SOUTH-CENTRAL ALASKA

The tectonic history along the eastern end of the Aleutian Arc and adjacent parts of south-central Alaska may be interpreted from the geologic record of folding and faulting. This record suggests that the present orogenic cycle, which probably began in Pliocene time, has resulted in regional compressive deformation in a general northwest-southeast to north-south direction around the margin of the Gulf of Alaska. It further indicates that at least three previous major orogenies culminated in south-central Alaska during (1) late Eocene to early Oligocene time, (2) Late Cretaceous to earliest Tertiary time, and (3) Middle(?) Jurassic to Late Jurassic or Early Cretaceous time. These earlier orogenies are indicated by major unconformities that divide the exposed section into four laterally continuous time-stratigraphic units that constitute gross subdivisions of the stratigraphic record. For brevity they are referred to in the following discussion as the late Cenozoic, early Cenozoic, late Mesozoic, and early Mesozoic and older sequences. They are described in the order named because it is the youngest deformation that is of primary concern here and because each successive orogeny tends to mask earlier events and thereby obscure to a large extent the earlier tectonic history.

Each of the four orogenies involved significant structural shortening of thick eugeosynclinal or geosynclinal sequences along the continental margin through folding and imbricate faulting. Deformation of coeval rocks inland from the continental margin was significantly less severe. This relationship may reflect a progressive reduction in horizontal compressive stress away from the continental margin, an increase in crustal competence, or a combination of both factors. In the mountains bordering the Gulf of Alaska and on the continental margin, the four major sequences form laterally continuous outcrop bands, commonly bounded by faults, which progressively increase in age from south to north (fig. 29). The distribution of coeval sequences to the north of the coastal mountains is not shown in figure 29 because the sequences exhibit complex overlapping relationships and are obscured to a large extent by plutonic intrusions, young volcanic rocks, water, or a veneer of unconsolidated deposits. The larger plutons and active or dormant volcanoes in south-central Alaska are delineated on figure 29.

A concise summary of the physiography and general geology of the area affected by tectonic movements during the earthquake, based on the compilation by Wahrhaftig (1966), has been given by Hansen and Eckel (1967) in the previous paper of this volume. It is not necessary to repeat it here. The broad tectonic setting and structural history of Alaska has been presented by Payne (1955) and by Gates and Gryc (1963). The stratigraphy and general geology of sedimentary basins in south-central Alaska were discussed by Miller, Payne, and Gryc (1959). Burk (1965) synthesized the geology of the western Alaska Peninsula and analyzed the relationship of the peninsula to the Aleutian Arc and continental margin. Grantz (1966) summarized data on strike-slip faults in Alaska and evaluated their role in the tectonic evolution of Alaska. All these writers included exhaustive bibliographies in their publications. Recent geologic maps along the Gulf of Alaska margin include a 1:500,000-scale compilation of the area between Prince William Sound and southeastern Alaska (Plafker, 1967a) and a 1:250,000-scale compilation of most of the Kodiak group of islands (Moore, 1967). The following section is based largely on the publications cited above, but includes some modifications of the Cenozoic history based on previously unpublished U.S. Geological Survey data.

POST-MIOCENE DEFORMATION

The orogeny, which began in Pliocene time and continued to the present, resulted in differential uplift and faulting throughout southern Alaska (Miller and others, 1959, p. 17). Folding was severe along the margin of the Gulf of Alaska, but gentle elsewhere except in the immediate vicinity of major faults. During this orogeny, the coastal mountains were uplifted and in places, especially to the west of Yakutat Bay, were thrust relatively southward against the Pacific basin along a system of high-angle faults (fig. 29). Major faults and folds in the late Cenozoic sequence tend to parallel the trends of the older structures in the Pacific Border Ranges; there is a general increase in the intensity of folding and magnitude of fault displacements from south to north across the deformed belt.

Transverse trends occur in the structurally complex Controller Bay area east of Prince William Sound where folds involving Oligocene and Miocene strata are typically of small amplitude, tightly compressed, and asymmetric or overturned; axial planes are inclined to the west or north.

Horizontal shortening of upper Oligocene and lower Miocene strata along one 5-mile north-south structure section in the Controller Bay area averages close to 25 percent (Don J. Miller, unpub. data).

To the east of the Controller Bay area the upper Cenozoic rocks form broad synclines and tightly appressed asymmetrical anticlines cut by north-dipping overthrust faults that strike roughly parallel to the coast. At least some of these faults probably represent the leading edges of thrust sheets developed by gravitational gliding off the uplifted Chugach-Saint Elias Mountains. On the south limbs of many of these anticlines, strata as young as late Pliocene are steeply dipping or overturned towards the north. At least two major intraformational unconformities in the upper part of the sequence record pronounced folding and uplift during late Pliocene time. Minor unconformities and thick beds of coarse conglomeratic sediments in the sequence reflect intervals of local uplift and erosion beginning in early Miocene time.

Marine sedimentary rocks of early Pleistocene or younger age on Middleton Island near the edge of the Continental Shelf have been titled northwestward at an average angle of 28°, truncated, raised above sea level, and displaced by active minor faults. A pervasive conjugate system of shear joints cutting the sequence reflects compressive stress directed northwest-southeast, normal to the strike of the beds.

Bedded rocks of Oligocene through middle Miocene age exposed in narrow belts along the southeast coast of the Kodiak Islands, and Oligocene rocks on Chirikof Island, are tightly folded about northeast-trending axes and are locally overturned (Moore,

1967). Relatively undeformed Tertiary rocks are exposed along the margin of the Gulf of Alaska only in the Trinity Islands and on Chirikof Island. On Chirikof, late Pliocene strata are exposed in homoclines with dips of less than 10°.

Late Cenozoic deposits along the Aleutian Volcanic Arc, in the Cook Inlet-Susitna lowland and around the Copper River lowland, were uplifted and slightly deformed during Pliocene and Quaternary time into generally open folds, most of which trend nearly parallel with the main arc or at a slightly oblique angle (Payne, 1955; Coats, 1962, p. 93; Burk, 1965, p. 121; Wolfe and others, 1966, p. A13). Most of the Eocene or younger Tertiary sedimentary rocks around the margin of the Cook Inlet lowland are nearly flat lying, gently tilted, or folded into broad, open structures with flank dips generally less than 10°. Thinning of individual stratigraphic units over anticlinal crests in the subsurface and the occurrence of topographic anomalies in areas mantled with Quaternary deposits suggest continuous active growth of some of these structures during late Cenozoic time (Kelly, 1963, p. 289, 296).

LATE EOCENE TO EARLY OLIGOCENE DEFORMATION

A major episode of deformation and plutonic activity began in late Eocene time and probably culminated in early Oligocene time. This episode resulted in complex folding, faulting, and mild metamorphism of early Tertiary rocks in the coastal belt (Plafker and MacNeil, 1966, p. 68) and probable minor warping and faulting of the age-equivalent strata exposed in the northern part of the Cook Inlet-Susitna lowland (Miller and others, 1959, p. 18). Folds

in the southern belt commonly are of short wavelength, tightly appressed with flank dips in excess of 50° and locally overturned both toward the north and south. Individual folds are of small amplitude and lateral extent and are complicated by intricate drag folding and minor overthrust faults. Horizontal shortening across a typical folded section, such as that shown in figure 31, commonly exceeds 45 percent, exclusive of imbrication on faults. Net shortening across the outcrop belt of lower Tertiary rocks is indeterminate because the structure has not been mapped in detail and traceable key horizons are generally absent. Conceivably, it could average as much as 45 percent or more across the entire outcrop belt; a net surface shortening of at least 30 miles in the Prince William Sound area. In a gross sense the strikes of bedding planes and fold axes tend to parallel the structural trends of the older rocks. They are notably divergent and complex in northeastern Prince William Sound and in the area immediately east of the sound (fig. 29), possibly because these areas are situated close to the axis of Carey's postulated Alaska orocline (1958, p. 209–212). Postorogenic potash-rich granite plutons of probable early Oligocene age (Lanphere, 1966, p. D197) with pronounced thermal aureoles are intrusive into the early Tertiary and older rocks in and near the Prince William Sound region.

Deformation of the early Tertiary rocks in the Cook Inlet-Susitna lowland during the early Cenozoic and later orogenies is characterized by broad open folding, flank dips commonly being less than 50° except in the immediate vicinity of faults. The strike of fold axes and of the steeply dipping faults of moderate dis-

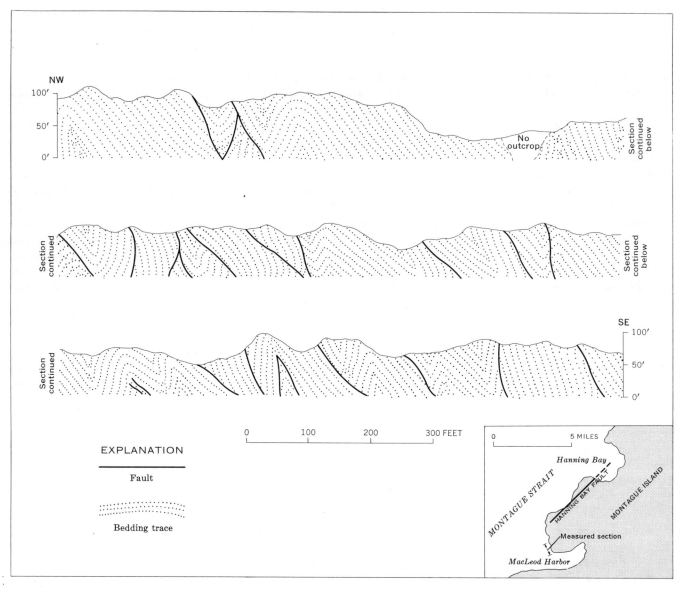

31.—Structure of the early Tertiary Orca Group exposed in a sea cliff along the north shore of MacLeod Harbor, Montague Island, Prince William Sound.

placement that offset the sequence is roughly parallel or at a slightly oblique angle to the trend of the adjacent mountain ranges. Horizontal shortening of Paleocene or Eocene strata through folding and faulting along a 5-mile-long northwest-southeast section across the Matanuska Valley (Barnes, 1962, section A–A') is about 25 percent. This figure undoubtedly approaches the approximate maximum amount of shortening in the sequence, because the section is located in a narrow structurally complex trough bounded on its north side by the active Castle Mountain fault.

LATE CRETACEOUS TO EARLY TERTIARY DEFORMATION

A major episode of diastrophism, corresponding to an early phase of the Laramide orogeny in the time interval from Late Cretaceous to early Tertiary, resulted in regional deformation and widespread intrusive activity in the Kodiak-Kenai-Chugach Mountains (Chugach Mountains geosyncline of Payne, 1955) and in the Alaska Range (Alaska Range geosyncline of Payne, 1955), with relatively slight deformation of rocks in the intervening area (Matanuska geosyncline of Payne, 1955). Figure 32 shows the style of deformation in one particularly well exposed outcrop area of probable late Mesozoic rocks along the south coast of the Kenai Peninsula immediately west of Prince William Sound. Structural shortening by folding across the section is about 55 percent, and there is an unknown amount of additional

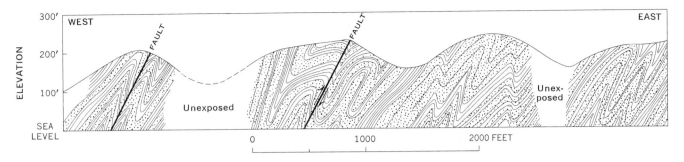

32.—Structure of probable late Mesozoic rocks along the southeast coast of the Kenai Peninsula immediately west of Prince William Sound (Martin and others, 1915, p. 216).

shortening by imbrication on overthrust faults. A c o m p a r a b l e amount of deformation across the entire late Mesozoic outcrop belt would have resulted in a net shortening of the original sequence by 40–60 miles. Deformation of the sequence was accompanied by emplacement of stocks and small batholiths, predominantly of quartz diorite and related plutonic rocks, and by metamorphism and penetrative deformation of rocks in the cores of the eastern Chugach Mountains, the Saint Elias Mountains, and the Fairweather Range.

During the Late Cretaceous to early Tertiary orogeny, deformation inland from the coastal mountains was mainly by uplift, broad open folding, and displacement on steeply dipping faults as indicated diagrammatically on section A–A', figure 29. Published structure sections across the sequence around the margins of the Copper River lowland (Grantz, 1965, sheet 3; Miller and MacColl, 1964) and on the Alaska Peninsula (Burk, 1965, figs. 21, 22) indicate structural shortening of Late Cretaceous strata that ranges from 5 to 20 percent and probably averages no more than 10 percent.

MIDDLE (?) JURASSIC TO EARLY CRETACEOUS DEFORMATION

All the older rocks in south-central Alaska were strongly affected by the major orogenic episode, roughly corresponding to the Nevadan orogeny, that began between latest Early Jurassic and earliest Middle Jurassic time and may have continued intermittently into earliest Cretaceous time. Rocks in the Seldovia geanticline were folded, complexly faulted, and regionally metamorphosed; deformation in the Talkeetna geanticline was considerably more variable and depended largely upon proximity to major batholiths. The orogeny was accompanied or immediately followed by emplacement of (1) numerous plutonic masses that range in composition from peridotite to granodiorite in the coastal mountains belt and (2) plutons of felsic composition and of batholithic size on the Alaska Peninsula and in the Talkeetna Mountains, with resultant contact metamorphism of the enclosing bedded rocks. The prevailing schistosity and slaty cleavage in the rocks of the coastal mountains are nearly vertical and have a variable strike that generally parallel roughly, or is at a small oblique angle to, the trend of the mountains.

A slight unconformity between rocks of Permian and Middle Triassic age in the Talkeetna Mountains (MacKevett and others, 1964) and the apparent absence of bedded rocks of Pennsylvanian, part of Permian, and Early Triassic age throughout the region suggest that these times were intervals of uplift and erosion.

MAJOR SURFACE FAULTS IN SOUTH-CENTRAL ALASKA

The longer coastal faults, or systems of faults, in south-central Alaska tend to follow the arcuate grain of the mountain ranges and the margin of the Gulf of Alaska; larger faults inland from the coast trend obliquely across some of the mountain ranges (fig. 29). In detail the faults do not form simple arcs but instead consist of linear segments of variable length, the included angles between adjacent segments being as little as 150°. Two minor north-south trending faults with Holocene movement intersect the regional grain at large oblique angles in the Controller Bay area (Ragged Mountain fault) and in the central Kenai Mountains (Kenai lineament).

Of the major faults delineated on figure 29, all but the Bruin Bay fault and the reverse fault along the northwest side of the Kodiak Island group exhibit evidence of post-Miocene movement; several have been active during post-Pleistocene (Holocene) time. Surface deformation was recorded in Alaska in conjunction with only three previous historic earthquakes along the Gulf of Alaska, at Chirikof Island in 1880 (George W. Moore, 1962, unpubl. data), at Yakutat Bay in 1899 (Tarr and Martin, 1912), and along the Fairweather fault in 1958 (Tocher,

TABLE 5.—*Radiocarbon-dated samples used in determining the relative ages of shoreline features*

[Locations of sample sites shown on fig. 33]

Locality No.	Lab. No.	Location	Age (B.P.)	Submergence (−) or emergence (+) relative to preearthquake datum (feet)	Data source	Comments
1	P-1039	Kodiak Island	3,279	[1]−3. 3	Clark (1966, p. 370)	Archaeologic site in submerged beach deposits.
2	P-1034	Sitkalidak Isalnd	5,519±78	Slight emergence	do	Archaeologic site in elevated beach ridge.
3	P-1036	do	3,945±65	do	do	Do.
4		Kukak Bay, Shelikof Strait	1,460±95	No apparent change	D. E. Dumond (written commun., March 28, 1966).	Archaeologic site in present beach ridge.
5		do	1,450±130	do	do	Do.
6		do	1,075±100	do	do	Do.
7		do	775±110	do	do	Do.
8	P-138	Yukon Island, Kachemak Bay	1,369±102	−4 to −10	Rainey and Ralph (1959)	Antler bone from archaeological site in submerged beach deposits.
9	P-139	do	2,706±118	[1]−16	do	Do.
10	W-299	Girdwood, Turnagain Arm	2,800±180	[1]−15	Karlstrom (1964, p. 48)	Peat in tidal silts and bog deposits. Possible significant surficial subsidence.
11	W-175	do	700±250	−2½	do	Do.
12	W-1720	Seward	≈200	[1]−7	Plafker and Rubin (1967)	Rooted stump on delta. Indicated submergence may be due to significant surficial slumping of unconsolidated deltaic deposits.
13	W-1589	Perry Island, Prince William Sound.	3,680±300	−11. 2	do	Rooted stump on submerged beach.
14	W-1588	Point Nowell, Prince William Sound.	930±200	−17	do	Wood fragment from interbedded peat and gravel on submerged beach.
15	W-1592	Columbia Bay, Prince William Sound.	1,140±250	−6	do	Rooted stump on submerged beach.
16	W-1591	Latouche Island, Prince William Sound.	230±200	−8. 5	do	Do.
17	W-1590	MacLeod Harbor, Prince William Sound.	560±200	−9. 7	do	Do.
18	W-1764	do	380±200	[1]−8	M. J. Kirkby (written commun., 1967).	Rooted stump in submerged river delta.
19	W-1766	Patton Bay, Montague Island	600±200	[1]−12	do	Wood fragment from submerged peat and gravel deposits.
20	W-1770	do	2,070±200	[1]+20	do	Peat on elevated beach deposits.
21	LJ-943	Copper River Delta area	1,360±50	−16. 8	Reimnitz (1966, p. 85)	
22	LJ-945	do	380±20	−13. 9	do	Rooted stumps on deltaic and marsh deposits. Submergence may be exaggerated owing to surficial subsidenc.
23	LJ-0032	do	700±50	−16. 8	do	
24	LJ-939	do	725±35	−15. 8	do	
25	LJ-938	do	700±30	−16. 8	do	
26	I-6	Katalla area	7,650±330	[1]+180	Heusser (1960, p. 94)	Peat from elevated terrace.
27	I-7	do	3,770±200	[1]+40	do	Do.
28	W-376	Cape Suckling	390±160	[1]−14	Rubin and Alexander (1958).	Rooted stump on submerged rock platform.
29	W-1729	do	710±200	−14	Plafker and Rubin (1967)	Do.
30	W-462	do	5,120±220	[1]+20	Rubin and Alexander (1958).	Shells on elevated terrace.
31	W-1724	Middleton Island	1,350±200	+22	do	Driftwood on elevated terrace.
32	W-1404	do	2,390±200	+58	Levin and others (1965, p. 392).	Do.
33	W-1405	do	4,470±250	+137	Levin and others (1965, p. 392-393).	Do.
34	W-1722	Stockdale Harbor, Prince William Sound.	>200	−8	Plafker and Rubin (1967)	Rooted stump on submerged beach.
35	LJ-0033	Copper River Delta area	860±50	−15. 9	Reimnitz (1966, p. 85)	Rooted stump on deltaic and marsh deposits.
36	LJ-0034	do	1,700±100	−22. 0	do	Do.

[1] Approximate.

1960). Although surface breakage may have occurred along faults during other earthquakes in Alaska, such features could easily have gone undetected had they occurred in the vast uninhabited parts of the State.

The sense of late Cenozoic displacement on the faults shown in figure 29 is given where known. In general, faults in south-central Alaska that trend northeast or east are predominantly overthrusts or oblique overthrusts that dip northward at moderate to steep angles, with north sides relatively upthrown. Horizontal movements on major longitudinal faults are largely restricted to the northwest-trending Fairweather fault and to the northwest and east-west trending parts of the Denali fault system, both of which are predominantly right-lateral. Geologic relationships across many of the faults suggest that they have undergone recurrent movement during Cenozoic and much of Mesozoic time and that the sense of displacement along some of them has changed with time. The orientation and the Quaternary displacement on these faults reflects tangential compression oriented north-south to northwest-southeast along the margin of the Gulf of Alaska, perhaps rotating to a more nearly east-west direction in central Alaska. The broad fault pattern implies that the Pacific Ocean basin is moving north to northwest relative to the mainland. Thus, the ocean basin appears to be shearing relatively past the mainland of British Columbia and southeastern Alaska along the system of northwest-trending right-lateral strike-slip faults, whereas it shears relatively beneath the continental margin and Aleutian Arc in central and western Alaska along a system of imbricate thrust (underthrust?) faults.

THE PREEARTHQUAKE HOLOCENE (RECENT) RECORD OF VERTICAL SHORELINE MOVEMENTS

Numerous records of preearthquake differential shoreline movements relative to sea level provide data on the history of vertical tectonic movements during Holocene time. Reconnaissance studies of the displaced shorelines have brought out (1) a general similarity between the pattern of earthquake displacements and the long-term trend of Holocene coastal emergence or submergence, and (2) a remarkable recent widespread submergence over much of the zone that was uplifted during the 1964 earthquake and over at least part of the zone that subsided. In addition, radiocarbon dating of material from coastal sites has provided quantitative data on the duration and rates of these Holocene movements.

Data and interpretations presented in this section are largely taken from a preliminary paper by Plafker and Rubin (1967). All radiocarbon-dated samples referred to, sources, and other pertinent data are listed in table 5; sample locations are shown on figure 33.

As used herein, the terms "uplift" and "subsidence" describe a tectonic rise or fall of the land; "emergence" and "submergence" indicate relative movements that may be the sum of both tectonic

movements and eustatic sea-level changes. Tectonic movements include those that result from both diastrophic and isostatic processes. "Long-term" refers to shoreline changes relative to sea level having durations measured in thousands of years; "short-term" refers to the general submergence that occurred during the 1,350 years or less prior to the earthquake.

Some of the observed recent submergence in areas shown on figure 33 is undoubtedly exaggerated by the local vibration-induced compaction or slumping of unconsolidated deposits during the earthquakes that frequently rock this seismically active region. As was demonstrated during the 1964 earthquake, surficial submergence may be substantial in areas of thick unconsolidated saturated deposits—especially in those deposits that are not constrained on one or more sides, such as deltas, spits, and barrier beaches. Consequently, rooted tree stumps, on bedrock or on thin beach deposits overlying bedrock, were used to determine amounts and rates of pre-1964 vertical displacement wherever possible.

In the absence of a reliable local eustatic sea-level record for southern Alaska, it is assumed that Holocene sea levels were probably comparable to those in more tectonically stable parts of the world where the sea-level record has been worked out in some detail. Three recent interpretations of eustatic sea levels are shown on figure 34. Most of these studies suggest either (1) a rather rapid rise in sea level at an average rate of about 0.08 inch per year until it reached approximately its present level between 2,000 and 6,000 years ago (Coleman and Smith, 1964), or (2) that sea level has been rising slowly and continuously from about −33 feet to its present level

during the past 7,000 years with a generally rising, but fluctuating, sea level between about 15,000 and 7,000 years B.P. (Curray, 1961). Some authorities believe that sea level reached its present position from 3,000 to 5,000 years ago and has been fluctuating above and below its present position by about 3–6 feet ever since (Fairbridge, 1961). For present purposes, it is significant to note that none of these studies suggest that eustatic sea-level fluctuations during the last 10,000 years were large enough alone to explain the relative shoreline displacements found along the coast of south-central Alaska.

LONG-TERM HOLOCENE EMERGENCE AND SUBMERGENCE

The record of Holocene displacements in the area affected by the earthquake, as deduced from shoreline morphology and from radiocarbon dates, is outlined in the following section. Places referred to and the spatial distribution of radiocarbon-dated shoreline samples in relation to the 1964 deformation are shown in figure 33. The age and pre-1964 position of these samples relative to sea level is shown in figure 34.

Much of the shore in the mountainous southern part of the area that subsided during the earthquake exhibits the characteristic features of a deeply drowned coast. Submerged shorelines occur along most of Kodiak and the adjacent islands, the southern Kenai Peninsula, the south shore of Kachemak Bay, and part of Turnagain Arm. The northern and eastern parts of the Prince William Sound region also appear to be submergent, although the evidence for relative shoreline movements is somewhat obscured by recent glaciation in most of the fiords. In these submerged mountainous areas, former rocky ridges are now peninsulas or islands, and

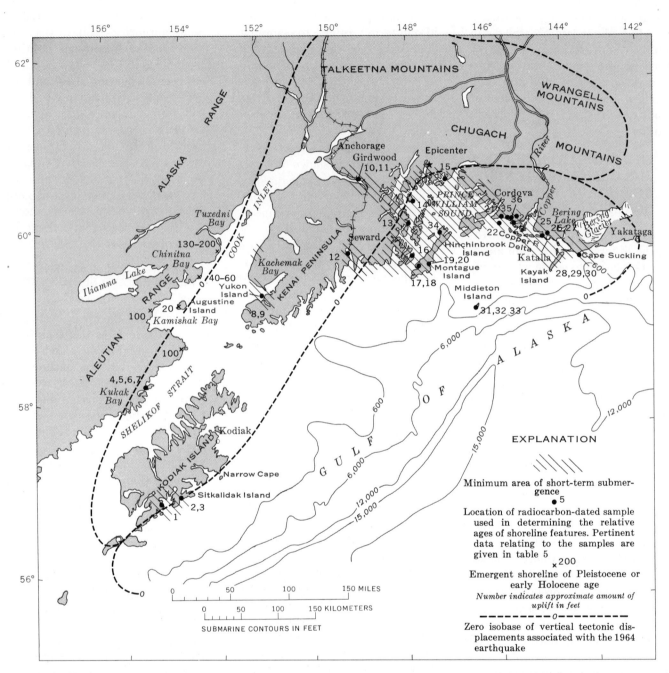

33.—Areal distribution of vertical displacements associated with the 1964 earthquake, areas of preearthquake submergence, and locations of radiocarbon-dated samples used to determine relative ages of shoreline features.

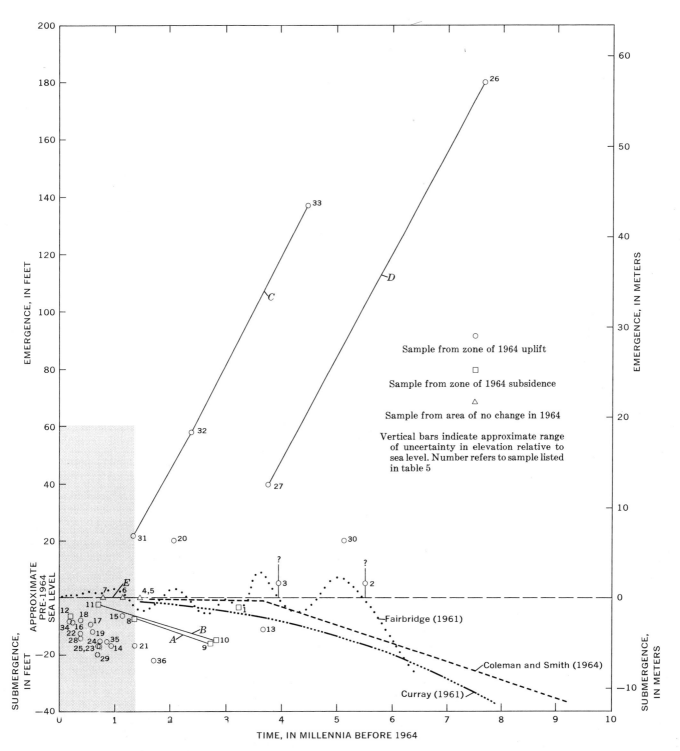

34.—Pre-1964 positions of radiocarbon-dated samples relative to the pre-1964 sea level and proposed eustatic sea levels of Curray (1961), Fairbridge (1961), and Coleman and Smith (1964). The duration of the inferred period of short-term subsidence is indicated by the stippled area. Sample locations at Yukon Island (*A*), Girdwood (*B*), Middleton Island (*C*), Katalla (*D*), and Kukak Bay (*E*) are connected by solid lines.

35.—Deeply submerged coast along the southern Kenai Peninsula. Embayments, which give the shore a distinctive scalloped appearance, are cirques whose floors are drowned to depths of as much as 300 feet below sea level. Shoreline shown was submerged an additional 2–5 feet in 1964. Photograph by T. L. Péwé.

drowned river valleys or glacial cirques have become embayments (fig. 35). The general scarcity of well-developed sea cliffs, beaches, and similar shore features attests to the recency of the submergence. Elsewhere in the subsided zone, coastal bogs of terrestrial peat and some aboriginal dwelling sites that are now inundated by high tides also indicate long-continued submergence relative to sea level.

The most pronounced submergence appears to be in the vicinity of the axis of maximum subsidence during the 1964 earthquake—a region which roughly coincides with the crest of the Kenai and Kodiak Mountains (pl. 1). Although the absolute maximum amount of postglacial submergence cannot be determined, an indication of it is provided by differences in the altitudes of cirque floors of probable Wisconsin age along this part of the coast which presumably were formed at a fairly uniform level. The lowest cirque floors along the outer coast of Prince William Sound and in

most of the Kodiak Island group— areas away from the region of maximum submergence—lie at altitudes ranging from 800 to 1,000 feet above sea level, but cirque floors along the south coast of the Kenai Peninsula range in altitude from 300 feet below sea level to 800 feet above sea level. This difference in cirque levels suggests at least 300, and perhaps as much as several hundred feet, of submergence in the Kenai Peninsula area.

In contrast to the zone of subsidence, the coast in those areas where the land has risen relative to the sea is generally smoother in outline and commonly exhibits, among other features, one or more wave-cut terraces or uplifted beaches rising to elevations of at least 200 feet (figs. 36, 37). In the major zone of uplift such features are characteristic of the points and capes on the seaward side of Kodiak Island, the islands of the southern and eastern Prince William Sound region, much of the mainland coast east of Cape Suckling, and Middleton Island on the

Continental Shelf. Comparable emergent shores with postglacial terraces as much as 1,700 feet high occur all along the mainland coast to the east of the area that was affected by the 1964 earthquake.

Relatively stable or emergent shores occur along parts of the Cook Inlet and Shelikof Strait coasts in areas that either subsided slightly, remained unchanged, or were slightly uplifted during the 1964 earthquake (fig. 33). Many of these emergent shorelines are probably pre-Holocene features related to high eustatic sea levels rather than to tectonic movements (Hopkins and others, 1965, p. 1113; Karlstrom, 1964, p. 34–37).

The record of long-term Holocene deformation within the major zone of uplift in the area between the Copper River Delta and Cape Suckling is seemingly anomalous in that uplifted surfaces described as marine terraces, and drowned forests or sphagnum-peat horizons, occur in close association with one another. Dated marine terraces at Katalla (nos. 26, 27, fig. 34) and Cape Suckling (no. 30, fig. 34) record net Holocene emergence; recent net submergence is indicated by (1) a dated wood sample from the Copper River Delta (no. 36, fig. 34) that was submerged 22 feet in the 1,700 years prior to the earthquake but was uplifted only about 6 feet at the time of the earthquake, (2) a widespread horizon of terrestrial peat of unknown age that was penetrated in borings at depths as much as 40 feet below sea level in the lower Copper River Delta and to a depth of 30 feet at Bering Lake (Tarr and Martin, 1914, p. 462–463), and (3) forest horizons in the Katalla and Cape Suckling areas submerged prior to the earthquake by amounts that were considerably larger than the earthquake-related uplift at these same

36.—Muskeg-covered preearthquake marine terrace on Middleton Island at an altitude of 110–125 feet. It is one of five uplifted terraces on the island, and surf-cut rock platform exposed between the base of the sea cliff and the new high-tide level is a sixth terrace formed by uplift of about 11 feet in 1964. White specks are seagulls. Photograph taken near 7-foot tide stage, April 4, 1964.

37.—The linear tree-covered beach ridge in this view is one of nine elevated beach ridges near Katalla, east of the Copper River Delta. Uplift of about 9 feet in 1964 shifted the shoreline several hundred feet seaward where another beach ridge is in process of formation. Photograph taken near zero tide stage, July 28, 1964.

localities (A–E) in the area for which multiple samples are available are shown in figure 34. Points on the graph are the preearthquake position relative to mean lower low water plotted against age in millenia of radiocarbon-dated material from these five sites. The available dated samples were collected by several different workers over a period of 30 years and were analyzed in three different laboratories. In spite of the small number of samples at each site, uncertainties in their exact positions relative to sea level, and the ever-present problem of analytical or sampling errors, it is noteworthy that the results appear to be remarkably consistent with one another and with the displacements that occurred in 1964.

These data indicate that the two localities at Yukon Island (A) and Girdwood (B) have subsided relative to present sea level at an average rate of about 0.7–1.0 foot per century during the time interval from 2,800 to 700 years B.P., whereas those at Middleton Island (C) and Katalla (D) in the uplifted area have risen at the much greater average rate of at least 3.3 feet per century between 7,650 and 1,350 years B.P. The rate of uplift would be increased somewhat if any of the deduced eustatic sea levels are used in place of the 1964 sea level. The shore at Kukak Bay (E), which was not affected by the earthquake, has apparently undergone no detectable net change in its present position relative to sea level since at least 1,450 B.P.

Detailed study of the emergent shorelines shows that the long-term vertical movements occurred, at least in part, as a series of upward pulses separated by intervals of stability or even gradual submergence. Evidence for periodic uplift is exceptionally well displayed on Middleton Island

localities. The relative ages of dated samples in these areas suggest that the long-term displacement may have reversed direction from uplift to submergence during the time interval between about 3,770 and 1,700 years B.P.

Radiocarbon dating of organic material from terraces, peat bogs, and archaeological sites in coastal areas affected by the earthquake has provided some preliminary data on average long-term displacement trends relative to sea level at a number of localities. Displacement-time curves at the five where the surface consists of a flight of five gently sloping and well-developed marine terraces separated by wave-cut cliffs or rises ranging from 20 to 30 feet each (Miller, 1953; Plafker, unpub. data, 1963, 1964, 1965). The highest terrace, forming the flat central part of the island, has a general altitude of 130–165 feet. Sudden uplift of 10–13 feet during the 1964 earthquake, which exposed a sixth surf-cut terrace (shown on fig. 36), suggests that perhaps the earlier terraces may also have been exposed by a series of upward pulses during previous earthquakes. Radiocarbon-dated driftwood from the highest and lowest of these preearthquake platforms on Middleton Island dates initial uplift of the island at 4,470±250 years ago and uplift of the lowest preearthquake terrace at approximately 1,350±200 years B.P. (nos. 33, 31, table 5). Thus, the extrapolated average time interval between successive uplifts of the three intervening terraces would be close to 800 years.

Because most of the dated samples were taken from deposits laid down when the postglacial eustatic sea level was rising gradually or was at about its present stand, the emergent shorelines probably result almost entirely from tectonic movements. Although some slightly submerged shorelines may be attributed to the effects of a late Holocene rise of sea level and to local surficial subsidence of unconsolidated deposits, in most instances the submergence is so large when compared to deduced eustatic curves that it must also be at least partly due to tectonic subsidence.

Regional submergence of the Kenai and Kodiak Mountains is clearly anomalous in that the movements are in a direction that tends to reduce the elevation of these youthful mountain ranges. Furthermore, because the net load of glacial ice on the mountains has been steadily diminished since the Pleistocene, isostatic adjustments, if any, should be upward. Thus, the submergence is a counter-isostatic process that can only be attributed to regional diastrophic movements.

Less certain is the extent to which the regional postglacial uplift reflects isostatic compensation resulting from unloading of ice and the extent to which it is caused by diastrophic movements. Both processes are undoubtedly involved. However, the known seismic activity of the region, the evidence for pulsating rather than continuous emergence, and the apparent late Holocene reversals in the sense of the net displacements over part of the region suggest that the movements were also, to a large extent, diastrophic in nature.

SHORT-TERM TECTONIC SUBMERGENCE

Much of the coast in the region affected by tectonic movements during the 1964 earthquake had experienced a pronounced submergence for several centuries prior to that event. This phenomenon was probably first recorded by the great English navigator, George Vancouver, who explored Prince William Sound between May 25 and June 17, 1794 (Vancouver, 1801, v. 5, p. 335–336). He noted that on northern Montague Island "The shores are in general low, and as had been already observed, very swampy in many places, on which the sea appears to be making more rapid encroachments than I ever before saw or heard of * * * [trees along the shore] were reduced to naked, dead white stumps, by the encroachment of the sea water to their roots; and some stumps of trees, with their roots still fast in the ground, were also found in no very advanced state of decay nearly as low down as the low water of spring tides." The fact that low water of spring tides is about 13 feet below the normal lower growth limit of trees in this area indicates almost that amount of submergence prior to 1794. The characteristic appearance of these drowned forests in Prince William Sound and along the coast at Cape Suckling east of the Sound is illustrated by figures 38 and 39.

Evidence for active submergence along the coast of the type first described by Vancouver was subsequently noted by geologists, archaeologists, and botanists in the following places: (1) the Controller Bay area east of Prince William Sound (Tarr and Martin, 1914), (2) the Copper River region (Schrader, 1900, p. 404; Reimnitz, 1966, p. 112–125), (3) around Prince William Sound (Grant and Higgins, 1910; Moffitt, 1954; Dachnowski-Stokes, 1941; De Laguna, 1956, (4) around Kachemak Bay on the southern Kenai Peninsula (De Laguna, 1934), (5) in the upper Cook Inlet region (Karlstrom, 1964, p. 48), and (6) in at least two localities on Kodiak Island (Clark, 1966).

Reconnaissance studies by the Geological Survey of all these shorelines after the 1964 earthquake suggest that the submergence observed is a regional phenomenon that has affected much, if not all, of the Prince William Sound region, the mainland coast and islands east of Prince William Sound, the south coast of the Kenai Peninsula at least as far as Kachemak Bay, parts of Turnagain Arm, and segments of the southeastern coast of the Kodiak group of islands. Undoubtedly, many more such localities could be found by detailed examination of the shorelines. Areas within

38.—Bleached trunks of spruce trees on Latouche Island, Prince William Sound, killed by salt-water immersion and partially buried in beach gravel as a result of about 8 feet of submergence below preearthquake extreme high-tide level. The locality was exposed by 8 feet of uplift in 1964. Photograph taken May 28, 1964.

39.—Spruce tree stumps (foreground) rooted in a thin layer of peat on a surf-cut bedrock surface about 14 feet below preearthquake extreme high water (indicated by the top of the line of driftwood below the present forest edge in the background). Radiocarbon age of a stump near the base of the stadia rod was 710±200 years (no. 29, fig. 34). These stumps were exposed by about 16 feet of uplift in 1964. Photograph taken July 24, 1964.

which there is evidence of pre-earthquake submergence are indicated on figure 33 and the ages and positions relative to sea level of the dated samples are shown on figure 34. In a few scattered localities within Prince William Sound, evidence of stable shorelines or of possible recent slight uplift (no more than 4 ft) was found. This evidence suggests that small areas may have acted as independent tectonic units that did not take part in the general submergence.

The available data is insufficient for determining whether the submergence, which affected the off-shore islands from Kayak Island to the Copper River Delta, extended as far out on the Continental Shelf as Middleton Island. Preearthquake sea levels that reached to the base of the prominent sea cliff encircling much of the island indicate either a long period of relative stability and erosion or some submergence since the last uplift of the island roughly 1,350 years ago.

The record of preearthquake submergence in the zone that was lowered in relation to sea level is much less complete than that for the zone that was raised, mainly because much of the evidence is now below lowest low tide. Available data suggest that submergence occurred along parts of the coast of the Kenai Peninsula and the Kodiak group of islands but that submergence probably was much less than in the area from Prince William Sound to Cape Suckling. No change in mean sea level attributable to tectonic movements was detected in a 21-year tidal record at Seward and a 15-year record at Kodiak. An apparently large preearthquake submergence on the delta of Spruce Creek near Seward of about 6.9 feet in less than 200 years, as indicated by drowned rooted tree stumps (no. 12, fig. 34), may be partly due to slumping and (or) compaction of deltaic deposits.

Radiocarbon dates from drowned terrestrial plants that were probably killed by sea-water encroachment provide data that permit a crude estimate of the duration and average rate of the short-term preearthquake submergence. Ages in radiocarbon years versus amount of submergence of samples taken from the most deeply submerged terrestrial vegetation at each site are plotted in the stippled area on figure 34. The fairly regular linear distribution of 14 out of 16 samples, all from the area between Seward and Cape Suckling, suggests a general submergence at a rate that averaged roughly 1.7 feet per century for about 930 years. On the other hand, positions of two samples (nos. 15, 21, fig. 34) from this same general area, both of which are older than 930 years, reflect lower rates of submergence, as do three samples from the Cook Inlet region (nos. 8, 11, 15, fig. 34). The maximum indicated average rate of submergence is 8.6 feet in 230 years or about 3.7 feet per century on Latouche Island in Prince William Sound.

Absence of historic records of sudden earthquake-related relative sea-level changes and of geomorphic evidence for such movements suggest that the submergence was probably gradual or that it occurred in numerous small increments over a long period of time. This time interval, as inferred from dated submerged shorelines, was at least 930 years in the Prince William Sound region. The upper limit for the duration of the submergence is far less certain; if it corresponds to the oldest dated submerged-forest sample along the coast (no. 21, fig. 34) and the time of uplift of the

lowest preearthquake marine terrace on Middleton Island (no. 31, fig. 34), it could be as much as 1,350 years.

Short-term submergence occurred at a time when sea level was at or near its present stand and in a region where overall isostatic displacements in response to glacial unloading should have been upward. Isostatic adjustments between major earthquakes such as the 1964 event could conceivably be responsible for some of the submergence in areas of tectonic uplift. However, such adjustments are inadequate to explain either short-term submergence in the Copper River Delta-Cape Suckling area that exceeds earthquake-related uplift or submergence in areas of the Kenai Peninsula and Kodiak Island that subsided both before and during the earthquake. By implication, this fact suggests that the submergence was caused at least partly by diastrophism that involved a significant downward-directed component of regional strain of variable amount and rate over much of the coastal belt affected by vertical displacements during the 1964 earthquake.

TECTONIC IMPLICATIONS OF THE RECORD OF HOLOCENE VERTICAL MOVEMENTS

The history of Holocene vertical movements in the region affected by the 1964 earthquake, and in nearby areas, is a fragmentary one based largely on a rapid reconnaissance after the earthquake and on incidental investigations by others. Additional work—involving far more radiocarbon dating—is required to obtain detailed data on vertical movements at selected localities in areas of net Holocene emergence and submergence. However, the following four tentative conclusions regarding the prehistoric tectonic move-

ments seem to be indicated by the available data:

1. Areas of net Holocene emergence or submergence broadly correspond with those areas in which significant amounts of uplift and subsidence occurred during the 1964 earthquake. Thus, the tectonic movements that accompanied the earthquake were apparently but one pulse in a long-continuing trend of deformation. This trend has resulted in regional emergence of parts of the continental margin, simultaneous submergence of the Kenai-Kodiak Mountains belt, and either relative stability or emergence along the shores of Cook Inlet and parts of Shelikof Strait.

2. The amounts of net long-term Holocene emergence and submergence of the coast, which are locally considerably larger than the postulated eustatic sea-level changes for the same time interval, indicate that differential displacement of the shoreline results largely from tectonic movements. Progressive submergence of youthful mountains recently unloaded of ice and pulsating emergence of the Continental Shelf and Gulf of Alaska coast are suggestive of a dominant regional diastrophic deformation.

3. Steplike flights of Holocene marine surf-cut terraces at a number of localities along the coast suggest that the long-term vertical movements occurred as a series of upward pulses that were separated by intervals of stability or even gradual subsidence that locally average 800 years or more in duration. These upward pulses probably represent earthquake-related movements comparable in origin to those which affected parts of the same coast in 1964.

4. Gradual tectonic submergence prevailed during at least the past 900 years, and perhaps as long as 1,360 years, over much of the zone that was uplifted and over at least part of the zone that subsided during the 1964 earthquake. This widespread submergence is tentatively interpreted as direct evidence for a significant downward-directed component of regional strain preceding the earthquake and its duration as the approximate time interval since the last major tectonic earthquake in this same region.

MECHANISM OF THE EARTHQUAKE

GENERAL CONSIDERATIONS

According to the classic elastic rebound theory of earthquake generation (Reid, 1911), which is generally accepted by western geologists and geophysicists, shallow earthquakes are generated by sudden fracture or faulting following a period of slow deformation during which energy is stored in the form of elastic strain within rock adjacent to the fault. When the strength of the rock is exceeded, failure in the form of faulting occurs, the material on opposite sides of the fault tends to rebound into a configuration of elastic equilibrium, and elastic strain potential is released in the form of heat, crushing of rock, and seismic-wave radiation. The drop in elastic strain potential is possibly augmented or partially absorbed by net changes in gravitational potential associated with vertical tectonic displacements.

Field investigations demonstrate that there is little likelihood that the primary fault along which the 1964 earthquake occurred is exposed at the surface on land, nor is there evidence for movement on any of the known major continental faults. If the earthquake originated by rupture along one or more faults, the two most plausible models for the orientation and sense of movement on the primary fault consistent with the available fault-plane solutions and dislocation-theory analyses of the re-

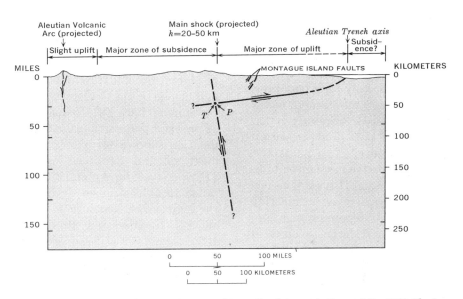

40.—Diagrammatic section showing two alternative interpretations of the 1964 Alaska earthquake based on focal mechanism studies (S. T. Algermissen, written commun., March 1965) and analyses of residual vertical displacements by dislocation theory (Savage and Hastie, 1966). Section is oriented through the focus of the main shock and roughly normal to the regional structural trend. P and T axes are the approximate orientations of the principal pressure and tension axes, respectively, at the hypocenter of the main shock indicated by the focal mechanism studies.

sidual vertical displacements are (1) relative seaward thrusting along a fault that dips northwestward beneath the continental margin at a low angle, and (2) dip-slip movement on a near-vertical fault, the ocean side being relatively upthrown, that strikes approximately along the zero isobase between the major zones of uplift and subsidence (fig. 40). These two models, which are discussed in the following sections, are referred to as the "thrust-fault model" and the "steep-fault model."

Whether the postulated shearing resulted from the overcoming of frictional resistance to sliding, as set forth in the elastic rebound theory of Reid (1911), or from some other process such as brittle fracture, creep instability, or propagation of flaws cannot be ascertained from available data. Several writers (O r o w a n, 1960; Griggs and Handin, 1960; Evison, 1963, p. 863–884) have pointed out deficiencies in the elastic rebound mechanism for earthquakes at depths of more than a few miles, where frictional stress on dry fault planes must vastly exceed the rock strength. However, such considerations generally do not take into account the effect of pore fluids which must exist in the real earth down to the depths of the deepest hydrated mineral phases. Recent laboratory studies (Raleigh and Patterson, 1965, p. 3977–3978; Griggs and Blacic, 1965; Raleigh, 1967) suggest the possibility that the Reid mechanism may extend to depths at least as great as the lower crust and upper mantle in regions where frictional resistance to sliding on faults may be reduced by local anomalously high pore pressures or where the strength of the rock is lowered sufficiently in the presence of pore fluids to permit brittle fracture.

An alternative mechanism to be considered is one that explains tectonic earthquakes as originating from sudden expansion and (or) contraction of large volumes of rock due to rapid phase changes (Evison, 1963). According to this concept, faulting is the result rather than the cause of earthquakes. No evidence has yet been found from either natural or experimental petrologic systems to support the idea that reconstructive solid-solid or solid-liquid reactions can occur fast enough throughout sufficiently large volumes of rock to generate major earthquakes or to produce regional vertical displacements (Ghent, 1965). Aside from the theoretical objections, it is difficult to conceive of a reasonable combination of equidimensional volume changes that could cause the observed pattern of vertical and horizontal displacements that accompanied this earthquake. For these reasons, there is little likelihood that phase changes were a primary mechanism for the 1964 earthquake, and this possibility will not be pursued further.

THRUST-FAULT MODEL

Most of the preliminary data available by the end of the 1964 field season suggested that the earthquake and the associated tectonic deformation resulted from a relative seaward thrusting along the continental margin that was accompanied by elastic horizontal extension behind the thrust block (Plafker, 1965, p. 1686). The t h r u s t - f a u l t model has been strongly reinforced by data subsequently obtained from (1) more detailed fieldwork on the surface displacements and preearthquake movements by the Geological Survey during 1965, (2) comparison of pre- and post-earthquake triangulation surveys for a large segment of the deformed region (Parkin, 1966, fig. 4), and (3) detailed focal-mechanism studies of the main shock and larger aftershocks (Stauder and Bollinger, 1966). The essential features of the suggested model, which are illustrated diagrammatically by figure 41, are presented below.

OUTLINE OF THE MODEL

According to the thrust-fault model, the earthquake resulted from shear failure along an inferred major zone of movement, or megathrust, which dips northwestward beneath the continental margin from the vicinity of the Aleutian Trench, and on subsidiary faults within the overthrust plate. The zone within which movement occurred, as delineated by the belt of major aftershocks, parallels the Aleutian Trench on the northwest for a distance of some 600 miles and is from 110 to 180 miles wide (fig. 2). It lies almost entirely within the major zone of uplift and the portion of the adjacent zone of subsidence that is on the seaward side of the axis of subsidence.

The pattern of earthquake-related horizontal displacements (fig. 16) and the evidence for regional preearthquake shoreline submergence along the continental margin (fig. 33) suggest that shear failure followed a long period of elastic strain accumulation (930–1,360 years) during which the upper plate was horizontally compressed roughly normal to the trend of the Aleutian Arc and probably simultaneously depressed relative to sea level. A hypothetical deformation cycle is illustrated diagrammatically in figure 42. The data suggest that the dynamic drive was probably provided by underthrust of the lower plate, with a downward-directed component of movement. R. K. Hose has pointed out that distortional drag due to an underthrust would have generated a shear couple in which the relative strains and orientation of potential shear planes coincide reasonably well with those deduced from fault-plane solutions for the main shock and many or the larger aftershocks (oral commun., Nov. 1965). Alternative mechanisms such as movement of the continental margin over the oceanic basin, or almost horizontal movements, could not be responsible for the combination of both horizontal shortening and regional submergence indicated by the available data.

Previous seismicity in the region during the strain-accumulation phase of the 1964 earthquake may have resulted from adjustments within the strained volume of rock involving predominantly lateral offsets or relatively local dip-slip displacement. This possibility is suggested by the fact that, although prior historic earthquakes with magnitudes of 7 or more have been recorded

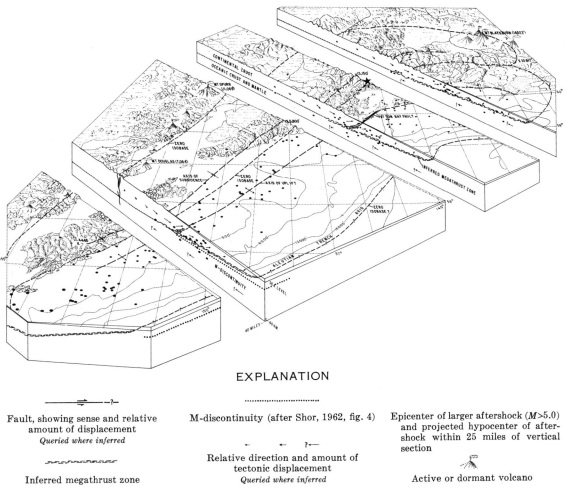

EXPLANATION

Fault, showing sense and relative
amount of displacement
Queried where inferred

M-discontinuity (after Shor, 1962, fig. 4)

Epicenter of larger aftershock (*M*>5.0)
and projected hypocenter of aftershock within 25 miles of vertical
section

Inferred megathrust zone

Relative direction and amount of
tectonic displacement
Queried where inferred

Active or dormant volcano

★

Epicenter of main shock

41.—Schematic block diagram showing the postulated relationship of the seismic activity and tectonic displacement associated with the 1964 Alaska earthquake to major structural elements of south-central Alaska. Horizontal and vertical scales equal below sea level; vertical scale above sea level exaggerated × 4. Drawn by H. T. Koelbl.

(Wood, 1966, p. 24), none of these were accompanied by known regional tectonic deformation—and certainly none with deformation on the scale of the 1964 earthquake.

Faulting at the time of the earthquake presumably was initiated at the hypocenter of the main shock in northern Prince William Sound, from which point it propagated simultaneously updip towards the Aleutian Trench and along strike both towards the southwest and east within the area encompassed by the aftershocks. Shear failure was accompanied by elastic rebound in the upper plate

above the thrust, which resulted in (1) relative seaward displacement and uplift of a part of the continental margin by movement along the inferred megathrust and the subsidiary reverse faults that break through the upper plate to the surface, and (2) simultaneous elastic horizontal extension and vertical attenuation (subsidence) of the crustal slab behind the upper plate. These movements, possibly in combination with unidentified submarine faulting and (or) underthrusting of the lower plate in the opposite direction, resulted in the observed and inferred

tectonic displacements at the surface.

Indicated stress drops at the surface across the zone of subsidence (on the order of a few hundred bars) are comparable in magnitude to those reported for other tectonic earthquakes. For the idealized case of homogeneous strain and purely elastic distortion of the crust, the stress drop (*P*) is a function of Young's modulus (*E*) of the slab and the reduction of horizontal strain (ε) across it:

$$\triangle P = E\epsilon$$

For an average *E* of 3×10^5 bars

[179]

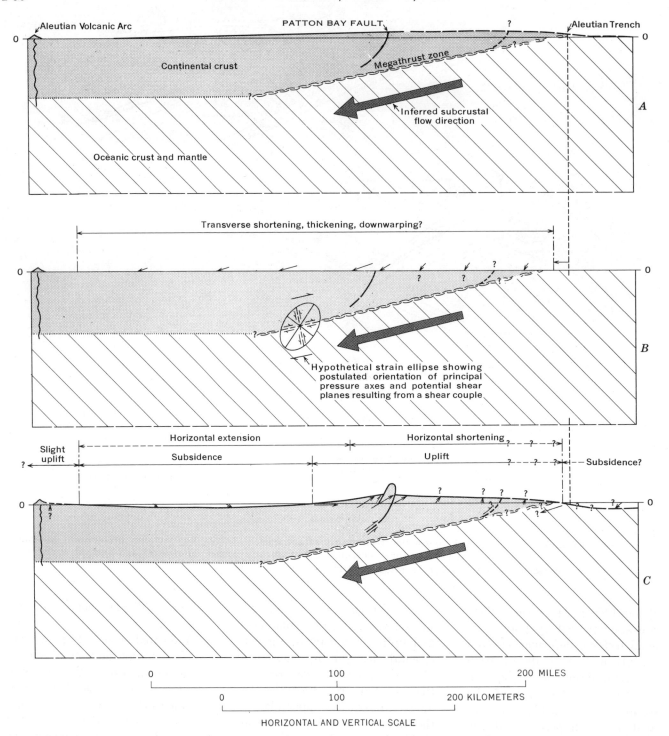

42.—Diagrammatic time-sequential cross sections through the crust and upper mantle in the northern part of the region affected by the 1964 earthquake. A, Relatively unstrained condition after the last major earthquake. B, Strain buildup stage during which the continental margin is shortened and downwarped. C, Observed and inferred displacements at time of the earthquake during which a segment of the continental margin is thrust seaward relative to the continent. Datum is the upper surface of the crust beneath the cover of water and low-velocity sediments. Vertical displacements at the surface, which are indicated by the profiles and by arrows showing sense and relative amount of movement, are about × 1,000 scale of the figure.

(7×10^{11} dynes cm^{-2}), and average and maximum strain across the subsided zone of 1.1×10^{-4} and 3×10^{-4}, respectively, the average stress drop was only about 77 bars (77×10^6 dynes cm^{-2}). The maximum drop, which occurs near the axis of subsidence, was about 210 bars (210×10^6 dynes cm^{-2}).

The megathrust in the earthquake focal region dips north to northwest at an angle of $9°$–$15°$, according to fault-plane solutions of the main shock and several aftershocks, but its precise depth and configuration are uncertain. The limited available data on focal depths of the earthquake (p. I 4) and on deep crustal structure (Shor, 1962, fig. 4; Hales and Asada, 1966, p. 420) suggest that the megathrust may coincide with the unstable interface at the base of the continental crust beneath the continental slope and shelf. It probably extends into the upper mantle toward the north to some unknown depth (no deeper than the deepest hypocenters in the region) where stress relaxation is sufficiently rapid to absorb the applied force by plastic, rather than elastic, deformation.

MAJOR UNRESOLVED PROBLEMS

The cause of the slight uplift that occurred to the north of the major zone of subsidence is uncertain. Presumably, this uplift involves an elastic distortion related to strain changes resulting from seaward thrusting along the continental margin at the time of the earthquake. It could represent an increase in vertical strain (Poisson bulge) resulting from a sudden increment in the regional horizontal compressive strain o r i e n t e d roughly normal to the zone (R. O. Burford, written commun., 1966). If this explanation for the uplift is correct, retriangulation within

the areas of slight uplift should show transverse horizontal shortening. A test of the suggestion could be made if the postearthquake triangulation net were extended northward into this zone.

A second major problem is that there exists an apparent asymmetry in the volumes of uplift (89 cu mi, 372 cu km) and subsidence (29 cu mi, 122 cu km) in the two major zones that implies a substantial increase in net gravitational potential. By making the assumptions that the displacements decrease linearly from a maximum at the surface to zero at the base of the continental crust, that there were no density changes within the affected volume of crust, and that the crust has an average density of 2.7, the approximate upper limit for this change may be calculated. An average lowering of $2\frac{1}{2}$ feet (75 cm) in a crustal block having the dimensions of the zone of subsidence would result in a potential energy loss of 2.7×10^{19} ft-lbs (3.6×10^{26} ergs). The increase in gravitational potential in the uplifted area would be about 4.1×10^{19} ft-lbs (5.6×10^{26} ergs), assuming an average uplift against gravity of roughly 6 feet (1.8 m) for a wedge-shaped block with a length of 475 miles (760 km), a width of 115 miles (185 km), and an average thickness of about 11 miles (18 km).

These data suggest an apparent net increase in gravitational potential of about 1.5×10^{19} ft-lbs (2×10^{26} ergs). Even with the assumption that vertical displacements extend only halfway through the slab, the indicated gravitational potential increase is still roughly two orders of magnitude larger than the total released seismic-wave energy of about 1–2×10^{24} ergs (calculated from the empirically derived Gutenberg-Richter relationship between

energy and earthquake magnitude $log\ E = 11.4 + 1.5\ M$; Richter, 1958, p. 366).

In fact, however, the net change in gravitational potential due to elastic-rebound mass redistribution in the crust must be considered as indeterminate because data are unavailable on (1) the seaward and continentward limits of the displacement field, (2) possible elastic density changes attendant upon stress drops within and behind the upper plate, and (3) the extent to which the movements may have been compensated by elastic depression of the denser mantle beneath zones of uplift and a corresponding rise beneath the zone of subsidence.

REPRESENTATION BY DISLOCATION THEORY

Savage and Hastie (1966) and Stauder and Bollinger (1966) have used dislocation theory to compare theoretical profiles of vertical surface displacement for various gently dipping and horizontal overthrust models to the observed and inferred profile. Their assumed models, with the corresponding profiles along a vertical plane oriented normal to the fault strike, are plotted to a common scale on figure 43. These models have, of necessity, been highly generalized to permit a mathematical analysis by dislocation theory, and, in part, the studies are based upon preliminary and incomplete observational data.

The basic assumption in this procedure is that the observed displacements can be modeled by the corresponding fields of a planar dislocation sheet in a homogeneous, isotropic, elastic half-space with displacement discontinuity matching the observed or inferred fault slip. Inasmuch as the depth, configuration, and net slip on the postulated faults are to a large degree speculative, considerable latitude exists in the parameters used for those calculations. Furthermore, because faults that break to the surface are not dislocations in a semi-infinite medium, their contribution to the deformation can only be examined qualitatively.

Figure 43 shows that, although each of the assumed models can approximately account for the observed subsidence, none of them gives a close fit between the theoretical and actual profiles in the uplifted zone. Stauder and Bollinger (1966, p. 5293) suggest that the observed tectonic surface displacements can be approximated to any desired degree by assuming combined differential-slip motion and a shallowly dipping thrust plane. Such a model would be more nearly in accord with the data which suggest a dipping master fault having the approximate configuration shown in figure 43A with differential slip as indicated in figure 43B. To be realistic, however, it would also have to include the effects of (1) imbrication along known and suspected thrust or reverse faults that break to the surface, (2) possible breaking to the surface along the shallowing leading edge of the megathrust, and, perhaps (3) possible simultaneous underthrusting of the lower plate along an inclined fault plane.

STEEP-FAULT MODEL

OUTLINE OF THE MODEL

According to the steep-fault model, the earthquake resulted from elastic rebound on a near-vertical fault that strikes approximately along the line of zero change in land level, with the southeast block up and the northwest block down relative to sea level. A steeply dipping fault was suggested by a preliminary fault-plane solution based on surface waves (Press and Jackson, 1965,

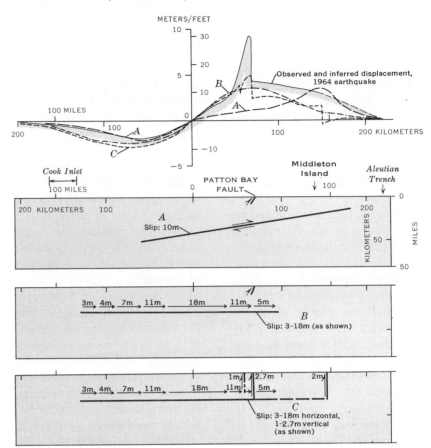

43.—Comparison of observed and inferred profile of surface displacement along line B–B' of plate 1 (shaded line) with computed profiles for movement on faults of slip and cross-sectional configuration shown in diagrams below the profiles. Model A from Savage and Hastie (1966, fig. 3); models B and C from Stauder and Bollinger (1966, fig. 7).

p. 867; Press, 1965, p. 2404). However, Savage and Hastie (1966, p. 4899–4900) have pointed out that a unique surface-wave solution for the fault orientation cannot be inferred from the surface waves, inasmuch as the direction of rupture propagation is along the null axis and therefore the radiation of seismic waves will be essentially the same for either of the two possible fault planes.

The main appeal of the steep-fault model is that it can readily account for the gross distribution of uplift and subsidence in two major zones, as well as the occurrence of the earthquake epicenter close to the zero isobase between these zones.

However, as noted elsewhere (Plafker, 1965, p. 1686), there are no compelling geologic, seismologic, or geodetic data in support of the steep-fault model. Aftershocks are not grouped along its postulated trace, but instead lie mainly in a broad belt along the continental margin mainly to the south of the zero isobase (fig. 2). Furthermore no field evidence exists for new surface breakage in the vicinity of the zero isobase—despite the fact that it intersects the coast in more than 15 localities (fig. 3). And finally there is no evidence that the line corresponds to a major geologic boundary with the seaward side relatively upthrown, as might be expected if it marked the trace of a major fault

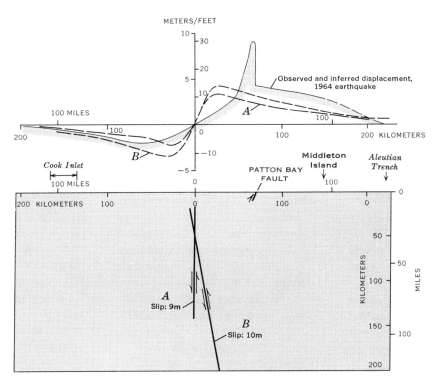

44.—Comparison of observed and inferred profile of surface displacement along line B–B' of plate 1 (shaded line) with computed profiles for movement on steeply dipping faults of slip and cross-sectional configuration shown in the diagram below the profiles. Model A from Press and Jackson (1965, fig. 1); model B from Savage and Hastie (1966, fig. 3).

along which vertical movement has occurred in the past. On the contrary the overwhelming majority of surface faults that parallel the coast in this part of Alaska have exactly the opposite sense of displacement (fig. 29).

The apparent absence of a surface dislocation along the zero isobase between the major zones prompted the suggestion that the displacement represents flexure above a near-vertical fault at depth (Press and Jackson, 1965, p. 868; Press, 1965, p. 2405). Such a fault would have to extend to the considerable depth of 62–124 miles (100–200 km) below the free surface to account for the areal distribution of residual vertical displacements normal to its inferred strike.

REPRESENTATION BY DISLOCATION THEORY

Observed residual tectonic displacements have been compared to the theoretical surface displacements that would occur on faults of varying inclination, slip, and dimension by application of dislocation theory (Press and Jackson, 1965; Press, 1965; Savage and Hastie, 1966). These analyses are subject to the same basic assumptions as were previously outlined. Assumed models, with corresponding profiles along a vertical plane oriented normal to the fault strike, are plotted to a common scale on figure 44. The resultant profiles show the same general spatial distribution of uplift and subsidence as the profile of observed and inferred vertical

displacements along a northwest-southeast line through the southwest tip of Montague Island. They differ fundamentally, however, in that the axes of uplift and subsidence are too close together by at least 50 miles (80 km), or a factor of one-half, and the indicated changes within the two major zones are notably more equal in amplitude than in the observed profile. The distance between the two axes would tend to decrease even further if the faulting is shallow—as is suggested by the spatial distribution of the aftershocks. Even if the vertical displacements could be explained by these models, no reasonable combination of fault dimensions, slip, and dip could also duplicate the systematic horizontal displacements observed in the field (fig. 18).

SUMMARY AND CONCLUSIONS

The earthquake of March 27, 1964, was accompanied by regional vertical and horizontal displacements over an area probably in excess of 110,000 square miles in south-central Alaska. Major deformation and related seismic activity were largely limited to an elongate segment of the continental margin lying between the Aleutian Trench and the chain of late Cenozoic volcanoes that comprise the Aleutian Volcanic Arc.

Geologic evidence in the earthquake-affected region suggests that the earthquake was but the most recent pulse in an episode of deformation that probably began in late Pliocene time and has continued intermittently to the present. The net effect of these movements has been uplift along the Gulf of Alaska coast and continental margin by warping and imbricate faulting; subsidence or relative stability characterized most of the adjacent landward zone extending inland approximately to the Aleutian Volcanic Arc. The length of time since the last major tectonic earthquake that involved regional warping, as inferred from radiocarbon-dated displaced shorelines in the epicentral region, appears to have been about 930–1,360 years.

Because the primary fault or zone of faulting along which the earthquake is presumed to have occurred is not exposed at the surface on land, a unique solution for its orientation and sense of slip cannot be made. Nevertheless, the vertical displacements, when considered in relationship to the focal-mechanism studies and spatial distribution of seismicity, strongly favor the hypothesis that the primary fault was a major thrust fault, or megathrust. The data suggest that the segment of the megathrust along which slippage occurred was 550–600 miles long and 110–180 miles wide and that it dips from the vicinity of the Aleutian Trench at a gentle angle beneath the continental margin.

According to the thrust-fault hypothesis, the observed regional uplift and transverse shortening along the continental margin during the earthquake resulted from (1) relative seaward displacement of the upper plate along the dipping primary thrust, (2) imbrication on the known subsidiary reverse faults that break through the upper plate to the surface, and (3) crustal warping. Movement on other subsidiary submarine reverse faults, as well as rebound of the lower plate toward the continent, may have contributed to the uplift. Simultaneous subsidence in the zone behind the fault block presumably reflects an elastic horizontal extension and vertical attenuation of previously compressed crustal material. Stored elastic-strain energy within the thrust block and the segment of crust behind the block that was affected by subsidence was the primary source of energy dissipated during the earthquake in the form of seismic waves, heat, crushing of rock, and, perhaps, net changes in gravitational potential. Major unresolved problems are the cause of the slight uplift in the area north of the two major zones of deformation and the apparent large increase in potential energy over the displacement field.

The implication of a genetic relationship between the 1964 Alaska earthquake and the Aleutian Arc appears inescapable in view of the nature of the surface deformation and seismic activity associated with the earthquake. Available geologic, geodetic, and geophysical data from the region affected by tectonic deformation during the earthquake are compatible with the concept that arc structures are sites of down-welling mantle convection currents and that planar seismic zones dipping beneath them mark the zone of shearing produced by downward-moving material thrust against a less mobile block of the crust and upper mantle. Conversely, the data provide severe constraints for alternative hypotheses that relate deformation in the eastern Aleutian Arc, at least, primarily to transverse regional extension or to movement on major longitudinal strike-slip faults or shallow steep dip-slip faults.

Preearthquake strain directed at a gentle angle downward beneath the arc in the epicentral region is suggested by geodetic evidence for horizontal shortening of as much as 64 feet roughly normal to the Gulf of Alaska coast and by geologic evidence for progressive coastal submergence in the same region in excess of 16 feet. If the duration of preearthquake strain accumulation, as inferred from radiocarbon-dated drowned shorelines, was about 930–1,360 years, average annual horizontal displacement was about 0.59–0.83 inch per year (1.5 to 2.1 cm per year). The indicated shortening, which is probably a minimum value inasmuch as there probably also was some permanent shortening, is reasonably compatible with sea-floor spreading rates of about 2.9 cm per year in a northwesterly direction from the Juan de Fuca ridge. Such rates and spreading directions have been deduced from paleomagnetic studies of the northeastern Pacific ocean floor (Vine, 1966, p. 1407). Alternative driving mechanisms, in which the upper plate overrides the ocean basin or in which the regional strain is directed horizontally, do not readily account either for the widespread preearthquake subsidence relative to sea level that accompanied horizontal shortening in coastal areas affected by earthquake-related tectonic deformation or for the orientation of principal stress axes at the hypocenter of the main shock and many of its aftershocks.

REFERENCES CITED

Alaska Department of Fish and Game, 1965, Post-earthquake fisheries evaluation; an interim report on the March 1964 earthquake effects on Alaska's fishery resources: Juneau, Alaska, 72 p.

Algermissen, S. T., 1965, Prince William Sound, Alaska earthquake of March 28, 1964, and aftershock sequence [abs.]: Geol. Soc. America Spec. Paper 82, p. 2.

Balakina, L. M., Shirokova, H. I., and Vvedenskaya, A. V., 1961, Study of stresses and ruptures in earthquake foci with the help of dislocation theory: Ottawa Dominion Observatory Pub., v. 24, no. 10, p. 321–327.

Barnes, D. F., 1966, Gravity changes during the Alaska earthquake: Jour. Geophys. Research, v. 71, no. 2, p. 451–456.

Barnes, F. F., 1962, Geologic map of the lower Matanuska Valley, Alaska: U.S. Geol. Survey Misc. Geol. Inv. Map I–359, scale 1 : 63,360.

Benioff, Hugo, 1951, Earthquakes and rock creep; pt. 1, Creep characteristics of rocks and the origin of aftershocks: Seismol. Soc. America Bull., v. 41, no. 1, p. 31–62.

——— 1954, Orogenesis and deep crustal structure—additional evidence from seismology: Geol. Soc. America Bull., v. 65, no. 5, p. 385–400.

Bollinger, G. A., and Stauder, William, 1965, Geometry of earthquake foci stresses [abs.]: Seismol. Soc. America, Eastern Sec., Earthquake Notes, v. 36, nos. 3–4, p. 22.

Bolt, B. A., 1964, Seismic air waves from the great 1964 Alaska earthquake: Nature, v. 202, no. 4937, p. 1095–1096.

Brazee, R. J., 1965, A study of T phases in the Aleutian earthquake series of March and April 1957: Seismol. Soc. America, Eastern Sec. Earthquake Notes, v. 36, nos. 1–2, p. 9–14.

Burk, C. A., 1965, Geology of the Alaska Peninsula—island arc and continental margin: Geol. Soc. America Mem. 99, pt. 1, 250 p.

Carey, S. W., 1958, The tectonic approach to continental drift, in Continental drift—a symposium: Hobart, Australia, Tasmania Univ. Geol. Dept. [1956], p. 177–355.

Clark, D. W., 1966, Perspectives in the prehistory of Kodiak Island, Alaska: Am. Antiquity, v. 31, no. 3, p. 358–371.

Coats, R. R., 1962, Magma type and crustal structure in the Aleutian Arc, in The crust of the Pacific Basin: Am. Geophys. Union. Geophys. Mon. 6, p. 92–109.

Coleman, J. M., and Smith, W. G., 1964, Late Recent rise of sea level: Geol. Soc. Am. Bull., v. 75, no. 9, p. 833–840.

Curray, J. R., 1961, Late Quaternary sea level—a discussion: Geol. Soc. Am. Bull., v. 72, no. 11, p. 1707–1712.

Dachnowski-Stokes, A. P., 1941, Peat resources in Alaska: U.S. Dept. Agriculture Tech. Bull. 769, 84 p.

De Laguna, Frederica, 1934, The archaeology of Cook Inlet, Alaska, with a chapter on Skeletal material, by Bruno Oetteking: Philadelphia Univ., Pa., Pennsylvania Press, 263 p.

——— 1956, Chugach prehistory; the archaeology of Prince William Sound, Alaska: Seattle, Washington Univ. Press, 289 p.

Detterman, R. L., and Reed, B. L., 1964, Preliminary map of the geology of the Iliamna quadrangle, Alaska: U.S. Geol. Survey Misc. Geol. Inv. Map I–407, scale 1 : 250,000.

Dietz, R. S., 1961, Continent and ocean basin evolution by spreading of the sea floor: Nature, v. 190, no. 4779, p. 854–857.

Earthquake Research Institute, 1964, Report of the Niigata earthquake of June 16, 1964: Spec. Bull. Tokyo Univ., Earthquake Research Inst., v. 8, 133 p. [In Japanese].

Eckel, E. B., 1967, Effects of the earthquake of March 27, 1964, on air and water transport, communications, and utilities systems in south-central Alaska: U.S. Geol. Survey Prof. Paper 545–B, p. B1–B27.

Evison, F. F., 1963, Earthquakes and faults: Seismol. Soc. America Bull., v. 53, no. 5, p. 873–891.

Ewing, Maurice, Ludwig, W. J., and Ewing, John, 1965, Oceanic structural history of the Bering Sea: Jour. Geophys. Research, v. 70, no. 18, p. 4593–4600.

Fairbridge, R. W., 1961, Eustatic changes in sea level, in Physics and chemistry of the earth: New York, Pergamon Press, v. 4, p. 99–185.

Florensov, N. A., and Solonenko, V. P., eds., 1963, The Gobi-Altai earthquake: Izdatelo Akad. Nauk SSSR, 391 p. [in Russian; English translation, U.S. Dept. of Commerce, 1965.]

Foster, H. L., and Karlstrom, T. N. V., 1967, Ground breakage and associated effects in the Cook Inlet area, Alaska, resulting from the March 27, 1964, earthquake: U.S. Geol. Survey Prof. Paper 543–F, p. F1–F28.

Furumoto, A. S., 1967, Analysis of Rayleigh waves, pt. 2 of Source mechanism of the Alaska earthquake and tsunami of 27 March 1964: Pacific Sci., v. 21, no. 3, p. 311–316.

Gates, G. O., and Gryc, George, 1963, Structure and tectonic history of Alaska: Am. Assoc. Petroleum Geologists Mem. 2, p. 264–277.

Gates, Olcott, and Gibson, W. M., 1956, Interpretation of the configuration of the Aleutian Ridge [Alaska]: Geol. Soc. America Bull., v. 67, no. 2, p. 127–146.

Ghent, E. D., 1965, Comments on phase changes and shallow focus earthquakes: New Zealand Jour. Geology and Geophysics, v. 8, no. 5, p. 820–832.

Grant, U. S., and Higgins, D. F., 1910, Reconnaissance of the geology and mineral resources of Prince William Sound, Alaska: U.S. Geol. Survey Bull. 443, 89 p.

Grantz, Arthur, 1965, Geologic map and cross sections of the Nelchina area, south-central Alaska: U.S. Geol. Survey open-file map, 4 sheets, scale 1 : 63,360.

——— 1966, Strike-slip faults in Alaska: U.S. Geol. Survey open-file report, 82 p.

Grantz, Arthur, Plafker, George, and Kachadoorian, Reuben, 1964, Alaska's Good Friday earthquake, March 27, 1964, a preliminary geologic evaluation: U.S. Geol. Survey Circ. 491, 35 p.

Griggs, D. T., and Blacic, J. D., 1965, Quartz—anomalous weakness of synthetic crystals: Science, v. 147, no. 3655, p. 292–295.

Griggs, D. T., and Handin, J. W., 1960, Observations on fracture and a hypothesis of earthquakes: Geol. Soc. America Mem. 79, p. 347–363.

Gutenberg, Beno, and Richter, C. F., 1954, Seismicity of the earth and associated phenomena, 2d ed.: Princeton, N.J., Princeton Univ. Press, 310 p.

Hales, A. L., and Asada, T., 1966, Crustal structure in coastal Alaska, in The earth beneath the continents: Am. Geophys. Union Geophys. Mon. 10, p. 420–432.

Hamilton, Warren, and Myers, W. B., 1966, Cenozoic tectonics of the western United States; Reviews of Geophysics, v. 4, no. 4, p. 509–549.

Hanna, G D., 1964, Biological effects of an earthquake: Pacific Discovery, v. 17, no. 6, p. 24–26.

Hansen, W. R., and Eckel, E. B., 1966, A summary description of the Alaska earthquake—its setting and effects, in Hansen, Eckel, and others, The Alaska earthquake, March 27, 1964: Field investigations and reconstruction effort: U.S. Geol. Survey Prof. Paper 541, p. 1–37.

Hatori, Tokutaro, 1965, on the tsunami which accompanied the Niigata earthquake of June 16, 1964— source deformation, propagation, and tsunami run-up: Tokyo Univ., Earthquake Research Inst. Bull., v. 43, no. 1, p. 129–148.

Henderson, J., 1933, The geological aspects of the Hawke's Bay earthquakes [New Zealand]: New Zealand Jour, Sci. Technology, v. 15, no. 1, p. 38–75.

Hess, H. H., 1955, The oceanic crust: Jour. Marine Research, v. 14, no. 4, p. 423–439.

——— 1957, The Vening Meinesz negative gravity anomaly belt of island arcs 1926–56: Koninkl. Nederl. Geol.-Mijnbouwk. Genoot., Verh., Geol. Ser., v. 18, 183–188.

——— 1962, History of ocean basins, in Petrologic studies (Buddington volume): Geol. Soc. America, p. 599–620.

Heusser, C. J., 1960, Late-Pleistocene environments of North Pacific North America—an elaboration of late-glacial and postglacial climatic, physiographic, and biotic changes: Am. Geog. Soc. Spec. Pub. 35, 308 p.

Hoare, J. M., 1961, Geology and tectonic setting of lower Kuskokwim-Bristol Bay region, Alaska: Am. Assoc. Petroleum Geologists Bull., v. 45, no. 5, p. 594–611.

Hodgson, J. H., 1957, Nature of faulting in large earthquakes: Geol. Soc. America Bull., v. 68, no. 5, p. 611–643.

Hopkins, D. M., MacNeil, F. S., Merklin, R. L., and Petrov, O. M., 1965, Quaternary correlations across Bering Strait: Science, v. 147, no. 3662, p. 1107–1114.

Iida, K., 1963, A relation of earthquake energy to tsunami energy and the estimation of the vertical displacement in a tsunami source: Nagoya [Japan] Univ. Inst. Earth Sci., Earth Sci. Jour., v. 11, no. 1, p. 49–67.

Imamura, Akitsune, 1930, Topographical changes accompanying earthquakes or volcanic eruptions: Japan Imperial Earthquake Inv. Comm., Foreign Languages Pubs., no. 25, 143 p.

Inoue, E., 1960, Land deformation in Japan: Japan Geog. Survey Inst. Bull., v. 6, pt. 2–3, p. 73–134.

Jordan, J. N., Lander, J. F. and Black, R. A., 1965, Aftershocks of the 4 February 1965 Rat Island Earthquake: Science, v. 148, no. 3675, p. 1323–1325.

Karlstrom, T. N. V., 1964, Quaternary geology of the Kenai Lowland and glacial history of the Cook Inlet region, Alaska: U.S. Geol. Survey Prof. Paper 443, 69 p.

Kaye, C. A., 1964, The upper limit of barnacles as an index of sea level change on the New England Coast during the past 100 years: Jour. Geology, v. 72, no. 5, p. 580–600.

Kelly, T. E., 1963, Geology and hydrocarbons in Cook Inlet basin, Alaska: Am. Assoc. Petroleum Geologists Mem. 2, p. 278–296.

Lamb, Horace, 1932, Hydrodynamics, 6th ed.: England, Cambridge Univ. Press, 738 p.

Lanphere, M. A., 1966, Potassium-argon ages of Tertiary plutrons in the Prince William Sound region, Alaska, in Geological Survey research 1966: U.S. Geol. Survey Prof. Paper 550–D, p. D195–D198.

Lensen, G. J., 1961, Principal horizontal stress directions as an aid to the study of crustal deformation, in A symposium on earthquake mechanism: Ottawa Dominion Observatory Pub., v. 24, no. 10, p. 389–397.

Levin, Betsy, Ives, P. C., Oman, C. L., and Rubin, Meyer, 1965, U.S. Geological Survey radiocarbon dates VIII: Radiocarbon, v. 7, p. 372–398.

Lyell, Sir Charles, 1874, Principles of geology: New York, D. Appleton and Co., v. 2, 652 p.

McCulloch D. S., 1966, Slide-induced waves, seiching, and ground fracturing caused by the earthquake of March 27, 1964, at Kenai Lake, Alaska: U.S. Geol. Survey Prof. Paper 543–A, p. A1–A41.

MacKevett, E. M., Jr., Berg, H. C., Plafker, George, and Jones, D. L., 1964, Preliminary geologic map of the McCarthy C–4 quadrangle, Alaska: U.S. Geol. Survey Misc. Geol. Inv. Map I–423, scale 1 : 63,360.

Malloy R. J., 1964, Crustal uplift southwest of Montague Island, Alaska: Science, v. 146, no. 3647, p. 1048–1049.

——— 1965, Gulf of Alaska—Seafloor upheaval: Geo-Marine Technology, v. 1, no. 5, p. 22–26.

Marmer, H. A., 1951, Tidal datum planes, revised ed.: U.S. Coast and Geodetic Survey Spec. Pub. 135, 142 p.

Martin, G. C., Johnson, B. L., and Grant, U.S., 1915, Geology and mineral resources of the Kenai Peninsula, Alaska: U.S. Geol. Survey Bull. 587, 243 p.

Martin, G. C., and Katz, F. J., 1912, Geology and coal fields of the lower Matanuska Valley, Alaska: U.S. Geol. Survey Bull. 500, 98 p.

Miller, D. J., 1953, Late Cenozoic marine glacial sediments and marine terraces of Middleton Island, Alaska: Jour. Geology, v. 61, no. 1, p. 17–40.

———1961, Geology of the Katalla district, Gulf of Alaska Tertiary province, Alaska: U.S. Geol. Survey open-file map, scale 1: 96,000, 2 sheets.

Miller, D. J., and MacColl, R. S., 1964, Geologic map and sections of the northern part of the McCarthy A–4 quadrangle, Alaska: U.S. Geol. Survey Misc. Geol. Inv. Map I–410, scale 1: 63,360.

Miller, D. J., Payne, T. G., and Gryc, George, 1959, Geology of possible petroleum provinces in Alaska, with an annotated bibliography by E. H. Cobb: U.S. Geol. Survey Bull. 1094, 131 p.

Moffit, F. H., 1954, Geology of the Prince William Sound region, Alaska: U.S. Geol. Survey Bull. 989–E, p. 225–310.

Moore, G. W., 1967, Preliminary geologic map of Kodiak Island and vicinity, Alaska: U.S. Geol. Survey open-file map, scale 1: 250,000.

Muto, K., 1932, A study of displacements of triangulation points: Tokyo Univ., Earthquake Research Inst. Bull., v. 10, p. 384–392.

Orowan, E., 1960, Mechanism of seismic faulting: Geol. Soc. America Mem. 79, p. 323–345.

Page, R. A., Jr., 1967, Aftershocks as a near-surface phenomenon [abs.]: Am. Geophys. Union Trans., v. 48, no. 1, p. 205.

Pararas-Carayannis, G e o r g e, 1967, Water waves, pt. 1 of Source mechanism study of the Alaska earthquake and tsunami of 27 March 1964: Pacific Science, v. 21, no. 3, p. 301–310.

Parkin, E. J., 1966, Horizontal displacements, pt. 2 of Alaskan surveys to determine crustal movement: U.S. Coast and Geodetic Survey, 11 p.

Payne, T. G., 1955, Mesozoic and Cenozoic tectonic elements of Alaska: U.S. Geol. Survey Misc. Geol. Inv. Map I–84, scale 1: 5,000,000.

Peter, G., Elvers, D., Yellin, M., 1965, Geological structure of Aleutian Trench southwest of Kodiak Island: Jour. Geophys. Research, v. 70, no. 2, p. 353–66.

Plafker, George, 1965, Tectonic deformation associated with the 1964 Alaskan earthquake: Science, v. 148, no. 3678, p. 1675–1687.

———1967a, Geologic map of the Gulf of Alaska Tertiary Province, Alaska: U.S. Geol. Survey Misc. Geol. Inv. Map I–484, scale 1: 500,000.

———1967b, Surface faults on Montague Island associated with the 1964 Alaska earthquake: U.S. Geol. Survey Prof. Paper 543–G, p. G1–G42.

Plafker, George, and Kachadoorian, Reuben, 1966, Geologic effects of the March 1964 earthquake and associated seismic sea waves on Kodiak and nearby islands, Alaska: U.S. Geol. Survey Prof. Paper 543–D, p. D1–D46.

Plafker, George, Kachadoorian, Reuben, Eckel, Edwin B., and Mayo, L. R., 1969, Effects of the earthquake of March 27, 1964, on various communities: U.S. Geol. Survey Prof. Paper 542–G, G1–G50.

Plafker, George, and MacNeil, F. S., 1966, Stratigraphic significance of Tertiary fossils from the Orca Group in the Prince William Sound region, Alaska, in Geological Survey research 1966: U.S. Geol. Survey Prof. Paper 550–B, p. B62–B68.

Plafker, George, and Mayo, L. R., 1965, Tectonic deformation, subaqueous slides, and destructive waves associated with the Alaskan March 27, 1964, earthquake—an interim geologic evaluation: U.S. Geol. Survey open-file report, 21 p.

Plafker, George, and Rubin, Meyer, 1967, Vertical tectonic displacements in south-central Alaska during and prior to the great 1964 earthquake: Jour. Geosciences (Osaka City Univ.), v. 10, art. 1–7, p. 1–14.

Press, Frank, 1965, Displacements, strains, and tilts at teleseismic distances: Jour. Geophys. Research, v. 70, no. 10, p. 2395–2412.

Press, Frank, and Jackson, David, 1965, Alaskan earthquake, 27 March 1964—vertical extent of faulting and elastic strain energy release: Science, v. 147, no. 3660, p. 867–868.

Rainey, F. G., and Ralph, Elizabeth, 1959, Radiocarbon dating in the Arctic: Am. Antiquity, v. 24, no. 4, p. 365–374.

Raleigh, C. B., 1967, Tectonic implications of serpentinite weakening: Royal Astron. Soc. Geophys. Jour., v. 14, p. 113–118.

Raleigh, C. B., and Patterson, M. S., 1965, Experimental deformation of serpentinite and its tectonic implications: Jour. Geophys. Research, v. 70, no. 16, p. 3965–3985.

Reid, H. F., 1911, The California earthquake of April 18, 1906. The mechanics of the earthquake: Carnegie Inst. Washington Pub. 87, v. 2, 192 p.

Reimnitz, Erk, 1966, Late Quaternary history and sedimentation of the Copper River Delta and vicinity: California Univ., San Diego, unpublished Ph. D. thesis, 160 p.

Richter, C. F., 1958, Elementary seismology: San Francisco, Calif., W. H. Freeman and Co., 768 p.

Ricketts, E. F., and Calvin, Jack, 1962, Between Pacific tides; an account of the habit and habitats of some 500 of the common, conspicuous seashore invertebrates of the Pacific Coast between Sitka, Alaska, and northern Mexico, 3d ed.: Stanford, Calif., Stanford Univ. Press, 516 p.

Rigg, G. B., and Miller, R. C., 1949, Intertidal plant and animal zonation in the vicinity of Neah Bay, Washington: California Acad. Sci. Proc., 4th ser., v. 26, no. 10, p. 323–351.

Row, R. V., 1966, On the ionospheric long-period acoustic-gravity wave pulse launched by the great Alaskan earthquake of March 1964 [abs.]: Am. Geophys. Union Trans., v. 47. no. 1, p. 51.

Rubin, Meyer, and Alexander, Corrinne, 1958, U.S. Geological Survey radiocarbon dates IV: Science, v. 127, no. 3313, p. 1476–1487.

Saint-Amand, Pierre, 1957, Geological and geophysical synthesis of the tectonics of portions of British Columbia, the Yukon Territory, and Alaska: Geol. Soc. America Bull., v. 68, no. 10, p. 1343–1370.

———1961, Los terremotos de mayo – Chile 1960 * * * an eyewitness account of the greatest catastrophe in recent history: China Lake, Calif., Michelson Lab., U.S. Naval Ordnance Test Sta. Tech. Art. 14, 39 p.

Savage, J. C., and Hastie, L. M., 1966, Surface deformation associated with dip-slip faulting: Jour. Geophys. Research, v. 71, no. 20, p. 4897–4904.

Schrader, F. C., 1900, A reconnaissance of a part of Prince William Sound and the Copper River district, Alaska, in 1898: U.S. Geol. Survey 20th Ann. Rept., pt. 7, p. 341–423.

Shor, G. G., Jr., 1962, Seismic refraction studies off the coast of Alaska 1956–1957: Seismol. Soc. America Bull., v. 52, no. 1, p. 37–57.

———1966, Continental margins and island arcs of western North America, in Continental margins and island arcs: Canada Geol. Survey Paper 66–15, p. 126–222.

Small, J. B., 1966, Vertical bench mark displacement, pt. 1 of Alaskan surveys to determine crustal movement: U.S. Coast and Geod. Survey, 24 p.

Stauder, William, 1967, Seismic evidence of present deformation in island arc structures [abs.]: Am. Geophys. Union Trans., v. 48, no. 1, p. 218–219.

Stauder, William, and Bollinger, G. A., 1964, the S wave project for focal mechanism studies—Earthquakes of 1962: Seismol. Soc. America Bull., v. 54, no. 6, pt. B, p. 2199–2208.

———1966, The focal mechanism of the Alaska earthquake of March 28, 1964, and of its aftershock sequence: Jour. Geophys. Research, v. 71, no. 22, p. 5283–5296.

Stephenson, T. A., and Stephenson, Anne, 1949, The universal features of zonation between tide-marks on rocky coasts: Jour. Ecology, v. 37, p. 289–305.

Tarr, R. S., and Martin, Lawrence, 1912, The earthquake at Yakutat Bay, Alaska, in September, 1899, with a preface by G. K. Gilbert: U.S. Geol. Survey Prof. Paper 69, 135 p.

———1914, Alaskan glacier studies of the National Geographic Society in the Yakutat Bay, Prince William Sound and lower Copper River Regions: Washington, D.C., Natl. Geog. Soc., 498 p.

Thorsteinson, F. V., 1965, Effects of the Alaska earthquake on pink and chum salmon runs in Prince William Sound: Auke Bay, Alaska, U.S. Bur. Commercial Fisheries Biol. Lab., 16 p.

Tobin, D. G., and Sykes, L. R., 1966, Relationship of hypocenters of earthquakes to the geology of Alaska: Jour. Geophys. Research, v. 71, no. 6, p. 1659–1667.

Tocher, Don, 1960, The Alaska earthquake of July 10, 1958—Movement on the Fairweather fault and field investigation of southern epicentral region: Seismol. Soc. America Bull., v. 50, no. 2, p. 267–292.

Toksoz, M. N., Ben-Menahem, Ari, and Harkrider, D. G., 1965, Source mechanism of Alaska earthquake from long-period seismic surface waves [abs.]: Am. Geophys. Union Trans., v. 46, no. 1, p. 154.

U.S. Coast and Geodetic Survey, 1964, Tide tables, high and low water predictions, 1964, West Coast North and South America including the Hawaiian Islands: U.S. Coast and Geod. Survey, 224 p.

Vancouver, John, ed., 1801, A voyage of discovery to the North Pacific Ocean and around the world * * * in the years 1790–1795 * * * under the command of Captain George Vancouver * * *, new ed.: London, printed for J. Stockdale, 6 v.

Van Dorn, W. G., 1965, Source mechanism of the tsunami of March 28, 1964, in Alaska: Coastal Eng. Conf., 9th, Lisbon 1964, Proc., p. 166–190.

Vine, F. J., 1966, Spreading of the ocean floor—new evidence: Science, v. 154, no. 3755, p. 1405–1415.

Von Huene, Roland, Shor, G. R., Jr., and Saint-Amand, Pierre, 1966, Active faults and structure of the continental margin in the 1964 Alaskan aftershock sequence area [abs.]: Am. Geophys. Union Trans., v. 47, no. 1, p. 176.

Wahrhaftig, Clyde, 1965, The physiographic provinces of Alaska: U.S. Geol. Survey Prof. Paper 482, 52 p.

Waller, R. M., 1966a, Effects of the earthquake of March 27, 1964 in the Homer area, Alaska with a section on Beach changes on Homer Spit, by K. W. Stanley: U.S. Geol. Survey Prof. Paper 542–D, p. D1–D28.

Waller, R. M., 1966b, Effects of the March 1964 Alaska earthquake on the hydrology of south-central Alaska: U.S. Geol. Survey Prof. Paper 544–A, p. A1–A28.

Wolfe, J. A., Hopkins, D. M., and Leopold, E. B., 1966, Tertiary stratigraphy and paleobotany of the Cook Inlet region, Alaska: U.S. Geol. Survey Prof. Paper 398–A, p. A1–A29.

Wood, F. J., ed., 1966, Operational phases of the Coast and Geodetic Survey program in Alaska for the period March 27 to December 31, 1964, v. 1 of The Prince William Sound, Alaska, earthquake of 1964 and aftershocks: U.S. Coast and Geodetic Survey, 263 p.

Wyss, Max, and Brune, J. N., 1967, The Alaska earthquake of 28 March 1964—A complex multiple rupture: Bull. Seis. Soc. America, v. 57, no. 5, p. 1017–1023.

CLARIFICATIONS

Seismology & Geodesy Vol. Page	USGS Page	Column	Line	Remarks	Remarks
116	I4	1	21, 22	Later computed as 61.04°N; 147.73°W	
145	I31	1	5	Unpublished data from a 1967 USC&GS retriangulation across Shelikof Strait and part of Cook Inlet showed the predicted transverse extension normal to the trend of the isobase contours.	
157	I43	Table 4	3	More complete data on deformation related to this earthquake are given in George Plafker and J. C. Savage, "Mechanism of the Chilean earthquakes of May 21 and 22, 1910," GSA Bull., v. 81, p. 1001–1030.	
169	I55	3	4	B.P. = before present.	

J. C. SAVAGE*
L. M. HASTIE†
UNIVERSITY OF TORONTO

Reprinted with minor changes from
Journal of Geophysical Research, Vol. 71, No. 20,
"Surface Deformation Associated with Dip-Slip Faulting"

Surface Deformation Associated with Dip-Slip Faulting

A fault surface may be represented by a rectangular surface of horizontal length $2L$, width W, and dip δ embedded in an elastic half-space with the top of the fault a depth h below the free surface. The vertical displacement of the free surface for a dip-slip motion Δu on such a fault surface can be calculated from the theory of Maruyama. This calculation has been made for fault models of three different earthquakes, and the results compared with the observed surface deformation in each case. For each calculation the dip of the fault plane was taken from the P wave fault plane solution. The preferred fault models are as follows: Alaska earthquake of March 28, 1964 (magnitude 8.4), $2L = 600$ km, $W = 200$ km, $\delta = 9°$, $h = 20$ km, and $\Delta u = 10$ m. Fairview Peak, Nevada, earthquake of December 16, 1954 (magnitude 7.1), $2L = 24$ to 48 km, $W = 6$ km, $\delta = 62°$, $h = 0$ km, and $\Delta u = 2$ m. Hebgen Lake, Montana, earthquake of August 18, 1959 (magnitude 7.1), $2L = 30$ km, $W = 15$ km, $\delta = 54°$, $h = 0.4$ km, and $\Delta u = 10$ m.

INTRODUCTION

The applications of static, elastic dislocation theory to the study of surface deformation accompanying faulting have been reviewed by *Press* [1965]. Whereas previous papers have been concerned with fault surfaces that are either parallel or perpendicular to the free surface of the elastic half-space, this paper is concerned with fault surfaces having reasonable values of dip. However, attention is restricted to the vertical component of the surface displacement since, in general, this is the only component which is reliably determined by field studies of earthquake deformation.

Figure 1 shows the coordinate system used to describe the fault surface and the elastic half-space. Only a rectangular fault of the type shown in the figure has been considered. It is assumed that the fault motion is dip slip and that it is the same everywhere on the fault surface, even out to the edges. The depth of the top of the fault h may have any value; $h = 0$ corresponds to a fault which breaks the surface. The dip of the fault plane δ must lie in the interval $0 < \delta < \pi/2$. Details of the calculation, which is merely an integration of expressions given by *Maruyama* [1964], are given in the appendix.

As an example of the results, we have shown in Figure 2 the vertical deformation of the surface in the plane $x_2 = 0$ which should be as-

sociated with faulting. For this example we have considered a reverse fault and shown how the deformation differs for high-angle and low-angle faulting. It is notable that the surface deformation is primarily uplift, particularly at dip 45°. Had we considered normal faulting, the sign of the vertical displacement would be changed, and the deformation would be primarily subsidence.

THE 1964 ALASKA EARTHQUAKE

The vertical displacements due to the March 28, 1964, Alaska earthquake (magnitude 8.4) are well documented over an area of approximately 2×10^5 km² [*Whitten*, 1965; *Plafker*, 1965]. The focal depth lies between 20 and 50 km. The fault plane solutions yield planes that strike between azimuths 60° and 70°. One plane, dipping 80°SE, is well defined by the solution, but the complementary low-angle plane is poorly defined. The belt of major aftershocks lies over the continental shelf and attains a maximum width of about 320 km and an average focal depth of 22 km.

Press and Jackson [1965] and *Press* [1965] have suggested that faulting occurred on the near-vertical plane defined by the fault plane solution. Using dislocation theory, those authors demonstrated that the observed uplift and subsidence could be accounted for by dip-slip motion on a near-vertical plane extending

---

*Now with U.S. Geological Survey.
†Now with Queensland Institute of Technology, Brisbane, Australia.

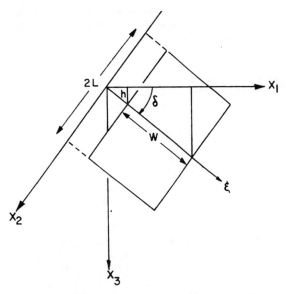

Fig. 1. Relation of fault plane to coordinate system.

from a depth of about 15 km down to perhaps a depth of 150 km or more. The dip slip re-

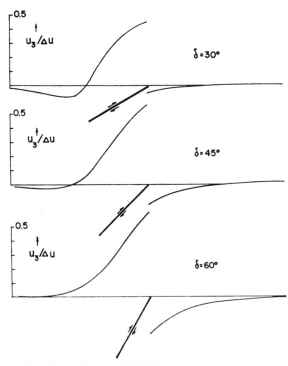

Fig. 2. Vertical displacement of free surface produced by dip-slip motion on a fault plane intersecting the surface. The profile is in the plane $x_2 = 0$ (Figure 1). The fault plane, drawn to scale, is shown as the heavy line segment. The fault length is four times the fault width. The vertical displacement is given as a fraction of the slip on the fault.

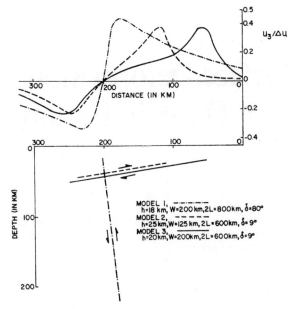

Fig. 3. Vertical surface displacements along the x_1 axis due to three plausible fault models of the 1964 Alaska earthquake. The fault surfaces for each model are sketched in the lower figure.

quired was about 10 m and the fault length 600 to 800 km.

On the other hand, *Plafker* [1965], on the basis of field studies, has suggested that thrust faulting occurred on the low-angle plane defined by the fault plane solution. He has shown by a qualitative argument that thrust faulting could produce the observed surface deformation. Here we shall make that argument quantitative by calculating the surface deformation associated with a dislocation model of thrust faulting. In this way both the thrust fault model and the near-vertical reverse fault model may be compared with the observed surface deformation to determine which offers the better explanation.

Figure 3 shows profiles of the vertical displacement along the free surface in the plane $x_2 = 0$ for three different fault models. Model 1 is essentially the model proposed by Press (a dip of 80° rather than 90° has been used both to fit the observed P wave fault plane solution and to conform to the observed asymmetry in vertical displacement). Comparison with Figure 4 shows that this model places the zone of maximum subsidence too close to the zone of maximum uplift. This difficulty can be overcome by using model 2 (Figure 3), which represents a low-angle thrust fault. Thus we

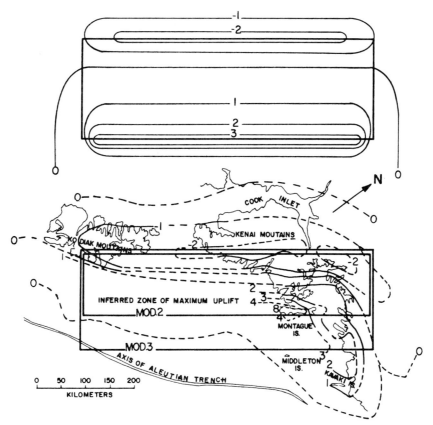

Fig. 4. (Upper) A plan of vertical surface displacements (in meters) calculated for fault model 3 of Figure 3. (Lower) A plan of the observed vertical displacements due to 1964 Alaska earthquake [after *Plafker*, 1965]. Outlines of the surface projections of fault planes for models 2 and 3 are shown as heavy rectangles. The projection of model 1 would be a narrow rectangle enclosing the epicenter and following the E-W trend of the zero contour. It has been omitted for clarity. Positive contour values represent uplift in meters.

believe model 2 is a better fit to the data than model 1. However, we believe that the best fit is provided by another model, model 3. The choice of model 3 is based upon the premise that the zone of observed maximum uplift passing through Montague Island (see Figure 4) is a product of secondary faulting. Both Press and Plafker seem to agree to this premise. We therefore expect the zone of maximum primary uplift to be about 75 km seaward from Montague Island, as is suggested by the observed contours on the right edge of Figure 4. If this is so, model 3 is to be preferred, and we believe that this is the model Plafker has suggested. The fault parameters for this model are $2L = 600$ km, $W = 200$ km, $\delta = 9°$, $h = 20$ km, and about 10 m of dip-slip motion on the fault surface. Figure 4 shows a comparison of the surface deformation calculated for this model with the observed deformation.

It should be recalled that the theoretical model of faulting requires constant slip right up to the edge of the fault. A more realistic model would permit the slip to decrease near the edge of the fault. This effect would tend to broaden the surface deformation pattern. In particular, the rather abrupt decay of vertical surface displacement on the right edge of both models 2 and 3 would become somewhat more gradual. However, the observational data are not adequate to justify attempts to include such refinements in the theory.

We should like to comment on the assertion [*Press*, 1965] that the surface wave fault plane solution requires that the 1964 Alaska earthquake was associated with a near-vertical fault plane. The double-couple fault representation does not distinguish between the fault plane and the auxiliary plane. It follows that the radiation from that representation will not make such a distinction. It is true that in many cases the distinction can be made on the basis of the inferred direction of rupture propagation. However, in the 1964 Alaska earthquake the direction of rupture propagation was along the null axis, and once again no distinction between the fault plane and the auxiliary plane can be made. Thus we believe that no first-order effects will distinguish the two planes. If second-order effects are capable of making the distinction, we doubt whether the effects will be so well observed as to be unambiguous.

Press [1965] has noted that the Kipapa strain seismograph indicated that the Alaska shock produced a permanent strain of about 10^{-8} in Hawaii. He indicated that such a strain could probably be explained by model 1 if there was some strike slip on the fault. Subject to the same proviso, models 2 and 3 will also yield strains at Hawaii of the correct order of magnitude.

It appears that the nature of the faulting associated with the Alaska earthquake must be decided by criteria other than those furnished by dislocation theory. Such criteria have been discussed by *Plafker* [1965], and the discussion need not be repeated here. It is our own opinion that the case for thrust faulting is the stronger, but the issue is by no means resolved.

FAIRVIEW PEAK EARTHQUAKE

The Fairview Peak, Nevada, earthquake of December 16, 1954 (magnitude 7.1), left extensive fault scarps trending in the N-S direction. U. S. Highway 50 crosses those scarps in an E-W direction just 2 km north of the epicenter. An accurate measure of the vertical movement along the highway was obtained by comparing leveling surveys performed before and after the earthquake [*Whitten*, 1957; *Reil*, 1957]. A U. S. Coast and Geodetic Survey level line, run along Highway 50 in 1934, and the highway survey itself (presumably run much more recently), form the pre-earthquake data. Both surveys were repeated after the earthquake, and the change in elevation of individual survey points indicates the ground deformation produced by the earthquake plus any regional subsidence that may have occurred in the intervening years. The highway surveys appear to yield changes $+\frac{1}{3}$ m greater than the USCGS surveys. Whether this represents re-

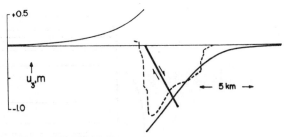

Fig. 5. Vertical displacement of surface produced by a fault with 2.2-m dip-slip motion at dip 62° that breaks the surface. The dashed line represents the observed surface displacement [*Slemmons*, 1957] after the Fairview Peak, Nevada, earthquake. Both profiles are in the plane $x_2 = 0$ (Figure 1).

gional subsidence or accumulated error in the highway survey is not known. We have followed *Slemmons* [1957] and adjusted this difference out of the highway survey data. The strike-slip movement across the highway was also measured directly [*Slemmons*, 1957]. It appeared to be about 2 m right lateral at the main fault and perhaps an additional 0.6 m about 6 km farther east. Thus we have an unusually complete set of surface deformation data along a line perpendicular to the fault trace.

The fault plane solution [*Romney*, 1957] indicated a plane striking at azimuth 349° and dipping 62°E; the east side of the fault moved in an azimuth of 155° and downward at an angle of 24° relative to the west block. This solution implies that the dip-slip motion is only half the strike-slip motion. The relative motion indicated by the fault plane solution is remarkably consistent with that found by geodetic measurement [*Romney*, 1957, p. 318]. However, the fault scarp trends along azimuth 5°, an azimuth 16°E of that indicated by the fault plane solution. In view of the excellent agreement between the relative movements deduced from the fault plane solution and the geodetic measurements, the discrepancy between the fault strike as indicated on the one hand by fault plane solution and on the other by the fault scarps may indicate that the fault scarps are no more than secondary features associated with the primary buried fault (W. Stauder, personal communication, 1966).

In Figure 5 we have attempted to fit a dislocation model of faulting to the surface deformation observed along Highway 50. The possible fault models have been restricted to those which break the surface and dip 62°E. If these restrictions were relaxed, a somewhat better fit could be obtained. The horizontal length of the fault is at least 24 km (length of Fairview Peak scarp alone) and perhaps more than 48 km (length of Fairview peak scarp plus Gold King scarp). Fortunately, the fault length is not a critical parameter in determining the fit to the observational data, and the solution proposed is consistent with either length. The observed vertical displacement of the ground surface is not continuous, but rather is made up in a large part by five fault scarps. Furthermore, the vertical deformation of the surface is probably affected to some extent by surficial settling. Nevertheless, a rough fit can be obtained, and the indicated value of the fault width (*W* in Figure 1) is about 6 km. The location of the model fault is consistent with the location of the epicenter, but the focal depth given by *Romney* [1957], 15 km based upon $_pP$, is about three times the depth

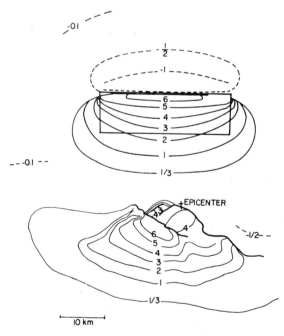

Fig. 6. Contour maps of subsidence (in meters) associated with Hebgen Lake earthquake. Upper map represents dislocation model and the lower figure the observed subsidence [after *Myers and Hamilton*, 1964]. The heavy rectangle in the upper figure represents the projection of the fault upon the surface; in the lower figure the heavy lines represent fault scarps. Dashed contours represent elevation rather than subsidence.

of the base of the model fault. It is, of course, possible that, although rupture initiates at depth, major slip is confined to the near-surface layers. The dip-slip movement on the fault model which best fits the observed data is about 2 m. Notice that the fault model proposed here involves only the dip-slip motion; the strike-slip motion would produce only negligible vertical displacement along this profile.

It can hardly be claimed that the model fits the observed profile closely. The most serious discrepancy is, of course, the lack of appreciable uplift on the upthrown side. This discrepancy may be attributed to the compaction of the alluvium by the shock. Such compaction, which is known to occur, would minimize the uplift and exaggerate the subsidence. The discrepancy may also be associated with the difference between the USCGS surveys and the highway surveys. Had we used the highway survey results, the observed profile would have been raised ⅓ m.

Chinnery [1964] (see also *Kasahara* [1958]) has proposed a dislocation model to fit the observed horizontal displacement of triangulation stations in the Fairview Peak area. His model consists of strike-slip motion along a vertical fault, and the strike of his model fault coincides with the fault plane solution rather than with the observed fault scarp. He finds that the best fit to the data is obtained for fault depths of 16 and 10 km for fault lengths of 45 and 60 km, respectively. The data do not fit the theoretical curves very closely (see *Kasahara* [1958] for an example of the fit), but part of the discrepancy is undoubtedly caused by failure to take account of the dip of the fault plane. Perhaps the best over-all estimate of the fault width would be about 10 km, a rough mean of the various estimates from dislocation theory.

THE HEBGEN LAKE EARTHQUAKE

The Hebgen Lake, Montana, earthquake (magnitude 7.1) of August 18, 1959, produced extensive fault scarps north of Hebgen Lake and an obvious downwarp of the lake basin. Subsidence was proved over an area of about 1250 km² (Figure 6). The maximum subsidence was about 7 m, and approximately 150 km² subsided more than 3 m. In contrast to the ample evidence for subsidence, there appears to be very little evidence of compensating uplift. Bench marks on the upthrown side of the fault near the eastern end (right edge in Figure 6) indicated an uplift of 0.5 m, while those at the western end showed an uplift of 0.1 m. It is true, however, that the region of suspected uplift is so mountainous as to offer few opportunities to prove elevation change. Nevertheless, field studies after the earthquake indicated that changes in altitude during the earthquake were almost entirely downward; both of the major interpretations of the evidence agree on this point. *Myers and Hamilton* [1964] interpret the field evidence to suggest that the major fault scarps produced by the earthquake are secondary features, and that 'the deep structure controlling the surficial subsidence is either a normal fault striking about N80°W and dipping southward or an abrupt monocline with the same orientation.' In this paper we shall follow the interpretation of Myers and Hamilton, but it must be mentioned that *Fraser et al.* [1964] interpret the evidence somewhat differently. Those authors believe that 'the principal, controlling structures for this change in relief are deep-seated earthquake-generating faults which either extend directly to the surface or are represented there by derivative faults.' In other words, the fault scarps are primary features.

The fault plane solution [*Ryall*, 1962] yielded only one plane, but the field evidence is sufficient to identify this as the fault plane. The fault motion was then dip-slip on a plane striking at azimuth 280° ± 10° and dip 54°S ± 8°. This solution is completely consistent with the interpretation of *Myers and Hamilton* [1964] and is probably not inconsistent with the interpretation of *Fraser et al.* [1964].

In Figure 6 we have compared the subsidence which would be produced by a buried fault dipping 54°S with the observed subsidence as

given by Myers and Hamilton. The model fault reaches to within about 0.4 km of the free surface and extends to a depth of about 12 km. The fault length is 30 km and the width 15 km. The dip-slip movement is about 10 m. It is clear from Figure 6 that the model offers a general explanation of the observed subsidence, though the detailed fit is not good. However, considering the simplicity of the model, perhaps one should not expect better agreement.

Press [1965] has noted that the strain seismograph at Isabella, California, indicated a permanent strain of 5×10^{-9} induced by the Hebgen Lake shock. Dislocation theory suggests that the fault model proposed above should induce a strain not greater than 2×10^{-10} at Isabella and that the strain in the direction of azimuth 326° (direction of the Isabella strain rod) should be an order of magnitude less. Thus it appears that the model does not account for the strain observed at Isabella. In this respect *Press*'s [1965] comments concerning a collapse mechanism remain pertinent.

To do justice to the interpretation suggested by *Fraser et al.* [1964], we should note that their isobase map is what would be expected from dislocation theory to be produced by three normal faults, one for each of the principal fault scarps. This, of course, is exactly what their interpretation requires.

CONCLUSIONS

The results of the application of dislocation theory to three earthquakes are summed up in Table 1. It should be recalled that each of the models is unsatisfactory in some respect (e.g., the Alaska earthquake may have been associated with a reverse fault dipping under the ocean rather than thrust fault dipping toward the continent as assumed in the model, the Nevada earthquake did not show the uplift predicted by theory, and the Montana earthquake model was based upon one of two

TABLE 1. Fault Parameters for Preferred Dislocation Models

Earthquake		Magnitude	Length, km	Width, km	Dip-slip, m	Dip, deg
Alaska	1964	8.4	600	200	10	9
Nevada	1954	7.1	36	6	2	62
Montana	1959	7.1	30	15	10	54

interpretations of the subsidence pattern). Also, only dip-slip motion has been taken into account. In the Nevada shock the strike-slip movement was estimated to be as large as twice the dip-slip movement, whereas in the Montana and Alaska shocks the strike-slip movement was small in comparison with the dip-slip movement. This presumably explains why the Montana and Nevada shocks have equal magnitudes even though the fault parameters in Table 1 suggest the latter shock to be much smaller.

The dislocation models shown in Table 1 all indicate that faulting probably was confined to the crust and did not penetrate into the mantle.

Appendix

Theoretical expressions for the surface displacement field produced by a sloping dislocation surface have been given by *Maruyama* [1964]. The evaluation of these expressions merely involves integration over the dislocation surface. The integrals for the surface displacement can be evaluated exactly, but for a sloping dislocation surface the evaluation of the integrals representing the displacement at depth is probably too complicated to be done other than numerically.

In our calculations, one of us (Savage) has evaluated the vertical component of the surface displacement by exact integration. The result has been checked by Hastie as a special case of a more general numerical integration designed to evaluate the displacement at depth. The strain calculations were made by Hastie by numerical integration.

From equation 2.30 in *Maruyama* [1964] we find for the vertical component of the ground displacement $u_3/\Delta u = -\iint [\frac{1}{2}(W_{33}{}^3 - W_{11}{}^3) \sin 2\delta + W_{13}{}^3 \cos 2\delta] \, d\xi_2 d\xi$, where ξ is the coordinate along the fault plane (Figure 1) in the ξ_1, ξ_3 plane (i.e., $\xi_1 = \xi \cos \delta$ and $\xi_3 = \xi \sin \delta$), Δu is the dip-slip on the fault surface, and δ is dip of the fault plane. (Except for the introduction of ξ and δ we follow the notation of Maruyama.) The integrals of $W_{33}{}^3$ and $W_{13}{}^3$ are straightforward and require no comment. However, the integral of $W_{11}{}^3$ must be treated with some care to avoid introducing singularities at $r = 0$ into some of the integrals. The best procedure appears to be to utilize the relation $(1 - \zeta) = r^2/[\rho^2(1 + \zeta)]$ to eliminate r^2 from the denominator of the expression for $W_{11}{}^3$. Noting that

$$B(\zeta) = -(1 - \zeta) + \zeta(1 - \zeta^2)$$

$$E(\zeta) = 2(1 - \zeta) - \zeta(1 - \zeta^2) - 6\zeta(1 - \zeta^2)^2$$

we can write

$$W_{11}{}^3 = \frac{1}{4\pi} [\zeta/\rho^2 - 6x^2/\rho^4 - {}^{-2}/(1 + \zeta) + x^2\rho^{-2}/(1 + \zeta)^2 + x^2\rho^{-4}/(1 + \zeta)]$$

where $x = x_1 - \xi_1$. None of the above terms is singular at $r = 0$, and the expression may be integrated over ξ and ξ_2 either numerically or with the aid of standard tables of integration. The exact integration over the rectangular fault surface in Figure 1 leads to

$$u_3/\Delta u = -(4S_1 + S_2 + S_3) \sin 2\delta/(8\pi x_1) - (S_4 + bS_1/a) \cos 2\delta/(2\pi x_1)$$

where

$$S_1 = \frac{a^3}{x_1{}^2} \left[\frac{-v(u^2 + b(3 - b^2/a^2)u + 3b^2)}{(u^2 + a^2)\rho} + \frac{b^3 vu}{a^2\rho(v^2 + a^2)} + \ln\left(\frac{\rho - v}{\rho + v}\right) + (b/a)(3 + b^2/a^2) \tan^{-1}\frac{uv}{a\rho} \right]\|$$

$$S_2 = \left[-2a \ln\frac{\rho - v}{\rho + v} - 4b \tan^{-1}\frac{uv}{a\rho} - \frac{2va(bu - v^2 - a^2)}{(v^2 + a^2)} \right]\|$$

$$S_3 = \frac{-x_1{}^2}{b} \left[-\tan^{-1}\frac{bu - a^2}{x_1 v} + \tan^{-1}\frac{vx_1}{bu - a^2} + \tan^{-1}\frac{vb(bu - a^2 - v^2)}{(a^2 + v^2)x_1(u + b) - \rho a(x_1{}^2 + v^2)} \right]\|$$

$$S_4 = a^2 \left[\frac{v(1 - b^2/a^2)u + 2b}{(u^2 + a^2)\rho} - \frac{uvb^2/a^2}{(v^2 + a^2)\rho} - \frac{1}{a}(1 + b^2/a^2) \tan^{-1}\frac{uv}{u\rho} \right]\|$$

and where $a = x_1 \sin \delta$, $b = x_1 \cos \delta$, $u = \xi - x_1 \cos \delta$, $v = \xi_2 - x_2$, $\rho^2 = u^2 + v^2 + a^2$, and $f(u, v)\| = f(u_2, v_2) - f(u_2, v_1) - f(u_1, v_2) + f(u_1, v_1)$. Here u_2 and v_2 are the upper limits of integration over u and v, respectively, and u_1 and v_1 are the lower limits.

In evaluating these integrals some attention must be paid to continuity in using the arctangent. In Fortran IV programming this may be taken care of by using ATAN2 for the arctangent and writing $(v/|v|) \tan^{-1}[(bu-a^2)/(x_1|v|)]$ for the first term in S_3.

Acknowledgment. This research was supported by the National Research Council of Canada.

REFERENCES

Chinnery, M. A., The strength of the earth's crust under horizontal shear stress, *J. Geophys. Res., 69,* 2085–2089, 1964.

Fraser, G. D., I. J. Witkind, and W. H. Nelson, A geological interpretation of the epicentral area—The dual basin concept, *U. S. Geol. Surv. Profess. Paper 435,* pp. 99–106, 1964.

Kasahara, K., Physical conditions of earthquake faults as deduced from geodetic data, *Bull. Earthquake Res. Inst., Tokyo Univ., 36,* 455–464, 1958.

Maruyama, T., Statical elastic dislocations in an infinite and semi-infinite medium, *Bull. Earthquake Res. Inst., Tokyo Univ, 42,* 289–368, 1964.

Myers, W. B., and W. Hamilton, Deformation accompanying the Hebgen Lake earthquake of August 17, 1959, *U. S. Geol. Surv. Profess. Paper 435,* pp. 55–98, 1964.

Plafker, G., Tectonic deformation associated with the 1964 Alaska earthquake, *Science, 148,* 1675–1687, 1965.

Press, F., Displacements, strains, and tilts at teleseismic distances, *J. Geophys. Res., 70,* 2395–2412, 1965.

Press, F., and D. Jackson, Alaskan earthquake, 27 March, 1964: Vertical extent of faulting and elastic strain energy release, *Science, 147,* 867–868, 1965.

Reil, O. E., Damage to Nevada highways, *Bull. Seismol. Soc. Am., 47,* 349–352, 1957.

Romney, C., Seismic waves from the Dixie Valley–Fairview Peak earthquakes, *Bull. Seismol. Soc. Am., 47,* 301–319, 1957.

Ryall, A., The Hebgen Lake, Montana, earthquake of August 18, 1959: *P* waves, *Bull. Seismol. Soc. Am., 52,* 235–271, 1962.

Slemmons, D. B., Geological effects of the Dixie Valley—Fairview Peak, Nevada, earthquakes of December 16, 1954, *Bull. Seismol. Soc. Am., 47,* 353–375, 1957.

Whitten, C. A., Geodetic measurements in the Dixie Valley area, *Bull. Seismol. Soc. Am., 47,* 321–325, 1957.

Whitten, C. A., Cartographic and geodetic effects of Alaskan earthquake (abstract), *Geol. Soc. Am. Spec. Paper, 82,* p. 222, 1965.

(Manuscript received April 28, 1966;
revised June 13, 1966.)

SAMUEL T. HARDING
S. T. ALGERMISSEN
U.S. COAST AND GEODETIC SURVEY *

Reprinted with minor changes from
U.S. Coast and Geodetic Survey Volume II-B,C: Seismology and Marine Geology,
"The Focal Mechanism of the Prince William Sound Earthquake
of March 28, 1964, and Related Earthquakes"

The Focal Mechanism of This and Related Earthquakes

ABSTRACT

Focal mechanisms for the Prince William Sound Earthquake of March 28, 1964, Greenwich Mean Time (G.M.T.), two preshocks, and eight aftershocks are presented. A combination of P-wave first motion and S-wave polarization data made possible the determination of both nodal planes for the main shock of March 28, 1964. For the main shock, two nodal planes for P were determined using a combination of P-wave first motion and S-wave polarization data and from S-wave data alone. The S-wave polarization error, $\delta\bar{\epsilon}$, is slightly lower for a type II than for a type I mechanism. The type I mechanism solution indicates predominately dip-slip faulting on a steeply dipping plane. The preferred solution is a type II mechanism with the following P nodal planes: strike N. 62° E., dip 82° S., (a plane); strike N. 22° W., dip 52° W., (b plane). Two solutions are possible: right lateral faulting which strikes northeast; or, left lateral faulting which strikes northwest. Both possible fault planes dip steeply. Left lateral faulting is suggested by the mechanism solutions of the majority of aftershocks. Composite mechanism studies of short-period P-wave first motions of groups of small aftershocks did not yield a clear pattern. No significant change in the ratio of compressions to dilatations for aftershocks recorded at local stations during the first 4 months after the main shock could be detected.

INTRODUCTION

The focal mechanism of the Prince William Sound, Alaska, Earthquake of March 28, 1964 (Greenwich Mean Time), one of the largest earthquakes known to have occurred in North America in historical times, has received considerable attention in geographical literature. Because of the nature and geophysical distribution of the

data available to study the problem, published results are not unanimous in their interpretation of the nature of the focal mechanism of the main shock and the related preshocks and aftershocks.

The nature of faulting in the main shock has been discussed by a number of authors [Algermissen, 1964, 1965, 1966; Berg, 1965; Plafker, 1965; Press and Jack-

---

*Now in part Earth Sciences Laboratories, National Oceanic and Atmospheric Administration.

[197]

son, 1965; Press, 1965; Pararas-Carayannis and Furumoto, 1965; and Toksöz, Ben-Menahem, and Harkrider, 1965]. Stauder and Bollinger [1966] have inferred the nature of faulting in the main shock from a consideration of the focal mechanisms of aftershocks and preshocks, since the seismological data for preshocks and aftershocks are much better than the materials available for a study of the main shock. In general, two greatly differing interpretations of the data have been presented. The faulting associated with the main shock has been interpreted both as a near vertical fault and also as a low-angle thrust fault.

In this paper, focal mechanism solutions are presented for the main shock, two preshocks, and six aftershocks (fig. 1). For the purpose of plotting all focal mechanism

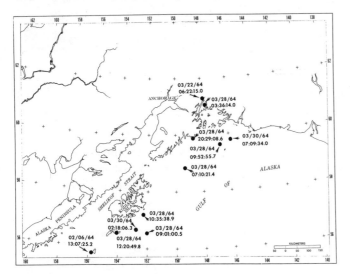

FIGURE 1.—Map of the epicentral area showing the earthquakes studied.

data, a crustal thickness of approximately 50 kilometers was assumed with a velocity of 6.0 kilometers per second and an upper mantle velocity of 8.0 kilometers per second. This section is in general agreement with the available crustal data [Woollard, *et al.*, 1960]. The focal depths of the earthquakes studied were assumed to be above the Mohorovičić discontinuity. Near stations, in the distance range from 3° to 12°, were plotted on a critical circle [Romney, 1957] of radius 48.5°. Composite focal mechanisms, based on an analysis of the first motions recorded from aftershocks at seven temporary seismograph stations installed after the March 28 earthquake, and on readings from the College Observatory (COL) are also presented.

THE MAIN SHOCK OF MARCH 28, 1964

The epicenter of the main shock was located by Sher-

burne, Algermissen, and Harding [1969] near the north shore of Prince William Sound on the small peninsula separating College Fiord and Unakwik Inlet. The coordinates of the epicenter are 61.04° N. latitude and 147.73° W. longitude. The focal depth is considered normal, or less than 70 kilometers.

The directions of first motion recorded by both long- and short-period seismographs at 122 stations were used to obtain a *P*-wave focal mechanism solution. The seismograms from 90 of these stations were read by the authors, and the remaining 32 readings were obtained from stations that reported directions of first motions for this study. The first motions are listed in table 1, and the resulting solution is shown in figure 2. When there was a difference in polarity registered by the long- and short-period seismographs, the long-period first motion was used. Kap Tobin and Weston are the only two stations where a difference in polarity between the first motions recorded by long- and short-period seismographs was noted.

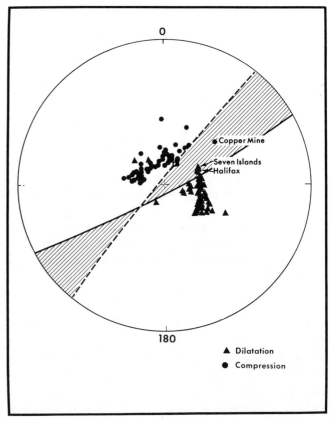

FIGURE 2.—*P*-wave focal mechanism solution of the Prince William Sound Earthquake of March 28, 1964 (Wulff net). Two possible orientations of the single plane determined from the *P*-wave data are shown as solid and dashed lines.

TABLE 1.—*P-wave data: Prince William Sound Earthquake of March 28, 1964*

[Origin time 03:36:14.0. Coordinates 61.04° N., 147.73° W. Magnitude $(M_s) = 8.3$]

Station	Short period	Long period	Station	Short period	Long period
Abuyama	$C\dagger$		Longmire	D	$D\dagger$
Alert	$C\dagger$		Malaga		$C\dagger$
Ann Arbor		$D\dagger$	Manila		$C\dagger$
Anpu	$C\dagger$	$C\dagger$	Matsushiro	C	$C\dagger$
Apatity*	$C\dagger$		Milford	D	
Arequipa		$D\dagger$	Mineral	$D\dagger$	
Athens	C	$C\dagger$	Minneapolis		$D\dagger$
Atlanta	D	$D\dagger$	Moscow	$C\dagger$	
Baguio City	C	$C\dagger$	Mould Bay	$C\dagger$	
Balboa Heights	$D\dagger$		Mount Wilson	$D\dagger$	
Barrett	$D\dagger$		Nana	D	$D\dagger$
Berkeley		$D\dagger$	Nanking*	$C\dagger$	
Bermuda	(D)	$D\dagger$	New Delhi	C	$C\dagger$
Blacksburg	D	$D\dagger$	North Pole	$C\dagger$	
Blue Mountains*	$D\dagger$		Nurmijärvi		$C\dagger$
Bogota		$D\dagger$	Ogdensburg		$D\dagger$
Bozeman	D	$D\dagger$	Oroville		$D\dagger$
Caracas	$D\dagger$		Oslo	$C\dagger$	
Changchun*	$C\dagger$		Palomar	$D\dagger$	
Chengtu*	$C\dagger$		Pasadena	D	$D\dagger$
China Lake	$D\dagger$		Peking*	$C\dagger$	
College	$C\dagger$		Petropavlovsk*	$C\dagger$	
Columbia	D	$D\dagger$	Porto	C	$C\dagger$
Copenhagen		$C\dagger$	Rabaul		$C\dagger$
Copper Mine	$C\dagger$		Rapid City	D	$D\dagger$
Canton*	$C\dagger$		Raton*	$D\dagger$	
Corvallis		$D\dagger$	Resolute	$C\dagger$	
Cumberland Plateau*	$D\dagger$		Riverside	D	$D\dagger$
Dallas	$D\dagger$		Sapporo	$C\dagger$	
Dugway	$D\dagger$		Scarborough	$D\dagger$	
Durango	$D\dagger$		Schefferville	$D\dagger$	
EK1*	$D\dagger$		Seattle	$D\dagger$	
Eltsovka*	$C\dagger$		Semipalatinsk*	$C\dagger$	
EV1*	$D\dagger$		Seven Islands	$D\dagger$	
Florissant	D	$D\dagger$	Shillong	C	$C\dagger$
Fordham	$D\dagger$		Shiraz	C	$C\dagger$
Fort Tejon	$D\dagger$		Sian*	$C\dagger$	
Fresno	$D\dagger$		Simferopol*	$C\dagger$	
Frobisher Bay	$C\dagger$		Sitka	$D\dagger$	
Frunze*	$C\dagger$		Spokane	$D\dagger$	
Georgetown		$D\dagger$	Spring Hill	D	$D\dagger$
Golden	D	$D\dagger$	State College	D	$D\dagger$
Guam		$C\dagger$	Stuttgart	$C\dagger$	
Halifax	$(C)\dagger$	C	Sverdlovsk*	$D\dagger$	
Hayfield		$D\dagger$	Tiksi*	$C\dagger$	
Helwan	C	$C\dagger$	Tinemaha	$D\dagger$	
Hong Kong	C	$C\dagger$	TK1	$D\dagger$	
Honiara		$C\dagger$	Toledo		$C\dagger$
Irkutsk*	$C\dagger$		Tonto Forest*		$D\dagger$
Kap Tobin	(C)	$D\dagger$	Trieste		$C\dagger$
Kevo	(C)	$C\dagger$	Trinidad		$D\dagger$
Kheis*	$C\dagger$		Troy		$D\dagger$
King Ranch	$D\dagger$		Tucson	D	$D\dagger$
Kirovabad*	$C\dagger$		Tumwater	$D\dagger$	
KN1*	$D\dagger$		Valentia		$C\dagger$
Kongsberg	C	$C\dagger$	Vladivostok*	$C\dagger$	
Kunming*	C		Wellington	$(D)\dagger$	
Lahore		$C\dagger$	Weston	C	$D\dagger$
Lanchow*	$C\dagger$		Wichita Mountain	D	$D\dagger$
L'Aquila	C	$C\dagger$	Yakutsk*	$D\dagger$	
Las Cruces	$D\dagger$		Yuzhno-Sakhalinsk*	$C\dagger$	
Lhasa*	$C\dagger$		Zo-Se*	$C\dagger$	
London	$D\dagger$				

*Seismograms not read by the authors.
†Station used in solution.
( )Doubtful reading.

C—Compressional.
D—Dilatational.

The first motions recorded by long-period seismographs were preferred because they were, in general, impulsive while the first motions recorded by short-period seismographs were frequently emergent and difficult to read, because of background noise. It can be seen from figure 2 that the first motions are divided into two fields. Consequently, only one plane can be determined from the data. Two possibilities for this plane are indicated, depending upon the interpretation of the first-motion data. The two extremes in orientation that are possible for this nodal plane are: (1) strike N. 62° E.; dip 82° S., and (2) strike N. 40° E.; dip 87° W. The difference in these two possible interpretations is small, amounting to 22° in strike and 11° in dip. The orientation of the plane depends upon the direction of first motion at several Canadian stations. A definite compression is indicated on the long-period seismogram from Halifax. Short-period instruments at Scarborough, Schefferville, and London indicate dilatations. There is, consequently, some ambiguity in assigning a definite orientation to the nodal plane. The area on the Wulff net resulting from the ambiguity in the interpretation is shown shaded in figure 2. A consideration of the S-wave data for the main shock indicates that the lowest average polarization error [Stauder and Bollinger, 1964], which is also called the average deviation of the polarization angle, for a type I force system is obtained if the orientation of the P-wave nodal plane is taken as N. 40° E. strike and 87° W. dip. If a type II system is assumed, the plane striking N. 62° E. and dipping 82° S. yields the lowest average polarization error. The S-wave data will be discussed later in this paper.

Several investigators have presented P-wave focal mechanism solutions of the main shock [Algermissen, 1964, 1965, 1966; Berg, 1965; Stauder and Bollinger,

TABLE 2.—S-*wave data: Prince William Sound Earthquake of March 28, 1964*

[Origin time 03:36:14.0. Coordinates 61.04° N., 147.73° W. Magnitude $(M_s) = 8.3$]

Station	Instrument	Instrument constants	Azimuth	Distance	ϵ_o	ϵ_{cII}	$\epsilon_o - \epsilon_{cII}$
			Degrees	*Degrees*			
Akita................	Electromagnetic, N.–S. & E.–W.............	$T_o = 5.0$ $V = 101$	278.1	47.9	−33.6	−39.1	5.5
Chihuahua.............	Wiechert, N.–S. & E.–W Mass 1,200 kg.............	$T_o = 6.0$ $V = 250$	120.4	42.6	15.8	15.8	0.0
Guadalajara...........	Wiechert, N.–S. & E.–W Mass 200 kg.............	$T_o = 6.5$ $V = 200$	122.2	50.8	−3.5	13.9	17.4
Hachinohe.............	Electromagnetic N.–S. & E.–W	$T_o = 5.0$ $V = 101$	277.6	46.6	−36.6	−38.2	1.6
Hamada...............	Wiechert, N.–S. & E.–W Mass 200 kg.............	$T_o = 5.0$ $V = 80$	280.9	55.6	−47.5	−46.0	1.5
Jena.................	Wiechert, N.–S. & E.–W Mass 1,200 kg.............	$T_o = 8.0$ $V = 200$	14.1	67.1	13.3	−22.4	35.7
Mazatlan..............	Wiechert, N.–S. & E.–W Mass 200 kg.............	$T_o = 4.5$ $V = 80$	124.3	47.3	−20.8	9.6	30.4
Mori.................	Wiechert, N.–S. & E.–W.............	$T_o = 4.8$ $V = 91$	279.8	45.8	−46.6	−39.1	7.5
Oaxaca...............	Wiechert, N.–S. & E.–W Mass 200 kg.............	$T_o = 6.0$ $V = 80$	117.5	56.8	28.6	22.2	6.4
Padova...............	Wiechert, N.–S. & E.–W Mass 200 kg.............	$T_o = 4.1$	15.0	72.6	−27.3	−24.4	2.9
Raciborz.............	Mainka, N.–S. & E.–W Mass 1,050 kg.............	$T_o = 6.22$ $V = 155$	9.8	68.6	4.4	−13.5	17.9
San Salvador..........	Wiechert, N.–S. & E.–W Mass 100 kg.............	$T_o = 1.50$ $V = 23$	111.7	63.1	27.0	31.2	4.2
Stuttgart.............	Wiechert, N.–E. & N.–W Mass 17,000 kg.............	$T_o = 1.5$ $V = 1860$	16.2	68.9	2.6	−26.6	29.2
Tacubaya.............	Wiechert, N.–S. & E.–W Mass 1,200 kg.............	$T_o = 6.0$ $V = 250$	118.7	53.6	40.3	19.9	20.4
Toyama...............	Wiechert, N.–S. & E.–W.............	$T_o = 4.9$ $V = 90$	278.0	51.7	−62.2	−43.4	18.8
Trieste..............	Wiechert, S.–E. & N.–E	$T_o = 4.9$ $V = 183.0$	12.6	72.5	−49.0	−19.6	29.4
Vera Cruz.............	Wiechert, N.–S. & E.–W Mass 200 kg.............	$T_o = 5.0$ $V = 80$	115.6	55.1	−21.6	24.8	46.4

ϵ_o Observed polarization.
ϵ_{cII} Computed polarization, Type II mechanism.

1966]. Berg [1965] attempted to determine the orientation of a second nodal plane based on the interpretation of a dilatation at one station, Yellowknife, and on the orthogonality criteria. Copies of seismograms from all the array elements at Yellowknife were obtained. The first motion recorded at Yellowknife is difficult to read because of background noise and the emergent nature of the first motion. This station was not used in the authors' solution.

A thorough search of seismograms was undertaken in an effort to find *S* waves that were sufficiently well recorded to be used in a mechanism solution. Seismograms from 17 stations were deemed suitable for calculation of *S*-wave polarization angles. All of the stations from which data were used are equipped with very low-magnification electromagnetic or mechanical seismographs. The seismograms are, in general, of poor quality and are difficult to digitize accurately because of slow recording speed and other recording problems. Of the 17 stations employed in the *S*-wave analysis, only the instrumentation at Stuttgart and Trieste, both Worldwide Standard Seismograph stations, was sufficient to provide both *P*-wave first motions and *S*-wave data. The 15 remaining stations had either very low magnification vertical instruments or no vertical seismographs at all. The stations used, together with other pertinent data, are listed in table 2. The general approach in the *S*-wave studies was to compute the theoretical *S*-wave polarization for various models, assuming both single- and double-couple force systems. The theoretical polarizations were then compared with the actual polarizations at each station, and the average error, δε̄, [Stauder and Bollinger, 1964] was computed. These techniques are essentially the same as those used by Udias [1964] and Udias and Stauder [1964].

Three separate approaches were tried in an effort to derive a suitable focal mechanism solution, assuming a single-couple force system and making use of all available *P*- and *S*-wave data. The results are listed in Table 3. First, an attempt was made to fit the data to Plafker's [1965] hypothesis of faulting. Plafker has suggested that the faulting associated with the main shock was an overthrust on a low-angle plane. For Plafker's hypothesis to agree with the first-motion data available, the nodal plane, which was determined from the *P*-wave data, must be considered the auxiliary plane. Figure 3 shows the theoretical *S*-wave polarization for a single-couple (type I) force system, assuming that a plane striking N. 62° E. and dipping 82° S. is the auxiliary plane. A plane striking N. 62° E. and dipping 82° S. is one pos-

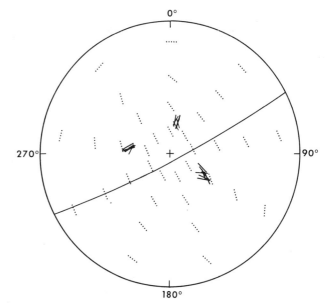

THEORETICAL POLARIZATION
OBSERVED POLARIZATION

FIGURE 3.—Prince William Sound Earthquake of March 28, 1964. Comparison of computed and observed *S*-wave polarization, type I force system. The *S*-wave polarization was computed assuming an auxiliary plane striking N. 62° E. and dipping 82° S.

sible choice for the orientation of the plane determined from *P* data. This orientation of the auxiliary plane is necessary so that the direction of the motion vector (strike N. 28° W., dip 8° N.) is compatible with low-angle overthrusting. The actual *S*-wave polarization for 17 stations is also shown in figure 3. The polarization at Central American stations shows fair agreement with this type of solution, but the polarization at other stations is in poor agreement. The average polarization error is 39°.

A second type I solution was computed using the technique developed by Udias [1964] and Stevens [1964] to calculate the best auxiliary plane in a least-squares sense. The auxiliary plane computed has a strike of N. 87° E. and a dip of 14° S. The average polarization error is δε̄ 22°. This plane is not orthogonal with the plane determined from *P*-wave data. However, only slight adjustment of the orientation of the plane would be necessary to satisfy the orthogonality criteria. This solution indicates a predominantly dip-slip motion on a steeply dipping plane.

Two other type I solutions were attempted, assuming first as the fault plane a nodal plane striking N. 40° E. (fig. 4) and dipping 87° W. and secondly, assuming for the fault plane a nodal plane striking N. 62° E. and

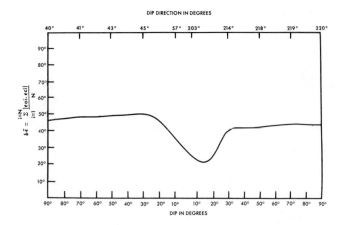

FIGURE 4.—Prince William Sound Earthquake of March 28, 1964. Average polarization error, $\delta\bar{\epsilon}$, of possible auxiliary planes satisfying the orthogonality criteria for a fault plane striking N. 40° E. and dipping 87° W. A type I force system is assumed.

TABLE 3.—*Summary of type I focal mechanisms computed for the Prince William Sound Earthquake of March 28, 1964*

[Origin time 03:36:14.0. Coordinates 61.04° N., 147.73° W. Magnitude $(M_s) = 8.3$]

Fault plane	Auxiliary plane	$\delta\bar{\epsilon}$	Remarks
	N. 62° E., 82° S.	39°	Low-angle over-thrust case (fig. 3).
	N. 87° E., 14° S.	22°	Least-squares solution; Stevens' [1964] program.
N. 40° E., 87° W.*	N. 64° W., 13° S.	22°	Auxiliary plane given has smallest $\delta\bar{\epsilon}$ of all planes orthogonal to the specified fault plane (fig. 4).
N. 62° E., 82° S.*	N. 5° E., 14° W.	29°	Auxiliary plane given has smallest $\delta\bar{\epsilon}$ of all planes orthogonal to the specified fault plane.

* Plane used to constrain the choice of the auxiliary plane.

dipping 82° S. Average polarization errors were computed for possible auxiliary planes orthogonal [Adkins, 1940] to the assumed fault planes.

The results of all type I focal mechanism computations are summarized in table 3. For a type I force system, the following conclusions are stated.

1. Assuming that the plane determined from P-wave

data has a strike of N. 62° E. and a dip of 82° S. and is the auxiliary plane, the S-wave solution yields a rather high polarization error of 39°. This does not appear to support the concept of low-angle over-thrusting.

2. The least-squares auxiliary plane determined from the S-wave data alone indicates predominant dip-slip faulting on a steeply dipping plane.

3. Assuming that the plane determined from the P-wave solution is the fault plane and has a strike of N. 40° E. and a dip of 87° W., and assuming further that the choice of auxiliary planes is restricted by the orthogonality criteria, the S-wave data yield a minimum average polarization error of 22° for an auxiliary plane which indicates principally dip-slip motion.

A summary of type II solutions is given in Table 4. For a type II force system, the theoretical S-wave polarization, corresponding approximately to that which would be expected for a low-angle overthrust, was calculated to determine how well the hypothesis of faulting proposed by Plafker [1965] fits the available S-wave data. One possible orientation (strike N. 62° E., dip 82° S.) of the plane determined from the P-wave solution was used to define one axis of the type II or double-couple focal mechanism model. A second P-wave nodal plane with a strike of N. 62° E. and a dip of 8° N. was used to define the other axis of the model. While the direction of faulting cannot be uniquely determined for a type II focal mechanism model, the nodal planes of P that have been assumed could result in faulting approximately equivalent to that proposed by Plafker. A comparison of the theoretical S-wave polarizations for this model with the actual S-wave polarization observed is shown in figure 5. The average polarization error for this particular model is $\delta\bar{\epsilon} = 44°$.

A second (type II) solution was computed using another possible orientation of the plane determined from the P-wave study (strike N. 62° E., dip 82° S.) to define one axis of the S-wave solution. The results are shown in figure 6. The other plane shown (strike N. 22° W., dip 52° W.) is the plane that yielded the smallest average error $(\delta\bar{\epsilon} = 16°)$. The average polarization error is shown in figure 7 for all values of the dip and strike of the b plane. Only planes orthogonal to a plane striking N. 62° E. and dipping 82° S. were considered. There is clearly a minimum error at approximately 52° dip. S-wave data were obtained from stations in three principal geographical areas: Japan, Europe, and Central America. Figure 8 shows the average polarization error, $\delta\bar{\epsilon}$, for each of these areas separately as a function of the

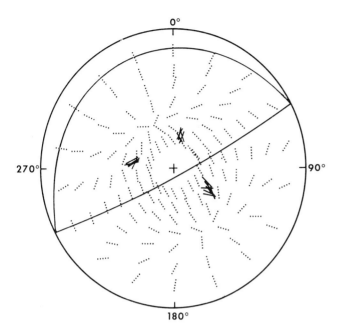

FIGURE 5.—Prince William Sound Earthquake of March 28, 1964. Comparison of computed and observed *S*-wave polarization, type II source. Two *P*-wave nodal planes (strike N. 62° E., dip 82° S.; strike N. 62° E., dip 8° N.) were used to define the *x* and *y* axes of the *S*-wave solution (Wulff net).

dip of one plane. One plane is taken, as before, as the plane determined from the *P*-wave solution. The polarization errors for each of the three areas show minima in the range of dips from 52° to 85°. Only data from the Japanese stations indicate a pronounced minimum.

A third type II solution was computed using a plane striking N. 40° E. and dipping 87° W. to define one axis of the *S*-wave solution. As discussed earlier, a *P*-nodal plane with the above orientation represents one possible interpretation of the *P*-wave data. The average polarization errors for all planes orthogonal to the specified plane were then computed. The plane with a minimum polarization error had a strike of N. 50° W. and a dip of 80° S. The minimum polarization error was 12°, a rather high value.

Because of the slight ambiguity in the interpretation of the orientation of the plane determined from *P* data, a fourth type II focal mechanism model was computed using the technique and computer program developed by Stevens [1964]. In the method described by Stevens for a type II source, the nodal planes are determined only from a consideration of the *S*-wave polarization angles. The initial *P*-wave displacements are not used

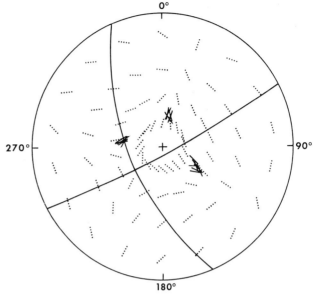

FIGURE 6.—*S*-wave focal mechanism of the Prince William Sound Earthquake of March 28, 1964 (Wulff net): type II force system. The nodal plane for *P* striking N. 62° E. and dipping 82° S. was used to define one axis of the *S*-wave solution. The other nodal plane for *P* which strikes N. 22° W. and dips 52° W. has the minimum average polarization error for the data shown.

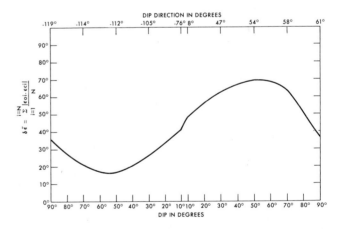

FIGURE 7.—Prince William Sound Earthquake of March 28, 1964. Average polarization error, $\delta\bar{\epsilon}$, as a function of the dip of one *P*-wave nodal plane. The second nodal plane (strike N. 62° E., dip 82° S.) is held constant. A type II force system is assumed.

as a control on the *S*-wave solution in any way. The nodal planes for *P* resulting from this calculation (solid lines) are shown in figure 9, together with the focal mechanism (dashed lines) already presented in figure 6.

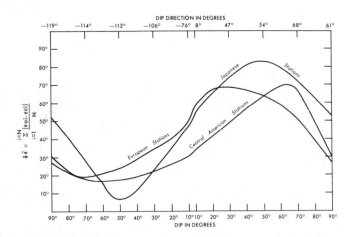

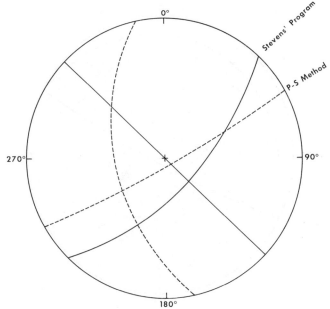

FIGURE 8.—Prince William Sound Earthquake of March 28, 1964. Average polarization error, $\delta\bar{\epsilon}$, as a function of the dip of one *P*-wave nodal plane. The assumptions are the same as for figure 7, but the average polarization error is shown for each geographical area from which data were available.

This solution, using *S*-wave data only, does not satisfy the *P* data and consequently cannot be considered as a solution. It should be pointed out that this solution obtained using only *S*-wave data has the same general nature (strike-slip faulting on steep planes) as the other solutions obtained using a combination of *P* and *S* data. A summary of type II solutions is given in table 4.

TABLE 4.—*Summary of type II focal mechanisms computed for the Prince William Sound Earthquake of March 28, 1964*

[Origin time 03:36:14.0. Coordinates 61.04° N., 147.73° W. Magnitude $(M_s) = 8.3$]

a plane	*b* plane	$\delta\bar{\epsilon}$	Remarks
N. 62° E., 82° S.*	N. 62° E., 8° N.*	44°	Low-angle overthrust case (fig. 5); two planes specified.
N. 62° E., 82° S.*	N. 22° W., 52° W.	16°	One nodal plane specified (fig. 6).
N. 40° E., 87° W.*	N. 50° W., 80° S.	42°	One nodal plane specified.
N. 45° E., 62° S.	N. 45° W., 90° E.	18°	Stevens' [1964] method (fig. 9).

*Plane specified in solution.

Assuming a type II force system, the following conclusions may be stated concerning the focal mechanism of the main shock:

1. The *P*-wave nodal planes for the *S*-wave solution with the lowest average polarization (16°) have the fol-

FIGURE 9.—Comparison of *S*-wave focal mechanism of the Prince William Sound Earthquake of March 28, 1964, obtained using Stevens' [1964] method (solid lines) with the *P-S* method (dashed lines) also shown in figure 6.

lowing orientations: strike N. 62° E., dip 82° S. (*a* plane); strike N. 22° W., dip 52° W. (*b* plane); this is the mechanism solution that we prefer. Right-lateral strike-slip faulting on a steeply dipping plane together with a significant component of dip-slip motion, is indicated by this solution if the fault plane is assumed to be related to the *a* nodal plane. If faulting is associated with the *b* plane, left lateral faulting is indicated.

2. The available *S*-wave data do not appear to support the hypothesis of overthrusting on a low-angle plane.

PRESHOCKS

THE EARTHQUAKE OF MARCH 22, 1964

A study was undertaken of the focal mechanisms of earthquakes in the 3 months preceding the main shock to find what relationships exist between the focal mechanism of these earthquakes and the main shock. One small, possible foreshock occurred 11 kilometers northwest of the main shock on March 22, 1964, at 06:22:15.0 (G.M.T.). The magnitude (m_b) published by the Coast and Geodetic Survey was 4.5. Because of its small magnitude, the shock was not widely recorded, and insufficient data were available to obtain a focal mechanism solution. It is constructive to compare the first-motion pattern for this earthquake with the first-motion pattern

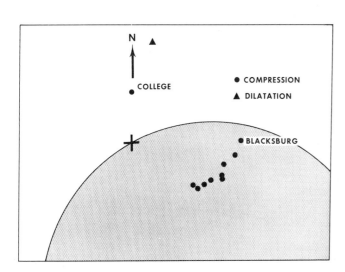

FIGURE 10.—Directions of first motion of *P*: preshock of March 22, 1964 (extended distance projection). The *P*-wave nodal plane shown is for the Prince William Sound Earthquake of March 28, 1964.

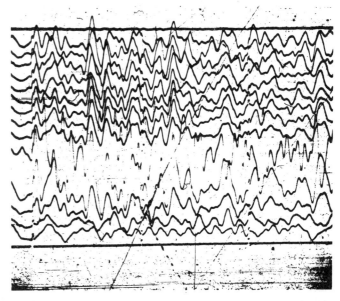

FIGURE 11.—First motions recorded at Blue Mountains Observatory (BMO) for the earthquake of March 22, 1964.

TABLE 5.—P-*wave data: preshock of March 22, 1964*

[Origin time 06:22:15.0. Coordinates 61.3° N., 147.8° W. Magnitude (m_b) = 4.5]

Station	Short period	Station	Short period
Blacksburg	*C*	Hungry Horse	*C*
Blue Mountains	*C*	Longmire	*C*
College	*C*	Nord	*D*
Eureka	*C*	Rapid City	*C*
Florissant	*C*	Uinta Basin	*C*
Golden	*C*		

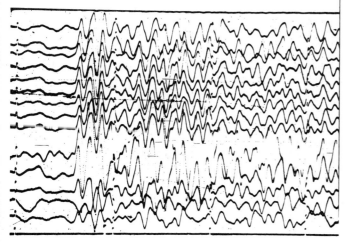

FIGURE 12.—First motions recorded at Uinta Basin Observatory (UBO) for the earthquake of March 22, 1964.

recorded for the main shock. The *P*-wave data are listed in table 5. In figure 10, the nodal plane from the *P*-wave fault-plane solution for the main shock has been shaded and superimposed on the first-motion data from the foreshock of March 22. Note that all stations lying within the shaded circle recorded very clear compressions. Examples of seismograms are shown in figures 11 and 12. For the main shock, all stations within the area of this same circle recorded dilatations. Thus, the earthquake of March 22, only 6 days before the main shock and located 11 kilometers northwest of the epicenter of the main shock, exhibited an entirely different first-motion pattern than the main earthquake.

THE EARTHQUAKE OF FEBRUARY 6, 1964

On February 6, 1964, a magnitude (m_b) 5.6 earthquake occurred southwest of Kodiak Island. Excellent data were available for this earthquake and both *P*- and

TABLE 6.—*P-wave data: preshock of February 6, 1964*

[Origin time 13:07:25.2. Coordinates 55.7° N., 155.8° W. Magnitude $(m_b) = 5.6$]

Station	Short period	Long period	Station	Short period	Long period
Addis Ababa		C†	Lahore		C†
Ann Arbor		C†	Lanchow*	C†	
Abuyama*	C†		Lhasa*	C†	
Afiamalu		D†	Longmire	D	D†
Alert*	C†		La Paz		D†
Albuquerque		D†	La Palma		D†
Anpu		C†	Lvov*	C†	
Apatity*	C		Malaga		C†
Athens University	C	C†	Manila	C	C†
Baguio City		C†	Mould Bay*	C†	
Boulder City*	D†		Minneapolis		C†
Bermuda-Columbia	C	C†	Moscow*	C†	
Bergen*	D†		Moxa*	C†	
Balboa Heights		D†	Mount Tsukuba*	C†	
Byerly		D†	Nanking*	C†	
Bensberg*	C†		New Delhi		C†
Bogota		C†	Nhatrang		C†
Bozeman	(C)	D†	Nord	C	C†
Caracas		C†	Naples*	C†	
Chiengmai	C	C†	Nurmijärvi	D	C†
Copper Mine	C	C†	Ogdensburg		D†
Changchun*	C†		Ottawa*	C†	
Canton*	C†		Ponta Delgada		C†
Chengtu*	C†		Peking*	C†	
College	C†		Petropavlovsk*	C†	
Copenhagen		C†	Phu-Lien	C†	
Corvallis	(C)	D†	Port Moresby		C†
Charters Towers	C†		Pruhonice*	C†	
Dallas	(C)	D†	Piszkesteto*	C†	
De Bilt*	C†		Porto		C†
Dugway	D	D†	Quetta	C	C†
Durham*	C†		Quito		D†
Edmonton*	D†		Rapid City		C†
Frobisher Bay*	C†		Riverview		D†
Florissant		C†	Schefferville*	C†	
Frunze*	C†		State College		C†
Garm*	C†		Semipalatinsk*	C†	
Godhavn		C†	Seoul		C†
Georgetown		C†	Spring Hill		D†
Golden	D	D†	Shiraz		D†
Goldstone		D†	Shillong	C	C†
Guam		C†	Sian	C†	
Hong Kong		C†	San Juan	D†	
Helwan		C†	St. Louis*	C†	
Honiara		C†	Spokane*	D†	
Howrah		C†	Stuttgart		C†
Huancayo*	D†		Sverdlovsk*	D†	
Irkutsk*	C†		Tiksi*	C†	
Istanbul		C†	Toledo	C	C†
Kevo	C	C†	Trinidad		C†
Kew*	C†		Tromsoe†	C†	
Kheis*	C†		Tucson		D†
Khorog*	C†		Umea*	C†	
Kiruna		C†	Uppsala*	C†	
Koumac*	D†		Valentia		C†
Kongsberg	C	C†	Warsaw*	C†	
Kirkenes*	C†		Weston		C†
Kirovabad*	C†		Yakutsk*	C†	
Kap Tobin	(C)	C†	Yuzhno-Sakhalinsk*	C†	
Kunming	C†		Zagreb*	C†	
Kurilsk*	C†				

*Not read by authors.
( ) Doubtful reading.
†Used in solution.

C—Compressional.
D—Dilatational.

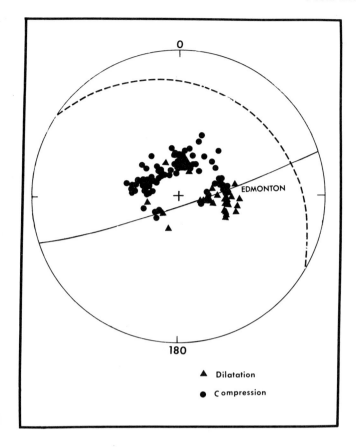

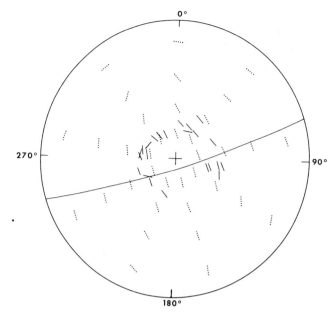

LEGEND
.· THEORETICAL POLARIZATION
/ OBSERVED POLARIZATION

FIGURE 13.—*P*-wave focal mechanism solution of the pre-shock of February 6, 1964 (Wulff net). The dashed line representing the *b* plane was determined from *S*-wave data.

FIGURE 14.—*S*-wave focal mechanism solution of the earthquake of February 6, 1964 (Wulff net): type I force system. The nodal plane was determined from *P*-wave data.

S-wave focal mechanisms were computed. Readings from 121 stations were used in the *P*-wave solution shown in figure 13 (Wulff stereographic projection).

Seismograms from 76 stations were read by the authors. Data from the remainder of the stations were obtained by direct inquiry to the station or from station bulletins. The *P*-wave data are summarized in table 6. Ten first motions were inconsistent with the solution shown in figure 13, resulting in an error of 8 percent. Only one nodal plane could be determined with confidence from the *P*-wave data. The strike of this plane is N. 72° E. and the dip is 82° S.

The one well-defined nodal plane from the *P*-wave solution was assumed to be the auxiliary plane, and the corresponding *S*-wave polarization pattern for a type I force system was computed, plotted, and compared with the *S*-wave polarization observed (fig. 14). The stations from which data were used, together with the polarization residuals and related data, are tabulated in table 7. The average error, $\delta\bar{\epsilon}$, is 22°.

The theoretical *S*-wave polarization for a type II

TABLE 7.—*S-wave data: preshock of February 6, 1964*

[Origin time 13:07:25.2. Coordinates 55.7° N., 155.8° W. Magnitude $(m_b) = 5.6$]

Station	Azimuth	Distance	ϵ_o	$|\epsilon_o - \epsilon_{oII}|$	$|\epsilon_o - \epsilon_{oI}|$
	Degrees	*Degrees*			
Afiamalu	196.5	70.6	−54	17	18
Anpu	279.1	65.5	−81	22	30
Baguio City	274.3	73.0	70	19	7
Balboa Heights	96.3	74.9	57	9	7
Chiengmai	292.9	82.9	−74	47	52
Copenhagen	7.1	68.6	−50	7	21
Dallas	94.1	46.3	66	6	1
Godhaven	30.5	43.3	−75	22	17
Golden	94.3	36.6	60	14	7
Guam	251.6	61.8	84	13	10
Hong Kong	283.6	71.9	81	9	16
Honiara	225.6	74.6	−66	2	3
La Palma	101.3	65.2	−14	78	73
Malaga	22.7	84.7	83	20	38
New Delhi	315.2	84.6	−12	42	42
Nhatrang	281.0	82.8	75	4	8
Port Moresby	237.2	80.2	50	57	56
Ponta Delgada	38.3	77.7	−81	2	19
Quetta	323.9	87.0	0	18	21
Shiraz	335.6	91.7	0	0	7
Tucson	107.8	39.0	66	2	11
Valentia	22.0	69.0	−72	1	26
Weston	66.4	53.6	74	7	17

Notes: ϵ_o Observed polarization.
  ϵ_{oI} Computed polarization angles for type I solution.
  ϵ_{oII} Computed polarization angles for type II solution.

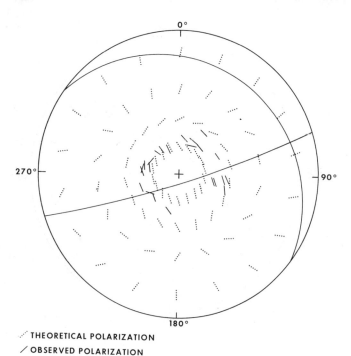

THEORETICAL POLARIZATION
OBSERVED POLARIZATION

FIGURE 15.—*S*-wave focal mechanism of the earthquake of February 6, 1964 (Wulff net). The nodal plane for *P* striking N. 72° E. was used to define one axis of the *S*-wave solution. The other nodal plane for *P* striking N. 79° E. has the minimum average polarization error for the data shown.

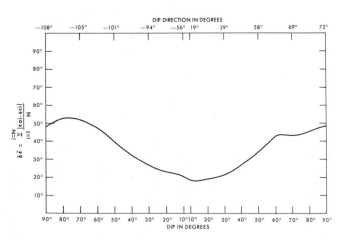

FIGURE 16.—Earthquake of February 6, 1964. Average polarization error, $\delta\bar{\epsilon}$, as a function of the dip of one *P*-wave nodal plane. The second nodal plane (strike N. 72° E., dip 82° S.) is held constant. A type II force system is assumed.

source was computed using the nodal plane determined from the *P*-wave solution to define one axis of the type II model. A comparison of the computed and observed polarizations for a type II source is shown in figure 15.

Figure 16 shows the polarization error, $\delta\bar{\epsilon}$, for various orientations of a second plane, assuming the other plane is defined by the nodal plane determined from the *P*-wave solution. The minimum average polarization error is 18° for a plane striking N. 55° W. and dipping 13° E. The type II mechanism solution has significantly lower error than the type I solution.

The *S*-wave polarization study of the February 6 preshock that occurred near Kodiak shows that the focal mechanism is probably a type II or double-couple force system and indicates, as pointed out by Stauder and Bollinger [1966], that the faulting probably occurred along a plane dipping at a low angle to the northeast beneath Kodiak Island.

AFTERSHOCKS

THE EARTHQUAKES OF MARCH 28, 1964

A search was made of the available seismograms of large aftershocks immediately following the main shock to determine the nature of faulting in the aftershock zone, and to attempt to relate the focal mechanisms of these aftershocks to that of the main shock. Seismograms from stations throughout the world were partially obscured for several hours by surface waves from the main shock. It was possible to obtain sufficient first-motion data to study six of the larger aftershocks that occurred within the initial 17 hours after the main shock. It was hoped that a study of these earthquakes would give an indication of the general nature of faulting in the aftershock area.

P-wave first-motion focal mechanism studies were made for each of the six earthquakes using the Byerly extended distance technique and Jeffreys-Bullen [1940] traveltime curves. Because of the sparcity of data, no *S*-wave focal mechanism studies were attempted for these earthquakes. The six earthquakes for which *P*-wave solutions were constructed occurred in the time interval between 07:10 and 20:29 hours (G.M.T.) of March 28, 1964. The *P*-wave data for these six earthquakes are tabulated in table 8. Only first motions from short-period seismograms are listed in table 8, because long-period seismograms were completely masked by phases from the main shock. A study was made of the following six aftershocks, all of which occurred on March 28.

Origin time 07:10:21.4, 58.8° N., 149.5° W., m$_b$ = 6.1.—No satisfactory *P*-wave solution could be obtained for this shock which occurred 3 hours and 34 minutes after the main shock. The majority of the first motions recorded are dilatations, with compressions scattered throughout in no recognizable pattern. The pattern of

TABLE 8.—*P-wave data: aftershocks of March 28, 1964*

Station	07:10:21.4	09:01:00.5	09:52:55.7	10:35:38.9	12:20:49.8	20:29:08.6	Station	07:10:21.4	09:01:00.5	09:52:55.7	10:35:38.9	12:20:49.8	20:29:08.6
Alma-Ata		C	D			C	Longmire					D	D
Alert	D		C	D	D	C	Malaga			C		D	C
Ann Arbor						C	Manila					D	C
Anpu						D	Milford	D	C	C	D	D	D
Apatity		D	C	C	D	D	Mineral	D	C	C	D	D	
Athens	D	C			C	D	Minneapolis	D	C			C	
Atlanta	D		C	C	D	D	Moscow	D	C		D	D	
Baguio City		C		D	D	C	Mould Bay			C	C	C	C
Balboa Heights			D				Nana	D					C
Barrett	D	D	C	D	D		Nanking		C	C	D	D	C
Bermuda	C	D	C	C	D	C	New Delhi	D	C	C	C	D	D
Blacksburg	D	D	C	C	D	D	Nahtrang		C		D		C
Bozeman						C	Nurmijärvi	D	C	C	D	C	D
Byerly	D		C	C			Oroville		C	C	D	D	D
Canton						C	Peking		C	C	D		C
Caracas		D		D	D	C	Petropavlovsk					C	C
Changchun		C	C		D	C	Porto	D	C				
Chengtu		C	C	D	D	C	Pulkovo		C			D	
Columbia		D	C		D		Quetta		C	C	D	D	C
Copenhagen				D		C	Rabaul					C	D
Corvallis	D	D	C	C	D		Rapid City						D
Dallas	C	D	D			D	Resolute	D		C	D	C	D
Dugway						D	Riverside	D	C	C	D	D	
Florissant	D		C	C	D		Scarborough				D		
Frobisher Bay	D	C	C	D	D		Schefferville		D	C	D		
Frunze	C	C	C	D			Seven Falls		D	D	D		
Georgetown		C	C	C	D	C	Shillong	D		C	D	D	D
Golden						D	Shiraz	D	C	C	D	D	C
Guam					C	C	Sian		C	C	D		C
Halifax	C					D	Simferopol				D		
Helwan	D						Spring Hill	D	C		D	C	D
Hong Kong						C	State College		C	D		D	D
Honolulu	D						Stuttgart	D	C		D	D	C
Irkutsk					C		Tiksi						C
Isabella	D	C	C	D	D		Trieste						C
Kap Tobin	D				D		Trinidad				C	D	
Kevo	D	C		D	D	C	Tucson		C		D	D	
Kheis			C	D	D	C	Valentia	D			D	D	C
Kirovobad	D	C		D	D		Vladivostok		C	C	D		
Kongsberg	D	C	C	D	D	C	Weston		C	D	D	D	
Kunming		C		D	D	C	Yakutsk			D	C	D	D
Lahore						C	Yuzhno-Sakhalinsk			C	D		C
Lanchow		C	C	D	D	C	Zo-Se		C	C			
L'Aquila	D	D	D		D	D							
Lhasa		C	C		D	C							

the first motions is markedly different from that recorded for the main shock. The distribution of dilatations indicates that any possible nodal plane that could be constructed would result in motion along a fault plane dipping approximately 45° (fig. 17).

Origin time 09:01:00.5, 56.5° N., 152.0° W., m_b = 6.0.—It was possible to construct two well-defined nodal planes for this aftershock which occurred 5 hours and 25 minutes after the main shock. The P-wave solution is shown in figure 18. The *a* plane is restrained by Blacksburg, and has a strike of N. 85° E. and a dip of 86° N. This plane dips steeply and is similar to the one nodal plane determined for the main shock. If the focal mechanism is a single couple and the *a* plane is selected

as the fault plane, the fault motion would be left lateral. The fault motion is right lateral if the *b* plane, with a strike of N. 3° W. and a dip of 63° E. is assumed to be the fault plane. Fifty P-wave first motions were used in this solution. Seven percent of the observations were inconsistent.

Origin time 09:52:55.7, 59.7° N., 146.6° W., m_b = 5.5.—The majority of first motions recorded were compressions (fig. 19). A solution with low error can be constructed which depends primarily on the first motions at Weston and State College (nodal plane *b*), and Yakutsk (nodal plane *a*). Mould Bay is inconsistent with this solution. Balboa Heights, Alma-Ata, and L'Aquila are also inconsistent, but there was no possible solution

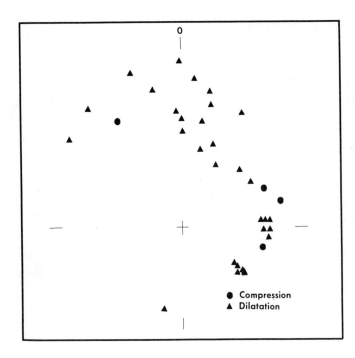

FIGURE 17.—*P*-wave first motion plot of the aftershock of 07:10:21.4, March 28, 1964 (extended distance projection). No focal mechanism solution was possible.

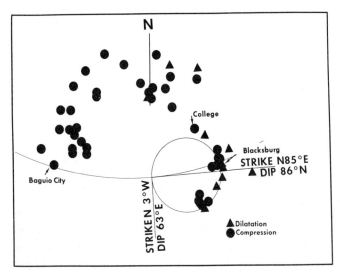

FIGURE 18.—*P*-wave focal mechanism solution of the aftershock of 09:01:00.5, March 28, 1964 (extended distance projection).

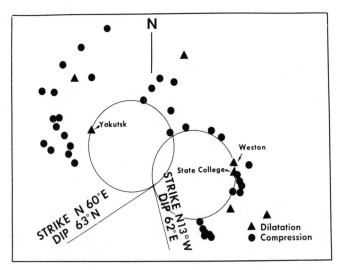

FIGURE 19.—*P*-wave focal mechanism solution of the aftershock of 09:52:55.7, March 28, 1964 (extended distance projection).

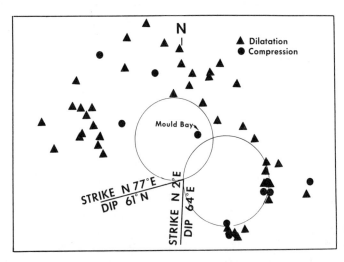

FIGURE 20.—*P*-wave focal mechanism solution of the aftershock of 10:35:38.9, March 28, 1964 (extended distance projection).

for which readings from these stations would be consistent without appreciably increasing the error. The *b* plane, with a strike of N. 13° W. and a dip of 62° E., is the better defined of the two planes. The *a* plane has a strike of N. 60° E. and a dip of 63° N. If the *a* plane is considered the fault plane, the motion is right lateral.

Conversely, the motion is left lateral, if the *b* plane is taken as the fault plane.

Origin time 10:35:38.9, 57.2° N. 152.4° W., m_b = 6.0.—The *P*-wave focal mechanism solution shown in figure 20 for this earthquake has an error of 12 percent, which is slightly higher than the average for the six earthquakes in the series.

The *b* plane was drawn to include the largest area possible with consideration for the compression recorded at Mould Bay. The circle representing the *b* nodal plane could have been drawn considerably smaller without affecting the precision of the solution as long as Mould Bay remains within the circle. The strike and dip of the *a* plane are N. 2° E. and 64° N., respectively. The *b* plane has a strike of N. 77° E. and a dip of 61° N. The fault motion is left lateral if the *a* plane is chosen as the fault plane, and right lateral if the *b* plane is selected as the fault plane.

Origin time 12:20:49.8, 56.5° N., 154.0° W., m_b *= 6.1.*—The *P*-wave solution for this earthquake is similar to the solution for the preceding earthquake, with the exception of a slight counterclockwise rotation of both planes. The position of the *a* plane is based on compressions at Minneapolis, Mould Bay, and Resolute. It has a strike of N. 46° E. and a dip of 66° N. The *b* plane is defined by Petropavlovsk and Irkutsk and has a strike of N. 31° W. and a dip of 64° E. If the *a* plane is taken to be the fault plane, the motion is predominantly left lateral, and if the *b* plane is the fault plane, the motion is right lateral. The focal mechanism solution is shown in figure 21.

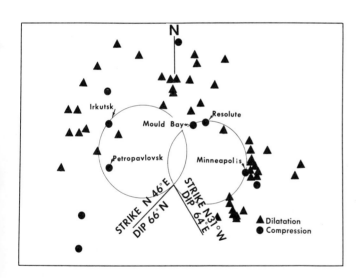

FIGURE 21.—*P*-wave focal mechanism solution of the aftershock of 12:20:49.8, March 28, 1964 (extended distance projection).

Origin time 20:29:08.6, 59.8° N., 118.7° W., m_b *= 5.8.*—The solution for this earthquake has a high percentage of inconsistent first motions, but the general nature of the solution is similar to the *P*-wave solution for the main shock. Seventeen first motions are inconsistent with the solution shown in figure 22. However, it should be pointed out that the inconsistent first motions do not form any definite pattern that would permit an alternate solution with comparable error. Left-lateral faulting is indicated if the *a* plane is the fault plane. The

faulting is right lateral if the *b* plane is selected as the fault plane. The *a* plane shown in figure 22 has a strike of N. 77° E. and a dip of 84° N., but the dip could be increased to nearly 90° with little change in strike of the plane and no change in the percent error.

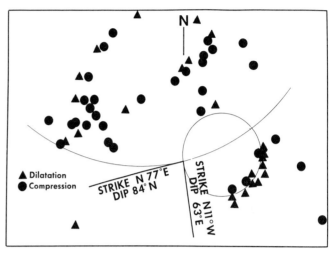

FIGURE 22.—*P*-wave focal mechanism solution of the aftershock of 20:29:08.6, March 28, 1964 (extended distance projection).

THE EARTHQUAKES OF MARCH 30, 1964

Origin time 02:18:06.3, 56.6° N., 152.9° W., m_b *= 5.8.*—Both *P*- and *S*-wave focal mechanism solutions were attempted for this aftershock. Seventy-three first motions were used in the *P*-wave solution shown on a Wulff stereographic projection in figure 23. Four first motions were inconsistent with the solution shown. The *P*-wave data are listed in table 9. The well-determined nodal plane shown in figure 23 has a strike of N. 63° E. and a dip of 87° S. The orientation of this plane is nearly the same as the one plane determined for the main shock from *P*-wave data. The second plane shown dashed in figure 23 was determined from *S*-wave data. A second orthogonal plane (not shown in figure 23) may be drawn which has a strike of N. 25° W. and a dip of 67° W., but it depends solely on the dilatation reported at Petropavlovsk. The interpretation of a second plane dipping to the west and passing between Petropavlovsk and Yuzhno-Sakhalinsk is not supported by the *S*-wave solution discussed below.

The theoretical *S*-wave polarization for a type I force system was computed with the assumption that the one well-determined plane from the *P*-wave solution is the auxiliary plane. All the pertinent *S*-wave data are listed

TABLE 9.—P-*wave data: aftershock of March 30, 1964*

[Origin time 02:18:06.3. Coordinates 56.6° N., 152.9° W. Magnitude (m_b) = 5.8]

Station	Short period	Long period	Station	Short period	Long period
Addis Ababa		C†	Manila	(D)	C†
Alert	C	C†	Minneapolis		(D) †
Ann Arbor		D†	Mould Bay*	C	
Anpu		C†	Nana	(C)	(D)
Athens*	C†		Nanking*	C	
Atlanta	D	D†	New Delhi	C	C
Baguio City		C†	Nhatrang	(D)	(D)
Balboa Heights		D†	Nurmijärvi	(D)	C†
Bermuda		D†	Oroville	C	C†
Blacksburg		D†	Ottawa*	(C)†	
Bogota		D†	Pasadena	D†	
Bozeman	D†		Peking*	C†	
Canton*	C†		Petropavlovsk*	D†	
Caracas		D†	Porto		C†
Changchun*	C†		Pulkovo*	D†	
Chengtu*	C†		Quetta	C	C†
China Lake	D†		Rabaul		C†
Copenhagen	(D)	C†	Rapid City	D	D†
Corvallis		D†	Resolute	C	C†
Dallas			Riverside		D†
Dugway	D†		Schefferville*	C†	
Golden		D†	Shiraz	C	C†
Helwan		C†	Sian*	C†	
Honiara		(D)†	State College	D	D†
Irkutsk			Stuttgart	C	C†
Isabella	(C)†		Sverdlovsk*	D†	
Kevo	C	C†	Tiksi	C†	
Kheis*	C†		Tinehama	D†	
King Ranch		D†	Troy		D†
Kongsberg		C†	Trieste		C†
Kunming*	C†		Trinidad		D†
Lahore		(C)†	Valentia		C†
Lanchow	C†		Vladivostok*	C†	
L'Aquila	C	C†	Weston	D	D†
Lhasa*	C†		Yuzhno-Sakhalinsk*	C†	
Longmire	D†		Zo-Se	C†	
Malaga	(D)	C†			

*Seismograms not read by the authors.   C—Compressional.
†Station used in solution.   D—Dilatational.
( ) Doubtful reading.

TABLE 10.—S-*wave data: aftershock of March 30, 1964*

[Origin time 02:18:06.3. Coordinates 56.6° N., 152.9° W. Magnitude (m_b) = 5.8]

Station	Azimuth	Distance	ϵ_o	$\|\epsilon_o - \epsilon_{cI}\|$	$\|\epsilon_o - \epsilon_{cII}\|$
	Degrees	*Degrees*			
Athens	2.7	85.7	−15	18	29
Atlanta	86.4	51.3	90	22	0
Bermuda	72.1	62.7	70	11	12
Balboa Heights	99.0	73.4	70	14	6
Caracas	87.5	79.1	79	11	7
Copenhagen	8.9	67.4	−59	18	0
Eskdalemuir	18.4	65.8	−85	35	18
Georgetown	76.1	51.2	22	55	59
L'Aquila	10.2	80.7	−53	13	0
La Palma	104.3	63.8	58	6	4
Nhatrang	283.2	84.2	74	21	17
Port Moresby	239.6	82.0	−80	5	5
Rabaul	237.6	75.1	89	7	7
Toledo	23.8	80.3	−54	0	12
Trinidad	82.9	82.0	−85	25	22
Trieste	9.5	77.4	−60	20	6
Valentia	23.8	67.6	−86	31	16

ϵ_o Observed polarization angle.
ϵ_{cI} Computed polarization angle for type I solution.
ϵ_{cII} Computed polarization angle for type II solution.

in table 10. The results were plotted and compared with the actual polarization as shown in figure 24. The average polarization error, $\delta\bar{\epsilon}$, for this solution is 19°.

The least-squares analysis technique of Udias [1964] was used to determine the auxiliary plane for a type I mechanism independent of the P-wave data. An auxiliary plane with a strike of N. 87° E. and a dip of 34° S. was computed from the S-wave data. This plane compares very favorably with the plane obtained from the P-wave solution. The S-wave study shows that if the earthquake has a type I focal mechanism, then the one plane determined from the P-wave solution is the auxiliary plane. The fault plane is indeterminate from both the P- and S-wave data for a type I focal mechanism.

The S-wave polarization, assuming a type II force system, was computed for this earthquake using the plane determined from the P-wave solution to define one force axis of the S-wave solution. The computed polarizations are shown plotted and compared with the observed

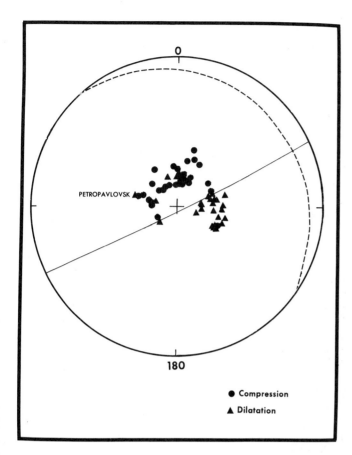

FIGURE 23.—*P*-wave focal mechanism solution of the after-shock of 02:18:06.3, March 30, 1964 (Wulff net). The dashed nodal plane was determined from *S*-wave data.

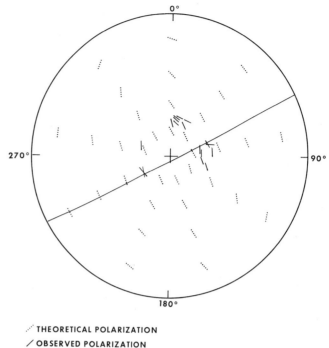

∴ THEORETICAL POLARIZATION
∕ OBSERVED POLARIZATION

FIGURE 24.—*S*-wave focal mechanism solution of the after-shock of 02:18:06.3, March 30, 1964 (Wulff net): type I force system. The nodal plane was determined from the *P*-wave data.

polarizations in figure 25. The *P*-wave nodal plane (*b* plane) determined from the *S*-wave polarization for a type II source has a strike of N. 47° W. and a dip of 9° N. This plane is quite different from the possible *b* plane from the *P*-wave solution which was suggested on the basis of the dilatation at Petropavlovsk. The *b* plane determined from the *S*-wave data is preferred. The average error for this solution is 14°. The average error, $\delta\bar{\epsilon}$, as a function of dip and strike of one plane is shown in figure 26. The solution presented here, which is based on a type II source, *S*-wave polarization data and the one well-determined plane from the *P*-wave solution, is in general agreement with the solution published by Stauder and Bollinger [1966].

Origin time 07:09:34.0, 59.9° N., 145.7° W., m_b = 5.6.—A *P*-wave solution was attempted for the aftershock of 07:09:34.0, March 30, 1964. The solution, based on 67 observations, is shown in figure 27. The *P*-wave data are listed in table 11. One nodal plane is reasonably well defined (strike N. 35° W., dip 72° W.). The second plane is not well determined, but is con-

strained by the data to a strike between due east and south and to dips between 24° and 32° NE. The two dashed circles shown in figure 27 indicate the two possible extreme orientations of the second nodal plane. The interpretation of the *P*-wave data presented here is somewhat different than the solution published by Stauder and Bollinger [1966] for this earthquake; the principal difference in the two solutions is the position of the *b* plane. Stauder and Bollinger [1966] also computed an *S*-wave solution for this earthquake.

Table 12 summarizes the data on the focal mechanisms computed for the two preshocks and eight aftershocks considered. In table 12, pressure and tension axes have been completed for all solutions, assuming a type II mechanism. Stauder and Bollinger [1966] presented focal mechanism solutions for 27 aftershocks. The mechanism diagrams for the earthquakes studied are shown in figure 28. Pressure and tension axes are shown for those earthquakes for which *S*-wave solutions were computed. The pressure axes are also shown for earthquakes studied by Stauder and Bollinger [1966]. The following conclusions are stated:

1. For earthquakes discussed in this paper that were also studied by Stauder and Bollinger [1966], the focal

TABLE 11.—P-*wave data: aftershock of March 30, 1964*

[Origin time 07:09:34.0. Coordinates 59.9° N., 145.7° W. Magnitude (m_b) = 5.6]

Station	Short period	Long period	Station	Short period	Long period
Alert	(D)	C†	Lhasa*	C†	
Ann Arbor		C†	Malaga	C	C†
Anpu		C†	Manila	(D)	(C)†
Arequipa		C†	Minneapolis	C	(C)†
Atlanta	C	C†	Moscow	D*	
Balboa Heights		C†	Mould Bay	C†	
Barrett	D	C†	Nana	(D)	(C)†
Bermuda		C†	Nanking	C†	
Blacksburg	C	C†	New Delhi	(D)	C†
Bogota		C†	Nhatrang	(C)	(C)†
Byerly	C	C†	Nurmijarvi		C†
Caracas		C†	Oroville	C	C†
Changchun*	C		Ottawa*	C†	
Chengtu*	C		Pasadena	C†	D†
China Lake	C		Peking*	C†	
Copenhagen		C†	Petropavlovsk*	D†	
Corvallis		C†	Porto		C†
Dallas	(C)	C†	Quetta	C	C†
Dushawbe*	D		Rabaul		(D)†
Florissant	C	C†	Rapid City	C	C†
Frunze	C*		Resolute	C	C†
Golden	C†		Schefferville	C	C†
Helwan		C†	Semipalatinsk*	(D)†	
Hong Kong		C†	Shillong		C†
Honiara		D†	Shiraz	(D)	C†
Irkutsk	C		Simferopol*	C†	
Isabella	C†		Tiksi*	C†	
Kevo	(C)	C†	Tinemaha		C†
Kheis	C		Trieste	(D)	C†
Khorog	C		Trinidad		(C)†
King Ranch		C†	Troy		C†
Kizyl–Arvat*	C†		Vladivostok*	D†	
Kongsberg	C	C†	Yuzhno-Sakhalinsk*	C†	
Lanchow*	C†				

*Seismograms not read by the authors.
†Station used in solution.
( ) Doubtful reading.

C—Compressional.
D—Dilatational.

TABLE 12.—*Summary of focal mechanisms computed for preshocks and aftershocks*

Date	Time (G.M.T.)	Latitude	Longitude	Magnitude (m_b)	P solution — a plane strike/dip	P solution — b plane strike/dip	P — Direction and plunge	T	Type I strike/dip	P–S method, type II strike/dip
		Degrees	Degrees		Degrees	Degrees	Degrees		Degrees	Degrees
02/06/64	13:07:25.2	55.7 N.	155.8 W.	5.6	N. 72 E. 82 S.	....	171* 36*	330* 52*	N. 52 E. 48 E.	N. 72 E., N. 55 W. 82 S. 13 E.
03/22/64	06:22:15.0	61.3 N.	147.8 W.	4.5	No solution					
03/28/64	07:10:21.4	58.8 N.	149.5 W.	6.1	No solution					
03/28/64	09:01:00.5	56.5 N.	152.0 W.	6.0	N. 85 E. 86 N.	N. 3 W. 63 E.	218 22	314 16		
03/28/64	09:52:55.7	59.7 N.	146.6 W.	5.5	N. 60 E. 63 N.	N. 13 W. 62 E.	294 01	203 41		
03/28/64	10:35:38.9	57.2 N.	152.4 W.	6.0	N. 2 E. 64 E.	N. 77 E. 61 N.	221 41	129 2		
03/28/64	12:20:49.8	56.5 N.	154.0 W.	6.1	N. 46 E. 66 N.	N. 31 W. 64 E.	187 37	278 01		
03/28/64	20:29:08.6	59.8 N.	148.7 W.	5.8	N. 77 E. 84 N.	N. 11 W. 63 E.	208 23	306 14		
03/30/64	02:18:06.3	56.6 N.	152.9 W.	5.8	N. 63 E. 87 S.		161* 41*	324* 47*	N. 87 E. 34 S.	N. 63 E., N. 47 W. 87 S. 9 N.
03/30/64	07:09:34.0	59.9 N.	145.7 W.	5.6	N. 35 W. 72 W.					

*P and T from type II S-wave solution; remaining P and T axis computed from P-wave solution assuming a type II focal mechanism.

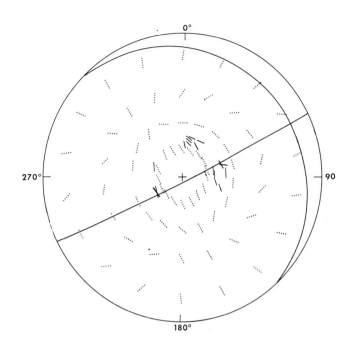

THEORETICAL POLARIZATION
OBSERVED POLARIZATION

FIGURE 25.—*S*-wave focal mechanism solution of the after-shock of 02:18:06.3, March 30, 1964 (Wulff net): type II force system. The nodal plane for *P* striking N. 63° E. was used to define one axis of the *S*-wave solution. The other nodal plane for *P* striking N. 47° W. has the minimum average polarization error for the data shown.

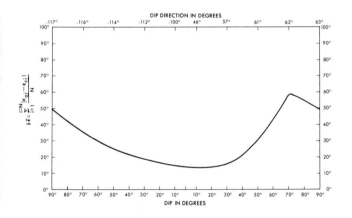

FIGURE 26.—Earthquake of 02:18:06.3, March 30, 1964. Average polarization error, $\delta\bar{\epsilon}$, as a function of the dip of one *P*-wave nodal plane. The second nodal plane (strike N. 63° E., dip 87° S.) is held constant. A type II force system is assumed.

mechanisms computed are in general agreement. Two exceptions are the orientations of the *b* planes of the earthquake of March 28, 1964, at 20:29:08.6, and the

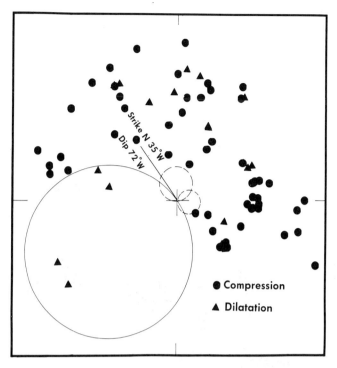

FIGURE 27.—*P*-wave focal mechanism solution of the after-shock of 07:09:34.0, March 30, 1964 (extended distance projection).

earthquake of March 30, 1964, at 07:09:34.0. The *P*-wave data for these earthquakes, however, are poor but several interpretations are possible.

2. The possible foreshock of March 22, 1964, at 06:22:15.0 which occurred 11 kilometers northwest of the main shock, only 6 days before, is of interest because the first-motion pattern is completely different from the known pattern for the main shock.

3. The strikes of the *P*-wave nodal planes are not oriented parallel to the main trend of the aftershock zone from Kodiak Island to Prince William Sound. The strike of the aftershock zone is approximately N. 35° E. The average strike of the *P*-wave nodal planes most nearly parallel to the aftershock zone is approximately N. 60° E. Stauder and Bollinger [1966] also commented on this orientation of the strike of the nodal planes.

4. There is some evidence of left-lateral movement for the aftershock studied.

COMPOSITE FOCAL MECHANISM STUDIES

Shortly following the Prince William Sound Earthquake of March 28, 1964, the Coast and Geodetic Survey installed seven temporary seismograph stations in the Prince William Sound-Kodiak Island area. The

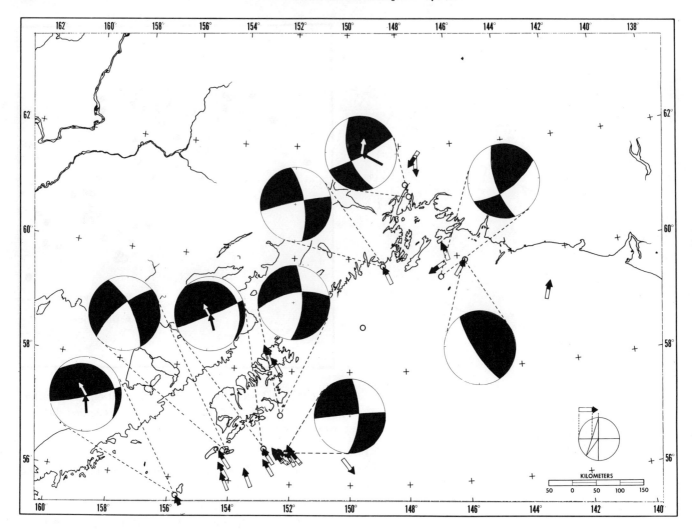

FIGURE 28.—Mechanism diagrams (Wulff net) of the earthquakes in the Prince William Sound–Kodiak Island region. Shaded areas represent compression quadrants. Arrows in compression quadrants represent direction and dip of the tension axis. Arrows in dilatation quadrants represent direction and dip of compression axis. Partially shaded arrows represent direction and dip of pressure axis taken from Stauder and Bollinger [1966].

directions of first motions recorded at these stations were used to construct composite focal mechanism solutions for specified areas. Figure 29 shows the regions selected for study and the distribution of seismograph stations. Data were also used from the Worldwide Network Seismograph Station at College, Alaska. Earthquake epicenters in a particular region were plotted at the center of a Wulff net stereographic projection. The direction of first motion recorded at each station for each earthquake in the region was then located at the proper distance and azimuth from the center of the Wulff net. An attempt was then made to construct nodal lines for *P*. Stated another way, the composite focal mechanism solutions constructed are the superposition of a number of individual *P*-wave solutions for a small selected area, treating the total data as if it originated from a single source. The method is not designed to give distinct nodal planes since the areas studied have considerable size. It would also be unreasonable to assume that the nodal planes for each earthquake would be exactly the same. However, it should be possible to construct nodal lines for *P* for each composite solution if the earthquake focal mechanisms in a particular region are similar. The method should permit a better understanding of the mechanism of faulting in the aftershock area, particularly for the smaller earthquakes which were not well recorded at teleseismic distances. A total of 859 first motions were used. The aftershock area was broken into 12 groups. A summary of the composite focal mechanism solutions is given in table 13.

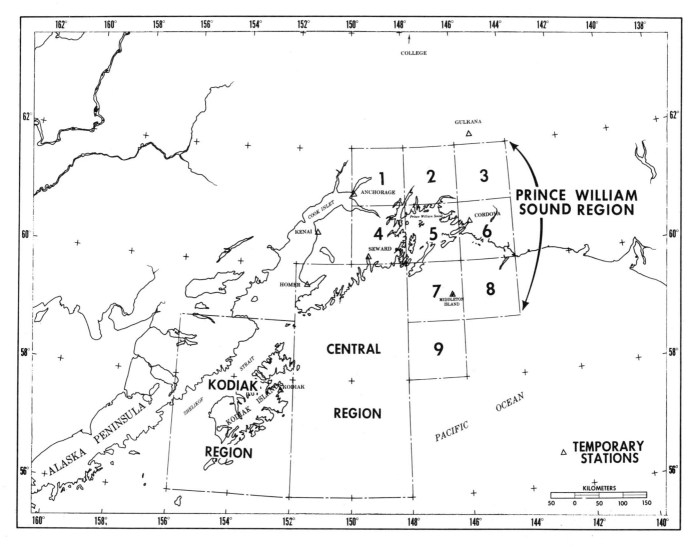

FIGURE 29.—Location map of the aftershock zones showing seismograph stations and regions for which composite focal mechanism solutions were attempted.

Figure 30 is a plot of all P_n first motions versus time. There appears to be no systematic change in the focal mechanism pattern over the aftershock area in this 4-month time span considered. Of the 859 first motions plotted, 473 are compressions and 386 are dilatations. Similar plots were constructed for each individual region. For each separate region there appeared to be no significant change in the distribution of compressions and dilatations with time.

Figure 31 shows all of the first motions recorded during the 4-month period plotted on a Wulff net. All first motions are considered to be P_n and are plotted on a critical circle with a radius of 48.5°; this radius corresponds to an assumed crustal thickness of 50 kilometers, a crustal velocity of 6 kilometers per second,

and an upper mantle velocity of 8 kilometers per second. For clarity, compressions were plotted slightly outside the critical circle, and dilatations were plotted slightly inside the critical circle. The plot is weighted by data from the northeastern end of the aftershock zone. Areas of predominantly compressional or dilatational first motions can be identified, but no clear pattern is evident. There is clearly a predominance of compressions over dilatations in the northwest quadrant, but the distribution of compressions and dilatations in the other three quadrants is about equal. This result is perhaps not unexpected because of the very large area over which the aftershocks occurred. The P_n first-motion data for each of the nine areas into which the aftershock zone was divided will now be discussed.

TABLE 13.—*Summary of composite focal mechanism solutions*

Region	Area boundaries		Number of P_n first motions	Remarks
	Longitude	Latitude		
	Degrees	*Degrees*		
Kodiak Island........................	152 W.–156 W.	56 N.–59 N.	19	Two planes constructed (fig. 32).
Central................................	143 W.–152 W.	56 N.–60 N.	240	Two planes constructed (fig. 33).
Prince William Sound				
Area 1...............................	148 W.–150 W.	61 N.–62 N.	37	Two planes constructed (fig. 34).
Area 2...............................	146 W.–148 W.	61 N.–62 N.	81	Two planes constructed (fig. 35).
Area 3...............................	144 W.–146 W.	61 N.–62 N.	4	Data insufficient for solution. (fig. 36).
Area 4...............................	148 W.–150 W.	60 N.–61 N.	59	Two planes constructed (fig. 37).
Area 5...............................	146 W.–148 W.	60 N.–61 N.	136	Two planes constructed (fig. 38).
Area 6...............................	144 W.–146 W.	60 N.–61 N.	49	Two planes constructed (fig. 39).
Area 7...............................	146 W.–148 W.	59 N.–60 N.	160	Two planes constructed (fig. 40).
Area 8...............................	144 W.–146 W.	59 N.–60 N.	58	Data insufficient for solution (fig. 41).
Area 9...............................	146 W.–148 W.	58 N.–59 N.	16	Two planes constructed (fig. 42).

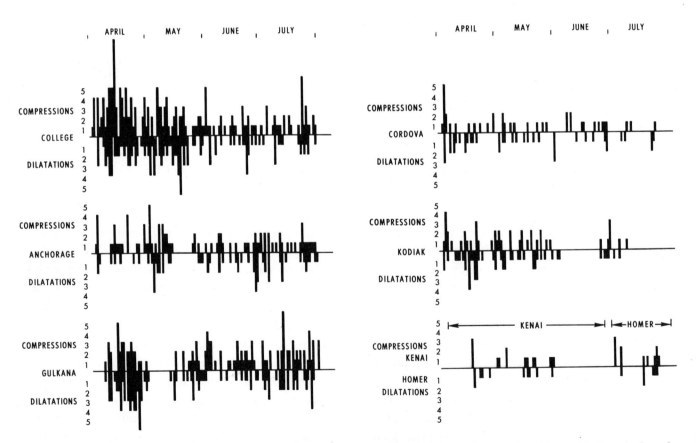

FIGURE 30.—Direction of first motion recorded at five temporary seismograph stations and College, Alaska, during the period April 1–July 31, 1964 (Wulff net).

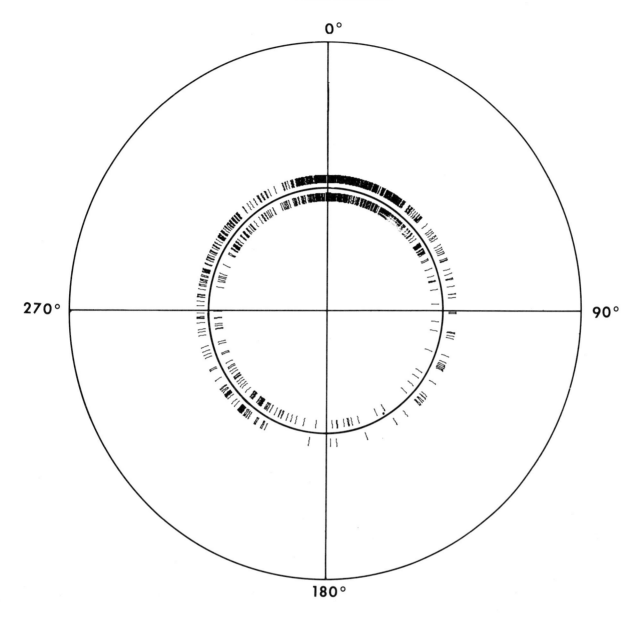

Compressions plotted outside of critical circle

Dilatations plotted inside of critical circle

FIGURE 31.—Prince William Sound Earthquake aftershock: direction of first motion recorded at temporary seismograph stations and College, Alaska, during the period April 1–July 31, 1964 (Wulff net).

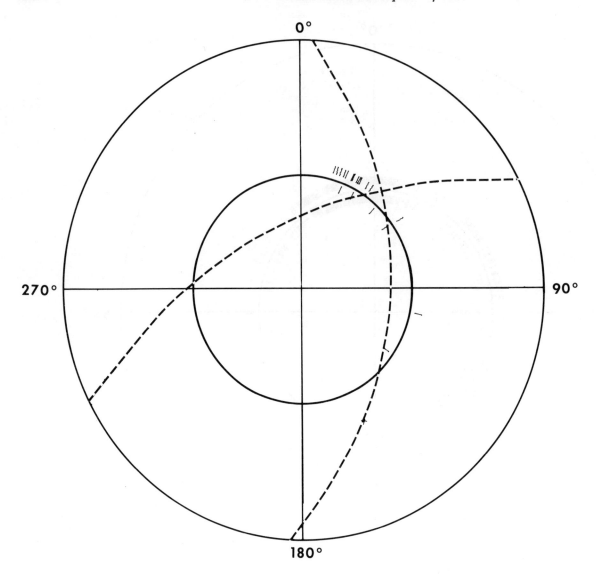

Compressions plotted outside of critical circle

Dilatations plotted inside of critical circle

FIGURE 32.—Kodiak region: direction of first motions recorded at temporary seismograph stations and College, Alaska, during the period April 1–July 31, 1964 (Wulff net).

Kodiak Region: Only 19 first motions could be used in this region. Most of the region falls outside the net of temporary seismograph stations; consequently, aftershocks were difficult to locate. Two tentative nodal planes are shown dashed in figure 32, but it is obvious that they are rather arbitrary. It should be noted that there is a predominance of compressions in the northeast quadrant.

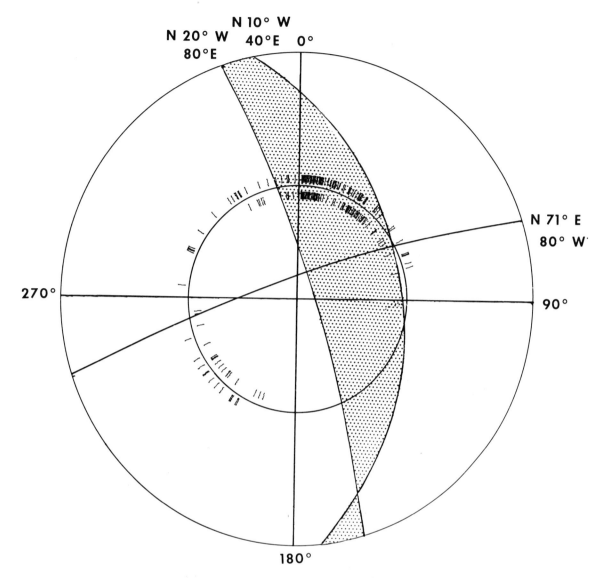

Compressions plotted outside of critical circle

Dilatations plotted inside of critical circle

Shaded area covers apparent rotation of plane

FIGURE 33.—Central region: composite focal mechanism solution from P_n first motions recorded at temporary seismograph stations and College, Alaska, during the period April 1–July 31, 1964.

Central Region: Two hundred and forty P_n arrivals were used in the study of the central region. The data and suggested nodal lines of P are shown in figure 33. The nodal plane striking N. 71° E. is based on the larger number of compressions in the northwest quadrant and the predominance of dilatations in the southwest quadrant. The proposed plane striking northwest could strike between N. 20° W. and N. 10° W. and vary in dip between 80° E. and 40° E. and still conform with the orthogonality criteria.

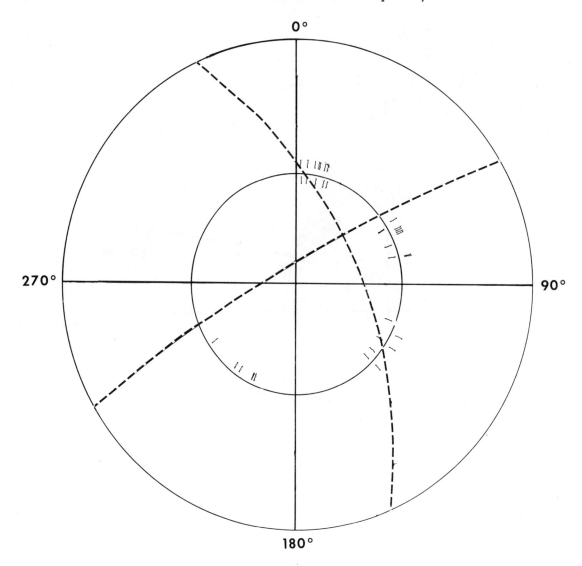

Compressions plotted outside of critical circle

Dilatations plotted inside of critical circle

FIGURE 34.—Prince William Sound region—area 1: composite focal mechanism solution from P_n first motions recorded at temporary seismograph stations and College, Alaska, during the period April 1–July 31, 1964.

Prince William Sound Region—area 1: This area contains 37 recorded P_n first motions (figure 34). The quadrants show about equally mixed compressions and dilatations with the exception of the southwest quadrant which contains predominantly dilatations. Two nodal planes are suggested.

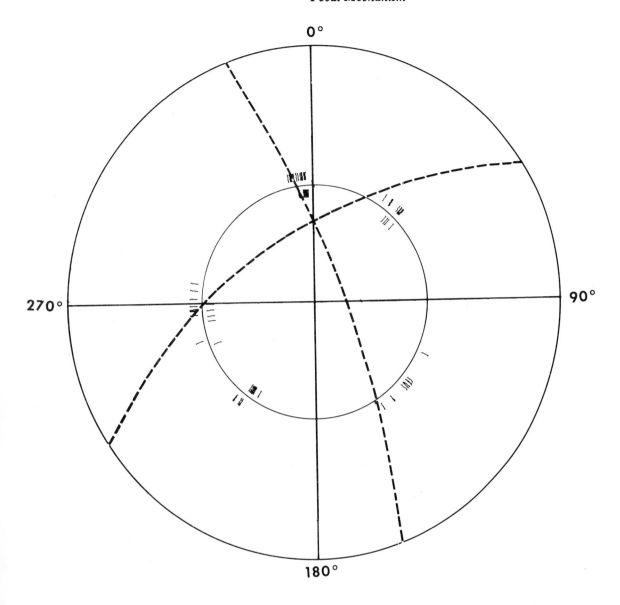

Compressions plotted outside of critical circle

Dilatations plotted inside of critical circle

FIGURE 35.—Prince William Sound region—area 2: composite focal mechanism solution from P_n first motions recorded at temporary seismograph stations and College, Alaska, during the period April 1–July 31, 1964.

Prince William Sound Region—area 2: This area contains 81 recorded P_n first motions. Compressions and dilatations are divided into fairly well-defined regions. The two orthogonal nodal planes that fit the data reasonably well are shown in figure 35.

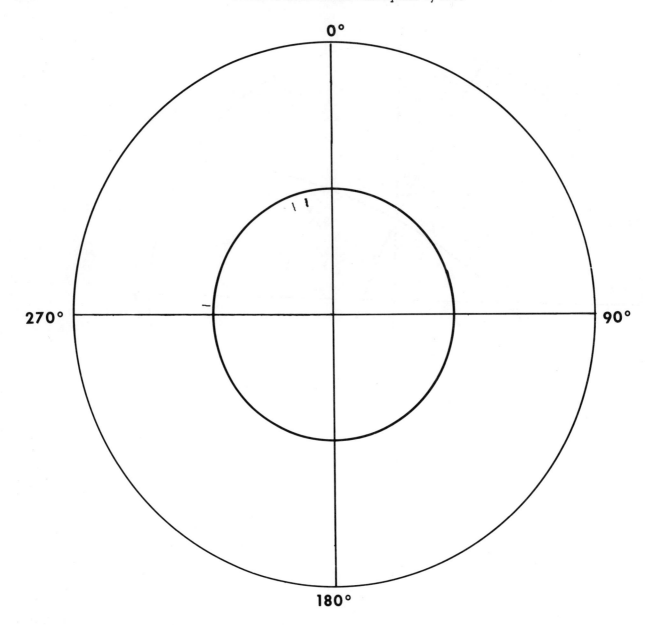

Compressions plotted outside of critical circle

Dilatations plotted inside of critical circle

FIGURE 36.—Prince William Sound region—area 3: P_n first motions recorded at temporary seismograph stations and College, Alaska, during the period April 1–July 31, 1964.

Prince William Sound Region—area 3: This area contained only four first motions (fig. 36)—an insufficient number of observations to attempt an interpretation.

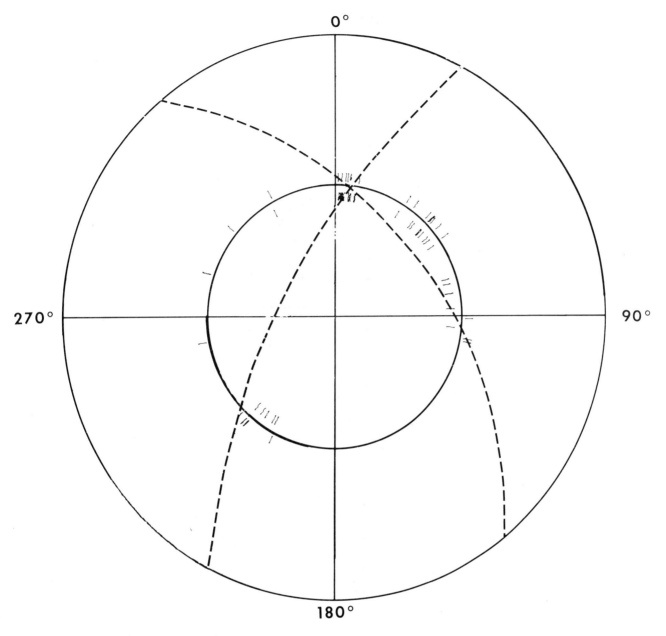

Compressions plotted outside of critical circle
Dilatations plotted inside of critical circle

FIGURE 37.—Prince William Sound region—area 4: composite focal mechanism solution from P_n first motions recorded at temporary seismograph stations and College, Alaska, during the period April 1–July 31, 1964.

Prince William Sound Region—area 4: Two nodal planes striking northeast were drawn for this area (fig. 37). The northwest quadrant is almost solely compres-sional. Fifty-nine P_n first motions were recorded from earthquakes in this region.

214

Prince William Sound Earthquake of 1964

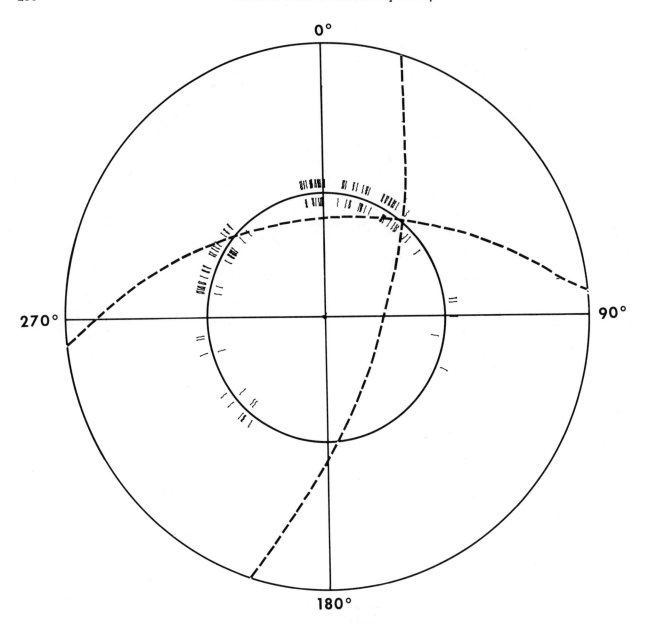

Compressions plotted outside of critical circle

Dilatations plotted inside of critical circle

FIGURE 38.—Prince William Sound region—area 5: composite focal mechanism solution from P_n first motions recorded at temporary seismograph stations and College, Alaska, during the period April 1–July 31, 1964.

Prince William Sound Region—area 5: Compressions and dilatations are quite evenly distributed. One hundred thirty-six P_n first motions were used. Two nodal planes have been defined, but the dilatational lune near the top of figure 38 is arbitrarily defined since the number of compressions and dilatations are about equal. Area 5 is in the center of Prince William Sound, a region where the strikes of known geological structure change rather abruptly from northwest to northeast. The nearly equal distribution of compressions and dilatations in all azimuths is not surprising, since faulting in this region probably occurs on planes with widely varying strikes. This interpretation is supported by the focal mechanism solutions of earthquakes in this general area presented by Stauder and Bollinger [1966] who found a change in the strike of nodal planes from east to west across Prince William Sound.

[226]

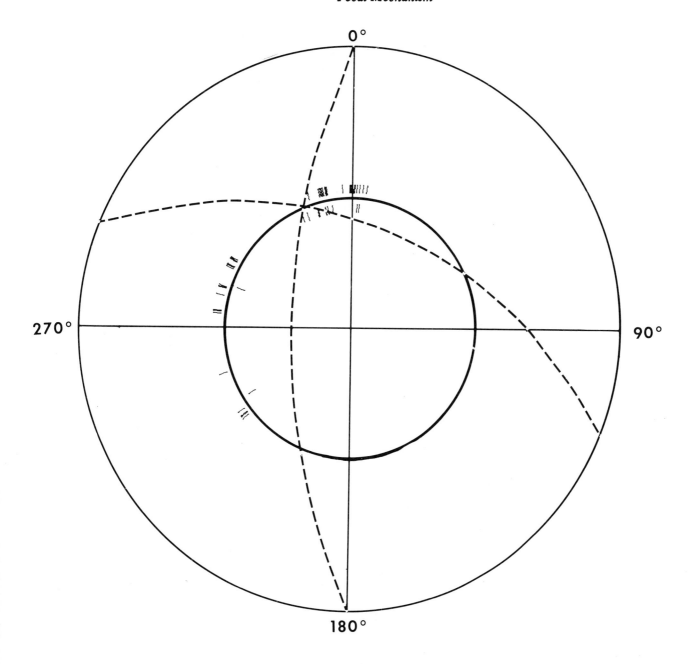

Compressions plotted outside of critical circle

Dilatations plotted inside of critical circle

FIGURE 39.—Prince William Sound Region area 6: composite focal mechanism solution from P_n first motions recorded at temporary seismograph stations and College, Alaska, during the period April 1–July 31, 1964.

Prince William Sound Region—area 6: Most of the 49 first motions recorded for this area were compressions. The interpretation presented in figure 39 is quite speculative, but consistent with the data. The solution is similar to the focal mechanism presented by Stauder and Bollinger [1966] for their earthquake number 8, which occurred in the same general area.

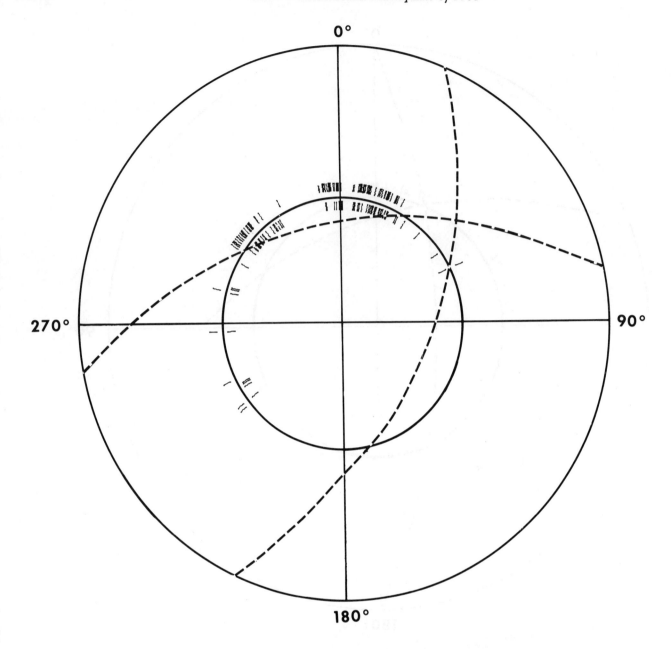

Compressions plotted outside of critical circle

Dilatations plotted inside of critical circle

FIGURE 40.—Prince William Sound region—area 7: composite focal mechanism solution of P_n first motions recorded at temporary seismograph stations and College, Alaska, during the period April 1–July 31, 1964 (Wulff net).

Prince William Sound Region—area 7: Two possible nodal planes were drawn, based on the 160 P_n first motions used (fig. 40). This area is along the southeast margin of the aftershock zone, and most of the shocks were of small magnitude.

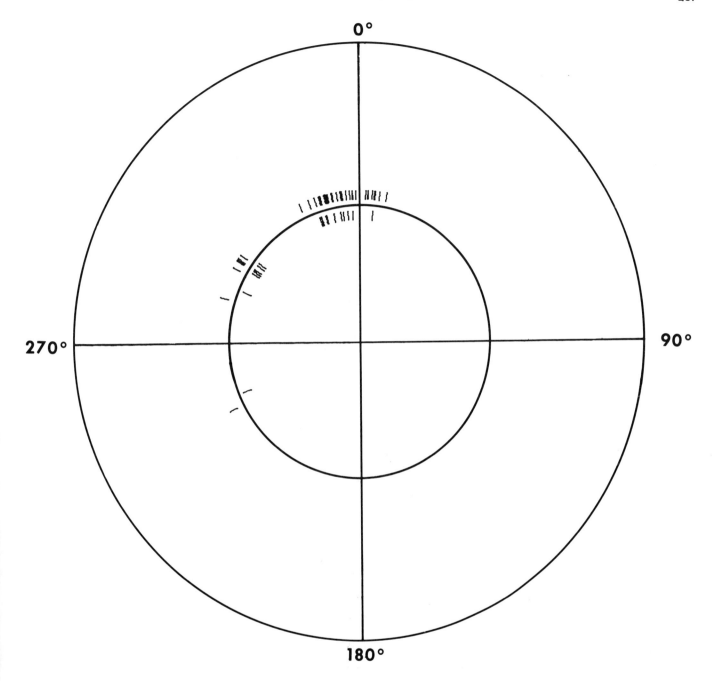

Compressions plotted outside of critical circle

Dilatations plotted inside of critical circle

FIGURE 41.—Prince William Sound region—area 8: composite first motion plot of P_n first motions recorded at temporary seismograph stations and College, Alaska, during the period April 1–July 31, 1964 (Wulff net).

Prince William Sound Region—area 8: The distribution of dilatations and compressions is about equal in all azimuths where data were available, except to the north where compressions are predominant (fig. 41). No solution was attempted.

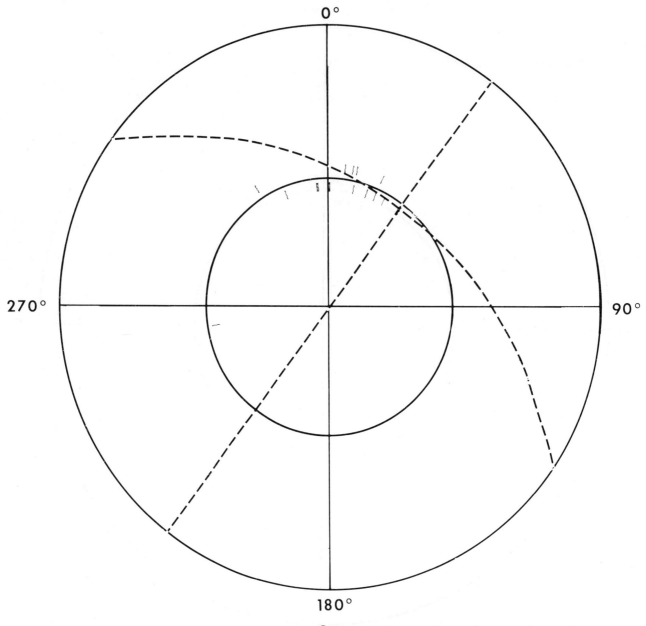

Compressions plotted outside of critical circle

Dilatations plotted inside of critical circle

FIGURE 42.—Prince William Sound region—area 9: composite focal mechanism solution of P_n first motions recorded at temporary seismograph stations and College, Alaska, during the period April 1–July 31, 1964 (Wulff net).

Prince William Sound Region—area 9: There are 16 P_n first motions, 5 compressions, and 11 dilatations (fig. 42). The data are poorly distributed. However, two planes have been somewhat arbitrarily drawn. It should be noted that the first motions in this area were mainly dilatations, but in areas 7 and 8 immediately to the north, the predominant type of first motion was compression.

The composite focal mechanism solutions are, for the most part, inconclusive. For most of the regions, the data are poorly distributed in azimuth and insufficient in quantity. The most important conclusions from the study are:

1. The number of compressions and dilatations recorded for each of the regions are approximately equal.

2. There appears to be no change in the pattern or ratio of compressions to dilatations with time during the first 4 months after the main shock.

3. The focal mechanisms (orientation of the nodal planes) seem to vary considerably for all regions studied.

DISCUSSION AND CONCLUSIONS

Focal mechanism solutions for the Prince William Sound Earthquake of March 28, 1964, two preshocks, and eight aftershocks, together with composite focal mechanism studies of 12 regions in the aftershock zone have been presented. The principal limitation in studying the focal mechanism of the main shock was the paucity of data available. This general lack of data may be attributed to three somewhat unrelated causes. First, the geographical location of the epicenter precluded identification of more than one *P*-wave nodal plane, even if all seismograph stations throughout the world in operation at the time of the earthquake had recorded clear, impulsive first motions. The distribution of stations north and west of the epicenter was totally inadequate to define a second nodal plane. Second, the *P*-wave first motion recorded at many stations was emergent. The ambiguity in the orientation of the one nodal plane defined by the *P*-wave data is principally caused by this problem. Third, only a very small number of seismograms from long-period seismographs were available for *S*-wave studies. The long-period data available were obtained from low-magnification, mechanical seismographs. The long-period seismographs of the World-Wide Network of Standard Seismograph Stations and the majority of long-period seismographs operated at other stations were off scale within a few seconds after the first motion from the earthquake.

The following conclusions have been reached regarding the mechanism of the main shock, aftershocks, and preshocks, based upon studies by the authors and the available geophysical literature at the present time.

1. Wyss and Brune [1967] have discussed the possibility that the Prince William Sound earthquake consisted of a series of ruptures occurring within a 72 sec time span following the initial motion. The majority of the *S*-wave data used for our study of the main shock were recorded by seismographs of intermediate period. If the Prince William Sound earthquake was a multiple rupture, the mechanism derived from *S*-waves of intermediate period (9 to 15 seconds, approximately) probably represents the mechanism of the initial rupture and may not be representative of the total mechanism of the earthquake. The same conclusion is obviously also true for solutions derived from *P*-wave data.

2. The analyses of *P*- and *S*-wave data for the main shock presented here favor a steeply dipping fault plane regardless of whether a type I or type II mechanism is assumed. The motion is mostly dip-slip on a steeply dipping fault plane for a type I mechanism and predominantly strike slip if a type II mechanism is assumed. The type II mechanism is preferred because it yields the lowest polarization error. The orientation of the *P*-wave nodal planes in the preferred solution are: strike N. 62° E., dip 82° S. (*a* plane); strike N. 22° W., dip 52° W. (*b* plane).

It should be pointed out that only the general nature of the faulting can be inferred for a type II mechanism since the fault plane cannot be uniquely specified. Assuming faulting related to the *a* plane along a northeast-southwest line more or less parallel to the length of the aftershock zone, our preferred type II solution is in general agreement with the results reported by Press and Jackson [1965] and Toksöz, Ben-Menahem and Harkrider [1965].

3. There appears to be some other data for the main shock suggestive of faulting along a steep plane. Von Huene, *et al.*, [1967] have defined a zone of high-angle surface faulting extending from the vicinity of Montague Island to Kodiak Island. While this faulting may be a secondary effect of the main shock, it establishes that the surface faulting in this area south and west of the epicenter of the main shock occurred along a steep plane. This evidence suggests that the one steeply dipping nodal plane commonly found for many aftershocks in the Kodiak Island area may be the plane or approximately the plane depending upon whether a type I or type II mechanism is assumed along which faulting has occurred. Von Huene, *et al.* [1967], state that, "Probably the most difficult feature to explain, if the continent is overriding the ocean basin, occurs off the continental margin. It has been found [Von Huene, *et al.*, 1967], that a thick sequence of horizontal strata in the Aleutian trench as well as the strata of the adjacent abyssal plains, are impressively undeformed by compressional folds or faults."

Case, *et al.* [1966], in their discussion of the prominent positive Bouguer gravity anomaly in Prince William Sound have commented that the zero isobase and uplift during the main shock approximately coincide with the steepest part of the gravity gradient along the northwest side of Prince William Sound, and the zero isobase locally parallels the gravity contours. They state that at least a portion of this gravity anomaly could be accounted for by a near vertical fault at depth, but they do not favor this interpretation of the data. Case, *et al.* [1966], also show that gravity surveys after the March 28, 1964, earthquake indicate that the gravity gradient along the northwest side of Prince William Sound is steeper and causes a much greater gravity difference across the Sound than had been previously indicated by surveys of Woollard, *et al.* [1960]. The earlier surveys and Bouguer gravity maps of Prince William Sound were based on much less data than are currently available, and it is difficult to evaluate how much of the increase in the Bouguer gravity in Prince William Sound resulted from the earthquake. Barnes [1966] discusses other gravity resurveys and concludes that mass changes within or just beneath the crust in the vicinity of Valdez may have occurred during or since the earthquake, but he believes that the uncertainties in the limited data available prevent a more detailed interpretation. If a mass change within or just beneath the crust in the Prince William Sound area was caused by or was associated with the main shock, the accompanying faulting probably occurred along a steep plane. Continued reobservation of the gravity and geodetic networks in south-central Alaska is essential to document any possible crustal changes still occurring in Prince William Sound.

4. Another interpretation of our preferred type II solution is possible if faulting is assumed to be related to the *b* plane, that is, left-lateral faulting along a line striking northwest-southeast. If the earthquake was a series of ruptures as suggested by Wyss and Brune [1967], a more complex fault pattern can be visualized. McKenzie and Parker [1967] have suggested that the general area of Prince William Sound represents a transition in regional tectonics from the right lateral faulting associated with the Fairweather fault system in southeastern Alaska to an overthrust system in the Aleutian Islands. It is possible that the initial faulting in the Prince William Sound earthquake was along a transform fault (striking northwest) near the eastern end of an Aleutian Island thrust fault system. Subsequent aftershocks west of Prince William Sound in the vicinity of Kodiak Island may represent fault movement along the Aleutian overthrust.

This interpretation would explain the fault plane solutions obtained by Stauder and Bollinger [1966] for some aftershocks near Kodiak that indicated faulting on a low angle thrust plane. This interpretation would at least partially account for the large lateral movements reported by Parkin [1966] as a result of the earthquake.

5. *S*-wave studies of the preshock of 13:07:25.2, February 6, 1964, and the aftershock of 02:18:06.3, March 30, 1964, indicate that both of these earthquakes have a type II mechanism. These results are in agreement with the conclusions of Stauder and Bollinger [1966].

6. The magnitude 4.5 preshock of 06:22:15.0 March 22, 1964, located only 11 kilometers northwest of the epicenter of the main shock, exhibited an entirely different first-motion pattern than the great earthquake 6 days later.

7. The *P*-wave mechanism solutions for the series of six aftershocks that occurred within 17 hours of the main shock suggest left-lateral movement. The strike of the regional geologic features in the Kodiak Island—Prince William Sound area is about N. 35° E. This strike also represents the assumed strike of the major faulting associated with the March 28, 1964, earthquake. The average strike of steeply dipping *P*-wave nodal planes of the six aftershocks is approximately N. 60° E. Thus, the strike of these planes present an en échelon pattern with the regional features between Kodiak Island and Prince William Sound. This pattern was also noticed (for different aftershocks) by Stauder and Bollinger [1966].

REFERENCES

Adkins, J. N., "The Alaskan Earthquake of July 22, 1937," *Bulletin of the Seismological Society of America,* vol. 30, pp. 353–376, 1940.

Algermissen, S. T., "Prince William Sound, Alaska Earthquake of March 28, 1964, and Aftershock Sequence," (abstract), Program 1964 Annual Meeting of the Geological Society of America, p. 2, 1964.

Algermissen, S. T., "Seismological Investigation of the Prince William Sound, Alaska, Earthquake and Aftershocks," (abstract), *Transactions of the American Geophysical Union,* vol. 45, no. 4, p. 633, 1964.

Algermissen, S. T., "Mechanism of the Prince William Sound Earthquake," in *ESSA Symposium on Earthquake Prediction,* U. S. Department of Commerce, Environmental Science Services Administration, 167 pp., 1966.

Barnes, David F., "Gravity Changes During the Alaska Earthquake," *Journal of Geophysical Research,* vol. 71, pp. 451–456, 1966.

Berg, E., "The Alaska Earthquake, Its Location and Seismic Setting," in Science in Alaska, 1964: *Proceedings of the 15th Alaskan Science Conference, College, Alaska, American Association for the Advancement of Science,* 1965.

Case, J. E., Barnes, D. F., Plafker, George, and Robbins, S. L., "Gravity Survey and Regional Geology of the Prince William Sound Epicentral Region, Alaska," *U. S. Geological Survey Professional Paper 543-C,* 12 pp., 1966.

Honda, H., "The Mechanism of the Earthquakes," *Science Reports,* Tokyo University, series 5, vol. 9, supplement, pp. 1–46, 1957.

Jeffreys, Harold and Bullen, K. E., *Seismological Tables,* British Association for Advancement of Science, London, 1940.

McKenzie, D. P. and R. L. Parker, "The North Pacific: an Example of Tectonics on a Sphere," *Nature,* vol. 216, pp. 1276–1280, 1967.

Pararas-Carayannis, G., and Furumoto, Augustine S., "Source Mechanism of the Alaska Earthquake and Tsunami of 27 March 1964," Report to the National Science Foundation, U. S. Department of Commerce, Clearinghouse for Federal Scientific and Technical Information, 42 pp., 1965.

Parkin, Ernest J., "Alaskan Surveys to Determine Crustal Movement: Part II—Horizontal Displacement," Paper presented at the annual meeting of the American Congress of Surveying and Mapping, Washington, D.C., March 10, 1966.

Plafker, George, "Tectonic Deformation Associated with the 1964 Alaska Earthquake," *Science,* vol. 148, pp. 1675–1687, 1965.

Press, Frank, "Displacements, Strains and Tilts at Teleseismic Distances," *Journal of Geophysical Research,* vol. 70, pp. 2395–2412, 1965.

Press, Frank and Jackson, D., "Alaska Earthquake, 27 March 1964: Vertical Extent of Faulting and Elastic Strain Energy Release," *Science,* vol. 147, pp. 867–868, 1965.

Romney, C., "The Dixie Valley-Fairview Peak, Nevada, Earthquake of December 16, 1954—Seismic Waves," *Bulletin of the Seismological Society of America,* vol. 47, pp. 301–320, 1957.

Sherburne, R. W., Algermissen, S. T., and Harding, Samuel T., "The Hypocenter, Origin Time, and Magnitude of the Prince William Sound Earthquake of March 28, 1964," this volume.

Stauder, William, "The Alaska Earthquake of July 10, 1958: Seismic Studies," *Bulletin of the Seismological Society of America,* vol. 50, pp. 293–322, 1960.

Stauder, William and Bollinger, G. A., "The S-Wave Project for Focal Mechanism Studies: Earthquakes of 1962," *Bulletin of the Seismological Society of America,* vol. 54, pp. 2199–2208, 1964.

Stauder, William and Bollinger, G. A., "The Focal Mechanisms of the Alaska Earthquake of March 28, 1964, and of Its Aftershock Sequence," *Journal of Geophysical Research,* vol. 71, pp. 5283–5296, 1966.

Stauder, William, and Udias, Agustin, "S-Wave Studies of Earthquakes of the North Pacific, Part II," *Bulletin of the Seismological Society of America,* vol. 53, pp. 59–77, 1963.

Stevens, Anne E., "S-Wave Earthquake Mechanism Determination by S-Wave Data," *Bulletin of the Seismological Society of America,* vol. 54, pp. 457–474, 1964.

Stevens, Anne E., "S-Wave Earthquake Mechanism Equations," *Bulletin of the Seismological Society of America,* vol. 57, pp. 99–112, 1967.

Toksöz, M. Nafi, Ben-Menahem, Ari, and Harkrider, David G., "Source Mechanism of Alaska Earthquake from Long Period Seismic Surface Waves," (abstract), *Transactions of the American Geophysical Union,* vol. 46, p. 154, 1965.

Udias, Agustin, "A Least Squares Method for Earthquake Mechanism Determination Using S-Wave Data," *Bulletin of the Seismological Society of America,* vol. 54, pp. 2037–2047, 1964.

Udias, Agustin and Stauder, William, "Application of Numerical Method for S-Wave Focal Mechanism Determinations to Earthquakes of Kamchatka-Kurile Islands Region," *Bulletin of the Seismological Society of America,* vol. 54, pp. 2049–2065, 1964.

von Huene, Roland, Malloy, Richard J., Shor, George G., Jr., and St. Amand, Pierre, "Geologic Structures in the Aftershock Region of the 1964 Alaskan Earthquake," *Journal of Geophysical Research,* vol. 72, no. 14, pp. 3649–3660, 1967.

von Huene, Roland, Shor, George G., Jr., and Reimnitz, Erk, "Geological Interpretation of Seismic Profiles in Prince William Sound, Alaska," *Bulletin of the Geological Society of America,* vol. 78, pp. 259–268, 1967.

Woollard, G. P., Ostenso, N. A., Thiel, E., and Bonini, W. E., "Gravity Anomalies, Crustal Structure and Geology in Alaska," *Journal of Geophysical Research,* vol. 65, no. 3, pp. 1021–1037, 1960.

Wyss, Max and Brune, James N., "The Alaska Earthquake of 28 March 1964: A Complex Multiple Rupture," *Bulletin of the Seismological Society of America,* vol. 47, no. 5, pp. 1017–1024, 1967.

WILLIAM STAUDER
G. A. BOLLINGER*
SAINT LOUIS UNIVERSITY

Reprinted with minor changes from
Journal of Geophysical Research, Vol. 71, No. 22,
"The Focal Mechanism of the Alaska Earthquake of
March 28, 1964, and of its Aftershock Sequence"

The Focal Mechanism and Aftershock Sequence

Focal mechanisms have been determined for one preshock, for the main shock, and for more than 25 aftershocks of the Alaska earthquake of March 28, 1964. For the main shock a single nodal plane with a strike azimuth of 66°, dip 85° southeast, is determinable from the polarity of the P wave. This plane may be taken either as a plane normal to the fault motion (thrust faulting) or as the fault plane (dip-slip motion on a near-vertical plane). A combination of P wave first motion and S wave polarization data make possible the determination of both nodal planes in each shock studied of the aftershock sequence. One of these planes is near vertical and closely resembles the nodal plane of the main shock; the other dips 5° to 15° to the northwest or north. For earthquakes of the Kodiak Island region, the near-vertical plane has the same orientation as that of the main shock. For earthquakes to the east of Prince William Sound, this plane shows a systematic change in orientation corresponding to the change in trend of the tectonic features. Three earthquakes that have foci at increasing depths along the line of greatest flexure of the tectonic features differ from the others. The difference in character of these foci probably provides an important clue to the right interpretation of the motion in the main shock. Although the focal mechanism solutions for the shocks are subject to the same ambiguity of interpretation as that of the main shock, criteria which favor a thrust hypothesis are advanced from the interrelation of the foci. From dislocation theory it is shown that differential slip and/or a dipping thrust plane explain satisfactorily the observed vertical displacements at the surface.

INTRODUCTION

Considerable discussion has been occasioned concerning the character of the fault motion in the great Alaska earthquake of March 28, 1964. On the basis of field observations of tectonic deformations, especially of vertical movements in coastal areas, *Plafker* [1965] has proposed predominantly thrust motion on a low-angle thrust plane. *Press* [1965] and *Press and Jackson* [1965], by applying dislocation theory, have used the vertical surface movements associated with the earthquake to infer predominantly dip-slip motion on a near-vertical fault extending deep into the earth. Fault plane solutions (see discussion below) based on the polarity of the first motion of P waves are consistent with either interpretation.

In this paper we present focal mechanism solutions for as many as possible of the earthquakes associated with the main shock. We hope thereby to be able to infer in greater detail the character of the total fault motion and, if possible, of the motion in the main shock.

THE MAIN SHOCK

The main shock, of magnitude 8.4 to 8.6,

occurred on March 28, 1964, 03h 36m 12.7s UT. Its hypocenter, as published by the U. S. Coast and Geodetic Survey, was 61.05°N, 147.5°W, in the vicinity of Prince William Sound. In the determination the depth was restrained to 20 km, but in references to this earthquake the depth of focus is generally regarded as lying between 20 and 50 km. The waves generated by this earthquake were so large that only the first motion of P waves could be used in finding the body wave solution for the focal mechanism. The P wave first-motion data, however, yield a rather remarkable nodal plane determination. Although on short-period records the initial P wave is small and irregular for the first few seconds, on long-period records the P wave begins abruptly; the direction of first motion is unambiguous and the apparent period of the initial P wave is of the order of 40 to 60 sec.

We have read the polarity of the initial long-period P motion directly from the 70-mm microfilm copies of records from 71 WWSSN stations. The data so obtained form a coherent set—all are from similar instruments and the polarity has been read by the same interpreter. These, plus data from 10 stations of the Canadian

*Now with Virginia Polytechnic Institute.

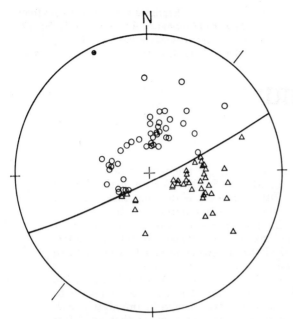

Fig. 1. Equal-area projection of the focal mechanism solution for the Alaska earthquake of March 28, 1964, based on first motion of P waves. Circles indicate compression; triangles indicate rarefaction.

network, form the basis of the focal mechanism solution presented in Figure 1.

The P wave data are clearly divided into two first-motion fields. Thus only one nodal plane is determinable. This plane has a strike azimuth of 66° and a dip 85° to the southeast. The second nodal plane, though not determined, is restricted by the data to have a dip varying from less than 25° to the northeast through 5° to the northwest to less than 60° to the southwest. Probably, on the basis of the aftershock data, the dip is to the northwest and is of only a few degrees. All of the 81 P wave first motions are consistent with the solution shown.

The solution presented in Figure 1 is in close agreement with that of *Algermissen* [1964] and with that of *Berg* [1965]. Berg proposes an orientation of the second nodal plane with a strike azimuth of 344° and a dip of 26° to the northeast, but his choice of this plane is based on readings at the single station Yellowknife and on the orthogonality criterion. In our opinion the second plane may be regarded as undetermined from the P wave data.

If the nodal plane of Figure 1 is taken as the fault plane, the motion was predominantly dip-slip on a near-vertical fault, the southeast side moving up relative to the northwest. In this case the fault would have the strike azimuth indicated, 66°. If the nodal plane is taken as normal to the motion, the fault would be predominantly of a thrust character, the north-

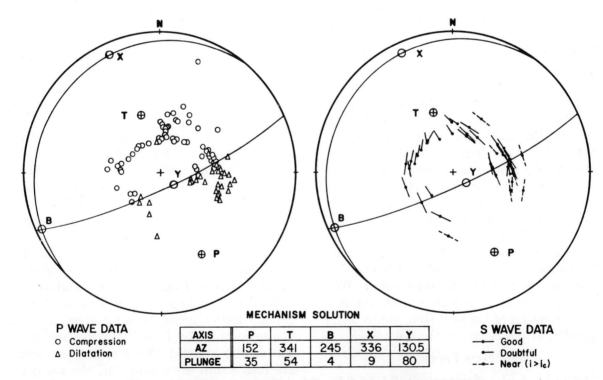

AXIS	P	T	B	X	Y
AZ	152	341	245	336	130.5
PLUNGE	35	54	4	9	80

MECHANISM SOLUTION

P WAVE DATA
o Compression
△ Dilatation

S WAVE DATA
—•— Good
—•- Doubtful
---•-- Near ($i > i_c$)

Fig. 2. Equal-area projection of the preshock of February 6, 1964.

TABLE 1. The Alaska Earthquake Sequence: Earthquakes Investigated and Focal Mechanism Determinations

No.	Date 1964	Origin h m s	Lat., N	Long., W	h, km	m_b	Plane 1 Strike Azimuth	Plane 1 Dip	Plane 2 Strike Azimuth	Plane 2 Dip	P Axis Trend, deg	P Axis Plunge, deg	T Axis Trend, deg	T Axis Plunge, deg	B Axis Trend, deg	B Axis Plunge, deg	S Data N	δ_e, deg	S_e, deg
A	Feb 6	13 07 25.2	55.7	155.8	33	5.8	66°	81°SE	40°	10°NW	153	36	341	54	246	5	49	9.9	12.5
M	Mar 28	03 36 12.7	61.05	147.5	20	8.5	66°	85°SE											
1	Mar 28	20 29 08.6	59.8	148.7	40	5.8	72°	85°SE	24°	7°NW	158	40	348	50	252	5	30	11.5	15.3
2	Mar 29	06 04 44.5	56.1	154.3	30	5.6	73°	80°SE	85°	10°N	165	35	340	55	73	3	40	11.3	14.0
3	Mar 29	16 40 57.9	59.7	147.0	15	5.8	333°	73°NE	333°	17°SW	63	27	243	63	333	0	38	13.4	17.1
4	Mar 30	02 18 06.3	59.9	152.9	25	5.6	67°	90°	337°	09°SW	148	45	345	44	247	9	35	12.3	14.3
5	Mar 30	07 09 34.0	59.9	145.7	15	5.6	310°	84°SW	275°	6°N	215	40	43	50	309	3	33	13.1	16.0
6	Mar 30	16 09 28.4	56.6	152.1	25	5.5	54°	87°SE	348°	8°W	137	42	331	47	233	7	47	10.1	12.8
7	Apr 3	22 33 42.2	61.6	147.6	40	5.7	76°	60°S	349°	85°W	37	25	299	16	179	59	42	14.9	17.0
8	Apr 4	04 34 56.9	60.3	146.5	5	5.0	279°	86°S	17°	30°W	164	34	36	41	277	30	22	16.4	19.0
9	Apr 4	08 40 29.8	56.5	152.6	15	5.0	35°	80°SE	359°	12°W	119	35	313	55	214	5	38	11.0	13.9
10	Apr 4	17 46 08.6	56.3	154.4	25	5.7	53°	80°SE	87°	12°N	148	35	315	55	54	06	55	13.2	17.5
11	Apr 5	01 22 13.3	56.2	153.5	25	5.4	65°	83°SE	83°	07°N	157	37	333	52	65	03	46	10.2	12.5
12	Apr 12	01 24 31.2	56.6	152.2	22	5.6	63°	83°SE	29°	08°NW	148	38	339	52	242	3	44	11.8	14.8
13	Apr 15	15 30 47.1	56.5	154.4	35	5.5	65°	85°SE	357°	12°W	145	39	347	48	244	12	39	15.9	19.0
14	Apr 16	19 26 57.4	56.4	152.9	30	5.5	64°	84°SE	19°	08°NW	149	40	339	50	243	5	47	13.1	16.2
15	Apr 17	04 49 30.5	56.4	152.9	25	5.3	63°	85°SE	27°	08°NW	148	37	339	52	242	3	41	14.7	17.4
16	Apr 20	11 56 41.6	61.4	147.3	30	5.7	21°	46°SE	312°	69°SW	357	47	251	15	148	39	33	15.3	20.4
17	May 6	15 26 35.5	56.7	152.1	15	5.4	68°	85°SE	21°	6°NW	153	39	343	50	247	4	35	13.6	17.0
18	May 12	18 16 41.9	56.6	152.4	10	5.3	57°	85°SE	355°	11°W	137	40	338	49	235	10	55	10.8	13.2
19	May 17	00 50 17.9	59.4	142.7	35	5.1	102°	80°S	329°	15°NE	201	34	360	54	104	10	43	13.4	16.3
20	Jun 29	07 21 32.8	62.7	152.1	33	5.6	41°	45°SE	74°	50°NW	328	04	228	73	59	17	14	9.5	11.7
21	Aug 2	08 36 16.9	56.2	149.9	31	5.4	70°	80°SE	307°	19°NE	322	52	173	33	74	15	30	20.8	27.1
22	Aug 24*	21 56 54.2	58.4	150.3	22	5.8	11°	38°E	71°	67°N	200	55	318	17	58	29	28	22.6	27.2
23	Sep 16*	01 50 34	60.0	147.1	29	5.5	24°	27°N	82°	75°S	155	27	20	54	256	21	17	8.2	10.9
24	Sep 27	15 50 54.7	56.6	152.0	27	5.4	60°	78°SE	35°	13°NW	144	33	339	57	239	4	25	16.9	21.7
	1965																		
25	Jun 23	11 09 15.3	56.6	152.6	36	5.7	52°	84°SE	1°	11°W	142	38	344	55	239	10	50	9.1	13.4
26	Sep 4	14 32 47.3	58.2	152.7	19	6.1	59°	85°SE	59°	5°NW	149	40	329	50	59	0	45	10.7	13.6
27	Dec 22	19 41 23.0	58.4	153.0	50	6.5	50°	85°SE	307°	20°NE	158	37	300	46	52	20	32	20.4	27.6

* Tentative solutions; not included in figures.

Notes: P axis is the axis of greatest compressive stress. T axis is the axis of least compressive stress. B axis is the null axis. N, number of station records used for S data.

west side riding over the southeast. Either hypothesis is completely in accord with the first-motion data.

PRESHOCK AND AFTERSHOCKS

Our interest was first drawn to the Alaska earthquake sequence when, in the course of routine procedures under the S Wave Project [see *Stauder and Bollinger*, 1964], the P wave first motion and S wave polarization were investigated for an earthquake which occurred southwest of the island of Kodiak on February 6, 1964, preceding the main shock by 7 weeks. The P wave first-motion data (see Figure 2) were found to be identical in distribution with that of the main shock of March 28. In this case S wave data of exceptional quality were also available. These latter make possible the full determination of the focal mechanism. The second nodal plane has a strike azimuth of 40° and dips 10° to the northwest.

The S wave polarization has been determined for this earthquake at 49 stations. Assuming a double-couple source, on which the above solution is based, the average error, δ_ϵ, of the S wave polarization at each station from that expected at that station for the solution of

Figure 2 is 9.9°. The standard deviation, S_ϵ, of the polarization from the expected value is 12.5°. These errors are exceptionally small and are comparable to the accuracy of measurement of the quantities involved.

In passing, we note that a single-couple solution corresponding to the P nodal plane of Figure 2 (in which case the nodal plane would be a plane normal to the motion) may also be obtained using S wave data alone. In this event the measures of error as defined above are $\delta_\epsilon = 15.0°$ and $S_\epsilon = 18.9°$. Similar results are obtained for the other earthquakes: the measures of error of the S wave data are notably smaller for the double-couple point source than for the single couple. This evidence is in keeping with previous experience and with all theoretical approaches to the mechanism problem. It would seem to confirm the assumption that, in general, a double-couple model for earthquakes is an equivalent point source representation of the focus.

Unfortunately, although both nodal planes are well determined for the earthquake of February 6, the ambiguity of interpretation noted above for the main shock applies equally well to this preshock. It is not resolvable by the P

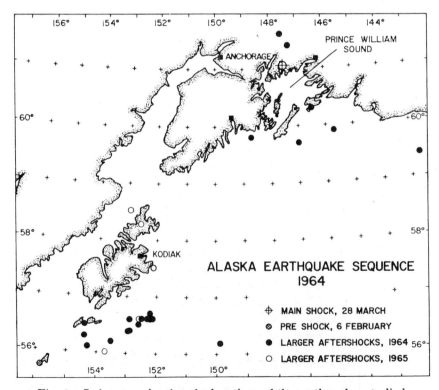

Fig. 3.   Index map showing the locations of the earthquakes studied.

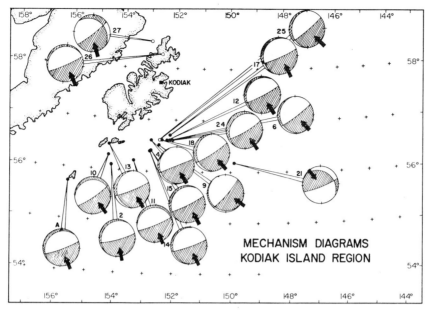

Fig. 4. Mechanism diagrams (stereographic projection) of earthquakes in the Kodiak Island region. Shaded areas represent rarefaction quadrants; arrows represent direction of P (pressure) axes.

and S wave data directly. The conflict of interpretation of vertical dip-slip motion versus overthrust, however, is more clearly emphasized by the fact that the second nodal plane is in this instance well determined and corresponds to the thrust plane hypothesized by Plafker.

After this discovery of the close parallelism between the main shock and the large preshock, an effort was made to investigate as many as possible of the aftershocks. Altogether, in addition to the preshock of February 6, twenty-four aftershocks ranging in magnitude from $5.0 < m_b < 5.8$, occurring between March 28 and September 27, 1964, have been investigated and focal mechanism solutions obtained. Five other shocks which occurred between June 23, 1965, and April 22, 1966, are also under investigation and our findings are partially reported here.

Identification of all shocks studied, including the preshock and the main shock, are given in Table 1. Hypocenters and magnitudes are those published by the U. S. Coast and Geodetic Survey. At our request personnel of the USCGS Washington Science Center have kindly recomputed the hypocenters. The revised hypocenters provide interesting information on focal depth to be considered below, but the epicentral coordinates agree so closely with those originally published that the latter are retained in Table 1. The locations of the earthquakes are further

shown on the index map (Figure 3). One epicenter, that of June 29, 1964, is off the map.

The larger aftershocks cluster, as is not infrequent in the aftershock sequences of large earthquakes, at either end of the region over which the epicenters of the sequence are distributed. One group is located near Kodiak Island, the other in the Prince William Sound, implying, very likely, rupture propagation from northeast to southwest.

In our investigation the focal mechanism determinations for the shocks to the southwest were found to differ systematically from those for earthquakes to the northeast. A convenient reason over and above geographic separation is thereby provided for discussing the mechanism of the two groups separately.

AFTERSHOCKS OF KODIAK ISLAND REGION

The focal mechanism determinations for the earthquakes concentrated in the region near Kodiak Island are all remarkably similar. For purposes of comparison, and to illustrate the similarity of the solutions of this group, all solutions are indicated by the mechanism diagrams (stereographic projections) displayed in Figure 4. The focal mechanism of the earthquake of February 6, 1964 (see Figure 2), is truly representative of the source mechanism for all these shocks. In all cases only one steeply

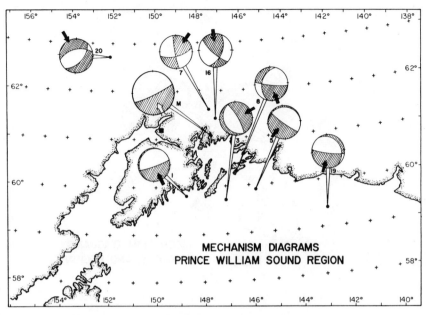

Fig. 5. Mechanism diagrams of earthquakes in the Prince William Sound region. Shaded areas and arrows as in Figure 4.

dipping nodal plane of P is determinable from the P wave first-motion data. The S wave data make possible in each instance the determination of the second nodal plane. The dip of this plane is very slight—only 5° to 14° in a direction usually west or northwest. Although the strike determined for this plane varies considerably from shock to shock, this effect may be more apparent than real; in the case of a nearly horizontal plane, small errors in the observations give rise to large variation in strike but only small variation in the spatial orientation of the plane.

The first-motion field for all these shocks consists of rarefactions on the southwest side of the near-vertical plane and of compressions on the northwest. The sole exception is earthquake 21. For this shock the first-motion field is exactly the reverse of the general rule. This latter shock is separated in space from the others. Its epicenter is located on the seaward side of the Aleutian Island trench, whereas the epicenters of all the remaining shocks of this group are on the landward side of the trench.

In addition to the concentration of aftershocks south of Kodiak Island, only two aftershocks of sufficient magnitude for a focal mechanism determination have occurred in the more central part of the assumed fault region. The mechanism solutions for these shocks, earthquakes 26 and 27, are also indicated in Figure 4; both occurred late in the aftershock sequence. The first is of normal focal depth. Its focal mechanism solution is well determined, as is evidenced by the measures of error of the S wave data given in Table 1, and is identical with those of the aftershocks at the southwest extremity of the aftershock region. The second had a focal depth of 60–65 km determined by exceptionally clear $pP - P$ intervals of 14–15 sec and $sP - P$ intervals of 19–20 sec. The polarities of the pP arrivals can be read without ambiguity except at stations corresponding (for the mechanism shown in the figure) to a nodal plane for pP, and they serve to confirm the position of the steeply dipping nodal plane. For some reason the S wave particle motions observed at stations in the United States for this earthquake are particularly irregular. This may be due to a combination of effects such as the influence of the depth of focus, irregular geometric spreading of the waves along the paths in question, epicentral distance unfavorable for determining the polarization of S waves, and relatively rapid spatial variation of polarization of S waves at stations in the United States corresponding to the solution shown. The S wave data for this earthquake from other regions are good. The second nodal plane is therefore less well determined than for other earthquakes of the sequence, but the solution indicated agrees satisfactorily with those for the earthquakes to the south of Kodiak Island.

The mechanism solutions for earthquakes 26 and 27 suggest that the motion at the source in aftershocks in the central region (and by inference the motion along the entire northeast-southwest extent of the fault in the main shock) corresponds to the motion determined for the aftershocks at the southwest extremity of the zone active in the sequence. Since the diagrams in Figure 4 represent the lower half of the focal sphere, the pressure axis is oriented approximately normal to the trend of the tectonic features and is inclined upward from the seaward side at an angle from the vertical of about 50°.

PRINCE WILLIAM SOUND REGION

For the earthquakes in the Prince William Sound region (Figure 5), as for those of the Kodiak Island region and for the main shock, only a single steeply dipping nodal plane is determinable from the P wave first-motion data. The second nodal plane has been determined by the S wave polarization data. Examination of the S wave measures of error for these shocks (Table 1) shows that our solutions are in good agreement with the data.

At first sight the mechanisms for this group of earthquakes do not seem to manifest the same uniformity as those for the Kodiak Island group. However, attention is called to the

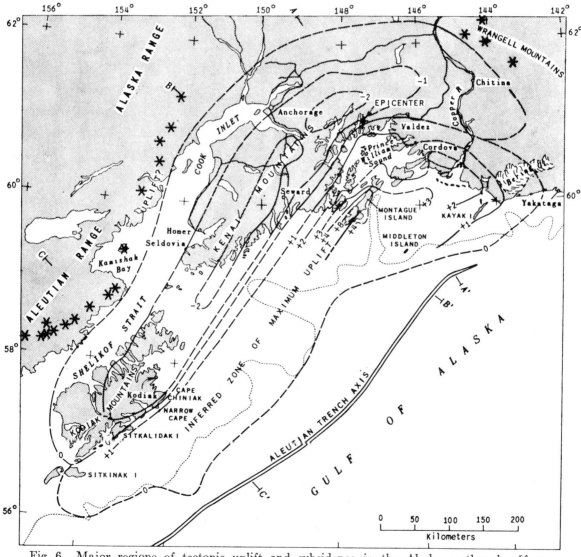

Fig. 6. Major regions of tectonic uplift and subsidence in the Alaska earthquake [from *Plafker, 1965*].

[241]

mechanism diagrams for earthquakes 1, 8, 5, and 19. For these shocks the orientation of the steeply dipping nodal plane varies systematically and parallels, more or less, the local trend of the tectonic structure. The fault motion corresponds either to dip-slip motion on an east-west trending fault or to an overthrust, the landward side moving south or south-southwest over the oceanic side.

Whether dip-slip or thrust faulting be the correct interpretation, the change in trend of the steeply dipping nodal plane which is here documented for aftershocks to the east of Prince William Sound is evidence of a change in trend of the fracture system in the same region. The corresponding trends of the fracture system and of the regional tectonics both correspond more or less to the configuration of the regions of

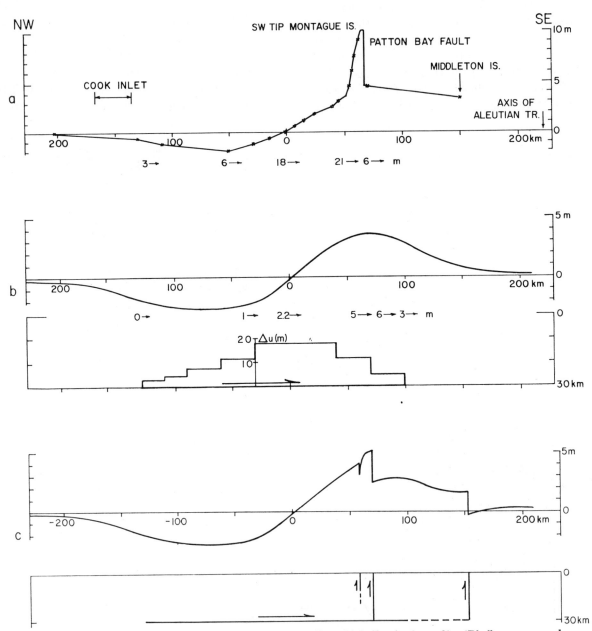

Fig. 7. Tectonic displacements of the free surface. (a) Revised profile (Plafker, personal communication) of observed uplift and subsidence along line BB' of Figure 6. (b) Computed vertical surface motion u_3, for differential slip Δu, for model indicated below profile: horizontal fault, $h = 30$ km, $W = 230$ km, $2L = 600$ km. Arrows beneath the profile represent the horizontal surface motion. (c) Superposition on 7b of vertical surface motion due to vertical faults, as indicated on the model below the profile.

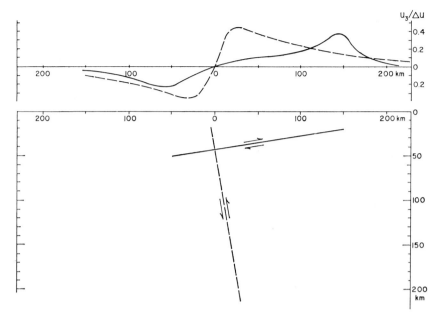

Fig. 8. Ratio of computed vertical surface motion u_3 to slip motion Δu on a dipping fault [*Savage and Hastie*, 1966]. Model 1 (dashed line): $h = 18$ km, $W = 200$ km, $2L = 800$ km $\delta = 80°$. Model 2 (solid line): $h = 20$ km, $W = 200$ km, $2L = 600$ km, $\delta = 9°$.

uplift and subsidence illustrated in Figure 6. The extent of the vertical displacements, which are too large for the magnitudes of the aftershocks, and the phenomena reported by witnesses indicate that most of the permanent vertical displacements occurred during the major shock. Assuming that the motion in the aftershocks is related to that of the main shock, the implication of the focal mechanism solutions for aftershocks 1, 8, 5, and 19 is that the direction of motion in the main shock differed somewhat in the region to the east of Prince William Sound from the direction of motion to the southwest of Prince William Sound.

Finally, attention is called to earthquakes 3, 16, 7, and 20.[1] The epicenters of these shocks are distributed along the line of greatest flexure of the tectonic structure (see Figure 6), and the foci are at increasing depths (based on pP readings) from Montague Island north and north-northwest toward Prince William Sound and into the interior. The corresponding focal mechanisms, included among those presented in Figure 5, differ notably from those of the earth-

quakes considered to this point. The characteristics of these shocks are most likely related to the difference in motion at the focus for earthquakes whose epicenters are distributed along the southwest-trending structures (west of 148°W) as opposed to those distributed along the east-west trending structures (east of 148°W).

RELATION TO DISLOCATION THEORY

Entirely independent of the focal mechanism solutions presented here, a primary evidence for the character of the ground motion in the Alaska earthquake is found in the observations of tectonic uplift and subsidence (Figures 6 and 7a) and of horizontal movement. These are documented by *Grantz et al.* [1964], *Malloy* [1964], *Plafker* [1965], *Plafker and Mayo* [1965], and *Whitten* [1965].

In the introduction to this paper we mentioned the dual interpretation of these observations. On the basis of field investigations, *Plafker* [1965] has proposed thrust faulting on a low-angle thrust plane. On the other hand, *Press and Jackson* [1965] and *Press* [1965] have proposed dip-slip motion on a near-vertical fault. These latter authors applied dislocation theory to demonstrate that the observed uplift and subsidence can be explained by the fault mo-

---

[1] Earthquake 20 is included tentatively. It is relatively removed from the general aftershock region and may represent only the normal seismic activity of the region and may not be directly related to the main sequence.

tion they suggest. To account for the extent of the vertical displacements at distances normal to the fault, they require the fault to break to depths of 100 to 200 km; to account for the absence of a discontinuity in vertical displacement at the earth's surface along the trace of a fault, they require the fault break to extend no nearer to the surface than 15 to 20 km. The magnitude of the uplift and subsidence requires a dip-slip motion of 6 to 9 meters.

More recently, *Savage and Hastie* [1966] have reviewed the implications of the vertical displacements. In particular they have examined quantitatively the surface deformation as-

The model of Savage and Hastie, as also that of Press, requires constant slip over the whole of the fault surface, right up to the edge of the fault. As a small further contribution, we would like to consider an approximation to differential movement in the direction of slip. For this we utilize case (1-3) in section 2-2 in *Maruyama* [1964]. The approximation to differential movement is obtained by allowing the displacement on the fault, Δu, to vary piecewise along the direction of slip. For the case of interest—that is, for displacements in the x_1 direction on a horizontal fault—Maruyama's equations give

$$u_3 = -\frac{Lh^2}{\pi}\left\{\frac{\Delta u_1}{[(x_1 - a_1)^2 + h^2][(x_1 - a_1)^2 + L^2 + h^2]^{1/2}}\right.$$

$$+ \sum_{i=2}^{n-1}\frac{\Delta u_i - \Delta u_{i-1}}{[(x_1 - a_i)^2 + h^2][(x_1 - a_i)^2 + L^2 + h^2]^{1/2}}$$

$$\left. - \frac{\Delta u_{n-1}}{[(x_1 - a_n)^2 + h^2][(x_1 - a_n)^2 + L^2 + h^2]^{1/2}}\right\}$$

sociated with the thrust faulting of the type proposed by Plafker. Following *Maruyama* [1964], they also have applied dislocation theory. In so doing, however, they have advanced the treatment of the problem by concerning themselves with fault surfaces having reasonable angles of dip. The inclusion of the dip of the fault plane is more realistic, and it also accounts for the asymmetry observed in surface displacements either side of the line of zero displacement.

Two models are considered by Savage and Hastie: (1) an adaptation of Press's model to include the dip of the fault plane and (2) thrust faulting. The two models, and the corresponding profiles of vertical surface motion, are indicated in Figure 8. The profiles are for a fault that begins at a depth h from the free surface, extends downward a distance W into the earth, has a length $2L$, and has a dip δ. The x_2 axis is chosen parallel to the strike of the fault; the x_1 axis is horizontal and normal to the fault. The profiles of Figure 8 are in the plane $x_2 = 0$.

Savage and Hastie comment that the first model places the zone of maximum subsidence too close to the zone of maximum uplift. In the second model a value of fault-slip $\Delta u \approx 10$ meters will yield vertical displacements that approximate those observed.

where a_i are the end points of segments of width $W_i = a_{i+1} - a_i$, the total width $W = \sum_{i=1}^{n-1}W_i$, and Δu_i is the slip in the x_1 direction in the interval $a_i < x_1 < a_{i+1}$. The horizontal fault is chosen to be symmetric about the plane $x_2 = 0$, slip occurs in the direction of the width, chosen along the x_1 axis, and h is the depth of the fault. The equation gives the vertical displacement u_3 at the surface along the profile $x_2 = 0$. If Δu_i varies with x_1 in the manner indicated in the lower part of Figure 7b, the vertical displacement profile of the upper part of Figure 7b is obtained. Like the dip of the fault, differential motion on the fault introduces asymmetry in the vertical surface displacements.

Differential slip of the form proposed seems reasonable because it is generally agreed that the surface faulting on Montague Island is a secondary effect. Plafker has further suggested in personal conversation that uplift of Middleton Island and inferred uplift of the region between Montague and Middleton may be due to imbricate faulting. Breaking upward to the surface along the shallowing and leading edge of the fault, or, even more so, imbricate faulting, would likely promote differential motion on the thrust plane.

To carry the consideration one step further, we show in Figure 7c the effect of superposing on the displacements of Figure 7b the vertical motion due to vertical faults corresponding to the surface fractures which were observed on Montague Island and which may be hypothesized for Middleton Island. Although the superposition of Figure 7b is entirely in keeping with dislocation theory, that of 7c is only qualitative; we are no longer considering a dislocation in a semi-infinite medium, but rather in a slab in frictional contact with another surface. The figure, however, is suggestive.

The two possible fault surfaces and fault motions indicated in the lower part of Figure 8 correspond to a double-couple model of the focus. *Savage and Hastie* [1966] rightly comment that in the double-couple representation the fault plane cannot be distinguished from the auxiliary plane and that the radiation of seismic waves will be the same for either orientation of the fault. Savage and Hastie further comment that, since for the Alaska earthquake the direction of propagation is along the null axis, no distinction between the two fault orientations can be made on the basis of the direction of rupture propagation inferred from a surface wave solution. Similarly, far-field observations noted in this earthquake can be equally explained by either model.

It would seem that by a combination of differential slip motion and a shallowly dipping thrust plane the observed tectonic surface displacements can be closely approximated. The thrust model is entirely in keeping with dislocation theory. We are inclined to agree with Savage and Hastie that a thrust model (their model 3, the model of Figure 7b above, or a combination of these two) is the preferred model. To the extent, however, that the observational data are not adequate to distinguish between the model of Plafker and that of Press, we are also in agreement with Savage and Hastie that criteria other than those furnished by dislocation theory are required.

OTHER EVIDENCE FAVORING THRUST FAULTING

Arguments favoring the overthrust model have been carefully advanced by *Plafker* [1965] in his interpretation of the field observations. In addition to the arguments he has proposed, we wish to bring forward evidence favoring the thrust hypothesis from the mechanism solutions presented here. In doing so we proceed with

caution, being ourselves aware and wishing the reader to bear in mind that, taken individually, the focal mechanism determination for each of the earthquakes of this sequence is subject to the same ambiguity as that of the main shock. Although the focal mechanism solutions taken individually are open to interpretation either as thrust faulting or as dip-slip motion on a near-vertical fault, the following considerations are advanced which in our opinion favor the thrust hypothesis.

1. *The P nodal plane of the main shock.* The single P nodal plane of the main shock is exceptionally well determined. The strike azimuth of this plane is 66°, whereas the tectonic trend of the region, as well as the trend of the region over which the aftershocks are distributed, is about azimuth 35°. More precisely, the trend of the contour of zero uplift (see Figure 6) has this same orientation, azimuth 35°. Whatever the dip of the fault, this direction surely corresponds to the strike of the major part of the fault. It does not seem possible, then, that the steeply dipping P nodal plane with strike azimuth 66° can represent the fault plane. Nor is it likely that the P nodal plane represents only a 'first motion' along some initial localized part of the fault; the P waves used in the solution were of a period varying from 40 to 60 sec. The P waveform on the seismograms is not that of the 'impulse response' of the instrument, and hence the long-period trace motion on records represents true ground motion. By implication the motion at the source involved a movement of mass of large proportion and of some time duration. We are currently investigating this additional aspect of the problem.

2. *The P nodal planes of the aftershocks.* A similar argument applies to the aftershocks. For the most part the steeply dipping P nodal planes of the mechanism solutions for these earthquakes do not follow the strike of the geologic features any more closely than that of the main shock. To assume that these planes are the fault planes would imply a sequence of en echelon faults oblique to the trend of the fault zone. We prefer to regard the near-vertical nodal plane to represent the auxiliary plane and the consistent orientation of this plane to indicate a uniform direction of tectonic motion.

3. *The spatial distribution of foci.* The

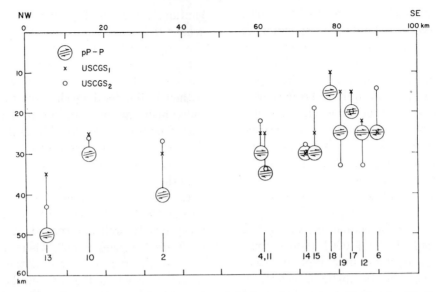

Fig. 9. Projection of depths of focus and nodal plane for earthquakes in the Kodiak Island region. Plane of projection is a vertical section in a line along azimuth 130° through the southern tip of Kodiak Island.

spatial distribution of aftershock hypocenters of all magnitudes has been investigated by others. Here we shall be concerned only with the foci under examination. Primary attention is directed to the earthquakes of the Kodiak Island region. Three different determinations of focal depth may be considered: (a) those originally published by the USCGS, (b) the revised hypocenters computed by the USCGS by request for the preparation of this paper, and (c) focal depths based on pP readings from station bulletins. In Figure 9 these focal depths are projected onto a vertical section. The plane of projection passes through the southern tip of Kodiak Island and is aligned along azimuth 130°, that is, normal to the trend of the regional tectonic features. The motion diagram symbols in the figure represent the nodal plane and direction of thrust projected onto the plane of projection at the $pP - P$ focal depth. The other focal depths are indicated by the symbols designated. The spatial distribution of foci and the corresponding motions are seen to conform well to the hypothesis of overthrust on a shallowly dipping thrust plane.

4. *The mechanisms and foci of shocks 3, 16, and 7.* The mechanisms of shocks 3, 16, and 7 differ from those of the other earthquakes studied. The foci of these earthquakes lie along a line near the region of greatest flexure of the tectonic features. Their foci, based on $pP - P$

data, are also progressively deeper (20, 60, and 65 km, respectively) with distance inland. Both the peculiarity of mechanism of these three shocks and their spatial distribution seem to be accounted for by their situation in a region of 'pinch' for an overthrust of the character here proposed. For earthquake 3, which is shallow and near the leading edge of the thrust sheet, the P axis is parallel to the trend of the tectonic features; for foci 16 and 7, which are deep and on the inland extreme of the thrust plane and possibly situated in the underthrust block, the T axis is parallel to the trend of the tectonic features and the P axis is in the direction of thrust.

In addition to the above, two other points of evidence are worthy of mention. First, Plafker's revised profile, shown in Figure 7a, includes an indication of the horizontal surface displacements found in triangulation measurements. Although the control on these measurements is not as accurate as that for the vertical displacements, the very magnitude of the numbers implies that horizontal surface displacements were notable. For comparison we have computed the horizontal displacements, u_1, for the model of Figure 7b; these are indicated by the arrows immediately below the profile of the vertical displacement. The computations do not include the effect of a fault breaking to the surface or of imbrication.

Second, a point of discussion has centered around the asymmetry of the vertical uplift and the greater volume of rock that was uplifted along the profile of Figure 7a as opposed to the subsidence. This is partially explained by the dip of the thrust plane. Another factor is the possibility that the uplift in the vicinity of Montague Island is the effect of motion along the profile BB' of Figure 6 and also of motion along a north-south profile, corresponding to the change in trend of the thrust plane to the east of Prince William Sound.

CONCLUSIONS

This paper has made the following contributions to the understanding of the Alaska earthquake of March 28, 1964.

First, by consideration of the focal mechanism of one preshock, the main shock, and more than 25 aftershocks, we have illustrated the uniformity of motion in the entire earthquake sequence and have indicated a systematic change in the fracture system corresponding to the change in trend of the tectonic features.

Second, by the use of polarization data of shear waves we have removed the indeterminacy of the second nodal plane of the P wave first-motion solutions and have demonstrated that the second nodal plane, at least in the aftershock sequence, corresponds to the thrust plane of Plafker's hypothesis.

Third, by an application of dislocation theory, we show that differential motion along a horizontal fault produces asymmetric vertical surface displacements similar to those observed and suggest that a combination of differential slip and a dipping thrust plane allows an arbitrarily close approximation to the surface observations.

Fourth, we have advanced criteria, over and above dislocation theory and the interpretation by Plafker of the field studies, which favor the hypothesis of thrust faulting. These criteria follow from a consideration of the results of the mechanism solutions taken as a group.

Thus, on the basis of the fault plane solutions, except for earthquakes 3, 16, and 7, the motion at the source of the great Alaska earthquake and of its aftershocks may, taken individually, be almost entirely of a reverse character on a steeply dipping fault, the seaward side moving up relative to the landward side, or the motion may be of an overthrust character, the land side moving over the seaward side at azimuth 155° in the Kodiak Island region southwest of Prince William Sound or at 190° to 195° in the region to the east of Prince William Sound.

On the basis of the fault plane solutions considered in relation to one another, however, in the former case the faulting follows a sinuous path roughly paralleling the curving trend of the tectonic features and is possibly en echelon in character. In the latter case the thrust plane has a dip of only about 10° to the northwest or north—that is, under the continent, and the tectonic motion consists of a thrust of the continent over the ocean, the direction of thrust varying with the change in trend of the tectonic features. In our opinion the evidence here and elsewhere presented favors the thrust hypothesis.

Notice. A report is available [*Stauder and Bollinger*, 1966] containing a listing of all the data on which the mechanism solutions given in Table 1 are based. The report also contains a graphical presentation on an equal-area projection of the data for each solution, the mechanism diagram, and a discussion of the factors relevant to individual solutions.

Acknowledgments. This research was supported by the Air Force Cambridge Research Laboratories, contract AF 19(628)-5100, and by the Air Force Office of Scientific Research, grant AF-AFOSR 62-458, as part of the Advanced Research Projects Agency's Project Vela-Uniform.

REFERENCES

Algermissen, S. T., Seismological investigation of the Prince William Sound earthquake and aftershocks (abstract), *Trans. Am. Geophys. Union, 45,* 633, 1964.

Berg, E., The Alaska earthquake, its location and seismic setting, in *Science in Alaska, 1964: Proc. Alaskan Sci. Conf., 15th, College, Alaska, Aug. 31–Sept. 4, 1964,* pp. 218–232, College, Alaska, Division, American Association for the Advancement of Science, 1965.

Grantz, A., G. Plafker, and R. Kachadoorian, Alaska's Good Friday earthquake, March 27, 1964, *U. S. Geol. Surv. Circ. 491,* 1964.

Malloy, R. J., Crustal uplift southwest of Montague Island, Alaska, *Science, 146,* 1048–1049, 1964.

Maruyama, T., Statical elastic dislocations in an infinite and semi-infinite medium, *Bull. Earthquake Res. Inst., Tokyo Univ., 42,* 289–368, 1964.

Miller, D. J., T. G. Payne, and G. Gryc, Geology of possible petroleum provinces in Alaska, *U. S. Geol. Surv. Bull. 1094,* 1959.

Plafker, G., Tectonic deformation associated with the 1964 Alaska earthquake, *Science, 148,* 1675–1687, 1965.

Plafker, G., and L. R. Mayo, Tectonic deformation, subaqueous slides and destructive waves associated with the Alaskan March 27, 1964 earthquake: an interim geologic evaluation, *U. S. Geol. Surv. Open-file Rept.,* 1965.

Press, F., Displacements, strains, and tilts at teleseismic distances, *J. Geophys. Res., 70,* 2395–2412, 1965.

Press, F., and D. Jackson, Alaska earthquake, 27 March 1964: vertical extent of faulting and elastic strain energy release, *Science, 147,* 867–868, 1965.

Savage, J. C., and L. M. Hastie, Surface deformation associated with dip-slip faulting, *J. Geophys. Res., 71*(20), 1966.

Stauder, W., and G. A. Bollinger, The *S*-wave project for focal mechanism studies: earthquakes of 1962, *Bull. Seismol. Soc. Am., 54,* 2199–2208, 1964.

Stauder, W., and G. A. Bollinger, The *S*-wave project for focal mechanism studies: the Alaska earthquake sequence of 1964, Sci. Rept. prepared for Air Force Cambridge Research Laboratories, OAR, under contract AF19(628)-5100 for ARPA Project Vela-Uniform, AFCRL 66-572, 1966.

Whitten, C. A., Crustal movements associated with the Alaskan earthquake (abstract), *Trans. Am. Geophys. Union, 45,* 633, 1964.

(Received July 7, 1966.)

GEORGE PARARAS-CARAYANNIS*

UNIVERSITY OF HAWAII

Reprinted with minor changes from
Pacific Science, Vol. 21, No. 3,
"A Study of the Source Mechanism of the Alaska Earthquake and
Tsunami of March 27, 1964: Part I, Water Waves"

Source Mechanism of the Water Waves Produced

ABSTRACT: The geologic history and the general geomorphology of the area affected by the March 27, 1964 Alaska earthquake are given. The tsunami-generating area is determined and the extent of crustal displacement and the limits of the areas of subsidence and uplift, as revealed by geologic evidence, are discussed. The dimensions of this tsunami-generating area, its volume of crustal displacement, and the energy associated with the tsunami are calculated. Wave activity within and outside the generating area and the possible generating mechanisms for the tsunami are discussed. A wave refraction diagram of the Alaska tsunami for the north Pacific Ocean area is presented in Figure 6.

THE ALEUTIAN ISLAND ARC and the Aleutian Trench extend for 2800 km from Kamchatka to south-central Alaska along remarkably smooth curves which are convex toward the south (Fig. 1). The Arc forms the Alaska Peninsula and, according to Wilson (1954), intersects, north of Cook Inlet, a second tectonic arc that extends northward from the vicinity of the Wrangell Mountains. However, Plafker (1965) regards this second segment as a continuation of the Aleutian Arc. Where the trench impinges on Alaska it loses its identity, although an offshore range of seamounts suggests it may once have extended around to the south to parallel the continental slope, as postulated by Menard and Dietz (1951). Concavity in the former shape of the trench on its eastern segment is also suggested by the sedimentary arc defined by Wilson (1954), which embraces Kodiak Island and the Kenai Peninsula. As shown by Wilson, such concavity is to be expected where two arcs meet at an acute angle, as is well exemplified where the Aleutian and Kuril-Kamchatka arcs intersect. It is also quite possible that large horizontal movements of crustal blocks have helped to change the shape of the Trench and Arc on their eastern segments. However, no such evidence was found in a field study following the Good Friday earthquake (Berg et al., 1971).

*Now with the Coastal Engineering Research Center, Washington, D.C.

The nature of the termination of the eastern segment of the Aleutian Trench is obscured by thick sediments washed in from the continental shelf against which it abuts offshore from Cape Suckling. The sediments are of geosynclinal-dimensions in the sedimentary arc on Kodiak Island (Menard and Dietz, 1951) and as shown by drilling on the Kenai Peninsula. Woollard et al. (1960) show there is geophysical evidence for at least 7 km of sediments in Cook Inlet, a graben separating the primary arc from the offshore sedimentary arc. Sediment is about 2 km thick off Kodiak Island along the Aleutian Trench, thinning out to about 0.7 km south of Unimak Island in the deep water area, according to seismic measurements by Shor (1962).

THE GENERATING AREA OF THE ALASKA TSUNAMI

According to Van Dorn (1965), the tectonic dislocations associated with the Alaska earthquake of March 27, 1964 ranged over a distance of 800 km, from the upper portion of Prince William Sound to southwest of the Trinity Islands. The dislocations follow a dipole pattern of positive and negative displacements on either side of a zero-line which, intersecting the east coast of Kodiak Island, continues northeast to the western side of Prince William Sound. There, changing direction, it

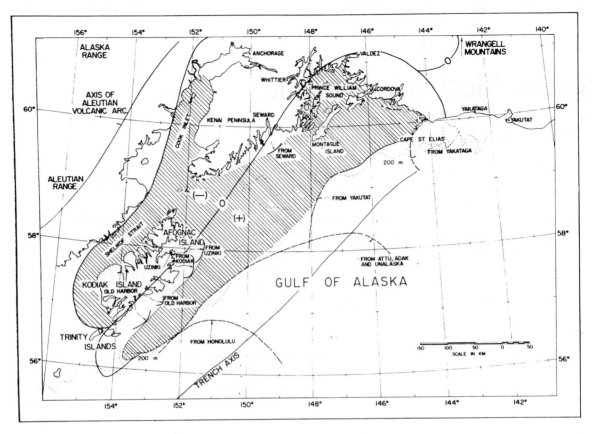

FIG. 1. Generating area of the Alaska tsunami. *Crosshatched area* indicates (−) area of subsidence and (+) area of uplift. *Heavy dashed lines* indicate the backward-refracted wave fronts. *Solid line marked by a zero* is the axis of rotation (no elevation change). *Other solid lines* indicate tectonic axes.

runs east along the upper part of the sound. The line roughly parallels the Aleutian Trench axis and separates the Kodiak geosyncline from the shelf geanticline.

The areas north and west of this line have undergone negative elevation changes, whereas the east and south underwent positive changes. An extensive pattern of positive surface dislocations under the sea is suspected to lie east of the island of Kodiak and along the continental shelf bordering the Gulf of Alaska. The extent of these dislocations still needs to be confirmed by detailed bathymetric surveys of the area, although large positive displacements have been observed as far south as Middleton Island and southwest to Sitkinak Island. Wave refraction studies, described here, also strongly indicated that the tsunami-generating area was mainly in the belt of uplift and included a large segment of the continental shelf and slope.

The zone between the known areas of tec-

tonic uplift closely corresponds to a major crustal fault defined by crustal seismic measurements conducted by the Department of Terrestrial Magnetism of the Carnegie Institution of Washington (Woollard et al., 1960). In view of the shallowness of the earthquake (20 km), it was concluded that the crustal dislocations occurred alongside a zone of tilting or a surface rupture (Grantz et al., 1964), but a survey of the area failed to identify such a feature. The focal depth corresponds, however, to the base of the granitic layer defined by Woollard's analysis of the crustal measurements made by the Carnegie Institution.

The total area of tectonic displacements associated with the Alaska earthquake of March 27, 1964 is estimated to be approximately 215,000 km². This is the largest area known to be associated with a single earthquake within historic time.

The magnitude of the Alaska earthquake was estimated to be from 8.4 to 8.75, which is greater than the 1906 San Francisco earthquake (8.3), and equal to or greater than the 1960 Chile earthquake (8.4). The epicenter of the earthquake was at 61.05°N, 147.7°W (USCGS, 1964), near the east shore of Unakwik Inlet in northern Prince William Sound.

Geological investigations have defined the land areas affected by the earthquake. To the east, the zone of deformation appears to die out between the Bering Glacier and Cape Yakataga. The northwestern limit of tectonic changes extends at least to the west side of Shelikof Strait and Cook Inlet (Plafker, 1965). The north inland limit is known only along the highway connecting Valdez and Fairbanks; it appears to extend in a northeasterly direction to the vicinity of the Wrangell Mountains, and quite possibly into the Alaska Range.

The area of uplift covers about 105,000 km² and extends from southern Kodiak Island northeast to Prince William Sound. It includes the southern and eastern parts of Prince William Sound, the coastal area as far east as the Bering Glacier, and the continental shelf and part of the slope to a depth contour of approximately 200 m. The maximum uplift on land was 10 m at the southwest end of Montague Island, but is suspected to have been considerably more offshore. Uplift also occurred along the extreme southeastern coasts of Kodiak Island and Sitkalidak Island, and part or all of Sitkinak Island. The maximum measured uplift of Sitkalidak Island was 0.4 m. The estimated uplift of Sitkinak Island was from 0.35 to 0.65 m and possibly as much as 1.5 m (Plafker, 1965).

The area that subsided included the northern and western parts of Prince William Sound, the western segment of the Chugach Mountains, portions of the lowlands north of them, most of the Kenai Peninsula, and almost all of the Kodiak Island group. This area of subsidence covers approximately 110,000 km², and is 800 km long and 150 km wide. Plafker (1965) estimates that the volume of crust that has been depressed below its pre-earthquake level is about 115 km³.

The seaward limits of the earthquake and the tsunami-generating area were determined by means of a series of refraction diagrams based on Snell's Law of Refraction using the velocity equation for shallow water waves, $C = \sqrt{gd}$.

Such a method of preparing refraction diagrams has shown good results, especially if carried out on large-scale charts with detailed bathymetry (Johnson, O'Brien, and Isaacs, 1948).

In constructing the refraction diagrams for the Alaska tsunami, the marigrams of different tide gauge stations around the Pacific were consulted and the total travel time of the first wave at each station was determined. Then refraction diagrams were constructed toward the earthquake area from each tide gauge station in lengths of time equal to the calculated travel time for that station. It was assumed that the last wave front in each refraction diagram would correspond to a point on the boundary of the generating area, and if enough refracted wave fronts from different stations were plotted, an envelope defining the tsunami-generating area could be drawn.

Wave fronts were refracted from Yakatat, Cape Yakataga, Seward, Uzinki, Kodiak, Old Harbor, Unalaska, Adak, Attu, and Honolulu. The last front of each of the refracted waves is shown by a heavy dashed line in Figure 1. The seaward boundary of the generating area is near the 200-m depth contour which defines the edge of the continental shelf. Maximum displacement of the ocean floor occurred along the continental shelf, from an area southeast of Kodiak Island, to an area close to Cape St. Elias south of the island of Kayak (Fig. 1). Geologic evidence, however, has shown positive land displacements as far north as Cape Suckling and as far east as the Bering Glacier. It is quite probable, therefore, that the tsunami-generating area extended farther to the northeast, although waves generated in such shallow water would reach tide gauges much later and their origin would not be identifiable.

Unfortunately, this same wave refraction technique could not be used to define the northern and western boundaries of the main tsunami-generating area, because conditions in Prince William Sound and elsewhere along the coast of Alaska were further complicated by local tsunamis, oscillations, and surge. In addition, no tide gauge stations were operating in the area, and personal accounts were conflicting as to arrival times of the different waves.

The northward limit is assumed to be restricted by the land boundaries, and the western limit to extend to the west side of Shelikof Strait and Cook Inlet.

In estimating the travel time of the tsunami, corrections were made for the delay at the island of Kodiak in the arrival of the ground shocks from Prince William Sound. These corrections ranged from 1 minute to 6 minutes and were based on the fact that the Navy Weather Central on the island of Kodiak listed the time of the principal shock in Prince William Sound as 6 minutes later than the time listed by the U. S. Coast and Geodetic Survey. This would imply that the wave front generated on the northeast side of the disturbance area had a 6-minute head start on the wave front generated southeast of Kodiak.

The tsunami-generating area covers an area 700 km long by 150 km wide, a total of about 105,000 km². The volume of the uplifted crust along the continental shelf is about 96 km³. The energy associated with the tsunami has been estimated by Van Dorn (1965) to be of the order of 2.3 × 10²¹ ergs. This estimate is based on the source dimensions of an area 240 nautical miles by 100 nautical miles and an uplift of 1.8 m (6 ft) at the northeastern end of this area and zero at the southwestern end. This estimate, however, is considered low because the generating area had dimensions that were larger than those estimated by Van Dorn.

Using our source dimensions, and assuming that the total energy was equal to the potential energy of the uplifted volume of water, the total energy for the tsunami in the Gulf of Alaska was calculated as follows:

$$E_t = \frac{1}{6}\rho gh^2 A$$

$$= \frac{1}{6}(1.03)(.980)(10^3)(10^4)(1.83^2)(1.5$$

$$\times 10^7)(7 \times 10^7) = 5.88 \times 10^{21} \text{ ergs}$$

where

$E_t = E_p = $ total energy
$\rho = 1.03 \text{ g/cm}^3 = $ density
$g = 980 \text{ cm/sec}^2$
$h = $ height of displacement $= 1.83$ m
$A = $ area
$1 \text{ erg} = \text{g cm}^2 \text{ sec}^{-2}$

The waves generated in the Gulf of Alaska were of an unusually long period, on the order

of an hour or more. Their energy radiation was preferentially directed toward the southeast and this is why more damage was done to the North American coast than anywhere else east or south of the generating area. This preferential directivity of energy radiation can be attributed to the orientation of the tectonic displacements along the continental shelf of the Gulf of Alaska, and the long period of the waves can be related to the long seiche period of the shallow shelf.

According to Japanese seismologists (Iida, 1958), the generating area of a tsunami roughly corresponds to the distribution of the major aftershocks. This appears to be indeed the case in the Gulf of Alaska.

There were 52 aftershocks of the Alaska earthquake. The largest had a magnitude of 6.7. The aftershocks occurred in an area from about 15 km north of Valdez to about 55 km south of Trinity Islands, and were heavily concentrated on the northeast and the southwest of the uplifted region (USCGS, 1964), which also was the main tsunami-generating area.

The vast area of tectonic movements indicates that wave crests were generated along one or more line sources from the region of maximum uplift. Thus, the shores of the Kenai Peninsula were struck within 20 minutes after the start of the earthquake, and those of Kodiak Island, within 34 minutes.

Unfortunately, the violence of the earthquake left south-central Alaska without a tide gauge in operation. The only reliable record from the generating area is the one that was obtained by personnel of the U. S. Navy Fleet Weather Station at Kodiak; it is shown in Figure 2. This record has been corrected for the 1.7-m (5.6-ft) submergence of the area.

Outside the immediate generating area, the record of Cape Yakataga, as constructed from the personal account of C. R. Bilderback, a resident of the area, is the next most reliable record. This record is the only one obtained outside the generating area that shows an initial drop in the water level (Berg et al., 1971). Withdrawal of the water immediately following the earthquake has been reported from Kayak, Middleton, and Hinchinbrook islands, as well as from Rocky Bay and Nuka Bay, at the end

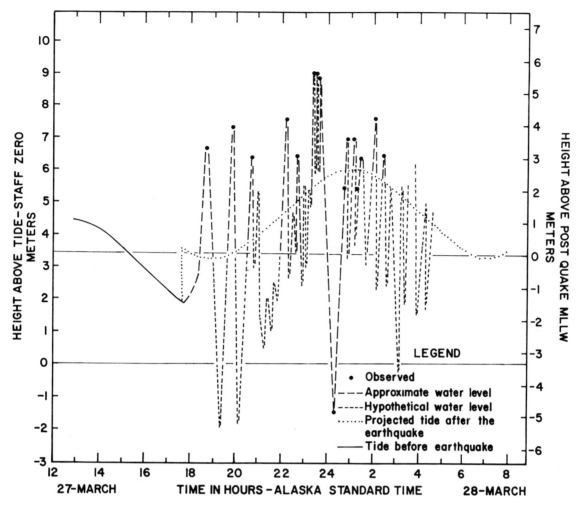

FIG. 2. Diagram of wave activity at Women's Bay, Kodiak Island. (From visual observations made at Marginal Pier, Nyman Peninsula.)

of the Kenai Peninsula, but these islands are inside the generating area.

Yakatat, a coastal town 170 km southeast of Cape Yakataga, had a tide gauge in operation, and the marigram shows that a positive wave arrived first (Fig. 3).

It is quite possible, therefore, that the first waves to arrive at Cape Yakataga had a different origin from that of the first waves to arrive at Yakatat. It could very well be that the Cape Yakataga waves traveled over the shallow portion of the shelf, whereas the Yakatat waves came from the open ocean.

An interesting aspect of these two records is that of the difference in amplitude and period of the first waves to arrive at these two sites—which also supports the hypothesis of difference in origin (see Figs. 3 and 4).

TSUNAMI GENERATED IN PRINCE WILLIAM SOUND

The shallow continental shelf and the islands bordering the southern side of Prince William Sound, as well as the pattern of crustal displacements, confined the waves generated in this area to the Sound itself; very little energy escaped this closed region. Most of the energy was expended in the narrow, deep fjords of the Sound, creating catastrophic waves and setting up resonating oscillations and surges that lasted for hours. In certain places maximum inundation occurred 5 or 6 hours later, at high tide. At Valdez, for example, the third wave came in at 2300, March 27, and the fourth one at 0145, March 28 (Brown, 1964). This last wave took the form of a tidal bore and inundated the

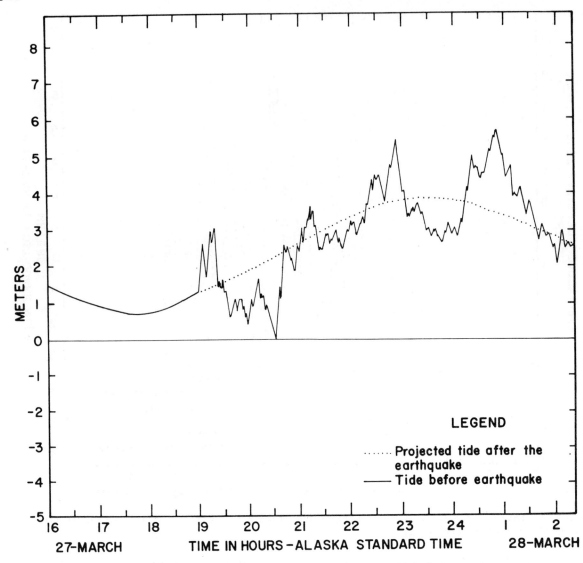

FIG. 3. Marigram of wave activity at the town of Yakutat.

downtown section of Valdez, ruining almost all the merchandise in the stores. These waves could not have come from the generating area outside Prince William Sound because if this were so, it would have taken them only 34 minutes to reach Valdez. It is more likely, then, that the waves at Valdez arrived in resonance at high tide, from the immediate area of Port Valdez.

Maximum positive crustal displacement in Prince William Sound occurred along the northwest coast of Montague Island and in the area offshore. These earth movements caused a gradient in hydrostatic level and the resulting short-period wave raced through Knight Island Passage within 10 minutes and on toward Che-

nega Island, inundating the village of Chenega to an elevation of 15.5 m and completely destroying it. This same wave continued north through Knight Island Passage and inundated Perry and Naked islands, but to lesser heights (Berg et al., 1971).

Bathymetric surveys by the USCGS (1964) in the area off Montague Island and at the north end of Latouche Island revealed a number of large submarine slides. It is possible, therefore, that the combination of submarine slides and the tilting of the ocean floor due to uplift created the solitary wave reported at Chenega village and at Perry and Naked islands.

A second wave about 40 m high (125 ft) was reported coming out of the Valdez Narrows

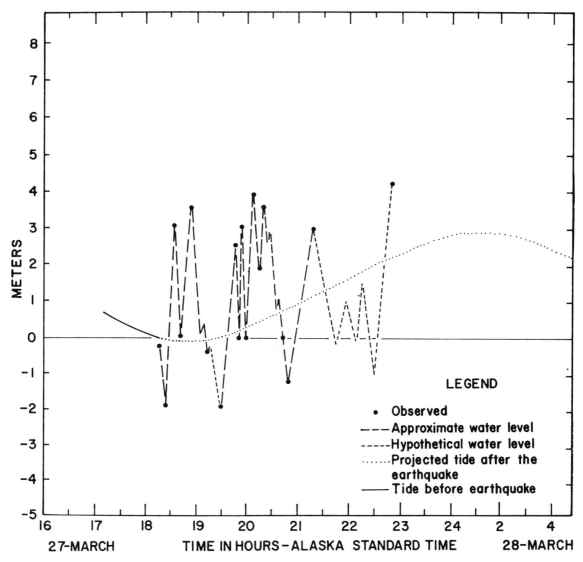

Fig. 4. Diagram of wave activity at Cape Yakataga.

and spreading across the Sound (Plafker and Mayo, 1965). This wave was caused by slumping of the glacial deltas in Port Valdez which had been shaken loose by the force of the earthquake.

TSUNAMI MECHANISM

Most tsunamis result from earthquakes having focal depths of less than 60 km. Iida (1958) has derived an empirical relation giving the maximum focal depth H (in km) for an earthquake of magnitude M which has resulted in a detectable tsunami:

$$M = 6.42 + 0.01 \ H \qquad (1)$$

where M is the Richter magnitude given by

$$\log \mathrm{E(ergs)} = 11.8 + 1.5 \ M \qquad (2)$$

The focal depth of the Alaska earthquake was about 20 km. This was shallow enough to create tsunami waves even though the epicenter of the main shock was as much as 100 km inland from the coast. A number of shallower aftershocks over a large area ranging from Hinchinbrook Island to southeast Kodiak Island indicate that crustal movements over a wide area were involved. Undoubtedly these shallow aftershocks created smaller waves that could not be separated, in the tide gauge records, from reflections of the initial tsunami.

If the tsunami waves that hit the island of Kodiak were the result of crustal movements only, then the first wave could be expected to be the highest, at least within the generating area. At Uzinki, Kodiak City, Women's Bay, and elsewhere on the island of Kodiak, however, the third and fourth waves were the highest. A theory of generation from a single pattern of crustal deformation is therefore not satisfactory here. Such factors as reflection from coastal boundaries, wave interaction, and resonance should be taken into consideration.

Slumps or avalanches, similar to the ones that occurred in Prince William Sound, are usually localized; they can produce no large tsunamis that would travel across wide portions of the ocean. According to Wiegel (1954), not more than 2% of the potential energy of a falling or sliding body is converted into wave energy. In Prince William Sound, however, slumping and sliding when added to tectonic movements created tsunami waves of very large energy, but their effect was catastrophic only locally; very little of the energy escaped the Sound.

SUMMARY AND CONCLUSIONS

The Alaska earthquake of March 27, 1964 affected an area of approximately 215,000 km², extending from the Wrangell Mountains at the northeast to the Trinity Islands in the southwest, and from the west side of Shelikof Strait and Cook Inlet east to the vicinity of the Bering Glacier.

Geologic evidence has revealed a dipole pattern of positive and negative tectonic movements resulting from this earthquake. The area of subsidence covers approximately 110,000 km² and the volume of crust that has been depressed below its pre-earthquake level is about 115 km³.

The area of uplift covers about 105,000 km² and includes the southern and eastern parts of Prince William Sound, the coastal area as far east as the Bering Glacier, and a great part of the continental shelf and slope bordering the Gulf of Alaska.

The seaward limits of the area affected by the Alaska earthquake and the tsunami-generating area were determined by means of a series of wave refraction diagrams as shown in Figure 5, based on Snell's Law of Refraction. The tsunami-generating area covers 140,000 km² and includes the whole of the region of uplift and part of the region of subsidence. It extends from the Trinity Islands to the Bering Glacier and includes Shelikof Strait, Cook Inlet, and the continental shelf bordering the Gulf of Alaska to a depth of approximately 200 m. The total volume of displaced material in the tsunami-generating area was estimated to be 120 km³, and the energy associated with the tsunami was calculated to be in the order of 6×10^{21} ergs.

As a result of this work the following conclusions are drawn:

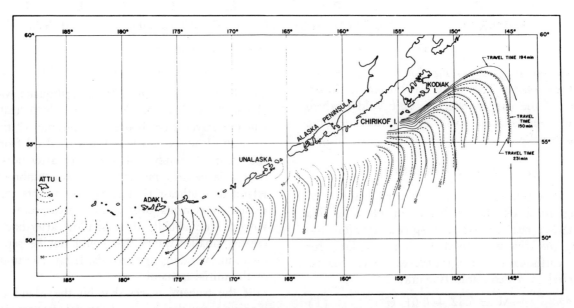

Fig. 5. Diagram of wave fronts refracted toward the earthquake area from Attu Island (*dashed line*), Adak Island (*solid line*), and Unalaska Island (*dotted line*).

1. Two main tsunami-generating areas can be distinguished: one along the continental shelf bordering the Gulf of Alaska; the other in Prince William Sound.

2. The main generating area in the Gulf of Alaska roughly corresponds to the geographic distribution of the major aftershocks.

3. The energy of the tsunamis generated in Prince William Sound was expended inside the Sound; not much energy escaped this closed region.

4. The long period of the waves generated in the Gulf of Alaska is related to the long seiche period of the shallow shelf.

5. The preferential radiation of energy toward the southeast is attributed to the orientation of the tectonic displacements along the continental shelf of the Gulf of Alaska.

6. The waves arriving at Cape Yakataga had their origin in the shallow coastal area near the Bering Glacier, whereas the waves arriving at Yakatat traveled through the deeper waters.

7. In Prince William Sound two major tsunamis were distinguished: one had its origin near the west coast of Montague Island, the other originated in the Port of Valdez.

8. Two types of tsunami-generating mechanisms were associated with the Alaska earthquake: (a) waves generated directly by tectonic movements of the sea floor, and (b) waves generated indirectly from landslides, mudflows, and slumping of alluvial deposits.

9. In Prince William Sound both generation mechanisms were evident, while in the generating area along the Gulf of Alaska, the generated tsunami was the direct result of tectonic movements.

ACKNOWLEDGMENTS

The work on which this paper is based was supported in part by the National Science Foundation under the United States–Japan program for cooperative research in the Pacific, through grant No. GF-153, and in part by the Office

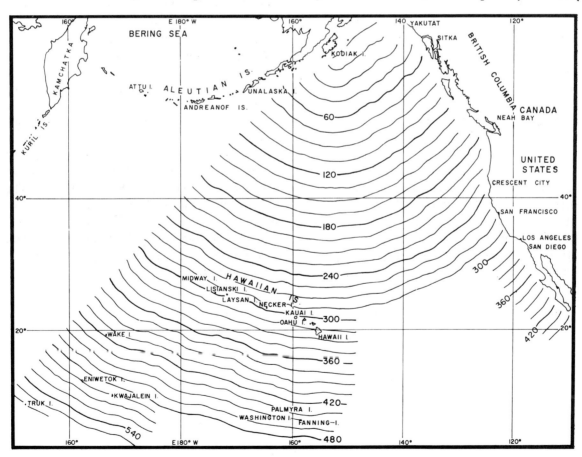

FIG. 6. Wave refraction diagram of the Alaska tsunami for the north Pacific Ocean (time interval: 15 minutes).

of Naval Research through contract Nonr-3748(03).

I am particularly indebted to D. C. Cox, W. M. Adams, and G. P. Woollard for their advice and constructive criticism.

I would also like to acknowledge with appreciation the advice, comments, and suggestions given to me by A. S. Furumoto, K. Kajiura, G. W. Groves, H. G. Loomis, G. R. Miller, and Robert Harvey.

I also thank the members of the United States–Japan Cooperative Field Survey (E. Berg, D. C. Cox, A. S. Furumoto, K. Kajiura, H. Kawasumi, and E. Shima) for permission to use data from their report prior to publication.

REFERENCES

BERG, E., D. C. COX, A. S. FURUMOTO, K. KAJIURA, H. KAWASUMI, and E. SHIMA, 1971. Field Survey of the Tsunamis of 28 March 1964 in Alaska. Hawaii Inst. Geophys. Rept. Series.

BROWN, D. L. 1964. Tsunamic Activity Accompanying the Alaskan Earthquake of 27 March 1964. U. S. Army Engr. Dist., Anchorage, Alaska. 20 pp.

GRANTZ, A., G. PLAFKER, and R. KACHADOORIAN. 1964. Alaska's Good Friday Earthquake March 27, 1964: A Preliminary Geologic Evaluation. U. S. Geol. Surv. Circ. 491. 35 pp.

IIDA, K. 1958. Magnitude and energy of earthquakes accompanied by tsunami, and tsunami energy. J. Earth Sci., Nagoya Univ. 6:101–112.

JOHNSON, J. W., P. O. O'BRIEN, and J. D. ISAACS. 1948. Graphical construction of wave refraction diagrams. H. O. Publ. No. 605.

MENARD, H. W. 1964. Marine Geology of the Pacific. McGraw-Hill Book Co., New York. Pp. 97–116.

——— and R. S. DIETZ. 1951. Submarine geology of the Gulf of Alaska. Bull. Geol. Soc. Am. 62:239–253.

PLAFKER, G. 1965. Tectonic deformation associated with the 1964 Alaska earthquake. Science 148:1675–1687.

——— and L. R. MAYO. 1965. Tectonic Deformation, Subaqueous Slides and Destructive Waves Associated with the Alaskan March 27, 1964 Earthquake: An Interim Geologic Evaluation. U. S. Geol. Surv., Open File Rept. 19 pp.

SHOR, G. G., JR. 1962. Seismic refraction studies off the coast of Alaska: 1956–57. Bull. Geol. Soc. Am. 52:37–57.

U. S. COAST AND GEODETIC SURVEY. 1964. Preliminary Report, Prince William Sound, Alaskan Earthquakes; March–April 1964. 83 pp.

VAN DORN, G. W. 1965. Source mechanism of the tsunami of March 28, 1964 in Alaska. Chap. 10. In: Proc. Ninth Conference on Coastal Engineering, Am. Soc. Civil Engr., pp. 166–190.

WIEGEL, R. L. 1954. Laboratory studies of gravity waves generated by the movement of a submerged body. Univ. Calif. Inst. Engr. Res., Ser. 3, Issue 362.

WILSON, J. T. 1954. The development and structure of the crust. Chap. 4. In: Gerard P. Kuiper, ed., The Solar System, Vol. 2. The Earth as a Planet. Univ. of Chicago Press.

WOOLLARD, G. P., N. A. OSTENSO, E. THIEL, and W. E. BONINI. 1960. Gravity anomalies, crustal structure, and geology in Alaska. J. Geophys. Res. 65:1021–1037.

AUGUSTINE S. FURUMOTO

UNIVERSITY OF HAWAII

Reprinted with minor changes from
Pacific Science, Vol. 21, No. 3,
"A Study of the Source Mechanism of the Alaska Earthquake and Tsunami
of March 27, 1964: Part II, Analysis of Rayleigh Wave"

Source Mechanism Study by Rayleigh Wave Analysis

ABSTRACT: The source mechanism of the Alaska earthquake of March 27, 1964 has been investigated by analyzing the Rayleigh wave recorded on the strain seismograph at Kipapa Station, Hawaii. The parameters that give the best fit to the observed data are: rupture length of 800 km, rupture velocity of 3 km/sec, and direction of rupture line of S30°W. The results of this analysis compare favorably with field data of elevation changes, with distribution of epicenters of aftershocks, and with the area of generation of the tsunami as obtained from sea-wave refraction diagrams.

THE UNITED STATES–JAPAN Cooperative Field Survey of the Alaska Earthquake of March 27, 1964 (Berg et al., 1971), resulted in an estimate of the length and size of the rupture zone of the earthquake. Corroboration for these results was sought from seismic data. Toksöz et al. (1965) have published a source mechanism analysis using surface wave data. Their results are as follows: rupture velocity, 3.0 km/sec; rupture length, 600 km; azimuth of rupture, S50°W from the epicenter. These results, however, are at variance with the field survey data.

Shortly after the field survey, an attempt at source mechanism analysis by surface wave methods was made by using the record of the strain seismograph at Kipapa Station, Hawaii.

The results of this analysis are presented here because they are in somewhat better accord with field survey data.

This study was supported by funds from the National Science Foundation under Grants GP-2257 and GP-5111.

METHOD OF ANALYSIS

The analysis of source mechanism based on earthquake surface waves was developed by Ben-Menahem (1961). According to this method, if the Rayleigh wave is used the ratio of the amplitude spectrum of R_3 to the amplitude spectrum of R_2 can be related to directivity function $D(f)$,

$$D(f) = \frac{\left|\left(\frac{C}{V} + \cos\theta\right)\right] \sin\frac{\pi Bf}{C}\left(\frac{C}{V} - \cos\theta\right)\right]\right|}{\left|\left(\frac{C}{V} - \cos\theta\right)\right] \sin\frac{\pi Bf}{C}\left(\frac{C}{V} + \cos\theta\right)\right]\right|} \tag{1}$$

where C is the phase velocity of the curve at frequency f, V is the velocity of rupture propagation, B is the length of the rupture, and θ is the angle which the rupture line makes with the great circle path through the epicenter and observing station. A method using the Love

wave has also been developed, but the present study utilizes the Rayleigh wave only.

Ben-Menahem and Toksöz have applied the method of surface wave analysis to the study of the source mechanism for the Mongolian earthquake of 1958 (Ben-Menahem and Toksöz, 1962), the Alaska earthquake of 1958 (Ben-Menahem and Toksöz, 1963b), and the Kamchatka earthquake of 1952 (Ben-Menahem and

[1] Hawaii Institute of Geophysics Contribution No. 185. Manuscript received June 22, 1966.

Toksöz, 1963a). Wada and Ono (1963) have applied the method for the Chile earthquake of 1960.

For the Alaska earthquake of 1964, copies of records from the strain seismograph at Kipapa Station, Hawaii, were used. This strain seismograph consists of a quartz rod 80 ft long. It was installed by the California Institute of Technology in the spring of 1963. Figure 1 shows the traces of R_2, R_3, and R_4.

RESULTS OF ANALYSIS

The Fourier spectra of R_2, R_3, and R_4 are given in Figure 2. To form the ratios of amplitudes R_3/R_2 and R_3/R_4, the decay of amplitudes with travel distance must be considered because the decay coefficient is frequency-dependent. The decay coefficient determined by Ben-Menahem and Toksöz (1963a) from empirical data was used for the corrections.

The amplitude ratios of R_3/R_2 and R_3/R_4 are given in Figure 3. There is coherence between the two ratio spectra at certain frequencies. Troughs of the spectra coincide at 0.0027 cps, 0.0056 cps, 0.0080 cps, and 0.0010 cps. Peaks agree at 0.0088 cps and 0.0111 cps. There is a peak at 0.0038 cps for R_3/R_4 and a peak

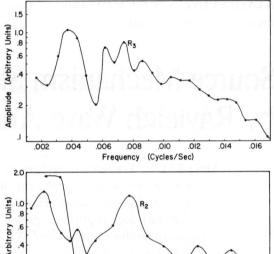

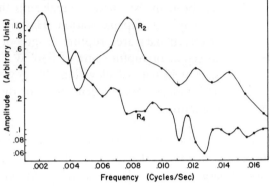

FIG. 2. *Upper*: Fourier spectrum of R_3. *Lower*: Fourier spectra of R_2 and R_4. The amplitude coordinate is in arbitrary units.

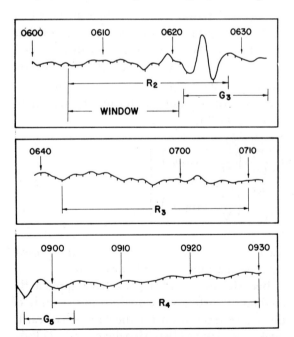

FIG. 1. *Upper*: Phases R_2 and G_3. Window indicates the section of R_2 that was used as data. *Middle*: Trace of R_3. *Lower*: Trace of R_4 and G_5.

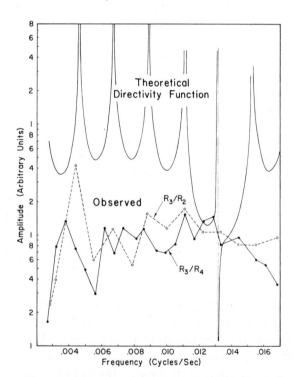

FIG. 3. Directivity function, theoretical and observed. The amplitude coordinate is in arbitrary units. For the theoretical curve, $V = 3$ km/sec, $\theta = 15°$, and $B = 800$ km.

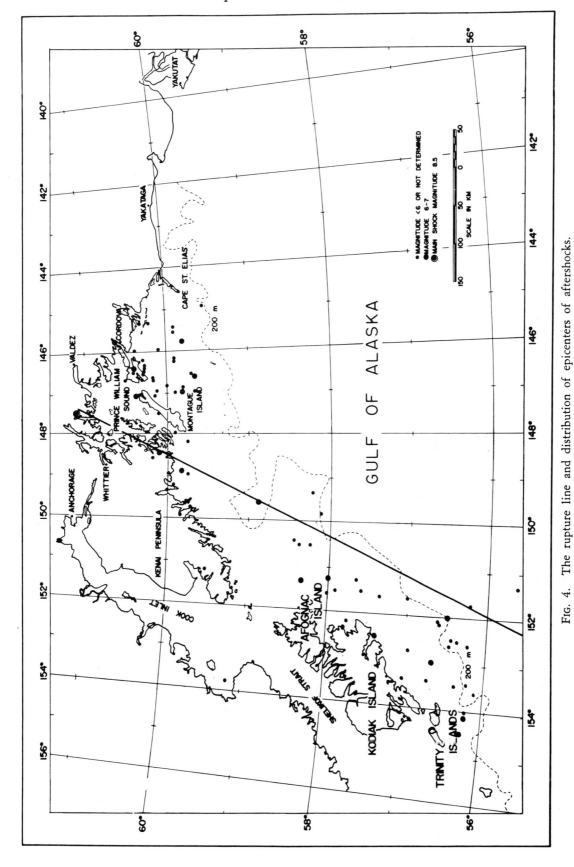

FIG. 4. The rupture line and distribution of epicenters of aftershocks.

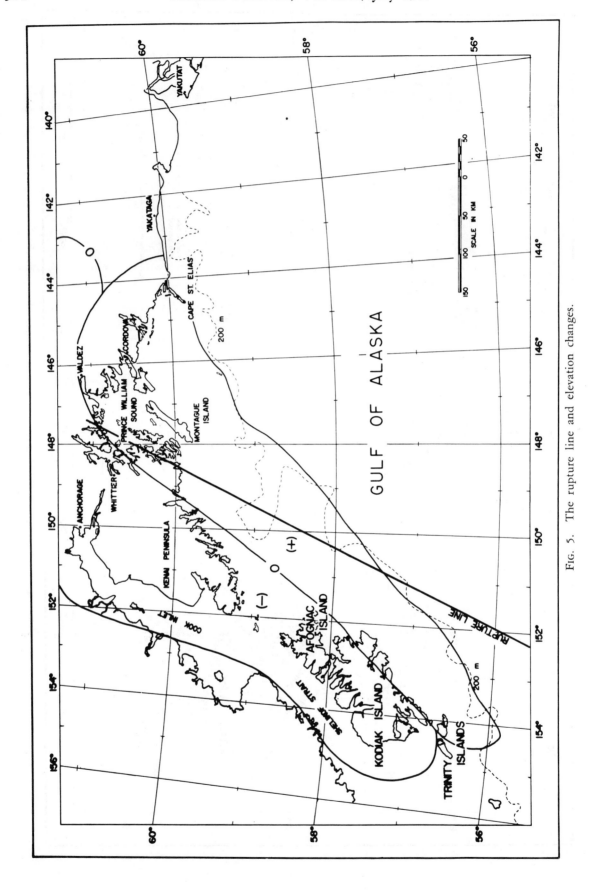

FIG. 5. The rupture line and elevation changes.

at 0.0044 cps for R_3/R_2. These two peaks probably coincide, and the apparent lag between the two is due to inadequate resolution of the Fourier analysis at these frequencies. There are opposing patterns at 0.0068 cps.

The best-fitting curve of the directivity function with the R_3/R_2 spectrum is plotted on the upper section of Figure 3. In this curve the parameters are: $B = 800$ km, $V = 3.0$ km/sec, and $\theta = 15°$. R_3/R_4 fits the curve also, except for the mismatch in the neighborhood of 0.0067 cps.

The epicenter determined by the U. S. Coast and Geodetic Survey (1964) was 61.05°N, 147.5°W. The coordinates of the Kipapa Station are 21°25′24″N and 158°00′54″W. The direction of the station from the epicenter is S15.3°W. This defines the direction of the rupture line from the epicenter as S30°W.

In Figure 4, the rupture line, as obtained from the present study, is superimposed on a map prepared by the U. S. Coast and Geodetic Survey (1964) which shows the epicenters of the main shock and the aftershocks of the Alaska earthquake. In general, the aftershock area defines the area of rupture. In the present case, the rupture line obtained from Rayleigh wave analysis extends 100 km beyond the aftershock area.

Surveys of elevation changes after the Alaska earthquake show positive changes in the Prince William Sound area, and negative changes in the Kodiak Island area. In Figure 5, the calculated line of rupture is superimposed on the map of elevation changes as prepared by Pararas-Carayannis (1967, Figure 1, and this volume). The rupture line runs diagonally across the section of positive changes. In this calculation the direction of the rupture line may vary about 5°. (This value is determined by the resolving power of the Fourier analysis.) If the direction of the rupture line is turned 5° clockwise, with the epicenter as the pivotal point, the rupture line will agree with the line of zero displacement from field observations.

An inspection of the directivity function $D(f)$ in equation (1) shows that the periodicity in terms of frequency of the peaks and troughs of the function is controlled by the length B of the rupture line. The peaks and troughs of R_3/R_2 and R_3/R_4 in Figure 3 are

such that a length of $B = 800$ km fits the data best. The superimposition of the rupture line on the elevation-change map shows that the rupture line extends to the south 100 km beyond the zone of elevation changes. On the other hand, if the total area of the observed elevation changes is considered, the zone has a length of 700–800 km (Plafker, 1965).

The present analysis shows a discrepancy between the direction of the calculated rupture line and the direction expected from field survey, but the discrepancy is within the limits of error of the calculation. The length of the calculated rupture line agrees with that from field data.

DISCUSSION

The results of the field survey by the United States–Japan Cooperative Team (Berg et al., in preparation) have heavily influenced the analysis presented here since the author was a member of the survey team. Perhaps because of this bias, the analysis should not be considered as an independent study but, rather, as additional evidence to strengthen the results proposed by the field survey. The rupture zone of the Alaska earthquake of 1964 has now been outlined consistently by four different methods: (a) field survey of elevation changes (Berg et al., 1971; Plafker, 1965); (b) plot of epicenters of aftershock (U.S. Coast and Geodetic Survey, 1964); (c) tsunami refraction diagrams (Pararas-Carayannis, 1967, and this volume); and (d) seismic surface wave method (this paper).

REFERENCES

BEN-MENAHEM, A. 1961. Radiation of seismic surface waves from finite moving sources. Bull. Seism. Soc. Am. 51:401–435.

———— and M. N. TOKSÖZ. 1962. Source mechanism from spectra of long period seismic surface waves, 1. The Mongolian earthquake of December 4, 1957. J. Geophys. Res. 67:1943–1955.

———— 1963a. Source mechanism from spectra of long period surface waves, 2. The Kamchatka earthquake of November 4, 1952. Ibid. 68:5207–5222.

———— 1963b. Source mechanism from spectra

of long period seismic surface waves, 3. The Alaska earthquake of July 10, 1958. Bull. Seism. Soc. Am. 53:905–919.

BERG, E., D. C. COX, A. S. FURUMOTO, K. KAJIURA, H. KAWASUMI, and E. SHIMA, 1971. Field Survey of the Tsunamis of 28 March 1964 in Alaska. Hawaii Inst. Geophys., Rept. Series.

PARARAS-CARAYANNIS, G., 1967. A study of the source mechanism of the Alaska earthquake and tsunami of March 27, 1964: Part I, Water waves. Pacific Science, 21 (July), 301–310. Also *in* The Great Alaska Earthquake of 1964: Seismology and Geodesy. NAS Pub. 1602. Washington: National Academy of Sciences, 1972.

PLAFKER, G. 1965. Tectonic deformation associated with the 1964 Alaska earthquake. Science 148:1675–1687.

TOKSÖZ, M. N., A. BEN-MENAHEM, and D. HARKRIDER. 1965. Source mechanism of Alaska earthquake from long period seismic surface waves. (Abstr.) Trans. Am. Geophys. Union 46:154.

U. S. COAST AND GEODETIC SURVEY. 1964. Preliminary Report, Prince William Sound, Alaskan Earthquakes, March–April 1964. 83 pp.

WADA, T., and H. ONO. 1963. Source mechanism of the Chilean earthquake from spectra of long period surface waves. Zisin 16 (ser. II):181–187.

HIROO KANAMORI*

MASSACHUSETTS INSTITUTE OF TECHNOLOGY

Reprinted from
Journal of Geophysical Research, Vol. 75, No. 26,
"The Alaska Earthquake of 1964: Radiation of
Long-Period Surface Waves and Source Mechanism"

Radiation of Long-Period Surface Waves and Source Mechanism

The records of multiple Love and Rayleigh waves of the Alaska earthquake of 1964 were recovered from the 30–100 seismograph records at the WWSSN stations. The seismograms were equalized to a propagation distance of $9\pi/2$ (equivalent to G5 and R5 at $\Delta = \pi/2$). These seismograms were compared with synthetic seismograms for radiation pattern and amplitude to estimate various source parameters. The synthetic seismograms were computed from the normal mode solutions. One simple, yet plausible, source model was found. The nature of the fault is essentially that of a low-angle thrust faulting. The direction of rupture propagation does not coincide with the strike of the fault. This enables one to distinguish between the fault plane and the auxiliary plane. The source parameters determined are as follows: force system, double couple, reverse dip slip; fault plane, dip angle 20°, dip direction N 24°W; rupture length, 600 km; rupture velocity, 3.5 km/sec towards S25°W; moment, 7.5×10^{29} dyne-cm; average slip dislocation, 7 meters in N24°W direction; stress drop, 28 bars; strain drop, 0.4×10^{-4}; released strain energy, 1.5×10^{25} ergs. The moment and the width of the fault plane of this earthquake are much larger than those of any other earthquakes reported.

The Prince William Sound, Alaska, earthquake of March 28, 1964, is one of the largest earthquakes in history. Despite its tectonic importance, however, considerable ambiguity still exists concerning the nature of the faulting. This is clearly due to the lack of reliable seismological data, particularly S-wave and surface-wave data.

The debate about the source mechanism of this earthquake is well-known. *Algermissen* [1966] who used P-wave data, suggested that it is a predominantly normal fault along a steeply dipping plane. *Press and Jackson* [1965], and *Press* [1965], showed that the surface deformation can be explained in terms of a nearly vertical fault extending to a depth of 100–200 km. On the other hand, *Plafker* [1965] proposed on the basis of the tectonic deformations associated with this earthquake that the source of this earthquake is a low-angle thrust fault. *Savage and Hastie* [1966] advocated Plafker's interpretation. *Stauder and Bollinger* [1966] also preferred this interpretation from considera-

tions of the source mechanisms of the preshocks and aftershocks, together with the long-period P-wave data. Recently, *Harding and Algermissen* [1969], using S-wave polarization data from the low-magnification seismograms, proposed predominantly strike-slip faulting (double-couple). *Toksöz et al.* [1965] used long-period surface waves obtained at several stations; they found that a double-couple source with both strike-slip and dip-slip motions on a steeply dipping plane can explain the surface-wave data. The fault length and the rupture velocity were estimated to be 600 km and 3 km/sec (in S50°W direction), respectively.

Stimulated by these discussions, we made a thorough survey of the standard 30–100 long-period seismograms obtained at the WWSSN stations. It was found that the seismograms from some of these stations show recoverable, though complicated, multiple surface waves with large amplitude. In the hope of obtaining a new set of data to resolve the nature of the faulting, considerable effort was made to recover multiple surface waves from as many stations as possible. This paper presents those records in an equalized form, and interprets them, on the

TABLE 1.   Station Data for the Alaska Earthquake of March 28, 1964
(Origin time, 3h 36m 13.0s; latitude, 61.1°N; longitude, 147.6°W; depth, 33 km; M_s = 8.5)

Station	Δ, deg	l, km	$l + L$, km	ϕ, deg	ϕ', deg	Component	Phase	Magnification
ADE	112.739	12540.4	40020.6	238.7	30.4	UD, EW	R4, R5, G5, G6	750
AFI	77.194	8586.8	40011.7	204.1	11.8	UD, EW	R5, G4, G5	750
ARE	97.712	10867.7	40023.1	110.0	331.6	EW	G5, G6	1500
BAG	76.670	8520.5	40024.5	279.7	29.9	EW	G5, G6	1500
CHG	84.444	9382.0	40021.2	299.1	26.6	UD	R6	3000
COP	62.506	6936.5	40009.8	12.6	349.2	UD, EW	R4, R5, G4, G5	375
GDH	36.452	4045.4	40014.8	36.8	305.4	NS	G4, G5	750
GEO	47.707	5299.0	40024.8	84.1	321.7	NS	G4, G5	350
HKC	74.612	8289.9	40023.4	288.1	29.9	UD	R5	750
HNR	81.381	9051.5	40019.0	232.3	22.9	UD	R5	1500
KEV	49.385	5479.6	40009.1	2.5	356.6	UD	R5, R6	750
LAH	81.578	9058.5	40014.4	324.8	19.2	UD, EW	R5, R6, G4, G5	750
LPS	62.554	6953.7	40022.8	111.4	332.2	UD	R5	750
MAN	77.932	8661.2	40024.6	278.3	29.8	UD	R4, R5	750
MUN	119.648	13307.6	40024.3	258.8	33.8	UD, EW	R4, R5, G5, G6	750
NAI	120.238	13358.1	40009.2	354.9	2.5	UD, EW	R5, R6, G5, G6	1500
PDA	70.795	7860.8	40017.1	45.4	334.1	UD	R5	750
RIV	106.840	11884.6	40018.3	229.7	26.4	EW	G4, G5	750
SHI	87.901	9759.6	40010.5	342.3	9.8	UD, EW	R5, R6, G5, G6	1500

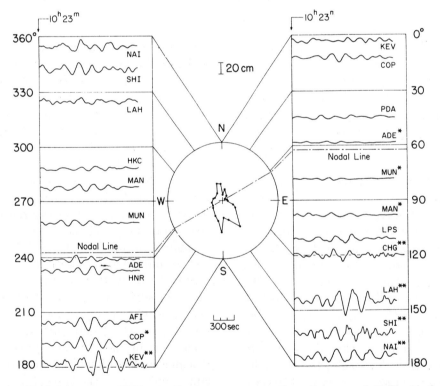

Fig. 1.   Rayleigh waves (R5) equalized to a propagation distance of $9\pi/2$, Alaska earthquake of March 28, 1964. The vertical scale gives the amplitude on the standard 30–100 seismogram with a magnification of 1500. Upward motion on the trace shows upward ground motion. For stations without asterisk, the equalization is made for R5; for those with an asterisk or with two asterisks, the equalization is made for R4 and R6, respectively. The nodal lines for the model shown in Figure 5B are shown.

basis of synthetic seismograms, to determine various source parameters. A method similar to that used by *Kanamori* [1970] is employed.

DATA

Actual-size copies of the long-period seismograms from WWSSN stations were collected. Although the traces are usually entangled because of the excessively large amplitude, it was possible to recover many multiple surface-wave trains such as R4, R5, R6, G4, G5, G6, etc. Table 1 lists the data used here. Rayleigh waves were windowed, between group velocities 3.47 and 3.75 km/sec, from vertical components; Love waves were windowed from horizontal components between group velocities 4.3 and 4.5 km/sec. The traces were digitized at every 4 sec and equalized to a magnification of 1500,

and to a propagation distance of $9\pi/2$. The latter equalization, which involves geometrical spreading, attenuation, and the phase shift due to propagation, was made as follows.

We let $U(\Delta, \omega)$ be the complex spectrum of the seismogram at a station of propagation distance Δ. The equalized seismograms at a distance Δ_0 (here $\Delta_0 = 9\pi/2$) as a function of time can then be written as

$$u(\Delta_0, t) = \left(\left|\frac{\sin \Delta}{\sin \Delta_0}\right|\right)^{1/2} \int_{-\infty}^{+\infty} U(\Delta, \omega)$$

$$\cdot \exp\left\{i\left[\omega \frac{\Delta - \Delta_0}{C} - \frac{\pi}{2} M\right]\right\}$$

$$\cdot \exp\left[k^*(\Delta - \Delta_0)\right] \exp(i\omega t) \, d\omega$$

where C and k^* are phase velocity and attenuation coefficient as a function of frequency, re-

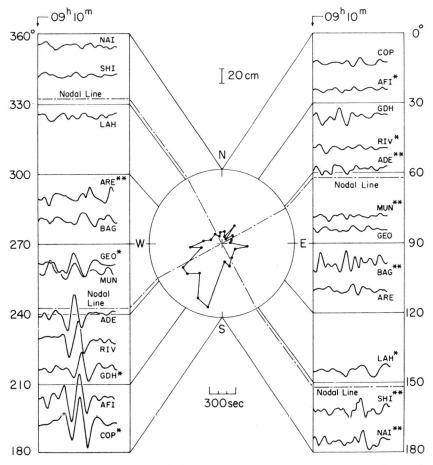

Fig. 2. Love waves (G5) equalized to a propagation distance of $9\pi/2$, Alaska earthquake of March 28, 1964. The vertical scale gives the amplitude on the standard 30–100 seismogram with a magnification of 1500. The counter-clockwise motion around the epicenter is taken upward on the trace. For stations without asterisk, the equalization is made for G5. For those with an asterisk or with two asterisks, the equalization is made for G4 and G6, respectively. The nodal lines for the model shown in Figure 5B are shown.

spectively. For C and k^*, the values listed in Tables 2 and 3 of *Kanamori* [1970] were used. The integer M is the number of polar or antipolar passages in going from Δ_0 to Δ.

The equalized seismograms thus obtained are shown in Figures 1 and 2. These traces correspond to R5 and G5 that would have been observed if the stations with the standard 30–100 seismograph having a magnification of 1500 were located at a distance of $\pi/2$. The circular plots at the center show the radiation patterns of the maximum trace amplitude. The important features of these seismograms are: (1) the maximum amplitude of Love waves is considerably larger than that of Rayleigh waves; (2) for both Love and Rayleigh waves, the radiation is nearly one-lobed; (3) the azimuth of the lobe of Love waves does not coincide with that of Rayleigh waves: the difference is about 45°.

Interpretation

For interpretation, we shall make extensive use of the synthetic seismograms of surface waves calculated by the method described by *Kanamori* [1970]. Since the focus of the main shock is considered to be shallow [*Sherburne et al.*, 1969] we first place a point source at a depth of 33 km in computing the synthetic seismograms.

Radiation pattern. The radiation pattern is determined by the force geometry of the source and the source dimension; the former determines the lobe pattern and the latter the asymmetry. Usually a crude guess of the force geometry can be made from the observed lobe pattern. For this great earthquake, however, the lobe pattern is too obscured because of so large an asymmetry for the force geometry to be recoverable. We shall therefore combine the body-wave data to construct a source model.

Most reliable body-wave data so far obtained are the first-motion data of P waves. One of the nodal planes has been determined very well; it has a dip angle between 82°SE and 87°NW, and a strike between N66°E and N40°E [*Harding and Algermissen*, 1969; *Stauder and Bollinger*, 1966] (see Figure 3). Because of the unfavorable distribution of the stations, the second nodal plane has not been determined. We shall therefore take the following procedure for interpreting the surface-wave data. We fix the

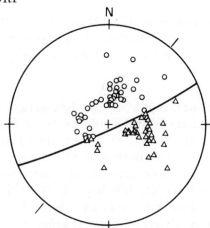

Fig. 3. Equal-area projection of the focal mechanism solution based on the first motion of P waves. Circles indicate compression and triangles indicate rarefaction. The nodal plane has a strike azimuth of N66°E and a dip 85° to the southwest (after *Stauder and Bollinger* [1966]).

first nodal plane with a dip angle of 82°SE and a strike N60°E, move the second nodal plane, and calculate the synthetic seismograms until a good fit between the synthetic and the observed seismograms is achieved. Before doing this, a brief inspection of the radiation pattern on the basis of Figure 7 of *Kanamori* [1970] which is reproduced in Figure 4 is useful. The depth and the propagation distance are different between Figure 4 and the present case. However, this difference is not very serious as long as Figure 4 is used as a guideline. We make the strike of the fault in Figure 4 parallel to the strike of the first nodal plane of P waves (N62°E). It is then evident that all the pure strike-slip sources (both vertical and 45°) are inadequate for this earthquake because the direction perpendicular to the fault is the node direction for the synthetic Rayleigh waves whereas it is the loop direction in the observed Rayleigh waves. On the other hand, the radiation patterns for the dip-slip sources can be reconciled with the observed radiation patterns; in particular, the 45° dip-slip source seems most appropriate because the lobe direction differs 45° between Love and Rayleigh waves. Further, from the amplitude ratio of Love to Rayleigh waves, the double-couple source may be preferable to the single-couple source.

On the basis of this reconnaissance, we start with a double-couple pure dip-slip with a dip angle of 82° and dip direction of S28°E (strike N62°E, see Figure 5B); one of the P-wave

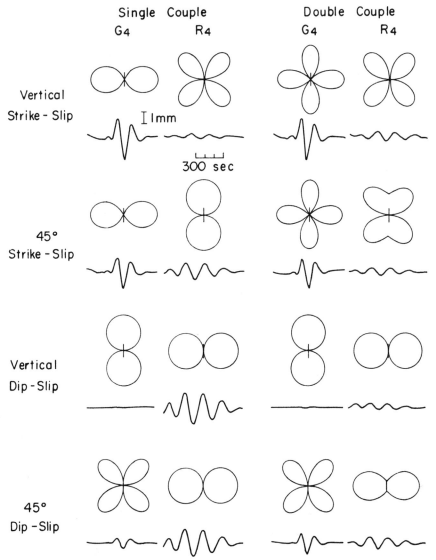

Fig. 4. Radiation patterns and wave forms in the direction of maximum amplitude of synthetic Love (G4) and Rayleigh (R4) waves for eight fundamental force geometries. The depth is 53 km (after *Kanamori* [1970]).

nodal planes for this model coincides with the observed nodal plane of *P* waves; the other nodal plane has a dip angle of 8° and dip direction of N28°W. The radiation pattern of synthetic seismograms computed for this model is shown in Figure 5B, where we see that the amplitude ratio of Love to Rayleigh waves is not consistent with the observations; the Rayleigh wave excitation relative to Love wave excitation is much larger than that observed. We found two ways of modifying this model so that it gives appropriate amplitude ratio of Love to Rayleigh waves. First, slight strike-slip component was superposed as shown in Figure

5C. Since Love waves are excited much more efficiently than Rayleigh waves by strike-slip sources, this model gives the right amplitude ratio. However, the surface-wave nodal lines are rotated with respect to the strike of the *P*-wave nodal planes. In order to obtain the best fit between the radiation patterns of synthetic and observed seismograms, a rotation of the fault planes by about 15° is necessary. This, of course, alters the strike of the *P*-wave nodal planes but not to such an extent as to be incompatible with the observed data (see Figures 3 and 5D). This model is designated model 1.

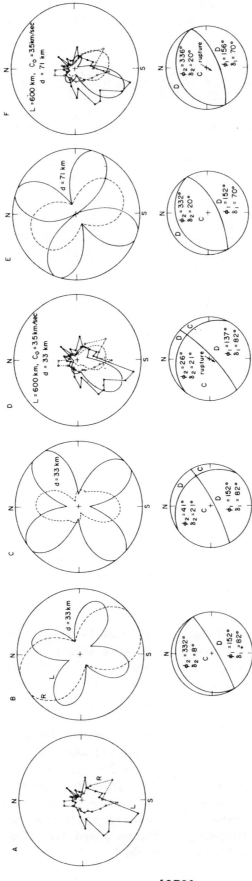

Fig. 5. Surface-wave (R5 and G5) radiation patterns and P-wave nodal planes for three models: A, observed Rayleigh-wave (R) and Love-wave (L) radiation patterns taken from Figures 1 and 2. B, surface-wave radiation patterns for a double-couple pure dip slip with dip angles $\delta_1 = 82°$ and $\delta_2 = 8°$; dip directions $\phi_1 = 152°$ (S28°E) and $\phi_2 = 332°$ (N28°W); depth, 33 km. C, model 1 (point source). D, model 1 (moving source) as compared with observed radiation patterns. E, model 2 (point source). F, model 2 (moving source) as compared with observed radiation patterns. In D and F the nodal planes are rotated.

The second possible model is shown in Figure 5E. The amplitude of Rayleigh waves of 100- to 200-sec period decreases sharply as the focal depth increases from 0 to 100 km. Thus, by increasing the depth from 33 to 71 km, the amplitude ratio of Love to Rayleigh waves can be made consistent with the observed ratio. This depth, 71 km, may seem incompatible with the depth of the main shock determined by the onset times of P waves at teleseismic stations. However, the onset times of P waves determine the location of the very beginning of the brittle fracture. It is possible that for such a great earthquake, the major fracture associated with the excitation of long-period surface waves involved a relatively large region extending to depths of 100 km or so. The depth 71 km should be considered as the average depth of the focal region. In the model given in Figure 5E, the dip angles are also changed from 82° to 70°,

and from 8° to 20°. These changes also contribute to bringing the amplitude ratio of Love to Rayleigh waves up to the right value. This model is called Model 2 and will be discussed later.

Asymmetry. The asymmetry can be explained by introducing a moving source. The direction of the rupture can be inferred from the asymmetry of the radiation pattern. Since the Rayleigh wave radiation pattern shows a large asymmetry in the direction perpendicular to the strike of the fault, the rupture velocity must have a horizontal component normal to the strike of the fault. On the other hand, for Love waves, the largest asymmetry occurs in the NE–SW direction suggesting that the rupture velocity has a component in this direction. From these observations we can constrain the direction of rupture in a fairly narrow range, S20°W to S30°W. The rupture velocity and

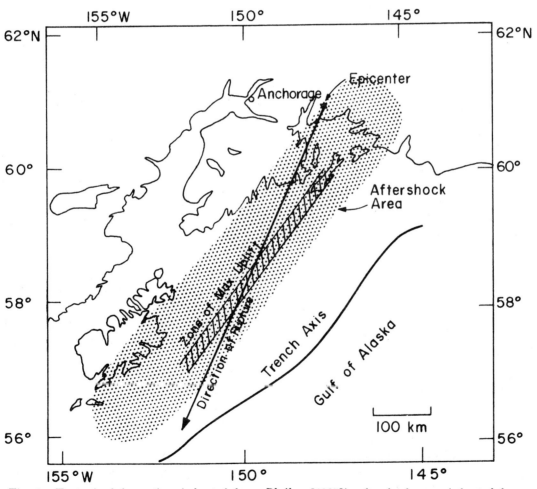

Fig. 6. Tectonic deformation (adopted from *Plafker* [1965]), aftershock area (adopted from *Algermissen et al.* [1969]), and the direction of rupture.

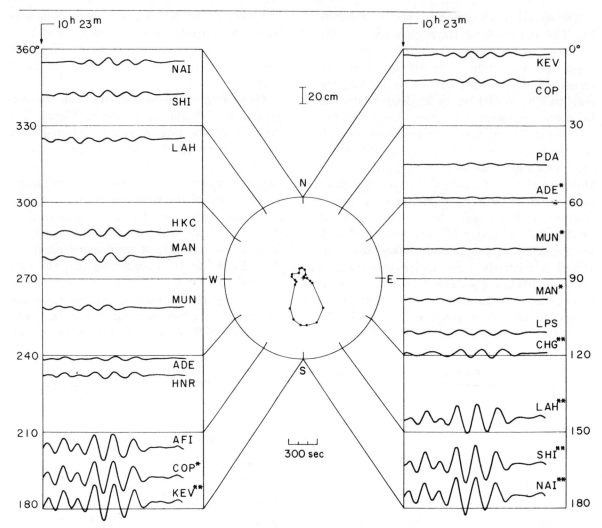

Fig. 7. Synthetic Rayleigh waves (R5 at $\Delta = 9\pi/2$) for model 2: double-couple pure dip slip; fault plane dip, 20°; dip direction, N24°W; rupture length, 600 km; rupture velocity, 3.5 km/sec toward S25°W; moment (time-function, step-function), 7.5×10^{29} dyne-cm; depth, 71 km. The vertical scale gives the trace amplitude on the standard 30–100 seismogram with a magnification of 1500. Station names correspond to those in Figure 1.

the rupture length are difficult to determine independently [see *Benioff et al.*, 1961; *Kanamori*, 1970] from observations over a limited frequency band: either rupture velocity or rupture length has to be somewhat restrained. If we take a rupture velocity of 3.5 km/sec, one of the representative values for major earthquakes [see *Benioff et al.*, 1961; *Press et al.*, 1961; *Ben-Menahem and Toksöz*, 1962; *Kanamori*, 1970], we find a rupture length of 600 km most appropriate, as shown in Figures 5D and 5F, where the effect of the moving source is superposed on the point-source radiation pattern. The method of computation is the same as that used by *Kanamori* [1970]. For rupture

velocities of 2.5 and 4.5 km/sec, rupture lengths of 450 and 750 km, respectively, are appropriate. Considering the extent of the tectonic deformation [*Plafker*, 1965] and the aftershock activity [*Algermissen et al.*, 1969], the combination (3.5 km/sec, 600 km) seems most appropriate (see Figure 6) and will be used hereafter. The rupture velocity and the rupture length obtained here are consistent with those obtained by *Toksöz et al.* [1965], allowing for the uncertainties mentioned above.

In Figures 5D and 5F, minor adjustments are made by slightly rotating the fault plane. The resulting *P*-wave nodal planes are not completely consistent with the observed first-motion data but are still tolerable (see Figure 3) considering that the fault motion associated with the excitation of long-period surface waves may be slightly different from that of P waves.

As has been noted, the radiation pattern of Rayleigh waves has a large asymmetry in the direction normal to the strike of the steeply dipping nodal plane of P waves. This observation precludes the possibility that the actual rupture took place on this plane; no rupture propagation on such a steep plane can produce such a large asymmetry in the direction per-

pendicular to it. This leads to an important conclusion that the fault plane of this earthquake is the gently dipping plane, not the steep plane. Thus, in model 1, the fault plane has a dip of 21° toward N26°E, and the rupture propagates up-dip on this plane in the direction nearly perpendicular to its strike. One difficulty then arises. The rupture, after starting from a depth around 33 km or so, reaches the earth's surface when it propagates up-dip over a distance of about 100 km. Thus at least six parallel fault planes, en echelon from NE to SW, are

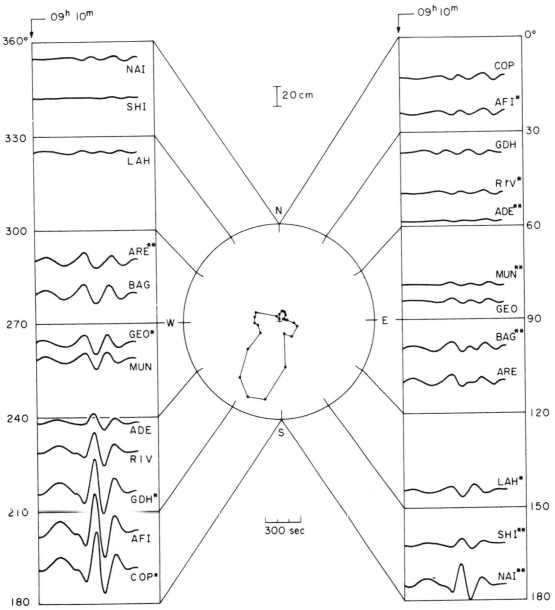

Fig. 8. Synthetic Love waves (G5 at $\Delta = 9\pi/2$) for model 2. For explanations, see the legend of Figure 7.

necessary to represent the entire rupture length, 600 km. This picture is somewhat artificial and physically implausible.

In model 2, on the other hand, the rupture starts from the NE end of the focal region and propagates, slightly up-dip, on a fault plane having a dip angle of 20° and dip direction of N24°W; the direction of rupture propagation is more or less parallel to the strike of the fault so that the entire rupture process may take place on a single fault plane. This model is simpler and perhaps physically more plausible than model 1. The faulting of model 2 is essentially a low-angle thrust fault, the oceanic block underthrusting beneath continent. This picture is generally similar to the one proposed by *Plafker* [1965], *Savage and Hastie* [1966], and *Stauder and Bollinger* [1966]. Because of its simplicity and plausibility we shall take model 2 as our final solution. From the direct comparison of the amplitude between synthetic and observed seismograms, the seismic moment can be estimated as 7.5×10^{29} dyne-cm, the largest value ever reported.

For the overall comparison we computed synthetic seismograms G5 and R5 for model 2 at azimuths corresponding to those of the stations used here. The results are shown in Figures 7 and 8. A remarkable similarity between Figures 1 and 7, and between Figures 2 and 8 is found. At some of the stations (e.g., COP*, GDH* for Love waves, COP* for Rayleigh waves), even the wave form and the phase agree very well. Since the equalized seismograms at these stations were derived from R4 and G4, they are more reliable than those derived from R5, R6, G5, and G6.

DISCUSSION AND CONCLUSIONS

In the computations of the effect of the moving source, we ignored the change of the depth as the point source propagates. Although the change of the depth could be taken into account by changing the excitation functions in the computations of the synthetic seismograms as the depth changes, we did not think it worthwhile, considering the gross simplification made in modeling the moving source.

From the geometry of the fault plane and the rupture propagation, the lateral dimension of the focal region can be estimated at about 300 km. To represent such a 'two-dimensional' fault,

the one-dimensional rupture discussed above is clearly an oversimplified model. A more sophisticated two-dimensional rupture model as discussed by *Hirasawa and Stauder* [1965] may be more appropriate. We tried several two-dimensional rupture models according to Hirasawa and Stauder. However, we found that the radiation pattern is relatively insensitive to the rupture parameters in the lateral direction, and could not determine those parameters from the observed radiation patterns. We therefore consider that the one-dimensional rupture model introduced above represents those two-dimensional models that have an overall movement in S25°W direction.

Wyss and Brune [1967] believe that this earthquake is a multiple shock consisting of at least six independent shocks greater than $m_b = 6.6$ within 70 sec after the onset of the earthquake. From the long-period surface waves, however, it is difficult to resolve these individual events; the present result neither supports nor rejects their conclusion.

This earthquake is probably the first earthquake that positively shows that the rupture propagation has appreciable component in the direction normal to the fault strike. This removes the otherwise inherent ambiguity in the selection of the fault plane out of the two *P*-wave nodal planes of double-couple dip-slip sources.

The uniqueness of the solution cannot be guaranteed fully. However, as we saw in the comparison between Figure 3 and Figures 1 and 2, only one out of the eight fundamental force geometries was found to be reasonably consistent with the data; it would be rather surprising if a force geometry that is simple yet entirely different from either model 1 or model 2 can be found to be consistent with the observed radiation patterns and the amplitude ratio of Love to Rayleigh waves.

Implicit in model 2 is the extension of the focal region to a relatively large depth, 100 km or so. At first this depth seems a little too large in the light of the depth of aftershock activity. *Algermissen et al.* [1969] and *Page* [1968] concluded that most of the aftershocks occurred within a depth of 40 km. However, the local quadripartite and tripartite observations of micro-aftershocks [*Hori et al.*, 1966; *Aki et al.*, 1969; *Matumoto and Page*, 1969] did indicate considerable mantle activity. Although it is not clear whether this mantle activity is activated by the Alaska earthquake [*Aki et al.*, 1969] or is due to a fluctuation of the background seismic activity in this region [*Page*, 1968], the present result seems to favor the former idea. It is possible that the faulting involves a considerable depth range, whereas the aftershock activity peaks at a relatively shallow depth.

The nature of the faulting of this earthquake is very similar to that of the Kurile Islands earthquake of 1963 [*Kanamori*, 1970] in that they are both low-angle thrust faultings. This is probably typical of island-arc earthquakes. The width of the fault plane, about 300 km, is much larger than that of typical transcurrent or transform faults such as the San Andreas fault.

Following *Aki* [1966], we can estimate from the observed moment the slip dislocation, stress drop, strain drop, and released strain energy using the slip dislocation theory of the faulting. We take the fault dimension as 500×300 km^2 (estimated from the geometry of the fault plane and the rupture propagation), and the rigidity, 0.7×10^{12} dyne-cm^{-2}. The results are: average slip dislocation, 7 meters in N24°W direction; stress drop, 28 bars; strain drop, 0.4×10^{-4}; released strain energy, 1.5×10^{25} ergs. The displacement of 7 meters can be compared with the figure 10 meters, estimated from the tectonic deformation by *Savage and Hastie* [1966]. In view of the large difference in the time scale and the method, we consider the agreement reasonably good. This agreement suggests that the slip-dislocation model is adequate for representing earthquake source. The value of the seismic moment estimated here, 7.5×10^{29} dyne-cm, is largest of all the values heretofore reported.

Acknowledgments. I am grateful to Drs. Keiiti Aki and Frank Press for kindly reading the manuscript and making many suggestions. In constructing the final model, I benefited from discussions with Drs. Keiiti Aki, Nafi Toksöz, and Tomowo Hirasawa.

This work was supported by the Air Force Office of Scientific Research under contract AF49 (638) 1632.

REFERENCES

Aki, K., Generation and propagation of G waves from the Niigata earthquake of June 16, 1964, 2, Estimation of earthquake moment, released energy, and stress-strain drop from the G wave spectrum, *Bull. Earthquake Res. Inst. Tokyo Univ., 44*, 73, 1966.

Aki, K., M. Hori, and H. Matumoto, Microaftershocks observed at a temporary array station on the Kenai Peninsula from May 19 to June 7, 1964, in *The Prince William Sound, Alaska, Earthquake of 1964 and Aftershocks*, vol. 2, edited by L. E. Leipold, pp. 131–156, U.S. Department of Commerce, Environmental Science Services Administration, Washington, D. C., 1969.

Algermissen, S. T., Mechanism of the Prince William Sound earthquake, in *ESSA Symposium on Earthquake Prediction*, pp. 20–25, U.S. Department of Commerce, Environmental Science Services Administration, Washington, D. C., 1966.

Algermissen, S. T., W. A. Rinehart, R. W. Sherburne, and W. H. Dillinger, Jr., Preshocks and aftershocks of the Prince William Sound earthquake of March 28, 1964, in *The Prince William Sound, Alaska, Earthquake of 1964 and Aftershocks*, vol. 2, edited by L. E. Leipold, pp. 79–130, U.S. Department of Commerce, Environmental Science Services Administration, Washington, D. C., 1969.

Benioff, H., F. Press, and S. Smith, Excitation of the free oscillations of the earth by earthquakes, *J. Geophys. Res., 66*, 605, 1961.

Ben-Menahem, A., and M. N. Toksöz, Source mechanism from spectra of long-period seismic surface waves, 1, The Mongolian earthquake of December 4, 1957, *J. Geophys. Res., 67*, 1943, 1962.

Harding, S. T., and S. T. Algermissen, Focal mechanism of the Prince William Sound, Alaska earthquake of March 28, 1964, *Bull. Seismol. Soc. Amer., 59*, 799, 1969.

Hirasawa, T., and W. Stauder, On the seismic body waves from a finite moving source, *Bull. Seismol. Soc. Amer., 55*, 237, 1965.

Hori, M., H. Matumoto, and K. Aki, Observation of microaftershocks of the Alaska earthquake of March 28, 1964 (in Japanese), *J. Seismol. Soc. Japan, 19*, 187, 1966.

Kanamori, H., Synthesis of long-period surface waves and its application to earthquake source studies—Kurile Island earthquake of October 13, 1963, *J. Geophys. Res., 75*(26), this issue, 1970.

Matumoto, T., and R. A. Page, Jr., Microaftershocks following the Alaska earthquake of March 28, 1964: Determination of hypocenters and crustal velocities in the Kenai Peninsula-Prince William Sound area, in *The Prince William Sound, Alaska, Earthquake of 1964 and Aftershocks*, vol. 2, edited by L. E. Liepold, pp. 157–173, U.S. Department of Commerce, Environmental Science Services Administration, Washington, D. C., 1969.

Page, R., Aftershocks and microaftershocks of

the great Alaska earthquake of 1964, *Bull. Seismol. Soc. Amer.*, *58*, 1131, 1968.

Plafker, G., Tectonic deformation associated with the 1964 Alaska earthquake, *Science, 148*, 1675, 1965.

Press, F., Displacements, strains, and tilts at teleseismic distances, *J. Geophys. Res., 70*, 2395, 1965.

Press, F., and D. Jackson, Alaskan earthquake, 27 March 1964: Vertical extent of faulting and elastic strain energy release, *Science, 147*, 867, 1965.

Press, F., A. Ben-Menahem, and M. N. Toksöz, Experimental determination of earthquake fault length and rupture velocity, *J. Geophys. Res., 66*, 3471, 1961.

Savage, J. C., and L. M. Hastie, Surface deformation associated with dip-slip faulting, *J. Geophys. Res., 71*, 4897, 1966.

Sherburne, R. W., S. T. Algermissen, and S. T. Harding, The hypocenter, origin time, and magnitude of the Prince William Sound earthquake of March 28, 1964, in *The Prince William Sound, Alaska, Earthquake of 1964 and Aftershocks*, vol. 2, edited by L. E. Leipold, pp. 49–69, U.S. Department of Commerce, Environmental Science Services Administration, Washington, D. C., 1969.

Stauder, W., and G. A. Bollinger, The focal mechanism of the Alaska earthquake of March 28, 1964, and of its aftershock sequence, *J. Geophys. Res., 71*, 5283, 1966.

Toksöz, M. N., A. Ben-Menahem, and D. G. Harkrider, Source mechanism of Alaska earthquake from long-period seismic surface waves (abstract), *Trans. Amer. Geophys. Union, 46*, 154, 1965.

Wyss, M., and J. Brune, The Alaska earthquake of 28 March 1964: A complex multiple rupture, *Bull. Seismol. Soc. Amer., 57*, 1017, 1967.

(Received March 30, 1970.)

ROLAND VON HUENE
U.S. GEOLOGICAL SURVEY

Geologic Structure of the Continental Margin

ABSTRACT: Observations in the area affected by the 1964 Alaska earthquake show that little Recent faulting is occurring in Prince William Sound near the initial earthquake epicenter. A large fault zone just off Montague and Kodiak islands was, however, a major tectonic element during late Tertiary time. Landward, the area has been uplifted; seaward, subsidence has occurred. The basin formed by subsidence is as much as 4-km deep. Its seaward flank forms a broad complex arch at the edge of the Continental Shelf and is the transition from the shelf to the rugged continental slope. The base of the slope and a downwarped area of the sea floor form the Aleutian Trench, which is filled with undeformed strata and with undeformed pretrench sediment.

The large fault zone off Montague and Kodiak islands is indicated by discontinuous fault scarps. It contains steep normal and reverse faults. Because this fault zone is in the belt of most intense recorded aftershock activity, it may have been the structure along which the 1964 earthquake occurred. The absence of strong evidence for a large thrust fault in the Aleutian Trench is a major weakness of a thrust-fault model. Neither the vertical- nor horizontal-fault model seems to explain all observations from the earthquake.

In the first week following the Alaska earthquake, earth scientists searching for a surface expression of a causative fault on land found earth slides rather than fresh fault scarps. But changes in elevation along shore lines were very noticeable, and, even at that time, it appeared that crustal uplift increased toward the Gulf of Alaska. The first plots of aftershocks showed large concentrations of epicenters along the inner Continental Shelf, and this evidence—along with the preliminary location of the area where the major tsunami may have originated—pointed to a causative fault off shore. About a week after the earthquake, while waiting for weather calm enough to land on Hinchinbrook Island, I was able to make two fathograms off Cape Hinchinbrook. A sharp 25-m-high scarp, striking approximately parallel to the regional northeast structural trend, was located in an area of irregular sea floor—an area later shown to be in the general vicinity of intense aftershock activity. Plafker's subsequent discovery of large uplift and fault scarps on Montague Island and Malloy's report of their extension offshore strengthened my suspicion of extensive faulting on the sea floor. This paper summarizes observations (made at sea during the two summers following the earthquake) by Scripps Institution of Oceanography, the U.S. Coast and Geodetic Survey, and the Naval Ordnance Test Station; many of these observations have been reported elsewhere (Malloy and Merrill, 1969, and Oceanography and Coastal Engineering volume; von Huene, 1966; von Huene, Malloy, Shor, and St.-Amand, 1967; von Huene and Shor, 1969; von Huene, Shor, and Reimnitz, 1967). These data are then related to other geologic and seismological data.

GEOLOGIC FRAMEWORK OF THE CONTINENTAL MARGIN AFFECTED BY THE EARTHQUAKE

The area in which strain was released by the Alaska earthquake is best delineated by the distribution of aftershocks, by horizontal and vertical surface deformation, and by the location where the major tsunami was generated. It includes a belt of land and Continental Shelf from south of Kodiak Island to east of Kayak Island (Figure 1). Rather than being completely linear, as were the areas affected by the 1906 San Francisco earthquake and the 1960 Chilean earthquake, the area affected during the Alaska earthquake has a bend at its northeastern end near Prince William Sound, where strain was first released (Figure 1). Geological and seismological data indicate that the bend is caused by the intersection of a northeasterly and a westerly trending structural system. For convenience, the former system is here called the Aleutian System and the latter the Alaska Mainland System (Figure 1).

The Aleutian System extends from the Aleutian Islands Arc to Prince William Sound. As a seismic trend, however, it extends inland some 400 km past the Sound (Tobin and Sykes, 1966; Algermissen and others, 1969, and this volume). Morphologically, it includes an uplifted terrestrial area, a broad Continental Shelf, and a rugged continental slope leading into the eastern Aleutian Trench. In contrast, the Alaska Mainland System, which extends from Prince William Sound eastward at least to Yakutat Sea Valley (Figure 1), has been seismically less active (Algermissen and others, 1969, and this volume). It has a rather smooth continental slope that makes a transition to the Gulf of Alaska through a shallow trough.

That strain was released mainly along the Aleutian System during the Alaska earthquake is best shown by the aftershock strain-release pattern (von Huene, Malloy, Shor, and St.-Amand, 1967; Algermissen and others, 1969, and this volume), and by the trend of the initial tsunami wave front (Van Dorn, 1965; Spaeth and Berkman, 1969). The significance of earthquake effects along a short segment of the Mainland System is unclear. The System may have been virtually passive, or strain may have been released because of triggering by activity along the Aleutian System. In the discussion that follows, the possible side effects along the Mainland System are carefully separated from those along the trend responsible for the earthquake.

STRUCTURAL ELEMENTS OF THE ALEUTIAN SYSTEM

The Aleutian System includes the continental margin and the Aleutian Trench as well as large adjacent land areas, the geology of which is treated here only as it pertains to an understanding of structures in the marine areas. A generalized section across the Aleutian System outlines its major structural elements (Figure 2). These elements include the uplifted Kenai–Kodiak block (represented in Figure 2 by Kodiak Island), a fault zone, and a deep Tertiary basin confined seaward by an arch at the outer Continental Shelf. The shelf

breaks off to a continental slope that makes a sharp juncture with the floor of the Aleutian Trench.

KENAI–KODIAK BLOCK

The fiords of Kenai Peninsula and Kodiak Island presumably are sculptured by glaciers along older structural lineaments in hard metamorphosed Cretaceous and lower Tertiary rocks (von Huene, 1966; von Huene, Shor, and Reimnitz, 1967). Little movement is known along the submarine extensions of the numerous faults on land since the last major glacial recession nor is there any indication in the postglacial sediments of repeated local tilting of Prince William Sound. In limited but representative surveys only one small fault with sea-floor expression was found in the fiord area and in the open-ocean area between the Kenai Peninsula and Kodiak Island. Since the last major glaciation, therefore, the Kenai Peninsula, Kodiak Island, and the marine area between them seem to have reacted to tectonic disturbance by flexing or tilting, with little movement along individual faults.

OFFSHORE FAULT ZONE FROM COPPER RIVER DELTA TO TRINITY ISLANDS

The most evidence of tectonic activity on the Continental Shelf is found in a wide fault zone just seaward of Kodiak, Montague, and Hinchinbrook islands (Figure 3). The existence of the fault zone is not well established between Portlock Bank and Kodiak Island because data are sparse, but it is thought to continue through this area. Its southern terminus has not been located but must lie somewhere in the vicinity of the Trinity Islands because it has not been seen south of them. Its northern end is probably in the complexly deformed area of the Copper River Delta.

The fault zone is a fundamental geologic boundary. Along Hinchinbrook and Montague islands it separates the uplifted metamorphosed rocks of Prince William Sound from a subsiding area of upper Tertiary and Quaternary rocks on the Continental Shelf. Some faults of the zone cross a platform of lithified rocks around southern Montague Island. Along the southeastern Kodiak coast, this fault zone separates thick upper Tertiary sediments on the Continental Shelf from metamorphosed rocks that make up most of the island.

Some faults within the zone have sharp, apparently recent, sea-floor expressions. However, they may not have occurred during the 1964 earthquake; activation during that event can be established only for the faults south of Montague Island. Fault scarps are not continuous along the whole zone and sometimes thin, undisturbed strata cover a fault. The present evidence indicates that some faults are 20- to possibly 30-km long, but most faults in the zone are probably shorter. Strikes, where established, are parallel to the regional trend. In seismic records, steep reverse faults and probable normal faults are

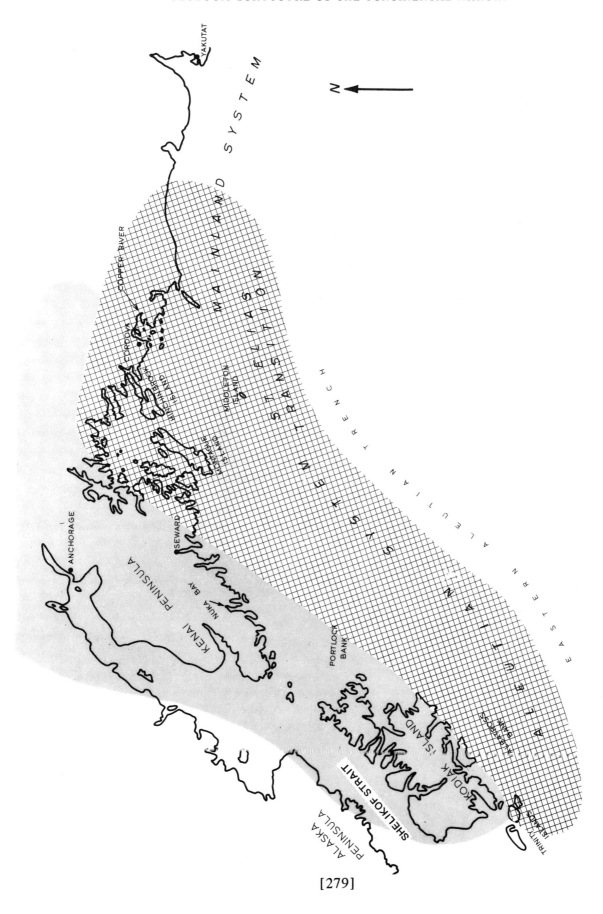

FIGURE 1   Location map showing areas where Plafker (1969, and this volume) reports elevation changes. Shading indicates subsidence; crosshatching indicates uplift.

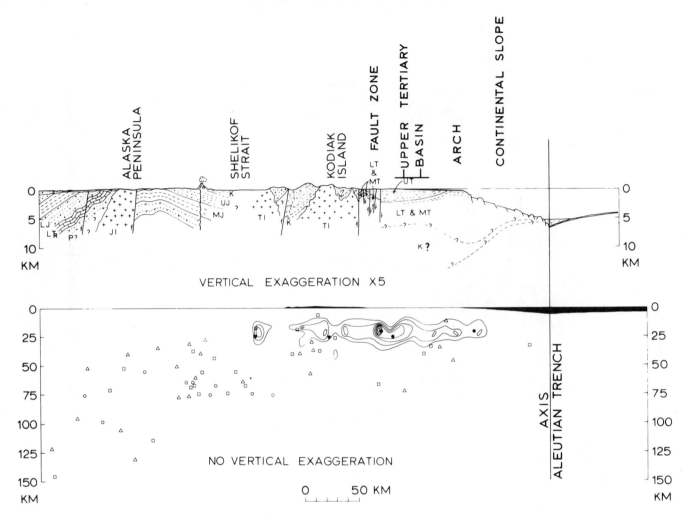

FIGURE 2 Section across the Aleutian structural System showing a composite of aftershock hypocenters from the latitude of Middleton Island to the southern end of Kodiak Island. Geology generalized from Burk (1965), Moore (1969), and seismic-refraction data from Shor (1964). P, Permian rocks; LTR, lower Triassic rocks; LJ, MJ, and UJ, lower, middle, and upper Jurassic rocks; Ji, Jurassic intrusive rocks; K, Cretaceous rocks; LT and MT, lower and middle Tertiary rocks; UT, upper Tertiary rocks; Ti, lower Tertiary intrusive rocks. Hypocenters are from Tobin and Sykes (1966); where location ○ is most accurate, □ is of intermediate accuracy, and △ is least accurate. Contours are strain release from aftershocks of the 1964 Alaska earthquake in 100-unit intervals of equivalent magnitude 3.0 earthquakes per 157 km². Individual aftershocks greater than magnitude 6.0 are shown with filled circles (●). Queried contacts extrapolated from seismic-refraction stations suggest a lower and middle Tertiary thickened section, possibly a continental rise, seaward of a similar Cretaceous feature.

seen (Figure 4). Because they are steep, the fault planes rarely show on the seismic records, but from the offset of other features their dip is thought to be steeper than 60°.

Reverse and normal faults are found close to each other, much like faults along the southeast coast of Kodiak Island. In fact, the steep faults seen in the marine seismic records are probably part of the subaerial Kodiak fault system. Capps (1937) observed that faults along the southeast coast of Kodiak Island are nearly vertical and are accompanied by local severe folding. Moore (1967; and *in* Grantz, 1964) describes these faults as part of a high-angle fault system separating Tertiary from Cretaceous (?) metamorphosed rocks with fault planes dipping either landward or seaward. On southern Montague Island, Plafker (1969, and this volume)

reports dips 55° northwest to vertical on faults that were active in 1964. Therefore the fault zone is probably best characterized as a system of normal and reverse faults dipping both landward and seaward, separating an uplifted area of metamorphosed Cretaceous and lower Tertiary rocks from a subsiding area of upper Tertiary rocks on the outer Continental Shelf.

TERTIARY BASIN AND ARCH ON THE OUTER CONTINENTAL SHELF

A deep basin of probable late Tertiary age lies between the fault zone off Kodiak Island and a broad arch at the edge of the Continental Shelf (Figure 2). Seismic-refraction studies

[280]

have indicated this basin to be 3-km deep off Kodiak (Shor, 1965). Between the Trinity and Chirikof islands to the southwest, the apparent thickness of truncated strata is about 4 km (von Huene, Malloy, Shor, and St.-Amand, 1967; and Figure 3, record VIII). A late Tertiary age of this basin fill is inferred because upper Miocene strata are exposed in a truncated part of the arch (von Huene and Shor, 1969). The basin has not been shown north of the Kodiak group of islands because of insufficient data.

The arch that bounds the basin varies in size along the strike. Seismic-reflection records northeast of Kodiak Island do not always show the arch in the upper 200 m of strata; however, the presence of a gravity ridge suggests that the arch may be continuous at depth (Barnes and others, 1966). The arch is seen around Middleton Island, which is the last of what was probably a series of late Tertiary islands on this arch in the Kenai–Kodiak area.

The crest of the arch is locally truncated by erosion. One erosion surface is now 400-m deep, or deeper than the lowest eustatic level of the sea. Repeated episodes of deformation involving both uplifted and limited subsidence seem to have locally affected the arch but probably never as a single regional event. The net effect, however, is one of uplift because fossils from intermediate ocean depths are found on the sea floor off Kodiak at the core of the arch (von Huene and Shor, 1969). Data are still grossly insufficient to determine what type of a stress field has formed this complex structure.

THE CONTINENTAL SLOPE

Along the Aleutian Trench the continental slope is rugged and is in the form of an irregular series of steps (Figure 5). In many respects the steps resemble some basin and range fault zones. Strata in small troughs are tilted and deformed in a manner suggestive of small graben or half graben. In at least one instance, the deformed strata suggest compressive folding. Individual blocks are often rotated both landward and seaward. In one instance the sediments may have slumped;

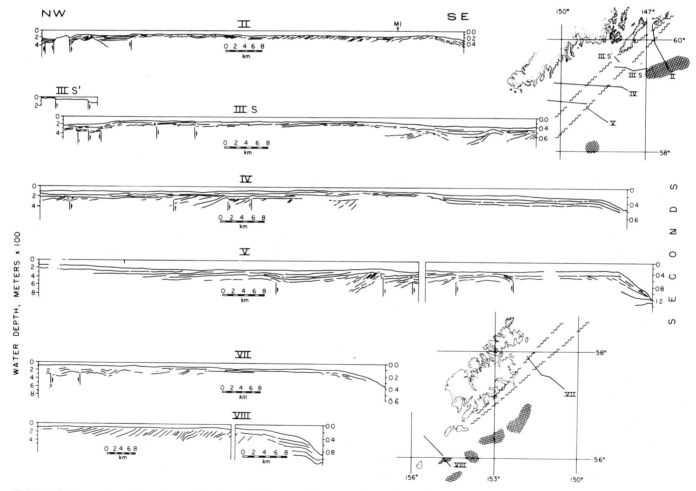

FIGURE 3 Simplified tracings of selected seismic-reflection records across the Continental Shelf. The offshore fault zone is indicated in the location map by a series of sigmoid lines; observed anticlinal areas at Shelf edge whose extent is interpreted from bathymetry are indicated by crosshatching. All faults are drawn vertical, but dips may be 60° in some cases. MI in profile A indicates projection of Middleton Island into the transect.

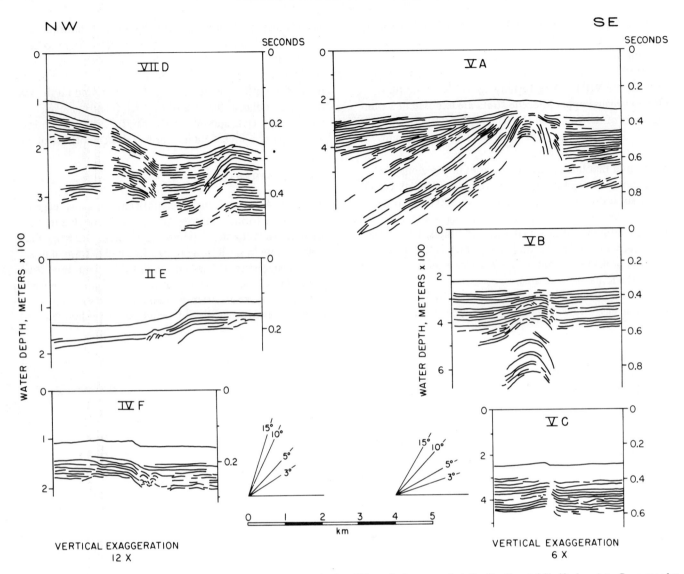

FIGURE 4 Tracing of seismic-reflection records across structures in the offshore fault zone and at the Continental Shelf edge. A to C are near lat. 58° 50′N and long. 149° 10′W, and A is included on transect D, Figure 3; B is 6 km southwest of A; C is 4 km southwest of B. Inset D was recorded at lat. 57° 55′N and long. 149° 20′W; inset E at lat. 60° 05′N and long. 146° 20′W, and it is part of transect A, Figure 3; and inset F at lat. 59° 35′N and long. 147° 30′W.

slumping is suggested by the series of hyperbolic reflectors at the foot of the slope in transect IV, although compressive folding cannot be ruled out. No magnetic anomaly, such as would be expected from a lava flow, is associated with these reflectors. Beneath a generally thin cover of sediment are hard rocks, below which no usable seismic reflections were received. Faint reflections that are occasionally seen in the records suggest that a lithified sequence of folded stratified rock may occur beneath the younger sequence. Structures in the thin sequence of sediment covering the slope indicate that the dominant deformational environment along the continen-

tal slope is one of extension, possibly resulting from uplift of the arch and depression of the Aleutian Trench.

EASTERN ALEUTIAN TRENCH

Seismic reflection records show three distinct rock units in the eastern Aleutian Trench. Lowest in the stratigraphic sequence is a unit beyond which no usable reflection information was observed—the so-called acoustic basement—which in turn is overlaid by two stratified units of different origin (Figure 5).

The acoustic basement has an undulating upper surface punctuated by seamounts. It is covered by an undeformed sequence of abyssal strata. The uniform thickness, uniform reflectivity, and parallel bedding of these strata suggest that they are deep-sea sediments of monotonous lithologies. Beneath the deep-ocean floor of the Gulf of Alaska these strata are horizontal, but they dip increasingly toward the continental slope (between 1° and 3°) as the abyssal plain gradually gives way to the Aleutian Trench. This dip of the abyssal section is assumed to have been caused by tilting during depres-

sion of the trench. In transects V, VI, and VII (Figure 5), tilting of undeformed strata occurs at a subtle hinge area, but in other transects the seaward limits of the Aleutian Trench are not defined by a sudden increase in tilt. An exception appears in transect V, where a small bump, a possible fold or basement high, marks a sharper hinge area.

The upper stratigraphic unit, deposited after the Aleutian Trench had developed (see Figure 3, transects V, III), is a wedge of subhorizontal strata along the axis of the Trench, confined seaward by the tilted abyssal strata and landward by

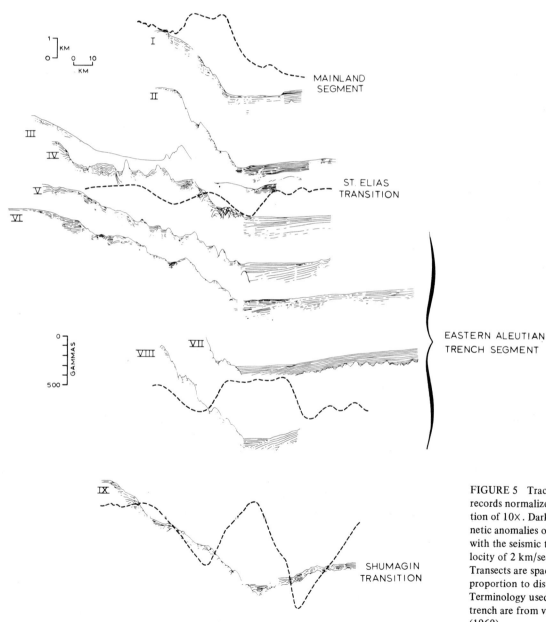

FIGURE 5 Tracings of seismic-reflection records normalized to a vertical exaggeration of 10X. Dark dashed lines are magnetic anomalies observed concurrently with the seismic transects. Assumed velocity of 2 km/sec used for vertical scale. Transects are spaced on illustration in proportion to distance along trench axis. Terminology used for segments of the trench are from von Huene and Shor (1969).

[283]

the continental slope. No major faulting seems to have occurred in the sedimentary wedge; only at Kodiak Seamount (Hamilton and von Huene, 1966) and to the northeast can a very gentle tilting of the trench fill be observed. The absence of deformation in the axial sediment wedge and its sharp contact with the underlying tilted abyssal sequence are most simply explained by assuming that an episode of sea-floor tilting was followed by an episode of sediment accumulation. The increase in cross-sectional area of the fill from the southwest to the northeast (Figure 5) may reflect different distances from the large sediment sources in the Alaska mainland rather than differential rates of subsidence.

The age of the eastern Aleutian Trench has been estimated from thicknesses of deep-ocean sediments that collected after the trench was depressed (von Huene and Shor, 1969). Calculated by using assumed rates of sedimentation, the maximum and minimum ages are 4.75 and 1.20 million years, respectively. A late Pliocene age is favored from consideration of these data and from the regional geology. If continuous ocean floor underthrusting is assumed, this estimate is the minimum age since the initiation of thrusting.

STRUCTURAL ELEMENTS OF THE MAINLAND SYSTEM

Less is known about the Mainland System, but it has similarities to and differences from the Aleutian System. The Mainland System has neither a well-developed trench (see Figure 5, transect I) nor an axial sediment wedge. Instead, there is a broad U-shaped trough formed by either tectonic or sedimentary processes. Strata draped over the lower continental slope continue into the trough without a tectonic or stratigraphic break (see Figure 5, transect I).

The continental slope is smooth, probably because of a relatively thick sediment cover. The juncture between slope and shelf is marked by a well-developed arch. Structurally this arch is similar to the arch of the Aleutian System, and it also forms the seaward wall of a large basin. The shoreward flank of the basin is not, however, a sharp geologic break such as the fault zone off Kodiak, Montague, and Hinchinbrook islands. From the few data available, there appears to be no sharp structural break near shore but rather a transition from more open structures on the shelf to tighter folds and large reverse faults on land. Structures on land adjacent to the Mainland System differ from those adjacent to the Aleutian System: They are dominantly steep reverse faults (Plafker, 1969, and this volume; Stoneley, 1967) rather than the nearly vertical fault of the type mapped around Prince William Sound (Condon, 1965; Condon and Cass, 1958) and on Kodiak Island (Moore, 1967).

TECTONIC HISTORY

Relative age of the two systems is not known and exactly how tectonic movement on the Aleutian System affects the Mainland System is unclear. In Prince William Sound, reverse faults of the Mainland System cross and apparently override faults of the Aleutian System (Condon and Cass, 1958), but the Aleutian System's continental margin appears tectonically more active and therefore younger. The possibility that the two systems are relatively independent and simultaneously active is suggested by their respective tectonic histories.

The Mainland System is thought by Stoneley (1967) to have been tectonically active throughout most of Tertiary time. There seems to have been no noticeable change of deformation style in Tertiary time, although changes in rates of deformation may have occurred.

The Aleutian System, on the other hand, has probably existed in its present form only during late Tertiary time. Development of the eastern Aleutian Trench, uplift of the outer continental margin, and subsidence of the large basin on the Continental Shelf probably occurred during the Pliocene, and possibly as late as the early Pleistocene. This deformation may have been simultaneous with uplift of the Alaska Peninsula (Burk, 1965).

Northeast of Kodiak Seamount, the trench subsided a little after it began to fill, but southwest of the seamount the trench appears tectonically quiet. After depression of the trench, the most active part of the Aleutian System appears to have been the continental slope and much of the Continental Shelf. On the Shelf a basin 3- to 4-km deep has formed since Pliocene (?) time, and on the basin's flanks, the fault zone and the arch at the edge of the shelf seem to be equally active tectonically.

RELATION OF DEFORMATION AND STRAIN RELEASE TO GEOLOGY OF THE CONTINENTAL MARGIN

The strain released by aftershocks of the 1964 earthquake was most intense under the Continental Shelf off Kodiak, Montague, and Hinchinbrook islands (Figure 6). A large amount of strain was released off Hinchinbrook Island in the structurally complex intersection between the Aleutian and Mainland systems. Because of this structural complexity, however, determining a correlation between strain release and faults in this area is difficult. At the southern end of the area a strong strain-release maximum occurs around Albatross Bank, a part of the arch at the edge of the Continental Shelf. Uplift and deformation of the arch are also indicated by the uplift of the area around Middleton Island (Plafker, 1969, and this volume), which, along with the origin of the tsunami

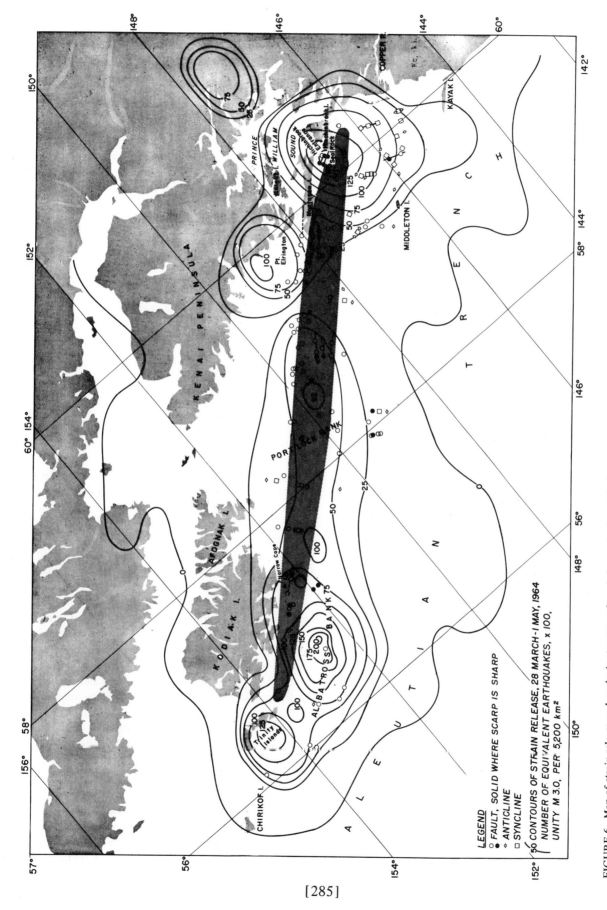

FIGURE 6 Map of strain release and geologic structures found along seismic and bathymetric traverses. Strain release summed in 0.4° radius circles. Contours are based on preliminary aftershock data from the U.S. Coast and Geodetic Survey and are smoothed graphically. Dark shaded area is the offshore zone of faults inferred from marine geophysical data.

at the outer edge of the shelf (Van Dorn, 1965; Spaeth and Berkman, 1969) indicates a possible surface expression of faulting; however, intense aftershock strain release was recorded along the arch only at Albatross Bank.

A linear belt of high strain release connecting the two terminal strain-release maxima follows closely the inferred offshore fault zone from Montague Island to Kodiak Island (Figure 6). Around Montague Island, in fact, well-developed segments of the fault zone and a portion of the area of maximum aftershock strain release coincide with an axis of maximum uplift and an axis of severe crustal flexure as delineated by Plafker (1969, and this volume). These axes may be virtually coincident around Montague Island. At the southern end of the aftershock area, where this fault zone dies out, the arch at the edge of the Continental Shelf may have been the structure most closely linked with strain release. Landward of the fault zone, a large area apparently deformed as a broad flexure (Plafker, 1969) without noticeable dislocation along faults. Seaward of the shelf, the amount of deformation during the 1964 earthquake cannot be determined. Sediment filling the Aleutian Trench is tilted only slightly, if at all, and strata are virtually undeformed.

A simple model explaining the mechanism of the earthquake is difficult to devise from the available data. It is important not to combine observations from the Mainland System with those from the Aleutian System and to recognize the structural complexities near their intersection. Both Press and Jackson (1965, and this volume) and Savage and Hastie (1966, and this volume) may have used elevation-change measurements from both structural systems and projected these points onto a plane normal to the strike of the Aleutian System to approximate the surface of deformation used in applying the dislocation theory to model the dip of the fault plane. Thus the deformation surface they used may descend too gradually beyond the area of maximum uplift. The area of uplift projected beyond the offshore fault zone has undergone net subsidence during late Tertiary time (Figure 2). Stauder and Bollinger (1966, and this volume) used a revised profile determined by George Plafker, but on the Continental Shelf between Montague and Middleton islands the surface of deformation is not known.

In the two models of a causative fault plane determined from the main-shock body wave (Stauder and Bollinger, 1966; Harding and Algermissen, 1969, and this volume), one fault plane is nearly vertical and the other is nearly horizontal. Stauder and Bollinger (1966) and Plafker (1969) have advanced reasons to favor the horizontal plane, whereas Harding and Algermissen (1969) favor the vertical plane. Nevertheless, von Huene, Malloy, Shor, and St.-Amand (1967) believe that neither plane can be decisively favored.

The model of a horizontal causative fault proposed by Plafker (1965, 1969) explains many observations from the 1964 earthquake. But it does not readily explain others,

especially those along the continental slope and in the Aleutian Trench (von Huene and Shor, 1969; von Huene, Malloy, Shor, and St.-Amand, 1967) (Figure 5). A near-vertical fault model satisfies data not readily explained by a large horizontal fault. In this model the fault zone just off Kodiak and Montague islands is a major zone of rupture, not a subsidiary fault. Its surface expression is a series of *en échelon* faults, some of which broke at the surface in 1964. The faults dip both landward and seaward at steep angles. Landward of the fault zone, an area has been uplifted by an unknown amount; seaward, an area has subsided as much as 4 km since Pliocene time. This fault zone corresponds roughly to the position of the sharp strain-release maximum, which is approximately 25-km deep and slightly seaward of the fault zone (see Figure 2).

The initial epicenter is about 100 km landward of the near-vertical fault. If the 1964 earthquake was a multiple rupture, as Wyss and Brune (1967, and this volume) suggest, the initial shocks would be the trigger for slippage along the offshore fault zone. This interpretation is consistent with the relatively mild ice breakup and landslide activity around the initial aftershock location, compared to the occurrences in the Copper River area and on the southern Kenai Peninsula that were observed on reconnaissance flights during the 2 weeks following the earthquake.

An appealing aspect of the near-vertical-fault model is that deformation during the 1964 earthquake is similar to net deformation during late Tertiary time. The vertical-fault model does not, however, explain some of the seismological evidence from the earthquake as well as does the horizontal-fault model, especially in the first-motion studies of Stauder and Bollinger (1966). The vertical-fault-plane model is also not compatible with the horizontal shifts observed by Parkin (1969, and this volume). The horizontal shift of Middleton Island, however, is difficult to explain with the horizontal-fault model.

The case for a horizontal megathrust as the causative fault has been forcefully argued by Plafker (1969). The most severe constraint on this hypothesis is the absence of strong indication of the megathrust in the Aleutian Trench, where it is thought to emerge at the sea floor. Plafker's model must be modified to explain the basin off Kodiak and the large vertical displacement in late Tertiary time on the major fault zone associated with aftershock strain release (von Huene, Malloy, Shor, and St.-Amand, 1967). Also, the area of sharp uplift at sea inferred by Plafker has been established only in the area south of Montague Island (Malloy and Merrill, 1969, and Oceanography and Coastal Engineering volume, in press), but in more than 12 crossings of this zone off Kodiak, no indication of a sharp area of uplift in 1964 has been noted.

The thrust-fault model is more appealing than a vertical-fault model because it explains many of the earthquake effects by postulating one large fault zone; it also agrees well with the popular hypothesis of sea-floor underthrusting; actually, however, neither model completely fits all the available data. The causative fault mechanism seems to be too complex to be explained by the data at hand. When supplemented by further study of the continental–oceanic crustal interaction and by detailed studies of the Continental Shelf, the data from the 1964 earthquake could lead to a better understanding of the hazards from future earthquakes along the Aleutian structural trend.

ACKNOWLEDGMENTS

I am particularly grateful to David S. McCulloch and Erk Reimnitz for their critical reviews. Their differences in opinion have contributed significantly to the development of the ideas presented.

POSTSCRIPT

After the 1964–1965 fieldwork that formed the basis for this report, additional fieldwork on the Continental Shelf (1967, 1968) and in the trench (1969, 1970) added significantly to knowledge of structure across the continental margin and modified my interpretation of geologic structure.

New seismic records across the continental slope off Kodiak Island indicate that the extensional structures seen in earlier seismic records are probably caused by gravity sliding. Slides are caused in part by oversteepening of the slope in response to uplift at the shelf break arch. Some slumps come to rest on the lower slope or even travel across the trench floor. These hummocky deposits generally mask reflections from below, including any deformed zones in underlying sediments. The probability of gravity sliding provides an explanation of the seeming paradox that the continental slope shows structures indicating extensional movement, while the assumed underthrusting should result in large-scale compression.

Seismic-refraction studies (Shor and von Huene, 1972) provide an estimate of maximum underthrust rate by showing the possible volume of deformed abyssal sediments incorporated into the continental margin. The estimated maximum rate is roughly equivalent to the rate derived from the plate tectonic model of Atwater (1970). However, estimated minimum rates show that a static or episodic model cannot be ruled out. Nevertheless, the continental margin crustal structure has a "thin skin" character that intuitively indicates lateral deforming forces.

Drill cores from Leg 18 of the Deep Sea Drilling Project indicate that tectonic processes on the slope and in the trench are more rapid than the estimates given in this paper. They establish that the oldest trench fill seen in seismic records was deposited 0.5 million years ago rather than in Pliocene time (von Huene and others, 1971). Deformed Quaternary sediment which appears as acoustic basement in the seismic records was recovered from a 2,000-m-high arch adjacent to the trench on the lower continental slope.

The ideas developed with the additional data are more compatible with the thrust-fault model for the 1964 earthquake than those discussed in this paper.

REFERENCES

Algermissen, S. T., W. A. Rinehart, R. W. Sherburne, and W. H. Dillinger, Jr., 1969. Preshocks and aftershocks of the Prince William Sound earthquake of March 28, 1964 *in* Volume II-B, C: The Prince William Sound, Alaska, earthquake of 1964 and aftershocks. Environmental Science Services Administration, U.S. Coast and Geodetic Survey. Washington: Government Printing Office. p. 79–130. Also *in* The Great Alaska Earthquake of 1964: Seismology and Geodesy. NAS Pub. 1602. Washington: National Academy of Sciences, 1972.

Atwater, Tanya, 1970. Implications of plate tectonics for the Cenozoic tectonic evolution of Western North America. *Geological Society of America Bulletin*, 81 (December), 3513–3535.

Barnes, David F., W. H. Lucas, E. V. Mace, and R. J. Malloy, 1966. Reconnaissance gravity and other geophysical data from the continental end of the Aleutian Arc (Abstract). *Proceedings, American Association of Petroleum Geologists*, 50 (March), 644.

Burk, C. A., 1965. Geology of the Alaska Peninsula—Island arc and continental margin. Geological Society of America Memoir 99. New York: The Geological Society of America. 250 p.

Capps, S. R., 1937. Kodiak and adjacent islands, Alaska. U.S. Geological Survey Bulletin 880-C. Washington: Government Printing Office. p. 111–184.

Condon, William H., 1965. Map of eastern Prince William Sound area, Alaska, showing fracture traces inferred from aerial photographs. U.S. Geological Survey Miscellaneous Geologic Investigations Map I-453. Washington: U.S. Geological Survey.

Condon, William H., and John T. Cass, 1958. Map of a part of the Prince William Sound area, Alaska, showing linear geologic features as shown on aerial photographs. U.S. Geological Survey Miscellaneous Geologic Investigations Map I-273. Washington: U.S. Geological Survey.

Grantz, Arthur, 1964. Committee report *in* Mineral and water resources of Alaska. 88th Congress, 2nd Session, p. 59.

Hamilton, Edwin L., and Roland E. von Huene, 1966. Kodiak Seamount not flat-topped. *Science*, 154 (December 9), 1323–1325.

Harding, Samuel T., and S. T. Algermissen, 1969. The focal mechanism of the Prince William Sound earthquake of March 28, 1964, and related earthquakes *in* Volume II-B,C: The Prince William Sound, Alaska, earthquake of 1964 and aftershocks. Environmental Science Services Administration, U.S. Coast and Geodetic Survey. Washington: Government Printing Office. p. 185–221. Also *in* The Great Alaska Earthquake of 1964: Seismology and Geodesy. NAS Pub. 1602. Washington: National Academy of Sciences, 1972.

Malloy, Richard J., and George F. Merrill, 1969. Vertical crustal movement of the sea floor associated with the Prince William Sound, Alaska, earthquake *in* Volume II-B,C: The Prince William Sound, Alaska, earthquake of 1964 and aftershocks. Environmental Science Services Administration, U.S. Coast and Geodetic Survey. Washington: Government Printing Office. p. 327–338. Also *in* The Great Alaska Earthquake of 1964: Oceanography and Coastal Engineering. NAS Pub. 1605. Washington: National Academy of Sciences, in press.

Matumoto, Tosimatu, and Robert A. Page, Jr., 1969. Microaftershocks following the Alaska earthquake of March 28, 1964: Determination of hypocenters and crustal velocities in the Kenai Peninsula–Prince William Sound area *in* Volume II-B,C: The Prince William Sound, Alaska, earthquake of 1964 and aftershocks. Environmental Science Services Administration, U.S. Coast and Geodetic Survey. Washington: Government Printing Office. p. 157–173. Also *in* The Great Alaska Earthquake of 1964: Seismology and Geodesy. NAS Pub. 1602. Washington: National Academy of Sciences, 1972.

Moore, George W., 1967. Preliminary geologic map of Kodiak Island and vicinity, Alaska. U.S. Geological Survey Open-File Map. Scale: 1:250,000. Washington: U.S. Geological Survey.

Moore, George W., 1969. New formations on Kodiak and adjacent islands, Alaska *in* Changes in stratigraphic nomenclature, 1967. U.S. Geological Survey Bulletin 1274-A. Washington: Government Printing Office. p. 27–34.

Parkin, Ernest J., 1969. Horizontal crustal movements determined from surveys after the Alaskan earthquake of 1964 *in* Volume III: The Prince William Sound, Alaska, earthquake of 1964 and aftershocks. Environmental Science Services Administration, U.S. Coast and Geodetic Survey. Washington: Government Printing Office. p. 35–98. Also *in* The Great Alaska Earthquake of 1964: Seismology and Geodesy. NAS Pub. 1602. Washington: National Academy of Sciences, 1972.

Plafker, George, 1965. Tectonic deformation associated with the 1964 Alaska earthquake. *Science*, 148 (June 25), 1675–1687.

Plafker, George, 1969. Tectonics of the March 27, 1964, Alaska earthquake. U.S. Geological Survey Professional Paper 543-I. Washington: Government Printing Office. 74 p. Also *in* The Great Alaska Earthquake of 1964: Seismology and Geodesy. NAS Pub. 1602. Washington: National Academy of Sciences, 1972.

Press, Frank, and David Jackson, 1965. Alaskan earthquake, 27 March 1964: Vertical extent of faulting and elastic strain energy release. *Science*, 147 (February 19), 867–868. Also *in* The Great Alaska Earthquake of 1964: Seismology and Geodesy. NAS Pub. 1602. Washington: National Academy of Sciences, 1972.

Savage, J. C., and L. M. Hastie, 1966. Surface deformation associated with dip-slip faulting. *Journal of Geophysical Research*, 71 (October 15), 4897–4904. Also *in* The Great Alaska Earthquake of 1964: Seismology and Geodesy. NAS Pub. 1602. Washington: National Academy of Sciences, 1972.

Shor, George G., Jr., 1964. Structure of the Bering Sea and the Aleutian Ridge. *Marine Geology*, 1 (No. 3), 213–219.

Shor, George G., Jr., 1965. Structure of the Aleutian Ridge, Aleutian Trench and Bering Sea (Abstract). *Transactions, American Geophysical Union,* 46 (March), 106.

Shor, George G., Jr., and Roland von Huene, in press. Marine seismic refraction studies near Kodiak, Alaska. *Geophysics.*

Spaeth, Mark G., and Saul C. Berkman, 1969. The tsunami of March 28, 1964, as recorded at tide stations *in* Volume II-B,C: The Prince William Sound, Alaska, earthquake of 1964 and aftershocks. Environmental Science Services Administration, U.S. Coast and Geodetic Survey. Washington: Government Printing Office. p. 223–307.

Stauder, William, and G. A. Bollinger, 1966. The focal mechanism of the Alaska earthquake of March 28, 1964, and of its aftershock sequence. *Journal of Geophysical Research*, 71 (November 15), 5283–5296. Also *in* The Great Alaska Earthquake of 1964: Seismology and Geodesy. NAS Pub. 1602. Washington: National Academy of Sciences, 1972.

Stoneley, R., 1967. The structural development of the Gulf of Alaska sedimentary province in southern Alaska. *Geological Society of London Quarterly Journal*, 123 (September 15), 25–27.

Tobin, Don G., and Lynn R. Sykes, 1966. Relationship of hypocenters of earthquakes to the geology of Alaska. *Journal of Geophysical Research*, 71 (March 15), 1659–1667.

Van Dorn, William G., 1965. Tsunamis. *Advances in Hydroscience*, 2 (Annual), 1–47.

von Huene, Roland, 1966. Glacial marine geology of Nuka Bay, Alaska, and the adjacent Continental Shelf. *Marine Geology*, 4 (August), 291–304.

von Huene, Roland, L. D. Kulm, J. R. Duncan, J. C. Ingle, S. A. Kling, L. M. Musich, D. J. W. Piper, R. M. Pratt, H. J. Schrader, O. Weser, and S. W. Wise, Jr., 1971. Deep Sea Drilling Project: Leg 18. *Geotimes*, 16 (October), 12–16.

von Huene, Roland, E. H. Lathram, and Erk Reimnitz, 1971. Possible petroleum resources of offshore Pacific-margin Tertiary basin, Alaska *in* American Association of Petroleum Geologists Memoir 15, Vol. I. Washington: American Society of Petroleum Geologists. p. 136–151.

von Huene, Roland, Richard J. Malloy, George G. Shor, Jr., and Pierre St.-Amand, 1967b. Geologic structures in the aftershock region of the 1964 Alaskan earthquake. *Journal of Geophysical Research*, 72 (July 15), 3649–3660.

von Huene, Roland, and George G. Shor, Jr., 1969. The structure and tectonic history of the eastern Aleutian Trench. *Geological Society of America Bulletin*, 80 (October), 1889–1902.

von Huene, Roland, George G. Shor, Jr., and Erk Reimnitz, 1967. Geological interpretation of seismic profiles in Prince William Sound, Alaska. *Geological Society of America Bulletin*, 78 (February), 259–268.

Wyss, Max, and James N. Brune, 1967. The Alaska earthquake of 28 March 1964: A complex multiple rupture. *Bulletin of the Seismological Society of America*, 57 (October), 1017–1023. Also *in* The Great Alaska Earthquake of 1964: Seismology and Geodesy. NAS Pub. 1602. Washington: National Academy of Sciences, 1972.

FRANK PRESS*

CALIFORNIA INSTITUTE OF TECHNOLOGY

Reprinted with minor changes from
Journal of Geophysical Research, Vol. 70, No. 10,
"Displacements, Strains and Tilts at Teleseismic Distances"

Displacements, Strains, and Tilts at Teleseismic Distances

Abstract. The dislocation theory representation of faulting of Vvedenskaya, Steketee, Chinnery, and Maruyama is used to compute the residual displacement, strain, and tilt fields at intermediate and large distances from major earthquakes. It is shown that the distant fields are large enough to be detected by modern instruments. The vertical displacement field from the Alaskan earthquake of March 27, 1964, indicates that the primary fault extended to a depth of 150 to 200 km and that it probably came to within 15 km of the surface. The residual strain observed at Hawaii amounted to 10^{-8}, a value which is reasonably consistent with the extent of faulting and the displacements near the source. The elastic strain energy release was about 10^{25} ergs. Other observations of residual strains and tilts are examined. In some cases nonfaulting sources are probably involved. In other cases the observations may be a spurious manifestation of instrumental hysteresis. The Mindlin-Cheng catalog of fields from various nuclei of strain in a half-space offers a convenient way to derive residual displacements from diverse sources, including those of Chinnery and Maruyama.

Introduction. The residual displacement, strain, and tilt fields associated with an earthquake are diagnostic of the source mechanism, possibly even to a greater extent than are the propagating waves. The latter typically involve polarity of P waves, plane of polarization of S waves, spectral radiation patterns of surface waves—all of which emphasize frequencies higher than the reciprocal time duration of action at the source. Only data that include very long mantle surface waves, free oscillations, and changes in the static fields are diagnostic of the entire source region and not just the region surrounding the initial rupture. Mantle surface waves and free oscillations are excited only by the larger earthquakes. Studies of source mechanism using these waves have been initiated [*Aki*, 1964; *Ben-Menahem and Toksöz*, 1963; *Brune*, 1962] and much progress has been made. However, applications have mostly been limited to waves with insufficient length in comparison with the source dimensions. The static fields have not received much attention, particularly because data are scarce and interpretation methods are not far advanced. The vertical extent of faulting has been inferred from near displacement fields and energy decay with distance [*Byerly and DeNoyer*, 1958; *Chinnery*, 1961; *Kasahara*, 1957; *Knopoff*, 1958]. The results of

these studies have yielded surprisingly shallow depths for major faults. For example, estimates of 2 to 10 km were obtained for the San Andreas fault from data of the San Francisco earthquake of 1906. Theoretical residual displacements in the near field have been computed and contoured by several authors [*Chinnery*, 1961; *Maruyama*, 1964].

Strains and tilts at intermediate and teleseismic distances have been reported, but no interpretations have been offered [*Benioff*, 1963; *Bonchkovsky*, 1962].

It is my purpose in this paper to review observations of displacements, strains, and tilts at various distances, to offer some new observations, and to take a position as to their reality. The method will be to obtain these fields theoretically from a plausible fault model and to ascertain whether these fields would be detectable by existing displacement meters (primarily tide gages at this time), strain seismographs, and tiltmeters. No effort will be made to deduce source mechanism in this paper because the data are too scarce. However, if distant static fields are observable, the possibilities are many for installing appropriate instruments and monitoring seismic belts. In a sense, the distinction between dynamic and static monitoring is an artificial one, and one may view the observation and interpretation of static fields as 'zero frequency seismology.'

The fault model. Geodetic observations indi-

---

*Now with Massachusetts Institute of Technology.

cate that strain accumulation is a continuing phenomenon in seismic belts. It is natural, therefore, to associate earthquakes, at least the shallow ones, with a sudden release of strain energy accompanying an abrupt change in strength over a surface. Unfortunately, the pre-existing strain field, the mechanism of fracture, and the extent of the surface are unknown. Theory is available only for simple strain fields and elementary geometries. For these reasons, only overly idealized cases have been discussed in the literature [*Knopoff*, 1958; *Archambeau*, 1964; *Press and Archambeau*, 1962].

Under these circumstances, *Vvedenskaya's* [1956] and *Steketee's* [1958] representation of a fault as a displacement dislocation surface in an elastic half-space has much merit, particularly if our interest is in computing the displacement, strain, and tilt fields at locations removed from the fault zone. The basic assumption in this procedure is that the displacements following an earthquake can be modeled by the corresponding fields of a dislocation sheet with displacement discontinuity matching the observed slip. *Chinnery* [1961, 1963] used Steketee's results in calculating the displacement and stress field in the vicinity of a vertical, rectangular, strike-slip fault. *Maruyama* [1964] made some formal extensions of Steketee's work and calculated the near displacement field for a vertical rectangular dip-slip fault. Maruyama summarizes the earlier work of Sezawa, Whipple, Soeda, and Yamakawa, who used various forms of internal strain nuclei to represent earthquake sources.

Steketee showed that the displacement field u_k corresponding to a displacement dislocation U_i across a dislocation surface Σ is given by

$$u_k = \frac{1}{8\pi\mu} \iint_\Sigma U_i \omega_{ij}{}^k \alpha_j \, d\Sigma \qquad (1)$$

Here a_j are the direction cosines of the normal to the surface element $d\Sigma$ and μ is the rigidity.

The $\omega_{ij}{}^k$ are obtainable from the displacements corresponding to nuclei of strain in a half-space (equation 5). Steketee showed a method of obtaining the six $\omega_{ij}{}^k$ fields by using a Green's function and derived $\omega_{12}{}^k$, which are pertinent to a vertical strike-slip fault. Maruyama derived the remaining five functions. Although both authors took advantage of a condensed formulation made possible by the use of the Galerkin vector strain function, the derivations are rather lengthy.

The appropriate value for $\omega_{ij}{}^k$ can be derived in a straightforward manner by using results by *Mindlin and Cheng* [1950], who gave explicit expressions for the displacement and stress fields for half-space nuclei of strain consisting of single forces and double forces with and without moment. It is only necessary to write the single force results since the other forms can be obtained by taking appropriate derivatives. These results for the half-space make possible the solution of many problems in terms of combinations of strain nuclei in the same way that the classical results for nuclei in solids of unlimited extent have been used.

The half-space occupies the region $x_3 > 0$. Point nuclei are at $\xi_1, 0, \xi_3$.

$$R^2 = (x_1 - \xi_1)^2 + x_2{}^2 + (x_3 - \xi_3)^2$$

$$Q^2 = (x_1 - \xi_1)^2 + x_2{}^2 + (x_3 + \xi_3)^2$$

λ, μ are Lamé's constants and ν is Poisson's ratio.

For a single force in x_1 direction with magnitude $8\pi\mu(\lambda+2\mu)/(\lambda+\mu)$,

$$
\begin{aligned}
u_1{}^1 = {} & \frac{3 - 4\nu}{R} + \frac{1}{Q} \\
& + \frac{2\xi_3 x_3}{Q^3} + \frac{4(1 - \nu)(1 - 2\nu)}{Q + x_3 + \xi_3} \\
& + (x_1 - \xi_1)^2 \left[\frac{1}{R^3} + \frac{3 - 4\nu}{Q^3} \right. \\
& \left. - \frac{6\xi_3 x_3}{Q^5} - \frac{4(1 - \nu)(1 - 2\nu)}{Q(Q + x_3 + \xi_3)^2} \right]
\end{aligned}
\qquad (2)
$$

$$
\begin{aligned}
u_2{}^1 = {} & (x_1 - \xi_1) x_2 \left[\frac{1}{R^3} + \frac{3 - 4\nu}{Q^3} \right. \\
& \left. - \frac{6\xi_3 x_3}{Q^5} - \frac{4(1 - \nu)(1 - 2\nu)}{Q(Q + x_3 + \xi_3)^2} \right]
\end{aligned}
$$

and

$$
\begin{aligned}
u_3{}^1 = {} & (x_1 - \xi_1) \left[\frac{x_3 - \xi_3}{R^3} + \frac{(3 - 4\nu)(x_3 - \xi_3)}{Q^3} \right. \\
& \left. - \frac{6\xi_3 x_3 (x_3 + \xi_3)}{Q^5} + \frac{4(1 - \nu)(1 - 2\nu)}{Q(Q + x_3 + \xi_3)} \right]
\end{aligned}
$$

For a single force in x_2 direction with magnitude $8\pi\mu(\lambda+2\mu)/(\lambda+\mu)$,

$$u_1{}^2 = (x_1 - \xi_1)x_2\left[\frac{1}{R^3} + \frac{3 - 4\nu}{Q^3}\right.$$

$$\left. - \frac{6\xi_3 x_3}{Q^5} - \frac{4(1 - \nu)(1 - 2\nu)}{Q(Q + x_3 + \xi_3)^2}\right]$$

$$u_2{}^2 = \frac{3 - 4\nu}{R} + \frac{1}{Q}$$

$$+ \frac{2\xi_3 x_3}{Q^3} + \frac{4(1 - \nu)(1 - 2\nu)}{(Q + x_3 + \xi_3)}$$

$$+ x_2{}^2\left[\frac{1}{R^3} + \frac{3 - 4\nu}{Q^3}\right.$$

$$\left. - \frac{6\xi_3 x_3}{Q^5} - \frac{4(1 - \nu)(1 - 2\nu)}{Q(Q + x_3 + \xi_3)^2}\right] \tag{3}$$

and

$$u_3{}^2 = x_2\left[\frac{x_3 - \xi_3}{R^3} + \frac{(3 - 4\nu)(x_3 - \xi_3)}{Q^3}\right.$$

$$\left. - \frac{6\xi_3 x_3(x_3 + \xi_3)}{Q^5} + \frac{4(1 - \nu)(1 - 2\nu)}{Q(Q + x_3 + \xi_3)}\right]$$

For a single force in x_3 direction with magnitude $8\pi\mu(\lambda + 2\mu)/(\lambda + \mu)$,

$$u_1{}^3 = (x_1 - \xi_1)\left[\frac{x_3 - \xi_3}{R^3} + \frac{(3 - 4\nu)(x_3 - \xi_3)}{Q^3}\right.$$

$$\left. + \frac{6\xi_3 x_3(x_3 + \xi_3)}{Q^5} - \frac{4(1 - \nu)(1 - 2\nu)}{Q(Q + x_3 + \xi_3)}\right]$$

$$u_2{}^3 = x_2\left[\frac{x_3 - \xi_3}{R^3} + \frac{(3 - 4\nu)(x_3 - \xi_3)}{Q^3}\right.$$

$$\left. + \frac{6\xi_3 x_3(x_3 + \xi_3)}{Q^5} - \frac{4(1 - \nu)(1 - 2\nu)}{Q(Q + x_3 + \xi_3)}\right] \tag{4}$$

and

$$u_3{}^3 = \frac{3 - 4\nu}{R}$$

$$+ \frac{8(1 - \nu)^2 - (3 - 4\nu)}{Q} + \frac{(x_3 - \xi_3)^2}{R^3}$$

$$+ \frac{(3 - 4\nu)(x_3 + \xi_3)^2 - 2\xi_3 x_3}{Q^3}$$

$$+ \frac{6\xi_3 x_3(x_3 + \xi_3)^2}{Q^5}$$

Noting that (1) assumes force nuclei of magnitude $8\pi\mu$ and taking into account that x_j and ξ_j

are interchanged in Mindlin vis-a-vis Steketee, we can show that

$$\omega_{ij}{}^k = \frac{\lambda + \mu}{\lambda + 2\mu}\left[\lambda\delta_{ij}\frac{\partial u_k{}^l}{\partial \xi_l}\right.$$

$$\left. + \mu\left(\frac{\partial u_k{}^i}{\partial \xi_j} + \frac{\partial u_k{}^j}{\partial \xi_i}\right)\right] \tag{5}$$

When $i = j$, the $\partial u_k{}^l/\partial \xi_l$ (summed over $1 = 1$, 2, 3) correspond to displacements from a center of dilatation and the $\partial u_k{}^i/\partial \xi_i$ correspond to double forces without moment. For $i \neq j$, the $(\partial u_k{}^i/\partial \xi_j + \partial u_k{}^j/\partial \xi_i)$ are displacements from two coplanar, mutually perpendicular double forces, each with moment. These force systems are shown schematically in Figure 1.

In this discussion we are interested in vertical strike-slip and dip-slip faults. If the fault is in the plane $\xi_2 = 0$ and extends horizontally and vertically over the ranges $-L \leq \xi_1 \leq L$ and $d \leq \xi_3 \leq D$, respectively, for strike-slip equation 1 takes the form

$$u_k = \frac{(\lambda + \mu)U_1}{8\pi(\lambda + 2\mu)}$$

$$\cdot \int_d^D \int_{-L}^L \left(\frac{\partial u_k{}^1}{\partial \xi_2} + \frac{\partial u_k{}^2}{\partial \xi_1}\right) d\xi_1\, d\xi_3 \tag{6}$$

and for dip-slip it is

$$u_k = \frac{(\lambda + \mu)U_3}{8\pi(\lambda + 2\mu)}$$

$$\cdot \int_d^D \int_{-L}^L \left(\frac{\partial u_k{}^3}{\partial \xi_2} + \frac{\partial u_k{}^2}{\partial \xi_3}\right) d\xi_1\, d\xi_3 \tag{7}$$

where U_1 and U_3 are the horizontal and vertical displacement dislocations across the fault. After somewhat lengthy evaluations and with the assumption $\lambda = \mu$, these integrations can be reduced to the following expressions for displacements, horizontal strains, and tilts at the free surface $(x_1, x_2, 0)$ where $R = Q$. We use Chinnery's notation $\|$ to represent the substitution $f(\xi_1, \xi_3)\| = f(L, D) - f(L, d) - f(-L, D) + f(-L, d)$.

For *strike-slip* the *displacements* are

$$u_1 = \frac{U_1}{8\pi}\left\{-\frac{x_2(x_1 - \xi_1)(3R + 4\xi_3)}{R(R + \xi_3)^2}\right.$$

$$\left. + 4\tan^{-1}\frac{x_2 R}{\xi_3(x_1 - \xi_1)}\right\}\Big\|$$

$$u_2 = \frac{U_1}{8\pi}\left\{\ln(R + \xi_3) + \frac{\xi_3}{R + \xi_3}\right.$$

$$\left. - \frac{x_2{}^2(3R + 4\xi_3)}{R(R + \xi_3)^2}\right\}\Big|\Big| \qquad (8)$$

$$u_3 = \frac{U_1}{4\pi}\left\{\frac{x_2(R + 2\xi_3)}{R(R + \xi_3)}\right\}\Big|\Big|$$

the *strains* are

$$\frac{\partial u_1}{\partial x_1} = -\frac{U_3}{2\pi}\left[\frac{x_2(x_1 - \xi_1)}{R^3}\right]\Big|\Big|$$

$$\frac{\partial u_1}{\partial x_2} = \frac{U_3}{2\pi}\left[\frac{R^2 - x_2{}^2}{R^3}\right]\Big|\Big|$$

$$\frac{\partial u_2}{\partial x_1} = -\frac{U_3}{2\pi}\left[\frac{x_2{}^2}{R^3}\right]\Big|\Big|$$

$$\frac{\partial u_2}{\partial x_2} = -\frac{U_3}{2\pi} \qquad (12)$$

$$\frac{\partial u_1}{\partial x_1} = \frac{U_1}{8\pi}\left\langle\frac{x_2}{(R + \xi_3)^2}\left\{1 - \frac{(x_1 - \xi_1)^2[3R(R + \xi_3) - (3R + 4\xi_3)(3R + \xi_3)]}{R^3(R + \xi_3)}\right\}\right\rangle\Big|\Big|$$

$$\frac{\partial u_1}{\partial x_2} = \frac{U_1}{8\pi}\left\langle\frac{(x_1 - \xi_1)}{R}\left\{\frac{4\xi_3}{x_2{}^2 + \xi_3{}^2} - \frac{7R + 8\xi_3}{(R + \xi_3)^2} - \frac{x_2{}^2[3R(R + \xi_3) - (3R + 4\xi_3)(3R + \xi_3)]}{R^2(R + \xi_3)^3}\right\}\right\rangle\Big|\Big|$$

$$\frac{\partial u_2}{\partial x_1} = \frac{U_1}{8\pi}\left\langle\frac{(x_1 - \xi_1)}{(R + \xi_3)^2}\left\{1 - \frac{x_2{}^2[3R(R + \xi_3) - (3R + 4\xi_3)(3R + \xi_3)]}{R^3(R + \xi_3)}\right\}\right\rangle\Big|\Big|$$

$$\frac{\partial u_2}{\partial x_2} = \frac{U_1}{8\pi}\left\langle\frac{x_2}{(R + \xi_3)^2}\left\{1 - \frac{2(3R + 4\xi_3)}{R} - \frac{x_2{}^2[3R(R + \xi_3) - (3R + 4\xi_3)(3R + \xi_3)]}{R^3(R + \xi_3)}\right\}\right\rangle\Big|\Big| \qquad (9)$$

and the *tilts* are

$$\frac{\partial u_3}{\partial x_1} = \frac{U_1}{4\pi}\left\{\frac{x_2(x_1 - \xi_1)[R(R + \xi_3) - (R + 2\xi_3)(2R + \xi_3)]}{R^3(R + \xi_3)^2}\right\}\Big|\Big|$$

$$\frac{\partial u_3}{\partial x_2} = \frac{U_1}{4\pi}\left\{\frac{x_2{}^2[R(R + \xi_3) - (R + 2\xi_3)(2R + \xi_3)]}{R^3(R + \xi_3)^2} + \frac{R + 2\xi_3}{R(R + \xi_3)}\right\}\Big|\Big| \qquad (10)$$

For *dip-slip* the *displacements* are

$$u_1 = \frac{U_3}{2\pi}\left[\frac{x_2}{R}\right]\Big|\Big|$$

$$u_2 = -\frac{U_3}{2\pi}\left[\frac{x_2{}^2(x_1 - \xi_1)}{R(x_2{}^2 + \xi_3{}^2)}\right]\Big|\Big| \qquad (11)$$

$$u_3 = \frac{U_3}{2\pi}\left[\frac{x_2\xi_3(x_1 - \xi_1)}{R(x_2{}^2 + \xi_3{}^2)}\right.$$

$$\left. + \tan^{-1}\frac{x_2 R}{\xi_3(x_1 - \xi_1)}\right]\Big|\Big|$$

the *strains* are

$$\cdot\left[\frac{x_2(x_1 - \xi_1)(2R^2\xi_3{}^2 - x_2{}^2\xi_3{}^2 - x_2{}^4)}{R^3(x_2{}^2 + \xi_3{}^2)^2}\right]\Big|\Big|$$

and the *tilts* are

$$\frac{\partial u_3}{\partial x_1} = \frac{U_3}{2\pi}\left\{\frac{x_2\xi_3}{R}\left[\frac{1}{R^2}\right.\right.$$

$$\left.\left. - \frac{1}{(x_1 - \xi_1)^2 + x_2{}^2}\right]\right\}\Big|\Big|$$

$$\frac{\partial u_3}{\partial x_2} = \frac{U_3}{2\pi}\left\{\frac{(x_1 - \xi_1)\xi_3}{(x_2{}^2 + \xi_3{}^2)}\right.$$

$$\cdot\left[\frac{\xi_3{}^2 - x_2{}^2}{R(x_2{}^2 + \xi_3{}^2)} + \frac{(x_1 - \xi_1)^2 + \xi_3{}^2}{R^3}\right.$$

$$\left.\left. + \frac{x_2{}^2 + \xi_3{}^2}{R[(x_1 - \xi_1)^2 + x_2{}^2]}\right]\right\}\Big|\Big| \qquad 13)$$

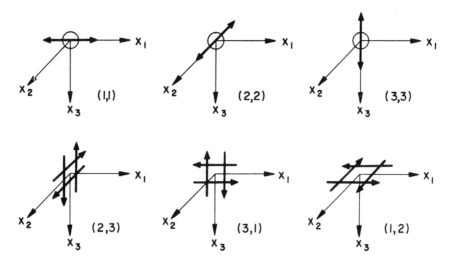

Fig. 1. Representation of force systems corresponding to ω_{ij}.

The displacements for strike-slip faults are the same as those given by *Chinnery* [1961]. The displacements for dip-slip faults correspond to those given by *Maruyama* [1964]. These investigators also presented numerical results for the near displacement field x_1, $x_2 \sim 2L$ for $d = 0$ and several values of D. In this paper we are mostly concerned with the distant field x_1, $x_2 \sim 10L$ for displacements, strains, and tilts.

The fields at teleseismic distances. Equations 8 to 13 have been programmed for automatically contoured output from an IBM 7094 computer. Results are given in Figures 2 to 10 for the two cases of $D = 0.1L$ and $D = 1.0L$ with $d = 0$. The map scale is in units of half-fault length. Dimensionless displacements u_k/U_1 or u_k/U_3 are plotted. The strain and tilt results assume slip values U_1 or U_3 of $\frac{1}{3} \times 10^{-4}L$. This corresponds to a 10-meter displacement for a fault with a total length of 600 km. Since strains and tilts are proportional to U_i the results can readily be transformed to correspond to any particular situation.

Several features of special interest emerge from these figures. Since modern instruments can detect residual strain and tilt changes in the range 10^{-9} to 10^{-8} under typical noise conditions, we see that when such changes accompany major earthquakes they are observable to distances of the order of several thousand kilometers. Displacements as large as a half-centimeter occur at these distances. Whether these surprisingly large residual displacements are detectable is questionable. Sea level changes of this magnitude are readily measurable, but the permanent offsets must be detected in the presence of waves, tides, seasonal changes, and local eustatic changes. Detection of residual displacements by pendulum seismographs would require multiple integration of trace motion in the presence of even larger transient waves, a difficult task which was recently attempted by *Berckhemer and Schneider* [1964].

Observations of displacements, strains, and tilts. A number of investigators have reported residual strains and tilts at large distances from earthquakes. *Benioff* [1963] displayed a strain seismogram with a residual offset following the Montana shock of August 18, 1959 (magnitude 7.2, distance 1200 km). *Bonchkovsky* [1962], *Nishimura* [1953], and *Tomaschek* [1955] reported tilts at large distances from major earthquakes. There is some question concerning the reality of these observations. The instruments are extremely sensitive and it is not impossible that they will undergo a permanent mechanical or electrical offset following the large impulses delivered by the transient waves. In what follows, I will attempt to make a case that the strain observations probably represent real deformation in the ground and that the tilts could be spurious. The procedure of comparing the observed values of strains and tilts with values expected from the fault model described earlier is followed, and local field evidence is used to estimate the source parameters of fault length, vertical extent, and slip. Preliminary results from a new photo-optical transducer on the

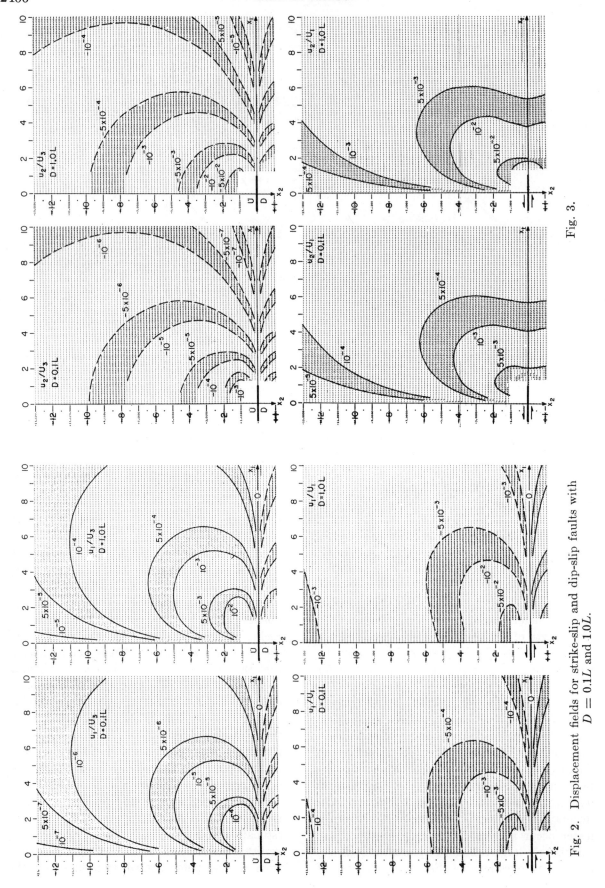

Fig. 2. Displacement fields for strike-slip and dip-slip faults with
$D = 0.1L$ and $1.0L$.

Fig. 3.

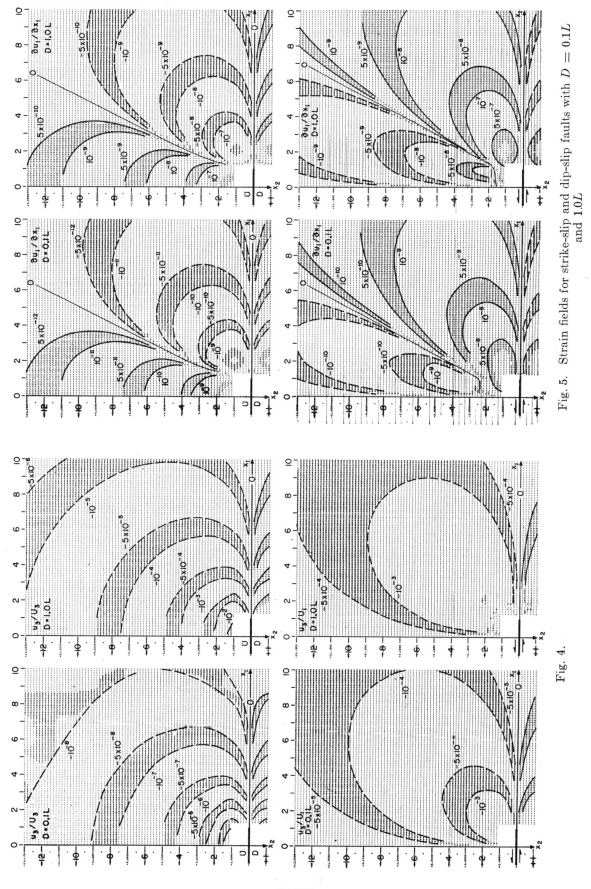

Fig. 5. Strain fields for strike-slip and dip-slip faults with $D = 0.1L$ and $1.0L$

Fig. 4.

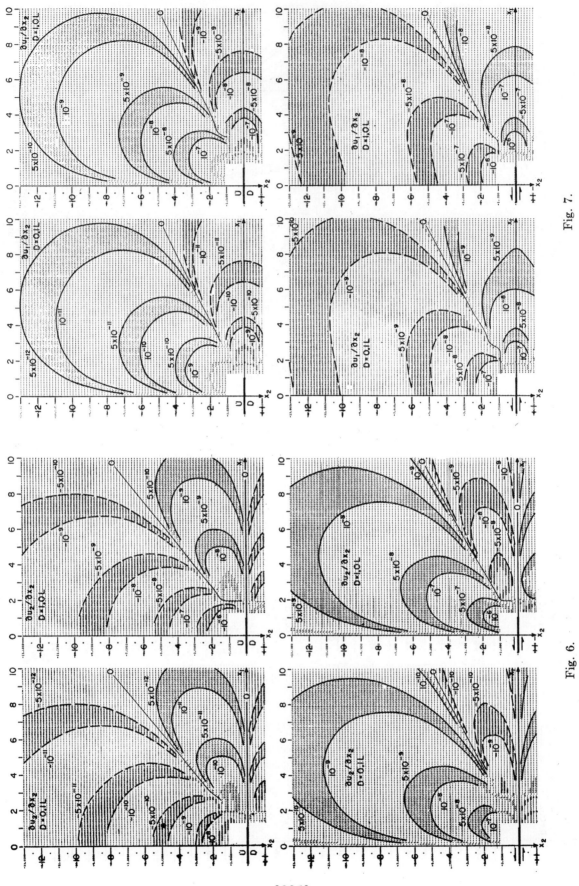

Fig. 7.

Fig. 6.

Fig. 9. Tilt fields for strike-slip and dip-slip faults with $D = 0.1L$ and $1.0L$.

Fig. 8.

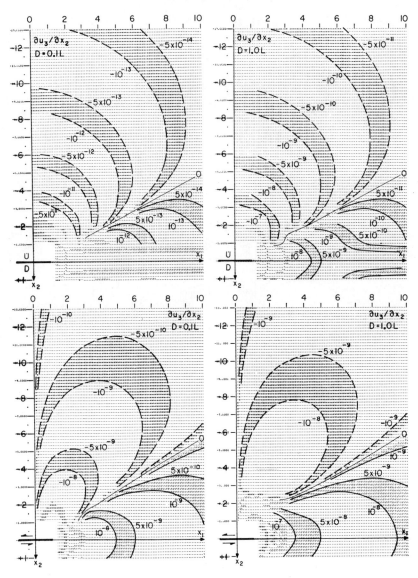

Fig. 10.

strain seismograph, designed by *Blayney and Gilman* [1965], are used to support the case.

The Alaskan earthquake of March 27, 1964. This great earthquake with Richter magnitude of 8.4 to 8.6 had epicentral coordinates 61.1°N and 147.4°W and a focal depth of about 50 km. More than 7500 aftershocks were instrumentally detected, defining a belt 800 km long and 250 km wide, azimuth 42°. The length of the belt is somewhat larger than the fault length of 650 km determined instrumentally using the directivity function (A. Ben-Menahem and M. N. Toksöz, personal communication, December 20, 1964). Average focal depths for some 200 aftershocks for which determinations were made was 20 km, the deepest event occurring at 60 km.

One fault plane solution for the main shock and aftershocks indicates dips of about 80°E and the azimuth of the strike is about 60°. [*Algermissen*, 1964]. Preliminary fault plane solutions from surface waves establish this as the unique solution (A. Ben-Menahem and M. N. Toksöz, personal communication, December 20, 1964). A special array of sensitive seismographs was installed by K. Aki after the earthquake. He was able to locate hundreds of aftershocks in a few weeks time, some of which occurred at depths as great as 200 km (Aki, personal communication, December 15, 1964).

Tectonic uplift and subsidence for this earthquake are comparatively well documented over large distances because permanent sea level changes along an irregular and lengthy coastline were evidenced in tide gage and shoreline data. The uplifted block extends southeast from the epicentral belt, its area exceeding 75,000 km². Most shorelines in this zone rose several feet. Montague Island lies in the zone of greatest tectonic activity. Local faults showing dominantly vertical slips as much as 5 m have been reported. A small part of the island rose more than 10 m and most of it rose 3 to 6 m [*Plafker*, 1965; *Grantz et al.*, 1964a, b]. Similarly the sea bottom southwest of Montague Island was predominantly uplifted 3 to 6 m, although very localized zones showed changes of more than 15 m [*Malloy*, 1964].

Available data for the down-dropped block to the northwest compiled by these investigators indicate that it exceeded 75,000 km² in area and sank as much as 2 m. The vertical movements do not imply a primary fault extending to the surface, but rather a zone of flexure between the uplifted and down-dropped blocks some 100 to 120 km wide, which to the precision of the data lies within the belt of epicenters of aftershocks. A plot of vertical movement projected on a section normal to the tectonic belt is shown in Figure 11. We consider the surface faulting and the local zones of intense uplift on Montague Island to be secondary features associated with the region of greatest flexure.

Preliminary results from geodetic resurveying show left lateral horizontal movement between Montague and Latouche islands amounting to 5 to 6 m [*Whitten*, 1964].

We use the following procedure to deduce the extent of the fault and the values for slip. We take the length of the fault $2L = 800$ km to be that given by the length of the epicentral belt. No significant change in our conclusions would occur had we used the length of 650 km indicated in the directivity function analysis. The distribution of vertical movements, the fault plane solutions from body and surface waves, and the distribution of focal depths imply a near-vertical plane for the primary fault. The occurrence of a zone of flexure rather than a primary scarp suggests that the upper boundary of the primary fault did not reach the surface. We shall deduce the vertical extent of faulting by assuming a vertical fault plane and using the observed movements and theory described earlier. This is the method of *Kasahara* [1957] and *Chinnery* [1961] among others. The vertical slip $U_3 \leq 20$ m since this is the difference between the maximum uplift and subsidence. If one weights the vertical movements in the zone of most intense deformation according to the area over which they occur, then 6 to 9 m is a more likely average value for U_3.

Two types of theoretical displacement curves, based on equation 11, are drawn through the data in Figure 11. The curves with $d = 0$ show the expected scarp when the fault breaks the surface. The curves with $d = 0.04L \sim 16$ km show a zone of flexure with zero displacement above the fault. The two curves are indistinguishable outside the zone of flexure, i.e. at distances greater than about 30 km normal to

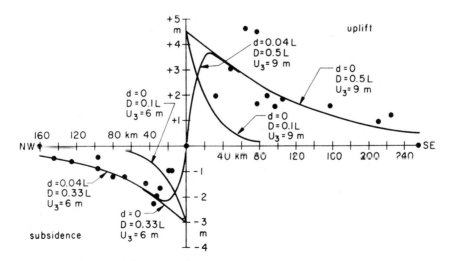

Fig. 11. Vertical movements associated with Alaskan earthquake projected on a section normal to belt of epicenters. Theoretical curves for different fault parameters are also shown.

the fault. Thus observations at distances smaller than 30 km are indicative of depth to the upper boundary of the fault, whereas data at larger distances are sensitive to the depth of the lower boundary.

The asymmetry in the data relative to the hingeline is probably due to dip of the fault plane, which was neglected in the theory. The simple procedure is used of interpreting displacements for both blocks separately. We conclude on the basis of the very gradual reduction of vertical deformation with distances that the fault could not have extended to depths as shallow as 50 km and that 100 to 200 km are more likely values. The fault probably came to within 15 to 20 km of the surface.

As a check, we note that the contours of field observations of vertical displacement lie roughly parallel to the strike of the fault, indicating a negligible contribution from the strike-slip component of faulting. This implies that $U_1/U_3 \ll 1$ or that $D/L \gg 0.1$. The first possibility seems to be ruled out by the preliminary geodetic indications of horizontal slip.

The vertical extent found for the fault of the Alaskan earthquake exceeds by an order of magnitude the values found for other earthquakes. Chinnery gives 2 to 6 km for the San Francisco earthquake of 1906. *Knopoff* [1958] gives 3 km, and *Byerly and DeNoyer* [1958] found a depth of 10 km. The last-named authors also found depths of 12 and 23 km for the Imperial Valley (1940) and the Fairview Peak earthquakes. Kasahara and Chinnery found depths between 10 and 15 km for the Tango and North Idu earthquakes in Japan. The larger magnitude associated with the Alaskan earthquake ($M = 8.4$) as compared with the others may partially explain the difference. In the case of the San Francisco earthquake, most of the displacement observations were within 5 km of the fault. Anomalously low rigidities in the fault zone could result in a misleading displacement-distance relationship [*Benioff*, 1962].

An estimate of the elastic strain energy released by the Alaskan earthquake can be made by evaluating the volume integral

$$\int_v \left[\lambda \varphi^2/2 + \mu \sum_{i,j=1}^{3} e_{ij}e_{ij} \right] dv$$

where e_{ij} are the strain components, φ is the dilatation, and $\mu = 5 \times 10^{11}$ dynes/cm². Using the fault parameters described earlier, and assuming that to a depth D the strains may be approximated by the surface values and are zero below, we obtain 10^{25} ergs, with the dip-slip component contributing about twice as much as the strike-slip component. Presumably this is an upper bound for the seismic wave energy radiated from the epicentral region. A more precise calculation is being undertaken in which the exact depth dependence of strain is taken into account.

The strain energy can also be obtained from $\frac{1}{2}\int\int_\Sigma U_i\tau_{ij}\nu_j d\Sigma$ where τ_{ij} are the stress components, Σ is the surface area of the fault, and the integral represents the energy required to produce the dislocation sheet. Approximate integration yields similar results. Assuming that an earthquake could be modeled by the formation of a crack in a material in a state of uniform strain, *Knopoff* [1958] derived a formula for energy release $E = \pi\mu U_1^2 L/8 = 2 \times 10^{24}$ ergs using the preceding values for the fault parameters. This is almost identical to our result for the U_1 component of slip. The elastic strain energy release may be compared to the seismic wave energy derived from the Gutenberg-Richter relation $\log E = 11.8 + 1.5M$. Using $M = 8.4$ yields a value of 3×10^{24} ergs.

A remarkable strain seismogram was written for this earthquake at the Kipapa station on Oahu, Hawaii (latitude 21°25′N, longitude 158°54′W, orientation N61°W). This instrument was recently installed by the California Institute of Technology and is operated by the U. S. Coast and Geodetic Survey. It incorporates both photo-optical and electronic transducers [*Blayney and Gilman*, 1965]. The seismogram is displayed in Figure 12 in such a way that the strain record for several days before and after the earthquake is shown. It is seen that the strain discontinuity of 10^{-8} associated with the shock is a unique feature. Subsequent tests in which large strains were induced artificially failed to show a permanent strain offset, minimizing the possibility that the Alaskan strain offset was due to an instrumental defect. Perhaps the best indication as to the reality of the observation is that it is reasonably consistent with the fault model, the fault dimensions, and the slips discussed earlier.

The Hawaiian strain seismograph is located at approximate coordinates $-8 \geq x_1/L \geq -11$,

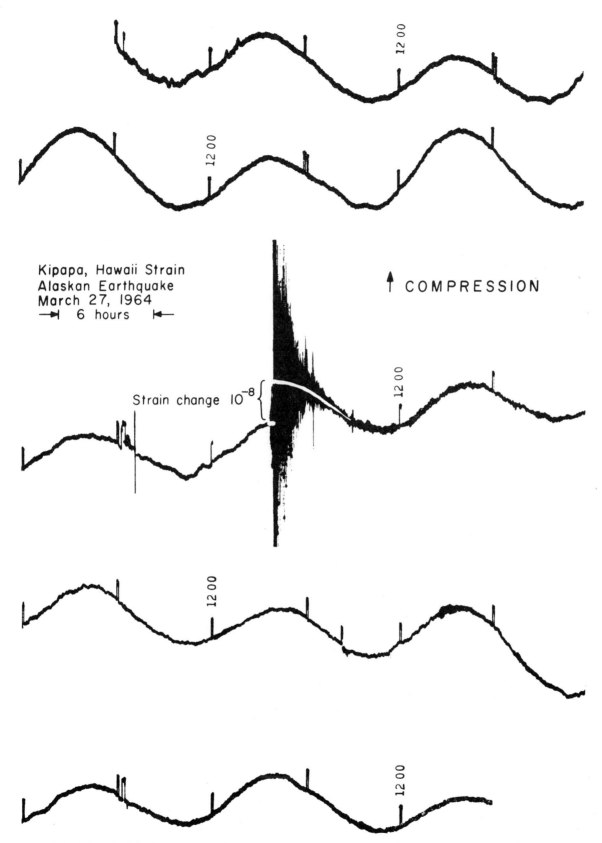

Fig. 12. Strain seismogram written at Kipapa, Oahu, for Alaskan earthquake of March 27, 1964. Several days of recording before and after the shock are shown to indicate uniqueness of residual strain.

$3 \leq x_2/L \leq 5$, depending on the fault length and orientation. Since the U_3 and U_1 values for the Alaskan shock are smaller by factors of about 2 or 3 than the values assumed in computing strains in Figures 5 to 8, we must reduce dip-slip and strike-slip strains by these amounts (also U_3 observed differs in sign from the value assumed in the figures). We note that strains of the order of 10^{-10} to 10^{-9} are present near Hawaii for $D = 0.1L$ and strains in the range 10^{-9} to 10^{-8} occur for the case $D = 1.0L$. These may be compared with the observed value of 10^{-8}. Actually, the comparison should be made with the total strain response of the instrument in which all the theoretical strain components are added, taking account of the orientation of the strain rod and the sign of the strain components. Unfortunately, the strain rod is oriented at right angles to the extension of the fault to within $\pm 5°$, and Hawaii falls near nodal lines of several strain fields. Small changes in the length and orientation of the fault lead to order of magnitude changes in the computed total strain response. For reasonable values of the fault parameters we find that the strike-slip component of $\partial u_2/\partial x_2$ contributes most of the strain. When $D = 0.1L$ the theoretical strain response is less than observed by several orders of magnitude, whereas $D = 1.0L$ yields a strain response of the right sign (compression) and within about an order of magnitude of that observed.

This indication of great depth of faulting substantiates the results from the near displacement fields, although it cannot carry as much weight since it is based on only one point in the strain field. The main contribution of this observation and the computation of theoretical values is the demonstration that strain observations from major earthquakes are observable at teleseismic distances and that they are diagnostic of source properties.

We have also examined the Isabella (California) strain seismograms for permanent deformation after the Alaskan earthquake. Although the records were not as convenient to read as those from Hawaii, we concluded that residual strain changes were smaller than the detection threshold of 5×10^{-9} (zero strain change being consistent with the data). In terms of fault coordinates Isabella is located at $0 \leq x_1/L \leq 2$ and $x_2/L \sim 9$. Here again we

have the unfortunate situation that the station is located near a nodal line for several strain components and that the instruments are oriented within about 10° to 20° of the cardinal directions defined by the fault axes. Thus small changes in fault parameters can change both the sign and order of magnitude of the strain response to the extent that the observation cannot be considered inconsistent with the Hawaiian data or the fault model.

Other observations of residual fields. *Berckhemer and Schneider* [1964] attempted to recover the true ground motion by integrating the trace motion of horizontal seismographs for several local earthquakes in the magnitude $4\frac{1}{2}$ to 5 range. They found residual displacements of the order of 5 to 10 μ at distances of about 60 km. Using the fault models described earlier, we can expect such displacements at this distance for faults about 1 km long and slips of about 5 cm (nuclear explosions with this equivalent magnitude produce residual movements of this order at about 1 km). These investigators also reported residual tilts of the order of 10^{-7}. These are three to four orders of magnitude too large for the above source. Mechanical hysteresis in the pendulum would be manifest as residual tilts and this possibility should be investigated.

Another example of a residual strain observation is shown in Figure 13, where two direct strain recordings for a local earthquake near Ñaña, Peru, are displayed. Unfortunately, the magnitude and distance of this event are not available. Note that on mechanically and electrically identical instruments one component shows a residual strain and the perpendicular component does not. This observation supports the notion that the strain offset is real and not due to an instrumental defect.

Several measurements of strains and tilts from earthquakes have been reported which are too large by several orders of magnitude to be explained by the fault mechanism assumed earlier. In the case of the strain instruments which have been tested for instrumental hysteresis and checked by the photo-optical transducer, we feel warranted in ascribing the strain changes to the source. The tilt observations could be real, but the possibility of spurious tilts due to mechanical hysteresis in the pendulums must be checked before their validity is taken seriously. Some examples follow.

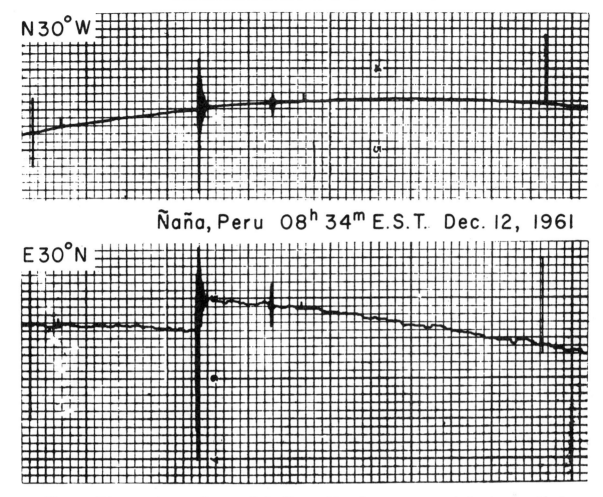

Fig. 13.   Direct strain recordings at Ñaña, Peru, with only one component showing a residual strain after a local earthquake.

Benioff [1963] published a direct strain seismogram from Isabella for the Montana earthquake of August 19, 1959, showing a strain change of 5×10^{-9}. The primary deformation in the epicentral region was subsidence, the earthquake resulting from a sudden collapse over a broad area. Although extensive faulting accompanied the earthquake over a length of some 30 km, with scarps as high as 6 m, both sides of the faults moved downward [*Witkind et al.*, 1962]. Meyers and Hamilton interpret the field data to indicate that the faults are secondary features, the primary tectonic action being basin collapse. Witkind and Fraser view the faults as primary features and believe that movements along the faults caused the earthquake. Taking $2L = 30$ km and 290° for the azimuth of the strike of the fault, we get for the coordinates of Isabella $x_1/L \sim 20$, $x_2/L \sim 75$. Using $U_3 = 3$ m for the average slip and $D/L =$

1.0 for the vertical extent of faulting, we find strain components in the range 10^{-12} to 10^{-11} at Isabella, values which are two to three orders of magnitude smaller than observed. We conclude that more extensive faulting occurs at depth than is manifest at the surface or that a non-faulting mechanism is responsible for subsidence in the epicentral region and the residual strain at Isabella. The possibility that volume changes at depth can account for these changes is now being examined.

Figure 14 is a direct strain seismogram written at Kipapa, Oahu, from the earthquake of October 11, 1964, off the west coast of Hawaii. This tremor had a magnitude of about 5. The strain change at Kipapa of 4×10^{-9} was measured with both the electronic and photo-optical transducers, as shown in the figure. An earthquake of magnitude 5, having a faulting mechanism, may be expected to have a fault length

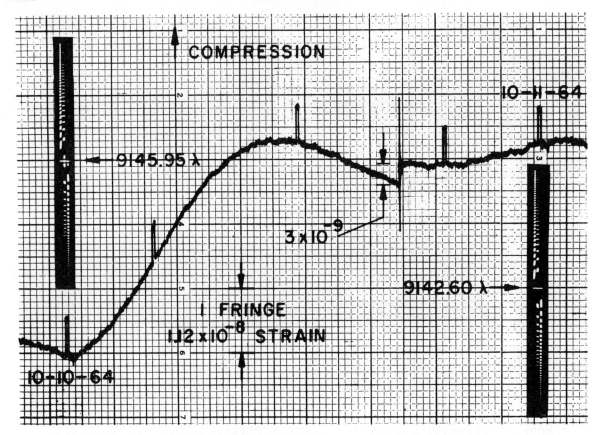

Fig. 14.   Direct strain recording at Kipapa, Oahu, for Hawaiian earthquake of October 11, 1964. Fringe pattern indicates separation of interferometer plates in wavelengths of mercury green line in agreement with trace motion derived from electronic transducer.

of well under 5 km. In terms of this length, Kipapa falls at a distance larger than $100L$ from the source. For a slip of $0.3 \times 10^{-4}L$ and vertical fault extent $D = 1.0L$ the strains are at least three orders of magnitude smaller than the observed value. We conclude that the source mechanism did not involve strain release from primary tectonic faulting of the type assumed in this paper. The result is not surprising since it is well known that earthquakes and deformation on Hawaii are associated with volcanism rather than tectonic faulting [*Eaton and Murata,* 1960].

Residual tilts connected with large teleseismic events have been reported by *Bonchkovsky* [1962], *Nishimura* [1953], and *Tomaschek* [1955]. Bonchkovsky studied tilts at Garm and Simferopol from the great Mongolian earthquake of December 4, 1957. He reported tilts of 10^{-5} and $\frac{1}{2} \times 10^{-5}$ for the two stations. The main fracture for this earthquake could be traced over a distance of 270 km. Aftershocks occurred in a belt 500 km long, and instrumen-

tal determination of fault length gave 560 km [*Ben-Menahem and Toksöz,* 1962]. Strike-slip movements of 3 to 3.5 m and dip-slips as much as 8 m were found at places along the fault. We represent the fault by the following approximate parameters. $2L = 500$ km, $U_1 = 3$ m, $U_3 = 6$ m. Using the reported orientation of the fault, we find that the coordinates of Garm are $x_1/L \sim 10$, $x_2/L \sim 2.5$ and the Simferopol coordinates are $x_1/L \sim 18$, $x_2/L \sim 7$. The theoretical tilts at these locations are of the order of 10^{-8} to 10^{-c}, or three to four orders of magnitude smaller than observed. The elastic strain energy change required to produce tilts of the order of those observed at these distances is impossibly high. The residual tilts reported by Tomaschek can also be shown to be too large. A discussion of the origin of these tilts is unwarranted until the instruments are tested for mechanical hysteresis induced by large-amplitude seismic waves.

Discussion. The previous discussion should be viewed primarily as a feasibility study in which an approximate theory and some single point observations show the possibilities of a more extensive experiment.

The use of residual displacements, strains, and tilts at intermediate and large distances from the epicenter offers new opportunities for studying the mechanism of earthquakes. The dimensions of the source, the elastic strain energy release, and the elucidation of primary mechanisms other than faulting ones are among the problems which may be studied by this approach. It is technically feasible to develop and deploy instruments to monitor the residual fields for an entire seismic belt. Without the former necessity for limiting observations to the epicentral region, data can be gathered in a relatively short period of time. Moreover, the installation of displacement-, strain-, and tilt-meters in arrays having continental dimensions offers the possibility of using correlation methods to improve signal-to-noise ratios so that residual fields from smaller events can be studied. Such an array might also monitor slowly varying fields or the more rapid variations associated with creep instability before an earthquake occurs.

Theoretical advances will be needed to exploit these observations fully. The dislocation theory representation of faults should be extended to include fault planes of arbitrary slip and orientation in a layered, spherical earth. Fields due to density changes over arbitrary regions should be programmed for computation. Methods will be needed to compute fields from realistic sources in which the mechanism of failure and the pre-existing strain field are taken into account.

Acknowledgments. I have benefited from many discussions with Drs. Stewart Smith, Hugo Benioff, Ari Ben-Menahem, and Don Anderson. Dr. Shawn Biehler generously adapted his automatic plotting routine for use in this paper. Dr. Keiiti Aki and Mr. George Plafker made their studies of the Alaskan earthquake available in advance of publication. Messrs. Ronald Victo, Robert Eppley, and Robert Munson of the U. S. Coast and Geodetic Survey station at Kipapa provided valuable assistance in operating the strain seismograph for us. Lawrence Turnbull checked the calculations.

I am grateful to Drs. Hugo Benioff, M. A. Chinnery, K. Aki, and M. Major for constructive comments on the paper. Dr. Aki mentioned a study which I have not yet seen by Dr. I. Ozawa of Kyoto University in which a similar conclusion about the reality of strain jumps is reached.

This work was partially supported by the National Science Foundation under grant GP-2806.

References

Aki, K., Study of Love and Rayleigh waves from earthquakes with fault plane solutions or with known faulting, *Bull. Seismol. Soc. Am., 54,* 511–570, 1964.

Algermissen, S. T., Prince William Sound, Alaska earthquake of March 28, 1964, and aftershock sequence (abstract), *Program 1964 Ann. Meeting Geol. Soc. Am.,* p. 2, 1964.

Archambeau, C., Elastodynamic source theory, Ph.D. thesis, California Institute of Technology, June 1964.

Benioff, H., Movements on major transcurrent faults, in *Continental Drift,* edited by S. K. Runcorn, pp. 103–134, Academic Press, New York, 1962.

Benioff, H., Source wave forms of three earthquakes, *Bull. Seismol. Soc. Am., 53,* 893–903, 1963.

Ben-Menahem, A., and M. N. Toksöz, Source-mechanism from spectra of long-period seismic surface-waves, *J. Geophys. Res., 67,* 1943–1955, 1962.

Ben-Menahem, A., and M. N. Toksöz, Source-mechanism from spectra of long-period seismic surface waves, *Bull. Seismol. Soc. Am., 53,* 905–919, 1963.

Berckhemer, H., and G. Schneider, Near earthquakes recorded with long-period seismographs, *Bull. Geol. Soc. Am., 54,* 973–987, 1964.

Blayney, J. L., and R. Gilman, A semi-portable strain meter with continuous interferometric calibration, to be submitted for publication in 1965.

Bonchkovsky, V. F., Deformation of the earth's surface accompanying certain disastrous earthquakes, *Bull. Acad. Sci. USSR, Geophys. Ser., English Transl., 2,* 190–193, 1962.

Brune, J. N., Correction of initial phase measurements for the southeast Alaska earthquake of December 4, 1957, *J. Geophys. Res., 67,* 3643, 1962.

Byerly, P., and J. DeNoyer, Energy in earthquakes as computed from geodetic observations, *Contributions in Geophysics,* vol. 1, pp. 17–35, Pergamon Press, London, 1958.

Chinnery, M. A., The deformation of the ground around surface faults, *Bull. Seismol. Soc. Am., 51,* 355–372, 1961.

Chinnery, M. A., The stress changes that accompany strike-slip faulting, *Bull. Seismol. Soc. Am., 53,* 921–932, 1963.

Eaton, J. P., and K. J. Murata, How volcanoes grow, *Science, 132,* 925–938, 1960.

Grantz, A., G. Plafker, and J. E. Case, Tectonics of Alaska's Good Friday earthquake (abstract), *Program 1964 Ann. Meeting, Geol. Soc. Am.,* p. 77, 1964a.

Grantz, A., G. Plafker, and R. Kachadoorian, Alaska's Good Friday earthquake, March 27, 1964, *U. S. Geol. Surv. Circ. 491,* 1964b.

Kasahara, K., The nature of seismic origins as inferred from seismological and geodetic observations, *Bull. Earthquake Res. Inst., Tokyo Univ.*, *35*, 473–532, 1957.

Knopoff, L., Energy release in earthquakes, *Geophys. J.*, *1*, 44–52, 1958.

Malloy, R. J., Crustal uplift southwest of Montague Island, Alaska, *Science*, *146*, 1048–1049, 1964.

Maruyama, T., Statical elastic dislocations in an infinite and semi-infinite medium, *Bull. Earthquake Res. Inst., Tokyo Univ.*, *42*, 289–368, 1964.

Mindlin, R. D., and D. H. Cheng, Nuclei of strain in the semi-infinite solid, *J. Appl. Phys.*, *21*, 926–930, 1950.

Nishimura, E., On some destructive earthquakes observed with a tiltmeter at a great distance, *Bull. Disaster Prevention Res. Inst., Kyoto Univ.*, *6*, 1–16, 1953.

Plafker, G., Tectonic uplift, subsidence, and faulting associated with Alaska's Good Friday earthquake, *Science*, in press, 1965.

Press, F., and C. Archambeau, Release of tectonic strain by underground nuclear explosions, *J. Geophys. Res.*, *67*, 337–343, 1962.

Steketee, J. A., On Volterra's dislocations in a semi-infinite medium, *Can. J. Phys.*, *36*, 192–205, 1958.

Tomaschek, R., Earth tilts in the British Isles connected with far distant earthquakes, *Nature*, *176*, 24–26, 1955.

Vvedenskaya, A. V., The determination of displacement fields by means of dislocation theory, Bull. Acad. Sci. USSR, *Geophys. Ser., English Transl.*, *3*, 277–284, 1956.

Whitten, C. A., Cartographic and geodetic effects of Alaskan earthquake (abstract), *Program 1964 Ann. Meeting, Geol. Soc. Am.*, p. 222, 1964.

Witkind, I. J., W. B. Meyers, J. B. Hadley, W. Hamilton, and G. D. Fraser, The earthquake at Hebgen Lake, Montana, on August 18, 1959: Geological features, *Bull. Seismol. Soc. Am.*, *52*, 163–180, 1962.

CLARIFICATION

Seismology & Geodesy Vol. Page	JGR Page	Column	Line	Remark
298	2404	1	5, 6	Later computed at 61.04°N and 147.73°W

II
FORESHOCKS
AND
AFTERSHOCKS

Introduction

Great earthquakes are not isolated events but are intricately related to the seismic history, tectonic processes, and geological structure of a region. Aftershock series, which nearly always follow great earthquakes, frequently alter the seismic patterns of large areas for years. Thus, it is important to understand the pre- and postearthquake seismicity of the area affected by the March 28, 1964 (GMT), shock as well as we can and to attempt its interpretation in terms of other earthquake parameters of significance.

It is often difficult to relate a great earthquake to the earlier seismicity of the area because great earthquakes seldom occur in regions that have undergone detailed geophysical investigation. Knowledge of crustal parameters in south central Alaska is limited (see, for example, Shor, 1962; Tatel and Tuve, 1956). In addition, the record of seismicity is probably incomplete for earthquakes of magnitude 6 or less before about 1935 and is questionable even for great earthquakes before 1904.

Only two Alaskan seismograph stations, College and Sitka, reported seismic observations in Alaska on a routine basis prior to the 1964 earthquake, although a few other stations operated for short periods of time in various parts of the state. Sitka became operational in 1904 with the installation of two low-magnification, mechanical, horizontal-component, Bosch–Omori pendulums and became a more-or-less modern station with the installation of an electromagnetic vertical seismograph in 1956. College commenced operation in 1935 with two low-magnification, optical–mechanical pendulums and became a first-rate high-magnification station with the installation of a three-component moving-coil Benioff system in 1949. The 1964 earthquake resulted in an upgrading of these two stations and the addition of many new seismograph stations in Alaska. (The present instrumentation at College and Sitka is described in the seismological bulletins of the Earth Science Laboratories of NOAA.) Information on the seismicity of Alaska before 1964 is based almost exclusively on data recorded at teleseismic distances and consequently nothing of significance is known about the pre-1964 low-level seismicity.

Despite the shortcomings of the seismicity data, some conclusions of interest can be drawn concerning the seismic setting of the Prince William Sound–Kodiak region and Alaska as a whole before 1964. We should first, perhaps, examine briefly the terminology used to describe the seismicity of an area prior to a large earthquake.

Many large earthquakes are preceded by smaller shocks that originate near the epicenter of the main shock and occur not long before it. These smaller earthquakes are commonly called *foreshocks*. Although the term has never been well defined and has been applied differently by various authors, it has been used mainly to describe earthquakes occurring before, but closely associated in time and space with, the main shock. Foreshocks are not considered to be part of the "normal" seismicity of a region; they represent some increase, or possibly other change, in the pattern of seismicity shortly before a major earthquake. The difficulties with such a definition are obvious, and it is doubtful whether the term as currently employed has a very useful meaning. Less ambiguous is the term *preshock*, which has been used recently to characterize in general the seismicity of a region prior to a large earthquake. A preshock is any earthquake that precedes a large earthquake in the same specified region, with no implication of relationship or lack of relationship to the main shock. By using this term one suggests that the seismicity of a region is preferably described simply as a time series of large earthquakes separated by smaller events.

The 1964 earthquake was accompanied by vertical deformation over an area of 170,000 to 200,000 km^2 (Plafker, 1965). The deformed zone, which includes the Prince William Sound–Kenai Peninsula–Kodiak Island area, the adjacent Continental Shelf, Shelikof Strait, Cook Inlet, and the Chugach Mountains, is roughly coincident with the area over which aftershocks were distributed. This zone also approximates the area over which strain was relieved by the main

[309]

shock and aftershocks. It is of some interest to examine the seismic activity of this zone of deformation before March 28, 1964.

Two earthquakes of about the same magnitude (7.2), with epicenters very near that of the 1964 earthquake occurred in Prince William Sound in 1912 and 1934 (Gutenberg and Richter, 1954). The seismicity of Prince William Sound remained low between 1935 and 1964, a point discussed by Algermissen and others, this section; Berg (1965), and Tobin and Sykes (1966). Large earthquakes ($M_s \geqslant 7.0$) did occur after 1934 in the Gulf of Alaska to the south (1947, 1949), in the vicinity of Kodiak Island (1938, 1951, 1952), and in central Alaska (1937, 1943, 1947, 1958). The Kodiak Island region at the southwest end of the aftershock zone of the 1964 earthquake was more-or-less continuously active before 1964. The seismicity in the immediate vicinity of the epicenter of the main shock showed no significant increase or other change that might be considered indicative of a great earthquake. During the year before March 28, 1964, the U.S. Coast and Geodetic Survey located eight events within a radius of 50 km of the epicenter for the main shock of 1964 (Sherburne and others, this volume). The International Seismological Centre (1967b) lists two additional small shocks. The first and largest of these ten earthquakes (April 3, 1963; m_b = 5.7, USC&GS) was 13 km northwest of the epicenter of the main shock; the last (March 22, 1964; m_b = 4.5, USC&GS) was 18 km to the north.

We should be cautious in inferring too much from the observation that ten earthquakes occurred near the epicenter of the main shock during the year preceding it. The seismicity of the whole region is high, and examination of the U.S. Coast and Geodetic Survey's Earthquake Data Reports (1963 and 1964) and of the bulletins for 1964 of the International Seismological Centre (1967a) suggests that the accuracy of location of small earthquakes such as these is not high. In Prince William Sound it is surely no better than ±25 km; some of the locations are much worse. It is very difficult, therefore, to propose a theory associating these earthquakes with the main shock until improved methods of determining hypocenters are available. Harding and Algermissen (this volume) have noted that the first motion pattern recorded for the March 22, 1964, earthquake was entirely different from that of the main shock, thus suggesting a different focal mechanism. More studies of this nature should be made to find out whether this phenomenon is characteristic of small events preceding large earthquakes.

The parameters of the aftershock sequence of this earthquake are probably more thoroughly known than those for any other great earthquake in history. Three kinds of seismograph station networks recorded the sequence: permanent stations throughout the world, located for the most part at teleseismic distances from the epicenter; temporary stations in the aftershock zone, some units of which began operation 2 days after the main shock; and several small, high-magnification arrays which were operated for short periods of time at one or more sites. These three recording networks served complementary functions. The teleseismic network yielded the most complete available record of the large shocks. The temporary local network provided information on some shocks that could not have been located teleseismically and supplied information critical to the calculation of accurate aftershock focal depths. The high-magnification arrays, operated intermittently, provided important insight into the microseismicity and magnitude distribution of earthquakes in specific areas.

An analysis of the aftershock data recorded by both the teleseismic and the temporary local stations is given by Algermissen and others. Combining data from the temporary stations and stations at teleseismic distances produced an exceptionally complete record of aftershock activity. Except for the first few hours after the main shock, data are probably complete for aftershocks of magnitude 5.0 and above. The aftershock sequence changed abruptly 520 days after the main shock, on September 4, 1965, when an earthquake with M_s = 6.9 occurred south of Kodiak. The aftershock zone showed increased energy release throughout the remainder of 1965 and during 1966, principally in the Kodiak Island area. The network of temporary seismograph stations also provided good quantitative control for computing focal depths by standard least-squares procedures and a check on depths calculated from observations of pP at teleseismic distances. Algermissen and others conclude that 79 percent of the aftershocks located had depths less than 40 km; the average depth was 15–20 km. Aki and others and Matumoto and Page also state that the majority of aftershocks and microaftershocks had shallow foci. Aki and his associates found about 10 percent of the foci located near their station site to be in the mantle. Matumoto and Page found evidence of a similar distribution of foci in the crust and mantle. Page (1968) discussed some of the implications of the observation that the majority of the aftershocks occurred at shallow depths.

The energy release in the aftershock sequence was about one tenth of the energy released in the main shock (Algermissen and others). Most of the activity and, consequently, most of the energy release in the sequence was confined to the Continental Shelf southeast of Kodiak Island and Prince William Sound. The area over which energy was released in the aftershock zone also corresponds roughly to the uplifted zone of deformation as described by Plafker (1965). Very little energy was released by aftershocks in Prince William Sound as compared to the remainder of the zone; this suggests that most of the strain in Prince William Sound was relieved by the main shock or perhaps a series of shocks as proposed by Wyss and Brune (this volume).

The 1964 earthquake was the first major earthquake for which high-gain, high-frequency seismographs were used to record microaftershocks. Two papers concerning the micro-aftershock activity following the earthquake are included in this volume. The paper by Aki and others discusses 9,061 microaftershocks recorded during a 20-day period that began 52 days after the main shock, on May 19, 1964. Hypocenters were determined for 797 of the 9,061 microearthquakes recorded. A quadripartite array of vertical seismographs was operated at magnifications as high as 1,700,000 at a period of 0.1 second. Matumoto and Page used both a small tripartite array, 1 km on a side, and a large tripartite array with sides ranging in length from 24 to 40 km to record microearthquakes. They located 249 microearthquakes and computed a crustal velocity model applicable to the eastern Kenai Peninsula. This model was used together with additional data by Algermissen and others to arrive at an average crustal-velocity model for the location of shocks throughout the entire aftershock zone.

Yet another question relating to the earthquake origin is raised in the paper by Berg. By correlating time of occurrence of the major shock and of the principal aftershocks with tide records, he suggests that the principal shock and the large aftershocks located on the Continental Shelf were possibly triggered by low-ocean-tide loads.

What has been learned from the study of the seismicity of Prince William Sound and the surrounding area before and after the 1964 earthquake? It is clear that this study was hampered by the lack of geophysical data for Prince William Sound and by the small number of seismograph stations in Alaska prior to 1964. Despite the small number of local stations, it was possible to locate by routine seismological methods a number of small earthquakes that had occurred very near the epicenter of the main shock during the year preceding the great 1964 earthquake. Twenty years earlier the small earthquakes could probably not have been located at all. Indeed, it would be interesting to examine the entire seismic history of Prince William Sound in more detail, relocating small earthquakes if necessary. An attempt could then be made to try Berg's (1966, and this volume) theory of tidal triggering of earthquakes on shocks occurring in Prince William Sound prior to 1964. Focal mechanism studies of preshocks and aftershocks of the 1964 earthquake should encourage a careful study of focal mechanisms of current earthquakes in the area. The great expansion of seismological instrumentation in Alaska after 1964 should greatly improve the accuracy of hypocenter locations and focal-mechanism solutions as well as stimulate such studies.

The world seismological network and the temporary stations installed in Alaska have provided us with the most complete record of aftershock activity available in the seismological literature. Microearthquake activity was investigated systematically for the first time, and evidence was found for activation of the mantle by a great earthquake in the crust (Aki and others; Matumoto and Page). Nonetheless, there is uncertainty regarding the numbers and magnitudes of aftershocks that occurred during about the first 10 hours after the main shock. The seismographs in operation could not discriminate between the numerous shocks, and many earthquakes were lost in the codas of earlier ones. This loss of data is important in any consideration of the multiple-rupture phenomenon proposed by Wyss and Brune (this volume). Instrumental and analytical techniques need additional development so that the nature of the aftershock sequence within the first few hours after a major shock will be clearly understood. With the possible exception of the first few hours after the main shock, very little strain energy was released in Prince William Sound by earthquakes in the aftershock sequence. The main shock, or series of shocks, apparently relieved most of the strain in Prince William Sound (Algermissen and others). This area of low energy release in Prince William Sound corresponds to the area in which the multiple ruptures proposed by Wyss and Brune (this volume) occurred.

It is hoped that the papers in this volume have contributed to a clearer understanding of the characteristics of seismic activity before and after major earthquakes and that these comments may stimulate further research.

S. T. ALGERMISSEN
Earth Sciences Laboratories, NOAA

REFERENCES

Berg, Eduard, 1965. The Alaskan earthquake, its location and seismic setting in Science in Alaska, 1964: Proceedings Fifteenth Alaskan Science Conference, College, Alaska, August 31 to September 4, 1964. George Dahlgren, editor. College: Alaska Division American Association for the Advancement of Science, March 15. p. 218–232.

Gutenberg, B., and Charles F. Richter, 1954. Seismicity of the earth and associated phenomena. Princeton: Princeton University Press. 322 p.

International Seismological Centre, 1967a. Bulletins for 1964, Vol. 1 (Nos. 1, 2, 3, 4). Edinburgh [Scotland]: International Seismological Centre.

International Seismological Centre, 1967b. Regional catalogue of earthquakes, 1964, January–June, Vol. 1 (No. 1). Edinburgh [Scotland]: International Seismological Centre. 219 p.

Page, Robert, 1968. Aftershocks and microaftershocks of the great Alaska earthquake of 1964. *Bulletin of the Seismological Society of America*, 58 (June), 1131–1168.

Plafker, George, 1965. Tectonic deformation associated with the 1964 Alaska earthquake. *Science*, 148 (June 25), 1675–1687.

Shor, George G., Jr., 1962. Seismic refraction studies off the coast of Alaska: 1956–1957. *Bulletin of the Seismological Society of America*, 52 (January), 37–57.

Tatel, H. E., and Merle A. Tuve, 1956. The earth's crust, seismic studies in Carnegie Institution of Washington Year Book 55. Washington: Carnegie Institution. p. 81–84.

Tobin, Don G., and Lynn R. Sykes, 1966. Relationship of hypocenters of earthquakes to the geology of Alaska. *Journal of Geophysical Research*, 71 (March 15), 1659–1667.

U.S. Coast and Geodetic Survey, 1963 and 1964. Earthquake Data Reports. Washington: Department of Commerce.

S. T. ALGERMISSEN
W. A. RINEHART
R. W. SHERBURNE*
W. H. DILLINGER, JR.
U.S. COAST AND GEODETIC SURVEY†

Reprinted with minor changes from
U.S. Coast and Geodetic Survey Volume II-B,C: Seismology and Marine Geology,
"Preshocks and Aftershocks of the Prince William Sound Earthquake of March 28, 1964"

Preshocks and Aftershocks

ABSTRACT

Data on 2,210 aftershocks and preshocks are presented. The aftershock area is approximately a rectangle 900 kilometers long and 400 kilometers wide. There was considerable temporal variation in aftershock activity with bursts of activity followed by periods of relative quiescence, although this pattern was superimposed on the general, well-known hyperbolic decrease of aftershock activity with time. Seventy-nine percent of the aftershocks for which a depth was actually computed (not restrained) by some method had depths less than 40 kilometers. The energy released in the aftershock sequence during the first 1,000 days was about one-tenth of the energy released in the main shock. Nearly all of the energy released in the aftershock sequence was confined to the shelf area adjacent to Kodiak Island, the Kenai Peninsula, and Prince William Sound.

INTRODUCTION

Portable seismographs were installed in the aftershock zone within 2 days following the occurrence of the main shock. Data for 2,210 aftershocks and other earthquakes that occurred in the Prince William Sound–Kodiak Island area from January 1, 1964, through December 31, 1966, were collected. A study of the energy release preceding and following the Prince William Sound Earthquake was undertaken to improve our understanding of the processes active in this region.

EPICENTERS AND RELATED DATA

A total of 2,178 aftershocks and other earthquakes was located, using data from all sources in the time period March 28, 1964, through December 31, 1966. Epicenters for 1,260 of the smaller shocks from March 28 through July 31, 1964, were located using data from the network of nine temporary seismograph stations established by the Coast and Geodetic Survey in Alaska shortly after the earthquake (fig. 1 and table 1). The station sites and instrumentation were described in detail in Volume 1 [1966] of this report.

The crustal and upper mantle velocities and structure in the Prince William Sound–Kodiak Island area, as presently known, are summarized in figure 2. The velocities for the area off the coast of Kodiak Island are from refraction profiles by Shor [1962]. The section shown for the Kenai Peninsula has been generalized from a study of aftershocks in this area by Matumoto and

*Now at Pennsylvania State University.
†Now in part Earth Science Laboratories, National Oceanic and Atmospheric Administration.

[313]

TABLE 1.—*Temporary stations: Instrument and site information*

Station name	Abbr.	Operating dates[1] and site description	Latitude N.	Longitude W.	Seismometer	Period Sec.	Reorder	Galvanometer period Sec.	Recording rate Mm./min.	Trace up (ground motion)	Noise level Micron	Period Sec.	Range of operating magnification $\times 10^3$	Abbr.
Anchorage	AN1	Mar. 30 to Apr. 27, 1964. Basement of BOQ Building 10-350, Elmendorf AFB; seismometer placed on cement basement.	61°14.54'	149°49.74'	Portable vertical Benioff.	1.0	Hot stylus, paper	0.75	60	up	0.93	0.6	1.5-4.8	AN1
	AN2	Installed Apr. 29, 1964.[2] Gould Hall of the Alaska Methodist University; seismometer located in basement of building and later placed in drum vault 31 meters from building.	61°11.36'	149°48.07'	Portable vertical Benioff.	1.0	Hot stylus, paper	0.20	60	up	0.30	0.9	6.0-15.5	AN2
Cordova	CD1	Apr. 2 to May 8, 1964. FAA Building at Cordova Airport; seismograph placed on concrete floor.	60°29.65'	145°27.86'	Portable vertical Benioff.	1.0	30-day photographic paper.	0.50	60	up	0.25	1.0	1.9-2.0	CD1
	CD2	May 9 to Oct. 3, 1964. FAA Building 2 km. S. E. of the Cordova Airport and 0.3 km. north of the Copper River Highway; seismometer placed on concrete floor.	60°29.27'	145°25.60'	Portable vertical Benioff.	1.0	30-day photographic paper.	0.50	60	up	0.10	1.0	2.4-7.8	CD2
Gulkana	GU1	Apr. 4 to Apr. 10, 1964. In building of FAA compound adjacent to Richardson Highway; seismometer placed on cement floor.	62°09.48'	145°27.67'	Willmore variable period vertical.	1.0	Photographic paper.	0.25	60	up	0.07	0.2	1.0-3.0	GU1
	GU2	Apr. 11 to May 7, 1964. Remote FAA standby transmitter building about 4 km. north of station GU1 and 0.3 km. from Richardson Highway.	62°11.62'	145 27.09'	Willmore variable period vertical.	1.0	Photographic paper.	0.25	60	up	0.02	0.2	3.0-10.0	GU2
	GU3	May 11 to Dec. 21, 1964. 14 km. south of the Gulkana FAA compound at the Copper Valley School; seismometer placed in storage room about 8 feet below surface of the ground.	62°02.78'	145°24.49'	Portable vertical Benioff.	1.0	Hot stylus, paper	0.20	60	up	0.01	0.2	4.6-16.0	GU3
	GU3	Installed Dec. 21, 1964.[2] Horizontal seismometers added to the system.	62°02.78'	145°24.49'	Portable vertical Benioff.	1.0	35-mm. film	0.20	15	up	0.01	0.2	4.6-16.0	GU3
					Portable horizontal Benioff.	1.0	35-mm. film	0.20	15	N., E.	0.01	0.2	10.0	
Homer	HOM	June 30 to Sept. 29, 1964. FAA warehouse at Homer Airport; seismograph placed on cement floor.	59°38.46'	151°29.85'	Portable vertical Benioff.	1.0	30-day photographic paper.	0.50	60	up	0.35	1.0	8.4-9.0	HOM
Kenai	KEN	Apr. 4 to June 26, 1964. Wildwood Military Reservation about 0.4 km. N. W. of Kenai; seismograph placed on cement floor in warehouse.	60°35.08'	151°17.78'	Portable vertical Benioff.	1.0	30-day photographic paper.	0.50	60	up	1.2	1.0	0.7-1.1	KEN
Kodiak	KD1	Apr. 2 to Apr. 10, 1964. Basement of Navy Fleet Weather Central.	57°44.84'	152°29.47'	Portable vertical Benioff.	1.0	Hot stylus, paper	0.20	60	up	0.26	0.8	2.6-5.5	KD1
	KD2	Apr. 10 to May 13, 1964. Abandoned wood frame building; seismometer placed on cement building pier and surrounded with sandbags for weather protection.	57°45.56'	152°29.61'	Portable vertical Benioff.	1.0	Hot stylus, paper	0.20	60	up	0.05	1.0	5.6-36.0	KD2
	KD3	May 14 to Aug. 17, 1964. Base pistol range; seismometer placed on bedrock and surrounded with sandbags for weather protection.	57°44.92'	152°30.88'	Portable vertical Benioff.	1.0	Hot stylus, paper	0.20	60	up	0.01	1.5	11.8-13.8	KD3
	KD4	Aug. 19 to Sept. 15, 1964. Equipment placed in wood frame building with cement floor.	57°44.92'	152°30.19'	Portable vertical Benioff.	1.0	35-mm. film	0.50	15	up	0.04	3.0	13.1-13.7	KD4
					Wood-Anderson.	0.8	35-mm. film		15	S.	[3]	[3]	2.8	
					Torsion.	0.8	35-mm. film		15	S.	[3]	[3]	0.1	
	KD5	Installed Sept. 15, 1964.[2] Underground reinforced concrete building.	57°44.87'	152°29.50'	Portable vertical Benioff.	1.0	35-mm. film	0.50	15	up	0.12	1.0	15.0-30.0	KD5
					Wood-Anderson.	0.8	35-mm. film		15	S.	[3]	[3]	2.8	
					Torsion.	0.8	35-mm. film		15	E.	[3]	[3]	0.1	
Middleton Island	MID4	Apr. 10, 1964 to Jan. 6, 1965. Seismometer in building about 1 km. S. W. of FAA compound.	59°25.67'	146°20.34'	Wood-Anderson.	0.8	35-mm. film		15	N.	[3]	[3]	2.8	MID[4]
					Torsion.	0.8	35-mm. film		15	E.	[3]	[3]	0.1	
					Torsion.	0.8	35-mm. film		15	E.	[3]	[3]	0.004	
	MID	Installed Dec. 6, 1964.[2] Same location as above but seismometers in outdoor drum-type vault.	59°25.67'	146°20.34'	Portable vertical Benioff.	1.0	35-mm. film	0.20	15	up	0.31	1.0	4.1-4.2	MID
					Portable horizontal Benioff.	1.0	35-mm. film	0.20	15	N., E.	0.31	1.0	4.1-4.2	
Seward	SEW[4]	Apr. 12, 1964 to June 13, 1965. Basement of Seward Hospital.	60°06.47'	149°26.71'	Wood-Anderson.	0.8	35-mm. film		15	N.	[3]	[3]	2.8	SEW[4]
					Wood-Anderson.	0.8	35-mm. film		15	E.	[3]	[3]	2.8	
					Torsion.	0.8	35-mm. film		15	E.	[3]	[3]	0.004	
Valdez	VAL	Installed Aug. 2, 1964.[2] Abandoned one-story apartment house.	61°07.05'	146°15.82'	Wood-Anderson.	0.8	35-mm. film		15	E.	[3]	[3]	2.8	VAL
					Torsion.	0.8	35-mm. film		15	S.	[3]	[3]	0.1	
					Torsion.	0.8	35-mm. film		15	S.	[3]	[3]	0.004	

1. All dates refer to 1964 unless otherwise noted.
2. Closeout date undetermined.
3. The Standard Wood-Anderson seismometer operates at a magnification of 2,800 and is relatively free of background noise.
4. Property of the California Institute of Technology.

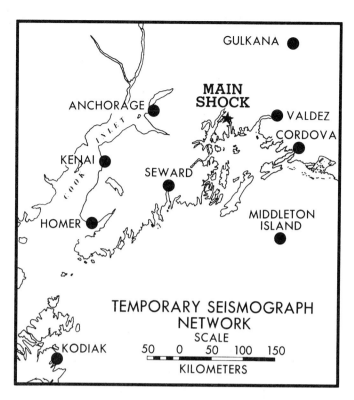

FIGURE 1.—Location of temporary seismograph stations.

Page [1968]. The crustal section in Prince William Sound and to the north were taken from refraction profiles published by Tatel and Tuve [1956] and reinterpreted by Woollard, *et al.*, [1960].

A generalized, single-layer, crustal model was assumed in order to simplify the computation of hypocenters. The model has a crustal thickness of 45 kilometers, *P*-wave velocity of 7 kilometers per second, and an upper mantle *P*-wave velocity of 8.2 kilometers per second. This model is a weighted average of the crustal data already discussed. For the location of hypocenters in and around Prince William Sound, the model appears to be a good approximation to the crust as presently known. The model is a poor approximation in the Kodiak region, being, in general, too thick. Figure 3 shows the traveltime curves based on the simplified structure for 11 depths of focus and distances up to 600 kilometers. The critical distances for each depth of focus above the Mohorovičić discontinuity are also shown. Rinehart's [1968] digital computer program was used to compute epicenters with data from the temporary seismograph stations. The computer program is described in detail elsewhere in this volume, and only an outline of the computation procedure is given here. The data for a particular earthquake were given an identification number and sorted into sequence by these numbers. For each

earthquake, time-difference hyperbola maps are plotted for pairs of stations. From these plots, data which are obviously in error are removed, and a preliminary hypocenter is calculated for use in the second part of the program, which is a least-squares iterative procedure.

If only three stations report *P*-arrival times, the hypocenter solution is underdetermined, and only an epicenter computation is made, the focal depth being fixed at 20 kilometers. Negative depths sometimes occur in computing hypocenters as a result of geologic model assumptions, poor azimuthal control, or a not-so-obvious data error. In these cases, the depth is constrained by the program logic to 20 kilometers, and only an epicenter is computed. The solution depth may also diverge downward for the same reasons. In these cases, the depth is constrained to 150 kilometers and again, only the epicenter is computed. In the summary listing (table 2), solutions for which the depth has been constrained are flagged.

Primarily because of azimuthal distribution of reporting stations, certain hypocenter solutions show a tendency to diverge or to oscillate. The tendency for divergence or oscillation of a solution can be identified on the time-difference plots by the near-parallelism of the hyperbolas. Program logic will terminate the processing of the hypocenter if its distance from the base latitude and longitude (60° N., 148° W.) is greater than 1,000 kilometers. The oscillating solution can usually be handled by constraining depth.

The magnitude M_L, as defined by Richter [1935], was computed by using data from the standard Wood–Anderson torsion seismometers in operation on Middleton Island and at Seward. Additional standard torsion seismometers were installed at Kodiak and Valdez in August 1964, but magnitudes computed from these stations are not included in this study.

Teleseismic data from seismograph stations throughout the world were used with a computer program described by Engdahl and Gunst [1966] and the Jeffreys–Bullen [1940] traveltime tables to compute the hypocenters of 1,231 of the larger aftershocks which occurred between March 28, 1964, and December 31, 1966. The magnitudes m_b were computed by the U. S. Coast and Geodetic Survey, and all were larger than 3.5. A summary of all hypocenters located by C&GS between March 28, 1964, and December 31, 1966, using local station data in Alaska and teleseismic data is given in table 2.

A requirement of the teleseismic computer location program is that at least five stations report *P*-wave

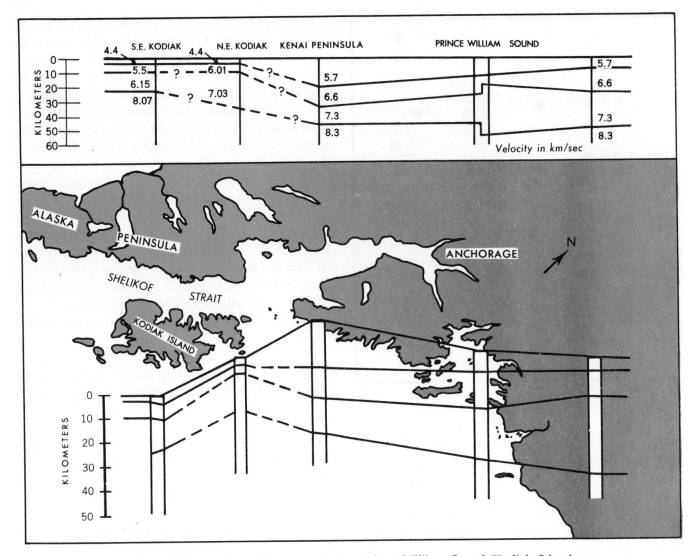

FIGURE 2.—Velocity and crustal structure in the Prince William Sound–Kodiak Island area.

arrival times before an attempt is made to compute the hypocenter. Occasionally, comparatively large aftershocks were not located because of a lack of teleseismic data and the five-station requirement of the computer program. An example is event 562, April 9, 1964, origin time 05:02:07.6, $M_L = 4.9$ (Earthquake No. 562, table 2). This recorded earthquake was located by using the temporary station network in Alaska.

A similar type of problem existed for locating aftershocks using the local computer program and the network of temporary stations. Operating downtime was fairly high at some of these stations during the first 2 months of their operation, and the magnification at all the stations was comparatively low. A total of 97 events located by the teleseismic method were not reported by at least three stations in the local Alaska station network. At least three of the temporary stations in Alaska

recorded P-wave arrivals for 173 aftershocks which were located using teleseismic data but could not be located with the temporary station data. The temporary network of stations was, in general, unable to locate aftershocks south and west of Kodiak Island in the Gulf of Alaska because of poor azimuthal distribution of the stations with regard to these earthquakes. The iterative process used in the hypocenter computer program diverged for many of the hypocenters for which the station distribution was poor.

A comparison of epicenters computed using teleseismic data with those using data from the temporary station network for the same earthquakes was made by Rinehart [1968]. He plotted the epicenters of earthquakes computed using data from the local stations relative to teleseismically determined epicenters plotted at the center of a grid. It was found that the scatter of the relative

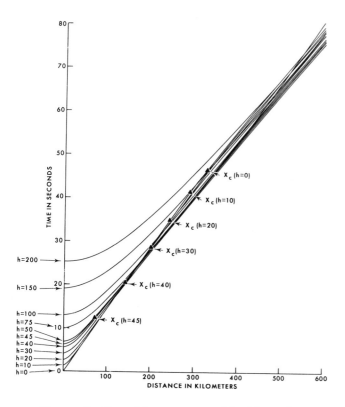

FIGURE 3.—Traveltime curves used in this study.

squares line of the form $\log N = a + bm_b$ fitted to the data for $m_b = 4.5$ and larger earthquakes yielded a slope of -0.95 and an intercept of 6.23 corresponding to data in 0.1 units of m_b.

This value of the slope is close to the value of -1.1 determined by Gutenberg and Richter [1954] for shallow shocks in Alaska and the Aleutian Islands for the time span 1904 to 1949.

Figure 8 shows the epicenters routinely located by the Coast and Geodetic Survey in south-central Alaska from January 1, 1964, until the main shock of March 28, 1964. The only large earthquake that occurred in this time span was the magnitude m_b 5.6 shock of February 6, 1964, off the southwest tip of Chirikof Island, 150 kilometers southwest of Kodiak Island. Two smaller earthquakes with m_b magnitudes 4.0 and 4.5 occurred near the epicenter of the main shock on January 28 and March 22, 1964. Both earthquakes are within 35 kilometers of the main shock.

Six large aftershocks occurred within the first 10 hours following the main shock. No other aftershock larger than $m_b = 6.0$ occurred in the aftershock zone until September 4—161 days after the main shock. The time sequence of these events indicates a progression of seismic activity from the main shock to the southwest end of the aftershock zone. The shocks can be interpreted as earthquakes associated with secondary faulting related to a master strike-slip fault [Harding and Algermissen, 1968]. Wyss and Brune [1967] have identified what they believe are six shocks greater than magnitude $m_b = 6.6$ within 70 seconds after the initial motion of the Prince William Sound Earthquake. They conclude that the rupture occurred in a series of events. These six earthquakes are shown in figure 9 as open circles. Thus, figure 9 shows all the known or postulated earthquakes with m_b magnitudes greater than 6.0 during the 10 hours following the initial earthquake at 03:36:14.0 G.M.T. on March 28.

Figure 10 shows the location of 370 aftershocks during the time span March 28 to April 2, 1964, or the first 5 days after the main shock. It should be noted that the aftershock activity is concentrated south of the main shock in the Gulf of Alaska in a band extending from the entrance to Prince William Sound to southeast of Kodiak Island. Very few aftershocks were located on Kodiak Island or the Alaska mainland.

Figure 11 shows the location of 249 aftershocks during the time April 3–12, 1964. The aftershock activity during this time span appears to be concentrated south of

locations (from local station data) had a mean or centroid 15 kilometers south and 8 kilometers west of the teleseismic location [Rinehart, 1968, figure 3]. The earthquakes whose epicenters were compared are located in Prince William Sound. It was pointed out by Rinehart that an increase of 0.1 kilometer per second in the crustal velocity of our model to 7.1 kilometers per second or a thickening of the crust by 7 kilometers to a thickness of 52 kilometers would correct this discrepancy.

The earthquake activity recorded by the individual temporary stations is shown in figure 4. Gaps in the registration of aftershocks at a particular station indicate that the station was inoperative for some reason.

The total number of earthquakes located per day in the aftershock zone from January 1, 1964, through December 31, 1966, is shown in figure 5. The number of earthquakes located per day from local station data is shown separately. Figure 6 shows the number of aftershocks of magnitude m_b 4.5 and larger and of magnitude m_b 5.5 and larger that occurred during the first 4 months after the main shock.

The frequency distribution of aftershocks with magnitude m_b for the period March 28 through December 31, 1964, is shown in figure 7. It was assumed that all aftershocks of magnitude 4.5 and larger were located. A least-

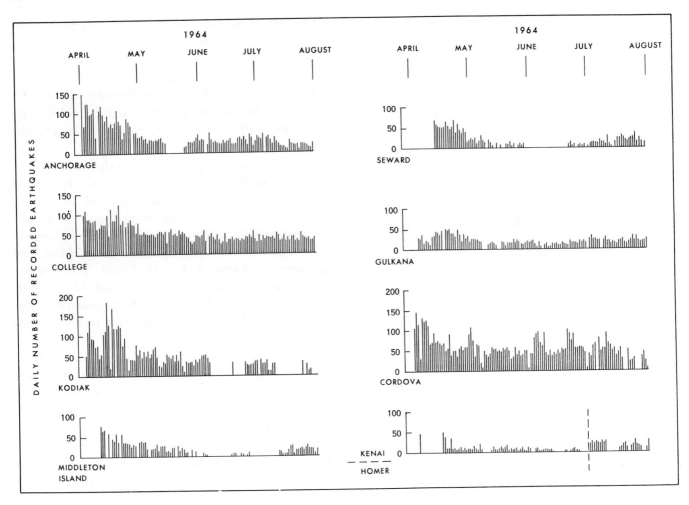

FIGURE 4.—Number of aftershocks recorded daily by the seismograph stations in Alaska, April through August 1964.

Kodiak Island and in the Gulf of Alaska near the entrance to Prince William Sound.

Figures 12 through 18 show the aftershocks and normal seismic activity in south-central Alaska from April 13, 1964, through December 31, 1966.

Figure 19 is a summary of all seismic activity in the aftershock zone from March 28, 1964, through December 31, 1965. During this time interval, 2,055 earthquakes were located.

It is difficult to outline the limits of the aftershock zone precisely because of the relatively high, normal seismicity of the area. The area of aftershock activity may be taken approximately as a rectangle 900 kilometers in length and 400 kilometers in width having an area of 3.6×10^5 km.[2] Assuming that the majority of all aftershock activity occurred at depths of 40 kilometers or less, the approximate volume of the aftershock zone is 14×10^6 km.[3] This volume is in good agreement with the volume of the aftershock zone that would be

expected for an 8.3 magnitude earthquake using the work of Båth and Duda [1964].

The aftershocks of magnitude $m_b = 4.5$ and greater that occurred during the interval March 28, 1964, through December 31, 1965, and fell within the area outlined in figure 20 were assigned coordinates proportional to their relative distances northeast or southwest from the midpoint of the aftershock zone. The relative position of each aftershock in the zone was then plotted versus time and the points connected. The purpose of the plot is to show any repetitive pattern in time for the aftershock sequence. In figure 21, A, B, and C illustrate idealized examples of possible aftershock occurrence. Figure 21A shows the space-time plot for a sequence of hypothetical aftershocks progressing from southwest to northeast along the length of an aftershock zone. Figure 21B shows a plot for a sequence of hypothetical aftershocks representing an oscillation of aftershock activity from the southwest to the northeast end of the aftershock

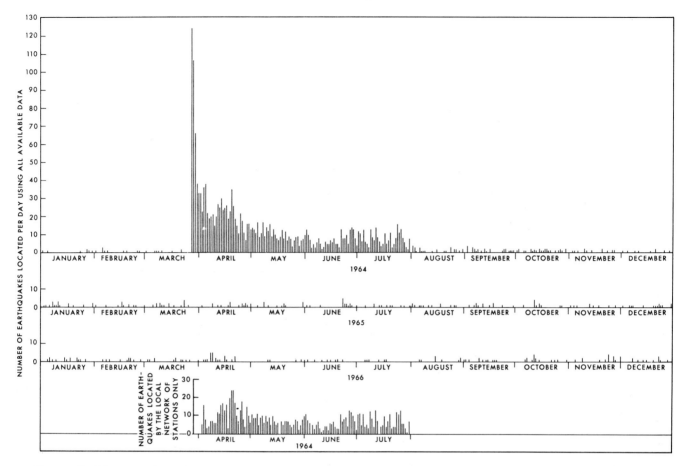

FIGURE 5.—Number of earthquakes located daily in the Prince William Sound–Kodiak Island region, 1964–1966.

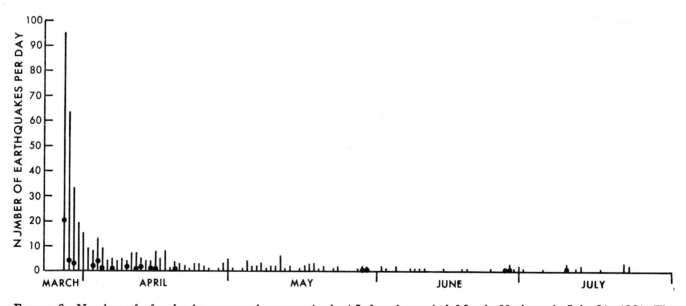

FIGURE 6.—Number of aftershocks greater than magnitude 4.5 for the period March 28 through July 31, 1964. The number of aftershocks greater than magnitude 5.5 are shown by circles.

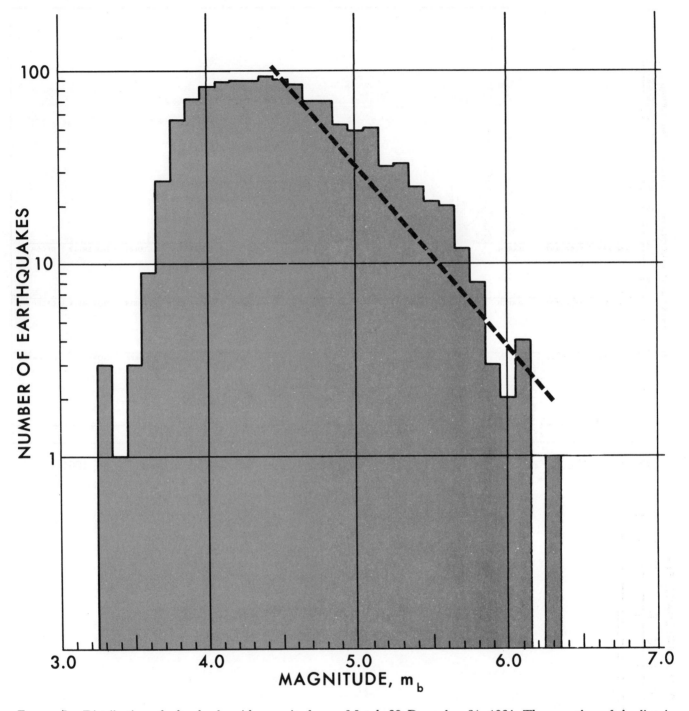

FIGURE 7.—Distribution of aftershocks with magnitude m_b, March 28–December 31, 1964. The equation of the line is:
$$\text{Log}_{10}\ N = 6.23 - 0.95\ m_b.$$

zone. Figure 21C shows the same type of plot for after-shock activity concentrated near one end of an aftershock zone. As described above, figure 22 is an actual plot of the earthquakes $m_b \geq 6.0$ that occurred during the first 10 hours after the main shock. Figure 9 is the epicenter map of these six earthquakes. Comparison of figure 9 with figure 22 shows the type of space-time plot to be

expected for a series of earthquakes which, in general, progressed from the northeast to southwest portion of the aftershock zone with some smaller oscillations. Figure 23 is a space-time plot of all of the earthquakes with magnitudes, $m_b \geq 4.5$ which were located in the after-shock zone between March 28, 1964, and December 31, 1966. Earthquakes of magnitude $m_b \geq 5.5$ have been

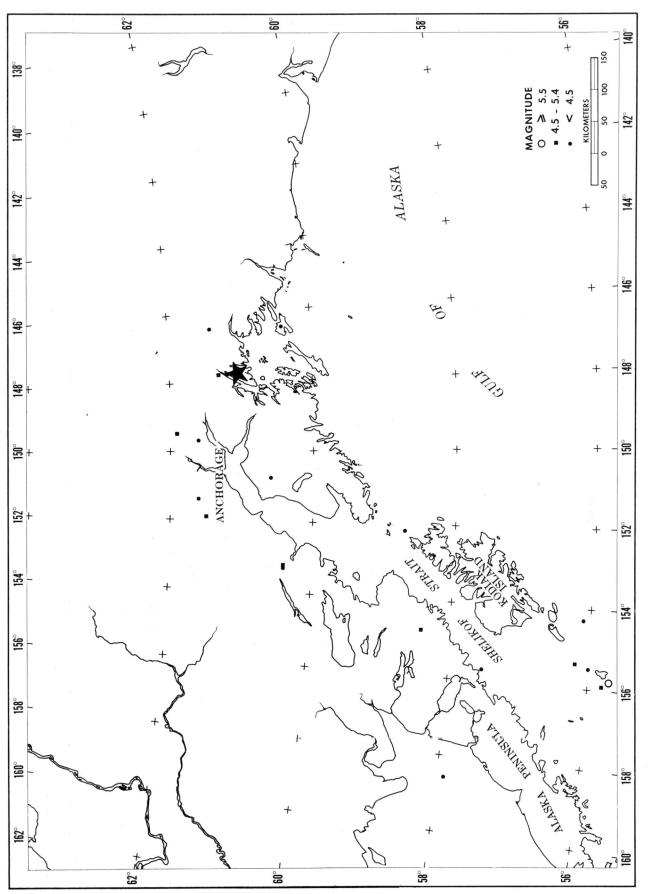

FIGURE 8.—Epicenters routinely located by the U.S. Coast and Geodetic Survey in the Prince William Sound–Kodiak Island area January 1 to March 28, 1964. The main shock is indicated by a star.

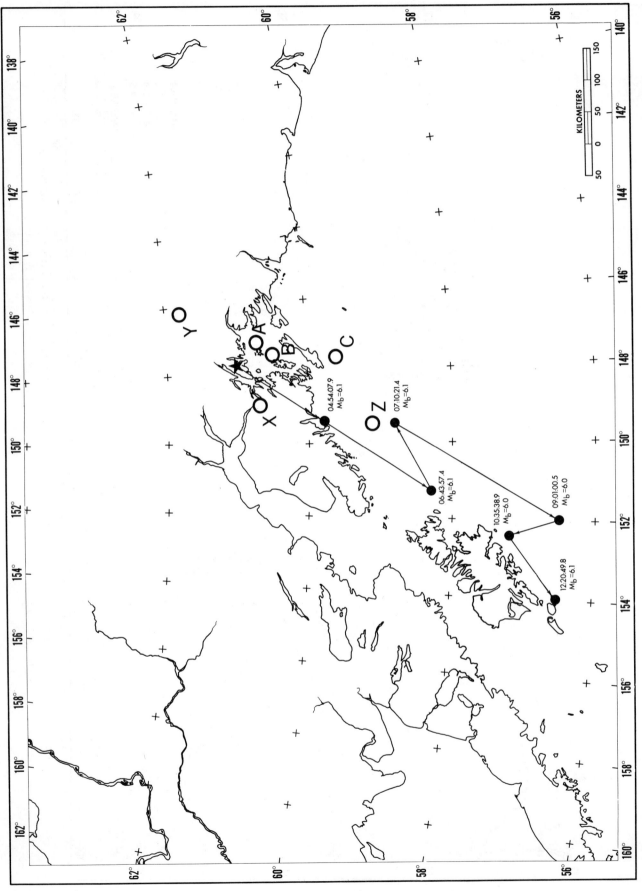

FIGURE 9.—Distribution of large aftershocks within 10 hours after the main shock. The open circles and letters refer to shocks identified by Wyss and Brune [1967].

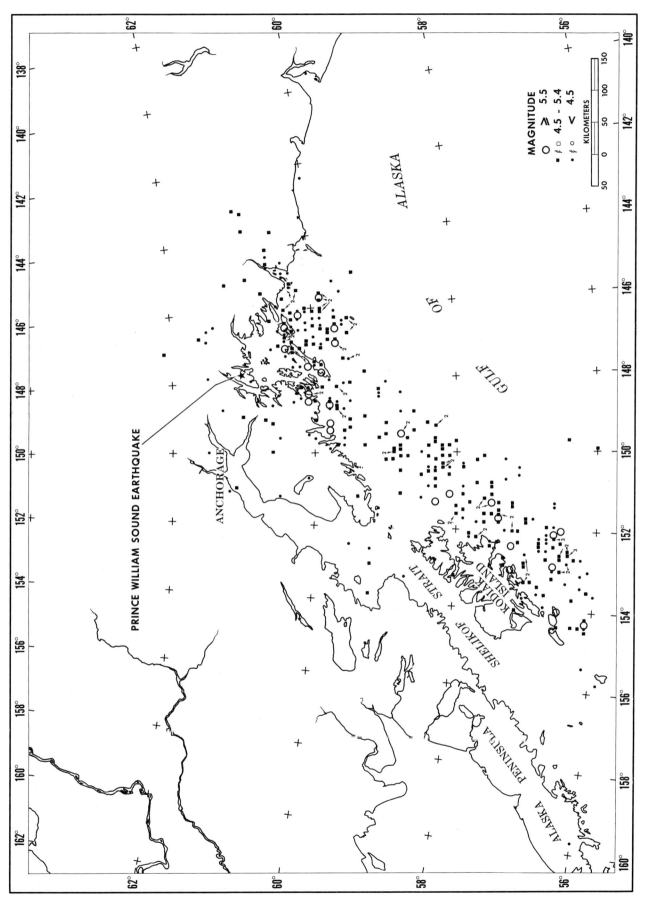

FIGURE 10.—The main shock and aftershocks through April 2, 1964. The small open squares and circles are aftershocks located with data from the temporary station network. All other shocks were located using teleseismic data.

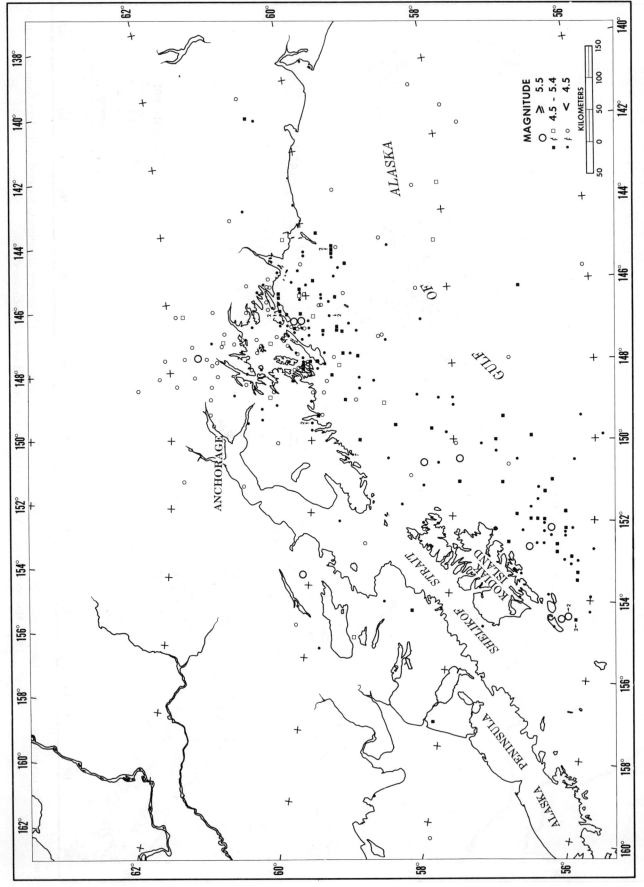

FIGURE 11.—Seismic activity, April 3–12, 1964. The small open squares and circles are aftershocks located with data from the temporary station network. All other shocks were located using teleseismic data.

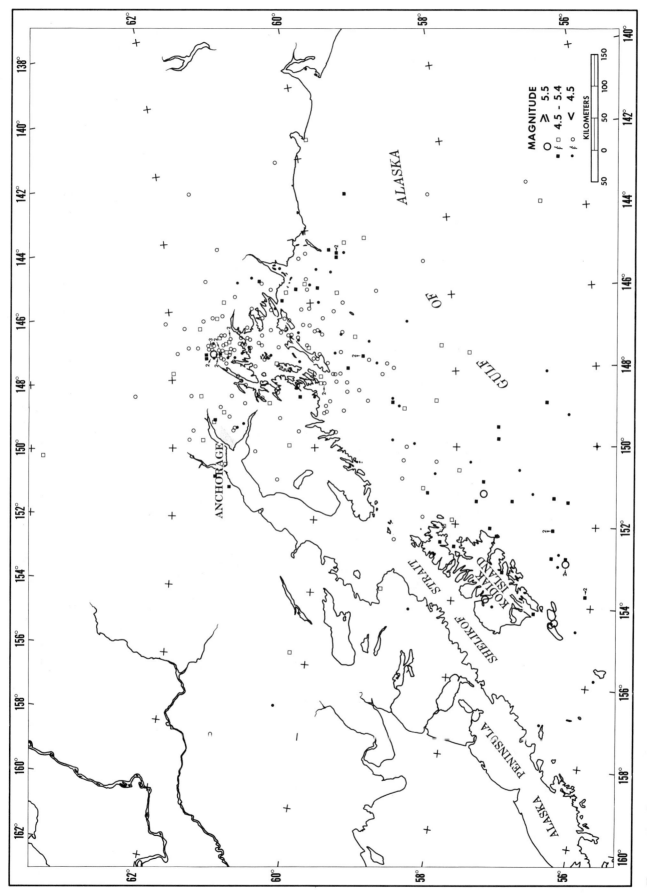

FIGURE 12.—Seismic activity, April 13–22, 1964. The small open squares and circles are aftershocks located with data from the temporary station network. All other shocks were located using teleseismic data.

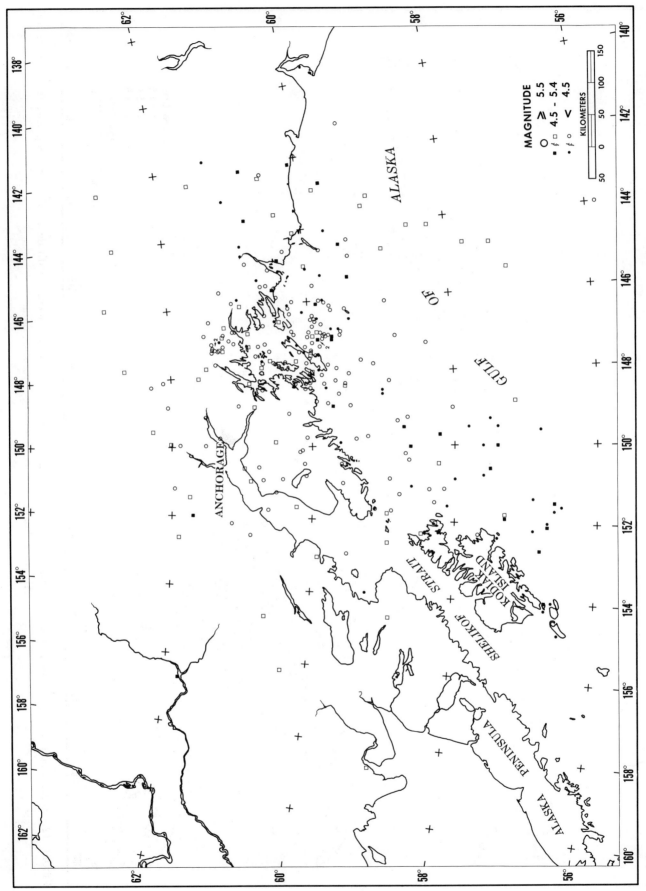

FIGURE 13.—Seismic activity, April 23–May 2, 1964. The small open squares and circles are aftershocks located with data from the temporary station network. All other shocks were located using teleseismic data.

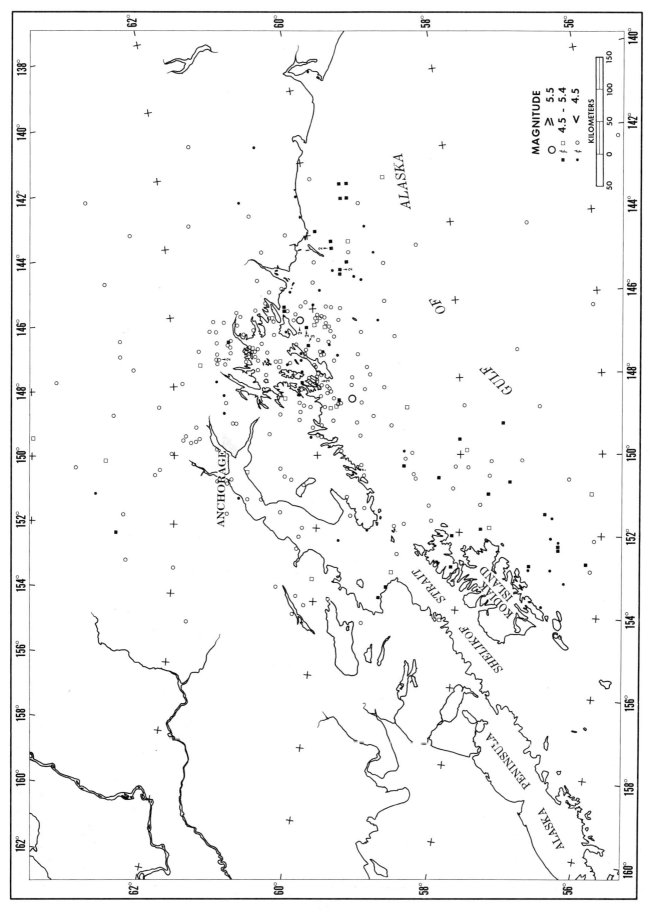

FIGURE 14.—Seismic activity, May 13–June 21, 1964. The small open squares and circles are aftershocks located with data from the temporary station network. All other shocks were located using teleseismic data.

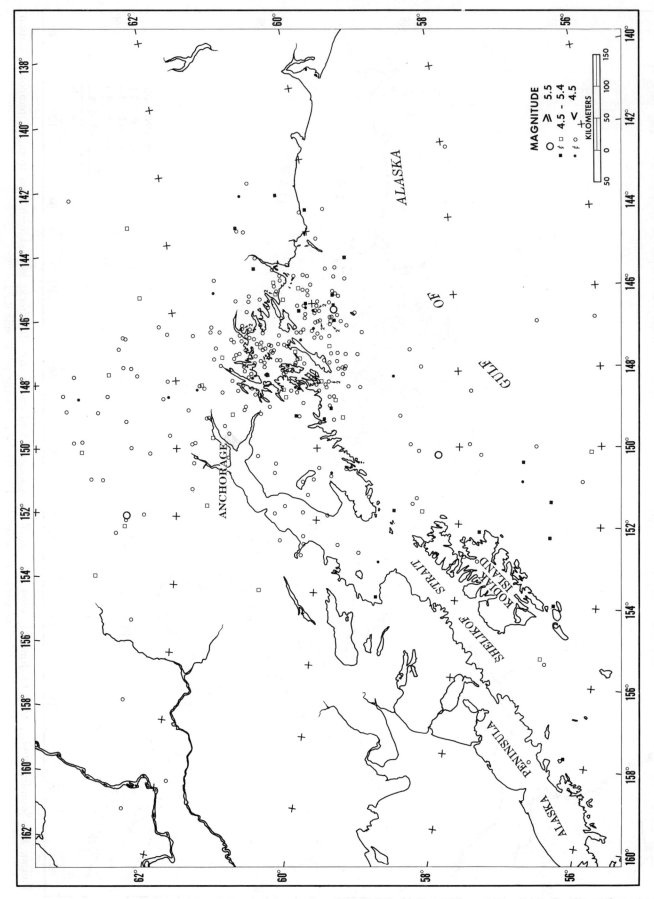

FIGURE 15.—Seismic activity, June 22–July 31, 1964. The small open squares and circles are aftershocks located with data from the temporary station network. All other shocks were located using teleseismic data.

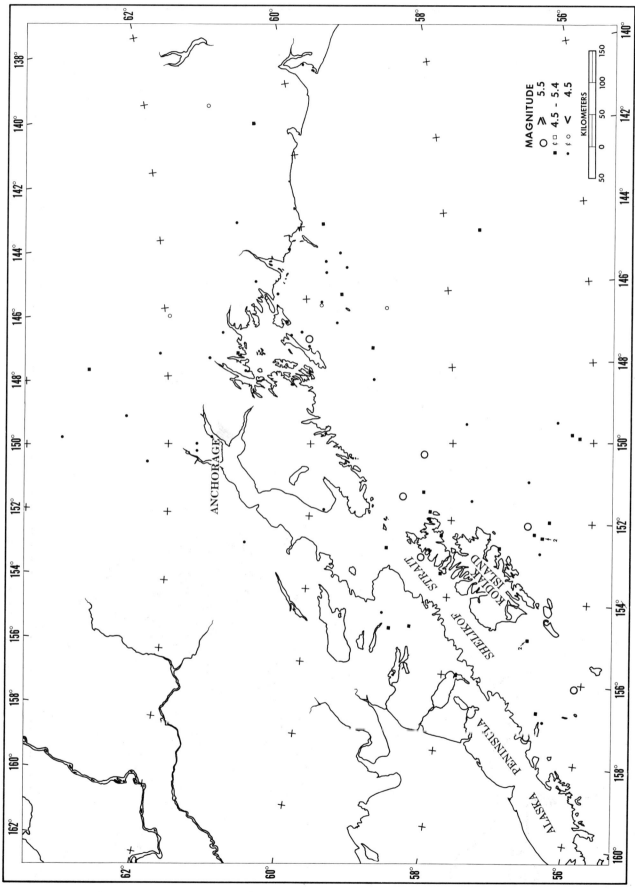

FIGURE 16.—Seismic activity, August 1–December 31, 1964. The small open squares and circles are aftershocks located with data from the temporary station network. All other shocks were located using teleseismic data.

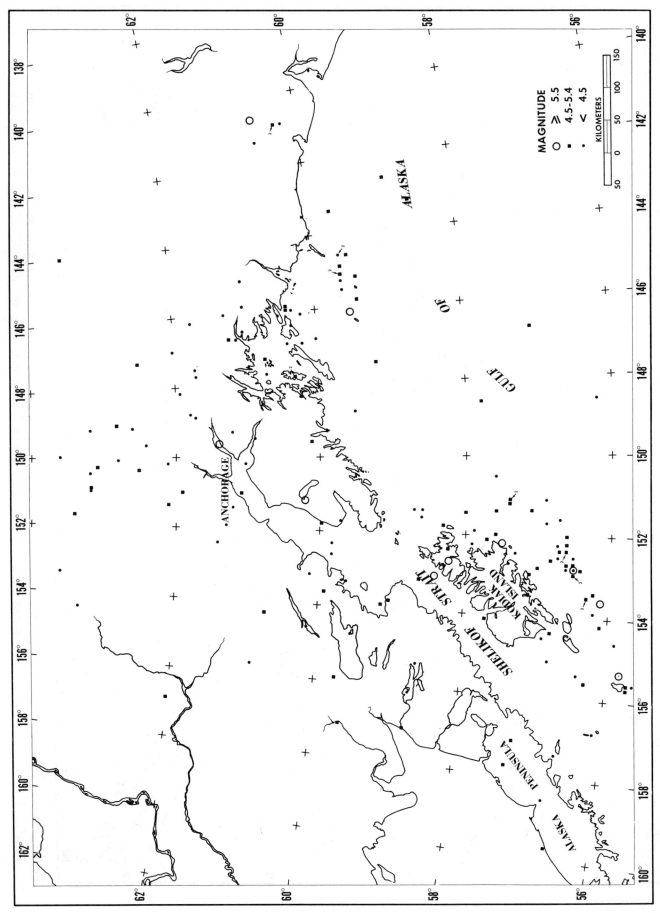

FIGURE 17.—Seismic activity, 1965. All epicenters computed using teleseismic data.

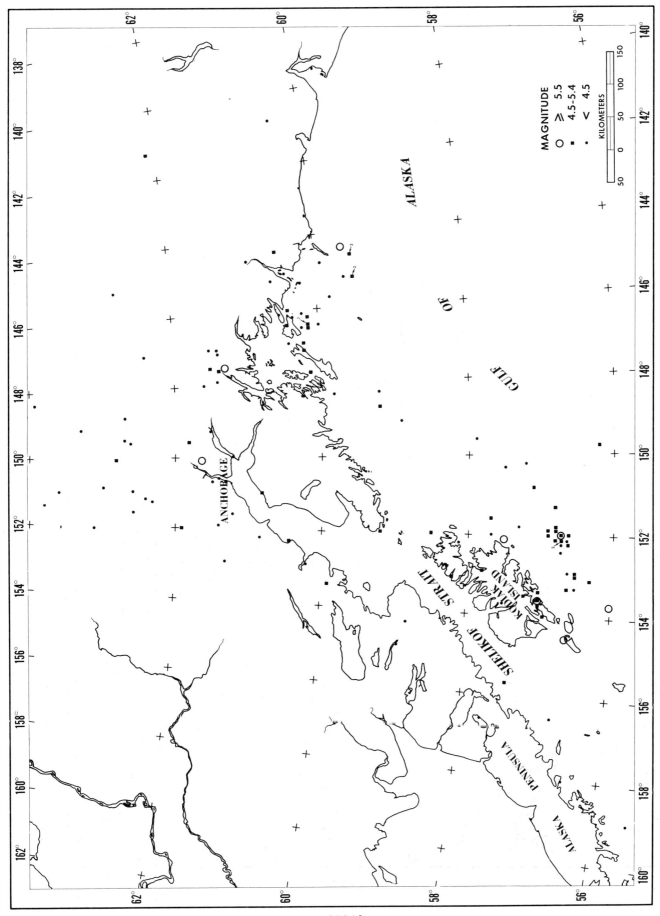

FIGURE 18.—Seismic activity, 1966. All epicenters computed using teleseismic data.

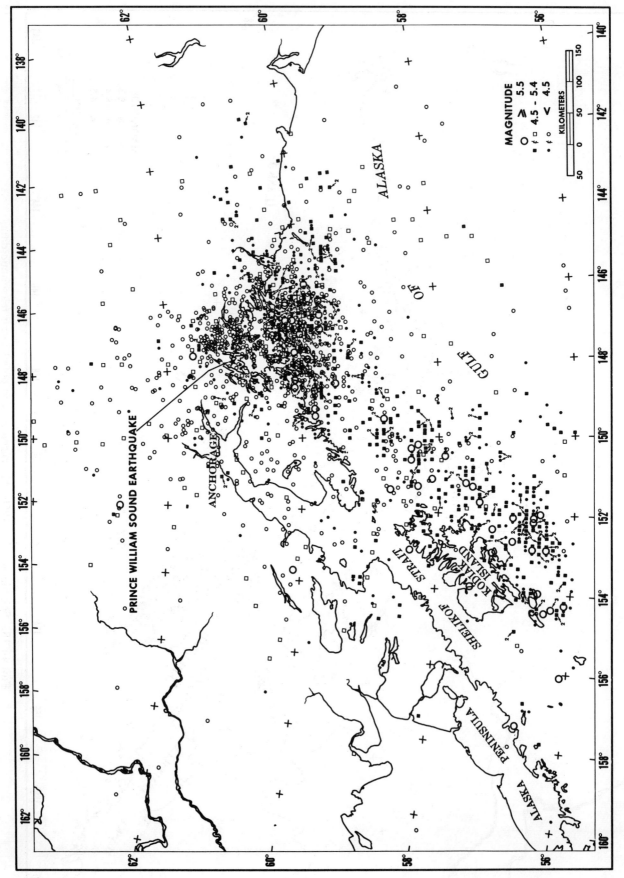

FIGURE 19.—All epicenters located between March 28, 1964, and December 31, 1965. The small open squares and circles are aftershocks located with data from the temporay station network. All other shocks were located using teleseismic data.

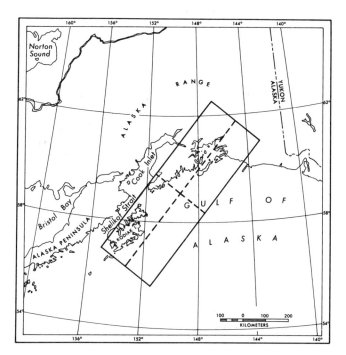

FIGURE 20.—Geographic area considered in the spatial-temporal plots of aftershock activity.

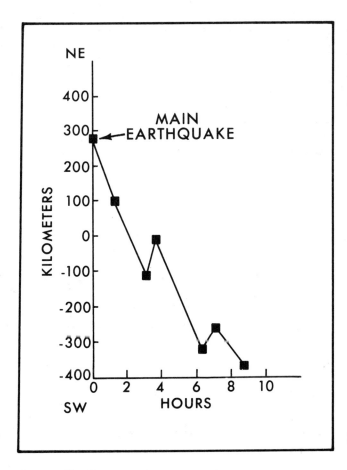

FIGURE 22.—Spatial-temporal plot of the six aftershocks shown in figure 9.

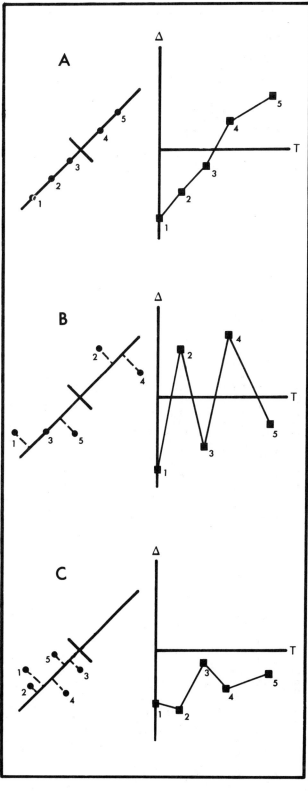

FIGURE 21.—Spatial-temporal plot of a hypothetical series of earthquakes. The left side is a hypothetical epicenter map; the numbers indicate chronological order:—A: progressing in space and time from southwest to northeast; B: oscillating in time from one end of the aftershock zone to the other; and C: activity concentrated in time at one end of the aftershock zone.

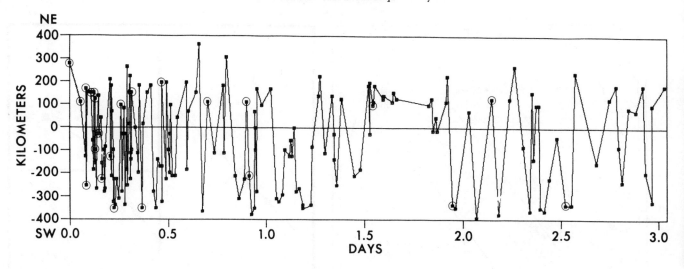

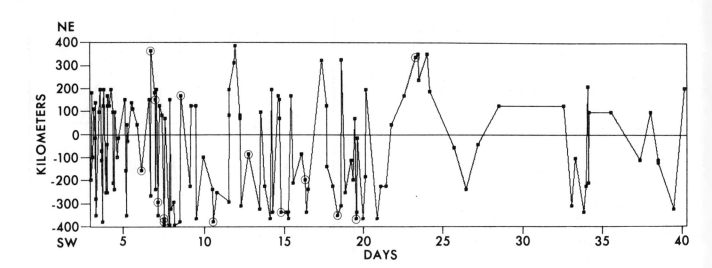

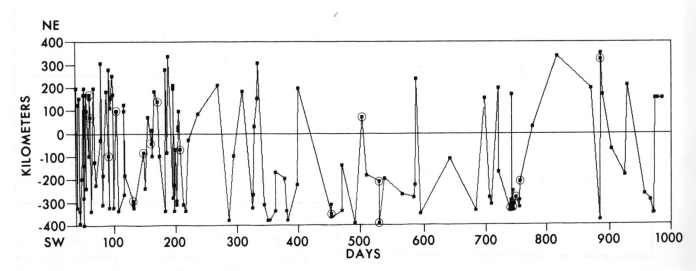

FIGURE 23.—Spatial-temporal plot of the earthquake activity in the Prince William Sound–Kodiak Island area, $m_b \geqq 4.5$, March 28, 1964, through December 31, 1966. Earthquakes with magnitude greater than or equal to 5.5 are circled.

circled. This plot shows several distinctive characteristics of the aftershock sequence.

1. There is considerable temporal variation in aftershock activity with bursts of activity followed by periods of relative quiescence. This pattern is superimposed on the general, well-known hyperbolic decrease of aftershock activity with time that is shown by figures 5 and 6.

2. The general pattern of aftershock occurrence appears to be oscillation of activity from one end of the aftershock zone to the other. Superimposed on this oscillatory pattern are spatial and temporal clusters of earthquakes. These clusters are often characterized by one or more large aftershocks either preceded or followed by a number of smaller shocks in the same geographic area. While it appears that the principal tendency is for aftershocks to oscillate from one end of the aftershock zone to the other with time, some large aftershocks appear to have their own individual foreshock and aftershock sequence.

3. There is a tendency for the large aftershocks to occur near the ends of the aftershock zone, particularly during the period 0.5 to 20 days following the main shock.

FOCAL DEPTHS

Focal depths were determined using four different methods.

1. Special studies of depth phases such as pP and sP together with P and S data from stations within 100 kilometers of the epicenter.

2. Analysis of depth phases only.

3. P and S data from local station data only.

4. Routine depths computed using teleseismic data with the standard C&GS hypocenter program.

The above techniques are listed in order of decreasing accuracy of focal depth determination. The focal depth listed in table 2 for each earthquake is the best estimated depth. The method used in each computation is indicated in the table.

A special study was made of 43 aftershocks that occurred between March 28 and October 31, 1964. Earthquakes were selected for study provided that (1) data were available from at least one temporary seismograph station within 100 kilometers of the epicenter, and (2) a focal depth could also be computed from depth phases such as pP and sP.

Focal depths were computed from local station data in the following manner: (1) The epicenter of each shock was fixed using teleseismic data ($\Delta \geq 25°$) and the Jeffreys–Bullen [1940] traveltime tables, and (2) with the epicenter fixed, the focal depth was determined from local station data.

Depth phases were, in general, well recorded for the aftershocks in this series. Seismograms recorded at various teleseismic distances for two aftershocks are shown in figures 24 and 25. Comparisons of depths computed, using local station data with those determined from depth phases recorded at teleseismic distances, are shown in figures 26 and 27. Figure 26 is a comparison of focal depths determined by the two methods for 29 earthquakes in the Prince William Sound area. Figure 27 compares depths computed by the two methods for 14 aftershocks in the vicinity of Kodiak Island. For aftershocks near Kodiak Island, there seems to be a tendency for focal depths determined from local station data to

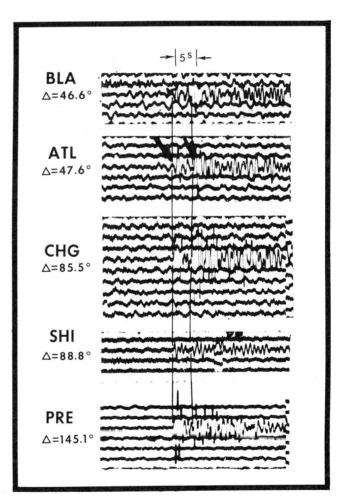

FIGURE 24.—Seismograms (vertical component) of the aftershock of May 1, 1964. Origin time 06:01:55.4, 60.5° N., 145.6° W., (h (ave.) = 14 km., m_b = 5.4) illustrating the identification of the phase pP at Blacksburg, Atlanta, Chiengmai, Shiraz, and Pretoria.

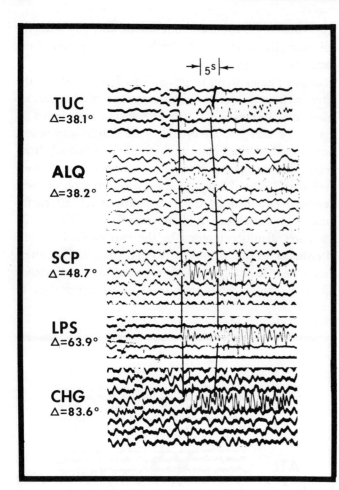

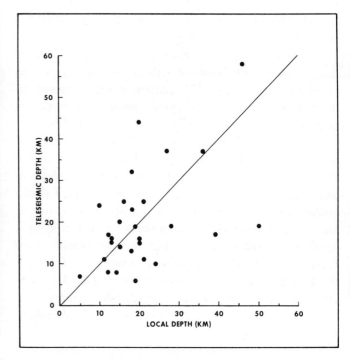

FIGURE 26.—Comparison of focal depths computed from local station data depths from analysis of the phases pP and sP (Prince William Sound area).

FIGURE 25.—Seismograms (vertical component) of the aftershock of May 4, 1964. Origin time 12:04:46.1; 58.2° N., 152.3° W.; (h (ave.) = 22 km.; m_b = 5.3) illustrating the identification of the phase pP at Tucson, Albuquerque, State College (Pennsylvania), La Palma (San Salvador), and Chiengmai.

be nearly twice as deep as the corresponding ones computed from depth phases. Assuming a crustal thickness of 22 kilometers [Shor, 1962] southeast of Kodiak Island, these data suggest that the depth phases are perhaps being reflected from the base of the crust rather than the earth's surface in this area. In addition to the 43 earthquakes included in the special study, depths were computed for 363 additional earthquakes using depth-sensitive phases recorded at teleseismic distances. These 363 aftershocks together with the 43 specially studied are shown in figure 28. Clearly, the aftershocks of the Prince William Sound are shallow earthquakes. The following is the percentage distribution with depth of the

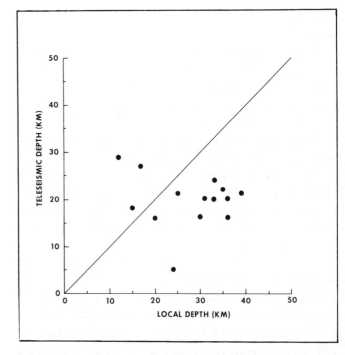

FIGURE 27.—Comparison of focal depths computed from local station data with depth from analysis of the phase pP and sP (Kodiak Island area).

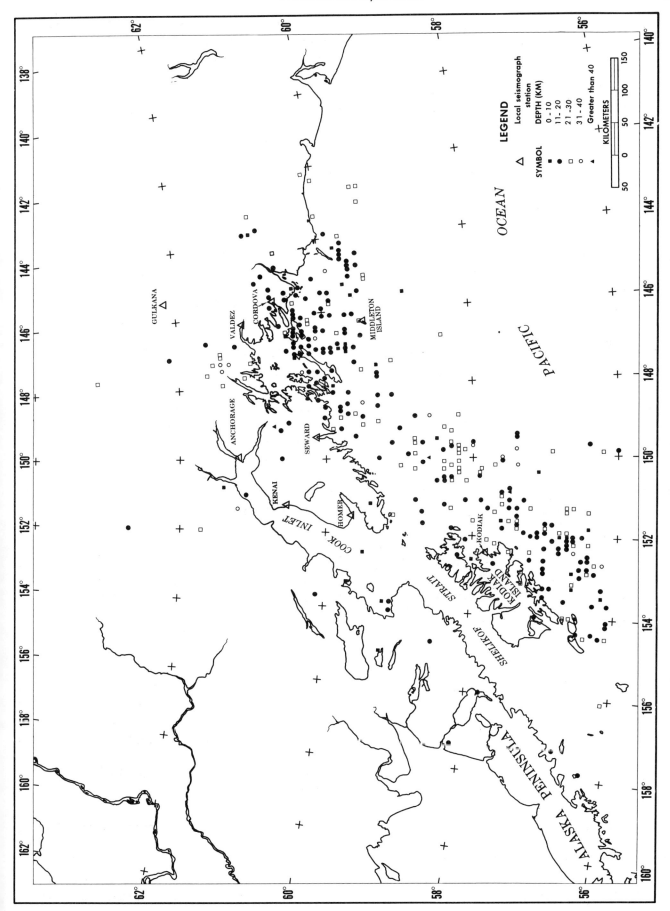

FIGURE 28.—Focal depths of selected aftershocks, March 28 to October 30, 1964.

406 aftershocks for which depth phases, local station data, or both were available:

h(km.)	Percent
Less than 20	62
20–40	37
Greater than 40	1

Of the total of 2,178 aftershocks located by C&GS between March 28, 1964, and December 31, 1966, focal depths were determined for 1,029 of the earthquakes, using one or more of the techniques discussed above. The focal depths of the remaining 1,149 aftershocks were restrained at either a depth of 20 to 33 kilometers in the hypocenter computation. The percentage distribution with depth for all aftershocks for which a depth was actually computed (not restrained) is given below:

h(km.)	Percent
Less than 20	33
20–40	46
Greater than 40	21

This table shows that when the focal depths determined by routine least-squares hypocenter computer programs are included, the percentage of deeper aftershocks increases. This is because the focal depths of many shallow earthquakes are often restrained at a depth of 33 kilometers by the computer program when the focal depth becomes negative (goes above the surface) in the computation.

Figure 29 is a northwest-southeast cross section through the location of the main shock. The foci of all aftershocks within 50 kilometers of the section were projected into the section.

The focus of the main shock is shown, arbitrarily, at a depth of 33 kilometers, since the depth of focus of the main shock was not precisely determined but is known to be shallow [Sherburne, *et al.*, 1968]. The Bouguer gravity (from C&GS data) and surface deformation resulting from the earthquake [after Plafker, 1965] are also shown. The aftershocks are very shallow beneath Prince William Sound, averaging 15 kilometers in depth. The foci dip gently at an angle of approximately 4° to 6° to the northwest under the Chugach Mountains. A cross section through Afognak Island in the Kodiak Island region is shown in figure 30. The aftershocks south and west of Kodiak Island are also very shallow, averaging 20 kilometers in depth. The foci do not increase in depth beneath the continent for the cross section considered in figure 30.

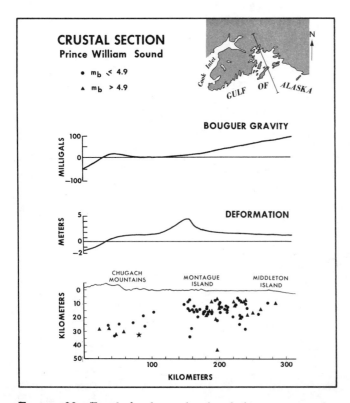

FIGURE 29.—Focal depths and related data on a section through the main shock (represented with a star).

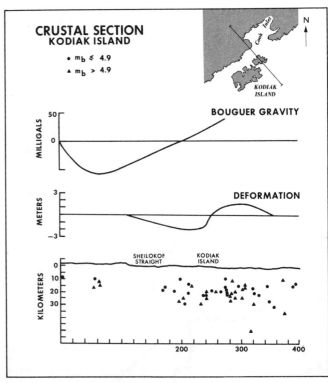

FIGURE 30.—Focal depths and related data on a section through Afognak Island in the Kodiak Island area.

The depths of focus of these aftershocks seem to be compatible with focal depths found in studies of the seismicity of this area [Tobin and Sykes, 1966] and other studies of the aftershock sequence of the March 28 earthquake [Matumoto and Page; Aki, *et al.*, 1968]. Matumoto and Page found that about 80 percent of the microearthquakes they were able to locate occurred at depths between 0 and 40 kilometers. Aki, *et al.*, found that nearly all of the shocks on the oceanic side of their station on the Kenai Peninsula occurred in the crust, but about half of the shocks on the continental side occurred in the mantle. Aki, *et al.*, also found shocks at depths up to 200 kilometers in the mantle; they concluded that all shocks occurring in the mantle were small, probably below magnitude 3.

ENERGY RELEASE

The temporal distribution of energy release was computed for Alaska and the Aleutian Islands from 1899 to the present to evaluate the relationship of regional energy release prior to 1964 with the energy released in the main shock and the resulting aftershock sequence. Seismicity data prior to 1951 was obtained primarily from *The Prince William Sound, Alaska, Earthquake of 1964 and Aftershocks*, Volume 1, table 2, p. 64 [1966], which was compiled from original sources—principally Gutenberg and Richter [1954]. Magnitudes of certain large shocks have been revised using data from Richter [1958]. No earthquakes with surface-wave magnitudes less than 6.0 have been considered, except in our study of the energy released in the aftershock sequence. Data may be incomplete on even the largest shocks prior to 1904, but the graph is plotted from 1899, primarily to include the Yakatat Bay earthquakes of that year. From 1904–1950 the completeness of the graphs depends primarily on the completeness of the data assembled by Gutenberg and Richter [1954]. The data are considered to be relatively complete for shocks of magnitude M_s greater than 6.0 since 1951. The C&GS began computing m_b magnitudes in 1963. For the interval 1951 to 1963, surface-wave magnitudes for shocks greater than 6.0, published by the University of California at Berkeley (BRK), California Institute of Technology (PAS), or the Lamont Geological Laboratory (PAL) were used if available. Otherwise magnitudes m_b were computed. Magnitudes m_b published by the C&GS were used for earthquakes since 1963 and were converted to M_s, using the least-squares relationship of Dillinger and Algermissen [1968] with the following

exceptions—because of the uncertainty of the relationship between m_b and M_s for $m_b \geq 6.0$, average values of M_s reported by PAL, BRK, and PAS were always used if available or, if not available, were computed for shocks in the range $m_b \geq 6.0$.

The M_s magnitude values were then converted to energy release using the relationship log $E = 11.8 + 1.5 M_s$ [Gutenberg and Richter, 1956]. For the display of spatial energy release, the longitude and latitude of all earthquakes were converted to x and y values on an Albers equal-area projection. The energies associated with each earthquake were then summed in grid squares whose dimensions were 25 kilometers on a side. A portion of the summed energy for each grid cell was distributed to surrounding grid cells, using the method adopted by Allen, *et al.*, [1965] to display a related quantity strain release. The distribution of energy was as follows: 40 percent of the energy originally in the grid cell remains; 10 percent is distributed to each grid cell north, east, south, and west of the original cell; and 5 percent is distributed to each grid cell to the northeast, northwest, southeast, and southwest. The initial energy distribution may be iterated any desired number of times, using a suitable digital computer program. Two iterations were used for the maps in this report. The final percent distribution of energy associated with earthquakes located in the center grid cell is shown in figure 31. The energy was

.25	1	1.5	1	.25
1	6	10	6	1
1.5	10	21	10	1.5
1	6	10	6	1
.25	1	1.5	1	.25

FIGURE 31.—Smoothing percentages used in distributing the strain energy.

distributed to take into account the uncertainty associated with the epicentral location of older shocks and to partially account for the release of energy over a greater area than 625 square kilometers which occurs in large earthquakes [Båth and Duda, 1964]. The energy release is expressed as contours in units of 10^{20} ergs.

Figure 32 illustrates the temporal energy release for Alaska and the Aleutian Islands from 170° E. to 130° W. longitude and from 50° N. to 66° N. latitude for the time period 1899–1966. The high seismicity of the area from the start of the graph in 1899 through about 1907 and the occurrence of great earthquakes in 1929 (Fox Islands), 1938 (southwest of Kodiak), 1957 (Andreanof Islands), 1958 (Lituya Bay), and 1964 (Prince William Sound) are clearly shown. The magnitudes of the shocks in 1929 and 1938 have been revised

upward from the original estimates of Gutenberg and Richter [1954]. The revised magnitudes for M_s are those of Richter [1958]. The two dashed lines which form an envelope for the saw-toothed curve indicate the range of energy release experienced during a single year or a few active seismic years. The average annual rate of energy release from 1899 through 1938 was roughly 0.7×10^{24} ergs per year. The curve shows, however, that the yearly energy release fluctuated widely during these years, ranging from 6.3×10^{20} ergs (1920) to approximately 7.1×10^{24} (1899). The rate of energy release since 1938 appears to have been substantially less than the average rate prior to 1938.

The temporal energy release in the Prince William Sound–Kodiak Island region (144°–156° W. long., 54°–63° N. lat.) for the period 1899–1966 (68 years) is shown in figure 33. The area considered corresponds to the area in which aftershocks of the Prince William Sound Earthquake occurred. No earthquakes were reported for this area between 1899 and 1908 by Gutenberg and Richter [1954] or Richter [1958] and hence, none appear on our plot. The high seismic activity shown for 1909–1911 results mainly from large shocks near Seward in 1909 and 1911, three large earthquakes in 1911 in the Cook Inlet–Shelikof Strait area, and a magnitude 7.3 shock north of Valdez in 1911. The periods 1913–1927 (15 years), 1935–1942 (8 years), and 1956–1963 (8 years) were periods of relatively low activity. Several other interesting trends should also be noted. The two dashed lines that form an envelope for the saw-toothed curve between 1912 and 1964 indicate that, on the average, amplitudes of the oscillations in the energy release curve were decreasing during this period. The energy releases for the periods 1943–1955 and 1956–1963 are particularly interesting. For the period 1943–1955, the rate of energy release averaged about 1.0 $\times 10^{22}$ ergs per year, more than double the average annual rate of energy release in the 8 years immediately preceding the earthquake. Energy was being released at a very slow rate in Prince William Sound in the 8 years before the 1964 earthquake.

The energy released in the aftershock zone during the 1,000 days following the main shock is shown in figure 34. All aftershocks with m_b (C&GS) magnitudes ≥ 4.5 are included in the graph. The energy released in the main shock is not shown in figure 34. Using the relationship $\log E = 11.8 + 1.5M_s$ [Gutenberg and Richter, 1956] and an M_s value of 8.3, the energy released in the main shock was about 1.8×10^{24} ergs. The energy released in the aftershock sequence during the first 1,000

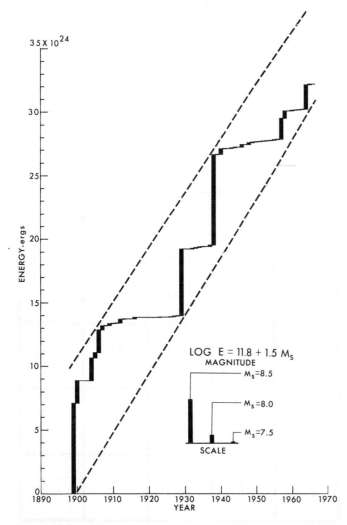

FIGURE 32.—Energy release, Alaska and the Aleutian Islands, 1899–1966, 50° to 66° N., 130° W. to 170° E., $M_s \geq 4.5$.

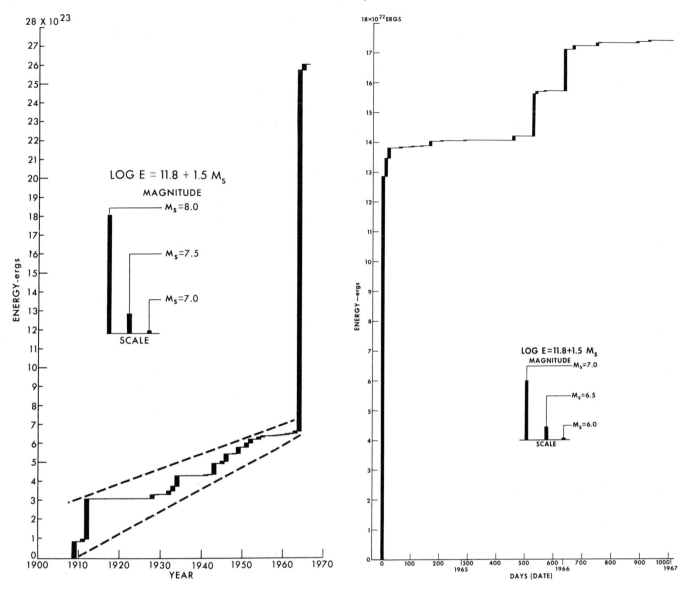

FIGURE 33.—Energy release, Prince William Sound–Kodiak Island area, 1909–1966, 54° to 63° N., 144° to 156° W., $M_s \geq 4.5$.

FIGURE 34.—Energy release, aftershocks of the Prince William Sound Earthquake, March 28, 1964, through December 31, 1966, $M_s \geq 4.5$.

days following the main shock was approximately 1.8×10^{23} ergs, about one-tenth of the energy released in the main shock. Actually, the energy release in the Prince William Sound aftershock zone in the 1,000 days following the main shock appears to consist of two parts. The first sequence terminates approximately 520 days after the main shock; the total energy release during this period being 1.43×10^{23} ergs or about 8 percent of the energy released in the main shock. A new sequence of activity was triggered on September 4, 1965, with an earthquake $M_s = 6.9$ off Kodiak Island. The increased energy release in the aftershock zone in 1965–1966 was

due principally to seismic activity in the vicinity of Kodiak Island.

Strain release in Alaska and the Aleutian Islands has been contoured by Milne [1967]. Consideration of Milne's work and figure 35 which shows the epicenters of the larger earthquakes that have occurred in the Prince William Sound area from 1899–1964, inclusive, points up two interesting features of the seismicity of south-central Alaska: (1) Although large earthquakes have occurred between 1899 and 1966 in the vicinity of Prince William Sound, the epicenters (when known) of all the larger shocks have been around the periphery of

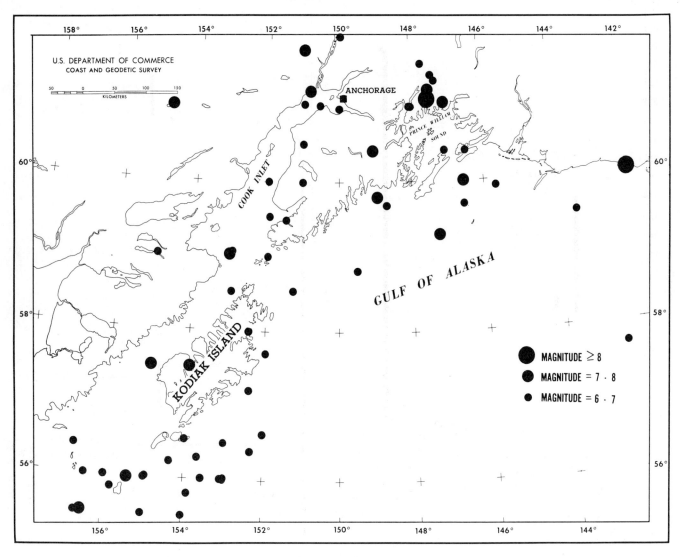

FIGURE 35.—Earthquakes with magnitude $M_s \geq 6.0$ in the Prince William Sound area, 1899–1964.

the Sound—the Sound itself having been relatively free of seismic activity until the aftershock sequence of the 1964 earthquake, and (2) the coastal area of Alaska in the vicinity of Kayak Island (59.6° N., 144.5° W.), about 150 kilometers southeast of Prince William Sound has been remarkably free of seismic activity for the past 68 years, even though great earthquakes have occurred 200 kilometers to the northwest (Prince William Sound, 1964) and 150 kilometers to the east (Yakatat, 1899) along the coastline.

Figure 36 shows the energy release in the vicinity of Prince William Sound and Kodiak Island from May 5, 1934, until the occurrence of the Prince William Sound Earthquake on March 28, 1964. The date May 5, 1934, was chosen to exclude from the map a magnitude 7.2 shock that occurred on May 4, 1934, approximately 160

kilometers northeast of Seward. This was the last large earthquake in the vicinity of Prince William Sound until 1964. Figure 36 shows the relatively low seismic activity of Prince William Sound and the Alaska coastal areas eastward from Prince William Sound to 139° W. longitude. Although there was some seismic activity slightly to the north of Prince William Sound adjacent to the epicenter of the initial rupture of the 1964 earthquake, Prince William Sound and the vicinity of Montague Island were particularly seismically quiet.

Figure 37 shows the areal distribution of energy release for the 1,000 days following the Prince William Sound Earthquake. This map shows the energy released by all shocks $m_b \geq 4.5$. Concentrations of energy release occur north of the Prince William Sound, south of Seward, and off the northeast and southeast tips of Kodiak Island.

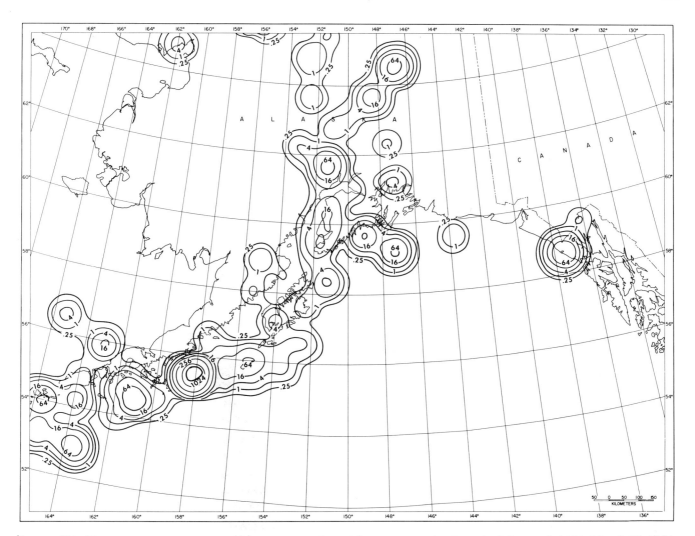

FIGURE 36.—Energy release in central Alaska and a portion of the Aleutian Islands $M_s \geqq 6.0$, May 5, 1934–March 28, 1964.

It is noteworthy that the energy released by the aftershock sequence in Prince William Sound was very small. Figure 37 also illustrates that from the point of view of energy release (1) the aftershock zone is irregular in shape, (2) energy release throughout the zone was not very uniform, (3) energy release was not concentrated near the ends of the zone but in the Gulf of Alaska south of Seward, and (4) nearly all of the energy release in the aftershock series was confined to the shelf area adjacent to Kodiak Island, the Kenai Peninsula, and Prince William Sound. Energy release of earthquakes beneath the continent has been very minor.

DISCUSSION AND CONCLUSIONS

Data have been presented on 2,178 aftershocks and other earthquakes that occurred in south-central Alaska between March 28, 1964, and December 31, 1966. Epi-

centers for 1,260 aftershocks during the first 4 months following the main shock were located using the network of temporary seismograph stations installed after the main shock. The capability of the temporary station network to locate earthquakes uniformly over the entire aftershock zone was not good because of poor azimuthal coverage—particularly for those shocks that occurred southwest of Kodiak Island. The temporary station network did provide significant magnitude data (M_L from torsion seismometers) and additional control on the computation of focal depths. Depth phases (notably pP and sP) were very distinct for earthquakes in the aftershock sequence, and the reliability of our interpretation of these phases could be checked using local station data. Consequently, focal depths for aftershocks in this sequence are much better known than for previous earthquakes in Alaska.

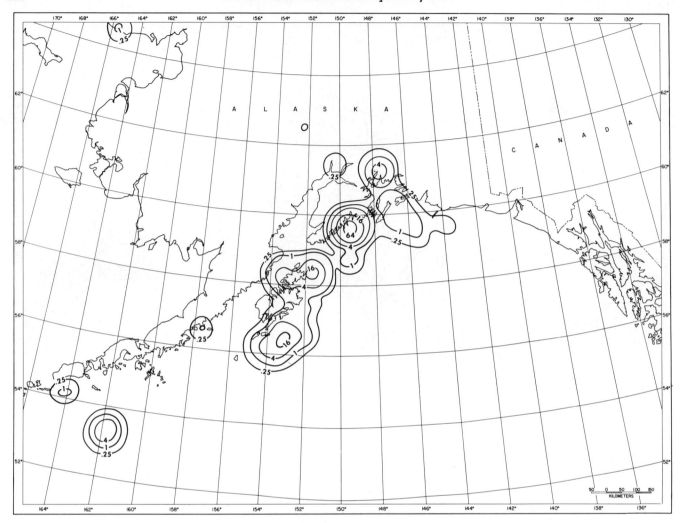

FIGURE 37.—Energy releases in central Alaska and a portion of the Aleutian Islands $M_s \geq 4.5$, March 28, 1964, through December 31, 1966.

The following conclusions are stated as a result of this study:

1. Comparison of epicenters computed using the network of temporary stations with locations based on teleseismic data shows that the epicenters computed from local station data have a mean centroid 15 kilometers south and 8 kilometers west of the teleseismic location [see also Rinehart, 1968].

2. The constants a and b in the equation $\log N = a + bm_b$ for the aftershock series are $a = 6.23$ and $b = -0.95$. These values are about the same as those obtained by Gutenberg and Richter [1954] for all Alaskan earthquakes.

3. The aftershock series was not distinguished by large shocks, except possibly within the first 10 hours following the main shock for the six aftershocks with $m_b \geq 6$ that occurred. The energy release in these shocks is uncertain because the relation between m_b and M_s for $m_b \geq 6$ has been shown to be uncertain [Dillinger and Algermissen,

1968]. Surface-wave magnitudes could not be determined because surface waves from the main shock tended to obscure those from the aftershocks.

4. The area and volume of the aftershock zone are approximately 3.6×10^5 km.² and 14×10^6 km.³

5. Aftershock activity showed considerable variation with time. Bursts of activity were followed by periods of relative quiescence. This pattern was superposed on the well-known hyperbolic decrease of aftershock activity with time.

6. The predominant space-time pattern of aftershock activity appears to be an oscillation of activity from one end of the aftershock zone to the other. Superposed on this oscillatory pattern are spatial and temporal clusters of earthquakes. These clusters are characterized by one or more large aftershocks preceded or followed by a number of smaller shocks in the same geographical area.

7. There is some tendency for large aftershocks to occur near the ends of the aftershock zone, but the larg-

est aftershock did not occur near either end of the aftershock zone.

8. The average focal depth of the aftershocks was 15 to 20 kilometers. Seventy-nine percent of all aftershocks located had depths less than 40 kilometers. Focal depths increase only slightly for shocks beneath the continent.

9. The annual rate of energy release in Alaska and the Aleutians since 1938 appears to have been substantially less than the average rate prior to 1938.

10. The annual rate of energy release in the Prince William Sound–Kodiak Island area during the 8 years preceding the 1964 earthquake was about 0.4 time the annual rate in the 1943–1955 period.

11. Prince William Sound area and the Alaska coast from the sound eastward to Yakatat Bay was relatively seismically inactive for 30 years preceding the 1964 earthquake.

12. The first portion of the aftershock sequence apparently ended approximately 520 days after the occurrence of the main shock. This sequence released 8 percent as much energy as the main shock. A new sequence of activity was started by a magnitude 6.9 earthquake off Kodiak Island on September 5, 1965.

13. Nearly all of the energy released in the aftershock sequence was confined to the shelf area adjacent to Kodiak Island, the Kenai Peninsula, and Prince William Sound. Energy release in earthquakes beneath the continental landmass was very small.

REFERENCES

Aki, Keiiti, Hori, Minoru, and Matumoto, Hideteru, "Microearthquakes Observed at a Temporary Array Station on the Kenai Peninsula," this volume.

Allen, C. R., St. Amand, Pierre, Richter, C. F., and Nordquist, J. M., "Relationship Between Seismicity and Geologic Structure in the Southern California Region," *Bulletin of the Seismological Society of America*, vol. 55, pp. 753–798, 1965.

Båth, Markus and Duda, S. J., "Earthquake Volume, Fault Plane Area, Seismic Energy, Strain, Deformation and Related Quantities," *Annali de Geofisica*, vol. 17, pp. 353–368, 1964.

Benioff, Hugo, "Earthquakes and Rock Creep (Part I: Creep Characteristics of Rocks and the Origin of Aftershocks)," *Bulletin of the Seismological Society of America,* vol. 41, pp. 31–62, 1951.

Dillinger, W. H., Jr., and Algermissen, S. T., "Magnitude Studies of Alaska Earthquakes," this volume.

Engdahl, E. R. and Gunst, R. H., "Use of a High-Speed Computer for the Preliminary Determination of Earthquake Hypocenters," *Bulletin of the Seismological Society of America,* vol. 56, pp. 325–336, 1966.

Gutenberg, B. and Richter, C. F., *Seismicity of the Earth and Associated Phenomena*, 2nd ed., Princeton University Press, Princeton, New Jersey, 310 pp., 1954.

Gutenberg, B. and Richter, C. F., "Magnitude and Energy of Earthquakes," *Annali de Geofisica*, vol. 9, pp. 1–15; 1956.

Harding, Samuel T. and Algermissen, S. T., "The Focal Mechanism of the Prince William Sound Earthquake of March 28, 1964, and Related Earthquakes," this volume.

Jeffreys, H. and Bullen, K. E., *Seismological Tables*, British Association for the Advancement of Science, Gray Milne Trust, London, England, 1940.

Matumoto, Tosimatu and Page, Robert A., Jr., "Microaftershocks Following the Alaska Earthquake of March 28, 1964, Determination of Hypocenters and Crustal Velocities in the Kenai Peninsula–Prince William Sound Area," this volume.

Milne, W. G., "Earthquake Epicenters and Strain Release," *Canadian Journal of Earth Sciences,* vol. 4, pp. 797–814, 1967.

Plafker, George, "Tectonic Deformation Associated with the 1964 Alaska Earthquake," *Science,* vol. 148, pp. 1675–1687, 1965.

Richter, C. F., "An Instrumental Magnitude Scale," *Bulletin of the Seismological Society of America*, vol. 25, pp. 1–32, 1935.

Richter, C. F., *Elementary Seismology*, W. H. Freeman and Company, San Francisco, 768 pp., 1958.

Rinehart, Wilbur, "A Digital Computer Program for the Location of Local Earthquakes," this volume.

Sherburne, R. W., Algermissen, S. T., and Harding, Samuel T., "The Hypocenter, Origin Time, and Magnitude of the Prince William Sound Earthquake of March 28, 1964," this volume.

Shor, G. G., Jr., "Seismic Refraction Studies Off the Coast of Alaska: 1956–1957," *Bulletin of the Seismological Society of America*, vol. 52, pp. 37–57, 1962.

Tatel, H. E. and Tuve, M. A., "The Earth's Crust, Seismic Studies," in *Year Book*, Carnegie Institute, Washington, 1955–56, pp, 81–85, 1956.

Tobin, D. G. and Sykes, L. R., "Relationship of Hypocenters of Earthquakes to the Geology of Alaska," *Journal of Geophysical Research,* vol. 71, pp. 1659–1667, 1966.

U. S. Department of Commerce, ESSA, Coast and Geodetic Survey, *The Prince William Sound, Alaska, Earthquake of 1964 and Aftershocks,* vol. I, 263 pp., 1966.

von Huene, Roland, Shor, G. G., Jr., and Reimnitz, Erk, "Geological Interpretation of Seismic Profiles in Prince

William Sound, Alaska," *Bulletin of the Geological Society of America*, vol. 78, pp. 259–268, 1967.

Woollard, G. P., Ostenso, N. A., Thiel, E., and Bonini, W. E., "Gravity Anomalies, Crustal Structure, and Geology in Alaska," *Journal of Geophysical Research*, vol. 65, pp. 1021–1037, 1960.

Wyss, Max and Brune, James N., "The Alaska Earthquake of 28 March 1964: A Complex Multiple Rupture," *Bulletin of the Seismological Society of America*, vol. 57, no. 5, pp. 1017–1024, 1967.

TABLE 2.—*Summary of aftershock data*

Earthquake number	Date	Origin time Hr.	Min.	Sec.	Latitude N. °	Longitude W. °	Depth Km.	Magnitude	Earthquake number	Date	Origin time Hr.	Min.	Sec.	Latitude N. °	Longitude W. °	Depth Km.	Magnitude
	1964									1964—Con.							
1	MAR. 28	3	36	14.2	61.00	147.80	33	8.3	51	MAR. 28—	10	17	27.7	60.30	146.60	15	4.4
2		4	54	7.9	59.80	149.40	25	6.1	52	Cont.	10	17	48.5	56.60	152.20	14†	5.1
3		5	31	5.4	58.10	150.10	33	5.3	53		10	20	29.9	57.70	152.20	33	4.3
4		5	33	52.6	60.20	146.20	7†	5.6	54		10	25	34.2	58.80	149.80	33	4.7
5		5	35	38.4	57.20	153.00	33	5.7	55		10	33	.2	57.70	152.20	22†	5.2
6		5	44	54.9	60.10	148.40	33	4.9	56		10	35	31.2	60.90	143.70	10†	5.1
7		6	8	44.2	60.10	148.60	20	5.6	57		10	35	38.9	57.20	152.40	22†	6.0
8		6	24	10.1	58.60	149.40	15	4.7	58		10	49	23.2	59.10	148.30	18†	4.6
9		6	29	17.4	57.70	150.80	20	5.1	59		10	53	44.8	60.10	147.60	18†	4.8
10		6	32	38.6	60.10	147.60	33	5.5	60		10	57	18.1	60.60	144.70	13†	4.7
11		6	36	55.2	57.90	151.50	33	5.1	61		10	59	16.3	57.40	151.60	24†	5.2
12		6	41	28.0	59.90	147.80	16†	5.5	62		11	2	22.7	58.20	149.90	23†	4.8
13		6	43	57.4	58.30	151.30	28†	6.1	63		11	4	16.3	58.00	151.40	33	4.7
14		6	50	48.9	57.10	152.30	33	5.0	64		11	7	13.2	58.30	150.70	33	4.6
15		6	53	35.6	58.80	149.50	20	5.7	65		11	8	26.0	60.10	148.40	16†	5.7
16		7	9	12.0	60.00	147.50	33	5.4	66		11	24	57.5	56.40	149.70	20†	5.0
17		7	10	21.4	58.80	149.50	22†	6.1	67		11	32	19.0	59.00	149.50	8†	4.9
18		7	24	21.7	59.30	149.80	20	5.0	68		11	50	1.9	58.20	149.80	20†	5.3
19		7	28	20.5	57.90	150.40	22†	5.0	69		11	56	48.3	57.60	151.80	19†	4.5
20		7	30	29.6	57.40	151.70	10†	5.7	70		12	3	16.5	60.30	146.60	16†	5.4
21		7	47	47.1	58.30	150.20	33	4.8	71		12	20	49.8	56.50	154.00	10†	6.1
22		7	48	47.8	57.00	153.30	20†	5.0	72		12	31	29.8	59.10	149.60	19†	4.7
23		7	52	.8	57.10	154.00	15†	4.8	73		12	48	34.0	60.50	145.90	33	4.3
24		7	55	8.4	58.40	150.10	21†	4.5	74		13	1	14.2	60.10	147.00	9†	5.1
25		7	59	40.7	57.90	150.30	21†	4.4	75		13	27	38.5	60.30	147.10	15†	4.9
26		8	13	9.5	59.60	148.80	24†	4.4	76		13	44	11.0	57.50	152.30	18†	4.4
27		8	30	11.7	60.50	147.00	11†	4.7	77		13	47	37.0	57.00	152.80	9†	5.0
28		8	32	33.7	61.00	143.10	15	4.5	78		13	54	19.9	62.10	147.10	14†	4.6
29		8	33	47.0	58.10	151.10	19†	5.6	79		14	1	57.6	56.50	154.40	25	5.1
30		8	39	54.9	57.50	151.60	22†	5.4	80		14	18	16.1	58.00	149.70	31†	4.8
31		8	42	31.3	60.30	147.20	33	4.7	81		14	33	13.6	57.80	152.10	22†	4.9
32		8	47	6.3	59.50	148.10	33	4.5	82		14	46	19.2	57.80	151.30	17†	4.8
33		8	52	44.6	60.30	147.60	35†	4.2	83		14	46	33.6	56.70	153.60	18†	4.9
34		8	54	24.6	57.00	154.50	33	3.9	84		14	47	37.1	60.40	146.50	20†	5.7
35		8	55	12.1	58.30	149.30	23†	4.6	85		14	49	13.7	60.40	147.10	13†	5.8
36		8	55	22.8	56.70	151.90	27†	5.1	86		15	20	28.6	57.40	151.30	13†	4.7
37		8	59	3.7	57.40	151.80	26†	5.1	87		15	22	36.4	60.40	146.80	13†	4.7
38		9	1	.5	56.50	152.00	14†	6.0	88		15	27	30.1	61.00	149.00	33	4.7
39		9	5	56.4	56.60	153.20	22†	5.3	89		15	34	10.4	59.50	146.70	18†	4.4
40		9	13	56.6	59.40	151.20	7†	5.2	90		15	36	22.3	58.30	150.90	25	4.7
41		9	17	52.6	57.40	151.60	8†	4.9	91		15	39	44.1	56.00	159.70	33	4.1
42		9	20	28.6	59.80	149.90	33	4.3	92		15	42	53.5	60.60	147.10	33	4.1
43		9	26	16.5	61.30	148.80	33	4.4	93		15	43	45.3	57.60	151.60	20†	4.5
44		9	28	36.7	56.70	153.90	33	4.0	94		15	51	50.7	58.80	149.90	25†	4.5
45		9	34	1.5	56.80	152.30	13†	5.0	95		15	55	25.8	59.70	146.30	8†	4.7
46		9	45	7.8	59.10	151.50	23†	4.2	96		16	4	33.8	57.50	150.80	17†	4.6
47		9	52	55.7	59.70	146.60	8†	5.5	97		16	15	2.9	59.60	149.60	33	4.0
48		9	58	23.5	58.80	150.10	33	4.6	98		16	26	16.9	57.50	150.90	51†	5.0
49		9	58	24.2	57.00	153.30	20	4.9	99		16	44	35.9	59.30	147.80	19†	5.3
50		10	15	41.9	59.60	149.40	17†	4.8	100		17	14	59.0	59.50	148.60	33	4.3

See footnotes at end of table.

TABLE 2.—*Summary of aftershock data*—Continued

Earthquake number	Date	Hr.	Min.	Sec.	Latitude N. °	Longitude W. °	Depth Km.	Magnitude	Earthquake number	Date	Hr.	Min.	Sec.	Latitude N. °	Longitude W. °	Depth Km.	Magnitude
	1964—Con.									1964—Con.							
101	MAR. 28—	17	47	17.0	60.40	145.70	27†	4.7	161	MAR. 29—	7	5	17.1	59.00	150.20	24†	4.7
102	Cont.	17	49	49.7	57.70	150.20	21†	4.9	162	Cont.	7	18	8.0	57.00	151.80	20†	4.8
103		18	2	54.9	59.50	149.30	33	4.6	163		7	37	22.8	55.90	154.80	33	4.0
104		18	24	2.2	60.10	149.50	15	4.0	164		7	39	40.7	57.10	152.00	17†	4.5
105		18	46	53.4	60.50	148.40	20	4.3	165		7	52	46.4	56.10	154.20	15†	4.8
106		19	1	51.5	60.10	146.90	15	4.5	166		8	6	3.7	56.60	152.40	25	4.5
107		19	21	38.8	61.60	146.70	12†	4.6	167		8	7	52.3	56.50	152.60	15†	4.9
108		19	29	2.4	58.10	150.40	20	4.4	168		8	11	54.2	61.40	146.40	20	4.2
109		19	45	21.4	56.40	152.60	20	4.5	169		8	18	42.5	60.10	146.60	33	3.9
110		20	5	44.6	60.60	144.50	33	4.0	170		8	31	30.0	60.20	148.50	15	4.4
111		20	29	8.6	59.80	148.70	13†	5.8	171		8	44	52.0	59.00	148.10	33	4.2
112		21	15	17.4	58.20	150.10	23†	4.7	172		8	50	3.6	56.70	152.10	33	4.3
113		21	37	48.7	59.60	145.60	10†	4.4	173		9	0	9.1	60.30	148.60	20	3.7
114		21	57	54.3	56.40	152.60	33	4.4	174		9	6	44.8	56.60	152.20	6†	4.8
115		22	9	43.2	58.00	153.20	15†	4.7	175		9	15	55.4	58.40	150.50	19†	4.6
116		22	13	22.9	57.50	152.90	25	4.4	176		9	22	1.0	59.60	149.80	33	4.3
117		22	16	20.8	59.80	148.80	33	3.9	177		9	28	57.6	56.50	151.20	20	4.3
118		22	22	3.1	60.30	145.30	16†	4.6	178		10	8	2.4	60.00	148.60	11†	5.3
119		22	28	47.0	58.20	150.40	21†	5.2	179		10	13	48.0	60.60	146.30	18†	4.6
120		22	47	.1	61.20	145.20	33	4.6	180		10	38	29.4	59.20	155.10	8†	4.1
121		23	14	46.7	57.60	151.20	33	4.1	181		10	42	42.8	57.90	151.70	33	3.9
122		23	21	5.7	61.50	146.50	33	3.8	182		10	49	40.3	58.20	150.40	23†	5.2
123		23	24	55.5	60.00	149.60	33	4.4	183		11	11	44.8	56.20	152.70	33	4.2
124		23	46	22.0	57.50	151.10	16†	5.2	184		11	17	14.2	58.50	151.20	33	3.9
125	MAR. 29	0	12	32.3	56.80	153.40	33	4.5	185		11	31	56.8	60.60	148.70	20	4.0
126		0	15	11.0	59.90	146.30	33	4.4	186		11	44	4.3	60.00	149.10	21†	4.9
127		0	21	3.8	58.40	150.40	33	4.2	187		11	54	41.0	58.80	151.10	13†	4.5
128		0	43	14.5	58.70	153.30	10†	3.9	188		11	56	33.0	58.00	151.60	19†	5.1
129		0	51	5.7	60.40	145.10	15	4.2	189		12	3	3.8	60.90	143.20	25†	4.7
130		0	51	45.1	60.60	150.00	16†	4.6	190		12	12	9.7	57.20	152.00	19†	4.6
131		0	53	5.8	57.40	151.50	19†	5.1	191		12	18	2.5	60.20	146.10	33	4.0
132		1	9	36.4	59.80	149.20	20†	5.5	192		12	33	10.1	59.20	153.80	10†	4.8
133		1	29	33.7	57.50	151.30	19†	5.6	193		12	48	5.9	59.90	145.60	25	4.5
134		1	48	18.5	56.30	153.70	16†	4.8	194		13	7	48.2	60.30	147.10	33	4.1
135		2	7	41.6	56.50	152.60	20	4.5	195		14	24	15.7	57.50	152.40	22†	4.7
136		2	14	2.4	59.50	149.10	22†	4.7	196		14	43	9.2	60.20	146.60	25	3.9
137		2	16	29.8	58.30	149.70	25†	4.9	197		14	51	30.2	60.00	148.90	20†	4.4
138		2	19	13.2	59.00	149.20	20†	4.4	198		15	7	13.1	54.30	157.00	8†	4.9
139		2	25	25.1	57.00	151.70	16†	5.2	199		15	30	33.9	57.20	152.00	13†	4.4
140		2	31	59.5	60.20	148.20	17†	4.7	200		15	39	28.6	56.10	154.40	25	4.2
141		3	7	19.5	59.70	148.80	20†	5.0	201		15	51	43.6	60.40	146.90	15†	4.4
142		3	15	16.6	57.90	150.90	33	3.9	202		16	9	15.3	60.30	146.60	14†	4.8
143		3	25	24.7	60.40	144.70	15	4.3	203		16	16	22.4	58.80	150.50	25	4.7
144		3	38	38.1	60.70	149.10	46†	5.1	204		16	18	29.3	60.40	146.00	17†	5.0
145		3	52	26.5	59.70	148.80	15	4.4	205		16	33	19.6	56.00	149.90	13†	4.6
146		4	1	21.9	59.80	148.50	15	4.1	206		16	40	57.9	59.70	147.00	15†	5.6
147		4	12	15.7	60.20	145.50	13|	5.3	207		16	45	33.6	59.80	146.90	12†	5.3
148		4	51	53.3	56.80	152.40	19†	4.8	208		16	53	20.0	60.30	146.10	16†	5.2
149		5	0	29.3	60.30	147.40	40	4.3	209		17	26	.2	56.40	153.30	33	4.1
150		5	8	25.8	56.70	152.70	20	4.6	210		17	38	12.5	59.90	147.00	12†	4.4
151		5	13	42.4	59.50	147.40	33	3.9	211		17	53	2.2	59.90	146.10	21†	5.0
152		5	21	9.8	57.10	150.40	20	4.4	212		17	55	30.2	60.00	146.10	20†	4.9
153		5	37	47.4	56.90	153.30	13†	4.8	213		17	57	56.8	60.00	147.00	11†	4.5
154		5	51	58.0	58.30	150.50	19†	4.7	214		18	58	37.1	59.80	146.70	15	4.5
155		6	4	44.5	56.10	154.30	20†	5.6	215		19	9	3.3	60.10	146.00	13†	4.6
156		6	29	39.4	58.10	149.80	23†	5.0	216		19	31	46.1	59.90	148.20	13†	4.6
157		6	36	16.2	59.90	146.00	20	4.3	217		19	45	24.0	56.40	152.80	33	4.1
158		6	38	9.2	58.60	148.90	36†	4.6	218		20	30	3.4	59.90	145.70	8†	4.0
159		6	48	52.3	58.10	150.60	24†	4.8	219		20	34	43.3	57.00	153.70	15	4.4
160		6	53	19.5	56.10	154.50	24†	4.8	220		20	59	25.6	59.20	153.00	20	4.6

See footnotes at end of table.

TABLE 2.—*Summary of aftershock data*—Continued

Earthquake number	Date	Origin time			Latitude N.	Longitude W.	Depth	Magnitude	Earthquake number	Date	Origin time			Latitude N.	Longitude W.	Depth	Magnitude
		Hr.	Min.	Sec.	°	°	Km.				Hr.	Min.	Sec.	°	°	Km.	
	1964—Con.									*1964*—Con.							
221	MAR. 29—	21	3	11.5	60.60	144.80	20	4.3	281	MAR. 30—	16	38	26.5	60.10	150.70	15	4.4
222	Cont.	21	9	30.5	59.50	152.50	9†	4.0	282	Cont.	16	53	7.7	56.60	152.20	14†	5.0
223		22	35	38.5	60.30	146.50	15	4.3	283		17	4	21.3	56.70	152.50	33	4.3
224		22	47	19.0	60.30	145.40	15	4.4	284		17	16	6.7	59.60	146.50	33	4.2
225		23	8	28.6	56.10	153.50	15	4.6	285		17	22	6.2	60.70	145.50	19†	4.6
226		23	25	35.1	59.20	152.60	33	4.1	286		17	41	13.4	61.50	150.00	40	4.3
227		23	27	55.3	59.70	148.20	30	4.6	287		19	18	20.5	60.50	143.80	15	4.7
228		23	40	54.8	61.10	151.00	12†	4.7	288		19	55	18.2	57.90	151.10	21†	4.5
229		23	49	28.6	59.90	147.10	14†	4.8	289		20	32	46.8	59.40	145.10	25†	4.5
230		23	55	51.9	58.90	150 00	20	4.7	290		21	32	14.9	59.90	147.60	17†	4.5
231	MAR. 30	0	8	24.9	60.20	146.30	33	3.7	291		22	5	3.9	60.20	145.50	15†	4.4
232		0	17	57.7	59.30	149.00	22†	4.5	292		22	21	25.2	60.30	146.90	15†	4.7
233		0	26	15.7	58.90	150.20	20	4.6	293		22	37	14.4	58.40	149.80	19†	4.6
234		0	53	55.8	60.00	146.30	15	4.2	294		23	3	34.5	57.30	152.70	15†	5.0
235		1	32	9.5	59.80	146.60	25†	4.6	295		23	33	31.6	56.10	153.00	33	4.1
236		1	41	38.6	60.60	144.30	27†	4.7	296		23	51	46.0	59.60	147.40	20†	4.6
237		2	18	6.3	56.60	152.90	8†	5.8	297	MAR. 31	0	44	53.3	59.50	146.30	21†	4.5
238		2	41	59.6	56.50	153.00	19†	4.9	298		1	17	11.3	58.80	148.90	20†	4.4
239		3	12	17.1	56.00	153.60	33	4.1	299		1	40	54.5	60.30	145.30	15	4.5
240		3	35	12.0	61.20	151.10	30	4.4	300		1	57	54.3	57.60	150.10	14†	4.8
241		4	1	35.7	56.40	152.80	33	4.3	301		2	43	35.6	56.70	154.00	21†	4.7
242		4	22	43.1	59.50	146.30	15	4.5	302		2	45	26.9	59.70	149.80	17†	4.7
243		5	4	15.3	60.40	145.00	33	3.8	303		4	4	48.5	59.10	148.40	20	4.2
244		5	14	21.5	56.20	154.40	33	4.5	304		4	20	16.3	60.30	146.30	17†	4.9
245		5	32	29.8	56.90	151.70	33	4.3	305		4	46	6.1	57.60	151.20	22†	4.7
246		6	28	58.5	59.70	148.60	15	4.1	306		5	42	22.4	56.20	153.40	33	4.3
247		7	9	34.0	59.90	145.70	12†	5.6	307		6	28	59.1	59.60	146.40	33	4.1
248		7	37	1.3	59.70	145.30	9†	4.2	308		7	8	54.5	58.30	149.30	20	4.5
249		7	52	43.6	59.90	146.50	20	4.0	309		7	15	10.6	59.80	148.00	33	3.9
250		7	56	29.1	56.30	154.40	21†	5.0	310		8	5	50.0	60.20	147.60	35	4.3
251		8	34	37.3	57.00	152.60	20	4.2	311		8	40	52.2	59.80	148.60	18†	4.7
252		8	40	10.7	56.50	153.00	20	4.3	312		9	52	32.8	57.80	152.20	15	4.1
253		8	53	17.9	56.20	153.10	33	4.3	313		10	13	29.1	58.80	148.40	20	4.1
254		9	23	5.0	59.90	145.60	8†	4.5	314		11	3	35.4	58.90	149.90	17†	5.0
255		9	57	32.5	60.90	145.10	18†	4.6	315		11	18	13.2	57.00	152.90	14†	4.5
256		10	15	51.7	60.40	146.60	16†	4.4	316		11	19	17.9	60.00	146.50	16†	4.9
257		10	31	22.0	60.50	149.60	30	4.4	317		11	24	57.4	58.20	150.30	33	4.3
258		10	35	42.3	60.40	146.90	33	3.8	318		11	52	13.9	60.10	146.40	13†	4.4
259		10	47	5.9	61.50	146.80	35	4.3	319		11	53	14.4	56.50	152.30	25	4.8
260		10	59	27.6	58.40	149.20	21†	5.0	320		12	30	35.7	58.40	150.90	25	3.8
261		11	5	47.4	60.40	146.80	12†	4.4	321		12	40	32.3	59.60	148.10	33	4.2
262		11	35	18.8	61.50	147.90	25	4.4	322		12	53	43.6	56.70	152.20	16†	4.3
263		11	48	40.4	56.40	152.50	19†	5.2	323		15	53	51.4	57.00	152.60	16†	4.4
264		12	5	43.5	60.10	147.00	25	5.0	324		16	32	7.2	57.30	152.00	33	4.3
265		12	14	28.4	58.00	151.60	23†	5.0	325		16	43	45.5	59.70	148.70	33	4.6
266		12	22	23.6	57.30	150.20	20	4.3	326		18	20	33.0	57.10	150.60	33	4.2
267		12	38	16.0	59.70	146.90	9†	5.0	327		18	30	21.3	58.50	150.00	33	4.3
268		12	55	12.5	59.70	147.00	12†	4.6	328		18	37	36.8	60.40	146.00	33	4.8
269		13	3	34.9	56.50	152.70	20	5.3	329		20	29	40.8	57.30	150.70	33	4.3
270		13	18	24.3	56.80	152.50	15	4.1	330		21	4	1.1	58.20	150.30	23†	5.2
271		13	32	18.5	56.40	152.60	15†	4.8	331		21	12	32.5	58.50	150.60	15†	4.6
272		13	41	1.9	60.50	146.60	8†	4.2	332		21	20	38.2	56.30	152.70	29†	4.6
273		13	51	2.9	56.60	151.90	33	4.0	333		22	50	36.5	56.80	152.20	33	3.9
274		13	58	19.7	60.20	145.50	33	3.9	334	APR. 1	23	36	56.0	59.90	145.80	29†	4.8
275		14	10	48.6	57.40	152.30	19†	5.1	335	APR. 1	0	1	10.6	60.40	146.40	13†	4.9
276		14	25	16.0	60.40	147.30	33	4.3	336		0	36	32.4	58.30	150.40	20	4.3
277		14	53	16.6	60.00	146.80	25	4.1	337		1	12	17.1	60.30	145.00	33	4.2
278		15	7	49.3	58.70	149.60	20†	5.3	338		1	21	5.4	60.60	149.20	34‡	4.6
279		15	46	12.8	57.70	151.80	33	4.2	339		1	54	9.3	59.70	146.10	15	4.3
280		16	9	28.4	56.60	152.10	12†	5.5	340		2	14	9.0	59.50	146.70	33	3.9

See footnotes at end of table.

TABLE 2.—*Summary of aftershock data*—Continued

Earthquake number	Date	Hr.	Min.	Sec.	Latitude N. °	Longitude W. °	Depth Km.	Magnitude	Earthquake number	Date	Hr.	Min.	Sec.	Latitude N. °	Longitude W. °	Depth Km.	Magnitude
	1964—Con.									1964—Con.							
341	APR. 1—	3	5	49.9	60.10	146.10	15	4.4	401	APR. 3	0	37	38.5	58.20	148.90	23†	
342	Cont.	3	23	17.2	57.20	151.30	29†	5.1	402		1	14	40.0	59.30	148.30	19†	4.4
343		3	43	47.4	59.90	146.10	33	3.8	403		1	40	26.5	59.30	147.70	10†	4.6
344		4	32	40.7	58.70	150.10	17†	4.8	404		4	51	26.8	57.00	154.00	33	4.3
345		4	49	26.3	57.20	151.40	20	4.8	405		6	23	11.3	60.00	149.50	33	
346		4	53	59.6	59.50	147.40	33	3.9	406		6	56	9.7	60.70	149.40	33	3.9
347		5	33	2.9	59.90	146.00	15	4.5	407		8	38	42.8	59.60	144.70	15†	5.4
348		6	16	21.4	60.20	147.10	17†	4.8	408		8	46	26.9	57.90	150.50	17†	5.5
349		6	39	48.5	60.40	146.70	10	4.4	409		9	48	15.7	57.10	150.50	33	4.4
350		7	26	2.6	59.60	150.10	33	4.1	410		10	46	51.6	59.30	147.00	33	3.7
351		7	56	7.7	56.60	151.30	33	3.9	411		11	9	28.2	56.70	152.30	24†	3.8
352		8	9	1.2	56.60	151.40	25	4.4	412		11	55	20.2	61.44	148.81	20§	(*)
353		8	28	9.4	60.00	147.60	20	4.4	413		12	14	4.6	60.68	140.32	20§	(*)
354		8	33	22.0	59.90	146.60	10	4.5	414		12	43	37.6	61.42	148.45	20§	(*)
355		8	54	3.8	56.70	152.30	4†	4.1	415		12	53	36.4	60.30	147.10	15	4.2
356		10	23	10.4	56.80	153.60	33	4.1	416		13	3	8.6	60.16	155.11	20§	(*)
357		10	45	13.6	59.10	148.50	33	4.0	417		13	52	1.7	58.90	147.30	33	
358		11	1	25.5	60.40	146.50	10	4.6	418		16	2	18.9	59.81	146.29	20§	(*)
359		13	33	23.4	59.70	148.20	20	4.5	419		19	57	53.3	60.10	148.00	20†	4.8
360		13	54	31.9	57.50	151.30	14†	4.9	420		20	23	25.0	57.00	146.10	25	4.6
361		15	22	38.3	57.30	152.90	21†	4.8	421		20	47	24.7	60.60	140.90	15	4.5
362		16	29	9.0	59.70	146.50	11†	4.7	422		22	15	48.3	57.10	151.90	23‡	5.1
363		17	23	12.1	56.10	155.40	20	4.4	423		22	33	42.2	61.60	147.60	39†	5.7
364		18	48	32.9	60.00	142.40	22†	4.4	424	APR. 4	1	58	40.9	58.40	146.80	30†	4.4
365		20	7	24.2	56.60	153.00	33	4.4	425		3	35	9.3	59.84	146.29	20§	(*)
366		20	13	8.3	58.30	149.60	25†	5.1	426		3	45	40.7	61.47	147.64	26	(*)
367		22	0	58.7	58.90	150.00	20	4.6	427		3	59	37.4	61.33	147.76	20§	(*)
368	APR. 2	0	16	44.7	60.90	148.00	33	4.1	428		4	8	46.6	61.40	147.83	44	(*)
369		2	15	9.2	56.40	152.50	33	4.3	429		4	34	56.9	60.30	146.50	19†	5.0
370		2	40	30.7	60.10	148.20	33	3.7	430		4	54	1.7	60.10	146.70	32‡	5.6
371		3	50	25.1	56.20	153.00	33	4.3	431		5	10	34.4	57.30	149.40	20	4.6
372		5	25	23.7	60.10	147.80	33	3.8	432		6	10	30.2	59.80	146.10	33	3.7
373		5	32	3.0	58.80	159.50	33	4.1	433		6	33	58.3	58.58	150.94	20§	(*)
374		6	7	16.6	58.90	150.50	33	3.9	434		6	53	25.9	60.40	146.00	15	4.8
375		6	18	16.1	60.40	146.80	20	4.0	435		7	14	31.0	61.35	146.32	20§	(*)
376		7	57	17.8	60.10	147.90	17†	4.5	436		7	37	51.3	60.32	147.37	20§	(*)
377		8	27	13.5	56.60	152.40	33	4.3	437		8	0	44.3	57.96	150.10	20§	(*)
378		8	31	36.5	55.80	154.30	33	4.2	438		8	40	29.8	56.50	152.60	17†	5.3
379		9	4	51.9	57.90	151.10	18†	4.8	439		9	10	55.1	56.90	152.70	15	5.9
380		9	23	57.7	60.40	146.20	33	3.9	440		9	49	27.9	56.90	151.70	33	4.2
381		9	57	54.5	56.50	152.80	19†	4.9	441		9	58	30.8	60.17	147.98	20§	(*)
382		10	9	47.0	56.70	152.60	33	4.2	442		10	37	36.2	59.80	150.00	10	4.3
383		10	58	9.1	59.30	150.00	11†	4.6	443		11	10	6.6	59.90	149.30	33	4.8
384		11	41	10.7	58.80	149.60	22†	5.4	444		12	4	49.3	58.00	148.90	33	4.4
385		12	14	58.5	60.10	145.30	33	4.0	445		13	47	10.9	60.49	150.05	20§	(*)
386		12	19	9.5	56.30	152.20	33	4.3	446		13	49	45.4	56.60	153.90	25	4.2
387		12	20	25.2	60.90	148.10	10	4.1	447		14	42	42.8	60.92	148.41	20§	(*)
388		13	28	38.6	60.20	147.60	20†	4.4	448		14	56	48.7	57.65	141.77	20§	(*)
389		14	22	3.4	60.50	149.00	17†	4.3	449		15	8	12.3	59.60	146.90	15	4.7
390		14	57	43.1	57.40	150.30	33	4.0	450		15	29	56.3	60.68	147.33	20§	(*)
391		18	17	31.5	56.80	151.20	33	4.4	451		17	18	28.3	60.38	147.22	84‡	(*)
392		18	25	21.0	60.00	147.80	13†	4.6	452		17	46	8.6	56.30	154.40	18†	5.7
393		19	3	52.4	60.40	145.30	10†	4.1	453		17	59	43.3	56.40	154.50	26†	5.5
394		19	38	24.7	60.70	145.80	17†	4.4	454		18	15	52.4	56.20	154.50	18†	5.0
395		19	40	19.9	59.60	144.80	15†	4.7	455		18	41	27.8	56.40	153.00	33	4.4
396		20	9	42.0	59.80	147.00	9†	5.0	456		20	1	44.8	59.50	147.60	24†	4.8
397		21	9	36.3	58.80	144.80	15	4.2	457		20	45	5.7	64.53	156.06	20‡	(*)
398		22	7	20.6	60.40	147.20	9†	4.4	458		22	16	54.5	59.40	145.20	29†	5.1
399		22	34	31.7	59.80	144.30	10†	5.0	459		23	37	4.5	57.84	163.86	20‡	(*)
400		23	29	59.3	60.50	146.30	15	3.9	460	APR. 5	0	16	41.6	58.40	152.20	33	4.1

See footnotes at end of table.

TABLE 2.—*Summary of aftershock data*—Continued

Earthquake number	Date	Origin time Hr.	Min.	Sec.	Latitude N. °	Longitude W. °	Depth Km.	Magnitude	Earthquake number	Date	Origin time Hr.	Min.	Sec.	Latitude N. °	Longitude W. °	Depth Km.	Magnitude
	1964—Con.									1964—Con.							
461	APR. 5—	1	22	13.3	56.20	153.50	9†	5.4	521	APR. 7—	3	17	43.4	59.60	145.50	15	4.0
462	Cont.	1	36	53.7	58.40	151.20	33	4.2	522	Cont.	3	53	57.2	61.10	148.70	33	4.2
463		1	41	45.0	56.20	153.30	14†	5.2	523		4	35	18.6	58.30	149.70	20†	4.7
464		1	49	24.0	57.20	147.91	20	(*)	524		4	54	42.0	58.10	157.40	20†	4.5
465		1	55	48.8	61.78	147.61	20‡	(*)	525		5	34	55.7	60.00	146.70	20	4.1
466		2	36	10.8	60.10	145.80	11†	4.9	526		6	1	59.7	60.00	145.70	33	4.0
467		3	47	57.2	56.70	151.30	22†	4.6	527		8	3	13.7	58.20	152.20	20‡	4.4
468		3	55	34.3	59.70	146.60	33	4.0	528		8	10	48.1	60.00	146.90	33	4.1
469		4	11	48.2	59.90	148.00	8†	4.4	529		9	15	28.5	56.08	145.70	20§	(*)
470		4	57	15.4	60.10	147.70	10	4.1	530		13	26	37.6	59.83	148.67	35	(*)
471		5	22	4.0	59.98	148.66	20‡	(*)	531		15	12	27.9	60.84	145.64	20§	(*)
472		5	30	17.5	61.91	148.42	20‡	(*)	532		16	19	58.8	60.70	148.00	33	3.8
473		5	55	59.0	60.34	147.07	20‡	(*)	533		16	28	38.2	59.60	145.00	23†	4.2
474		7	13	24.4	56.50	154.70	25	4.2	534		18	2	24.7	57.30	151.10	26‡	4.8
475		7	29	3.5	60.40	146.70	15	4.4	535		18	10	29.6	60.10	147.20	33	
476		7	44	50.6	60.00	144.80	15	4.2	536		18	17	8.6	57.00	153.40	33	4.1
477		8	13	12.4	56.90	152.00	15	4.5	537		18	33	1.9	60.47	144.99	20§	(*)
478		8	59	2.0	56.20	154.50	16†	4.7	538		19	28	24.7	55.70	151.90	29†	5.6
479		10	22	12.1	60.00	149.70	33	3.8	539	APR. 8	0	13	18.7	56.20	149.40	33	4.3
480		12	30	3.7	58.90	154.30	10	4.1	540		0	36	21.2	57.20	152.60	20†	4.8
481		12	59	15.1	61.40	147.20	33	3.6	541		4	0	1.1	60.00	149.50	33	4.1
482		13	30	55.4	56.30	150.50	33	4.0	542		4	35	18.0	59.40	147.60	33	4.0
483		13	44	16.5	56.30	153.10	33	4.0	543		5	9	55.3	60.16	146.91	20§	(*)
484		13	48	47.3	60.20	145.60	13†	4.1	544		5	53	32.0	60.56	146.34	20§	(*)
485		14	0	7.2	60.03	147.82	20	(*)	545		6	36	11.0	60.05	145.12	49	(*)
486		14	5	40.2	57.60	150.10	33	3.6	546		8	19	44.8	61.26	147.31	10§	(*)
487		15	21	47.0	60.70	149.10	33	3.8	547		9	43	50.8	60.30	146.80	5	4.2
488		15	49	30.2	56.00	154.30	25	4.1	548		9	54	16.6	60.50	141.00	20	4.3
489		16	8	23.6	59.00	147.19	20‡	(*)	549		11	22	35.4	59.35	148.91	20§	(*)
490		16	49	4.0	58.70	151.70	13†	4.4	550		15	12	35.5	60.03	145.95	20§	(*)
491		17	16	10.2	55.90	149.90	33	4.1	551		16	46	38.1	60.30	147.80	33	3.9
492		17	40	43.1	56.30	152.90	14†	4.9	552		17	32	26.7	59.70	146.20	33	3.8
493		17	42	7.4	59.60	144.90	13†	5.1	553		18	58	50.5	56.90	149.90	35	4.8
494		18	30	49.5	60.75	147.15	20‡	(*)	554		19	33	19.0	59.60	147.00	19†	5.1
495		19	28	18.1	60.20	146.70	16†	5.8	555		19	50	16.8	60.40	145.90	15†	5.3
496		19	50	41.3	57.00	153.20	18‡	4.4	556		20	49	53.1	59.30	148.60	20†	4.2
497		21	26	32.1	60.60	145.60	20	4.0	557		22	54	28.2	60.40	146.50	33	3.7
498	APR. 6	1	51	48.6	59.40	146.80	15	4.3	558		23	56	2.4	61.88	146.39	20‡	(*)
499		3	40	7.5	60.87	146.38	20‡	(*)	559	APR. 9	2	36	11.7	62.15	148.19	20‡	(*)
500		4	57	32.4	56.80	151.50	33	4.2	560		3	45	6.7	60.10	145.90	33	3.8
501		5	30	41.2	58.38	152.38	20§	(*)	561		4	4	29.7	61.23	147.20	20‡	4.6*
502		8	21	24.8	57.40	152.30	5†	4.8	562		5	2	7.6	61.77	146.40	20‡	4.9*
503		9	3	12.9	59.50	145.30	15	4.4	563		5	28	38.1	60.12	146.85	20‡	3.1*
504		9	29	31.6	59.70	146.60	33	3.8	564		5	43	24.0	60.00	148.20	33	4.1
505		10	42	36.3	59.90	145.60	17‡	4.8	565		6	19	31.3	60.06	146.90	20‡	3.7*
506		10	56	29.2	59.80	147.90	33	4.0	566		6	53	15.6	60.00	148.90	25	4.2
507		10	59	5.9	56.30	154.40	33	4.2	567		7	10	57.0	60.28	144.41	154‡	4.2*
508		12	7	54.0	58.20	150.60	20	4.1	568		8	19	55.1	58.00	149.10	33	3.7
509		14	50	57.3	56.70	152.10	33	4.0	569		10	37	14.9	59.10	148.40	20	4.1
510		15	1	32.0	58.10	154.40	33	3.8	570		12	33	23.9	59.50	148.90	20†	4.7
511		15	29	5.3	60.40	146.50	33	4.0	571		13	2	(**)				
512		16	0	28.6	56.40	152.40	33	3.9	572		13	6	15.2	59.60	146.10	15†	5.1
513		16	50	42.3	57.50	154.80	33	4.1	573		13	22	29.6	56.80	152.00	8†	4.7
514		17	35	50.6	59.90	147.80	18†	4.9	574		14	14	36.5	59.80	146.00	10	4.3
515		18	3	56.4	56.40	151.80	5†	4.7	575		16	11	31.5	58.10	152.50	30	4.4
516		18	59	11.9	60.00	147.10	33	4.1	576		17	14	45.3	60.10	146.10	33	3.9
517		19	40	44.5	56.00	153.90	25	4.2	577		18	25	.9	59.80	147.10	33	4.2
518		22	49	56.4	61.40	149.57	20§	(*)	578		21	20	3.1	60.80	146.80	33	4.1
519		22	57	53.3	57.10	153.30	15	4.2	579		22	12	30.7	59.80	155.70	33	4.4
520	APR. 7	1	43	28.7	58.50	154.50	30	5.1	580	APR. 10	0	29	46.2	60.30	147.10	33	4.0

See footnotes at end of table.

TABLE 2.—*Summary of aftershock data*—Continued

Earthquake number	Date	Hr.	Min.	Sec.	Latitude N. °	Longitude W. °	Depth Km.	Magnitude	Earthquake number	Date	Hr.	Min.	Sec.	Latitude N. °	Longitude W. °	Depth Km.	Magnitude
	1964—Con.									1964—Con.							
581	APR. 10—	1	8	.2	58.40	150.60	19†	5.5	641	APR. 12	22	22	48.8	60.04	145.63	20§	(*)
582	Cont.	2	46	35.5	58.50	148.80	33	3.7	642	APR. 13	0	14	5.7	60.91	146.58	20§	(*)
583		6	46	15.6	60.10	146.90	33	4.0	643		0	55	.6	59.50	144.70	33	3.9
584		7	4	11.3	60.20	147.00	33	4.0	644		1	17	36.2	56.60	157.00	33	4.0
585		7	57	15.9	60.24	146.84	20‡	3.2*	645		1	26	36.3	60.04	145.35	20§	3.3*
586		11	19	30.4	61.33	148.16	28‡	3.7*	646		7	6	39.6	59.70	147.40	33	3.9
587		12	6	24.5	59.60	152.20	25	4.3	647		7	25	3.7	61.27	147.21	34	3.3*
588		12	51	10.6	60.47	147.09	20‡	3.6*	648		7	28	35.5	58.90	149.80	25	4.0
589		15	39	9.2	60.19	147.62	20‡	3.9*	649		8	2	2.3	60.32	142.02	78	3.9*
590		17	54	57.5	56.70	152.00	9†	4.7	650		8	41	53.9	58.40	151.20	14†	4.8
591		18	4	1.0	60.10	146.00	5‡	4.3*	651		9	58	30.5	60.50	148.35	20‡	2.9*
592		19	5	52.6	59.70	148.20	18†	5.2	652		10	4	32.4	60.13	144.76	20‡	3.0*
593		19	35	36.7	60.03	147.89	20	3.8*	653		10	50	31.7	59.03	148.04	10‡	2.8*
594		21	44	6.7	60.10	153.70	15†	5.6	654		10	55	15.5	61.25	144.29	20‡	(*)
595	APR. 11	0	39	10.6	57.40	150.00	15	4.6	655		11	47	15.8	60.67	145.36	20‡	3.7*
596		4	40	.3	56.80	152.60	33	4.2	656		12	25	36.0	59.40	143.90	40	4.9
597		7	33	52.2	59.60	144.80	33	4.4	657		14	5	.0	57.60	151.20	28‡	5.5
598		8	23	29.1	59.80	147.60	33	3.9	658		16	14	6.3	56.60	152.10	14†	5.1
599		9	23	51.5	56.40	152.20	39†	4.6	659		17	43	26.3	61.10	147.40	24†	4.4
600		10	9	58.1	59.85	149.30	26	3.7*	660		18	14	21.4	59.20	147.10	20	4.3
601		10	20	39.5	60.80	143.50	20	4.2	661		19	16	48.6	57.30	153.20	23‡	4.8
602		11	4	57.7	60.58	146.11	41	3.4*	662		21	25	33.0	57.50	153.90	16†	5.5
603		11	36	.5	60.40	146.40	15†	4.8	663		21	43	16.5	59.40	143.10	22†	5.1
604		12	16	41.1	56.60	151.00	20	4.8	664		23	14	10.3	60.08	147.16	30‡	3.7*
605		14	8	(**)					665		23	19	25.5	59.98	146.79	98‡	3.2*
606		15	24	48.1	58.14	144.77	20§	4.3*	666		23	48	52.7	61.00	149.30	33	4.1
607		16	10	25.2	58.10	149.80	20	4.3	667	APR. 14	1	4	44.1	58.47	151.83	20‡	(*)
608		16	44	34.3	60.56	147.28	20§	4.3*	668		2	21	16.9	62.51	148.47	20	(*)
609		17	51	16.4	56.00	152.70	33	4.2*	669		5	14	28.5	61.00	146.85	41‡	(*)
610		18	16	30.4	61.67	147.28	35	3.8*	670		6	19	38.2	60.20	146.80	33	4.1
611		22	2	38.2	60.20	146.90	14‡	4.5	671		6	27	32.0	59.71	147.99	23‡	(*)
612		22	20	5.5	60.78	146.42	20§	3.6*	672		6	53	36.3	56.20	154.60	33	4.1
613		23	11	22.8	60.10	146.50	18‡	4.6	673		7	59	25.4	61.40	147.00	21†	4.4
614		23	34	35.3	59.50	147.00	33	4.5	674		8	8	25.4	61.00	145.30	33	3.9
615	APR. 12	1	15	37.9	60.00	144.90	30	4.4	675		9	48	10.9	56.00	150.00	25	4.3
616		1	24	31.2	56.60	152.20	25†	5.6	676		10	9	1.9	60.50	146.10	33	3.8
617		2	6	19.8	60.90	149.50	20	4.2	677		10	58	11.2	59.90	146.80	20	4.1
618		2	19	5.4	60.56	145.70	20§	(*)	678		12	13	48.2	59.95	147.55	20‡	3.6*
619		3	38	53.4	56.40	152.30	33	4.0	679		13	18	34.2	61.10	147.20	16‡	(*)
620		5	27	20.8	60.58	146.69	20§	(*)	680		13	23	49.8	61.35	147.34	20‡	(*)
621		5	44	23.2	58.80	148.90	33	4.0	681		13	35	49.6	59.06	145.78	30‡	(*)
622		7	33	43.6	59.30	147.50	25	3.6	682		14	0	33.9	58.25	143.34	20‡	(*)
623		8	0	49.2	60.63	147.43	24	(*)	683		14	16	(**)				
624		9	34	44.1	56.60	152.10	17†	5.1	684		14	29	51.5	60.48	147.18	20‡	(*)
625		10	27	34.9	58.28	150.39	20§	(*)	685		15	4	20.5	61.14	146.87	20	(*)
626		10	33	20.0	58.66	146.63	20§	(*)	686		15	16	37.4	61.79	146.51	20	(*)
627		12	13	1.5	60.14	146.17	20§	(*)	687		15	32	58.0	61.57	149.76	59‡	4.1*
628		12	36	22.7	56.40	151.40	23†	5.0	688		15	55	10.9	61.30	147.30	31†	5.4
629		12	48	2.2	56.60	151.30	26†	5.1	689		16	5	46.1	59.90	146.00	33	4.4
630		14	35	39.2	61.20	151.10	25‡	5.0	690		16	59	30.1	61.40	150.80	52‡	5.1
631		15	8	9.5	61.20	147.40	20	3.6	691		17	14	16.9	59.62	147.39	20	3.8*
632		17	22	2.2	60.20	145.60	16‡	5.0	692		20	52	20.9	60.52	147.63	20	4.3*
633		18	7	24.9	60.25	148.29	20§	(*)	693		20	59	6.3	61.15	146.90	20‡	(*)
634		18	50	41.2	56.50	152.70	33	4.2	694		21	33	37.3	61.00	147.30	27†	4.2
635		19	42	4.8	59.53	148.24	20§	(*)	695		22	29	31.1	59.90	145.60	22†	4.5
636		20	15	3.2	60.83	146.05	20§	(*)	696		22	55	31.3	58.00	152.60	8†	5.4
637		20	28	50.1	57.50	152.10	33	4.6	697	APR. 15	0	18	1.0	61.26	150.46	20‡	3.9*
638		20	53	40.9	60.76	147.03	20§	(*)	698		3	53	7.5	59.70	145.20	33	3.7
639		21	2	15.9	58.60	154.30	33	4.0	699		5	34	16.3	61.17	146.96	20‡	4.3*
640		21	52	43.5	59.84	148.85	40	(*)	700		8	2	24.4	61.05	145.68	5‡	(*)

See footnotes at end of table.

TABLE 2.—*Summary of aftershock data*—Continued

Earthquake number	Date	Origin time Hr.	Min.	Sec.	Latitude N. °	Longitude W. °	Depth Km.	Magnitude	Earthquake number	Date	Origin time Hr.	Min.	Sec.	Latitude N. °	Longitude W. °	Depth Km.	Magnitude
	1964—Con.									1964—Con.							
701	APR. 15—	8	23	27.4	57.40	149.50	14†	4.9	761	APR. 17—	11	52	49.4	60.81	147.68	89‡	3.3*
702	Cont.	9	1	34.1	59.91	148.05	16	4.0*	762	Cont.	12	5	59.9	60.40	145.00	33	3.8
703		9	24	11.1	60.00	148.60	33	3.7	763		13	26	57.5	61.16	148.51	20	3.8*
704		10	49	6.1	61.31	147.20	20§	(*)	764		18	5	40.7	60.57	146.12	20	(*)
705		11	2	25.4	60.54	145.55	4	(*)	765		18	29	6.0	60.04	146.63	20‡	3.1*
706		11	20	31.4	57.80	150.40	33	3.9	766		18	37	42.5	61.02	146.70	20	3.3*
707		13	0	45.9	60.63	148.75	10§	4.1*	767		20	27	18.5	60.21	146.95	27‡	3.8*
708		13	41	32.0	60.71	147.11	20	3.7*	768		21	32	50.6	60.48	149.16	20‡	3.3*
709		14	19	24.5	58.60	149.90	33	4.1	769		22	13	(**)				
710		15	30	47.1	56.50	154.40	13†	5.5	770		22	21	7.3	61.21	145.82	20	3.7*
711		16	1	27.0	60.87	147.16	15	3.9*	771		23	16	4.6	57.96	150.61	20‡	4.0*
712		16	29	2.1	60.30	146.86	20§	(*)	772	APR. 18	0	13	24.4	59.60	144.88	33	4.5
713		16	37	8.6	60.44	146.77	20§	3.6*	773		1	32	18.4	56.40	152.80	20†	5.0
714		16	46	15.7	60.81	147.69	20§	3.7*	774		3	6	43.5	56.70	148.90	33	4.5
715		17	22	57.5	61.21	147.02	30	4.1*	775		7	10	58.5	60.80	145.20	33	4.2
716		20	18	9.9	60.71	146.83	20§	(*)	776		7	16	36.4	59.10	147.70	33	4.3
717		20	30	35.9	56.80	154.20	20	4.7	777		7	44	3.4	60.20	147.60	33	3.9
718		21	33	35.6	59.87	148.23	27	3.4*	778		7	45	47.6	56.50	153.00	33	4.3
719		21	44	39.9	61.32	146.29	20§	4.5*	779		7	47	3.3	57.40	149.80	36†	5.1
720		21	58	15.2	59.21	147.60	20§	(*)	780		12	41	39.3	57.40	154.10	33	3.8
721	APR. 16	0	5	12.9	56.40	149.20	20	3.9	781		15	14	42.9	57.40	152.30	23†	4.5
722		3	19	34.8	57.20	151.40	10	5.0	782		15	59	(**)				
723		4	2	44.8	60.07	145.48	10§	4.3*	783		16	3	27.3	59.59	146.87	20	3.9*
724		4	50	41.2	56.52	141.31	20§	(*)	784		17	16	43.8	57.10	150.60	33	4.0
725		5	57	46.2	59.73	147.98	20§	3.7*	785		17	32	19.2	56.90	151.20	33	4.2
726		7	14	39.0	61.57	142.62	20§	(*)	786		19	25	23.5	58.90	148.70	33	3.9
727		7	37	35.8	59.60	146.90	33	4.3	787		20	8	19.7	56.10	153.70	19†	4.9
728		9	32	37.3	61.39	146.26	20§	(*)	788		20	16	16.3	56.10	153.70	13†	4.9
729		10	38	50.9	61.45	145.19	20§	3.4*	789		21	54	46.3	59.00	153.81	20	4.0*
730		11	29	54.4	60.36	146.69	20§	2.7	790		23	38	3.4	59.30	147.50	10†	5.1
731		11	56	4.5	58.30	150.70	33	4.4	791	APR. 19	0	9	48.8	55.90	155.80	33	3.8
732		12	11	15.7	58.20	152.50	16‡	4.5	792		3	47	30.0	59.71	149.58	20‡	(*)
733		12	31	24.7	61.02	148.00	20§	(*)	793		4	24	53.6	61.28	146.76	20‡	3.8*
734		14	21	36.2	57.60	150.90	13†	4.6	794		6	34	14.4	60.60	147.40	15	4.1
735		14	31	16.3	61.40	149.20	33	4.6	795		8	58	12.9	62.05	146.35	20	(*)
736		15	17	6.5	60.91	146.89	20§	(*)	796		10	4	44.2	61.70	149.49	20‡	(*)
737		15	21	49.7	59.25	148.74	20§	3.9*	797		12	30	24.3	61.73	148.49	20‡	(*)
738		17	8	27.2	59.50	147.80	33	4.5	798		14	52	49.9	59.63	147.97	20‡	3.5*
739		17	48	39.6	59.39	146.97	20§	4.3*	799		15	16	50.3	61.02	147.02	20	3.4*
740		19	26	57.4	56.40	152.90	23†	5.5	800		15	25	34.7	56.84	143.29	20‡	(*)
741		20	12	36.8	56.60	152.80	33	5.0	801		16	34	22.6	58.75	150.35	74	(*)
742		21	25	46.0	58.90	148.80	33	5.2	802		16	55	36.1	60.52	148.44	20	3.5*
743		22	28	(**)					803		17	35	45.4	58.87	147.84	82	3.8*
744		22	31	38.9	61.14	149.49	36	3.7*	804		17	39	8.7	59.83	149.00	34	3.0*
745		23	7	38.2	59.58	149.01	20§	3.8*	805		18	0	19.4	61.25	146.21	20§	(*)
746	APR. 17	1	26	20.3	60.06	147.23	34	4.3*	806		18	51	10.9	60.20	148.60	33	4.7
747		2	7	7.5	60.34	147.81	41	3.6*	807		20	21	48.5	61.90	147.24	20§	3.8*
748		2	22	17.7	60.30	146.90	33	3.6	808		20	26	5.9	60.38	146.40	20§	3.7*
749		2	39	38.2	60.13	146.60	20§	3.5*	809		20	51	39.1	59.99	148.52	28	3.7*
750		4	3	55.9	59.60	144.70	18†	4.9	810		21	16	16.4	59.46	144.42	20§	4.2*
751		4	16	59.4	59.60	144.70	17†	4.9	811		21	30	54.4	60.97	148.20	33	3.7*
752		4	49	30.5	56.40	152.90	15†	5.3	812		22	1	29.0	60.03	146.16	14	3.7*
753		6	11	22.3	58.77	150.85	20‡	(*)	813		23	54	19.6	60.00	147.53	20§	(*)
754		6	39	54.0	60.97	148.73	20	3.0*	814	APR. 20	0	3	30.2	58.71	149.99	77	(*)
755		7	26	39.0	61.10	149.40	33	4.4	815		0	32	(**)				
756		9	1	45.0	59.78	148.72	24‡	3.1*	816		1	11	26.5	59.92	148.23	34	4.0*
757		9	9	7.8	57.70	151.40	30‡	5.4	817		1	32	17.5	59.69	146.27	20§	2.0*
758		9	59	52.4	60.40	145.90	14‡	4.9	818		1	41	37.3	61.21	147.26	22	4.3*
759		10	5	27.7	60.88	146.92	36‡	2.9*	819		2	33	35.0	60.76	151.78	16	3.7*
760		11	48	44.7	60.00	145.50	12†	4.4	820		3	31	57.1	59.87	148.23	10§	3.2*

See footnotes at end of table.

TABLE 2.—*Summary of aftershock data*—Continued

Earthquake number	Date	Origin time Hr.	Min.	Sec.	Latitude N. °	Longitude W. °	Depth Km.	Magnitude	Earthquake number	Date	Origin time Hr.	Min.	Sec.	Latitude N. °	Longitude W. °	Depth Km.	Magnitude
	1964—Con.									*1964*—Con.							
821	APR. 20—	3	34	45.1	59.70	144.60	15†	4.7	881	APR. 22—	5	40	58.2	59.57	146.98	14‡	3.2*
822	Cont.	6	30	25.2	61.32	148.82	20§	(*)	882	Cont.	10	34	28.9	64.17	154.67	20	(*)
823		6	37	30.8	60.83	150.11	36	(*)	883		11	14	43.4	57.80	149.50	33	4.2
824		8	7	54.8	60.20	147.00	15	4.3	884		12	12	51.6	61.25	147.15	28	3.7*
825		8	25	6.5	59.91	147.42	14	3.4*	885		12	20	58.1	61.25	146.88	35	4.0*
826		10	58	5.4	59.87	149.05	21	3.4*	886		14	4	59.9	59.86	148.04	19	3.1*
827		11	14	48.9	56.70	148.10	30	4.3	887		14	21	5.3	61.37	147.24	20‡	(*)
828		11	15	32.0	59.80	147.68	20§	2.8*	888		14	50	16.1	59.80	142.97	79‡	4.1*
829		11	56	41.6	61.40	147.30	33†	5.7	889		15	39	7.0	59.83	147.06	42‡	3.4*
830		12	14	49.8	61.06	147.94	20§	(*)	890		16	20	31.6	59.13	143.54	20‡	4.1*
831		12	43	49.6	59.37	148.46	28	3.8*	891		18	43	49.9	60.65	145.50	39‡	2.9*
832		13	10	32.1	58.86	152.48	20§	3.9*	892		20	29	20.3	58.60	150.00	46†	5.1
833		13	25	51.7	61.29	147.41	46	3.8*	893		22	50	15.8	59.93	146.56	20	3.8*
834		13	46	45.4	61.15	147.17	20§	3.3*	894	APR. 23	1	11	19.5	61.08	145.90	20‡	3.5*
835		14	15	32.3	60.69	146.34	20§	3.7*	895		3	6	42.6	56.80	149.60	33	3.9
836		14	57	11.9	61.12	147.52	20§	3.4*	896		3	13	55.7	60.90	144.30	35	4.2
837		15	40	28.0	61.50	147.30	29†	5.0	897		3	31	7.9	59.11	151.68	78	4.4*
838		16	18	26.4	60.70	145.30	18†	4.9	898		5	1	35.1	61.16	146.98	22	3.7*
839		16	29	15.0	61.22	147.57	12	3.9*	899		7	2	20.8	61.88	149.94	20	(*)
840		16	39	30.0	59.90	145.10	10	4.1	900		9	39	26.6	60.88	148.21	5	4.0*
841		16	49	41.8	61.40	147.30	33	4.2	901		11	25	54.8	60.90	144.60	33	4.0
842		17	26	52.2	61.41	147.17	20§	3.4*	902		14	40	28.8	59.11	147.79	10§	3.7*
843		18	50	31.0	59.93	146.77	10§	3.2	903		14	56	30.9	57.30	151.90	26‡	5.3
844		19	25	48.0	61.40	147.40	33	3.8	904		15	47	15.1	59.90	147.50	33	4.1
845		20	3	57.9	61.76	149.75	13	(*)	905		16	47	44.5	59.84	146.65	10§	3.8*
846		20	48	14.7	61.23	146.76	20§	3.5*	906		18	46	45.6	59.65	147.86	113	3.8*
847		22	57	36.9	61.33	147.33	20§	3.8*	907		19	32	33.9	62.27	149.55	20§	4.0*
848		23	29	.8	59.87	146.89	20§	3.5*	908		22	57	37.4	59.98	147.96	80	4.0*
849	APR. 21	0	9	8.7	61.38	147.04	20§	(*)	909	APR. 24	0	48	21.3	60.03	148.24	25	3.6*
850		1	15	46.8	61.74	147.08	20§	(*)	910		0	59	33.4	56.50	151.60	33	3.8
851		1	30	48.3	61.26	147.46	20‡	(*)	911		1	39	10.9	60.34	149.09	20§	2.7*
852		2	12	41.3	60.36	149.93	20‡	4.9*	912		2	2	38.9	60.53	149.88	20§	4.6*
853		2	20	16.3	61.46	147.15	20‡	(*)	913		3	51	5.0	59.50	144.50	19†	5.2
854		3	23	7.1	61.16	147.26	20‡	4.0*	914		4	23	5.1	56.60	151.70	20	4.1
855		4	30	43.5	61.17	147.32	20	(*)	915		4	57	6.1	61.52	149.14	20§	(*)
856		4	32	43.0	61.32	147.20	43‡	3.9*	916		5	7	.9	60.04	146.98	88	3.2*
857		5	1	35.7	61.50	147.50	40	5.4	917		8	57	9.8	58.70	149.50	33	4.5
858		6	4	36.8	60.40	157.20	33	3.9	918		14	54	17.2	59.80	146.96	20§	3.9*
859		6	43	17.1	61.42	147.22	20‡	(*)	919		18	55	46.7	61.52	149.96	20§	3.8*
860		6	58	5.0	60.68	147.48	35	2.8*	920	APR. 25	0	17	56.1	60.30	147.00	33	3.9
861		7	0	16.6	61.47	147.04	20‡	(*)	921		0	51	8.0	59.90	147.10	33	4.1
862		7	17	1.3	61.52	146.33	71‡	(*)	922		1	59	14.4	60.00	145.10	33	4.0
863		8	59	33.4	60.34	145.67	20	4.5*	923		5	39	50.5	61.39	147.22	32	(*)
864		9	13	48.5	60.52	150.90	79‡	3.5*	924		6	55	19.1	60.18	150.16	22	3.3*
865		10	13	35.9	60.32	146.45	20‡	3.6*	925		7	1	19.7	59.80	145.30	33	3.8
866		12	6	30.0	61.39	147.05	20‡	(*)	926		9	43	30.7	59.90	144.90	36‡	5.0
867		12	29	49.8	59.53	148.50	20	3.7*	927		11	23	58.5	01.50	147.76	12	4.2*
868		13	4	13.1	61.97	147.80	20‡	4.4*	928		11	34	29.3	57.60	150.80	33	4.2
869		13	27	48.2	61.42	147.22	28‡	4.4*	929		12	58	50.8	59.36	144.83	20§	3.7*
870		13	47	42.8	58.96	147.72	74	3.4*	930		15	6	16.4	59.70	146.27	20§	(*)
871		14	36	5.8	61.61	147.10	20‡	(*)	931		16	10	1.3	59.90	146.10	24‡	4.6
872		16	59	27.5	60.34	146.87	20	3.8*	932		18	11	24.4	60.70	145.30	33	3.7
873		18	15	32.4	61.21	158.21	20‡	(*)	933		19	2	44.2	61.61	148.04	10§	4.0*
874		23	51	16.6	61.25	147.05	42‡	3.4*	934		19	51	27.5	60.66	146.61	20§	(*)
875	APR. 22	0	19	14.2	61.12	149.42	20‡	(*)	935		20	55	20.7	62.02	149.91	20§	4.6*
876		1	47	50.8	59.18	144.34	31‡	4.6*	936		21	7	(**)				
877		2	2	38.7	60.95	147.05	85‡	2.7*	937		21	27	59.6	62.06	148.85	20§	(*)
878		2	57	56.7	59.56	146.06	100	2.9*	938		22	8	52.1	61.41	147.30	20§	(*)
879		4	34	16.9	60.70	147.78	47‡	4.1*	939		22	13	31.2	60.88	150.98	20§	4.1*
880		4	36	54.7	61.24	146.83	36	(*)	940		22	46	20.5	59.78	146.06	20§	3.5*

See footnotes at end of table.

TABLE 2.—*Summary of aftershock data*—Continued

Earthquake number	Date	Origin time Hr.	Min.	Sec.	Latitude N. °	Longitude W. °	Depth Km.	Magnitude	Earthquake number	Date	Origin time Hr.	Min.	Sec.	Latitude N. °	Longitude W. °	Depth Km.	Magnitude
	1964—Con.									1964—Con.							
941	APR. 25	22	48	2.6	61.30	147.24	36	4.1*	1001	APR. 30—Cont.	10	58	36.4	58.26	152.05	10§	4.5*
942	APR. 26	1	2	50.3	61.51	146.81	20§	(*)	1002		11	2	47.4	61.26	147.26	65	4.1*
943		3	20	13.6	58.79	149.32	10§	3.8*	1003		11	50	47.4	61.30	147.00	33	4.4
944		6	48	50.0	59.95	147.49	20§	3.1*	1004		13	20	34.8	60.88	147.18	28	4.3*
945		7	46	16.1	58.36	147.25	20§	2.7*	1005		13	24	1.1	62.88	145.86	20§	4.4*
946		8	5	30.0	60.16	147.39	43	3.0*	1006		14	2	33.0	59.20	149.73	20	3.4*
947		8	56	6.2	59.45	148.03	130	3.4*	1007		16	25	30.6	59.00	148.60	33	4.2
948		9	7	38.0	61.09	147.07	30	3.6*	1008		17	26	29.9	60.10	142.20	28†	4.9
949		9	34	26.5	61.41	147.07	115	3.4*	1009		23	51	28.1	58.00	150.90	33	3.9
950		10	49	31.1	59.87	147.27	20§	3.5*	1010	MAY 1	0	17	22.0	56.60	151.50	30	4.5
951		11	36	35.5	60.43	150.92	12‡	3.1*	1011		3	13	3.5	57.40	150.00	37†	5.3
952		12	11	52.1	57.76	144.73	10	4.4*	1012		3	40	36.2	59.70	144.10	20	4.4
953		12	39	43.4	61.44	146.44	20‡	(*)	1013		4	40	55.1	60.31	144.57	10§	3.7*
954		18	33	47.2	57.39	144.78	20‡	4.5*	1014		5	33	42.3	61.96	151.20	20§	(*)
955		20	44	8.3	59.72	146.15	13	3.8*	1015		6	1	55.4	60.50	145.60	14‡	5.4
956		22	1	36.3	61.32	147.27	33‡	3.8*	1016		7	8	12.2	57.50	150.60	20	4.5
957		22	38	3.1	59.96	146.40	27	3.8*	1017		7	44	44.9	59.70	147.10	6‡	4.8
958		23	19	16.5	60.23	151.68	76‡	4.6*	1018		9	44	20.6	60.53	145.04	20§	3.5*
959		23	38	33.6	60.88	146.81	12‡	4.2*	1019		10	25	32.3	60.37	147.64	20§	3.4*
960	APR. 27	0	17	44.5	60.69	147.66	20‡	3.4*	1020		12	25	4.0	60.38	143.53	10§	4.3*
961		2	21	38.3	60.09	150.82	20	3.7*	1021		14	39	58.2	60.40	145.10	33	4.3
962		2	34	29.6	61.37	147.24	25	(*)	1022		18	3	26.6	59.82	146.97	20§	3.4*
963		3	4	9.3	60.02	148.00	25‡	3.4*	1023	MAY 2	2	23	47.4	58.35	151.17	20§	(*)
964		3	53	47.1	57.40	152.40	20	4.3	1024		4	43	50.1	58.60	151.10	33	4.0
965		13	59	59.0	57.15	148.86	92	4.0*	1025		5	38	42.7	61.10	146.74	20§	3.4*
966		14	29	33.4	60.22	145.97	42‡	3.4*	1026		5	49	46.3	60.54	147.66	20§	2.7*
967		15	47	54.5	58.78	147.02	20‡	3.5*	1027		9	45	50.8	58.22	150.46	30	4.0*
968		16	0	45.4	61.89	152.63	20	4.8*	1028		10	2	42.4	59.40	146.50	33	4.3
969		19	9	39.0	60.50	146.50	29†	4.4	1029		15	41	17.0	58.89	144.72	73	4.1*
970		20	25	4.1	59.80	148.40	33	4.3	1030		15	44	32.5	59.46	146.22	88	2.6*
971	APR. 28	8	38	12.4	59.60	149.90	33	3.9	1031		16	47	12.4	59.85	146.01	56	3.7*
972		10	51	32.2	55.84	143.99	20‡	(*)	1032		17	8	57.6	59.70	147.00	30	4.8
973		12	22	7.1	60.59	147.33	20‡	(*)	1033		17	17	59.8	60.64	146.32	21	3.7*
974		13	34	10.4	57.60	150.00	33	4.4	1034		18	40	8.0	61.05	148.84	20§	3.3*
975		13	54	(**)					1035		19	31	13.2	58.90	148.26	44	3.8*
976		17	33	14.5	60.30	146.17	20‡	3.5*	1036		22	16	53.8	59.51	148.36	27	4.1*
977		22	56	18.8	56.70	152.00	33	4.1	1037	MAY 3	2	57	27.5	58.90	146.08	81	3.3*
978	APR. 29	3	52	43.1	60.00	147.40	33	4.0	1038		7	9	38.9	58.88	151.74	47	3.7*
979		4	9	42.7	60.08	149.75	64	3.2*	1039		7	32	56.3	56.50	154.80	30	4.4
980		6	19	43.3	59.78	148.83	30	3.0*	1040		7	58	44.6	58.10	151.60	33	4.2
981		7	10	.9	60.41	147.82	30‡	2.8*	1041		11	51	45.7	62.65	147.74	20§	4.0*
982		8	57	50.2	60.03	148.39	37‡	3.5*	1042		12	40	3.9	60.09	148.27	22	3.2*
983		9	19	14.0	59.85	146.90	32	3.9*	1043		17	37	38.1	58.65	149.23	20§	(*)
984		9	40	15.3	59.28	147.68	0	3.4*	1044		19	50	35.9	58.90	150.90	20§	(*)
985		9	54	56.3	61.06	146.74	20	3.6*	1045		20	15	41.3	60.58	145.49	10§	3.9*
986		13	4	18.2	61.25	145.56	20‡	3.7*	1046		20	43	39.3	60.02	147.57	10§	3.4*
987		14	30	33.9	60.63	151.77	20	3.8*	1047		21	31	53.2	59.00	148.50	25	4.4
988		14	38	34.0	59.50	148.31	10	3.3*	1048		21	39	30.4	61.00	145.80	33	3.9
989		16	2	38.1	60.28	146.32	20	3.9*	1049		23	51	12.2	60.74	148.34	20§	3.4*
990		17	55	25.0	59.90	146.88	34	4.5*	1050	MAY 4	2	53	(**)				
991		18	9	(**)					1051		6	51	41.7	59.55	151.04	20	(*)
992		22	12	48.6	60.85	144.83	20	3.7*	1052		9	0	10.1	61.30	141.80	33	3.9
993		22	53	15.7	59.53	146.83	31	3.6*	1053		9	7	9.3	58.02	149.00	10‡	(*)
994	APR. 30	0	26	.1	56.90	152.20	33	3.9	1054		10	24	29.7	60.76	150.59	13‡	3.6*
995		2	41	57.8	58.28	151.50	20	(*)	1055		12	4	46.1	58.20	152.30	22‡	5.3
996		3	35	11.9	58.76	151.31	20‡	(*)	1056		13	9	26.5	60.08	147.26	20‡	(*)
997		3	50	34.8	59.36	144.38	20‡	3.4*	1057		17	37	31.4	59.92	145.59	30‡	(*)
998		5	31	51.1	56.80	152.70	33	4.5	1058		19	24	54.5	59.49	152.95	20‡	3.7*
999		9	55	(**)					1059		22	44	19.1	60.04	149.36	5‡	3.3*
1000		10	47	43.3	62.70	144.09	20	4.4*	1060		22	55	.9	60.52	147.69	20‡	3.6*

See footnotes at end of table.

TABLE 2.—*Summary of aftershock data*—Continued

Earthquake number	Date	Hr.	Min.	Sec.	Latitude N. °	Longitude W. °	Depth Km.	Magnitude	Earthquake number	Date	Hr.	Min.	Sec.	Latitude N. °	Longitude W. °	Depth Km.	Magnitude
	1964—Con.									1964—Con.							
1061	MAY 5	0	21	56.9	60.70	147.60	33	4.0	1121	MAY 9— Cont.	19	55	40.8	59.94	146.50	87	3.5*
1062		2	4	17.9	57.40	149.50	33	4.4	1122		21	6	12.2	61.70	152.00	26†	5.0
1063		2	32	42.3	60.40	147.10	18‡	4.4	1123		21	11	8.0	58.93	152.61	21	4.1*
1064		4	5	8.3	59.70	148.90	33	4.6	1124	MAY 10	2	0	27.5	59.90	146.50	33	3.6
1065		5	15	29.2	59.99	146.51	31‡	3.7*	1125		2	48	29.4	60.24	148.27	7	3.1*
1066		6	49	59.0	59.62	148.58	20‡	3.1*	1126		4	11	29.2	60.00	141.98	20§	(*)
1067		8	28	.7	59.83	148.28	15‡	3.6*	1127		6	25	26.3	60.02	146.86	20§	3.8*
1068		8	33	47.5	60.70	150.95	11	(*)	1128		7	24	26.7	57.18	145.45	20§	4.5*
1069		8	58	4.5	59.04	143.28	10	4.4*	1129		11	23	52.4	59.98	147.15	20§	3.2*
1070		11	30	27.4	57.67	152.32	20	(*)	1130		12	1	23.8	60.70	148.40	33	3.7
1071		12	8	9.6	59.77	147.76	26‡	3.3*	1131		13	25	38.0	62.28	148.25	20§	(*)
1072		13	54	32.0	61.37	147.65	34	3.5*	1132		13	28	9.8	60.65	147.12	20§	(*)
1073		14	46	56.9	58.87	154.56	20	4.2*	1133		14	46	15.3	59.90	147.10	15	4.5
1074		16	11	51.7	59.70	148.20	18‡	3.3*	1134		15	33	17.7	60.21	147.63	20§	4.0*
1075		16	13	44.5	58.20	149.70	35†	5.0	1135		15	40	53.3	60.10	146.30	15	4.3
1076		21	50	47.7	58.51	144.15	20	4.7*	1136		21	39	5.2	59.78	146.99	20§	3.3*
1077		22	41	7.1	61.80	156.70	13†	4.7	1137		22	48	3.0	60.48	145.59	20§	3.9*
1078	MAY 6	0	59	53.2	59.60	146.80	33	4.1	1138	MAY 11	0	10	29.3	60.70	148.42	20§	(*)
1079		4	44	13.3	57.50	149.30	33	4.2	1139		2	17	1.5	60.80	142.20	33	4.7
1080		9	38	11.6	59.70	142.80	33	4.6	1140		3	31	38.7	60.20	147.20	33	3.9
1081		10	15	53.6	60.07	147.70	8‡	3.4*	1141		4	50	29.7	60.00	147.36	20§	3.2*
1082		10	24	59.9	61.75	151.45	20‡	4.1*	1142		7	5	21.1	60.78	147.45	20§	(*)
1083		14	0	50.4	61.33	149.75	8‡	3.4*	1143		9	45	22.2	58.40	152.30	15	4.3
1084		15	26	35.5	56.70	152.10	26†	5.4	1144		11	47	27.0	60.46	147.76	90	(*)
1085		17	33	30.5	60.96	146.01	20‡	4.4*	1145		14	47	(**)				
1086		18	7	23.7	59.44	148.90	3‡	3.6*	1146		18	22	47.2	56.60	154.00	33	4.2
1087	MAY 7	0	15	48.9	60.10	147.40	33	4.2	1147		20	10	36.5	60.30	146.10	33	4.0
1088		0	28	3.4	60.58	147.59	20‡	4.4*	1148		20	13	30.0	60.02	145.01	20§	4.2*
1089		5	40	35.3	60.52	151.27	20‡	(*)	1149		22	2	42.4	62.11	148.12	20§	(*)
1090		7	30	52.3	60.44	146.54	20‡	4.8*	1150	MAY 12	0	29	59.2	60.87	152.51	20§	(*)
1091		10	5	15.8	60.23	146.92	26	3.4*	1151		2	4	15.5	56.90	151.40	25	4.0
1092		11	41	37.1	58.63	150.37	10‡	3.6*	1152		3	21	44.4	60.98	150.49	30‡	4.0*
1093		15	36	31.6	61.39	147.20	20	(*)	1153		9	16	(**)				
1094		18	10	8.6	58.46	152.34	20	4.2*	1154		11	47	32.2	60.10	147.00	18‡	4.7
1095		18	15	37.3	60.26	146.82	30	3.8*	1155		12	57	44.2	60.04	153.38	10	4.2*
1096		18	27	1.0	60.00	147.51	16	4.1*	1156		15	1	40.1	59.95	149.49	44	3.7*
1097		19	12	37.8	60.40	144.80	15	4.5	1157		16	55	46.9	59.50	144.80	32‡	4.9
1098	MAY 8	5	56	13.7	59.20	153.90	25	4.4	1158		18	16	41.9	56.60	152.40	37†	5.3
1099		6	5	46.8	56.70	154.20	33	3.9	1159		18	22	21.8	56.14	152.88	20‡	(*)
1100		7	29	46.7	60.14	150.11	38‡	3.8*	1160		18	28	57.5	56.60	152.20	8†	4.4
1101		7	34	6.0	60.11	150.49	80	3.5*	1161		19	10	7.7	59.83	146.42	85‡	3.4*
1102		9	23	33.1	59.40	145.40	20	4.5	1162		19	16	49.4	61.06	145.98	13‡	3.6*
1103		9	46	54.5	59.34	141.25	20§	3.7*	1163		21	40	32.6	60.93	147.03	25	3.5*
1104		10	14	48.4	59.74	146.96	20§	3.4*	1164		23	37	50.4	59.40	143.10	20	4.7
1105		11	15	19.8	59.93	153.05	20§	4.3*	1165		23	42	23.0	59.50	143.10	25	4.5
1106		14	20	39.1	58.94	151.82	10§	4.0*	1166	MAY 13	0	7	42.1	56.20	152.70	34†	4.9
1107		15	42	8.3	60.46	145.84	23	3.2*	1167		6	48	34.6	61.26	147.41	27	(*)
1108		16	21	49.8	56.70	154.00	22†	5.3	1168		7	43	.4	56.80	153.00	25	3.7
1109		18	6	10.9	59.97	146.70	25	3.9*	1169		11	55	10.5	59.74	148.67	23‡	4.0*
1110		19	42	(**)					1170		13	47	32.4	60.60	141.40	33	3.7
1111		21	34	40.6	60.80	143.60	17†	5.4	1171		15	6	3.2	60.00	145.90	13	4.2
1112		21	54	41.8	61.10	143.00	33	4.1	1172		15	47	3.0	62.96	150.15	20‡	4.3*
1113		22	15	22.5	60.49	146.32	20§	4.4*	1173		16	3	46.8	58.75	148.75	22‡	4.0*
1114		22	38	3.6	59.80	146.00	33	3.7	1174		23	56	40.5	61.37	146.49	20‡	3.7*
1115	MAY 9	1	16	9.8	59.70	146.80	33	3.8	1175	MAY 14	4	12	22.7	59.99	148.01	19‡	2.4*
1116		6	45	(**)					1176		10	25	(**)				
1117		10	12	27.1	58.14	151.15	20§	(*)	1177		11	9	52.1	60.84	147.10	10	(*)
1118		17	16	50.3	60.97	150.62	20§	4.1*	1178		11	55	28.2	62.80	152.30	15	4.6
1119		18	53	25.8	59.90	147.90	33	3.9	1179		12	42	22.0	62.65	153.09	20	(*)
1120		19	47	54.2	61.15	152.19	20§	3.9*	1180		13	18	17.8	60.28	154.37	20‡	(*)

See footnotes at end of table.

TABLE 2.—*Summary of aftershock data*—Continued

Earthquake number	Date	Hr.	Min.	Sec.	Latitude N. °	Longitude W. °	Depth Km.	Magnitude	Earthquake number	Date	Hr.	Min.	Sec.	Latitude N. °	Longitude W. °	Depth Km.	Magnitude
	1964—Con.									*1964*—Con.							
1181	MAY 14—	14	19	5.1	59.70	144.40	33	4.5	1241	MAY 20—	14	30	1.9	59.83	148.19	20§	3.3*
1182	Cont.	14	55	28.2	57.90	149.89	10	4.4*	1242	Cont.	16	53	58.3	59.81	153.90	20§	(*)
1183		15	12	4.5	59.80	147.00	33	4.1	1243	MAY 21	1	11	23.4	60.40	145.90	11‡	4.6
1184		15	57	48.5	59.89	142.47	20	(*)	1244		2	40	37.2	59.53	151.63	20§	(*)
1185		16	23	43.9	58.44	151.32	79‡	(*)	1245		8	9	31.7	59.79	149.06	41	3.0*
1186		16	36	31.6	59.89	146.22	24	3.7*	1246		9	51	11.8	61.25	146.24	20§	(*)
1187		23	43	35.2	60.61	146.20	20	2.7*	1247		11	10	9.4	61.77	149.63	20§	(*)
1188	MAY 15	2	56	15.2	60.10	147.00	33	3.8	1248		13	31	50.9	60.20	147.20	33	4.2
1189		4	2	39.3	57.60	152.20	20	3.9	1249		15	36	1.5	59.00	153.50	17†	5.3
1190		5	11	17.3	61.40	147.90	26†	3.7	1250		16	26	38.4	57.00	152.90	33	3.8
1191		10	35	41.5	62.54	147.46	20	(*)	1251		18	29	16.4	61.63	143.40	20	(*)
1192		11	15	50.9	60.25	153.87	20	(*)	1252		18	38	34.8	59.95	149.18	20‡	3.5*
1193		12	15	46.2	62.71	146.62	36‡	(*)	1253		19	7	16.2	58.79	151.81	20‡	3.8*
1194		15	21	26.1	59.95	148.40	20‡	(*)	1254		22	30	11.0	59.30	145.30	38	4.1
1195		23	5	45.0	62.04	149.95	20‡	(*)	1255	MAY 22	2	37	5.3	60.98	146.60	20	(*)
1196		23	8	8.0	58.98	144.90	20‡	3.2*	1256		3	50	34.5	60.20	151.99	20‡	(*)
1197		23	53	27.0	58.40	151.71	78‡	(*)	1257		6	51	12.9	60.97	151.23	30‡	(*)
1198	MAY 16	0	51	48.3	59.77	148.46	20	3.3*	1258		7	27	50.0	61.21	146.87	29	(*)
1199		2	40	9.7	59.60	145.00	33	3.8	1259		16	51	44.3	60.13	154.11	71‡	(*)
1200		5	15	21.6	60.00	149.45	20	(*)	1260		17	30	19.6	57.88	150.33	20‡	(*)
1201		9	53	55.4	61.20	150.68	20§	(*)	1261		21	36	22.0	61.40	150.74	20	(*)
1202		10	27	36.4	59.30	152.00	35	3.7	1262	MAY 23	3	44	32.5	60.25	149.02	21	(*)
1203		14	44	54.3	57.60	151.00	24†	5.4	1263		3	54	6.1	60.37	150.69	83‡	(*)
1204		16	49	21.1	58.94	153.12	20§	4.0*	1264		6	29	24.4	57.30	150.70	20	4.5
1205		17	21	47.6	58.87	152.62	20§	3.9*	1265		6	53	22.4	59.85	146.53	12	4.3*
1206	MAY 17	0	50	17.9	59.40	142.70	24†	5.1	1266		8	31	27.0	59.50	147.89	20	(*)
1207		4	44	(**)					1267		17	15	23.0	59.40	149.48	20	(*)
1208		15	42	31.8	59.25	147.84	20§	3.2*	1268		21	45	45.0	58.51	144.50	20‡	3.4*
1209		21	57	24.0	60.13	147.12	17	(*)	1269		23	50	49.1	59.96	146.35	20‡	3.2*
1210		22	9	49.1	59.00	145.90	77	3.4*	1270	MAY 24	0	40	21.9	60.20	148.00	14†	4.9
1211		22	18	20.0	57.71	151.28	20§	(*)	1271		6	52	44.4	59.70	148.50	19†	4.6
1212		23	7	59.9	60.26	146.96	20§	2.7*	1272		8	59	28.2	58.07	150.31	67‡	(*)
1213	MAY 18	4	46	41.2	61.13	149.10	76	(*)	1273		9	4	57.0	56.70	152.90	33	4.0
1214		5	12	32.2	60.40	146.60	14‡	3.9	1274		10	16	21.5	59.90	145.50	11‡	4.3
1215		7	28	48.3	58.68	149.95	20§	(*)	1275		15	5	50.2	59.34	151.41	20‡	(*)
1216		9	26	55.6	62.27	150.57	20§	(*)	1276		16	56	27.7	59.35	150.55	20‡	(*)
1217		10	12	10.6	63.06	142.45	20§	(*)	1277		18	31	13.1	59.91	146.27	20‡	3.2*
1218		13	47	22.7	59.60	145.00	15†	4.6	1278		20	40	6.9	59.25	143.27	20‡	3.4*
1219		13	56	(**)					1279	MAY 25	4	53	52.1	59.68	148.59	20‡	(*)
1220		18	14	48.7	59.70	145.00	33	4.0	1280		9	50	59.4	60.17	145.92	20	(*)
1221		21	12	46.2	59.50	142.70	21†	4.9	1281		15	44	41.6	57.93	148.74	20	(*)
1222	MAY 19	1	44	33.6	60.40	147.50	15	4.3	1282		22	14	56.4	60.10	145.80	20	(*)
1223		2	0	55.4	60.00	147.87	20§	(*)	1283	MAY 26	5	33	44.6	60.30	145.50	16‡	4.3
1224		2	23	45.2	59.40	145.20	20	4.3	1284		9	54	55.6	59.98	145.28	45‡	3.4*
1225		2	28	33.6	59.20	143.90	33	4.2	1285		16	4	27.6	62.46	143.49	20‡	(*)
1226		10	52	28.7	59.82	148.73	27	4.0*	1286		17	15	10.5	59.93	147.28	20‡	3.7*
1227		13	19	20.7	59.70	152.30	33	4.2	1287		19	0	37.2	62.70	151.74	12	(*)
1228		14	42	40.7	60.20	146.30	14‡	4.9	1288		19	38	12.8	59.33	148.23	85	3.4*
1229		15	37	35.9	57.00	152.80	19†	4.9	1289		21	58	34.1	60.10	147.00	33	4.1
1230		15	57	22.4	60.45	148.44	20§	4.2*	1290	MAY 27	4	44	42.9	58.97	149.22	20	(*)
1231		16	36	36.6	59.99	147.79	20§	(*)	1291		6	30	23.3	60.91	146.98	28	(*)
1232		19	8	47.8	59.45	149.11	20§	(*)	1292		8	15	22.1	60.80	147.03	20	(*)
1233		23	29	55.3	58.66	150.51	10§	3.7*	1293		13	27	45.3	59.41	147.29	19‡	(*)
1234		23	41	(**)					1294		15	25	4.6	59.60	151.14	20	(*)
1235	MAY 20	1	55	23.8	61.30	148.30	33	4.0	1295		16	0	36.1	63.38	150.34	20‡	(*)
1236		5	32	13.7	58.00	149.60	18†	4.9	1296		17	17	27.1	59.86	148.31	10	(*)
1237		6	21	29.9	61.84	149.44	20§	(*)	1297		17	52	8.4	59.10	146.40	33	4.0
1238		7	50	24.8	59.71	148.62	20§	3.5*	1298		22	59	57.9	59.86	148.13	17‡	(*)
1239		9	28	38.5	60.20	147.40	33	4.4	1299	MAY 28	8	58	53.8	61.51	141.14	20‡	(*)
1240		12	6	49.5	60.58	146.20	10§	4.0*	1300		9	57	12.3	61.76	154.77	20‡	(*)

See footnotes at end of table.

TABLE 2.—*Summary of aftershock data*—Continued

Earthquake number	Date	Origin time Hr.	Min.	Sec.	Latitude N. °	Longitude W. °	Depth Km.	Magnitude	Earthquake number	Date	Origin time Hr.	Min.	Sec.	Latitude N. °	Longitude W. °	Depth Km.	Magnitude
	1964—Con.									1964—Con.							
1301	MAY 28—	11	47	59.8	61.01	146.10	20§	(*)	1361	JUNE 4—	3	27	4.6	59.70	147.30	45	(*)
1302	Cont.	14	6	58.2	60.20	147.70	33	3.7	1362	Cont.	11	43	53.6	60.25	152.25	95‡	(*)
1303		14	17	.7	60.28	146.29	29	3.7*	1363		12	31	11.4	60.46	150.60	1‡	(*)
1304		16	18	4.2	58.30	150.60	25†	5.4	1364		12	42	49.7	61.18	149.09	20	(*)
1305		17	19	27.0	61.65	149.53	20§	(*)	1365		12	52	22.0	60.91	147.08	5	3.3*
1306		19	3	44.3	59.90	148.68	34	3.5*	1366		18	9	41.1	60.27	152.58	115‡	(*)
1307		21	47	52.2	59.89	147.26	10§	3.3*	1367	JUNE 5	9	50	35.0	60.40	146.00	15†	5.2
1308	MAY 29	3	25	34.5	56.07	146.33	20§	(*)	1368		11	50	24.9	63.10	151.10	94	4.2
1309		3	34	51.8	60.10	146.50	17‡	4.7	1369		22	6	53.0	58.10	152.10	13†	5.0
1310		10	17	34.5	60.20	146.30	20‡	5.6	1370	JUNE 6	5	24	4.0	60.10	148.02	20	(*)
1311		20	13	.7	60.31	143.93	20§	(*)	1371		5	43	55.4	60.00	148.02	20	(*)
1312	MAY 30	3	18	8.3	59.50	148.50	35†	5.5	1372		6	24	3.3	60.02	147.59	33‡	(*)
1313		6	38	9.4	59.39	150.27	24	(*)	1373		13	29	13.8	60.56	146.29	20	(*)
1314		11	29	23.9	61.26	150.81	20§	(*)	1374		23	29	20.9	61.37	147.39	20‡	(*)
1315		15	21	32.0	61.62	147.01	20§	(*)	1375	JUNE 7	2	42	30.2	61.87	147.91	20	(*)
1316		20	54	41.4	60.25	148.55	24	(*)	1376		10	47	40.9	56.49	154.51	45	(*)
1317		22	34	33.3	56.60	152.30	10†	4.7	1377		16	16	21.8	60.22	148.20	20	(*)
1318		22	57	33.8	59.68	149.90	35	(*)	1378	JUNE 8	0	50	46.0	60.56	146.66	20	(*)
1319	MAY 31	0	47	41.1	59.21	148.97	20§	(*)	1379		5	44	31.0	57.40	149.20	12†	4.6
1320		1	22	52.1	60.96	147.06	20§	(*)	1380		6	24	(**)				
1321		4	9	16.3	60.53	153.65	20§	(*)	1381		6	44	40.1	59.95	146.87	20	(*)
1322		13	16	58.3	58.10	150.88	16	(*)	1382		8	0	15.7	61.88	149.56	20	(*)
1323		13	42	13.7	63.64	147.78	20§	(*)	1383		15	58	34.7	60.15	147.24	20‡	(*)
1324		15	33	6.9	60.56	147.40	16	(*)	1384	JUNE 9	7	39	27.7	60.80	147.35	1‡	(*)
1325		17	26	7.4	60.78	143.31	20§	(*)	1385		9	24	17.8	59.60	145.10	12†	4.8
1326		19	2	39.6	60.07	149.24	20§	(*)	1386		10	33	47.4	59.75	145.99	20	(*)
1327	JUNE 1	2	7	1.6	56.10	152.13	20§	(*)	1387		17	56	45.1	61.70	149.60	5†	(*)
1328		3	41	49.6	58.89	146.86	20§	(*)	1388		18	51	41.9	60.51	151.58	20†	(*)
1329		4	34	(**)					1389		21	19	18.0	60.36	147.46	38	(*)
1330		6	21	44.4	59.78	146.64	20§	(*)	1390		21	24	36.9	59.85	146.26	5	(*)
1331		9	15	42.2	62.20	150.41	20§	(*)	1391		22	53	39.4	59.82	145.97	40‡	(*)
1332		16	54	41.8	61.06	146.34	51§	(*)	1392	JUNE 10	7	35	56.7	61.30	148.80	33	3.9
1333		17	32	7.3	59.94	148.09	0	(*)	1393		12	9	55.6	58.63	150.63	20‡	(*)
1334		18	22	20.5	59.35	146.70	96	(*)	1394		13	15	27.2	61.69	149.19	32‡	(*)
1335		18	37	27.1	60.67	149.41	20§	(*)	1395		17	0	7.2	59.81	146.93	18‡	(*)
1336		20	14	40.3	60.36	146.03	20§	(*)	1396		23	25	9.1	59.10	153.80	14†	5.1
1337	JUNE 2	5	19	41.2	61.36	147.30	24	(*)	1397	JUNE 11	16	25	20.2	61.18	146.95	20‡	(*)
1338		7	37	24.8	60:97	147.37	14	(*)	1398		17	27	13.4	58.10	152.90	30	5.0
1339		10	57	54.5	59.51	148.10	20§	(*)	1399	JUNE 12	0	23	4.6	60.10	142.90	33	4.2
1340		14	46	19.3	60.67	147.14	20§	(*)	1400		7	50	3.9	59.29	147.64	20‡	(*)
1341		16	9	23.5	59.70	144.40	14†	5.1	1401		22	59	16.3	60.52	150.38	66	(*)
1342		16	29	41.5	59.70	144.20	15†	4.8	1402	JUNE 13	1	13	31.9	58.80	149.90	33	4.4
1343		17	33	1.8	62.21	148.60	19	(*)	1403		2	46	27.3	56.50	153.20	33	4.0
1344		18	14	3.4	60.51	148.33	21	(*)	1404		3	10	24.7	61.40	146.20	20§	(*)
1345		19	38	31.6	62.72	147.06	7	(*)	1405		4	9	.2	60.74	146.89	20§	(*)
1346		21	49	42.1	60.00	146.45	20§	4.1*	1406		5	58	10.0	59.63	146.02	20§	(*)
1347		22	42	59.9	60.20	150.82	67	(¹)	1407		7	14	(**)				
1348		23	25	40.8	61.18	147.10	20§	(*)	1408	JUNE 14	8	18	7.9	61.38	147.27	20§	(*)
1349		23	43	19.5	60.14	147.31	20§	3.5*	1409		12	7	.2	60.11	146.52	20§	(*)
1350	JUNE 3	2	20	17.8	60.92	147.12	28	(*)	1410		14	56	(**)				
1351		5	47	32.1	60.84	147.24	5	(*)	1411		17	20	17.5	56.70	152.10	33	(*)
1352		6	55	32.2	61.98	153.27	20‡	(*)	1412		20	51	.9	59.06	148.19	5§	(*)
1353		7	26	49.2	59.45	144.54	20‡	(*)	1413	JUNE 15	4	21	11.5	61.37	147.12	20§	(*)
1354		9	31	59.5	60.24	148.81	10‡	(*)	1414		9	28	3.8	56.70	151.60	33	4.4
1355		11	25	45.5	61.10	151.20	33	3.8	1415		9	32	37.9	61.35	147.28	3	(*)
1356		13	16	54.0	60.03	147.57	18‡	(*)	1416		16	13	31.5	59.10	144.60	33	4.4
1357		14	3	42.4	59.90	143.90	16†	5.1	1417		20	19	14.7	58.80	150.30	22†	5.1
1358		17	41	53.4	59.93	147.19	5	(*)	1418	JUNE 16	0	29	22.5	62.87	144.87	20§	(*)
1359		19	7	37.7	59.98	146.27	20‡	3.0*	1419		4	8	26.4	60.80	145.94	20§	(*)
1360	JUNE 4	1	50	49.3	60.85	146.50	1‡	(*)	1420		4	9	52.8	62.84	148.81	20§	(*)

See footnotes at end of table.

TABLE 2.—*Summary of aftershock data*—Continued

Earthquake number	Date	Hr.	Min.	Sec.	Latitude N. °	Longitude W. °	Depth Km.	Magnitude	Earthquake number	Date	Hr.	Min.	Sec.	Latitude N. °	Longitude W. °	Depth Km.	Magnitude
	1964—Con.									*1964*—Con.							
1421	JUNE 16—	7	23	29.0	61.27	148.52	20§	(*)	1481	JUNE 25	3	25	32.5	59.61	147.99	20	(*)
1422	Cont.	10	23	39.7	61.20	146.80	12†	4.5	1482		4	34	4.4	59.69	152.65	20‡	(*)
1423		10	26	36.0	60.88	147.10	20§	(*)	1483		8	19	40.0	59.60	147.82	20‡	(*)
1424		19	53	52.3	59.66	146.35	20§	2.6*	1484		9	27	21.8	60.71	147.19	29‡	(*)
1425	JUNE 17	2	59	22.1	61.17	146.77	7	(*)	1485		9	40	29.7	63.46	147.81	20‡	(*)
1426		10	59	27.2	60.10	149.50	72	4.1	1486		11	23	.6	60.30	149.10	70	4.6
1427		12	45	27.8	57.58	150.54	132	(*)	1487		11	46	34.9	61.78	149.87	20	3.7*
1428		13	8	44.6	61.40	149.81	5§	(*)	1488		13	4	26.4	59.76	146.00	25	2.7*
1429		15	4	10.7	61.46	146.47	5§	(*)	1489		20	32	41.2	60.33	144.89	20‡	(*)
1430		17	58	1.8	60.42	145.40	20§	(*)	1490		22	42	32.4	59.73	148.69	28	4.0*
1431	JUNE 18	7	20	18.0	61.25	151.65	5§	(*)	1491	JUNE 26	5	28	49.0	61.70	148.30	33	4.3
1432		8	24	26.6	59.90	147.20	33	4.4	1492		6	53	17.8	60.22	146.04	20‡	2.9*
1433		10	47	49.1	59.73	146.80	19	2.8*	1493		7	23	32.6	61.38	145.14	11‡	(*)
1434		12	41	(**)					1494		11	53	3.6	59.93	148.16	28	4.0*
1435		15	7	41.4	59.81	148.27	16	(*)	1495		14	44	30.0	61.05	146.78	124‡	(*)
1436		15	46	58.5	60.70	147.76	20§	(*)	1496	JUNE 27	1	11	42.6	56.77	157.95	20‡	(*)
1437		16	9	32.3	59.93	147.80	109	2.7*	1497		2	39	18.9	62.37	150.14	20	(*)
1438		17	27	13.6	61.37	146.80	20§	(*)	1498		5	17	22.4	59.97	146.22	27	(*)
1439	JUNE 19	1	34	10.9	56.80	151.50	33	4.5	1499		5	55	30.2	62.67	146.68	20	(*)
1440		3	58	25.2	60.29	147.73	20§	3.1*	1500		6	13	49.0	63.35	149.80	20	(*)
1441		5	26	50.3	60.11	147.90	18	(*)	1501		7	22	9.3	61.27	150.27	16	(*)
1442		8	13	39.9	60.25	146.13	14	(*)	1502		12	24	20.7	58.51	151.71	120	4.0*
1443		21	52	41.2	60.10	148.67	25	(*)	1503		13	17	37.2	61.03	146.94	20§	(*)
1444	JUNE 20	0	51	20.8	60.19	148.64	20§	(*)	1504		15	48	28.8	60.28	147.63	20§	2.8*
1445		2	39	4.0	57.70	151.90	34	4.5	1505		18	39	34.0	60.96	146.81	20§	3.0*
1446		4	15	47.0	60.90	142.90	40	3.8	1506		19	49	34.2	60.96	147.97	20§	3.6*
1447		4	46	15.0	56.47	150.63	20§	(*)	1507		22	32	(**)				
1448		7	8	38.8	57.16	147.34	20§	(*)	1508		23	57	59.7	59.40	146.28	20§	2.4*
1449	JUNE 21	10	46	47.5	60.51	147.56	20§	(*)	1509	JUNE 28	4	41	46.1	61.76	150.44	20§	(*)
1450		21	58	40.2	59.75	147.45	20§	(*)	1510		4	46	23.9	60.16	147.65	20§	(*)
1451		22	58	30.6	59.97	146.27	7‡	(*)	1511		5	7	(**)				
1452	JUNE 22	2	15	4.2	60.29	147.09	20‡	(*)	1512		7	47	23.1	63.47	149.83	20§	(*)
1453		6	51	10.2	61.18	146.89	10‡	(*)	1513		10	18	(**)				
1454		8	32	2.1	62.10	148.50	33	4.1	1514		11	9	9.4	59.92	145.96	20§	3.8*
1455		11	18	31.6	63.11	148.91	10	(*)	1515		11	22	16.3	56.91	149.99	68	(*)
1456		12	11	9.4	60.00	146.70	33	4.0	1516		13	2	34.7	60.60	151.84	10§	(*)
1457		14	6	33.0	59.52	146.62	20‡	2.8*	1517		13	49	(**)				
1458		14	13	13.6	61.01	146.52	20	(*)	1518		19	2	34.8	60.45	146.36	20§	(*)
1459		15	8	42.9	60.92	148.30	34	3.5*	1519		19	9	5.4	58.30	150.20	25†	5.5
1460		15	29	15.8	61.01	146.58	10‡	3.3*	1520		19	53	5.3	60.11	146.28	20§	(*)
1461		16	33	42.3	60.51	145.59	20‡	2.5*	1521		19	56	25.1	59.10	153.10	33	4.4
1462		16	36	4.5	60.51	145.65	10	3.3*	1522		22	44	52.1	61.01	147.58	82	3.5*
1463		17	17	28.5	59.66	145.78	43	2.7*	1523	JUNE 29	1	1	42.4	60.86	146.90	41	(*)
1464		21	12	20.4	58.56	150.08	20†	(*)	1524		7	0	48.8	59.91	146.97	20§	(*)
1465	JUNE 23	0	24	27.6	59.94	146.09	20‡	3.4*	1525		7	6	45.3	57.82	148.54	73	(*)
1466		0	48	43.4	59.98	150.56	44‡	2.6*	1526		7	21	32.8	62.70	152.00	13†	5.6
1467		1	33	29.9	63.11	153.88	20‡	4.2*	1527		7	46	48.9	62.11	148.03	20§	3.7*
1468		5	52	10.8	60.60	150.44	20	2.5*	1528		7	49	12.8	57.94	142.16	53	(*)
1469		8	42	52.7	60.50	144.90	33	3.9	1529		10	42	46.1	56.70	151.40	22†	5.1
1470		9	27	53.6	59.77	146.60	20	(*)	1530		11	12	19.4	62.71	152.10	10§	(*)
1471		12	41	44.3	60.68	148.83	20	2.5*	1531		11	50	42.5	60.77	144.62	20§	(*)
1472		22	54	44.0	61.56	149.13	20‡	3.0*	1532		13	29	16.1	56.03	146.77	20§	(*)
1473	JUNE 24	1	59	49.6	61.01	148.81	20	2.6*	1533		19	4	49.9	61.00	143.70	16†	4.5
1474		9	29	47.0	59.83	148.17	20	(*)	1534		21	28	26.1	59.56	147.73	20§	(*)
1475		10	33	26.4	63.36	150.11	20‡	4.0*	1535		21	57	33.3	62.85	152.53	20§	(*)
1476		11	49	33.9	60.52	152.59	20‡	(*)	1536	JUNE 30	3	32	20.6	60.92	146.86	20§	3.9*
1477		11	57	16.6	61.04	148.20	8‡	(*)	1537		5	4	37.8	60.64	146.02	20§	(*)
1478		12	44	4.4	63.22	150.93	155	(*)	1538		5	46	53.3	59.10	154.00	17†	4.6
1479		13	25	12.8	60.30	147.69	20	(*)	1539		6	50	(**)				
1480		20	23	55.3	59.62	147.82	20	(*)	1540		13	57	(**)				

See footnotes at end of table.

TABLE 2.—*Summary of aftershock data*—Continued

Earthquake number	Date	Origin time Hr.	Min.	Sec.	Latitude N. °	Longitude W. °	Depth Km.	Magnitude	Earthquake number	Date	Origin time Hr.	Min.	Sec.	Latitude N. °	Longitude W. °	Depth Km.	Magnitude
	1964—Con.									*1964*—Con.							
1541	JUNE 30—	15	46	17.2	56.68	155.48	77	(*)	1601	JULY 8—	13	41	24.9	60.28	148.45	20§	3.2*
1542	Cont.	17	39	(**)					1602	Cont.	21	28	50.2	60.73	147.70	20§	3.4*
1543		20	14	45.9	58.82	149.14	20§	(*)	1603		23	50	45.2	60.90	142.80	33	4.1
1544	JULY 1	2	38	19.0	59.80	148.90	40	4.7	1604	JULY 9	0	21	17.7	59.80	150.70	15	4.3
1545		4	6	38.7	60.93	146.12	20§	(*)	1605		3	32	29.3	59.39	147.41	20§	3.4*
1546		6	5	33.7	58.90	151.70	20	4.6	1606		5	32	8.6	60.05	150.88	20§	3.4*
1547		8	48	58.8	62.59	157.55	20§	(*)	1607		6	3	9.1	60.50	147.53	20§	3.2*
1548	JULY 2	1	19	2.7	60.10	146.00	15†	5.1	1608		8	18	36.8	60.01	145.47	20§	(*)
1549		4	55	28.3	62.45	151.97	20§	(*)	1609		8	23	20.1	60.21	150.95	74	3.2*
1550		5	58	50.3	60.21	152.98	20§	(*)	1610		9	28	49.0	59.96	149.30	18	2.9*
1551		6	28	32.4	60.26	148.16	20‡	(*)	1611		10	50	34.8	60.63	147.11	10§	(*)
1552		7	46	53.0	55.54	143.69	20‡	(*)	1612		11	34	18.1	62.08	146.63	20§	(*)
1553		10	25	1.6	61.44	147.41	20	(*)	1613		15	12	51.5	62.18	148.55	28	(*)
1554		12	26	45.8	60.22	147.52	5	4.4*	1614		16	51	.3	56.85	146.78	10§	(*)
1555		16	30	(**)					1615		21	2	28.4	59.81	148.84	6	3.8*
1556		17	30	38.0	60.13	151.31	79	3.3*	1616		22	16	50.1	60.25	147.53	5§	3.2*
1557		17	50	42.3	57.72	152.96	20‡	(*)	1617	JULY 10	2	59	59.9	60.40	147.68	14	3.3*
1558		18	7	(**)					1618		4	40	41.3	61.82	148.89	20§	(*)
1559		22	42	52.2	60.78	147.52	28	3.7*	1619		7	23	10.4	55.60	154.10	33	3.9
1560	JULY 3	3	58	48.8	59.59	150.59	40	3.0*	1620		7	25	23.3	61.72	146.71	20§	(*)
1561		5	6	34.5	58.51	147.83	10‡	3.5*	1621		10	19	49.1	60.61	147.29	20§	3.4*
1562		5	29	5.0	60.59	147.25	20	(*)	1622		10	42	49.3	59.73	146.41	20§	(*)
1563		6	3	29.4	59.70	145.70	20‡	(*)	1623		13	28	45.3	60.43	147.11	20§	3.4*
1564		9	24	59.2	58.68	149.91	20	3.8*	1624		19	27	10.5	59.75	148.58	15	3.8*
1565		11	0	37.1	59.64	145.06	20‡	(*)	1625		20	32	3.1	57.69	150.21	20§	(*)
1566		13	29	10.0	60.89	145.68	20	(*)	1626	JULY 11	4	45	17.9	59.96	146.53	20§	3.1*
1567		14	4	32.7	60.74	147.22	20‡	(*)	1627		5	50	42.2	60.76	147.01	20§	(*)
1568		14	15	24.4	59.65	146.37	20	(*)	1628		6	28	15.6	62.71	149.18	20§	(*)
1569		18	11	57.3	59.38	152.88	20‡	(*)	1629		9	44	18.7	59.70	146.10	28‡	5.3
1570		23	39	22.6	60.05	145.76	20	(*)	1630		20	25	40.3	59.70	146.20	40	5.6
1571	JULY 4	8	17	57.9	60.91	146.62	20‡	(*)	1631		21	5	49.9	59.70	146.50	14†	4.9
1572		12	14	3.8	60.35	147.04	31‡	3.6*	1632		22	40	10.2	60.11	145.19	20§	(*)
1573		12	33	25.7	60.55	147.52	20‡	3.4*	1633	JULY 12	0	53	38.9	60.12	146.40	20§	(*)
1574		12	52	56.3	58.65	151.50	20	(*)	1634		1	39	18.2	59.57	147.45	20§	3.0*
1575		13	8	41.0	58.90	148.10	33	3.5	1635		7	1	50.4	61.74	149.83	12	(*)
1576		23	50	38.9	60.44	148.57	18‡	4.0*	1636		9	0	39.9	60.10	146.10	33	3.8
1577	JULY 5	0	53	52.3	61.49	149.69	39	4.0*	1637		10	27	3.5	59.96	146.85	17	3.6*
1578		3	14	33.3	60.80	144.90	12‡	4.9	1638		12	31	39.7	60.18	145.55	29	4.0*
1579		3	43	1.6	59.68	147.83	20‡	(*)	1639		13	30	8.0	61.47	146.64	20§	(*)
1580		4	44	29.6	59.80	150.78	77	3.6*	1640		17	6	31.6	61.46	146.50	13	(*)
1581		5	16	51.8	60.17	152.67	15	3.6*	1641		18	57	47.4	59.88	144.22	5§	3.2*
1582		6	45	11.3	60.90	145.84	20	(*)	1642		21	6	5.4	61.78	151.19	20§	(*)
1583		7	46	32.1	60.62	147.28	22‡	3.3*	1643		21	23	43.4	59.31	146.83	20§	2.9*
1584		9	9	34.3	60.77	147.14	47	4.2*	1644		21	27	56.4	62.97	148.42	20§	(*)
1585		9	48	51.8	60.26	149.12	10	2.5*	1645		21	56	15.6	61.02	146.60	20§	(*)
1586		15	23	51.7	59.79	147.20	10	4.0*	1646		21	58	40.4	59.96	146.19	10§	3.2*
1587		17	58	59.7	60.20	146.20	20‡	4.9	1647	JULY 13	0	3	40.1	61.12	147.32	20§	3.5*
1588		20	54	48.8	61.14	146.96	48‡	3.6*	1648		2	33	49.3	60.73	146.74	20§	(*)
1589		23	41	51.6	61.85	159.77	20‡	(*)	1649		2	59	51.6	60.52	147.08	20§	(*)
1590	JULY 6	2	22	1.7	60.15	146.71	20‡	(*)	1650		3	25	32.2	60.74	145.79	20§	3.9*
1591		3	20	59.4	56.70	152.30	16†	4.8	1651		11	41	47.1	59.63	149.16	28	3.7*
1592		13	46	11.9	59.68	147.40	20‡	3.7*	1652		15	52	4.8	56.60	154.00	27†	4.8
1593		16	23	28.6	60.65	147.10	20	3.6*	1653		16	2	47.2	62.43	145.48	20‡	4.3*
1594		23	9	8.7	57.77	152.49	20‡	(*)	1654		18	27	-5.8	60.87	147.58	20‡	(*)
1595	JULY 7	2	15	29.7	59.97	148.41	20	2.9*	1655		21	41	2.6	55.20	156.50	33	4.1
1596		3	57	59.2	62.64	149.97	20‡	4.4*	1656	JULY 14	3	1	54.9	60.98	147.21	20	(*)
1597		7	35	39.8	60.05	145.22	20	3.9*	1657		3	40	32.4	60.44	145.15	20	(*)
1598		13	49	12.2	59.53	148.31	20‡	(*)	1658		4	16	41.5	60.20	148.75	20	(*)
1599		19	58	35.1	60.43	147.87	20	3.5*	1659		5	22	20.0	60.40	142.90	10	4.8
1600	JULY 8	10	32	32.3	58.66	147.35	13	3.5*	1660		12	42	59.4	59.90	146.50	24‡	2.7*

See footnotes at end of table.

TABLE 2.—*Summary of aftershock data*—Continued

Earthquake number	Date		Origin time			Latitude N.	Longitude W.	Depth	Magnitude	Earthquake number	Date		Origin time			Latitude N.	Longitude W.	Depth	Magnitude
			Hr.	Min.	Sec.	°	°	Km.					Hr.	Min.	Sec.	°	°	Km.	
	1964—Con.										*1964*—Con.								
1661	JULY	14	22	59	9.2	59.50	144.80	10‡	5.1	1721	JULY	24	2	7	42.5	60.19	152.45	20§	3.8*
1662	JULY	15	0	14	40.2	60.27	146.63	26	(*)	1722			4	52	49.0	61.08	145.79	20§	3.0*
1663			4	18	33.9	61.11	148.36	20‡	(*)	1723			4	59	46.1	60.07	148.02	6	3.1*
1664			6	37	13.1	61.19	148.06	5	(*)	1724			5	48	15.4	60.79	154.01	15	4.8*
1665			6	44	8.1	59.78	145.06	71‡	3.4*	1725			7	6	48.4	60.53	145.42	46	3.4*
1666	JULY	16	2	10	22.3	61.66	148.19	20	(*)	1726			7	35	48.4	56.30	157.80	13†	5.2
1667			4	40	2.2	61.34	148.39	20‡	(*)	1727			8	17	30.8	62.15	164.97	20§	(*)
1668			8	2	3.9	61.61	148.23	5	(*)	1728			13	40	45.3	60.30	148.30	35	3.9
1669			11	28	31.9	61.34	146.66	25‡	3.6*	1729			13	58	29.4	60.44	145.28	20§	(*)
1670			14	12	48.3	60.89	147.25	46	3.4*	1730			15	17	40.9	60.46	151.63	20§	3.5*
1671	JULY	17	2	45	44.3	63.62	148.39	20	(*)	1731			17	44	44.4	62.61	147.57	20§	(*)
1672			2	59	45.3	62.73	152.32	7	4.4*	1732			18	14	35.4	57.90	152.87	5§	4.4*
1673			5	49	44.0	60.40	147.14	70	3.6*	1733			19	6	54.3	60.00	146.20	33	3.9
1674			7	28	4.8	60.06	145.62	31‡	2.7*	1734			21	53	48.9	61.25	149.58	9	3.8*
1675			8	10	3.0	60.13	145.59	20	(*)	1735			21	54	54.0	57.70	152.20	28‡	5.2
1676			11	11	(**)					1736			23	33	24.2	59.60	146.54	21	3.4*
1677			15	39	32.1	60.82	147.05	20	3.0*	1737	JULY	25	4	41	57.6	60.76	146.52	20§	(*)
1678			17	28	55.6	60.41	145.83	20	4.1*	1738			5	20	52.7	59.75	146.54	23	4.1*
1679			18	1	22.6	60.46	147.91	20‡	3.6*	1739			6	26	9.2	59.62	145.84	28§	3.2*
1680			18	39	45.9	57.10	150.90	33	4.2	1740			6	28	3.1	60.80	149.02	20§	3.3*
1681			19	58	8.4	59.79	146.93	23‡	3.6*	1741			7	32	31.1	59.80	147.65	39	2.8*
1682	JULY	18	3	13	3.2	62.19	146.39	20	(*)	1742			10	58	18.3	61.02	147.65	20§	3.1*
1683			7	45	57.6	61.03	148.90	20	(*)	1743			11	21	13.5	61.21	147.75	20§	(*)
1684			9	39	21.5	60.85	150.23	20	3.5*	1744			15	16	58.1	62.72	147.53	20§	(*)
1685			12	57	30.7	62.57	155.13	20‡	(*)	1745			15	20	33.8	59.77	147.40	36	3.5*
1686			23	36	21.0	60.00	143.40	22†	4.9	1746			17	28	34.4	61.54	149.11	20§	(*)
1687	JULY	19	2	14	11.9	60.85	147.39	23‡	3.4*	1747			22	29	31.1	60.93	147.39	20§	(*)
1688			7	1	49.4	62.09	149.62	20‡	(*)	1748	JULY	26	7	15	34.3	61.63	148.18	20§	4.1*
1689			12	50	(**)					1749			7	21	21.8	61.15	147.43	33	3.4*
1690			13	6	51.6	60.48	147.81	20‡	3.5*	1750			8	10	7.4	59.76	149.21	20§	3.0*
1691			17	45	48.6	60.73	147.58	32	3.4*	1751			9	16	39.4	60.76	142.50	20	3.5*
1692			23	16	28.6	61.57	151.66	83	4.0*	1752			9	34	50.7	59.93	146.50	12	2.8*
1693			23	22	4.5	60.28	147.32	20	4.1*	1753			10	9	(**)				
1694	JULY	20	1	7	10.1	59.85	151.85	20	3.3*	1754			11	20	19.3	59.88	147.59	22	3.2*
1695			6	40	36.0	60.08	143.46	20	3.1*	1755			11	47	49.6	57.85	149.92	20	(*)
1696			7	15	22.8	60.98	143.81	20	3.6*	1756			13	54	14.6	59.50	145.37	69	3.2*
1697			7	41	10.3	59.69	147.63	42	3.2*	1757			15	58	57.7	61.41	147.10	20‡	(*)
1698			9	58	22.8	60.54	144.97	92	3.0*	1758			18	36	2.5	60.20	147.00	52	3.8
1699			11	1	1.0	59.74	143.44	20	3.3*	1759			18	39	37.0	60.03	146.76	20‡	2.7*
1700			15	22	37.3	60.20	151.79	20	3.6*	1760			19	33	4.1	59.75	146.41	22	3.6*
1701			15	45	18.0	61.35	147.61	30§	3.8*	1761	JULY	27	4	13	9.7	60.87	148.49	20	(*)
1702			16	16	16.5	59.26	151.33	20§	3.4*	1762			5	31	29.4	60.00	146.96	20	3.5*
1703			18	58	12.5	62.53	147.80	20§	(*)	1763			15	30	16.8	59.37	148.35	10‡	3.9*
1704			21	28	23.3	59.95	148.84	20§	2.7*	1764			15	41	3.7	59.87	148.25	74‡	2.8*
1705	JULY	21	13	56	58.4	60.19	146.79	20§	3.9*	1765			15	53	23.6	63.40	148.50	115	4.2
1706			14	36	9.9	59.83	148.17	20§	3.0*	1766			16	9	22.1	60.37	147.82	43‡	4.3*
1707			16	57	12.0	61.32	147.38	13	4.0*	1767			22	35	5.8	60.00	148.24	105‡	2.9*
1708	JULY	22	12	15	15.8	62.71	146.65	74	(*)	1768			23	20	56.2	60.90	148.00	33	4.2
1709			17	51	14.8	59.70	153.40	33	(*)	1769	JULY	28	6	59	.3	61.20	149.04	20‡	4.0*
1710			21	11	59.7	60.24	145.20	20§	2.9*	1770			8	4	36.5	60.61	150.70	5	3.4*
1711			22	40	51.8	61.07	147.29	20§	(*)	1771			9	47	.4	59.90	146.22	26	3.6*
1712			23	36	35.8	63.05	150.96	20§	(*)	1772			10	19	51.3	59.90	146.46	20	2.7*
1713	JULY	23	7	11	28.5	60.70	147.90	9	3.9	1773			12	50	34.3	60.92	147.88	20‡	(*)
1714			10	23	19.7	59.86	148.32	23	3.1*	1774			22	19	50.7	61.01	147.79	20‡	(*)
1715			12	59	39.7	58.59	151.35	10§	3.6*	1775	JULY	29	3	4	9.3	56.26	150.88	20‡	(*)
1716			14	19	1.1	57.10	150.40	10†	5.1	1776			4	0	43.0	60.50	146.84	12‡	·(*)
1717			15	56	27.6	59.70	145.80	20	4.7	1777			16	56	36.8	59.81	148.59	20	3.1*
1718			19	8	6.6	59.90	149.20	21†	5.4	1778	JULY	30	5	26	24.7	62.78	146.98	20‡	(*)
1719			22	35	49.0	60.12	146.04	23	3.3*	1779			16	53	18.2	61.40	145.50	25	4.0
1720			23	56	12.4	60.89	143.85	20§	3.7*	1780	JULY	31	2	21	36.2	60.25	146.78	10	3.9*

See footnotes at end of table.

TABLE 2.—*Summary of aftershock data*—Continued

Earthquake number	Date	Hr.	Min.	Sec.	Latitude N. °	Longitude W. °	Depth Km.	Magnitude	Earthquake number	Date	Hr.	Min.	Sec.	Latitude N. °	Longitude W. °	Depth Km.	Magnitude
	1964—Con.									1964—Con.							
1781	JULY 31—	2	24	39.2	63.57	148.87	20	(*)	1841	SEPT. 25	4	55	21.6	57.50	144.50	33	4.5
1782	Cont.	4	11	7.4	61.10	140.30	20	(*)	1842		16	32	22.7	56.70	152.80	33	4.1
1783		9	12	25.6	58.88	146.32	58‡	3.1*	1843	SEPT. 27	15	50	54.7	56.60	152.00	13†	5.4
1784		9	25	51.6	59.70	145.00	33	4.4	1844	SEPT. 28	18	30	20.2	61.00	147.40	89	4.5
1785		9	55	58.1	60.56	145.89	10‡	3.2*	1845	SEPT. 29	2	0	1.7	57.80	149.50	44	3.8
1786		11	4	38.8	59.80	146.19	20‡	3.5*	1846	SEPT. 30	20	27	24.1	58.40	151.30	17	5.1
1787		15	10	44.9	61.93	146.24	20		1847	OCT. 2	22	23	32.4	59.70	144.50	15†	5.2
1788	AUG. 2	3	4	16.9	56.10	156.10	27†	5.6	1848	OCT. 3	13	39	39.9	61.40	147.10	23‡	5.2
1789		6	13	6.7	59.80	146.10	28	3.8	1849		15	5	19.5	59.10	153.20	60	4.1
1790		8	36	16.9	56.20	149.90	28†	5.4	1850	OCT. 6	1	37	20.5	56.50	152.70	33	4.4
1791		15	33	31.1	56.50	149.50	33	4.2	1851		20	5	36.7	59.00	148.80	33	
1792	AUG. 3	2	32	14.6	60.00	148.00	18	4.2	1852	OCT. 9	9	11	53.6	60.00	143.70	33	4.0
1793		6	11	37.8	60.20	144.60	20	4.1	1853		14	56	47.6	59.60	143.90	29	3.8
1794		16	56	18.2	56.70	152.40	20	4.1	1854		19	55	34.7	57.00	151.90	28‡	5.1
1795	AUG. 4	5	44	5.6	56.90	151.00	33	3.8	1855		22	7	12.9	59.50	144.40	16	4.5
1796	AUG. 6	7	5	48.6	56.30	149.80	33	4.5	1856	OCT. 10	19	38	47.7	60.40	146.10	15†	5.3
1797		13	11	31.1	60.40	145.80	33	4.0	1857		20	6	39.8	60.50	145.40	15†	5.4
1798		18	24	50.5	56.90	152.10	18†	5.6	1858	OCT. 11	22	1	46.2	57.40	150.20	31†	4.6
1799	AUG. 7	5	37	25.1	56.80	152.30	19†	5.2	1859	OCT. 12	6	6	8.0	56.60	152.60	33	4.6
1800	AUG. 8	9	48	35.6	56.70	152.40	33	5.1	1860	OCT. 13	14	0	12.3	58.50	151.40	33	4.9
1801		11	33	25.5	60.70	145.40	33	3.8	1861	OCT. 15	22	59	43.6	56.80	151.90	21†	5.2
1802	AUG. 10	1	7	44.1	59.80	151.80	33	4.2	1862		23	9	25.1	56.90	151.70	13†	5.3
1803	AUG. 13	8	38	11.4	59.70	145.30	33	4.2	1863	OCT. 16	4	6	30.7	57.10	151.00	33	4.2
1804	AUG. 16	2	57	5.6	61.60	150.20	63	4.1	1864	OCT. 17	2	0	3.3	59.50	145.50	11†	5.2
1805		12	38	20.6	62.10	147.30	56	4.1	1865	OCT. 18	15	58	10.5	59.10	148.20	33	4.8
1806	AUG. 20	14	3	34.4	61.40	147.50	34†	4.3	1866		21	45	10.4	60.30	152.30	96	4.1
1807	AUG. 21	6	24	16.3	55.00	158.20	33	4.4	1867	OCT. 19	1	30	18.4	59.20	151.20	33	4.5
1808	AUG. 24	1	36	23.7	61.20	146.80	47	4.0	1868		16	29	49.1	59.70	148.70	53	4.6
1809		5	48	13.3	60.00	147.30	33	3.8	1869	OCT. 20	6	24	11.9	56.90	152.60	48	4.1
1810		21	56	54.2	58.40	150.30	22†	5.8	1870	OCT. 21	14	32	57.6	58.50	151.90	33	5.6
1811	AUG. 26	17	22	55.3	60.90	147.90	33	3.9	1871	OCT. 24	7	51	30.7	60.90	146.70	33	3.7
1812		23	45	4.5	57.30	152.70	26‡	4.9	1872	OCT. 26	14	32	49.3	56.80	152.30	14†	5.0
1813	AUG. 27	10	31	59.7	63.60	148.20	106	4.2	1873	OCT. 27	12	44	27.3	57.70	152.10	33	3.9
1814		22	41	53.0	60.90	152.80	33	3.7	1874		19	3	14.9	59.60	144.40	33	4.7
1815	AUG. 29	4	8	3.2	57.80	156.00	15†	4.8	1875	OCT. 28	8	17	20.5	60.80	146.90	33	3.8
1816	AUG. 31	19	36	37.6	59.50	145.90	33	4.6	1876	OCT. 30	17	13	13.8	56.60	152.20	10†	5.1
1817		23	55	22.6	58.50	154.80	12†	5.2	1877		20	4	41.1	59.20	152.60	33	4.1
1818	SEPT. 3	2	45	7.2	59.50	144.80	19	4.2	1878	NOV. 3	9	14	40.1	57.00	150.90	33	4.2
1819		12	32	.6	59.40	145.20	35	4.4	1879	NOV. 4	4	44	34.9	58.80	151.60	34	4.6
1820		18	59	6.8	59.80	149.70	33	4.1	1880	NOV. 6	12	18	42.1	59.70	148.90	33	4.2
1821		21	4	13.3	59.70	144.00	21†	4.5	1881	NOV. 10	5	3	44.8	60.10	143.50	40	4.6
1822	SEPT. 6	15	58	15.4	58.70	151.40	12†	5.8	1882		6	7	49.6	59.80	144.30	42	5.0
1823		17	16	54.6	59.10	147.40	32†	5.1	1883	NOV. 11	8	1	26.1	59.40	144.60	10	5.2
1824		17	36	44.3	63.10	147.70	30†	4.8	1884	NOV. 14	10	42	14.9	60.20	149.40	47	3.7
1825	SEPT. 7	7	7	55.4	57.70	151.50	33	4.0	1885	NOV. 20	4	50	55.3	59.60	148.20	33	4.9
1826		7	12	2.3	58.30	152.00	18‡	5.1	1886		21	27	39.5	63.70	146.50	80	4.6
1827	SEPT. 8	2	43	17.1	60.10	146.90	34†	3.5	1887	NOV. 23	13	15	1.7	63.50	157.00	33	4.3
1828	SEPT. 9	2	41	46.1	58.90	154.50	33		1888	NOV. 26	16	36	50.6	58.70	152.00	33	5.4
1829		3	36	43.4	58.90	152.80	33	4.6	1889	NOV. 27	7	47	7.6	62.60	151.50	113	5.4
1830	SEPT. 11	0	26	29.9	60.30	146.60	18†	4.7	1890	DEC. 2	9	34	25.7	60.40	153.90	33	
1831	SEPT. 13	17	44	10.2	61.40	149.80	33	3.9	1891	DEC. 5	19	50	1.6	59.40	144.80	33	4.7
1832		19	40	44.4	58.80	154.90	83	4.7	1892	DEC. 9	7	21	18.1	60.80	144.20	33	4.0
1833	SEPT. 14	10	17	46.6	56.70	157.40	13†	5.7	1893	DEC. 11	11	18	23.0	60.10	146.60	33	4.0
1834	SEPT. 16	1	50	33.9	60.00	147.10	14†	5.5	1894	DEC. 18	2	29	10.4	60.70	147.40	33	3.8
1835		22	22	18.0	59.60	146.70	33	4.3	1895	DEC. 21	17	36	29.0	60.50	146.80	43	5.0
1836	SEPT. 17	2	6	26.8	59.10	148.30	33	4.2	1896		18	32	3.0	63.10	150.30	111	4.8
1837	SEPT. 18	19	9	3.9	58.30	151.80	20†	4.7	1897	DEC. 26	23	50	23.8	59.30	152.90	35	
1838	SEPT. 23	16	37	19.1	61.60	150.00	33	4.1	1898	DEC. 29	2	7	3.4	59.60	145.30	33	4.6
1839	SEPT. 24	2	39	38.2	56.50	157.00	33	4.3	1899	DEC. 31	3	14	25.9	60.00	147.00	58	4.1
1840		9	34	26.5	60.90	143.70	7	4.0									

See footnotes at end of table.

Prince William Sound Earthquake of 1964

TABLE 2.—*Summary of aftershock data*—Continued

Earthquake number	Date	Origin time Hr.	Min.	Sec.	Latitude N. °	Longitude W. °	Depth Km.	Magnitude
	1965							
1900	JAN. 1	20	2	38.0	61.70	148.90	33	4.3
1901		23	13	50.4	60.20	151.20	93	5.6
1902	JAN. 4	3	41	22.9	59.90	153.60	122	5.4
1903	JAN. 6	18	27	34.0	60.00	151.80	53	5.2
1904	JAN. 8	10	23	17.1	56.70	152.20	33	4.3
1905		10	31	38.1	56.70	152.50	33	4.3
1906		11	25	56.6	56.30	153.50	33	4.5
1907	JAN. 9	0	19	39.8	57.60	150.50	22	4.2
1908	JAN. 10	13	17	47.8	58.70	157.10	33	4.6
1909	JAN. 11	0	37	19.1	58.60	151.40	33	
1910		16	57	27.0	61.10	151.00	59	5.4
1911		19	25	38.5	60.30	146.00	33	3.9
1912	JAN. 12	12	49	36.0	60.30	147.80	33	4.1
1913	JAN. 17	0	58	28.8	56.90	151.70	33	4.4
1914		2	13	28.6	58.30	151.80	33	5.3
1915	JAN. 20	16	42	50.9	60.00	146.80	33	4.4
1916	JAN. 26	1	19	18.9	61.40	152.40	135	4.1
1917	JAN. 31	3	9	17.2	60.30	147.80	33	4.5
1918		11	5	1.4	60.20	146.10	33	4.3
1919	FEB. 2	16	36	30.5	60.70	154.30	10	4.5
1920	FEB. 15	11	22	35.4	56.70	152.40	33	4.9
1921	FEB. 17	4	1	35.5	57.10	153.40	20	4.9
1922		4	53	6.0	57.10	152.90	33	4.5
1923		11	6	29.9	59.70	151.70	33	3.8
1924	FEB. 18	19	30	19.9	59.20	147.50	30	5.3
1925	FEB. 24	1	13	1.1	60.10	149.60	30	4.8
1926	FEB. 25	2	2	37.4	61.20	146.70	40	4.5
1927	MAR. 1	13	56	7.4	61.70	147.70	43	4.0
1928	MAR. 6	3	32	29.5	56.80	154.40	30	4.8
1929	MAR. 8	12	4	21.0	62.50	150.40	104	4.5
1930		22	14	34.1	59.60	145.30	33	4.1
1931	MAR. 10	20	29	34.5	62.50	147.30	85	4.8
1932		21	52	57.6	56.30	155.60	33	5.0
1933	MAR. 11	1	44	25.0	56.10	156.80	33	4.4
1934	MAR. 12	6	51	40.0	55.70	155.60	16	4.6
1935	MAR. 15	12	35	29.8	55.90	154.60	23	4.3
1936		12	38	52.1	55.70	154.50	18	4.7
1937	MAR. 18	16	49	59.0	59.70	155.90	33	4.8
1938	MAR. 22	10	58	20.1	56.50	152.80	33	4.0
1939	MAR. 24	7	7	45.4	56.60	152.40	20	5.1
1940		7	36	46.6	56.60	152.00	20	5.1
1941		8	8	5.2	56.60	152.40	30	5.2
1942		13	30	4.5	57.80	148.60	13	5.0
1943	MAR. 26	1	41	57.4	59.60	145.10	33	4.5
1944	APR. 3	7	51	45.6	57.30	152.40	33	4.0
1945	APR. 9	1	28	48.2	57.60	151.40	33	4.6
1946		17	33	45.3	59.60	144.90	52	4.8
1947	APR. 12	3	59	40.2	56.60	152.70	33	5.3
1948	APR. 14	7	35	39.4	56.30	153.50	27	5.0
1949	APR. 18	20	35	51.8	57.30	157.80	33	4.5
1950	APR. 19	7	15	54.4	62.10	150.20	83	4.1
1951		8	52	51.8	60.60	141.30	33	3.8
1952		11	24	10.0	60.30	146.40	8	3.7
1953	APR. 24	10	20	50.2	58.60	153.20	58	4.7
1954	APR. 26	1	57	14.4	58.90	142.70	33	5.3
1955		6	31	36.9	57.90	151.90	33	4.0
1956	APR. 27	11	41	37.3	57.90	152.20	25	
1957	APR. 28	3	17	16.2	61.10	146.70	33	3.8
1958		9	40	19.2	58.60	143.30	5	4.9
1959	APR. 29	13	32	18.3	57.40	151.10	33	4.8
1960	MAY 1	1	58	2.9	60.40	145.90	13	4.6
	1965—Con.							
1961		21	27	54.4	60.40	146.00	33	5.3
1962	MAY 5	9	17	24.5	61.00	145.10	45	4.0
1963	MAY 9	10	59	51.3	56.20	148.60	33	4.0
1964		22	12	12.7	56.60	152.80	33	4.4
1965	MAY 11	17	37	38.3	61.40	149.60	58	5.5
1966	MAY 16	9	15	18.6	60.50	146.10	29	4.0
1967	MAY 19	5	24	47.6	60.90	155.70	33	4.1
1968	MAY 20	12	1	49.2	61.00	150.20	166	3.9
1969		22	51	45.1	59.80	152.60	96	4.3
1970	MAY 21	6	41	10.3	59.40	153.40	73	3.8
1971	MAY 31	10	52	55.3	56.90	154.50	33	4.2
1972		20	20	14.6	60.40	146.90	33	3.9
1973		23	27	10.4	57.40	152.70	33	4.1
1974	JUNE 2	0	43	4.3	62.10	151.40	24	4.5
1975	JUNE 4	13	16	39.3	61.70	146.20	45	3.8
1976	JUNE 23	11	9	15.7	56.50	152.80	33	5.7
1977		12	2	47.2	56.80	152.60	33	4.8
1978		12	23	23.9	56.50	152.70	33	4.7
1979		12	41	42.0	56.40	155.40	33	4.2
1980		14	22	44.9	56.40	152.80	47	4.8
1981	JUNE 24	1	45	50.7	58.70	151.40	33	3.9
1982		5	51	17.5	59.60	157.10	33	4.7
1983	JUNE 25	7	47	26.8	59.60	144.60	31	4.2
1984	JUNE 26	23	13	42.4	62.80	149.10	75	4.8
1985	JUNE 27	11	8	56.7	60.30	140.90	12	5.3
1986		11	24	49.1	60.30	140.90	28	4.8
1987		15	45	43.1	60.20	140.90	33	4.3
1988	JUNE 28	0	16	52.1	61.00	145.80	33	3.8
1989	JULY 1	19	54	46.9	56.50	152.50	33	4.1
1990	JULY 6	1	12	47.6	59.90	149.30	44	3.9
1991	JULY 11	6	12	7.1	56.60	152.20	33	4.7
1992		7	12	58.5	58.00	151.40	7	5.1
1993	JULY 14	2	29	29.4	57.10	146.80	33	4.5
1994	JULY 15	5	45	3.5	61.80	148.80	64	3.8
1995	JULY 18	9	41	25.8	56.90	151.10	33	4.3
1996	JULY 20	16	57	.2	62.00	147.00	33	4.0
1997	JULY 21	9	8	12.3	59.10	153.90	53	4.5
1998	JULY 26	16	50	11.1	61.30	151.90	60	3.8
1999	JULY 28	14	26	20.0	59.00	153.80	34	4.5
2000	JULY 31	11	16	3.5	56.20	153.40	20	4.9
2001	AUG. 1	5	31	11.6	56.10	154.20	39	4.5
2002	AUG. 2	7	26	59.6	59.60	145.50	43	4.0
2003		8	45	29.7	62.00	156.90	33	4.6
2004	AUG. 3	9	13	48.9	56.60	159.70	47	5.1
2005	AUG. 6	12	46	18.8	61.90	148.20	33	3.9
2006	AUG. 7	21	14	43.6	61.90	151.00	80	4.8
2007	AUG. 8	11	28	21.9	61.20	149.30	86	4.1
2008	AUG. 11	18	29	38.2	59.50	146.10	16	5.5
2009	AUG. 13	15	19	17.2	61.20	151.40	92	4.2
2010	AUG. 18	4	49	52.6	61.30	146.00	33	3.8
2011		14	0	34.7	57.70	152.10	33	4.6
2012	AUG. 24	13	12	21.1	59.40	145.80	33	5.3
2013	AUG. 26	5	0	46.2	60.90	149.50	33	3.8
2014	AUG. 27	14	53	1.8	59.60	145.10	39	3.8
2015	SEPT. 4	14	32	46.7	58.20	152.70	10	6.7
2016	SEPT. 7	12	57	55.0	61.70	147.50	33	3.7
2017	SEPT. 8	3	26	20.8	57.50	152.20	25	5.6
2018		11	16	32.0	55.80	155.03	14	5.5
2019	SEPT. 9	7	38	26.4	60.10	153.20	104	3.9
2020	SEPT. 12	6	3	30.0	60.70	147.70	33	4.3

See footnotes at end of table.

TABLE 2.—*Summary of aftershock data*—Continued

Earthquake number	Date	Origin time Hr.	Min.	Sec.	Latitude N. °	Longitude W. °	Depth Km.	Magnitude
	1965—Con.							
2021	SEPT. 12	9	15	38.4	55.40	150.90	33	4.0
2022	SEPT. 16	15	3	18.3	57.60	152.00	33	4.5
2023	SEPT. 18	20	46	36.5	59.40	145.20	5	5.3
2024		23	33	18.2	59.60	144.60	33	4.3
2025	SEPT. 23	7	17	17.5	59.80	152.30	57	3.9
2026	SEPT. 30	23	47	39.9	59.70	143.40	12	5.0
2027	OCT. 6	17	57	2.8	59.50	148.80	44	3.9
2028	OCT. 12	8	16	23.1	59.50	144.60	4	4.8
2029		13	40	59.4	56.10	153.60	29	5.5
2030		14	23	37.2	56.50	152.90	33	4.3
2031		14	58	14.4	56.20	153.90	24	4.2
2032	OCT. 13	16	25	38.0	56.70	151.60	33	4.0
2033	OCT. 15	4	58	30.6	55.60	155.60	33	3.8
2034		11	31	55.9	57.10	151.40	33	4.7
2035	OCT. 27	12	47	28.3	61.00	146.50	7	4.0
2036	OCT. 28	23	8	19.2	58.60	151.60	33	4.1
2037	NOV. 2	9	10	40.2	57.00	152.80	27	5.0
2038	NOV. 4	10	38	23.1	57.40	151.20	42	4.6
2039	NOV. 6	6	38	39.3	60.70	147.30	21	5.2
2040	NOV. 13	10	43	47.6	56.50	152.90	9	5.2
2041	NOV. 15	2	13	48.5	57.20	157.10	41	4.6
2042	NOV. 18	15	39	47.3	62.60	150.10	33	3.9
2043	NOV. 25	6	30	53.8	59.50	154.70	14	4.0
2044	DEC. 2	15	58	10.5	59.60	153.30	68	4.2
2045	DEC. 6	21	50	28.8	57.70	154.10	95	4.8
2046	DEC. 8	7	37	28.9	56.60	157.40	46	4.2
2047	DEC. 9	22	48	25.5	60.20	146.90	33	4.0
2048	DEC. 20	13	47	49.7	56.70	158.50	129	4.2
2049	DEC. 21	14	48	31.6	56.80	155.10	12	4.3
2050	DEC. 22	19	41	23.1	58.40	153.10	51	6.7
2051		2	14	50.0	58.60	155.40	114	4.4
2052		20	47	35.5	60.60	140.70	11	5.8
2053	DEC. 24	16	10	1.1	62.40	149.70	95	4.2
2054	DEC. 25	10	34	22.3	62.60	149.20	165	
2055	DEC. 30	16	33	43.8	58.20	152.40	33	5.3
	1966							
2056	JAN. 1	8	41	54.7	57.50	153.70	42	4.3
2057	JAN. 5	11	0	5.9	62.60	149.60	131	3.6
2058	JAN. 6	5	58	1.9	60.20	146.50	33	4.0
2059		12	16	6.8	60.40	146.90	62	3.8
2060	JAN. 8	20	30	14.2	56.70	156.50	33	4.4
2061	JAN. 10	6	1	22.5	62.70	148.90	57	3.7
2062	JAN. 15	11	59	58.9	59.50	144.60	33	5.3
2063		16	8	2.4	59.50	144.60	30	4.4
2064	JAN. 18	21	28	51.5	61.40	151.90	80	4.1
2065		21	46	1.5	61.50	150.70	69	4.1
2066	JAN. 22	11	27	7.9	56.00	153.70	33	5.8
2067		22	7	33.9	62.10	141.30	33	4.7
2068	JAN. 24	11	41	25.1	62.60	151.60	41	4.2
2069	JAN. 27	6	20	57.0	57.70	152.00	33	4.1
2070	FEB. 6	23	28	7.8	60.40	152.30	91	5.3
2071	FEB. 8	19	50	2.8	60.40	140.80	13	4.0
2072	FEB. 10	12	38	49.1	56.60	153.30	12	4.5
2073	FEB. 16	21	52	22.7	58.10	152.20	63	3.9
2074	FEB. 20	2	8	40.4	60.80	152.20	105	4.4
2075	FEB. 22	4	36	3.9	60.20	152.90	104	
2076		7	48	8.1	62.40	147.10	73	4.0
2077	FEB. 24	19	53	15.4	60.10	147.70	25	5.0
2078	FEB. 28	18	41	21.5	56.60	152.90	33	3.9
2079	MAR. 3	17	37	3.7	61.40	150.60	53	4.0
2080	MAR. 4	14	19	26.8	57.00	153.40	6	4.6
	1966—Con.							
2081	MAR. 7	20	21	31.3	56.80	151.30	22	4.8
2082	MAR. 18	18	11	7.5	60.40	146.40	17	5.0
2083	MAR. 19	6	10	48.8	57.80	152.90	13	4.6
2084		9	33	43.8	62.40	151.20	86	4.3
2085	MAR. 22	10	28	59.9	61.20	151.60	103	4.2
2086	MAR. 23	7	15	7.6	57.90	149.60	33	
2087	MAR. 25	1	15	11.8	62.60	151.00	106	4.4
2088	MAR. 27	15	44	46.3	60.50	146.10	33	4.0
2089	APR. 1	0	57	27.4	59.80	145.70	33	3.7
2090	APR. 5	14	10	53.3	61.60	148.00	107	3.6
2091	APR. 6	22	28	38.7	56.60	154.50	33	5.5
2092	APR. 8	9	19	9.6	56.90	152.00	33	4.7
2093		12	27	24.5	56.70	152.10	33	4.0
2094		22	10	59.3	56.80	151.90	33	5.1
2095		22	33	50.5	56.70	152.10	33	4.6
2096		22	37	6.3	56.70	152.20	33	4.7
2097	APR. 9	7	16	16.1	56.80	152.10	33	4.5
2098		8	48	15.2	56.70	152.40	33	4.4
2099		18	51	45.0	60.20	147.10	34	4.7
2100		20	8	38.6	56.70	152.00	33	5.5
2101		20	17	44.5	56.60	152.20	33	5.1
2102	APR. 11	18	26	11.8	57.20	153.50	33	4.9
2103		23	0	24.0	56.60	152.00	33	5.4
2104	APR. 13	0	31	58.2	56.80	151.80	33	4.8
2105	APR. 16	1	27	15.3	57.00	153.60	33	5.7
2106		4	40	44.9	57.00	153.70	33	4.5
2107		13	10	15.2	57.00	153.60	33	4.7
2108	APR. 20	11	18	29.7	57.70	156.60	33	4.1
2109		13	30	57.2	57.30	151.80	33	4.1
2110	APR. 22	7	23	47.6	56.70	152.00	9	4.7
2111		10	15	50.6	56.90	151.80	33	4.9
2112		23	27	20.5	57.50	152.10	22	5.9
2113	MAY 11	1	26	23.7	62.80	150.10	91	4.7
2114	MAY 13	13	16	6.9	59.20	148.70	16	4.5
2115	MAY 26	10	44	13.0	60.80	151.00	95	4.5
2116	MAY 29	6	46	34.0	60.90	144.60	9	3.9
2117	JUNE 1	13	52	20.7	61.40	147.10	124	3.6
2118	JUNE 3	11	22	6.8	59.20	148.30	14	3.7
2119	JUNE 10	14	12	14.6	57.40	155.70	67	5.2
2120	JUNE 13	12	2	48.2	59.20	152.00	11	4.5
2121	JUNE 22	11	38	53.7	61.40	147.60	53	5.2
2122	JULY 6	6	19	33.1	61.30	152.90	107	4.3
2123	JULY 7	4	49	5.9	56.60	152.10	33	4.3
2124	JULY 8	13	11	49.4	57.20	150.20	33	4.0
2125	JULY 14	12	18	17.0	56.20	149.80	33	5.2
2126	JULY 17	8	46	25.8	61.90	152.00	103	4.8
2127	JULY 18	3	28	19.2	62.80	145.20	33	3.9
2128	AUG. 6	15	48	54.9	62.30	151.30	49	4.0
2129	AUG. 7	14	11	51.2	59.60	144.40	4	5.5
2130	AUG. 15	10	58	51.7	58.20	153.10	41	4.9
2131		13	36	23.7	60.40	146.00	9	5.3
2132		19	37	15.7	61.20	150.00	98	4.3
2133	AUG. 19	3	10	4.2	59.50	144.60	33	4.6
2134	AUG. 29	22	30	22.8	56.30	153.10	33	4.7
2135	AUG. 30	20	20	54.0	61.30	147.50	36	
2136		20	23	18.2	61.50	147.50	33	
2137	SEPT. 1	23	19	9.8	61.80	149.60	77	5.2
2138	SEPT. 2	22	46	39.5	60.20	146.90	31	4.9
2139	SEPT. 9	12	24	1.4	61.40	147.00	24	4.1
2140		15	36	56.7	61.40	147.90	58	4.4

See footnotes at end of table.

TABLE 2.—*Summary of aftershock data*—Continued

Earthquake number	Date		Origin time			Latitude N.	Longitude W.	Depth	Magnitude	Earthquake number	Date		Origin time			Latitude N.	Longitude W.	Depth	Magnitude
			Hr.	Min.	Sec.	°	°	Km.					Hr.	Min.	Sec.	°	°	Km.	
	1966—Con.										*1966*—Con.								
2141	SEPT.	11	13	46	9.5	56.50	158.00†	33	4.2	2161	NOV.	9	2	35	12.2	57.10	150.80	33	4.5
2142	SEPT.	13	5	30	1.4	58.80	154.30	33	4.3	2162	NOV.	19	16	39	3.2	56.90	154.00	33	4.5
2143	SEPT.	14	14	34	39.8	61.50	147.00	44	4.1	2163	NOV.	22	21	38	12.4	59.80	148.30	33	3.8
2144	SEPT.	17	1	23	16.9	58.50	152.00	46	4.7	2164	NOV.	24	6	53	37.1	56.50	152.90	33	4.8
2145	SEPT.	18	9	54	15.2	57.50	150.30	33	4.4	2165			8	41	56.9	56.50	153.30	33	4.0
2146	SEPT.	19	3	49	56.7	60.60	145.20	33	3.8	2166			15	7	23.5	56.50	153.00	33	4.5
2147	OCT.	7	20	55	56.0	61.60	150.10	56	5.7	2167	NOV.	27	4	10	42.8	60.10	146.20	28	4.6
2148	OCT.	8	3	6	46.4	57.70	151.60	32	5.0	2168			4	15	30.8	60.00	146.40	11	4.3
2149			10	3	46.6	61.30	150.70	33	3.7	2169			14	23	42.0	60.30	146.20	31	4.0
2150	OCT.	11	16	49	49.0	62.70	149.50	85	4.4	2170	DEC.	1	4	29	23.3	60.10	146.40	38	4.6
2151			3	19	25.4	60.50	144.40	33	4.5	2171			7	23	11.7	60.20	146.10	21	4.1
2152			8	20	38.4	60.40	145.00	25	4.4	2172			16	10	9.7	60.10	146.40	33	3.9
2153			11	30	35.8	59.90	144.80	33	4.0	2173	DEC.	8	23	18	9.4	60.10	146.50	35	4.5
2154			16	40	40.6	60.20	145.30	33	4.1	2174	DEC.	11	19	22	3.6	63.00	150.90	110	4.1
2155	OCT.	13	2	15	45.2	59.50	145.20	10	5.0	2175	DEC.	16	21	59	47.2	61.50	149.30	65	3.8
2156			5	26	45.6	59.60	145.20	33	4.2	2176	DEC.	20	22	44	56.5	55.40	155.00	33	4.2
2157	OCT.	15	12	9	23.9	55.50	158.90	33	4.3	2177	DEC.	23	16	40	7.6	59.50	145.20	33	4.5
2158	OCT.	26	20	59	5.3	58.90	149.10	33	4.2	2178	DEC.	24	22	28	59.6	59.90	153.40	113	5.1
2159	NOV.	5	21	36	30.1	58.90	154.90	33	4.3										
2160	NOV.	9	2	17	20.8	58.00	153.30	33	4.3										

* This is a local earthquake, the magnitude is M_L.
† Teleseismic hypocenter depth restrained by $_pP$.
‡ Teleseismic hypocenter depth determined by special study.

§ The depth was restrained to force convergence in the local hypocenter program.
** Hypocenter poorly determined by local network of stations.

TOSIMATU MATUMOTO
ROBERT A. PAGE, JR.*
LAMONT-DOHERTY GEOLOGICAL OBSERVATORY

Reprinted from
U.S. Coast and Geodetic Survey Volume II-B,C: Seismology and Marine Geology,
"Microaftershocks Following the Alaska Earthquake of March 28, 1964:
Determination of Hypocenters and Crustal Velocities
in the Kenai Peninsula-Prince William Sound Area"

Microaftershocks Following the Earthquake: Determination of Hypocenters and Crustal Velocities

ABSTRACT

After the great Alaska earthquake of March 28, 1964, at 03:36:13.0 [C&GS–03:36:14.0] Greenwich Mean Time (G.M.T.), seismologists from the Lamont Geological Observatory initiated a program to study the microseismicity associated with a major aftershock sequence. As one phase of the program, a few hundred microshocks were recorded during a 4-day period in July 1964 by two tripartite arrays of high-gain, high-frequency seismographs situated on the Kenai Peninsula. Most of the 249 microshocks for which hypocenters were determined are interpreted as microaftershocks which occurred in the uplifted tectonic block—that is, in the region of Prince William Sound and eastern Kenai Peninsula. Several subcrustal microshocks were located beneath the Cook Inlet lowlands and western Kenai Peninsula; these may represent the usual intermediate-depth activity associated with this region. In the procedure to determine microshock hypocenters, a smoothed model of crustal velocities applicable to eastern Kenai Peninsula was constructed. The model was characterized by near-surface velocities in the range 5.2 to 5.5 kilometers per second and by a marked increase in velocity to 7.5 kilometers per second at about 30 kilometers in depth.

INTRODUCTION

In April, June, July, and September of 1964, several seismologists from the Lamont Geological Observatory carried out a field program on the Kenai Peninsula of Alaska for the purpose of recording microaftershocks following the March 1964 earthquake. As used here, the term "microaftershocks" refers to those aftershocks hav-

---

*Now with the U.S. Geological Survey.

ing energies too small to be recorded by a global network of short-period seismograph stations. The purpose in recording microaftershocks is to examine the spatial and temporal distribution of seismic activity within a major aftershock sequence on a scale not attainable with data from only larger aftershocks and to relate this activity to tectonic processes active within the aftershock region.

The content of this paper is limited to results obtained from microshock data recorded by an array of high-gain, high-frequency seismographs during the June and July field trip. In particular, hypocenter determinations based on array data are listed in the appendix to this paper for 249 well-recorded microshocks which occurred during July 2–5, 1964. A model of crustal structure applicable to the eastern portion of the Kenai Peninsula is also presented. Results from other phases of the Lamont aftershock program will be published independently, and will not be included in this volume.

Unlike most aftershock studies, including those follow-

ing the Alaska earthquake, the Lamont program utilized high-gain, high-frequency seismographs to record the high-frequency P and S phases from microshocks. Typically, a system with a magnification of about 2 million at 10 cycles per second (c.p.s.) was operated continuously for several days.

High-gain, high-frequency seismographs have been used by many investigators to record microearthquakes and to study the local seismicity of a region [Asada, 1957; Sanford and Holmes, 1962; Isacks and Oliver, 1964; Suyehiro, *et al.,* 1964; and others]. However, the practice of incorporating portable high-gain, high-frequency instrumentation in the elements of a temporary seismic array for the purpose of recording microaftershocks is a recent development [Miyamura, *et al.,* 1961].

During the initial Lamont field trip in April, data were recorded by a tripartite array of geophones at Lawing on the eastern elbow of Kenai Lake (fig. 1), but the data lacked the time resolution required for locating hypocenters. Using array recording techniques and the same recording site, a Japanese party from the Earthquake Research Institute of Japan, led by K. Aki recorded microaftershocks for 3 weeks during May and June. In late June, T. Matumoto and L. Sykes returned to Lawing to carry out the second Lamont field investigation. This investigation included an array recording with improved time resolution.

ARRAY RECORDING PROGRAM

During the second Lamont field effort, a small tripartite array, consisting of high-gain, high-frequency recording systems, was operating on a continuous basis for 11 days in late June and early July; a second tripartite array operated simultaneously for a 4-day period, July 2–5, 1964.

Figure 2 depicts the location and the geometry of the two arrays. The small array, with dimensions of about 1 kilometer, was located at Lawing; it incorporated three of the recording points also used by Aki and his colleagues in this volume. The large array had dimensions of about 30 kilometers and was centered about Kenai Lake with elements at Broadview (Guard Station), Seward, and Lawing. A total of five geophones was available, and Point 4, at Lawing, was common to both arrays.

The choice of instrumentation for array recording was influenced by two considerations. First, the predominant seismic energy observed at a distance of less than 200 kilometers from a microearthquake is contained in fre-

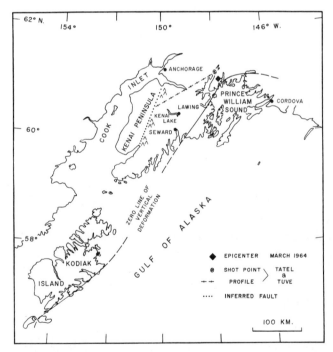

FIGURE 1.—The Prince William Sound–Kenai Peninsula–Kodiak Island section of Alaska. Lawing, the chief recording site used in the Lamont aftershock program is on Kenai Lake. The epicenter of the Alaska Earthquake of 28 March 1964, and the seismic-refraction profile of Tatel and Tuve are indicated. Nearly all of the aftershock and microaftershock epicenters that have been determined independently by several investigators lie southeast of the zero line of vertical deformation.

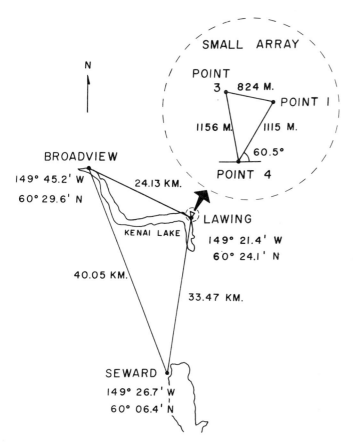

FIGURE 2.—Location and geometry of the 30-kilometer and 1-kilometer arrays. Point 4, at Lawing, was common to both arrays.

quencies above 2 c.p.s. [De Noyer, *et al.*, 1963]. Second, in order to locate microshocks from array data, one must be able to obtain accurate differences between phase-arrival times at the elements of the array.

A seismograph system with a magnification of about 1 million in the frequency range from 2 to 20 c.p.s. or more was considered a prime requisite for the general microaftershock recording program. Such sensitivity was attained in a basic system consisting of a vertical 2-c.p.s. geophone, a Lamont seismic amplifier [Thanos, 1964], and a paper chart recorder. The number of shocks per day occurring within an epicentral distance of 200 kilometers that were recorded with this system was more than a thousand times greater than the corresponding number with $m \geq 4.0$ reported on the U. S. Coast and Geodetic Survey *Preliminary Determination of Epicenters* (PDE) cards [Page and Matumoto, 1965].

For array recording, a 2-c.p.s. geophone and a d.c. amplifier were combined with either a paper chart recorder or a magnetic tape recorder. The system magnifications, during the phase of the Lamont aftershock pro-

gram reported here, were somewhat less than those used in other parts of the program.

In detail, the small array consisted of three matched seismic channels and a multichannel magnetic tape recorder. Each channel included a Texas Instrument S–36 2-c.p.s. vertical geophone (operating with a velocity sensitivity of 4 volts per inch per second at 0.6 of critical damping) and a Lamont seismic amplifier (providing a voltage gain of 6,000 over the range from d.c. to 40 c.p.s.). The amplified seismic signals together with time marks from a Sprengnether TS–100 crystal-controlled chronometer were recorded on a Precision Instrument PI 5104 FM magnetic tape recorder equipped with four data channels. The dynamic range of the tape recorder was 32 decibels; its response was nearly flat from d.c. to 15 c.p.s. and fell off sharply at frequencies above 17 c.p.s. The minimum recordable ground motion was calculated to be about 0.5 millimicron at 10 c.p.s. Upon playback of the tape, a total magnification of about 1 million at 10 c.p.s. produced an equivalent ground-noise level of 1 millimeter on the record.

The large array consisted of three independent seismograph systems. Point 4, at Lawing, was common to the small and large arrays. Similar instrumentation was used at Broadview and Seward—(1) A Hall-Sears HS–10 2-c.p.s. vertical geophone with a velocity sensitivity of 1.5 volts per inch per second, (2) a preamplifier unit from the Lamont seismic amplifier, and (3) a single-channel Sanborn paper chart recorder. With a preamplifier gain of 1,000 from d.c. to 40 c.p.s. and a recorder sensitivity of 10 millivolts per millimeter, the magnification at Broadview and Seward was about 400,000 at 10 c.p.s.

The calculated frequency response of the system used at Broadview and Seward is compared to the normalized response of an element of the small array in figure 3. The two systems have similar responses up to 17 c.p.s.; this similarity is necessary, if phases are to be correlated between elements of the large array. The response of a short-period system of the Worldwide Network of Standard Seismograph Stations operating at 100,000 gain is also shown. In the frequency range of 5 to 20 c.p.s., which contains much of the microaftershock energy, the magnifications of the Lamont systems are 5 to more than 100 times that of the standard short-period system.

As previously mentioned, accurate and precise timing is necessary to locate shocks on the basis of time differences between phase arrivals at the elements of an array. In the small array, data were recorded simultaneously on a multichannel tape recorder; hence, the precision of

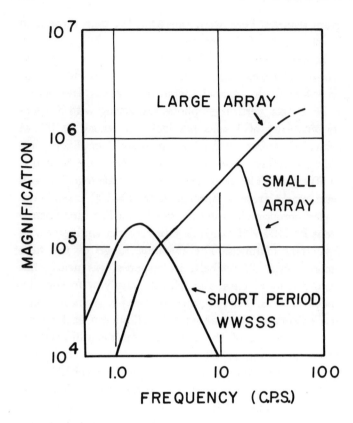

carried out in two stages: (1) The location of microshock hypocenters, assuming a crustal velocity model, and (2) the refinement of the assumed velocity structure and the relocation of hypocenters.

The first step in analyzing the data was to locate microshock hypocenters from data recorded by the small tripartite array, based on an assumed crustal model. After returning from the field, the tape-recorded data were played back and recorded by a pen-writing oscillograph. From these records, arrival-time differences between the three array elements were measured. Under the assumption of plane-wave fronts, the azimuth from the array to the event and the apparent velocity of the P wave were determined.

A tracing of a sample microaftershock from a playback record from the small array is shown in figure 4. Although the P wave has an impulsive character, there

FIGURE 3.—Magnification curves for two array seismograph systems and a short-period station of the Worldwide Network of Standard Seismograph Stations. The curve for the small array has been normalized to match that of the large array below 15 c.p.s. High-gain, high-frequency seismographs are essential for recording microearthquakes.

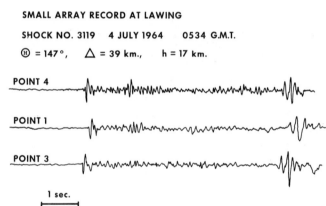

FIGURE 4.—A tracing of a sample playback of microaftershock No. 3119 recorded at 0534 (G.M.T.) on July 4, 1964, by the small tripartite array at Lawing. The epicenter of the shock was 39 kilometers from Lawing on an azimuth of 147° and at a focal depth of 17 kilometers.

relative timing between elements of the array was limited by the frequency content of the signal and the frequency response of the seismograph system. In contrast, independent timing was employed at each station of the large array. Sprengnether TS–100 crystal-controlled chronometers were used to provide minute time signals at Broadview and Lawing. At Seward, however, time was obtained from the chronometer incorporated in the California Institute of Technology's temporary seismograph system. Clock corrections for all three chronometer systems were computed using radio time signals from WWVH as a standard. The timing accuracies were estimated to be 0.1, 0.1, and 0.05 second at Seward, Broadview, and Lawing, respectively.

DATA ANALYSIS

Data for the 249 microshocks recorded in the interval July 2–5, 1964, have been analyzed. The analysis was

is considerable difficulty in determining arrival-time differences between traces to an accuracy of a few milliseconds, on the basis of first motion alone. A method of visual correlation of waveforms was used in measuring arrival-time differences.

The accuracy in the calculated azimuth and velocity depends on the spacing between geophones and the relative time resolution between elements of the array. The theoretical time resolution on the playback records was 2 milliseconds. In practice, however, a precision of 2 milliseconds was never realized, due to the 17-c.p.s. cutoff in the tape-recorder response and the uncertainty associated with an emergent first motion. The latter problem was partially overcome by visually correlating wave patterns between elements and by measuring the observed timelag. The possible error in this method of time analysis was judged to be about 5 milliseconds. The resultant uncertainties in the computed azimuth and apparent velocity were estimated to be 15° and 5 percent, respectively.

PRELIMINARY HYPOCENTER DETERMINATION

To locate a microshock, one must determine the epicentral distance, focal depth, and the azimuth. If the P- and S-wave velocities are known as a function of depth, then the measured S-P time interval and the apparent P-wave velocity across the array determine the depth and distance of the shock. Shor [1962] presented two models (MK 13 and MK 14) for crustal structure in the vicinity of Kodiak Island. A four-layer crustal model, largely patterned after MK 13 and MK 14, was used as a first approximation in the preliminary hypocenter determinations. The parameters for this model were:

Layer thickness	*P*-wave velocity	Poisson's ratio
Km.	*Km./sec.*	
0.7	2.19	
3.6	4.43	
12.2	5.47	Assumed to be constant at 0.25
20.0	7.03	
∞	8.03	

In order to evaluate the reliability of the tripartite method of locating hypocenters, some of the larger microshocks recorded by both arrays were located by using data from the small and large array independently. Figure 5 provides a comparison of the epicenters from the large array with those from the small array. In general, the accuracy of the location is better for the closer shocks. More than three-fourths of the pairs of epicenters agree within 20 kilometers of each other.

During this period, only one aftershock large enough to be located by the U. S. Coast and Geodetic Survey on the basis of teleseismic readings occurred. No hypocenter could be determined for the shock from the array data because the P wave saturated all the seismograph systems, and no S wave could be read. This aftershock, located about 160 kilometers SSE. of Lawing, was assigned a magnitude of $m = 3.5$.

As a further indication of the dependability of the

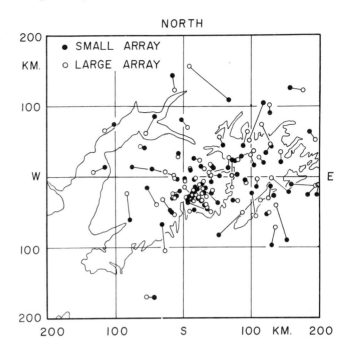

FIGURE 5.—Preliminary microshock epicenters based on data from the small and large arrays at Lawing (the center of the figure where the N.–S. and E.–W. lines intersect).

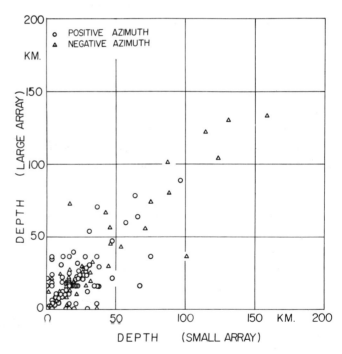

FIGURE 6.—Preliminary focal depths determined independently from two sets of array data.

tripartite-array method of location, the independently computed depths and azimuths of the larger microshocks are plotted against each other (figs. 6 and 7). Figure 6 shows that about 80 percent of the shocks

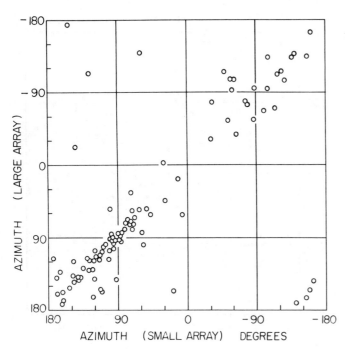

FIGURE 7.—Azimuths from Lawing to the preliminary epicenters located independently from two sets of array data.

occurred at depths between 0 and 40 kilometers. Of the focal depths based on the two sets of data, about 60 percent agree within 10 kilometers and about 85 percent agree within 20 kilometers. Figure 7 indicates that about two-thirds of the pairs of azimuths computed from the two sets of data lie within 15° of each other. It thus appears that the uncertainty in the preliminary hypocenter determinations for microaftershocks is of the same order of magnitude as the uncertainty associated with the preliminary teleseismic hypocenter determinations for Alaskan aftershocks made by the U. S. Coast and Geodetic Survey.

The velocity structure assumed in determining preliminary hypocenters was meant to represent only a first approximation to the actual velocity structure in the Kenai Peninsula–Prince William Sound region of Alaska. Thus, the second part of the data analysis was directed toward possible modification of the assumed structure and the subsequent relocation of hypocenters.

REFINEMENT OF ASSUMED VELOCITY STRUCTURE

The method that was used in modifying the assumed crustal structure is analogous to that of well shooting—a common technique in the oil prospecting industry [Nettleton, 1940]. The mean velocity as a function of depth

was determined from traveltime data of microshocks that occurred beneath the array. The velocity structure in the vicinity of the array was then calculated from the mean velocity-depth distribution.

In the first step, a perturbation scheme was employed to derive a refined mean velocity versus depth relationship. The time required for a P wave to travel along a straight path from a hypocenter (x_0, y_0, z_0) to a station (x_i, y_i, z_i) can be written as

$$t_i - t_0 = [(x_i - x_0)^2 + (y_i - y_0)^2 + (z_i - z_0)^2]^{1/2} / V_m \qquad (1)$$

where t_i is the P-wave arrival time at the station, t_0 is the origin time of the shock, and V_m is the mean P-wave velocity along the straight path. All the quantities in the equation are known: x_i, y_i, z_i are station constants; x_0, y_0, z_0 are the coordinates of the preliminary hypocenter; t_i is measured; t_0 is the origin time corresponding to the preliminary hypocenter; and V_m is calculated for the particular velocity model used in determining the preliminary hypocenter. When the hypocenter is not directly under the station, the right-hand side of the equation only approximates the observed traveltime, but the approximation is good when the focal depth is greater than the epicentral distance.

The origin time, focal depth, and mean velocity in the traveltime equation were perturbed by replacing the quantities t_0, z_0, and V_m by the quantities $t_0 + \Delta t_0$, $z_0 + \Delta z_0$, and $V_m + \Delta V_m$, while the epicentral coordinates, x_0 and y_0 remained fixed. The quantities Δt_0, Δz_0, and ΔV_m represent correction terms to be added to the initial values to obtain more accurate values for t_0, z_0, and V_m. Discarding second- and higher order perturbation terms, an equation of the form

$$a_i \Delta V_m + b_i \Delta z_0 + c_i \Delta t_0 = K_i \qquad (2)$$

was obtained, where a_i, b_i, c_i, and K_i are known constants.

There was one such equation for each of the five stations from the two arrays; hence, least-squares values of ΔV_m, Δz_0, and Δt_0 were obtained for each shock. The perturbation terms were then added to the original values to give corrected values for V_m, z_0, and t_0. This procedure was applied to 98 microshocks, using preliminary hypocenter determinations based on data from the small array. In this way, a more realistic mean velocity-depth relationship was constructed.

For successful results, the data should be preferably from shocks which occur beneath the array—that is, from shocks for which the focal depth exceeds the epicentral distance. The data available for this method consisted of arrival times of P waves from microshocks recorded by both arrays. For most of the shocks, the epicentral distance was larger than the focal depth, so that the straight-path assumption in the traveltime equation was violated. For these shocks, one would expect the computed mean velocity to be higher than the actual mean velocity.

Refined mean-velocity values were derived first from the four-layer crustal model. The refined values are denoted by the open circles in the mean velocity-depth plot in figure 8. The swarm of points representing mean

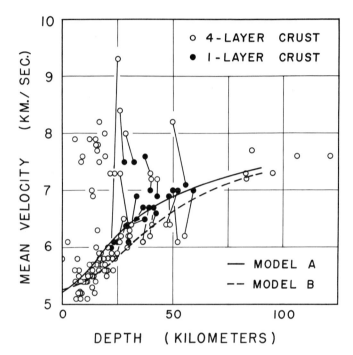

FIGURE 8.—Mean *P*-wave velocity as a function of depth. The points correspond to microshocks that were recorded by both arrays. For several shocks, two values of mean velocity and depth were determined by using two different crustal models; the two points for each shock are connected by a straight line. The two smooth curves represent mean-velocity functions from which the velocity-depth distributions were computed.

velocities in excess of 7 kilometers per second to depths of 50 kilometers corresponds to shocks for which the epicentral distance exceeded the focal depth by a factor of five or more. Ignoring the high mean velocities, the open circles define a mean velocity-depth function to a depth of about 25 kilometers. The few points at depths greater than 80 kilometers appear to be reliable; however, the form of the mean-velocity function at depths between 25 and 80 kilometers is somewhat ambiguous. In order to delineate the function in the depth range of 25 to 80

kilometers, a second set of refined mean-velocity values derived from the model of a 6-kilometer-per-second crust overlying an 8-kilometer-per-second mantle was calculated for microshocks that were located in this depth range. The closed circles in figure 8 represent the values based on the one-layer crustal model; pairs of values from the two models are connected by straight lines. The mean velocities derived from the one-layer crust are more consistent than those from the four-layer crust. For this reason, the closed circles are considered more indicative of the actual mean velocities in the depth range of 25 to 60 kilometers.

The solid curve in figure 8 was drawn to best represent the mean-velocity function defined by the two sets of points. The curve was restricted to a mean velocity of 5.2 kilometers per second at zero depth, because this was the minimum apparent velocity measured with the small array. In drawing the curve, the swarm of high, mean-velocity points mentioned above was ignored. A limit to the amount of curvature drawn into the line was set by the requirement that no low-velocity layer in the crust be allowed in the model.

The scatter in the points about the indicated function is due, in part, to the fact that some of the preliminary epicenters used in the perturbation scheme contradict the implicit assumption that the preliminary epicenter determinations are close to the true epicenters. In figure 5, a comparison of epicenter determinations based on data from the two arrays indicates that there was considerable uncertainty in some of the determinations—and, probably, more uncertainty for the more distant shocks.

Once the mean-velocity function was known, the velocity distribution in the crust was calculated. The points defining the mean-velocity function were presumed to represent straight line travelpaths or, equivalently, paths that were almost normally incident to the crustal layers. Under this condition, the velocity V_i in the ith layer is related to the mean velocity V_m by the equation

$$V_m \sum_i d_i = \sum_i V_i d_i \qquad (3)$$

where d_i is the thickness of the ith layer.

This equation was used to calculate the velocity distribution from the surface to a depth of 90 kilometers. In the calculation, the crust and upper mantle were assumed to be composed of horizontal layers—each layer being 5 kilometers thick and having a constant velocity. The mean velocities used in the computation were taken from the mean velocity versus depth curves in figure 8. Values for the mean velocity and the calculated velocity at 5-kilometer-depth intervals are listed in table 1. This velocity distribution has been labeled Model A (fig. 8).

TABLE 1.—*Velocity-depth distribution of Model A*

Depth	Mean *P*-wave velocity	*P*-wave velocity
Km.	*Km./sec.*	*Km./sec.*
0	5.20	5.20
5	5.33	5.46
10	5.50	5.86
15	5.74	6.59
20	5.99	7.19
25	6.21	7.58
30	6.39	7.73
35	6.55	7.84
40	6.68	7.92
45	6.79	7.95
50	6.88	7.99
55	6.97	8.11
60	7.05	8.16
65	7.12	8.21
70	7.19	8.29
75	7.25	8.27
80	7.30	8.20
85	7.34	8.15
90	7.39	8.20

In applying equation (3), one starts with the first layer and determines the velocities in successively deeper layers in a cumulative fashion. A discrepancy between the computed and the actual velocity in any layer will decrease the accuracy of the computed velocity in the underlying layers. For this reason, the computed velocity-depth distribution is judged to be less representative of the real velocity distribution at greater depths.

A velocity distribution (labeled Model B in figure 8) was calculated for a second mean-velocity function to determine how much the velocity might change, if the mean-velocity function were altered slightly. The dashed curve in figure 8 was drawn as the lower limit to the mean-velocity depth points. The velocities of the two models are compared in figure 9. The difference between the two models reaches a value of 0.5 kilometer per second in the depth range from 20 to 40 kilometers.

RELOCATION OF HYPOCENTERS

Finally, the 249 microshock hypocenters were relocated, using the data from the small array and the refined velocity distribution of Model A. A crust composed of layers 1 kilometer thick and with velocities interpolated from those in table 1 was employed in the relocation program. The relocated shocks are plotted in figure 10. In general, the position of the relocated hypocenters did not differ greatly from the preliminary hypocenters.

The final hypocenters determined in this program are listed in the appendix to this paper in terms of epicentral

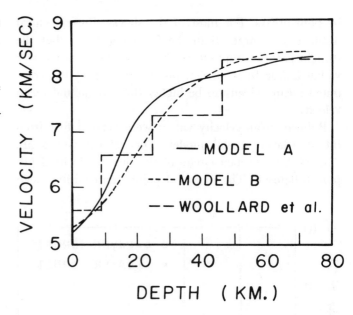

FIGURE 9.—*P*-wave velocity models proposed for the eastern part of the Kenai Peninsula. Models A and B are based on microshock-array data recorded in this program. The layered model of Woollard, *et al.*, is derived from seismic-refraction data.

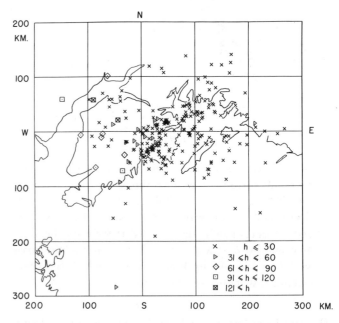

FIGURE 10.—Location and depth of final microshock epicenters listed in the appendix to this paper. The shocks included in this figure occurred during a 4-day interval (July 2-5, 1964), about 3 months after the Alaska earthquake. Lawing is at the intersection of the N.–S. and E.–W. grid lines.

distance, azimuth to the shock (progressing clockwise from the north), and focal depth. In addition, the assigned serial number, date of occurrence, *P*-wave arrival time, *S-P* interval, and apparent *P*-wave velocity are included. All the parameters are referred to Point 4, at Lawing.

CRUSTAL VELOCITY MODEL

Of the two velocity models that were computed from microshock data, Model A is considered to be more representative of the actual crustal velocity structure beneath the eastern part of the Kenai Peninsula. Model B was constructed primarily to estimate the degree of dependence of the calculated velocity values on the particular shape of the mean-velocity function, whereas Model A was designed to best represent the mean velocities obtained from the data.

If, in fact, the mean-velocity distribution differs systematically from that of Model A in table 1, the actual mean velocities are probably less than those of Model A —that is, between Models A and B. This is so because the most likely source of systematic error in this method of determining crustal velocities is a violation of the straight travelpath assumption. The occurrence of high values for mean velocities calculated for shocks associated with curved ray paths was mentioned earlier in the paper.

Model A is characterized by near-surface velocities in the neighborhood of 5.2 to 5.5 kilometers per second, by a rapid increase in velocities at depths between 10 and 30 kilometers, and by velocities ranging from 7.5 to 8 kilometers per second at depths from 30 to 50 kilometers. It must be kept in mind that the method used in constructing this model tends to accumulate errors as velocities for progressively deeper layers are determined. Hence, the discussion of Model A is limited to depths less than 50 kilometers.

Very little seismic information about the structure of the Kenai Peninsula has been published. Tatel and Tuve [1956] discussed a seismic refraction profile along a line extending from College Fiord, Prince William Sound, southwest across the Kenai Peninsula (refer to fig. 1 for location of the profile). The data were sparse, and the authors made no attempt to construct a detailed crustal model. Woollard, *et al.,* [1960] reexamined Tatel and Tuve's data and derived a flat-layered crustal model for the northeastern part of the Kenai Peninsula. They concluded that the seismic data indicated a crustal thickness of 46 kilometers—a value that was considered to be in agreement with their gravity data.

The crustal model proposed by Woollard, *et al.,* is shown in comparison with Model A in figure 9. There are differences between the two: (1) The surface velocity found by Woollard, *et al.,* is 0.5 kilometer per second greater than the minimum apparent velocity observed in this study, and (2) Model A has higher velocities in the depth range of 15 to 45 kilometers. For the Mohorovičić discontinuity, Woollard, *et al.,* suggested a velocity contrast of 7.3 to 8.3 kilometers per second at a depth of 46 kilometers. Due to the procedure followed in its derivation, Model A necessarily represents a smoothed velocity distribution; hence, a sharp velocity discontinuity would not appear as an abrupt step in the computed velocity distribution. A velocity of about 8 kilometers per second is reached at a depth of 50 kilometers in Model A. At this depth, the computed velocity values are expected to be accurate to a few tenths of a kilometer per second. Neither the data used by Woollard, *et al.,* nor those of this paper provide high resolution of the features of the crustal models; thus, there is no way of choosing the more accurate representation of the crust at present.

In summary, the model of crustal velocity presented here represents a smoothed velocity distribution that differs somewhat in character from the layered models obtained in seismic refraction work. In this paper, the smoothed model has been employed in determining hypocenters that are consistent with crustal structure.

DISTRIBUTION OF MICROSHOCK HYPOCENTERS

The distribution of the relocated microshock epicenters around Lawing is shown in figure 10. Only a portion of the entire zone defined by the larger aftershocks of the Alaska earthquake is included in the map, because the high-frequency response characteristics of the seismograph system and the attenuation of the seismic signal along the propagation path cause an apparent decrease in activity as the distance from the recording site increases.

The two dominant features seen on the map are the asymmetrical distribution of hypocenters around the station and the presence of subcrustal microshocks in the Kenai Peninsula–Cook Inlet region. Of the 249 microshocks recorded at Lawing, 210 were located southeast of a NE.-SW. line passing through the station. This is not surprising, because Lawing is on the northwestern edge of the zone of epicenters of larger aftershocks that were determined by the U. S. Coast and Geodetic Survey.

During the 4-day period of recording, microaftershock activity in the vicinity of Prince William Sound and near the eastern edge of the Kenai Peninsula was much higher than that in other equally distant areas to the north and west of Lawing. Microaftershock epicenters were concentrated in three local areas on the Kenai Peninsula: 35 kilometers SSE., 30 kilometers ENE., and 50 kilometers ENE. of Lawing. Such concentrations often appeared and vanished within a time-span of 12 hours. The fact that the shocks in a particular group all had about the same focal depth and often the same $S:P$ amplitude ratio suggests that they were generated by the same focal mechanism. A very low level of activity was observed for the southern portion of the Kenai Peninsula and the adjoining offshore areas.

The areal distribution of aftershocks is generally considered to be indicative of the length of the primary fault accompanying a shallow earthquake. In the case of the March 1964 Alaska earthquake, the epicenters of the larger aftershocks define a NE.-SW. trending belt about 800 kilometers long and 200 kilometers wide. This belt extends from the eastern coast of Kodiak Island, along the eastern edge of the Kenai Peninsula and through Prince William Sound. In a source-mechanism study using long-period surface waves, Toksöz, *et al.*, [1965] conclude that the primary rupture progagated a distance of about 600 kilometers in the direction S. 50° W.

In order to obtain a better picture of the distribution of microaftershocks in relation to the boundary of the aftershock belt and the regional geological structure, the hypocenters were projected onto a vertical plane that was oriented NW.-SE. and perpendicular to both the aftershock zone and the regional structural trend (fig. 11). The projected hypocenters, as well as the epicenters shown in figure 10, indicate a vertical discontinuity in the distribution of shallow microaftershocks in the vicinity of Lawing. This discontinuity is oriented NE.-SW., and 40 kilometers to the northwest, it parallels the zero line of vertical deformation that was determined by Plafker [1965] from measured changes in land levels (fig. 1). Nearly all the aftershocks listed on the U. S. Coast and Geodetic Survey PDE cards occurred on the seaward side of the zero line, that is, in the uplifted tectonic block. Many of the microaftershocks included in this study also were located in the uplifted block. If similar instruments had been distributed adequately throughout the Prince William Sound region, a map, such as that in figure 10, would have shown clearly a preponderance of micro-aftershocks in the uplifted block.

As seen in figure 11, very few microshocks occurred to the northwest of a NE.-SW. line passing through Lawing. Several authors have suggested the existence of a major fault in this region. On the basis of a traveltime

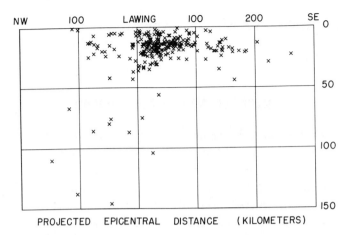

FIGURE 11.—The epicentral distances (in kilometers) of the final microshock hypocenters listed in the appendix have been projected onto a vertical NW.-SE. plane through Lawing. This section is perpendicular to the zero line of vertical deformation (fig. 1), which lies 40 kilometers southeast of Lawing.

offset in a seismic refraction profile across the northeastern part of the Kenai Peninsula, Woollard, *et al.*, [1960] have postulated the existence of a fault which intersects the profile (fig. 1) at a distance 84 kilometers southwest of the shot point. Karlstrom [1964] has inferred that the contact of the Cretaceous bedrock of the Kenai Mountains with the Tertiary formations underlying the Cook Inlet lowlands to the west is a steep westward-dipping normal fault that forms the eastern wall of the assumed graben structure of the Cook Inlet lowlands (fig. 1).

The very low level of microshock activity in this region northwest of Lawing might be attributed to the inability of strain energy to accumulate in a region that is heavily fractured as a result of earlier faulting. An alternative explanation is that the accumulated strain energy was low in this region at the time of the Alaska earthquake, due to energy release in one of more small earthquakes within the past few years. With respect to the latter explanation, Tobin and Sykes [1966] found that several shallow shocks occurred in the western part of the Kenai Peninsula during the past 10 years, but very few shocks occurred in the eastern part and in Prince William Sound. A detailed knowledge of recent seismicity in this area is essential for deciding which of the two explanations is the more likely.

The depth distribution of the microshocks is well defined in figures 10 and 11. Only 25 of the 249 microshocks for which final hypocenters have been determined were deeper than 30 kilometers; only 11 were deeper than 45 kilometers. The deepest focal depth computed was 146 kilometers. Except for one, all of the hypocenters with depths greater than 30 kilometers were located beneath the Kenai Peninsula or the Cook Inlet area; the exception had a depth of 35 kilometers and was east of Prince William Sound, near Cordova. No focal depths exceeding 35 kilometers were found for microaftershocks in the Prince William Sound area.

Intermediate-depth earthquakes are known to have occurred in the vicinity of Cook Inlet [Gutenberg and Richter, 1954]. Tobin and Sykes [1966] emphasized that the activity associated with the intermediate-depth shocks ($h = 70$ to 300 kilometers) occurred in a narrow zone extending from the Alaska Peninsula through the Cook Inlet lowlands to the northern edge of the Alaska Range. This zone has the highest level of intermediate-depth seismicity in the United States. Furthermore, the greatest reliable depth that they calculated for an intermediate-depth shock in this area was about 170 kilometers. It is clear that the microshocks deeper than 35 kilometers occurred in the zone defined by Tobin and Sykes. Hence, there is a question as to whether the microshocks that occurred at subcrustal depths under western Kenai Peninsula and Cook Inlet should be interpreted as microaftershocks or as independent microearthquakes.

To decide whether the subcrustal shocks represent aftershocks or independent shocks, one should compare the microseismicity following the Alaska earthquake with the usual seismicity prior to the earthquake. Unfortunately, the focal depths in this region often are unreliable, because of the absence of close stations and the poor azimuthal distribution of stations.

The nine microshocks, which occurred in the region bounded by latitudes 59° and 62°N. and longitudes 148° and 153° W. and which had depths ranging from 70 to 170 kilometers, may be explained in terms of the expected annual seismicity of this limited region. Assuming that as a regional average, no microshock smaller than magnitude 2 were recorded and that the value of b in the magnitude-frequency relationship is unity, the seismicity for shocks with magnitudes greater than 5 would be one or two shocks per year for this limited region. When compared with the observed seismicity, this figure agrees within the uncertainty of the calculation.

Although the paucity of the microshock data precludes any definite conclusions as to the nature of the subcrustal shocks, it is apparent that the Alaska earthquake produced a change in the seismicity associated with shallow shocks—a change that was several orders of magnitude greater than any change associated with intermediate shocks.

The distribution of hypocenters found in this 4-day period in early July is strikingly similar to that found by Aki, *et al.*, during a 3-week interval in May and June [Aki, *et al.*, unpublished results]. This fact indicates that the gross features of the spatial distribution of microaftershocks were stationary in time, for at least several weeks.

As previously mentioned, the areal distribution of aftershocks is often indicative of the horizontal length of the primary fault associated with a shallow earthquake. One might expect that other features of the tectonic processes associated with a major earthquake—such as the vertical extent of the primary fault—would be reflected in the spatial distribution of aftershocks. All but one of the few subcrustal microshocks included in this study occurred northwest of the zero line of vertical deformation. On the basis of the measured changes in land levels which accompanied the Alaska earthquake, Press [1965] has proposed the existence of a near-vertical fault plane extending from about 15 kilometers beneath the zero line of vertical deformation to a depth of 150 to 200 kilometers. As seen in figure 11, such a surface would represent a bounding surface for the intermediate-depth microshocks. Assuming that the subcrustal microshocks are independent shocks, the distribution of microaftershocks would serve to delineate only the projected fault trace on the surface and not the vertcial extent of the faulting.

On the other hand, assuming that together the shallow microaftershocks and the independent subcrustal microshocks define a fault zone, the pattern of hypocenters in figure 11 can be considered representative of a transverse section across a Pacific marginal arc-type structure [Benioff, 1954]. In this case, the hypocenters would define a focal zone 100 to 200 kilometers wide, dipping to the northwest. From the data presented in this study, it is not possible to decide which of the two tectonic models is more realistic.

SUMMARY

This study illustrates the value in using high-gain, high-frequency seismographs and array recording techniques to investigate the microseismicity within a major aftershock sequence. A smoothed velocity-depth distribution applicable to the eastern part of the Kenai Peninsula was obtained on the basis of microshock data recorded from two tripartite arrays. The derived velocity distribution was used in determining hypocenters for 249 microshocks which occurred in a 4-day period about 3 months after the great Alaska earthquake of March 1964.

The majority of the hypocenters located in this program corresponds to shallow microaftershocks that occurred in the zone of tectonic uplift in the eastern Kenai Peninsula-Prince William Sound region. Several subcrustal shocks were located on the landward (northwestern) side of the zero line of vertical deformation. Although the data are scanty, the subcrustal shocks may be explained in terms of expected intermediate-depth seismicity, and thus need not be considered aftershocks. The observed spatial distribution of microshocks is not sufficient evidence for deciding which of two proposed models of tectonic structure is more accurate—a near-vertical crust–mantle fault beneath the zero line of vertical deformation or a landward-dipping fault zone typical of Pacific marginal arc-type structures.

ACKNOWLEDGMENTS

The authors express their gratitude to the many people who have contributed to the Lamont aftershock program and to the publication of this paper. Dr. Jack Oliver of Lamont encouraged and promoted the program from the outset. Mr. Kenneth Klopf of the Geophyscial Institute of the University of Alaska and Dr. Lynn Sykes of Lamont, who participated in the field efforts of the program, are largely responsible for its success.

Several people, in particular, are to be thanked for their timely assistance during the initial stages of the program. Dr. Eduard Berg and Mr. Kenneth Klopf, both of the University of Alaska, were most helpful in expediting the first field trip. While still recovering from the earthquake disaster, residents of Seward and Lawing unselfishly supported our efforts. Police Chief Lloyd Heffner of Seward and District Ranger V. Parents of the Chugach National Forest suggested possible recording sites. Mr. and Mrs. Charles O'Leary of Lawing graciously permitted the authors to operate instruments on their property and provided shelter during all three field trips.

With respect to the array recording program, the authors are indebted to Dr. Keiiti Aki of the Earthquake Research Institute (University of Tokyo) for the loan of a signal cable used in the small array at Lawing, and to Mr. Walter Blue of Seward for providing time signals for the Seward array station from the California Institute of Technology's temporary seismograph station. Dr. Paul Pomeroy and others at Lamont helped in assembling the necessary recording instrumentation.

The authors have benefited from associations with several seismologists. For example, Dr. K. Aki and his colleagues kindly made available their unpublished hypocenter determinations for the microshocks that they recorded in May and June. Drs. Jack Oliver, Lynn Sykes, James Brune, Bryan Isacks, and Mr. Don Tobin of Lamont were consulted freely during the program. Drs. Oliver and Brune critically read the manuscript and offered suggestions for its improvement.

Research for this paper was supported by the Office of Aerospace Research through (1) the Geophysics Division of the Air Force Office of Scientific Research and (2) the Air Force Cambridge Research Laboratories under contracts AF 19(628)–4082 and AF 19(604)–8485 for the Advanced Research Projects Agency's Project VELA-UNIFORM, and by the American Chemical Society under grant PRF 756–A2.

APPENDIX

Final hypocenter determinations were made for 249 microshocks recorded during the period July 2 to 5, 1964. The locations are based on data from the small array and the velocities of Model A. The shocks are arranged in order by an assigned serial number. For each shock, the following quantities are listed: Assigned serial number, date of occurrence, *P*-wave arrival time, *S-P* interval, apparent *P*-wave velocity across the array, epicentral distance, azimuth (from Lawing to the shock measured clockwise from north), and focal depth. All parameters are referred to Point 4, at Lawing.

Alaska microshock locations, July 1964

Serial number	Date (July)	P-arrival time (G.M.T.)			S-P time interval	Apparent P-wave velocity	Distance	Azimuth	Depth
		Hr.	Min.	Sec.	Sec.	Km./sec.	Km.	Degrees	Km.
3001	4	23	55	52.9	5.6	6.2	41	88	13
3003	4	23	01	31.2	14.4	5.4	107	102	6
3004	4	22	54	18.2	5.6	5.4	40	123	6
3005	4	22	52	01.2	12.0	5.6	90	59	7
3007	4	22	41	26.0	23.5	7.2	219	50	20

Alaska microshock locations, July 1964—Continued

Serial number	Date (July)	P-arrival time (G.M.T.)			S-P time interval	Apparent P-wave velocity	Distance	Azimuth	Depth
		Hr.	Min.	Sec.	Sec.	Km./sec.	Km.	Degrees	Km.
3009	4	22	25	56.3	3.4	6.5	22	178	12
3011	4	22	19	49.8	12.4	7.4	111	71	23
3012	4	22	05	00.8	5.9	7.8	44	29	26
3013	4	21	54	07.0	12.9	6.3	105	92	14
3015	4	21	40	55.2	12.8	12.6	80	−153	104
3016	4	21	31	10.1	20.8	7.3	196	57	22
3017	4	21	03	51.0	5.3	7.4	38	148	21
3018	4	20	57	43.4	11.7	6.3	95	88	14
3021	4	20	05	56.5	5.3	5.4	38	−49	5
3022	4	20	04	48.0	4.5	7.5	30	71	20
3023	4	19	58	02.6	11.6	5.7	88	92	9
3027	4	19	48	51.3	4.7	6.3	33	153	13
3028	4	19	41	05.6	5.3	5.8	38	161	10
3029	4	19	31	43.5	13.6	6.2	110	95	13
3031	4	18	43	31.1	16.3	7.2	148	59	21
3032	4	18	10	52.3	5.2	5.4	37	120	4
3035	4	17	12	33.0	2.8	5.7	19	133	7
3036	4	17	04	13.6	13.6	9.9	108	−127	87
3038	4	16	40	50.0	3.6	6.4	24	154	13
3039	4	16	37	41.0	13.2	5.4	96	73	4
3040	4	16	29	10.6	5.4	7.7	39	−7	24
3041	4	16	10	06.0	17.6	6.2	144	126	13
3042	4	16	05	53.9	7.8	6.0	59	142	12
3043	4	16	04	28.5	7.5	7.5	61	87	24
3044	4	15	56	32.0	12.3	7.4	109	74	22
3047	4	15	42	21.1	18.4	5.8	143	48	10
3050	4	15	37	05.0	20.9	6.7	185	97	17
3052	4	15	22	41.6	7.2	6.6	56	161	16
3053	4	15	22	11.8	18.7	9.4	160	−68	110
3055	4	15	17	00.0	8.2	7.5	68	−83	24
3056	4	15	04	08.6	3.2	6.7	20	99	13
3057	4	15	03	25.1	4.8	11.3	25	−161	34
3060	4	14	49	54.5	6.7	7.5	52	65	24
3061	4	14	33	23.5	23.8	6.6	209	53	16
3062	4	14	30	40.2	8.6	6.4	68	−35	15
3064	4	14	15	00.3	10.0	5.6	75	144	8
3066	4	13	55	43.0	27.5	7.5	266	124	23
3067	4	13	46	35.2	13.6	6.7	116	73	17
3068	4	13	41	35.4	9.4	6.6	76	152	16
3069	4	13	34	05.3	23.0	7.7	224	129	29
3071	4	13	09	05.3	6.3	5.4	45	67	5
3073	4	12	52	00.0	13.2	5.7	100	85	9
3076	4	12	34	25.5	6.6	7.6	51	74	24
3077	4	12	33	39.6	21.8	5.3	158	93	3
3079	4	12	13	58.6	15.8	7.5	147	122	24
3080	4	12	02	41.8	22.9	7.2	213	88	20
3081	4	11	51	42.0	7.0	6.1	53	142	12
3082	4	11	42	48.9	21.8	7.7	212	86	35
3083	4	11	40	40.2	21.5	7.0	197	92	19
3084	4	11	35	56.8	14.0	5.3	101	−46	2
3086	4	11	24	15.9	6.4	6.8	49	64	17
3088	4	11	16	00.7	12.7	6.3	104	72	14
3089	4	11	12	35.1	14.4	5.4	106	112	5
3090	4	11	11	45.0	4.7	7.3	33	65	20
3091	4	11	09	01.1	8.4	0.1	65	141	13
3094	4	10	24	12.5	4.8	6.9	34	147	17
3095	4	10	20	17.3	15.7	7.2	143	70	21
3096	4	10	13	41.8	5.6	8.9	38	51	32
3098	4	10	06	21.0	4.3	7.0	29	82	17
3101	4	09	03	06.9	6.7	5.8	49	71	10
3103	4	08	39	25.2	7.6	8.2	60	−155	35
3105	4	08	34	51.2	7.5	7.5	61	−159	24
3106	4	08	32	50.0	4.7	6.4	33	−124	14
3107	4	08	19	46.0	3.4	6.9	21	73	14
3108	4	08	18	22.8	17.3	7.1	158	56	20

Alaska microshock locations, July 1964—Continued

Serial number	Date (July)	P-arrival time (G.M.T.)			S-P time interval	Apparent P-wave velocity	Distance	Azimuth	Depth
		Hr.	Min.	Sec.	Sec.	Km./sec.	Km.	Degrees	Km.
3109	4	07	39	35.2	17.3	6.2	142	69	13
3111	4	07	03	33.7	5.2	6.0	37	143	11
3112	4	07	01	29.8	12.7	6.8	109	80	18
3115	4	06	28	50.2	4.0	20.6	11	148	33
3116	4	06	19	48.2	9.3	5.4	68	−113	5
3117	4	06	12	51.5	16.0	6.3	133	71	14
3118	4	06	02	17.2	28.3	7.2	267	89	20
3119	4	05	34	37.4	5.3	6.8	39	147	17
3120	4	05	28	38.4	6.6	6.2	50	71	13
3121	4	05	21	17.5	1.1	14.7	2	−86	7
3122	4	04	44	43.2	4.3	8.0	28	66	22
3124	4	04	33	28.0	1.1	7.2	5	164	5
3126	4	03	57	26.3	6.3	6.0	47	139	12
3127	4	03	40	59.3	18.5	6.3	155	50	14
3128	4	03	36	35.4	11.1	6.7	93	60	17
3129	4	03	25	52.0	10.7	5.4	78	75	5
3131	4	03	10	25.2	13.8	5.4	102	62	6
3133	4	03	02	36.8	10.1	6.0	79	87	12
3136	4	02	46	45.3	6.6	6.8	51	118	18
3139	4	02	15	12.2	6.4	6.2	48	68	13
3142	4	02	00	32.3	10.8	10.7	76	−98	76
3146	4	01	45	35.2	1.2	11.2	4	135	7
3150	4	01	09	58.3	13.4	5.3	98	87	4
3152	4	00	48	25.9	1.3	6.0	8	29	4
3161	3	23	24	51.3	5.8	6.9	43	−178	18
3162	3	23	19	20.1	10.6	6.2	84	−46	13
3163	3	23	19	08.2	5.2	9.7	32	49	33
3164	3	23	14	39.4	20.2	6.2	167	−161	13
3165	3	22	56	05.0	11.8	5.6	88	70	7
3167	3	21	43	30.9	8.3	7.6	69	169	26
3168	3	21	38	55.1	2.6	8.7	13	−104	15
3169	3	21	35	26.0	28.5	6.2	238	104	13
3170	3	21	29	11.2	5.2	5.4	37	−155	6
3171	3	21	06	36.2	5.3	5.4	38	132	6
3172	3	20	53	05.5	9.2	6.6	74	52	16
3173	3	20	48	00.2	5.2	9.0	34	95	30
3175	3	19	41	33.2	16.8	6.5	142	76	15
3177	3	19	22	10.0	10.6	6.0	83	−26	12
3178	3	19	10	33.2	5.2	5.8	37	133	10
3179	3	18	52	52.3	10.2	6.2	81	−43	13
3180	3	18	49	37.6	5.2	7.2	38	164	20
3181	3	18	33	11.3	18.6	6.2	153	54	13
3182	3	18	12	40.6	11.4	6.3	92	40	14
3184	3	17	24	51.3	22.9	6.4	193	51	14
3185	3	17	18	36.2	5.8	7.6	43	163	24
3186	3	17	09	45.7	4.9	7.6	34	146	22
3187	3	17	09	04.5	9.4	6.5	76	144	16
3188	3	17	03	32.7	18.6	6.7	163	93	17
3190	3	16	33	28.6	7.9	6.5	62	125	15
3194	3	16	02	13.1	9.5	6.4	75	−32	14
3195	3	15	54	44.0	14.7	6.3	121	125	14
3199	3	15	21	10.5	8.6	6.8	70	95	17
3200	3	14	41	48.0	10.8	7.2	93	−95	20
3202	3	14	15	57.9	14.7	5.9	115	78	11
3203	3	14	07	33.1	10.2	6.3	82	76	14
3204	3	14	04	47.4	19.2	7.4	179	47	22
3206	3	13	35	25.9	1.3	5.6	8	74	3
3207	3	13	29	32.0	24.3	6.3	206	70	14
3208	3	13	17	31.6	5.3	7.2	39	−178	20
3209	3	13	16	32.1	6.7	5.4	48	−40	6
3210	3	13	07	03.7	5.2	6.0	37	84	11
3211	3	12	47	27.3	6.6	5.7	48	138	9
3214	3	12	06	24.9	9.6	5.5	71	78	6
3216	3	11	45	37.1	14.0	5.4	103	105	5
3218	3	11	32	32.2	13.7	8.7	120	−32	67

Alaska microshock locations, July 1964—Continued

Serial number	Date (July)	P-arrival time (G.M.T.)			S-P time interval	Apparent P-wave velocity	Distance	Azimuth	Depth
		Hr.	Min.	Sec.	Sec.	Km./sec	Km.	Degrees	Km.
3219	3	11	22	03.7	6.1	6.2	45	98	13
3220	3	11	04	52.1	11.4	5.8	88	149	11
3221	3	11	01	07.5	20.3	6.9	182	108	18
3222	3	10	52	02.0	8.0	5.4	58	−105	6
3225	3	10	29	01.2	5.1	5.3	36	128	4
3226	3	09	35	39.8	7.3	5.8	54	71	10
3229	3	08	46	23.7	10.3	5.9	79	135	11
3230	3	08	45	48.8	6.2	6.8	47	175	17
3233	3	07	53	18.9	16.0	5.2	114	−59	1
3234	3	07	51	59.2	8.6	7.6	72	125	26
3235	3	07	44	23.3	4.7	6.5	33	162	15
3237	3	07	21	13.4	7.0	7.0	55	173	19
3239	3	07	01	51.1	14.8	24.0	49	−64	146
3240	3	06	59	26.0	24.5	5.8	192	173	10
3241	3	06	54	40.9	26.8	7.3	254	91	21
3244	3	06	28	52.1	28.9	7.8	288	−170	44
3245	3	06	24	45.5	4.5	6.5	31	66	14
3246	3	06	24	13.6	9.0	6.6	73	110	16
3248	3	06	16	02.7	8.2	6.1	63	137	13
3249	3	06	08	08.9	14.0	9.6	114	−93	86
3252	3	06	04	00.6	22.3	6.8	198	97	17
3253	3	06	01	37.1	5.7	8.1	41	129	27
3254	3	05	58	46.7	12.1	5.5	89	72	6
3255	3	05	58	10.7	4.5	6.2	32	139	13
3258	3	05	47	02.0	17.8	7.0	160	60	19
3260	3	05	39	42.1	10.8	11.3	73	−93	80
3261	3	05	34	16.5	6.1	5.4	44	72	4
3262	3	05	29	15.2	19.5	7.1	180	119	20
3264	3	05	07	04.3	16.3	5.6	124	101	8
3265	3	04	56	17.0	15.1	6.5	127	95	15
3266	3	04	20	25.7	18.3	5.7	141	75	9
3267	3	04	17	13.1	15.9	5.5	119	73	7
3268	3	04	05	49.2	16.8	12.6	107	−57	138
3269	3	04	02	22.3	4.8	34.9	8	−58	43
3270	3	04	01	29.1	5.2	8.7	35	−157	29
3271	3	03	59	04.6	15.6	7.1	141	113	20
3272	3	03	31	09.1	20.3	6.2	167	102	13
3279	3	02	27	03.6	10.0	7.1	84	115	19
3280	3	02	23	27.0	12.3	6.3	100	69	14
3286	3	01	54	37.8	11.5	6.8	97	60	17
3290	3	01	30	02.7	10.7	5.5	80	88	7
3291	3	01	27	57.2	13.4	7.3	120	7	22
3294	3	01	23	44.4	14.9	6.2	121	100	13
3295	3	01	22	06.2	13.0	6.4	107	97	15
3298	3	00	54	55.9	13.8	6.5	115	21	15
3300	3	00	53	32.7	13.8	6.6	117	77	16
3301	3	00	52	35.9	13.6	7.1	121	18	20
3305	3	00	44	35.8	1.7	5.7	11	73	4
3309	3	00	11	55.3	16.7	6.7	143	119	16
3311	3	00	00	17.4	10.1	6.7	84	71	17
3312	2	23	50	39.9	18.1	6.9	161	31	18
3313	2	23	46	22.9	18.0	6.8	160	97	18
3314	2	23	42	13.1	4.8	6.4	34	108	14
3317	2	23	32	34.0	5.2	6.2	38	168	13
3319	2	23	22	54.9	20.2	6.0	161	109	11
3320	2	23	14	58.2	10.9	5.4	80	73	6
3322	2	23	10	08.2	5.1	9.3	32	127	31
3323	2	23	09	55.9	5.1	7.1	37	152	19
3324	2	22	59	05.0	4.8	6.9	34	144	17
3325	2	22	59	53.3	4.7	7.8	32	94	22
3326	2	22	55	22.2	12.0	7.2	105	147	20
3334	2	22	00	13.7	4.7	13.0	22	−140	36
3335	2	21	52	43.5	2.7	6.9	16	52	12
3341	2	21	11	14.1	5.8	7.5	43	59	23
3342	2	21	03	47.1	13.5	6.1	109	71	13

Alaska microshock locations, July 1964—Continued

Serial number	Date (July)	P-arrival time (G.M.T.)			S-P time interval	Apparent P-wave velocity	Distance	Azimuth	Depth
		Hr.	Min.	Sec.	Sec.	Km./sec.	Km.	Degrees	Km.
3343	2	20	58	46.2	16.7	5.8	130	88	10
3344	2	20	53	29.3	5.1	6.4	37	149	14
3345	2	20	42	48.3	12.6	5.4	92	−107	5
3346	2	20	36	39.1	4.9	6.8	35	−122	17
3347	2	20	24	38.6	4.6	7.3	32	−177	19
3348	2	20	22	05.0	12.8	5.2	91	94	1
3352	2	18	32	21.1	9.8	6.7	81	−78	17
3353	2	18	30	30.3	5.3	5.4	38	110	6
3356	2	18	18	36.0	4.5	11.1	23	121	31
3359	2	18	12	36.1	10.2	5.5	75	−53	7
3361	2	18	09	12.8	11.9	5.8	91	95	10
3362	2	18	08	49.1	11.2	6.4	90	92	14
3364	2	18	05	50.2	7.5	9.0	55	−76	42
3366	2	17	56	33.4	6.8	7.1	53	161	19
3367	2	17	52	51.0	11.4	6.0	90	67	12
3368	2	17	51	14.1	15.2	7.0	135	−167	19
3370	2	17	42	42.7	16.1	6.4	136	69	15
3371	2	17	40	35.2	17.7	5.2	127	59	2
3372	2	17	39	30.8	19.5	5.3	143	106	4
3375	2	17	30	42.8	9.2	13.0	53	−143	75
4067	5				8.3	6.1	64	140	12
4068	5				16.1	7.6	151	79	27
4069	5				13.0	6.3	106	−166	14
4071	5				15.8	5.3	115	62	3
4072	5				6.1	8.4	44	175	31
4073	5				4.5	8.2	29	73	23
4074	5				15.6	7.2	141	119	20
4075	5				21.3	6.4	182	75	15
4076	5				11.2	7.6	99	−12	25
4077	5		Time not availalbe for 5 July		5.7	10.1	35	−124	37
4078	5				15.7	7.1	142	114	20
4079	5				5.1	8.6	34	40	28
4080	5				8.5	7.2	70	71	20
4081	5				11.8	8.5	101	−156	56
4082	5				12.0	6.5	99	65	15
4083	5				4.9	6.9	35	179	17
4084	5				8.8	6.4	69	146	14
4085	5				4.9	6.9	35	144	17
4086	5				15.6	5.3	113	94	3
4089	5				16.5	7.6	155	94	27
4091	5				11.5	7.5	103	60	25
4094	5				6.2	6.2	46	70	13
4095	5				15.8	6.3	131	65	14
4098	5				24.5	7.2	230	90	21
4100	5				7.9	6.3	61	122	14
4105	5				11.3	6.6	94	127	16
4108	5				5.0	8.9	32	144	29
4109	5				6.2	6.6	47	68	16
4115	5				4.3	8.0	28	61	21

REFERENCES

Asada, T., "Observations of Near-By Microearthquakes With Ultra Sensitive Seismometers," *Journal of the Physics of the Earth*, vol. 5, pp. 83–113, 1957.

Benioff, H., "Orogenesis and Deep Crustal Structure, Additional Evidence From Seismology," *Bulletin of the Geological Society of America*, vol. 65, pp. 385–400, 1954.

De Noyer, J. M., Willis, D. E., and Wilson, J. T., *Measurements of Near and Regional Earthquakes Outside the Continental United States*, Technical Report, Institute of Science and Technology, University of Michigan, Ann Arbor, Mich., 1963.

Gutenberg, B., and Richter, C. F., *Seismicity of the Earth and Associated Phenomena*, 2nd ed., Princeton University Press, Princeton, N. J., 310 pp., 1954.

Isacks, B., and Oliver, J., "Seismic Waves With Frequencies From 1 to 100 Cycles Per Second Recorded in a Deep Mine in Northern New Jersey," *Bulletin of the Seismological Society of America*, vol. 54, pp. 1941–1979, 1964.

Karlstrom, T. N. V., "Quaternary Geology of the Kenai Lowland and Glacial History of the Cook Inlet Region, Alaska," *U. S. Geological Survey Professional Paper 443*, Government Printing Office, Washington, D. C., 1964.

Miyamura, S., Hori, M., Aki, K., Matumoto, H., and Ando, S., "Observation of Aftershocks of the Kita Mino Earthquake, August 19, 1961," *Bulletin of the Earthquake Research Institute,* vol. 39, pp. 895–908, 1961 (in Japanese).

Nettleton, L. L., *Geophysical Prospecting for Oil,* McGraw-Hill, New York, N.Y., 1940.

Page, R. A., Jr., and Matumoto, T., "A Study of Microaftershocks Following the Alaska Earthquake of March 28, 1964, Part I: Statistical Treatment of Sequences of Microaftershocks," paper presented at the American Geophysical Union's 46th Annual Meeting, 1965.

Plafker, G., "Tectonic Deformation Associated With the 1964 Alaska Earthquake," *Science,* vol. 148, pp. 1675–1687, June 25, 1965.

Press, F., "Displacements, Strains, and Tilts at Teleseismic Distances," *Journal of Geophysical Research,* vol. 70, pp. 2395–2412, 1965.

Sanford, A. R., and Holmes, C. R., "Microearthquakes Near Socorro, New Mexico," *Journal of Geophysical Research,* vol. 67, pp. 4449–4459, 1962.

Shor, G. G., Jr., "Seismic Refraction Studies Off the Coast of Alaska: 1956–1957," *Bulletin of the Seismological Society of America,* vol. 52, pp. 37–57, 1962.

Suyehiro, S., Asada, T., and Ohkate, M., "Foreshocks and Aftershocks Accompanying a Perceptible Earthquake in Central Japan," *Papers in Meteorology and Geophysics,* vol. 15, pp. 71–88, 1964.

Tatel, H. E., and Tuve, M. A., "Seismic Crustal Measurements in Alaska," (abstract), *Transactions of the American Geophysical Union,* vol. 37, p. 360, 1956.

Thanos, S. N., "A Low-Noise Transistorized Seismic Amplifier," *Bulletin of the Seismological Society of America,* vol. 54, pp. 347–368, 1964.

Tobin, D. G., and Sykes, L. R., "Relationship of Hypocenters of Earthquakes to the Geology of Alaska," *Journal of Geophysical Research,* vol. 71, pp. 1659–1667, 1966.

Toksöz, M. N., Ben-Menahem, A., and Harkrider, D. G., "Source Mechanism of Alaska Earthquake From Long-Period Seismic Surface Waves," (abstract), *Transactions of the American Geophysical Union,* vol. 46, p. 154, 1965.

Woollard, G. P., Ostenso, N. A., Thiel, E., and Bonini, W. E., "Gravity Anomalies, Crustal Structure, and Geology in Alaska," *Journal of Geophysical Research,* vol. 65, pp. 1021–1037, 1960.

Lamont Geological Observatory Contribution No. 1256
(Submitted for publication July 29, 1965.)

KEIITI AKI
MASSACHUSETTS INSTITUTE OF TECHNOLOGY
MINORU HORI
HIDETERU MATUMOTO
THE UNIVERSITY OF TOKYO

Reprinted with minor changes from
U.S. Coast and Geodetic Survey Volume II-B,C: Seismology and Marine Geology,
"Microaftershocks Observed at a Temporary Array Station
on the Kenai Peninsula from May 19 to June 7, 1964"

Microaftershocks Observed at a Temporary-Array Station on the Kenai Peninsula

ABSTRACT: Microaftershocks of the Alaska earthquake of March 28, 1964, were studied by means of temporary-array stations set up on the Kenai Peninsula. A quick effective analysis method developed in the last several years by the authors was successfully used in this experiment. With this method, we can complete the analysis of data within a few hours after their acquisition. Thus, most of the conclusions given in this paper were reached within a few weeks after the start of the observation, while we were still in the field. The most important conclusion is that about one tenth of the aftershocks originate in the upper mantle to a depth of about 200 km. For the first time, we observed an indication of activation of the upper mantle by a great earthquake in the crust.

INTRODUCTION

This paper describes the method used to observe microaftershocks associated with the Alaska earthquake of March 28, 1964 (G.M.T.) and the conclusions reached. Data were obtained by means of a temporary array seismograph station at Lawing, near Moose Pass on the Kenai Peninsula in Alaska. Continuous observations were made for a 20-day period which began on May 19, 1964—52 days after the main shock. During this 20-day period, 9,061 microearthquakes were registered. Of these, epicenters and focal depths were determined for 797 shocks. In addition, *P*- and *S*-wave arrival times, as well as the maximum trace amplitudes, were determined for 1,514 microearthquakes. Data were processed at the temporary station immediately after each recording, and most of the conclusions given in this paper were reached a few weeks after the observation was started. This rapid processing of data in the field was

made possible by the use of a special, selective-recording device, described later.

INSTRUMENTATION AND PROCEDURE

A seismograph system specifically designed for the purpose of locating microearthquakes was used to obtain the data for this study. Four vertical seismographs, each with a natural period of 1 second, were used to determine the apparent velocity and direction of approach of *P* waves, and matched horizontal seismographs were used to identify the *S* waves. The seismographs were placed at four sites where Mesozoic graywacke was exposed. Figure 1 is a diagram that shows the arrangement of the seismograph array. The geographic coordinates of the main site (No. 4 in fig. 1) are 60°24'15" N. and 149°21'26" W.

Seismic signals were sent to a central recording center by cable and were recorded either on magnetic tape or on pen-writing drum recorders (visible recording seismographs that use revolving drums on which a writing pen registers movement). The magnetic recorder consisted of an endless-tape recorder and a storing recorder.

---

* Now at the Department of Geology and Geophysics, Massachusetts Institute of Technology.

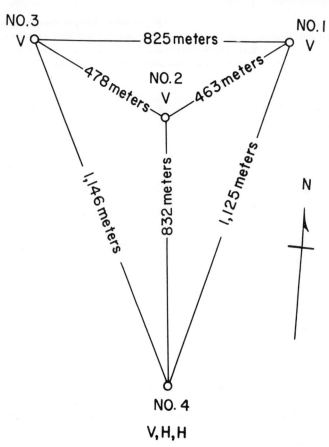

FIGURE 1.—This is a diagram of the seismograph array at Lawing (60°24′ N., 149°21′26″ W.). "V" and "H" refer to vertical- and horizontal-component seismographs, respectively.

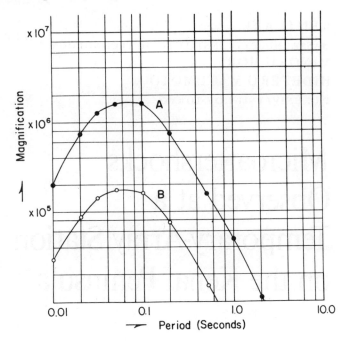

FIGURE 2.—Frequency response and magnification curves.

The endless-tape recorder continuously recorded signals, but erased them 30 seconds later. The storing recorder began to receive signals from the reproducing heads of the endless-tape recorder whenever a triggered mechanism became activated by an earthquake. This procedure enabled *P* waves to be recorded on the storing tape even though the triggered action was made by *S* waves or by later waves [Omote, *et al.*, 1955].

The drum recorders were used for monitoring purposes. Only signals from the vertical seismograph at the main site (No. 4) were registered on two of these recorders; one had a maximum magnification of 160,000 and the other of 1,600,000. The overall frequency response of the seismograph system is shown in figure 2. For comparative purposes, sample records for the same half day are given in figures 3 and 4. As shown in these figures, a time mark was superimposed on the trace every second, as well as for each minute and hour. This method to mark time signals is used widely in Japan for routine observations of microearthquakes [Matumoto, 1965].

The seismic signals recorded on the magnetic tape were reproduced on paper by a pen-writing oscillograph at a speed of 160 millimeters per second. This high speed enabled the authors to read the arrival-time difference between two points of the array with a precision in the order of 1 millisecond. Sample records are shown in figure 5.

To illustrate the uniformity of earthquake records obtained from the triggered mechanism (magnetic tape recorder), the number of shocks with given *S-P* time intervals for the 20-day period between May 19 and June 7 have been compared with shocks recorded by a low-magnification drum recorder. As shown in figure 6, the number varies with the *S-P* interval in an almost identical manner for the two types of recording—thus assuring that the sampling by a triggered mechanism would be uniform in the sense that the shocks recorded on the magnetic tape adequately represented those recorded on a drum.

METHOD OF LOCATING EPICENTERS AND FOCAL DEPTHS OF MICROEARTHQUAKES

For the successful location of microearthquakes by the use of an array as small as that described above, the following three requirements were fulfilled.

1. The seismograph must be placed on consolidated rock which is uniform throughout the array (otherwise,

MOOSE PASS, ALASKA   B

MAY 27, 1964 22^h - MAY 28. 10^h (AST)

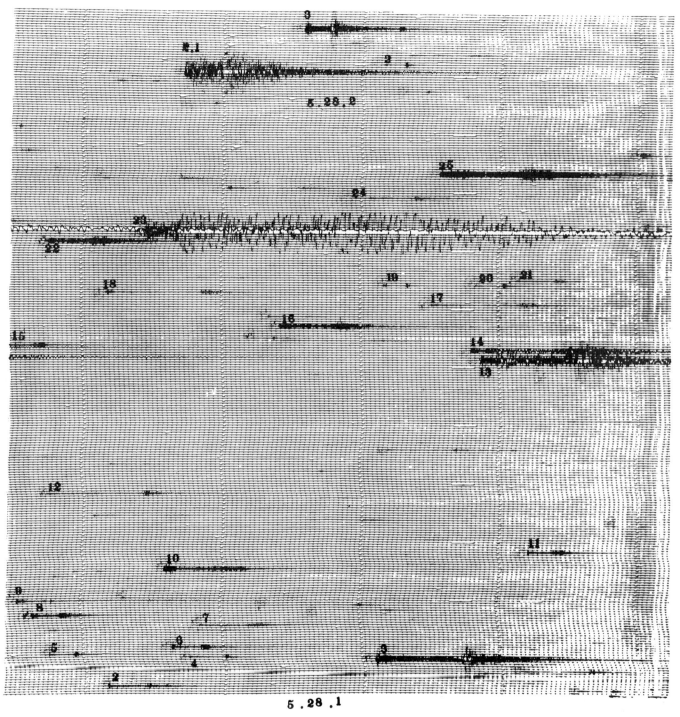

FIGURE 3.—A half-day record of a drum recorder with a peak magnification of 160,000.

the waveform will not be well correlated between seismographs). Also, if the seismographs are placed on soft superficial layers, a small difference in elevation between seismograph sites (or even the thickness of the layers at these sites) would be the source of serious error in establishing the apparent velocity and direction of the wave approach.

2. At least four seismographs must be used to equalize any local irregularity of the medium of the array. They must be located on a plane—preferably, horizontal. A

MOOSE PASS, ALASKA   A

MAY 27, 1964 22ʰ – MAY 28. 10ʰ (AST)

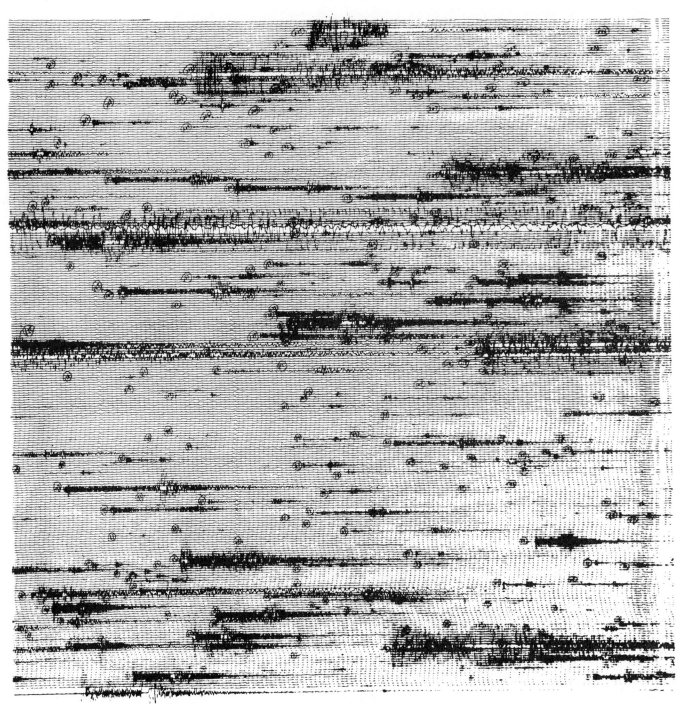

FIGURE 4.—The record of a drum recorder with a peak magnification of 1,600,000—for the same half day as shown in figure 3.

correction of the apparent velocity and direction of wave approach for the slope of this plane usually is applied if the slope is greater than 2° [Maruyama, 1965]. The use of four seismographs also permits an estimate of the error of the epicenter determinations, as explained later.

3. *P* waves must be measured by using vertical seismographs, and *S* waves must be identified through the use of horizontal seismographs.

Shock No.187   (Region A. Focus in the crust. Distance 174 km.)
1964 May 19 21ʰ 23ᵐ (A.S.T.)

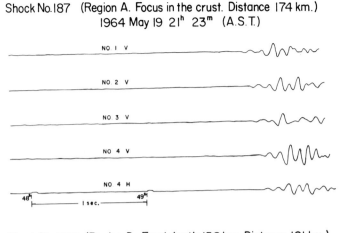

Shock No. 507   (Region D. Focal depth 156 km. Distance 181 km.)
1964 May 24 05ʰ 06ᵐ (A.S.T.)

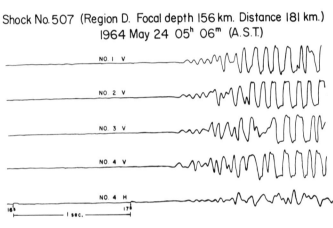

FIGURE 5.—Sample records (seismograms) of a pen-writing oscillograph. Shock 187 is the record of a shallow shock in the Prince William Sound (Region A). Shock 507 is the record of a mantle shock on the continental side of Station No. 4 at Lawing (Region D). "V" and "H" refer to vertical- and horizontal-component seismographs, respectively.

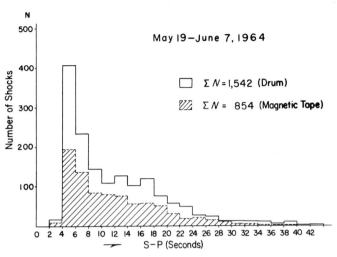

FIGURE 6.—This graph permits comparison of the number of shocks with given S-P time intervals that were recorded on a drum and on magnetic tape. A triggered mechanism was used to activate the magnetic tape recorder.

The difficulty with the former method is that the onset of P waves usually is not definable within the precision of a few milliseconds. The difficulty with the correlation method is that the time length of the wave portion required for obtaining well-defined correlation functions may include waves other than pure P waves, and also that the time and labor spent to evaluate each earthquake is too great—even with a specially designed electronic computer.

ACCURACY OF THE HYPOCENTER LOCATIONS

In the "waveform-visual-correlation method," the arrival-time difference at two seismographs was measured as follows: (1) A seismic signal from one of the seismographs was traced on transparent paper, (2) the tracing was placed over the other record, and (3) a comparison was made of the first several cycles of P waves. If the waveforms agreed only in the first cycle, later cycles were disregarded. However, usually a good fit in waveform was observed for several cycles of P waves. Then, the time shift (the arrival-time difference at the two seismographs) required for the best fit between the two waveforms was measured.

Through the use of four seismographs, it was possible to measure six time differences. These six measurements are independent, unlike the case of using the onset of P waves. From these time differences, six apparent velocities along the directions connecting each pair can be

The method, described above, has been developed by the authors since 1958, and has been applied to more than 1,000 earthquakes recorded at seven temporary array stations in various regions in Japan [Miyamura and Tsujiura, 1959; Miyamura, *et al.*, 1961, 1962; Aki, 1962; Aki and Matumoto, 1963].

The authors tested several techniques to determine the apparent velocity and direction of wave approach, using data obtained at these seven array stations. It was concluded that the most appropriate technique is what may be called the "waveform-visual-correlation method" —a compromise between two extreme methods—that is, one in which the times of initial onset of P waves are used, and the other in which a cross-correlation function is computed for a certain portion of P waves between seismographs [Aki, *et al.*, 1958; Aki and Tsujiura, 1959].

obtained. The velocities are plotted on a diagram with polar coordinates, with the value of the velocity considered as the radial length and the direction of the line connecting pair seismographs as the azimuth. The six points thus plotted must lie on a straight line—if the wave is a plane wave. First, a straight line which best fits these points is drawn, and then the normal to this line from the origin is plotted. The length of the normal is the apparent velocity, and its direction is the azimuth of the wave approach. The scatter of the points around the line indicates the magnitude of error in the determination. In the case of the Alaska aftershock study presented in this paper, the magnitude of error, estimated in this way, is about 5 percent for the apparent velocity and about 3° for the direction of the wave approach. In this method of estimating the error, however, the effect of the heterogeneous wave media in the path from the origin to the array station is neglected. Therefore, the final estimate of error in locating the earthquake origins must be made by comparing the authors' results with those made by the standard method of using many stations spread over a wide area.

During the 20-day period that the authors observed

microaftershocks in Alaska, 797 hypocenters were determined. Of these 797 shocks, 24 shocks are listed in the *Preliminary Determination of Epicenter* (PDE) cards of the U. S. Coast and Geodetic Survey. Table 1 compares the determinations computed by the two methods. The expected apparent velocity of the P waves and S-P intervals in the table were computed, assuming that the C&GS origin times are correct, on the basis of a simplified model of crustal structure of the Kenai Peninsula —a model in which a 35-kilometer-thick crust with a P-wave velocity of 6.0 kilometers per second overlies a mantle with a P-wave velocity of 8.0 kilometers per second [Hales, personal communication]. The authors also assumed that the Poisson's ratio was 0.25.

Table 1 shows that the deviation of the direction of approach of the P waves is less than 10° for about 70 percent of the shocks. The discrepancy of the apparent velocity is less than 10 percent for 50 percent of the shocks. Therefore, 10° for the direction and 10 percent for the apparent velocity are probably good estimates of the accuracy of the authors' method. If the epicentral distance is 100 kilometers, the above error will correspond to an error of about 17 kilometers in the position

TABLE 1.—*Comparison of observed* S-P *interval, direction of approach, and the apparent velocity of* P *waves with those computed from the epicenters determined by the U. S. Coast and Geodetic Survey*

Shock number	C&GS preliminary determination of epicenters								S-P interval			Direction of approach of P waves			Apparent velocity of P waves		
	Origin time (G.M.T.)					Epicenter		Depth	Distance to Moose Pass	Expected	Observed	Difference (Obs. − exp.)	Expected	Observed	Difference (Obs. − exp.)	Expected	Observed	Difference (Obs. − exp.)
	1964		Time of day			Lat. N.	Long. W.											
	Mo.	Day	Hr.	Min.	Sec.	Degrees	Degrees	Km.	Km.	Sec.	Sec.	Sec.	°N.	°N.	Degrees	Km./ sec.	Km./ sec.	Km./ sec.
82	5	19	13	19	21.	59.7	152.3	33	180	19.3	15.2	−4.1	244	220	−24	8.0	7.2	−0.8
90	5	19	14	42	40.7	60.2	146.3	33	175	18.8	26.9	+8.1	100	104	+4	8.0	8.6	+0.6
180	5	20	05	32	13.7	58.0	149.6	20	268	28.3	29.2	+0.9	193	172	−21	8.0	7.4	−0.6
198	5	20	09	28	38.5	60.2	147.4	33	120	13.8	15.5	+1.7	107	97	−10	8.0	6.6	−1.4
231	5	21	01	11	23.4	60.4	145.9	15	195	20.6	22.7	+2.1	90	91	+1	8.0	7.7	−0.3
415	5	23	06	29	24.4	57.3	150.7	20	354	36.1	33.8	−2.3	194	188	−6	8.0	7.7	−0.3
467	5	24	00	40	21.9	60.2	148.0	15	78	9.7	7.5	−2.2	116	122	+6	6.1	5.8	−0.3
481	5	24	06	52	44.4	59.7	148.5	20	91	11.5	9.1	−2.4	149	145	−4	6.2	6.2	0.0
493	5	24	10	16	21.5	59.9	145.5	15	215	22.5	27.9	+5.2	104	108	+4	8.0	6.6	−1.4
676	5	26	21	58	34.1	60.1	147.0	33	130	14.8	17.9	+3.1	104	108	+4	8.0	7.1	−0.9
743	5	27	17	52	08.4	59.1	146.4	33	248	25.5	25.2	−0.3	130	170	+40	8.0	7.3	−0.7
811	5	28	14	06	58.2	60.2	147.7	33	90	11.1	18.8	+7.7	103	95	−8	8.0	7.2	−0.8
823	5	28	16	18	04.2	58.3	150.6	25	245	25.8	42.5	+16.7	197	197	0	8.0	7.9	−0.1
858	5	29	03	34	51.8	60.1	146.5	15	161	19.1	22.3	+3.2	102	115	+13	8.0	7.7	−0.3
875	5	29	10	17	34.5	60.2	146.3	5	170	20.7	10 ?	−10.7	99	113	+14	8.0	7.1	−0.9
1234	6	2	16	09	23.5	59.7	144.4	15	286	30.6	31.8	+1.2	105	112	+7	8.0	6.9	−1.1
1235	6	2	16	29	41.5	59.7	144.2	10	297	32.0	32.8	+0.8	104	110	+6	8.0	7.4	−0.6
1299	6	3	11	25	45.5	61.1	151.2	33	120	13.8	15.3	+1.5	310	292	−18	8.0	7.2	−0.8
1308	6	3	14	03	42.4	59.9	143.9	20	307	32.2	41.5	+9.3	109	108	−1	8.0	6.8	−1.2
1351	6	4	03	27	05.	59.7	147.3	45	138	15.7	22.0	+6.3	123	117	−6	8.1	7.2	−0.9
1441	6	5	09	50	35.0	60.4	146.0	15	185	21.1	19.7	−1.4	89	98	+9	8.0	6.8	−1.2
1448	6	5	11	50	25.	59.3	151.1	94	314	32.0	31.9	−0.1	344	2	+18	8.2	11.4	+3.2
1477	6	5	22	06	53.0	58.1	152.1	15	300	30.3	49.5	+19.2	212	205	−7	8.0	8.4	+0.4
1635	6	8	05	44	31.0	57.4	149.2	33	340	33.9	35.4	+1.5	178	177	−1	8.0	7.0	−1.0

of the epicenter. The error in focal depth would be of the same order of magnitude.

The shocks listed in table 1 are too large to have been recorded by the authors' sensitive instruments, and most of the epicenters are far from the station. This made the identification of *S* waves especially difficult; table 1 shows rather large discrepancies between the observed and the expected *S-P* intervals. The error exceeds 3 seconds for 50 percent of the shocks. However, the error for the smaller shocks with an appropriate record amplitude must be much smaller than 3 seconds.

TIME AND SPACE DISTRIBUTION OF AFTERSHOCKS

The number of shocks recorded on the monitoring drum recorder with a peak magnification of 1,600,000 was 9,061 during the 20-day observation period. The number recorded was 4,626 in the first 10 days, and 4,435 during the last 10 days; this latter number is only 4 percent less than the first 10 days. If Omori's hyperbolic law applies, a 15 percent decrease was expected, since the midday of the first 10 days was the 57th day from the time of the main shock and that of the last was the 67th day. This indicates that the seismic activity during the 20 days was more nearly stationary than would be expected if following Omori's hyperbolic law. The stationariness is confirmed by a good fit of the Poisson's distribution to the shock numbers as shown below.

Table 2 gives the number of shocks (per 2-hour periods) recorded on the monitoring drum recorder having a magnification of 160,000 and the maximum double amplitudes greater than 2 millimeters. Table 3 shows the frequency of occurrence of these numbers (see also the solid line of fig. 7); the mean of the numbers is 6.39. The observed frequency is compared with the theoretical one corresponding to Poisson's distribution law for this mean value, as shown in table 3 and figure 7. The fit is excellent, and the x^2 test indicates that even at the significance level of 80 percent, the authors cannot deny the adequacy of fitting the Poisson's distribution to the data.

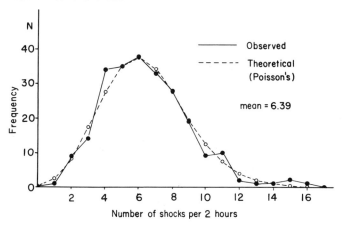

FIGURE 7.—This graph compares the frequency and the number of shocks (observed and theoretical) per 2-hour periods.

TABLE 2.—*Number of shocks per 2-hour periods*

Date (1964)	0000	0200	0400	0600	0800	1000	1200	1400	1600	1800	2000	2200	Total
May 19	7	4	5	13	7	8	10	8	5	9	8	8	92
20	4	4	7	5	5	3	2	7	7	16	8	7	75
21	9	6	5	4	7	7	8	8	7	10	6	6	83
22	10	4	5	6	5	4	4	5	8	4	11	3	69
23	6	5	9	3	9	6	2	5	3	5	6	7	66
24	4	5	8	6	5	7	11	11	6	15	8	4	90
25	4	5	8	3	2	4	6	6	5	8	2	6	59
26	5	6	2	8	8	6	6	6	4	9	10	5	75
27	3	7	5	14	9	4	9	6	5	6	4	15	87
28	6	1	11	7	6	7	9	4	4	2	5	6	68
29	7	4	9	7	3	7	8	6	5	8	5	0	78
30	10	8	3	4	8	7	11	7	12	7	4	6	87
31	9	4	11	8	6	6	7	5	9	4	11	5	85
June 1	6	12	8	8	11	6	4	4	11	6	4	7	87
2	9	7	10	9	5	3	8	4	10	8	7	7	87
3	5	7	5	8	8	10	6	7	4	4	10	6	80
4	6	6	2	5	4	4	6	9	6	6	4	9	67
5	8	6	2	7	3	9	9	3	5	7	7	7	73
6	5	2	4	5	4	5	3	5	3	7	8	4	55
7	7	9	11	8	5	3	5	6	6	......	......	......	60
Total	130	112	130	138	120	116	134	122	125	141	128	127	1523

TABLE 3.—*Comparison of observed and theoretical frequency of shocks per 2-hour periods*

Number of shocks per period	Observed frequency (f)	Theoretical frequency (F)	$\frac{(f-F)^2}{F}$
0	0 ⎫	0.4 ⎫	
1	1 ⎬10	2.5 ⎬11.0	0.091
2	9 ⎭	8.1 ⎭	
3	14	17.3	0.630
4	34	27.6	1.486
5	35	35.3	0.003
6	38	37.6	0.006
7	33	34.3	0.050
8	28	27.4	0.015
9	19	19.5	0.015
10	9	12.4	0.936
11	10	7.2	1.083
12	2 ⎫	3.8 ⎫	
13	1	1.9	
14	1 ⎬ 7	0.9 ⎬7.4	0.027
15	2	0.4	
16	1 ⎭	0.1 ⎭	

$$\text{Pr } (\chi_9^2 \geqq 5.380) = 0.80 \qquad \begin{aligned} \chi^2 &= 4.34 \\ n &= 9 \end{aligned}$$

The excellent fit of Poisson's distribution is rather unusual. Usually, an earthquake sequence deviates from Poisson's process in a manner that indicates a "swarmy" nature of earthquake occurrence [Aki, 1956; Knopoff, 1964]. The fit of Poisson's distribution implies not only that the process is stationary, but also that the occurrence of one earthquake is statistically independent from others. The interdependence of earthquakes is manifested best in the very existence of aftershocks, and this effect usually makes an earthquake sequence deviate from the Poisson's process. From this, the authors regard their result as showing that these small aftershocks are not accompanied by their own aftershocks, but rather that the occurrences are independent of each other.

The epicenters and focal depths were determined by the method already described for the 797 shocks recorded on magnetic tape. The results are listed in table 4. The first column in table 4 shows the reel number of the tape on which the shock listed is recorded; the reels were exchanged three times a day. (On May 21 and 29, the recorder did not work properly, and the shocks on tapes 5–21–1, 5–21–2, 5–29–3, and 5–30–1 could not be processed and so are not listed.) The second column shows the serial number assigned to all shocks recorded by a drum recorder which had a peak magnification of 160,000.

TABLE 4.—*List of aftershocks recorded at Station No. 4, Lawing[1]*

[Footnotes are at end of table.]

Tape number	Shock number	Date	P-wave arrival (A.S.T.)[2] Hr.	Min.	Sec.	Apparent velocity Km./sec.	Azimuth[3] °	$S-P$ time Sec.	Region	Epicenter distance Km.	Focal depth Km.	Maximum trace amplitude[4] Mm.	First motion[5]
5–19–1													
1	68	May 19	00	39	54.9	6.4	75	12.5	A	106	crust	7.0	C
2	69			52	36.0	6.0	146	6.8	B	54	5	40.0	D
3	70			59	10.3	6.0	163	4.8	B	37	5	3.3	....
4	71		01	04	43.5	6.3	42	13.9	A	121	crust	2.4	....
5	82		03	19	44.1	7.2	220	15.2	D	135	crust	23.0	....
6	86			37	27.6	....	....	8.5		....	....	5.4	C
7	90		04	43	04.0	8.6	104	26.9	A	263	114	36.0	C
8	97		05	38	33.5	....	....	18.3		....	....	15.0	....
9	98			51	19.3	6.7	149	23.2	C	222	crust	4.0	....
10	100			57	31.2	7.6	108	21.8	A	207	crust	10.4	....
11	101		06	04	58.9	....	....	4.6		....	....	6.0	....
12	107			49	15.6	6.3	155	5.0	B	38	14	10.1	C
13	108			50	02.0	8.6	338	19.9	D	176	88	3.3	....
14	109			59	05.1	6.6	153	5.0	B	36	18	5.3	C
15	110		07	03	52.5	6.4	120	7.7	A	59	24	3.5	....
16	116			48	38.4	6.7	87	11.2	A	91	crust	5.2	....
17	118			57	23.4	6.2	155	5.1	B	39	12	5.8	D
18	124		08	52	18.0	6.9	70	6.8	A	48	27	4.3	....
5–19–2													
1	131		10	24	30.8	5.7	158	5.0	B	38	3	15.0	C
2	138		11	10	25.3	6.7	36	7.3	A	52	26	2.4	....
3	141			52	31.2	8.0	208	19.6	C	183	crust	4.0	....
4	142			53	55.2	6.4	148	5.2	B	38	16	16.0	D
5	150		12	55	55.0	6.4	67	6.7	A	50	20	9.0	C
6	152		13	14	59.8	7.1	151	5.1	B	34	23	3.8	....
7	153			18	41.6	6.1	135	6.8	B	54	10	8.0	D
8	156			31	58.5	7.8	197	21.1	C	200	crust	4.7	....
9	157			42	15.2	6.4	146	11.0	C	84	30	33.0	D
10	159			59	43.4	6.8	73	11.0	A	89	crust	7.0	D

TABLE 4.—*List of aftershocks recorded at Station No. 4, Lawing*[1]—Continued

[Footnotes are at end of table.]

Tape number	Shock number	Date	P-wave arrival (A.S.T.)[2]			Apparent velocity	Azimuth[3]	S−P time	Region	Epicenter distance	Focal depth	Maximum trace amplitude[4]	First motion[5]
			Hr.	Min.	Sec.	Km./sec.	°	Sec.		Km.	Km.	Mm.	
5-19-2													
11	160	May 19	14	01	19.4	6.2	148	6.8	B	53	16	4.0	C
12	161			17	01.6	6.6	308	10.2	D	80	crust	3.0	C
13	163			45	12.4	5.8	156	5.5	B	43	5	5.0	C
14	165		15	14	42.1	5.9	142	9.4	B	75	5	2.1	....
15	167			25	06.3	6.7	34	7.6	D	55	28	5.0	....
16	169			55	27.6	....	....	30.8	....	....	....	21.6	C
17	170		16	11	26.7	....	....	16.5	....	....	....	7.2	....
18	171			37	35.9	7.7	53	20.0	A	187	crust	2.8	....
19	172			51	28.3	5.7	153	4.9	B	38	5	4.5	C
5-19-3													
1	174		17	24	27.3	7.2	113	20.2	A	190	crust	7.2	....
2	175		18	49	42.0	6.4	107	9.6	A	72	28	6.9	....
3	176			50	58.9	6.9	59	19.4	A	181	crust	8.1	C
4	177		19	03	06.0	6.8	108	11.9	A	98	crust	4.6	....
5	178			07	18.2	6.9	85	11.1	A	90	crust	6.0	....
6	179			21	28.7	....	....	9.3	....	....	....	2.0	....
7	180			32	53.5	7.4	172	29.2	B	289	crust	22.9	D
8	184		20	21	51.3	8.0	16	17.6	D	162	crust	25.0	C
9	186			28	41.6	....	....	8.6	....	....	....	4.0	D
10	187		21	23	50.0	6.7	51	18.7	A	174	crust	5.8	D
11	188			26	23.4	6.0	137	8.0	B	63	5	17.7	C
12	190			33	13.3	....	....	10.9	....	....	....	4.0	....
13	191			50	39.8	6.3	140	12.9	A	110	crust	20.8	D
14	192		22	08	16.6	5.8	142	8.2	B	67	5	34.0	D
15	193			30	25.7	....	....	24.9	....	....	....	6.2	....
16	194			52	24.5	6.5	159	5.3	B	38	18	4.2	....
17	195		23	04	25.0	6.2	152	5.6	B	43	14	10.5	....
18	196			06	27.9	6.3	153	4.6	B	34	13	5.0	D
19	197			28	18.6	6.5	140	8.6	B	64	28	9.8	D
20	198			28	58.6	6.6	97	15.5	A	138	crust	34.0	D
5-20-1													
1	199			53	13.2	6.5	151	4.2	B	30	14	19.5	D
2	200	May 20	00	48	20.9	5.9	136	8.0	B	63	5	2.8	D
3	201			50	09.1	6.4	53	12.6	A	107	crust	5.4	....
4	204		02	03	57.2	8.3	10	5.9	D	38	33	28.0	D
5	205			07	17.1	7.8	95	26.7	A	260	crust	18.3	C
6	206			09	34.5	7.4	75	4.9	A	32	23	6.2	D
7	207		03	22	18.5	6.8	95	16.3	A	146	crust	4.0	D
8	208		04	12	14.4	9.1	142	4.6	B	24	28	3.5	D
9	212		05	45	24.9	6.8	93	14.0	A	122	crust	10.3	C
10	213			48	17.3	6.3	162	4.8	B	36	13	6.3	....
11	214			59	30.2	6.0	151	6.9	B	54	5	2.6	....
12	215		06	01	25.3	9.0	38	4.9	A	26	30	7.0	....
13	216			18	09.6	6.7	163	4.6	B	32	18	19.0	C
14	217			54	22.4	8.2	33	17.2	D	154	60	7.6	....
15	218		07	09	40.1	6.6	62	17.1	A	156	crust	5.2	....
5-20-2													
1	220		08	39	12.0	7.3	108	13.9	A	121	crust	7.0	....
2	221			47	29.8	6.9	91	13.5	A	117	crust	3.5	C
3	222			56	35.2	10.6	235	14.3	D	98	100	7.0	C
4	223		09	21	04.9	....	....	16.5	....	....	....	4.0	....
5	224			26	09.3	6.9	101	12.3	A	102	crust	2.5	....
6	227		11	50	06.4	5.7	183	6.2	B	49	5	4.3	....
7	228		12	34	02.5	6.8	75	6.5	A	46	26	3.2	C
8	229		13	23	26.8	6.0	80	6.2	A	49	5	3.5	C
9	231		15	11	52.1	7.7	91	22.7	A	218	crust	30.0	....
10	232			22	38.8	6.7	169	33.4	C	335	crust	12.8	....
11	233			30	25.2	....	....	8.2	....	....	....	2.2	C
12	234			54	51.3	13.1	240	9.7	D	51	77	7.5	C
13	235			58	38.5	6.0	137	7.9	B	59	5	6.3	C
14	237		16	22	15.7	6.7	77	10.3	A	81	crust	5.0	D
15	240			55	52.1	6.9	66	5.9	A	42	24	13.7	C
16	241		17	05	32.8	5.5	154	5.3	B	42	0	2.2	....
17	242			17	56.3	6.4	91	10.6	A	80	33	26.0	....
5-20-3													
1	243			49	22.4	7.4	193	33.6	B	337	crust	8.8	D
2	244		18	15	53.3	6.9	65	16.4	A	148	crust	3.0	....

TABLE 4.—*List of aftershocks recorded at Station No. 4, Lawing*[1]—Continued

[Footnotes are at end of table.]

Tape number	Shock number	Date	P-wave arrival (A.S.T.)[2] Hr.	Min.	Sec.	Apparent velocity (Km./sec.)	Azimuth[3] (°)	S−P time (Sec.)	Region	Epicenter distance (Km.)	Focal depth (Km.)	Maximum trace amplitude[4] (Mm.)	First motion[5]
5-20-3													
3	245	May 20		19	09.2	6.9	115	14.1	A	123	crust	9.0	....
4	247			36	59.6	6.4	67	6.6	A	49	20	10.6	C
5	248			53	15.3	6.0	90	13.5	A	109	5	3.1	....
6													
7	252		19	03	45.3	7.0	156	12.5	B	106	crust	15.2	C
8	256			25	57.3	....		17.6	....		....	2.3	....
9	257			27	09.1↲	6.1	138	9.0	B	71	12	5.0	....
10	258			41	29.1	6.5	76	12.3	A	102	crust	14.0	C
11	260		20	04	10.6	....		10.9	D	....	....	3.0	D
12	261			10	28.3	8.8	230	16.2	D	136	83	38.0	C
13	263			14	11.4	5.6	146	8.3	B	66	5	3.5	D
14	264			16	41.4	5.6	151	8.0	B	63	5	2.6	D
15	266			58	06.1	7.0	73	12.0	A	100	crust	3.5	D
16	267		21	44	13.1	7.2	104	18.5	A	171	crust	2.0	....
17	268		22	06	14.6	....		4.3	....		....	9.0	C
18	269			09	39.9	....		5.9	....		....	37.0	C
5-21-3													
1	337	May 21	18	14	52.2	7.0	52	18.8	A	175	crust	8.8	....
2	339			53	02.0	7.8	105	15.1	A	134	crust	3.2	....
3	340			55	05.3	6.2	163	5.4	B	41	13	2.0	....
4	342		19	00	36.1	6.5	146	18.2	C	168	crust	3.6	....
5	343			10	06.9	6.3	74	6.7	A	51	17	5.3	C
6	344			22	55.5	7.6	44	14.6	A	128	crust	5.2	C
7	345			23	54.2	7.0	153	5.2	B	38	23	2.4	....
8	346		20	25	08.1	5.7	131	7.7	B	61	5	4.6	....
9	347			51	27.2	7.0	301	13.5	D	116	crust	36.0	....
10	348		21	06	11.0	6.5	67	16.1	A	144	crust	11.6	D
11	349			28	12.5	7.1	61	19.3	A	180	crust	7.0	....
12	352		22	05	57.0	....		5.1	....		....	9.6	C
5-22-1													
1	356		23	13	03.1	5.5	154	6.0	B	47	0	3.0	....
2	360	May 22	00	31	30.0	6.3	141	8.3	B	62	20	14.0	....
3	363			58	03.2	7.3	67	11.7	A	96	crust	2.8	....
4	364		01	10	15.6	6.2	116	14.5	A	127	32	6.6	D
5	366			23	18.5	6.7	74	13.7	A	118	crust	6.0	C
6	367			53	54.2	14.9	123	3.2	A	10	24	15.0	D
7	368		02	25	27.0	6.1	137	8.5	B	67	12	13.7	....
8	374		04	56	11.7	6.3	146	6.8	B	52	18	6.5	....
9	377		06	12	54.8	7.6	70	4.9	A	30	24	27.0	D
10	378			52	15.6	10.0	246	19.7	D	152	124	15.5	D
11	379		07	08	13.5	5.7	131	7.6	B	60	5	23.0	D
5-22-2													
1	385		08	28	53.2	6.6	72	6.7	A	49	23	2.6	....
2	386		09	34	22.1	6.3	162	7.4	B	57	19	12.5	C
3	387			51	53.9	7.2	113	8.2	A	58	crust	38.5	C
4	....		....	......	......	6.6	156	5.4	B	38	19	....	....
5	....		....	......	......	6.2	84	12.2	A	95	26	....	....
6	388		10	35	12.2	6.1	83	11.9	A	96	16	4.4	....
7	390		11	31	04.5	7.0	93	10.8	A	86	crust	5.0	D
8	391			36	38.3	12.3	312	15.7	D	96	122	37.0	....
9	392		12	37	32.4	....		14.8	....		....	3.8	....
10	393		13	10	18.8	6.7	147	5.5	B	41	21	3.5	C
11	395			43	41.8	14.2	283	9.4	D	44	76	10.2	C
12	397		14	30	36.4	7.0	123	15.2	A	134	crust	4.0	....
13	398			59	18.5	6.1	144	6.0	B	48	10	5.0	....
14	399		15	05	31.?	6.9	287	9.8	D	76	crust	2.7	....
15	401		16	14	08.9	7.2	178	5.1	B	35	23	12.0	C
5-22-3													
1	405		17	38	50.1	7.7	171	5.0	B	32	26	30.5	C
2	405′			44	12.1	6.9	63	5.5	A	40	24	1.9	....
3	406			44	38.5	6.3	140	8.5	B	66	22	29.0	....
4	407			50	08.0	7.1	167	5.5	B	38	26	7.5	D
5	408			54	14.8	8.0	269	9.5	D	72	crust	42.0	D
6	410		18	52	13.6	....		8.9	....		....	2.6	C
7	411		19	06	22.2	5.9	83	12.0	A	96	5	3.5	....
8	412			51	24.5	13.0	269	28.1	D	172	232	19.0	....

TABLE 4.—*List of aftershocks recorded at Station No. 4, Lawing*[1]—Continued

[Footnotes are at end of table.]

Tape number	Shock number	Date	P-wave arrival (A.S.T.)[2] Hr.	Min.	Sec.	Apparent velocity Km./sec.	Azimuth[3] °	S−P time Sec.	Region	Epicenter distance Km.	Focal depth Km.	Maximum trace amplitude[4] Mm.	First motion[5]
5-22-3													
9	414	May 22	20	23	23.1	10.1	138	4.5	B	24	30	7.0	....
10	415			30	15.4	7.7	188	33.8	B	339	crust	32.0	D
11	417			53	50.6	7.0	110	25.7	A	250	crust	3.6	
12	419			58	28.5	6.8	169	5.6	B	39	22	14.0	D
13	422		21	42	44.5	6.3	144	9.1	B	70	22	5.3	....
14	423			46	16.8	5.9	143	8.3	B	66	5	12.0	D
15	424		22	07	15.1	7.3	92	19.7	A	184	crust	4.8	....
16	425		22	31	42.8	7.3	163	14.5	B	127	crust	20.5	C
17	......			......	......	7.3	174	11.5	B	94	crust	......	
18	425′		23	09	57.0	......			17.4					
5-23-1													
1	426			28	10.5	10.7	138	4.3	B	19	28	4.3	
2	427	May 23	00	08	33.9	6.6	24	6.0	D	44	22	8.0	
3	428			10	18.1	7.1	174	5.6	B	38	25	8.5	C
4	429			19	14.0	5.8	154	5.6	B	44	5	28.0	D
5	430			41	05.9	7.4	113	19.4	A	181	crust	2.7	C
6	431		01	16	45.6	10.2	281	14.2	D	104	96	3.8	
7	433		02	58	44.6	6.1	122	7.3	A	58	10	7.5	C
8	435		03	32	59.7	6.8	180	5.9	B	42	24	20.0	
9	436			35	60.0	7.3	53	22.9	A	219	crust	3.3	C
10	437			49	48.3	6.9	353	18.8	D	174	crust	2.3	
11	438		04	15	35.2	6.9	204	5.2	C	36	22	4.0	
12	441			34	26.8	6.1	142	8.8	B	70	12	6.6	D
13	442			37	12.8	6.1	142	9.3	B	74	13	2.0	C
14	447		06	07	53.2	6.8	107	16.5	A	148	crust	2.7	
15	448		07	15	10.6	8.1	184	27.6	C	270	60	11.0	
16	449			33	29.0	7.5	56	23.1	A	221	crust	4.2	
17	450		08	01	55.0	6.8	49	18.0	A	166	crust	5.3	
18	451			12	21.5	6.9	79	15.1	A	134	crust	4.3	
19	452			17	37.8	8.5	27	13.7	D	114	62	2.5	
20	455			18	21.3	7.4	102	26.5	A	259	crust	2.4	
21	453			32	22.8	6.2	153	5.4	B	42	14	25.5	C
5-23-2													
1	454			58	15.1	6.8	107	11.3	A	92	crust	2.2	
2	457		09	15	06.1	5.9	151	6.9	B	54	5	5.7	
3	458		09	51	34.0	......	......	6.4				2.5	
4	460		10	42	28.8	11.9	257	22.0	D	148	166	3.1	
5	461		11	04	00.5	6.0	144	8.0	B	64	5	5.6	
6	462			12	00.6	7.7	101	10.9	A	88	crust	4.6	C
7	466		13	51	12.5	7.7	110	21.0	A	199	crust	4.2	D
8	467		14	40	36.5	5.8	122	7.5	A	60	5	40.5	C
9	468			48	44.1	7.0	70	12.2	A	101	crust	7.8	
10	469			57	41.3	6.3	139	7.7	B	59	20	7.3	C
11	471		15	18	08.5	7.3	92	22.1	A	211	crust	2.8	
5-23-3													
1	473		17	36	36.4	6.3	68	18.0	A	166	crust	5.5	C
2	477		18	48	58.5	10.9	313	10.0	D	62	70	5.1	C
3	478		19	10	12.8	5.6	112	11.2	A	90	5	6.?	C
4	479			12	49.5	6.4	311	5.4	D	40	17	18.5	
5	481		20	53	03.1	6.2	145	9.1	B	70	20	40.0	
6	482		21	00	34.5	6.3	71	17.9	A	165	crust	8.5	C
7	484			34	24.0	6.4	128	15.1	A	134	crust	8.0	
5-24-1													
1	486		22	17	07.0	6.4	155	5.6	B	43	18	39.0	
2	489			59	39.3	6.2	153	5.4	B	42	14	14.5	C
3	490		23	00	01.8	......	......	7.2				13.0	C
4	491			05	37.4	6.0	160	4.5	B	34	5	3.0	
5	493	May 24	00	16	56.0	6.6	108	27.9	A	275	crust	16.0	D
6	497		02	15	13.1	6.9	94	12.6	A	107	crust	3.0	
7	498		03	30	32.4	......	......	24.6				3.7	
8	499			47	56.7	6.6	167	6.8	B	49	24	13.0	C
9	501		04	04	46.6	6.5	123	10.0	A	78	34	3.2	
10	507		05	06	17.3	10.3	231	23.4	D	181	156	37.0	C
11	508			18	47.5	6.6	165	5.3	B	39	19	8.5	D
12	509			37	45.2	6.9	122	5.4	A	38	22	9.7	D
13	510		06	36	05.4	6.9	156	7.2	B	50	30	12.5	D

TABLE 4.—*List of aftershocks recorded at Station No. 4, Lawing*[1]—Continued

[Footnotes are at end of table.]

Tape number	Shock number	Date	P-wave arrival (A.S.T.)[2]			Apparent velocity	Azimuth[3]	S–P time	Region	Epicenter distance	Focal depth	Maximum trace amplitude[4]	First motion[5]
5-24-1			Hr.	Min.	Sec.	Km./sec.	°	Sec.		Km.	Km.	Mm.	
14	512	May 24		56	16.9	6.0	141	8.2	B	61	5	3.2	....
15	513			56	45.9	7.4	204	14.6	C	128	crust	6.1	....
5-24-2													
1	518		09	01	25.0	5.5	96	7.1	A	56	0	39.0	D
2	521		10	12	47.3	5.6	135	9.0	B	71	5	6.0	D
3	522			30	21.9	6.6	127	10.6	A	84	crust	3.2	....
4	523			30	52.2	10.2	83	4.0	A	19	26	4.3	D
5	524			40	35.8	6.2	104	16.1	A	144	crust	7.5	C
6	525			57	08.1	......	......	17.6	......			3.1	....
7	527		11	37	37.5	6.6	55	18.2	A	168	crust	2.7	....
8	528		12	31	18.9	6.0	144	12.8	B	104	5	9.5	C
9	529			58	42.0	7.4	187	2.5	B	15	12	6.0	D
10	530		13	04	52.0	6.5	91	11.7	A	96	crust	11.0	....
11	531			06	01.7	......	......	6.2	......			2.5	....
12	533			11	31.6	6.4	87	15.1	· A	134	crust	7.3	C
13	536			20	42.7	......	......	12.2	......			3.0	....
14	538			49	14.2	6.5	77	10.9	A	88	crust	5.0	....
15	539		14	17	36.2	6.5	131	16.5	A	149	crust	4.0	....
16	541			41	42.5	......	......	5.8	......			5.2	D
17	543		15	07	00.1	6.3	91	11.1	A	90	35	6.9	....
18	546			41	23.0	6.2	302	10.6	D	83	24	7.4	C
19	548			49	10.6	6.3	153	5.2	B	40	14	9.5	C
5-24-3													
1	553		17	26	14.4	6.6	70	10.9	A	88	crust	6.4	....
2	554			41	35.5	7.8	152	10.3	C	81	crust	3.7	D
3	555			45	49.6	6.5	93	11.7	A	96	crust	2.5	....
4	556		18	37	24.8	6.8	73	21.4	A	203	crust	5.3	....
5	557			43	39.5	5.9	141	7.2	B	57	5	6.5	C
6	558			44	48.6	5.7	139	5.4	B	43	5	25.0	D
7	559			48	31.8	5.9	141	7.2	B	57	5	5.3	....
8	560			54	00.3	5.8	140	7.4	B	59	5	29.0	....
9	562		19	03	55.2	6.1	116	8.0	A	63	9	2.8	C
10	562'			06	0.30	7.0	265	7.1	D	49	28	4.0	....
11	564			12	54.0	5.8	144	7.1	B	56	5	13.0	....
12	567			15	07.7	5.7	138	7.2	B	57	5	3.6	....
13	568			15	30.3	5.9	145	7.1	B	56	5	29.0	....
14	570			48	06.5	7.2	124	24.0	A	231	crust	3.5	....
15	572		20	13	51.1	6.1	143	6.6	B	52	10	2.0	....
16	573			26	00.6	......	......	4.3	......			3.3	D
17	574			31	19.1	7.4	282	10.0	D	78	crust	5.6	....
18	577		21	25	14.1	6.6	168	7.4	B	54	26	8.3	....
5-25-1													
1	579		22	45	02.0	5.8	53	14.6	A	118	5	9.5	....
2	580			56	56.8	8.8	183	5.5	C	31	33	5.8	C
3	582		23	51	17.8	6.3	125	20.2	A	190	crust	2.6	....
4	585	May 25	01	04	48.3	7.1	122	5.0	A	34	23	7.5	D
5	587		02	01	25.7	6.0	139	5.8	B	44	5	15.0	D
6	590			48	02.5	7.1	87	5.7	A	39	25	4.5	C
7	592		04	01	05.1	6.4	79	15.2	A	135	crust	3.6	....
8	594			15	41.2	6.8	63	15.9	A	142	crust	13.0	....
9	596			41	14.3	9.7	8	16.9	D	132	102	4.9	....
10	597			59	31.9	......	......	6.6	......			4.0	....
11	598		05	08	56.8	7.1	54	12.5	A	110	crust	2.2	....
12	599			45	20.2	7.3	181	25.1	C	244	crust	9.5	....
13	600		06	42	41.1	7.3	150	4.9	B	32	23	3.0	....
14	601		07	21	43.1	6.7	67	18.2	A	168	crust	5.3	....
15	602			34	44.0	8.0	184	6.0	C	36	32	7.5	....
5-25-2													
1	604		09	17	55.3	6.4	147	5.0	B	36	16	......	....
2	606		11	31	00.7	6.2	76	9.9	A	78	22	5.0	....
3	609		12	15	24.4	8.6	100	28.0	A	259	123	4.2	C
4	610			27	13.6	6.3	55	7.6	A	58	20	2.0	....
5	611			28	43.6	6.6	71	17.2	A	157	crust	3.8	C
6	614		13	41	55.4	6.5	153	4.6	B	33	16	20.0	C
7	615		14	11	17.2	8.3	189	6.5	C	39	crust	2.7	....
8	616			18	27.2	6.1	144	7.6	B	60	11	4.5	....

TABLE 4.—*List of aftershocks recorded at Station No. 4, Lawing*[1]—Continued

[Footnotes are at end of table.]

Tape number	Shock number	Date	P-wave arrival (A.S.T.)[2]			Apparent velocity	Azimuth[3]	S−P time	Region	Epicenter distance	Focal depth	Maximum trace amplitude[4]	First motion[5]
5-25-2			Hr.	Min.	Sec.	Km./sec.	°	Sec.		Km.	Km.	Mm.	
9	617	May 25		35	14.3	7.7	79	4.6	A	29	24	5.2	·D
10	619		15	35	15.0	6.9	155	4.6	B	32	19	2.1	D
11	622		16	14	43.8	6.5	152	4.6	B	34	16	27.5	D
5-25-3													
1	623		17	30	14.0	5.9	149	3.3	B	25	5	6.5	....
2	624			43	00.6	....	....	19.5				2.0	....
3	624′			43	49.0	7.9	185	5.7	C	35	31	1.5	....
4	625′			47	56.5	9.1	39	3.1	A	16	19	5.8	C
5	628		18	26	34.0	6.2	181	3.9	B	29	10	9.5	C
6	629			29	54.5	6.3	42	13.3	A	114	crust	4.0	....
7	630			53	22.4	7.2	106	21.9	A	208	crust	5.8	....
5-26-1													
1	635		21	42	54.2	5.9	133	14.6	A	116	5	3.2	....
2	637		22	56	16.3	6.6	185	5.7	B	42	20	2.1	....
3	638		23	10	35.4	8.4	251	24.5	D	227	99	2.8	....
4	639			12	03.6	5.6	147	8.6	B	68	5	5.1	D
5	640			38	54.7	6.4	75	6.2	A	46	19	4.8	D
6	641			55	55.3	8.1	114	38.2	A	(387	56)	4.2	....
7	642	May 26	00	39	56.4	5.5	147	3.5	B	27	0	7.6	C
8	647		02	07	02.2	5.6	149	5.2	B	40	2	7.2	....
9	648			42	11.3	6.6	190	5.2	B	38	19	4.2	....
10	651		03	48	08.0	6.4	77	12.6	A	107	crust	6.2	....
11	652			56	04.5	12.2	257	11.4	D	65	87	2.6	C
12	656		06	33	58.5	6.4	78	19.1	A	177	crust	13.1	C
13	657			36	18.0	6.5	68	16.6	A	150	crust	7.6	D
14	658			39	22.6	6.0	69	12.9	A	104	5	3.0	....
15	659			53	47.9	6.2	139	8.6	B	67	20	2.0	....
16	660		07	14	01.2	6.4	66	10.9	A	88	crust	5.0	....
17	661			15	28.5	6.4	108	15.9	A	142	crust	32.5	C
5-26-2													
1	664		08	57	04.8	6.5	189	6.4	B	48	21	2.0	D
2	665		09	01	17.7	10.4	352	34.4	D	280	226	10.0	....
3	666			30	18.8	6.6	138	8.0	B	59	27	3.8	C
4	667			38	28.3	6.1	146	13.6	C	110	15	38.5	C
5	668			43	55.0	7.2	67	21.0	A	198	crust	5.8	....
6	669			53	35.0	7.1	69	10.6	A	85	crust	3.9	....
7	671		10	40	31.3	6.7	54	7.1	A	52	24	4.0	....
8	674		11	34	26.9	7.4	119	4.8	A	32	21	16.0	....
9	675			36	05.8	6.8	107	17.6	A	162	crust	3.1	D
10	676			58	53.1	7.1	108	17.9	A	165	crust	33.5	....
11	678		12	03	29.6	6.8	107	17.6	A	162	crust	3.5	C
12	677			04	55.3	6.8	109	17.5	A	160	crust	4.0	D
13	680			22	32.4	5.6	146	3.3	B	25	3	13.0	C
14	685		14	44	12.9	7.2	26	11.2	D	91	crust	6.8	....
15	688		15	19	21.1	17.5	285	19.9	D	96	180	5.8	C
5-26-3													
1	691		17	42	37.8	....	....	5.7	....			3.5	....
2	693		18	06	14.4	6.8	107	11.0	A	89	crust	5.3	C
3	694			18	31.9	6.9	53	17.7	A	162	crust	6.3	C
4	696			45	12.0	8.5	218	18.0	D	163	80	6.6	....
5	697		19	02	07.8	6.7	63	6.6	A	49	23	2.8	....
6	698			16	33.2	7.3	114	6.2	A	42	28	21.0	C
7	700			18	20.1	11.2	234	13.4	D	90	96	6.2	....
8	702		20	19	10.7	6.8	171	19.4	C	181	crust	4.5	C
9	703			30	44.1	6.4	72	17.5	A	160	crust	30.0	C
10	706		20	59	38.6	....	....	3.4				4.0	....
11	707		21	16	21.0	7.7	15	11.2	D	91	crust	6.1	....
12	708			23	20.5	5.8	147	7.4	B	59	5	4.5	D
13	709			28	59.3	....	....	24.1				2.2	....
14	710			51	08.6	6.4	133	8.3	B	63	25	4.7	C
15	711			57	11.1	9.5	322	11.5	D	84	69	15.2	....
16	712		22	15	10.4	6.8	68	18.2	A	168	crust	....	....
17	713			17	....	....	....	26.4				5.0	....
18	714			20	32.5	6.4	61	6.3	A	47	20	19.0	C
5-27-1													
1	716			46	13.7	5.9	137	12.6	A	107	5	5.7	C
2	719	May 27	01	38	56.3	....	....	5.6	....			2.0	....

TABLE 4.—*List of aftershocks recorded at Station No. 4, Lawing[1]*—Continued

[Footnotes are at end of table.]

Tape number	Shock number	Date	P-wave arrival (A.S.T.)[2]			Apparent velocity	Azimuth [3]	S−P time	Region	Epicenter distance	Focal depth	Maximum trace amplitude [4]	First motion [5]
			Hr.	Min.	Sec.	Km./sec.	°	Sec.		Km.	Km.	Mm.	
5-27-1													
3	720	May 27	02	07	21.8	6.6	68	16.2	A	145	crust	4.4	C
4	721			12	11.4	12.7	323	24.8	D	156	204	4.7	....
5	723			49	30.6	7.3	167	4.6	B	29	21	8.1	C
6	724		03	28	10.8	6.6	104	18.0	A	166	crust	34.5	....
7	728		05	25	23.3	7.8	215	16.8	D	152	crust	3.6	....
8	729		05	32	32.9	6.4	133	8.3	B	62	26	8.7	....
9	733		06	01	23.2	....		24.6	....			5.5	....
10	735			18	01.5	5.9	142	8.3	B	66	4	2.1	....
11	738			39	14.1	6.5	136	8.8	B	65	29	3.6	C
12	739		07	13	59.5			18.3	....			3.8	....
13	740			17	38.9	5.7	125	10.5	A	84	5	37.5	C
14	741			28	02.7	8.0	279	7.9	D	53	crust	2.5	....
15	742			39	26.4	6.0	135	7.9	B	63	5	6.8	D
16	743			52	32.3	7.3	170	25.2	C	245	crust	19.0	D
17	744			57	31.3	7.9	220	16.6	D	150	crust	2.0	....
5-27-2													
1													
2	748		08	48	11.2	6.5	69	17.7	A	162	crust	5.1	C
3	751		09	13	14.8	7.0	164	5.7	B	40	25	4.5	....
4	754			48	58.8	7.0	164	5.5	B	37	23	29.0	D
5					....	5.7	154	5.8	B	46	5	....	....
6	755		10	33	26.1	7.7	185	7.8	B	53	crust	5.0	....
7	756			39	27.7	6.9	90	10.7	A	85	crust	3.0	D
8	757			42	16.8	7.1	182	7.2	B	49	32	21.0	D
9	759		12	00	16.4	6.6	120	14.1	A	123	crust	7.9	C
10	764		13	00	10.1	5.6	130	10.8	A	87	3	22.0	....
11	765			19	51.0	8.0	93	21.2	A	201	crust	3.0	....
12	766			34	03.9	6.8	157	6.2	B	44	24	10.0	D
13	768		15	32	10.0	6.4	153	7.6	B	57	24	3.5	....
14	769			35	11.8	6.4	151	4.0	B	29	13	7.8	D
5-27-3													
1	775		17	01	19.0	....		6.2	....			4.7	D
2	776			16	05.2	6.1	139	8.4	B	66	12	4.4	....
3	778			40	20.3	13.2	321	6.9	D	33	53	2.7	....
4	779		18	08	48.6	6.2	130	10.0	B	78	22	4.5	....
5	783		19	20	33.4	....		5.3	....			12.5	D
6	782			08	47.3	(8.4)	(282)	14.0	(D)	118	61	30.0	....
7	787		21	37	25.5	6.2	154	4.9	B	37	12	8.7	C
8	788			46	09.6	6.5	190	6.6	B	49	22	2.7	....
5-28-1													
1	790		22	15	22.9	7.1	130	13.7	A	119	crust	21.5	C
2	792			31	05.2	6.0	141	8.4	B	67	5	10.0	....
3	795			59	33.0	6.3	54	18.3	A	169	crust	25.0	D
4	796		23	01	22.7	6.5	113	7.6	A	56	25	4.3	D
5	797			03	22.8	6.1	159	5.7	B	44	9	5.4	C
6	798			11	19.2	7.3	180	6.2	B	41	29	11.3	....
7	799			33	53.8	6.6	90	10.8	A	87	crust	3.5	....
8	800			43	19.5	6.0	164	6.3	B	50	5	5.0	C
9	803			58	15.6	6.8	173	29.3	C	290	crust	4.5	....
10	806	May 28	00	31	17.3	10.3	274	11.5	D	78	77	7.0	C
11	807			50	06.8	6.8	183	5.7	B	40	23	4.5	C
12	809		01	48	22.3	7.6	74	20.0	A	188	crust	4.7	....
13	811		04	07	25.9	7.2	95	18.8	A	174	crust	35.0	C
14	812			17	23.9	7.6	101	21.2	A	201	crust	10.5	C
15	813			20	14.1	7.0	192	5.7	B	39	25	3.8	....
16	815			41	42.6	6.8	215	11.5	D	94	crust	11.8	....
17	817		05	04	45.4	....		19.0	....			2.8	D
18	818			16	05.3	6.9	72	20.5	A	194	crust	4.1	....
19	819			24	35.3	6.9	157	5.1	B	36	21	3.8	D
20	820			24	55.3	6.9	163	6.3	B	44	24	4.4	C
21	821			30	04.1	6.6	135	8.5	B	62	26	2.0	....
22	822		06	08	22.0	6.3	73	10.1	A	77	28	8.0	....
23	823			18	41.8	(7.9)	197	42.5)	B	402	crust	32.0	C
24	824			54	28.3	7.5	66	13.1	A	112	crust	2.8	....
25	827		07	19	46.4	9.0	0	17.4	D	145	93	13.7	....

TABLE 4.—*List of aftershocks recorded at Station No. 4, Lawing*[1]—Continued

[Footnotes are at end of table.]

Tape number	Shock number	Date	P-wave arrival (A.S.T.)[2]			Apparent velocity	Azimuth[3]	S−P time	Region	Epicenter distance	Focal depth	Maximum trace amplitude[4]	First motion[5]
			Hr.	Min.	Sec.	Km./sec.	°	Sec.		Km.	Km.	Mm.	
5-28-2													
1	832	May 28	09	03	52.0	5.9	136	8.0	B	63	5	37.5	D
2	833			12	04.6	6.7	166	4.5	B	32	16	6.0	C
3	834			49	17.6	6.5	157	5.4	B	40	18	34.3	D
4	836		11	20	37.6	6.8	183	7.5	B	53	30	35.5	D
5	837			40	45.3	8.4	28	12.9	D	106	58	2.6	....
6	838			41	27.1	6.6	146	5.2	B	42	20	24.5	C
7	839			44	54.8	7.0	126	16.9	A	153	crust	3.0	D
8	840			53	08.5	6.5	105	14.6	A	128	crust	15.0	....
9	841			54	38.3	6.3	103	14.2	A	124	crust	2.6	....
10	844		12	21	23.3	6.7	63	6.8	A	50	26	3.0	....
11	845			33	17.2	6.8	97	7.2	A	51	28	30.0	C
12	847			36	48.9	5.9	153	4.5	B	35	5	5.0	C
13	848		13	26	48.2	6.7	127	16.6	A	150	crust	3.4	....
14	849			44	56.1	6.6	159	5.7	B	42	20	11.0	D
15	850			46	42.2	6.6	76	10.8	A	86	crust	2.3	C
16	852			49	33.1	8.2	2	17.7	D	159	62	7.1	....
17	853		15	44	53.6	6.8	91	16.2	A	146	crust	7.2	C
18	854			48	43.8	6.7	185	5.0	B	36	19	22.0	C
5-28-3													
1	857		17	26	43.4	6.9	96	15.4	A	140	crust	7.0	C
2	857			30	20.?	10.2	214	23.2	C	182	153	....	
3	858			35	18.0	7.7	115	22.3	A	213	crust	33.0	C
4	859		18	40	14.5	7.7	65	4.5	A	28	23	4.0	....
5	860		19	18	39.2	6.8	148	5.4	B	39	22	3.5	....
6	862		20	52	36.7	7.7	84	4.6	A	28	23	3.6	D
7	863		21	01	49.5	....	....	16.9				3.8	C
8	864			23	52.1	6.7	68	17.9	A	165	crust	7.8	....
9	865			55	45.7	7.2	193	5.2	B	35	24	34.3	D
5-29-1													
1	866		22	23	26.8	7.4	178	5.7	B	37	28	5.7	D
2	867			26	50.6	7.7	66	4.6	A	29	24	3.6	....
3	868		23	07	55.3	6.8	150	7.6	B	50	28	14.4	C
4	870			29	33.9	....	....	28.2				2.5	....
5	871			43	27.7	6.4	147	3.5	B	25	12	5.2	C
6	875	May 29	00	18	01.7	7.1	113	10.?	A	80	crust	38.0	C
7	877			51	55.2	7.4	110	21.6	A	199	crust	4.8	D
8	878		01	39	07.5	6.3	313	11.0	D	89	crust	10 5	....
9	880		02	44	50.4	6.5	81	18.3	A	169	crust	21.5	C
10	882		03	59	44.4	7.1	116	15.1	A	132	crust	5.0	....
11	883		04	07	45.5	7.0	188	5.4	B	38	24	11.0	D
12	884			11	43.9	8.4	353	17.9	D	158	76	2.5	....
13	885			21	19.6	6.1	84	6.5	A	51	10	4.0	C
14	886			36	14.8	6.3	151	4.9	B	36	15	5.8	....
15	887			52	08.1	6.8	183	5.4	B	38	22	36.0	D
16	888		05	14	59.2	....	....	20.0	....	....	....	6.3	....
17	889			26	30.5	8.5	242	13.1	D	108	60	3.5	....
18	890			29	49.2	6.0	137	8.7	B	71	5	7.8	C
19	891			48	53.3	5.9	153	4.6	B	35	5	3.5	D
20	892		06	17	11.7	6.3	116	7.7	A	58	23	4.0	....
5-29-2													
1	893			38	38.7	6.0	137	7.5	B	60	5	5.7	C
2	894			45	50.0	6.3	72	6.5	A	49	20	6.3	....
3	897		07	47	50.1	6.3	70	11.2	A	86	27	4.7	....
4	898			49	58.0	10.3	265	18.8	D	141	126	3.3	....
5	900		09	47	24.3	6.1	89	5.7	A	45	10	3.5	....
6	900'			51	38.?	6.3	125	7.5	A	57	20	1.5	....
7	901			52	01.3	6.7	69	22.5	A	216	crust	5.2	....
8	902		10	02	08.5	7.6	90	16.0	A	143	crust	13.3	....
9				....	....	6.0	140	8.7	B	69	5	....	....
10	903			13	38.1	7.2	92	29.4	A	291	crust	4.6	C
11	905		11	11	08.8	....	....	5.1	....	....	....	3.9	C
12	907			29	44.1	7.0	166	5.2	B	36	23	8.1	C
13	909		12	25	13.9	6.9	25	5.2	D	37	22	3.9	....
14	912			56	15.5	8.2	333	12.5	D	103	50	7.8	....
15	913		13	10	53.4	7.0	184	4.6	B	31	20	6.8	C

TABLE 4.—*List of aftershocks recorded at Station No. 4, Lawing[1]*—Continued

[Footnotes are at end of table.]

Tape number	Shock number	Date	P-wave arrival (A.S.T.)[2]			Apparent velocity	Azimuth [3]	S−P time	Region	Epicenter distance	Focal depth	Maximum trace amplitude [4]	First motion [5]
			Hr.	Min.	Sec.	Km./sec.	°	Sec.		Km.	Km.	Mm.	
5-29-2													
16	914	May 29		23	20.2	7.2	94	21.4	A	204	crust	2.0	....
17	919		14	48	49.0	7.0	64	11.4	A	93	crust	7.0	....
18	920		15	02	33.2	7.1	152	4.9	B	33	22	5.5	....
19				19	11.3	......	....	17.6	.....	...	...	2.5	....
20	923		16	04	41.8	6.5	180	7.4	B	56	25	7.0	....
5-30-2		May 30											
1	976		08	15	45.5	6.6	181	6.2	B	45	22	4.5	C
2	979			45	59.2	11.6	321	14.9	D	96	112	7.1	....
3	980		09	04	30.2	7.4	93	16.6	A	150	crust	3.0	....
4	981			25	32.5	7.4	56	21.7	A	207	crust	3.5	C
5	982			58	24.1	5.8	143	7.2	B	57	5	3.5	....
6	983		10	31	14.8	......	....	19.3	.....	...	...	2.0	D
7	948			54	47.5	6.0	127	8.6	A	68	5	33.5	C
8	985			58	53.9	6.8	66	12.5	A	106	crust	6.7	D
9	986		11	00	32.3	5.7	120	12.3	A	98	5	6.5	C .
10	987			40	12.4	6.9	65	24.3	A	235	crust	3.0	....
11	988			50	06.2	5.9	160	5.5	B	44	5	3.6	....
12				50	57.8	......	....	5.3	.....	...	...	1.8	....
13	989			56	51.6	6.0	167	4.3	B	33	5	3.0	C
14	990		12	06	02.7	6.1	81	6.0	A	47	8	15.0	C
15	991			11	15.8	6.4	161	5.7	B	43	18	36.0	D
16	992			24	19.8	......	....	6.8	.....	...	...	7.3	....
17	996			57	47.1	7.0	174	22.3	C	213	crust	11.2	....
18	997		13	04	31.6	6.3	129	7.5	B	56	22	3.3	....
19	999			21	45.0	6.8	94	11.4	A	93	crust	3.0	....
5-30-3													
1	1000			53	38.4	6.5	67	7.2	A	52	24	3.3	C
2	1001		14	26	14.2	7.0	294	8.9	D	65	crust	6.5	....
3	1002			38	03.6	7.1	103	23.2	A	222	crust	3.8	....
4	1003			48	15.3	14.6	249	......	D	...	crust	9.5	....
5	1004			57	17.4	7.0	109	22.8	A	218	crust	4.2	....
6	1006		15	22	36.9	6.6	153	4.7	B	34	16	6.8	C
7	1007			23	12.0	6.9	67	18.5	A	171	crust	5.6	C
8	1008		16	06	54.3	......	....	5.0	.....	...	...	5.0	....
9	1009			57	31.9	6.3	156	5.8	B	44	16	13.0	D
10	1011		17	07	14.9	6.8	73	6.1	A	43	24	7.6	D
11	1018			55	10.7	......	....	4.9	.....	...	...	2.4	....
12	1019			59	59.2	6.9	150	14.9	C	132	crust	2.3	....
13	1020		18	09	33.5	......	....	......	.....	...	...	3.2	....
14	1021			39	36.2	7.2	182	5.1	B	34	24	15.0	....
15	1022		19	10	41.3	6.7	308	......	D	...	...	3.2	....
16	1024			40	30.9	......	....	20.5	.....	...	...	8.2	C
17	1025			43	21.9	6.6	78	13.5	A	117	crust	2.5	....
18	1028		20	44	00.1	10.8	267	13.2	D	88	94	7.8	....
19	1029		21	02	54.5	11.8	236	18.9	D	124	146	4.2	C
5-31-1													
1	1031		22	14	28.4	6.3	59	9.4	A	71	28	13.5	C
2	1032			17	12.6	6.4	150	5.2	B	39	17	5.8	C
3	1034			29	54.8	6.8	172	4.8	B	33	19	11.5	C
4	1035			48	24.4	6.6	92	12.6	A	107	crust	7.6	C
5	1037	May 31	00	48	49.7	6.8	76	13.8	A	120	crust	3.0	C
6	1039			54	43.3	6.1	128	7.2	B	57	11	3.8	....
7	1040			55	24.3	6.5	169	13.0	C	111	crust	18.9	....
8	1041		01	01	07.7	7.7	70	4.9	A	30	25	12.7	D
9	1044			44	25.0	6.4	49	12.5	A	106	crust	3.0	....
10	1045			53	12.5	7.3	76	11.8	A	97	crust	3.0	....
11	1047		03	17	35.5	7.6	188	37.?	C	374	crust	8.3	....
12	1048			42	51.9	8.0	98	28.0	A	276	crust	3.5	....
13	1051		04	30	47.2	6.1	86	17.1	A	156	24	4.0	....
14	1053			37	00.9	7.5	93	19.3	A	180	crust	6.4	....
15	1054			38	34.2	......	....	18.9	.....	...	...	3.6	....
16	1055		05	00	11.6	6.3	71	6.9	A	52	20	6.8	C
17	1057			33	12.5	6.7	137	20.0	C	188	crust	7.0	C
18	1061		06	28	48.0	6.3	154	5.4	B	41	16	8.4	C
19	1062			55	30.1	6.1	71	6.4	A	51	11	6.2	C

TABLE 4.—*List of aftershocks recorded at Station No. 4, Lawing*[1]—Continued

[Footnotes are at end of table.]

Tape number	Shock number	Date	P-wave arrival (A.S.T.)[2] Hr.	Min.	Sec.	Apparent velocity Km./sec.	Azimuth[3] °	S−P time Sec.	Region	Epicenter distance Km.	Focal depth Km.	Maximum trace amplitude[4] Mm.	First motion[5]
5-31-2													
1	1065	May 31	07	26	50.1	7.3	65	25.4	A	247	crust	16.5	....
2	1066			30	41.5	6.3	139	7.7	B	58	23	4.0	....
3	1067			31	27.0	8.1	189	5.8	B	35	32	2.6	....
4	1071		08	57	30.3	11.4	318	12.4	D	78	91	16.0	C
5	1072		09	02	45.3	6.6	182	7.2	B	53	25	35.0	D
6	1074			51	32.2	6.8	74	10.6	A	85	crust	2.9	D
7	1078		10	56	38.9	7.0	153	14.4	C	126	crust	16.5	C
8	1079		11	08	29.4	6.5	164	7.5	B	55	25	7.9	D
9	1080			29	18.4	6.4	117	26.8	A	262	crust	2.2	....
10	1081		12	10	34.7	6.8	81	8.5	A	61	32	3.7	D
11	1084		13	13	04.2	7.5	92	16.4	A	148	crust	7.0	....
12	1085			40	41.0	7.3	94	20.2	A	190	crust	3.7	....
13	1086			47	46.8	7.5	107	18.8	A	174	crust	5.4	C
14	1089		14	22	27.3	7.1	71	21.3	A	202	crust	8.3	....
15	1093		16	08	03.4	6.5	158	20.5	C	194	crust	8.7	C
5-31-3													
1	1096		17	01	39.5	6.3	60	9.2	A	70	25	21.1	D
2	1097			38	05.8	6.5	122	7.6	A	56	25	5.5	D
3	1098			42	22.7	6.7	111	20.9	A	188	crust	10.3	C
4	1099			47	53.2	6.2	169	6.9	B	53	16	4.0	C
5	1101			50	06.6	6.8	124	16.6	A	150	crust	4.5	....
6	1104		19	21	09.4	5.9	136	15.4	A	122	5	4.0	....
7	1105			47	51.5	6.1	152	5.1	B	44	9	13.3	D
8	1107		20	15	31.9	5.9	123	7.7	A	61	5	27.0	....
9	1108			22	09.8	7.2	119	25.3	A	246	crust	4.2	....
10	1111			46	26.4	6.5	152	4.6	B	34	16	2.9	....
6-1-1													
1	1119		23	16	12.6	7.5	351	24.0	D	231	crust	4.3	....
2	1125	June 1	01	41	42.8	6.0	140	8.6	B	68	5	4.0	....
3	1126			45	26.9	6.8	70	6.9	A	49	27	9.0	....
4	1127		02	05	32.3	6.4	167	7.1	B	53	22	11.0	C
5	1134		03	04	49.5	....	....	4.8	....	....	....	2.3	....
6	1136			34	47.9	7.8	73	5.1	A	33	29	5.9	D
7	1137			35	29.6	7.1	92	26.9	A	263	crust	5.8	C
8	1140		04	20	04.5	7.7	235	25.4	D	248	crust	2.7	....
9	1142		05	20	18.1	6.6	78	15.2	A	135	crust	4.7	....
10	1146			48	11.0	6.8	76	13.2	A	113	crust	3.5	....
11	1148		06	27	38.5	....	....	10.6	....	....	....	2.5	....
12	1149			30	24.4	6.9	69	12.5	A	106	crust	3.2	....
13	1153		07	32	17.5	5.9	145	14.5	C	117	5	32.5	....
14	1154			46	47.4	7.0	72	12.8	A	125	crust	2.3	....
6-1-2													
1	1155		08	03	31.4	6.7	145	13.1	C	112	crust	7.0	....
2	1156			15	02.3	6.7	67	16.6	A	150	crust	2.8	....
3	1157			22	39.5	6.8	130	16.8	A	152	crust	23.0	D
4	1161			35	57.1	9.3	336	18.8	D	154	106	2.5	....
5	1159			37	23.1	6.4	127	6.9	A	52	22	34.0	C
6	1162			48	17.6	6.5	150	4.9	B	36	16	11.5	D
7	1166		10	07	42.4	6.1	128	16.2	A	134	22	2.8	....
8	1167			15	04.6	7.0	107	31.9	A	319	crust	6.9	....
9	1169		11	32	00.1	8.6	357	16.4	D	140	75	6.3	....
10	1170			46	30.5	....	....	15.1	....	....	....	3.0	....
11	1171			59	46.6	7.3	334	5.4	D	36	26	5.9	C
12	1172		12	13	08.2	6.7	283	12.3	D	103	crust	2.9	....
13	1173		13	29	02.9	6.8	286	9.3	D	70	crust	3.8	....
14	1174			34	20.6	6.5	72	6.8	A	50	22	4.2	C
15	1176		14	45	17.2	5.9	142	8.9	B	71	5	3.3	....
16	1178		15	10	29.3	6.2	84	7.9	A	61	18	5.7	C
17	1179			21	20.6	....	....	8.6	....	....	....	3.7	....
6-1-3													
1	1181		16	28	20.8	5.9	146	10.2	C	82	5	9.6	D
2	1183		17	03	00.0	7.2	109	21.2	A	201	crust	3.5	D
3	1184			09	29.2	7.1	77	15.8	A	141	crust	2.5	....
4	1185			13	02.0	6.9	80	5.7	A	40	24	2.5	C
5	1189			36	31.5	6.9	139	9.9	A	77	crust	8.2	D

TABLE 4.—*List of aftershocks recorded at Station No. 4, Lawing*[1]—Continued

[Footnotes are at end of table.]

Tape number	Shock number	Date	P-wave arrival (A.S.T.)[2] Hr.	Min.	Sec.	Apparent velocity Km./sec.	Azimuth[3] °	S–P time Sec.	Region	Epicenter distance Km.	Focal depth Km.	Maximum trace amplitude[4] Mm.	First motion[5]
6–1–3													
6	1192	June 1	18	20	06.9	5.8	84	6.9	A	54	5	8.8	......
7	1193		19	10	34.1	8.3	55	4.6	A	26	26	26.0	C
8	1194			12	17.9	9.8	300	8.2	D	52	52	4.6	......
9	1195			20	03.9	6.4	54	18.8	A	174	crust	26.6	D
10	1196			31	07.4	7.3	48	18.0	A	166	crust	4.0	D
11	1197		20	46	37.4	6.4	77	9.3	A	70	28	5.4	C
12	1198			48	18.6	6.8	108	17.6	A	162	crust	6.9	C
13	1200		21	37	43.2	6.6	65	15.1	A	134	crust	22.0	C
6–2–1													
1	1201		22	19	05.4	7.2	164	4.7	B	31	21	11.0	......
2	1202			42	25.3	6.2	125	8.6	A	66	20	2.8	......
3	1204		23	31	16.5	8.5	28	6.3	D	37	crust	7.7	......
4	1206			52	27.2	6.6	147	10.6	C	85	crust	10.0	......
5	1209	June 2	00	13	30.3	6.5	140	10.3	A	81	crust	4.5	......
5'	1210			19	03.6	6.6	162	6.2	B	45	22	18.0	D
6	1211			34	36.6	7.0	73	15.4	A	137	crust	7.0	D
7	1212			35	49.8	7.0	73	15.5	A	138	crust	6.0	......
8	1219		02	22	40.3	......		5.8				4.?	D
9	1220			38	26.6	6.3	168	5.8	B	44	16	4.9	......
10	1223		03	37	44.0	6.3	154	5.1	B	39	14	9.1	D
11	1225		04	21	41.3	6.5	69	7.0	A	50	23	5.2	C
12	1226			27	04.8	12.5	249	23.4	D	150	188	8.5	D
13	1227			33	44.4	5.8	147	5.5	B	44	5	15.2	C
14	1228			46	36.4	6.3	78	15.0	A	133	crust	15.0	C
15	1231		05	26	57.5	6.9	115	20.1	A	189	crust	5.0	......
16	1234		06	10	02.4	6.9	112	31.8	A	318	crust	34.0	D
17	1235			30	19.4	7.4	110	32.5	A	326	crust	28.0	D
18	1238		07	33	31.4	7.3	26	23.6	D	226	crust	3.5	......
19	1239			38	35.6	6.0	154	5.2	B	41	5	7.5	C
20	1240			39	18.2	......		5.3				7.0	......
21	1241			48	01.4	5.8	167	4.9	B	38	5	12.0	C
22	1242			52	30.4	6.7	121	5.2	A	37	19	7.4	D
6–2–2													
1	1243		08	14	08.5	6.9	76	7.5	A	52	31	15.5	......
2	1244			57	45.0	10.4	306	4.0	D	19	26	2.1	......
3	1245		09	00	52.8	6.3	142	9.0	B	67	24	2.5	D
4	1246			01	27.2	7.3	91	27.3	A	268	crust	3.3	D
5	1247			30	01.0	7.0	70	6.8	A	47	29	25.5	......
6	1248		10	14	26.6	7.8	68	15.1	A	134	crust	3.8	......
7	1250		11	50	00.9	......		25.1				2.7	......
8	1251		12	25	21.4	6.4	164	5.2	B	38	16	4.0	......
9	1252			43	15.1	10.0	239	12.3	D	87	80	10.6	......
10	1253			50	26.3	6.0	139	8.5	B	67	5	2.6	C
11	1254		13	13	43.8	6.3	73	6.8	A	52	19	4.1	C
12	1255			25	58.9	7.1	56	17.4	A	159	crust	7.3	......
13	1256			43	35.9	7.0	110	15.1	A	134	crust	30.0	C
14	1258			59	56.1	6.2	156	5.4	B	42	13	9.3	......
15	......							4.8				......	......
16	1261		15	18	07.7	......		2.7				3.0	C
17	1262			34	14.6	6.0	125	12.0	A	96	5	9.5	C
6–2–3													
1	1263		16	00	35.2	6.1	112	10.8	A	86	16	4.8	C
2	1264			20	37.0	6.5	67	15.5	A	139	crust	36.2	D
3	1265			28	13.3	6.3	162	5.2	B	39	14	5.6	......
4	1266			43	54.1	......		19.3				3.1	......
5	1267		17	08	56.1	6.0	141	8.2	B	65	5	7.5	C
6	1270			32	43.0	......		18.2				2.1	......
7	1272			42	28.2	6.5	72	6.2	A	46	20	6.4	......
8	1274		18	13	44.4	7.0	86	5.2	A	36	23	4.9	......
9	1275			33	05.?	6.9	88	4.6	A	31	19	3.2	......
10	1279		19	20	56.2	6.7	164	5.5	B	40	20	15.2	D
11	1280			47	50.1	6.3	65	15.2	A	135	crust	24.5	......
12	1283		20	55	36.5	9.8	209	29.3	C	243	185	2.6	......
13	1284		21	07	51.4	8.6	192	28.8	C	268	123	2.3	......
14	1285			10	53.8	6.9	358	7.7	D	54	32	5.5	......
15	1286			27	20.9	7.4	109	25.0	A	242	crust	3.0	D

TABLE 4.—*List of aftershocks recorded at Station No. 4, Lawing*[1]—Continued

[Footnotes are at end of table.]

Tape number	Shock number	Date	P-wave arrival (A.S.T.)[2]			Apparent velocity	Azimuth [3]	S−P time	Region	Epicenter distance	Focal depth	Maximum trace amplitude [4]	First motion [5]
			Hr.	Min.	Sec.	Km./sec.	°	Sec.		Km.	Km.	Mm.	
6-3-1													
1	1287	June 2		37	23.1	7.2	95	5.6	A	38	26	2.2	....
2	1291		23	10	19.9	6.0	156	4.3	B	33	5	4.5	D
3	1292			14	51.5	6.8	31	8.6	D	61	34	5.3	....
4	1293			32	06.0	8.6	69	....	A	....	....	36.0	....
5	1293			....	....	8.3	64	4.8	A	28	26	....	....
6	1295	June 3	00	15	01.7	6.5	84	13.3	A	114	crust	4.7	....
7	1296		01	04	43.2	6.3	167	4.5	B	33	13	7.0	....
8	1297			06	22.1	6.4	150	11.7	C	96	crust	5.1	....
9	1299			26	03.9	7.2	292	15.3	D	136	crust	36.0	D
10	1300		02	13	15.1	6.6	49	12.0	A	100	crust	6.3	....
11	1304		03	17	14.1	6.2	75	11.8	A	92	26	24.5	C
12	1305			45	17.0	....	....	15.4	....	....	....	3.2	....
13	1306			58	15.9	6.7	68	15.7	A	140	crust	5.4	C
14	1308		04	04	19.8	6.8	108	41.5	A	392	crust	25.0	D
15	1309			18	28.1	7.3	290	8.8	D	64	crust	36.1	C
16	1310		05	13	42.3	5.8	144	8.7	B	67	5	3.0	....
17	1313		06	44	54.2	6.8	173	4.3	B	30	18	7.0	....
18	1315			46	19.4	6.9	105	13.9	A	121	crust	5.8	....
19	1317		07	17	56.3	6.4	79	12.6	A	107	crust	3.0	D
20	1318			35	47.6	....	....	18.0	....	....	....	3.1	....
21	1319			39	14.2	7.2	102	15.0	A	133	crust	12.0	....
6-3-2													
1	1320		08	59	23.5	5.8	138	12.2	A	98	5	8.5	....
2	1321		09	08	08.7	7.3	109	31.4	A	312	crust	7.0	....
3	1323			22	22.2	7.0	103	20.9	A	198	crust	11.9	C
4	1328		10	03	41.2	7.7	92	28.2	A	278	crust	8.1	....
5	1330			30	52.5	7.5	107	21.4	A	204	crust	7.6	....
6	1331			32	19.0	7.2	191	6.9	B	47	31	5.5	....
7	1337		11	48	07.0	7.1	166	25.5	C	248	crust	2.5	....
8	1338		12	51	39.5	9.0	2	16.0	D	130	85	3.4	....
9	1339			56	37.3	7.4	108	28.0	A	276	crust	4.7	....
10	1343		13	18	23.6	7.1	110	17.8	A	164	crust	4.3	....
11	1344		14	27	42.2	6.7	139	7.4	B	54	27	4.0	....
12	1349		15	51	12.8	6.7	77	20.2	A	191	crust	6.6	D
6-3-3													
1	1351		17	27	27.4	7.2	117	22.0	A	210	crust	33.0	....
2	1352			37	30.0	6.0	76	6.3	A	50	5	4.6	....
3	1353			39	29.9	9.9	232	9.6	D	64	62	10.9	C
4	1355		18	20	40.4	6.1	125	4.3	A	33	8	2.4	....
5	1356		19	06	34.9	7.7	70	5.1	A	33	27	3.0	D
6	1357			22	07.8	6.2	70	6.4	A	49	15	8.6	C
7	1358			51	45.4	7.4	90	11.1	A	92	crust	2.7	....
8	1359		20	20	08.4	5.8	83	6.2	A	49	5	4.1	....
9	1361			24	05.8	7.5	67	12.9	A	110	crust	5.2	....
10	1362		21	12	13.3	6.3	133	8.3	B	64	22	13.2	C
11	1365			28	54.6	6.2	122	14.2	A	124	crust	6.6	C
12	1367			44	59.5	6.2	72	6.7	A	52	16	3.8	C
13	1368			59	23.2	7.2	55	19.1	A	178	crust	5.6	....
6-4-1													
1	1370		22	33	58.4	6.2	137	9.1	B	72	21	3.3	....
2	1373			32	06.6	6.6	75	6.2	A	45	22	3.6	D
3	1374		23	34	11.3	6.1	153	4.8	B	38	8	19.5	C
4	1376	June 4	01	09	06.3	6.6	155	5.7	B	41	21	4.8	D
5	1380			44	16.8	11.1	241	16.9	D	117	123	0.0	D
6	1381		02	21	22.9	....	....	13.3	....	....	....	5.4	....
7	1382			31	24.3	7.3	288	10.2	D	80	crust	21.9	C
8	1383			52	36.4	7.7	91	19.9	A	187	crust	11.5	C
9	1387		04	09	02.3	8.1	0	21.4	D	202	54	2.1	....
10	1391		07	09	18.9	6.5	156	4.5	B	32	17	5.2	D
6-4-2													
1	1394		08	10	07.1	10.7	229	20.9	D	152	150	31.3	C
2	1395			23	48.8	6.4	168	10.9	C	88	crust	22.6	....
3	1397		09	14	15.3	6.8	93	10.8	A	87	crust	10.5	....
4	1398		10	32	48.8	9.1	336	12.2	D	93	68	3.9	....
5	1399			43	51.9	6.4	170	4.8	B	35	15	3.0	....

TABLE 4.—*List of aftershocks recorded at Station No. 4, Lawing*[1]—Continued

[Footnotes are at end of table.]

Tape number	Shock number	Date	P-wave arrival (A.S.T.)[2]			Apparent velocity	Azimuth[3]	S−P time	Region	Epicenter distance	Focal depth	Maximum trace amplitude[4]	First motion[5]
			Hr.	Min.	Sec.	Km./sec.	°	Sec.		Km.	Km.	Mm.	
6-4-2													
6	1400	June 4		51	55.7	10.0	241	11.1	D	76	72	11.5	C
7	1402		12	33	34.3	5.8	142	7.1	B	56	5	3.3	......
8	1403			46	23.6	6.4	141	11.8	B	97	crust	6.0	C
9	1405		13	01	41.6	5.5	154	5.2	B	41	0	3.9	C
10	1407			48	23.8	5.9	152	5.4	B	43	5	5.3	D
11	1409		14	24	58.2	7.4	176	5.7	B	38	28	9.6	......
12	1411			47	13.2	9.9	307	12.2	D	86	78	6.8	......
13	1414		15	31	06.7	12.7	262	17.2	D	103	140	12.6	C
14	1415			50	17.1	5.8	142	7.2	B	57	5	2.4	......
15	1417		16	03	37.4	6.0	68	13.8	A	111	5	39.0	......
16	1418			09	35.9	6.9	166	4.4	B	30	19	5.5	C
17	1419			14	32.6	7.3	72	10.3	A	81	crust	11.7	......
6-4-3													
1	1420			19	08.4	6.5	164	26.2	C	255	crust	2.3	D
2	1422		17	54	58.4	6.6	207	4.9	C	35	17	3.1	......
3	1423		18	31	25.2	7.2	105	23.5	A	226	crust	4.5	C
4	1424			33	36.7	6.8	114	11.4	A	93	crust	4.1	C
5	1426		19	22	31.9	6.8	92	13.8	A	120	crust	7.3	C
6	1427			41	13.2	9.7	286	12.2	D	88	75	3.0	......
7	1428			55	16.0	6.8	154	5.5	B	39	22	5.7	D
8	1430		20	35	10.7	6.4	157	5.1	B	38	16	9.8	C
6-5-1													
1	1433		22	22	09.7	6.7	125	8.7	A	63	32	8.6	C
2	1434			38	36.8	7.1	119	7.8	A	62	34	32.0	C
3	1435			40	17.5	6.0	142	8.5	B	68	5	7.3	D
4	1436			47	16.3	6.7	67	5.9	A	42	22	2.8	C
5	1437			59	46.8	10.3	225	12.7	D	89	85	12.8	D
6	1438		23	14	02.8	......	......	26.3		......	......	4.6	......
7	1441			51	04.8	6.8	98	19.7	A	184	crust	32.5	C
8	1422	June 5	00	04	26.4	6.2	149	5.2	B	40	13	7.5	C
9	1443			27	09.4	6.3	83	12.4	A	96	31	23.1	C
10	1446		01	17	09.6	7.7	181	40.9	C	384	crust	8.5	D
11	1448			50	58.2	11.4	2	31.9	D	232	236	9.8	......
12	1449			55	15.3	5.9	138	8.2	B	65	5	6.0	C
13	1455		03	43	08.8	6.5	107	10.9	A	88	crust	3.0	C
14	1456		05	20	12.1	7.1	107	18.4	A	170	crust	13.0	......
15	1457			59	04.4	7.2	110	25.4	A	247	crust	6.1	......
16	1458		06	06	03.1	7.7	95	24.2	A	234	crust	16.5	......
17	1459			10	20.4	6.4	150	4.6	B	34	14	4.1	......
18	1461		07	15	24.7	8.2	78	26.1	A	249	81	4.6	......
19	1462			23	20.8	8.7	203	14.2	C	116	71	21.6	D
6-5-2													
1	1464			38	41.7	6.1	151	5.5	B	43	10	10.0	C
2	1467		09	52	27.2	6.4	163	5.8	B	44	18	3.4	D
3	1468		10	09	29.5	5.8	152	4.7	B	36	5	18.0	C
4	1469			35	27.3	6.8	94	11.6	A	95	crust	13.3	C
5	1470			46	11.8	6.4	72	8.5	A	64	26	3.8	......
6	1472			58	21.3	8.2	97	24.5	A	232	92	20.1	......
7	1473		11	00	53.5	7.0	155	4.8	B	32	21	10.7	C
8	1474			20	21.5	5.8	154	4.5	B	35	5	4.6	C
9	1475			52	17.1	6.2	188	6.3	B	48	15	7.1	......
10	1476			56	13.2	......	......	26.6		......	......	2.4	......
11	1477		12	07	38.5	8.4	205	49.5	C	460	196	32.0	C
12	1478			12	16.6	6.2	166	6.0	B	46	14	6.7	......
13	1479			14	37.8	8.1	192	5.5	B	34	31	5.4	......
14	1480			53	25.6	10.6	267	12.6	D	87	86	7.0	......
15	1484		13	54	11.3	5.8	139	5.0	B	39	5	10.2	C
16	1487		14	25	56.7	8.0	96	27.5	A	271	crust	6.3	......
17	1487'			58	04.6	9.6	244	9.1	D	60	56	1.8	......
18	1488		15	35	09.8	6.0	139	8.8	B	70	5	3.8	C
6-5-3													
1	1491		17	11	07.5	6.4	72	12.7	A	108	crust	6.0	......
2	1492			42	20.3	7.2	108	19.0	A	176	crust	8.6	......
3	1494		18	18	18.7	6.2	127	7.4	A	57	17	5.0	C
4	1495			41	16.5	6.8	71	6.8	A	48	27	3.9	......
5	1496		19	09	33.8	7.1	76	16.2	A	146	crust	2.9	......

TABLE 4.—*List of aftershocks recorded at Station No. 4, Lawing*[1]—Continued

[Footnotes are at end of table.]

Tape number	Shock number	Date	P-wave arrival (A.S.T.)[2] Hr.	Min.	Sec.	Apparent velocity Km./sec.	Azimuth[3] °	S−P time Sec.	Region	Epicenter distance Km.	Focal depth Km.	Maximum trace amplitude[4] Mm.	First motion[5]
6–5–3													
6	1497	June 5		09	56.5	6.5	155	4.5	B	33	15	9.0	....
7	1498			24	21.3	6.7	90	12.0	A	100	crust	31.0	....
8	1499			44	14.2	6.6	93	12.5	A	106	crust	31.0	....
9	1500			52	21.4	6.8	85	10.5	A	84	crust	4.5	....
10	1501		20	03	21.0	6.1	87	11.0	A	86	15	13.0	....
11	1502			07	00.0	6.1	310	9.2	D	73	13	4.8	
12	1503			24	18.3	6.6	93	11.8	A	97	crust	24.0	....
13	1505			56	49.6	6.1	112	14.8	A	119	20	34.0	C
14	1506		21	09	54.6	6.6	73	12.0	A	100	crust	4.3	C
15	1507			20	33.0	5.8	147	5.0	B	39	5	2.3	D
16	1508		22	12	11.6	6.8	75	5.9	A	42	23	3.6	D
6–6–1													
1	1509			26	27.5	6.6	151	4.8	B	34	18	7.4	C
2	1511		23	07	57.3	6.9	288	19.3	D	180	crust	3.8	....
3	1514			57	32.6	6.1	117	6.9	A	54	10	2.5	....
4	1516	June 6	00	03	55.4	6.4	75	11.4	A	93	crust	4.4	....
5	1517			20	54.3	6.5	148	5.1	B	38	18	3.7	....
6	1520		03	00	56.0	7.0	183	7.9	B	54	38	5.2	C
7	1521			29	15.9	6.5	106	12.2	A	101	crust	10.2	D
8	1522		04	19	27.1	6.9	99	11.5	A	94	crust	3.4	....
9	1524		05	34	15.4	6.0	142	8.1	B	64	5	12.0	C
10	1525			58	17.7	20.7	215	4.3	D	10	33	45.0	D
11	1526		06	16	22.1	6.5	115	13.4	A	116	crust	2.9	....
12	1527			31	40.0	5.7	140	7.1	B	56	5	13.3	....
13	1529		07	39	50.6	8.1	0	10.6	D	84	39	8.6	....
14	1530			54	32.1	6.5	82	11.2	A	91	crust	2.6	....
6–6–2													
1	1532		08	58	19.0	5.9	141	7.0	B	56	5	2.0	....
2	1534		09	43	15.3	6.5	67	16.7	A	150	crust	2.9	....
3	1535		10	01	16.2	7.2	121	21.9	A	208	crust	14.8	....
4	1536			55	56.1	6.4	305	9.4	D	70	28	18.0	....
5	1537		11	36	32.2	7.0	100	14.6	A	128	crust	6.2	....
6	1538		12	07	52.9	6.8	125	16.3	A	146	crust	5.0	....
7	1542		13	29	13.4	6.5	51	18.6	A	172	crust	12.2	D
8	1544		14	18	36.5	6.7	131	8.5	B	61	30	2.8	C
9	1546		15	22	19.8	6.9	107	7.6	A	53	31	10.0	....
6–6–3													
1	1548		17	06	24.3	7.5	70	5.0	A	32	25	6.0	....
2	1549			12	20.0	6.8	150	4.5	B	31	18	4.8	....
3	1551		18	15	18.1	5.9	150	5.5	B	44	5	4.4	C
4	1552			43	45.8	6.7	65	12.7	A	108	crust	4.8	....
5	1557		19	56	06.5	7.1	183	7.2	B	49	32	12.4	D
6	1559		20	13	41.7	7.3	220	29.6	D	294	crust	2.3	C
7	1561			49	10.8	6.3	106	11.4	A	90	30	3.2	D
8	1562			51	52.5	9.5	244	15.2	D	117	92	3.0	....
9	1565		21	42	13.6	......	......	4.8	......	......	......	5.6	....
10	1566		22	18	36.3	11.7	291	9.6	D	56	72	3.3	....
6–7–1													
1	1567		23	30	26.1	......	......	13.2	......	......	......	2.8	....
2	1568			43	54.3	6.4	77	13.3	A	114	crust	5.3	....
3	1570	June 7	00	04	37.5	......	......	5.4	......	......	......	2.9	....
4	1571			44	11.7	......	......	9.6	......	......	......	3.0	....
5	1572			48	16.5	7.6	201	26.7	C	262	crust	6.8	D
6	1573			57	37.9	6.6	74	15.4	A	137	crust	5.0	C
7	1574		01	05	24.8	6.3	84	10.2	A	79	26	3.2	D
8	1575			13	40.2	5.7	148	4.9	B	38	5	5.0	....
9	1580		02	42	49.2	6.8	298	9.3	D	66	crust	9.0	....
10	1582		03	24	04.8	6.9	177	6.4	B	45	26	10.4	....
11	1584			36	06.3	7.0	106	7.3	A	50	32	17.6	C
12	1590		04	42	25.1	7.0	108	15.9	A	142	crust	3.0	....
13	1591			44	38.5	6.6	75	5.6	A	41	20	5.7	D
14	1592			54	37.4	5.7	127	7.2	A	57	5	17.9	....
15	1595		05	12	58.0	5.9	151	5.2	B	41	5	22.5	....
16	1597		06	01	38.6	6.5	151	7.7	B	57	25	4.2	....
17	1598			08	38.9	6.6	80	13.3	A	114	crust	4.2	C
18	1599			13	21.9	6.3	117	8.4	A	64	22	4.2	C

TABLE 4.—*List of aftershocks recorded at Station No. 4, Lawing[1]*—Continued

[Footnotes are at end of table.]

Tape number	Shock number	Date	P-wave arrival (A.S.T.)[2]			Apparent velocity	Azimuth [3]	S−P time	Region	Epicenter distance	Focal depth	Maximum trace amplitude [4]	First motion [5]
			Hr.	Min.	Sec.	Km./sec.	°	Sec.		Km.	Km.	Mm.	
6–7–1													
19	1600	June 7		16	28.5	5.8	144	12.4	C	99	5	20.4	C
20	1601			30	21.1	6.2	124	7.2	A	56	17	22.3	....
21	1604		07	30	32.2	6.4	72	17.8	A	163	crust	4.6	C
6–7–2													
1	1605		08	18	14.8	6.7	182	7.1	B	52	26	29.0	D
2	1607		09	16	31.0	6.7	151	4.5	B	32	16	5.9	....
3	1609			51	11.4	11.9	268	10.2	D	59	77	7.1	C
4	1612		11	42	08.9	6.5	133	8.6	B	64	28	4.2	C
5	1613		12	41	31.4	7.3	94	12.0	A	100	crust	6.4	D
6	1614		13	00	23.9	10.8	231	9.2	D	55	64	10.0	....
7	1616			11	36.5	10.4	327	12.8	D	88	88	2.2	D
8	1617			34	30.8	5.8	165	5.9	B	47	5	2.6	C
9	1619		14	12	13.3	8.1	84	4.5	A	26	24	9.9	D
10	1622			56	08.6	6.3	78	19.1	A	177	crust	10.4	C
11	1626		16	34	33.2	8.9	3	11.7	D	89	63	5.4	....
12	1629		17	58	33.0	7.1	153	4.6	B	31	21	10.8	D
13	1630		18	26	41.5	6.9	184	4.9	B	34	20	26.5	C
14	1632		19	20	26.5	6.4	185	7.1	B	53	22	5.5	C
15	1631			28	56.7	7.4	175	5.2	B	35	25	8.5	C
16	1634			39	36.2	6.5	72	7.1	A	52	23	12.0	....
17	1635			45	16.5	7.0	177	35.4	C	359	crust	31.5	....
18	1636			53	50.3	6.4	155	5.7	B	43	18	5.7	....
19	1637		20	03	28.8	7.7	170	4.5	B	28	23	9.7	....
20	1638			10	26.5	7.5	172	5.0	B	32	24	17.2	....
21	1639			25	02.1	7.5	118	23.1	A	221	crust	3.5	....
22	1640			30	26.6	7.0	167	5.4	B	38	24	4.0	....
23	1641			41	39.4	7.6	2	7.7	D	52	crust	3.5	D

[1] Lawing: Station coordinates are 149°21′26″ W. and 60°24′15″ N.
[2] A.S.T.=G.M.T.−10 hrs.
[3] Measured clockwise from north.
[4] Measured on a recorder with a peak magnification of 160,000.
[5] C=Compressional (up); D=Dilatational (down).

The *P*-wave arrival time is measured from the record written at Station No. 4. The time is shown as Alaska Standard Time (A.S.T. = G.M.T.−10 hours). In the next three columns, the apparent velocity of the *P* waves, the azimuth of the direction of approach of the *P* waves, and the *S-P* time intervals are shown. They are measured in kilometers per second, in degrees clockwise (from the north), and in seconds, respectively. The next column gives the general epicenter region, as shown in figure 8. Region A consists of Prince William Sound and its coastal area; Region B, the part of the Kenai Peninsula east of Seward and south of the array station; Region C̄, the Pacific Ocean south of Seward; and Region D, the continental side of the array (covering azimuths 0° to 35° and 215° to 360° clockwise from north of Station No. 4).

The next two columns give the epicentral distance from the Lawing station and the focal depth. In order to determine the distance and focal depth from the apparent velocity and the *S-P* time interval, the crustal structure must be known. According to Hales and others

(personal communications), explosion data for the Kenai Peninsula are compatible with a simplified crustal model in which the crust with a *P*-wave velocity of 6.0 kilometers per second and a thickness of 35 kilometers overlies a mantle with a *P*-wave velocity of 8.0 kilometers per second. Since the least apparent velocity observed at the array station was 5.5 kilometers per second, the authors modified Hales' model in such a way that the *P*-wave velocity at the top of the crust to a depth of 5 kilometers was 5.5 kilometers per second. The authors also assumed that the Poisson's ratio was 0.25. When the first motion was the refracted arrivals, it was not possible to assign an exact value to the focal depth and epicentral distance. In these cases, the table indicates that the shock originated in the crust, and that the epicentral distance is obtained by putting the focus at the base of the crust.

The epicenters listed in table 4 are plotted on figure 8. As discussed previously, the error in epicenter location was about 17 kilometers at a distance of 100 kilometers from the station, and about 35 kilometers at a distance of 200 kilometers. For convenience, a circle with a 200-

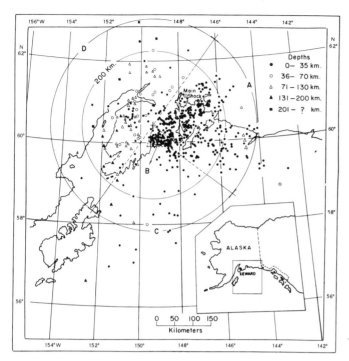

FIGURE 8.—Locations and depths of aftershock epicenters between May 19 and June 7, 1964. Data were obtained from table 4.

kilometer radius from the center of Station No. 4 is indicated on figure 8.

The map (fig. 8) shows several interesting features of the aftershock activity (for convenience of discussion, the authors indicated the previously mentioned Regions A, B, C, and D). About 85 percent of the total shocks occurred on the oceanic side of Lawing (Regions A, B, and C). About 40 percent of these shocks are, however, clustered in that part of the Kenai Peninsula east of Seward (Region B). Here, the intensive seismicity is due partly to the proximity of the area to the array station. It is, however, significant that Region B separates the generally active Region A (of the Prince William Sound area) from the relatively quiet Region C (the Pacific Ocean south of Seward). The number of shocks that occurred in Region C was only 42, as compared to 396 in Region A and to 256 in Region B. It seems as if the aftershock activity, at the time of the authors' observations, was blocked at Region B and did not penetrate south of it.

Practically all the shocks on the oceanic side of Lawing originated in the crust. On the other hand, out of the 114 shocks on the continental side of the station (Region D), 60 shocks originated in the mantle. These mantle shocks occurred in the northwestern half of the Kenai Peninsula along a belt parallel to the general trend of

Cook Inlet. Their focal depths averaged about 100 kilometers and tended to deepen westward. This zone is precisely the same as the one in which shocks of intermediate depths were plotted by Gutenberg and Richter [1949] on their seismicity map.

The next section considers whether these mantle shocks are aftershocks that were activated by the March 28th event or whether they were independent of it. If these mantle shocks are actually aftershocks, it must be concluded that a great shallow earthquake in the crust can activate the upper mantle to a depth of about 200 kilometers.

DISCUSSION

The most important result of the authors' observations is the finding that about one-tenth of the aftershocks originated in the upper mantle to a depth of about 200 kilometers. However, in order to conclude whether these are actually aftershocks activated by the March 28 event, one must examine the possibility that a random fluctuation in the normal activity of the upper mantle in the region might have generated these microshocks. Also to be considered is the question as to why there are practically no shocks with depths greater than 40 kilometers in the list of aftershocks compiled by the U. S. Coast and Geodetic Survey.

First, the authors considered the magnitude-frequency relationship of the microaftershocks for different regions and depths to determine whether there was any difference in the rate of decrease of frequency with magnitude between crustal and mantle shocks. Figure 9 shows the number of shocks with maximum trace amplitudes greater than specified values. The amplitudes were measured in millimeters on a drum recorder that had a peak magnification of 160,000. The shocks were plotted in all four regions, but those in Region D were further divided into two groups; in one of these, the shocks originated in the crust, and in the other, they originated in the mantle. As described before, all of the shocks in Regions A, B, and C originated in the crust. It is clear, from figure 9, that these groups show no significant difference in the rate of decrease of number with amplitude. For amplitudes greater than 4 millimeters, the logarithm of the frequency may be expressed by a linear function of the logarithm of the amplitude. From this linear coefficient, one can obtain the coefficient m in Ishimoto-Iida's formula $N(A)dA = N(1)A^{-m}dA$ [Ishimoto and Iida, 1939]. Under a reasonable assumption, it can be shown that this m value is equal to $b + 1$, where b

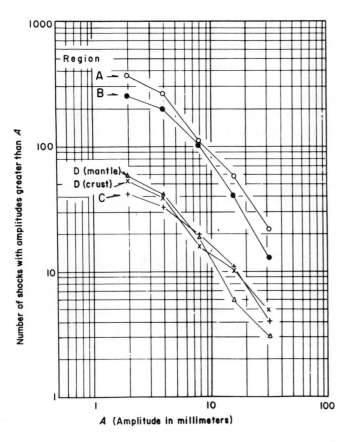

FIGURE 9.—Number of mantle and crustal shocks with maximum trace amplitudes greater than a specified value (*A*) for Regions A, B, C, and D.

is the linear coefficient in Gutenberg-Richter's formula for the magnitude-frequency relationship. Table 5 lists the *m* value for each region, with its 95 percent confidence limits [Aki, 1965].

TABLE 5.—*List of m values and their 95 percent confidence limits*

Region	*m* value	95 percent confidence limits
A	2.20	±0.26
B	2.30	±0.32
C	2.03	±0.69
D (crust)	1.98	±0.61
D (mantle)	2.25	±0.70

From the authors' observations, the number of shocks that originated in the mantle is 8 percent of the total number of shocks for which focal depths have been determined. If the shocks in Region B are excluded because of its proximity to Station No. 4, the rate exceeds 11 percent. The maximum amplitude-frequency relationship, as shown in figure 9 and table 5, suggests that this

rate may hold for larger shocks as well. The PDE cards of the U. S. Coast and Geodetic Survey list thousands of aftershocks, but the tabulation includes practically no shocks with depths greater than 40 kilometers. One explanation for this apparent inconsistency between the two observations is that there is an upper limit of earthquake magnitude for the aftershocks originating in the mantle. This upper limit of the magnitude, if it exists, is probably about 3.

Next, the authors examined the possibility that a random fluctuation in the normal activity of the mantle in the region might have generated the mantle shocks recorded by their observations. Within the general aftershock region during the 1-year period preceding March 28, 1964, the U. S. Coast and Geodetic Survey located 19 epicenters in the mantle. Therefore, C&GS was expected to locate 1.04 mantle shocks during the 20-day observation period—if the activity was not changed by the occurrence of the main shock.

The expected number of mantle shocks that can be observed by the authors' instruments in the 20-day period can be determined by multiplying the above number by a factor which depends on the magnitude-frequency relationship of shocks, as well as on the sensitivity and geographical distribution of seismograph stations used by the U. S. Coast and Geodetic Survey and by the authors. For shallow shocks, this factor can be obtained empirically by using data for the observation period. Between May 19 and June 7, 1964, the PDE cards of the U. S. Coast and Geodetic Survey listed 37 aftershocks with depths of 0 to 40 kilometers, but the authors located 737 aftershocks in the crust. Therefore, the factor is 20 for the shallow earthquakes. A reliable empirical estimate of the factor for mantle shocks during the observation period is impossible because the data are too limited. However, the factor obtained from shallow shocks may be applied to mantle shocks, if the same linear coefficient *b* (or $m-1$) in the magnitude-frequency relationship applies to both.

Thus, 21 mantle shocks were expected to be located by the authors' observations if the activity prior to the main shock continued without any change. The actually observed number of 60 deviated from the expected number by more than 8 times the standard deviation—on the assumption that the earthquake sequence is a Poisson's process. The chance is extremely small that these mantle shocks are not the aftershocks of the March 28, 1964, event but rather are due to a random fluctuation in the normal activity of the region.

The above statement can be fortified considerably if one considers a possible difference in the b value between shallow aftershocks of a great earthquake and shocks of the intermediate depths in the normal period. Mogi [1963] suggested that the value of b for aftershocks is somewhat larger than that for general earthquakes. On the other hand, Suyehiro [1960, 1962] showed that the b value for deep shocks of small magnitudes is significantly lower than that for larger deep shocks ($M > 6$) or that for large and small shallow shocks. If one takes into account these results, the expected number of mantle shocks will be fewer than 21, and the deviation of the observed number from the expected will be greater than what was stated before.

The most direct evidence for mantle aftershocks could be obtained by repeating the same observation at the same place after an appropriate period. If the number of mantle shocks decreases with time, the shocks must be aftershocks. From the foregoing discussions, however, the authors feel that their observations revealed favorable evidence for an activation of the upper mantle by a great earthquake in the crust.

ACKNOWLEDGMENTS

Dr. Shigeji Suyehiro of the Japan Meteorological Agency visited the aftershock area to determine whether it would be feasible and worthwhile to set up a temporary station for microaftershock observations by Japanese seismologists. The authors are indebted to him for the selection of a suitable observation site and for several other arrangements which facilitated setting up and operating the station.

Dr. Tosimatu Matumoto and his colleagues from the Lamont Geological Observatory of Columbia University made preliminary observations of microaftershocks at the same site. For their generosity to use the site they explored, the authors are grateful.

Dr. Eduard Berg of the University of Alaska; Dr. Ruth Schmidt of Anchorage; Mr. Walter Blue of Seward; District Ranger, Victor P. Parent, of the Kenai Ranger Station; and Mr. and Mrs. Charles O'Leary of Lawing greatly assisted in setting up and operating the station. The authors are also grateful to Dr. Anton L. Hales for permission to use his unpublished report on the crustal structure of the Kenai Peninsula.

Constant encouragement given to the authors throughout this investigation by Drs. Chuji Tsuboi, Hiroshi Kawasumi, and Setumi Miyamura is gratefully acknowledged.

Acknowledgment also is made of a grant from the Japan Society for the Promotion of Science (JSPS) as part of the Japan-United States Scientific Cooperation Program. This grant partially financed the authors' investigations.

REFERENCES

Aki, Keiiti, "Some Problems in Statistical Seismology," *Zisin,* Series 2, vol. 8, pp. 205–228, 1956.

——, "Study of Earthquake Waves by Seismometer Array, Part 1," *Bulletin of the Earthquake Research Institute,* vol. 40, pp. 371–389, 1962.

——, "Maximum Likelihood Estimate of the b Value in the Formula $\log N = a - bM$ and Its Confidence Limits," *Bulletin of the Earthquake Research Institute,* vol. 43, pp. 237–239, 1965.

Aki, K., and Matumoto, H., "Study of Earthquake Waves by a Seismometer Array, Part 2," *Bulletin of the Earthquake Research Institute,* vol. 41, pp. 279–292, 1963.

Aki, K., and Tsujiura, M., "Correlational Study of Near Earthquake Waves," *Bulletin of the Earthquake Research Institute,* vol. 37, pp. 207–232, 1959.

Aki, K., Tsujiura, M., Hori, M., and Goto, K., "Spectral Study of Near Earthquake Waves," *Bulletin of the Earthquake Research Institute,* vol. 36, pp. 71–98, 1958.

Gutenberg, B., and Richter, C. F., *Seismicity of the Earth and Associated Phenomena,* Princeton University Press, Princeton, N. J., 273 pp., 1949.

Hales, Anton L., personal communication.

Ishimoto, M., and Iida, K., "Observations sur les Séismes enregistrés par le Microsismographe construit dernièrement (1)," (in Japanese) *Bulletin of the Earthquake Research Institute,* vol. 17, pp. 443–478, 1939.

Knopoff, L., "The Statistics of Earthquakes in Southern California," *Bulletin of the Seismological Society of America,* vol. 54, pp. 1871–1874, 1964.

Maruyama, T., "Slope Corrections in Tripartite Net Observation," *Bulletin of the Earthquake Research Institute,* vol. 43, pp. 409–420, 1965.

Matumoto, H., *Accuracy of Timing in the Routine Observation of Micro-Earthquakes,* a paper read at the spring meeting of the Seismological Society of Japan, 1965.

Miyamura, S., and Tsujiura, M., "Direction of Approach and Apparent Velocity of Near Earthquake Initial Motion," *Bulletin of the Earthquake Research Institute,* vol. 37, pp. 359–374, 1959.

Miyamura, S., Hori, M., Aki, K., Tsujiura, M., and Ando, S., "Observation of Aftershocks of the Kita-Mino Earthquake, August 19, 1961," *Bulletin of the Earthquake Research Institute,* vol. 39, pp. 895–908, 1961.

Miyamura, S., Hori, M., Aki, K., Tsujiura, M., and Matumoto, H., "Simultaneous Operation of Two Seismograph-Array Stations in a Study of Micro-Earthquakes in the Kanto and Chubu Region," *Bulletin of the Earthquake Research Institute,* vol. 40, pp. 885–898, 1962.

Mogi, K., "The Fracture of a Semi-Infinite Body Caused by an Inner Stress Origin and Its Relation to Earthquake Phenomena," *Bulletin of the Earthquake Research Institute,* vol. 41, pp. 595–614, 1963.

Omote, S., Miyamura, S., and Yamazaki, Y., "Triggered Magnetic Tape Recorder for Routine Seismic Observa-

tion," *Bulletin of the Earthquake Research Institute,* vol. 33, pp. 397–410, 1955.

Suyehiro, S., "Deep Focus Earthquakes of Small Magnitude," *Papers in Meteorology and Geophysics,* vol. 11, pp. 97–143, 1960.

——, "Deep Focus Earthquakes in the Fiji Region," *Papers in Meteorology and Geophysics,* vol. 13, pp. 216–238, 1962.

EDUARD BERG

UNIVERSITY OF ALASKA

Reprinted with minor changes from
Nature, Vol. 210, No. 5039,
"Triggering of the Alaskan Earthquake of March 28, 1964, and Major Aftershocks by Low Ocean Tide Loads"

Triggering of the Earthquake and Major Aftershocks by Low-Ocean-Tide Loads

During the investigation of the tsunami in South-central Alaska, many of the interviewed inhabitants of the damaged harbours, villages, and isolated homesteads stated that it was very fortunate that the 'quake had occurred during the low tide levels. The tsunami thus did not cause nearly as much damage as if it had occurred at high tide level which is generally some 4–5 m higher. The low tide has therefore been considered as a possible trigger for the main earthquake and larger aftershocks. Stresses and strains induced in the crust either from atmospheric disturbances or from the solid earth tides have been considered possible influences on the occurrence of earthquakes. Knopoff,[1] however, has shown that the solid earth tides do not have a statistically meaningful influence in California. The peak-to-peak strains induced are about $1/2 \times 10^{-7}$.

Those induced in the area of the Gulf of Alaska are considerably higher. The results of other investigations seem to indicate the incidence of earthquakes in regions where some anomalous crustal loading occurs. D. S. Carder[2] reports earthquakes associated with the reservoir loading of the Boulder Dam area and his calculations indicate the correct relation between earthquake energy and deformation under the water load. Dr. and Mrs. Gough also reported a higher incidence of shocks as a result of waterloading in a dam area from Rhodesia.[3] McGinnis[4] investigated the earthquake incidence due to water load changes in the Mississippi Valley Region, where the earthquake frequency increases with an increase in the rate of change of river stage, and the rate of energy release increases with an increase in water mass, the addition of a water load only aiding the movement of a subsiding crust.

Very pronounced occurrence of earthquake swarms under low ocean tidal loads have been described in the Bay of Sagami by Matuzawa[5] (after research by the Imamura group). In this case, however, the tide variations at the coast are only about 1 m (peak to peak), whereas those in the shelf area of the Gulf of Alaska are about 4–5 m (peak to peak). In Japan,

ABSTRACT: This study indicates that the March 28 Alaska earthquake of 1964 and aftershocks of $m_B \geqslant 5.5$ (except for the first day) located on the Continental Shelf could possibly have been triggered by low-ocean-tide loads. The observation is consistent with the principal compressional stress system deduced from fault-plane solutions, and the stress variations of the ocean tidal loading are high enough to act as triggering force.

as in Alaska, the earthquakes occur during the low water half of the tide cycle.

The tidal diurnal ranges in the Gulf of Alaska are very high compared with elsewhere. In the preparation of Fig. 1, only those locations very close to open water have been chosen, to give an idea of the loading in the shelf area itself. This shelf area is here (more or less arbitrarily) considered to be limited by the 100-fathom line, since from there on the depth increases very rapidly towards the Aleutian Trench (or its extension) to about 2,000 fathoms within 70 km in the middle section of the aftershock area, and twice as fast south of Kodiak Island.[14] The tide ranges are highest in the north-eastern part and diminish progressively further out along the Aleutian Chain. Since Middleton Island, situated almost on the edge of the shelf, has a diurnal range of 10.3 ft, I feel that 3 m is a representative level for most of the Gulf area, compared with diurnal variations some 20 percent higher (12.3 ft) at Cordova in the Prince William Sound. Also, the absolute water levels have drastically changed throughout Alaska (by about 6 ft at Cordova, 20 ft in most of Montague Island, and 5 ft in Kodiak) although the tidal variations stood basically the same. Therefore, the predicted tides still could be used for the present investigation.

Fig. 2 shows the location of the epicentres of all the shocks of magnitude $m_B \geqslant 5.5$ to August 30, 1964, listed in the first part of Table 1, except for the main shock. The table includes all the aftershocks of $m_B \geqslant 5.5$ listed by the U.S. Coast and Geodetic Survey starting 24 h after the main shock. The aftershocks for the first 24 h are not included, since their occurrence is predominantly determined by the aftershock release mechanism.

Fig. 3 shows the tide levels for Cordova and partly for Kodiak (dashed lines) and the time (A.S.T.) of occurrence of the earthquakes with respect to the tides up to April 19. It is found that most of the quakes occur in the lower half of the

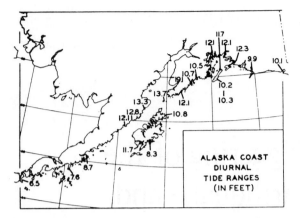

FIGURE 1 Tide ranges along the Alaskan coast (in ft.)

tide cycle or very close to the half ebb tide. The exceptions which may be explained are: two 'quakes at a depth of 39 and 40 km, the 'quakes inland or on Kodiak Island, and one off the shelf area. Since the stresses induced by the tide load diminish with depth and with the distance from the coastline and the tide levels also diminish with the depth of water, these exceptions may be expected.

The exceptions are marked on Figs. 2 and 3 by a cross. The 'quakes marked with an open half circle are those very close to the half ebb tide.

The remaining two 'quakes which are exceptions are those of May 29 at the north-eastern end of the aftershock zone and the one of August 2 at the very south-western end (off the map). No attempt has so far been made to consider shocks of magnitude $m_B < 5.5$.

No attempt is made to solve the problem of the fracture mechanism of rocks *in situ*, that is, at the earthquake failure zone. But if it is admitted that the 'quakes examined here have been effectively triggered by the unloading of the crust,

Table 1. EPICENTRES WITH $m_B \geqslant 5.5$ TO AUGUST 30 FROM U.S. COAST AND GEODETIC SURVEY PRELIMINARY EPICENTRE CARDS

64	03	28	033612·7	0·6	87	61·1	N.	147·6	W.	H	20	M		8·6	8·4	8·6	PAL	PAS	BRK	
64	03	29	060444·5	0·6	56	56·1	N.	154·3	W.	H	30	M5·6	0·2						CGS	
64	03	29	164057·9	0·7	72	59·7	N.	147·0	W.	H	15	M5·6	0·3						CGS	
64	03	30	021806·3	0·9	75	56·6	N.	152·9	W.	H	25	M5·8	0·4						CGS	
64	03	30	070934·0	0·8	80	59·9	N.	145·7	W.	H	15	M5·6	0·3						CGS	
64	03	30	160928·4	0·6	67	56·6	N.	152·1	W.	H	25	M5·5	0·3						CGS	
64	04	03	084627·0	1·4	13	57·9	N.	150·5	W.	H	15	M5·5	0·0						CGS	
64	04	04	045401·7	0·8	76	60·1	N.	146·7	W.	H	40	M5·6	0·2	Deep					CGS	
64	04	04	091055·1	0·7	74	56·9	N.	152·7	W.	H	15	M5·9	0·4						CGS	
64	04	04	174608·6	0·8	78	56·3	N.	154·4	W.	H	25	M5·7	0·4						CGS	
64	04	04	175943·3	0·7	48	56·4	N.	154·5	W.	H	25	M5·5	0·3						CGS	
64	04	05	192818·1	0·8	85	60·2	N.	146·7	W.	H	15	M5·8	0·3						CGS	
64	04	07	192824·7	0·7	55	55·7	N.	151·9	W.	H	20	M5·6	0·3	Off shelf					CGS	
64	04	10	010800·2	0·7	65	58·4	N.	150·6	W.	H	15	M5·5	0·4						CGS	
64	04	12	012431·2	0·9	95	56·6	N.	152·2	W.	H	22	M5·6	0·4						CGS	
64	04	13	140500·0	0·6	57	57·6	N.	151·2	W.	H	25	M5·5	0·2						CGS	
64	04	13	212533·0	0·8	68	57·5	N.	153·9	W.	H	30	M5·5	0·3	On Kodiak					CGS	
64	04	15	153047·1	0·6	74	56·5	N.	154·4	W.	H	35	M5·5	0·4						CGS	
64	04	16	192657·4	0·7	87	56·4	N.	152·9	W.	H	30	M5·5	0·4						CGS	
64	05	29	101734·5	0·9	24	60·2	N.	146·3	W.	H	5	M5·6	0·0	Exception					CGS	
64	05	30	031808·3	0·9	21	59·5	N.	148·5	W.	H		M5·5	0·4						CGS	
64	06	28	190905·4	0·9	55	58·3	N.	150·2	W.	H	23	M5·5	0·0						CGS	
64	08	06	182450·5	0·4	15	56·9	N.	152·1	W.	H	39	M5·6	0·0	Deep half ebb tide					CGS	
64	08	24	215654·2	1·0	46	58·4	N.	150·3	W.	H	22	M5·8	0·0						CGS	
Earthquakes not mapped																				
64	04	03	223342·2	0·7	80	61·6	N.	147·6	W.	H	40	M5·7	0·4	Inland					CGS	
64	04	10	214406·7	0·6	63	60·1	N.	153·7	W.	H	10	M5·6	0·4	Inland					CGS	
64	04	20	115641·6	0·8	87	61·4	N.	147·3	W.	H	30	M5·7	0·4	Inland					CGS	
64	06	29	072132·8	0·8	58	62·7	N.	152·0	W.	H	33	M5·6	0·0	Inland					CGS	
64	08	02	030416·9	1·0	19	56·1	N.	156·1	W.	H	33	M5·6	0·0	Out of map Possible exception					CGS	

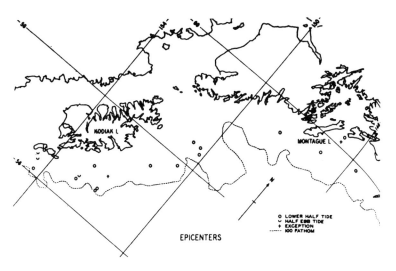

EPICENTERS

○ LOWER HALF TIDE
∪ HALF EBB TIDE
+ EXCEPTION
----- 100 FATHOM

FIGURE 2   Epicentre locations of shocks with $m_B \geqslant 5.5$, ○, lower half tide; ∪, half ebb tide; +, exception; - - -, 100 fathoms

some more data limiting the figures for rock strength in an important earthquake belt are obtained.

During a half-tide cycle of about 6 h duration the pressure varies approximately by 0.3 kg/cm² on the ocean floor of the shelf area. This pressure variation seems to act as a trigger for the main 'quake and the subsequent aftershocks (excluding the first 24 h) of $m_B \geqslant 5.5$. Since brittle fracture seems to be excluded at some depth, and on the other hand strain and tilt observations prior to large earthquakes point towards rapidly increasing values as the failure approaches, it is assumed that a 'creep' fracture is involved. The rocks *in situ* are already stressed far beyond the yield point into the strain-hardening portion of the stress-strain curve, possibly into the strain-softening areas, so that the additional shear force generated by the unloading of the crust (see Fig. 4) in the shelf area and applied during a few hours is sufficient to bring this material to the fracture point. It may be that the very shallow 'quake (5 km) of May 29, which did not occur during the unloading, is an indication that the creep or flow fracture is confined to greater depth and does not apply to very shallow depth earthquakes.

In laboratory experiments the shear strength of rocks is of the order of 100–400 kg/cm²,[7] but several workers pointed out that strengths of rocks *in situ* are reduced by up to 2 orders of magnitude.[8] It seems reasonable, therefore, to assume that the crustal unloading is able to initiate fracture when the pressure variation is of the order of 1 percent or less of the total fracture stress. Also, laboratory stress experiments with other materials indicate that failure occurs much more rapidly if a very small cyclic stress is superimposed on a continuous one, where the amplitude of the cyclic stress is even less than 1 percent of the continuous one. In a particular kind of steel under an 'equilibrium' stress of 120,000 lb/in² and strain of 4 × 10⁻² large flow rates of 5 × 10⁻³/sec in strain are initiated by only a 1.5 percent overstress.[9]

Assuming similar behaviour for rocks *in situ*, an upper limit for the failure stresses encountered can be obtained. Using 0.3 kg/cm² × 100, a value roughly of the order of 30 kg/cm² is found which will, however, diminish with increasing depth.

Balakina[10] has shown that for all the major earthquakes (with one exception) in the Aleutian Chain and the Alaska belt, the principal stress axis is compressional and more or less perpendicular to the tectonic trend. In addition it is directed slightly upward on the Pacific Ocean side for focal depths less than 100 km. I found[11] that this holds also for the main shock and major aftershocks (partly unpublished data) in the Alaska 1964 event.

The periodical unloading of the crust generates an additional upward directed component of force, introducing a periodic shear enhancing the existing stress system and the tectonic movement along the 'hinge' line. The 'hinge' line separates zones of land rise on its ocean side from land subsidence on its continental side[12,13] (Fig. 4).

The unloading of the crust by large ocean tides may be considered as a triggering mechanism for the Alaska earthquake of March 1964 and major aftershocks. The stress system is compatible with that deduced from fault plane solutions and land-uplift and subsidence which occurred during the main shock.

Since brittle fracture seems to be excluded at some depth, the time interval of a few hours and the pressure variation involved as a result of the ocean tide cycle seem to be significant in carrying the last part of the stress-strain curve in the 'strain-softening' region towards failure.

I thank Dr. Maurice Ewing, Dr. Jack Oliver, and Mr. William Best for valuable discussions and strong encouragement to publish these data.

This research was supported by the U.S. Air Force Office of Scientific Research as part of the Advanced Research Projects Agency's Vela Uniform programme.

[411]

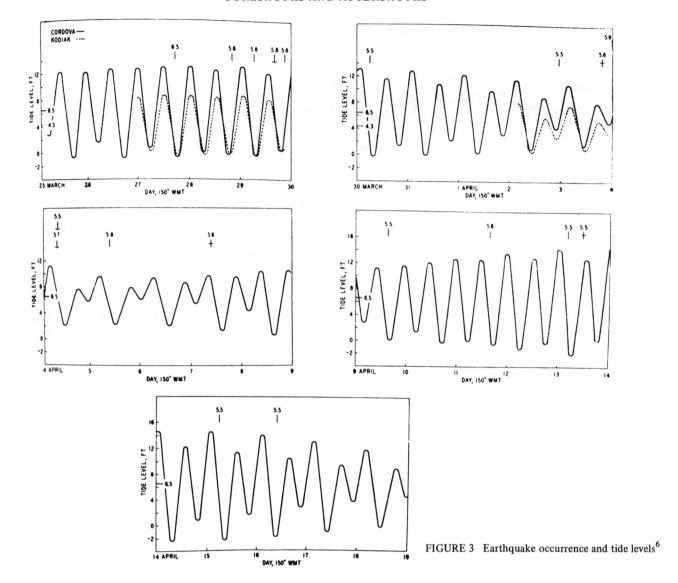

FIGURE 3   Earthquake occurrence and tide levels[6]

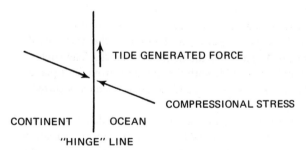

FIGURE 4   Stress system along the hinge line

[1] Knopoff, L., *Proc. U.S. Japan Conf. Res. Related to Earthquake Prediction*, 61(1964).

[2] Carder, D. S., *Seismic Investigations in the Boulder Dam Area, 1940–1944, and the Influence of Reservoir Loading on Local Earthquake Activity. B.S.S.A.*, 35, 175 (1945).

[3] Gough, D. I., and Gough, Mrs. D. I. (personal communication).

[4] McGinnis, L. D., *Illinois State Geol. Survey, Urbana, Circular 344* (1963).

[5] Matuzawa, Takeo, *Study of Earthquakes III, Swarms of Earthquakes, Foreshocks and Aftershocks*, 57 (1964).

[6] *Tide Tables, West Coast North and South America* (U.S. Coast and Geodetic Survey, 1964).

[7] Jaeger, J. C., *Elasticity, Fracture and Flow* (John Wiley and Son, Inc., New York, 1962).

[8] Chilton, F., Eisler, J. D. and Henbach, H. G., *Trans. Amer. Geophys. Union*, 46, 539 (1965).

[9] Bridgman, P. W., *Large Plastic Flow and Fracture* (McGraw-Hill, 1952).

[10] Balakina, L. M., *Bull. Acad. Sci., U.S.S.R., Geophys. Series No. 11* (in English), 909 (1962).

[11] Berg, E., *Proc. 15th Alaska Sci. Conf., College, Alaska*, edit. by Dahlgren, G. (Alaska Div. Amer. Assoc. Adv. Sci., 1965).

[12] Press, F., *J. Geophys. Res.*, 70, 2385 (1965).

[13] Plafker, G., *Science*, 148, 1675 (1965).

[14] *Gulf of Alaska (Navigation Chart), No. 8500, Strait of Juan de Fuca to Kodiak Island* (U.S. Coast and Geodetic Survey).

III
GEODESY
AND
PHOTOGRAMMETRY

Introduction: An Evaluation of the Geodetic and Photogrammetric Surveys

After every major earthquake, scientists and engineers ask geodesists to determine the geographical extent of the crustal disturbance and the magnitude of the displacement associated with the earthquake. Special resurveys after the San Francisco earthquake of 1906 provided such comparative information and helped to initiate within the United States a broad program of crustal movement study using geodetic techniques.

Before looking at the details and results of each phase of the resurveys after the Prince William Sound earthquake, a few basic concepts should be identified and reviewed as reference or background for any interpretation.

First, most conventional geodetic resurveying is related to local or regional engineering programs. Although the extensive geodetic surveys of former years were not designed to serve as a basis for crustal-movement studies, they do have a significant value for postearthquake investigations and provide a major source of information for these studies. Mapping and charting programs require a uniform spacing of control points, determined with a reasonable degree of accuracy. Thus, whenever an earthquake occurs in an economically developed area, there is an excellent chance that some type of geodetic reference framework exists. The probability of adequate survey coverage is smaller in remote or uninhabited areas.

A second point to be considered in interpreting studies of crustal displacement is the nature of the internal characteristics of a geodetic survey. Measurements of angles, lengths, and differences of elevation, and so forth are subject to error. Any mathematical treatment of these observed data may involve some uncertainty and should always be evaluated. When surveys are repeated, the new measurements are compared with the old. The differences are the essential data. The analysis depends on the so-called differentials, whether they be used to compute strain components or whether their effect be integrated or accumulated to show differences of positions or coordinates. Basically, the two methods complement each other and should be studied in combination.

A third point to be considered is the analytical method or computational technique that uses differences of position. When the major crustal disturbance can be identified as a sharp displacement—either horizontal or vertical—along a fault, and can be directly measured on the surface at the site of the displacement, the analysis is less complex because the accumulated positional changes or the sum of the differential effects can be equated to this accurately measured quantity, the real displacement. In the Prince William Sound earthquake, this less complex analysis has not been possible. The point of maximum uplift south of Montague Island can be related to the surface of the ocean, but the horizontal displacement in this area cannot be measured directly. The stable reference for horizontal control is, perhaps, from 100 to 200 mi away. Thus, the reliability of the vertical displacement is considerably better than that of the horizontal. The 15-m uplift of the ocean floor is well determined. The reliability of the vectors representing horizontal displacement depends on evaluations involving statistical data and engineering experience. In evaluating the entire horizontal positional disturbance, it is necessary to examine some of the individual or smaller areas and consider their relation to the entire area.

Wherever any of the triangulation networks in the vicinity of Prince William Sound were reobserved, there was evidence of change. It has not been possible to extend the resurvey operations far enough to include points where it can be stated with full confidence that there was no movement.

However, the data indicate that the mountain mass north of the Matanuska River and the Aleutian Range on the northwest side of Cook Inlet can be treated as stable, or fixed in position, for geodetic reference. The resurveys have indicated that the Chugach Mountains (which are south of the Matanuska River), the Kenai Mountains, and the islands in Prince William Sound have all shifted to the south, beginning with a slight elongation across the Matanuska Valley and accumulating to a maximum of the order of 15 m for the southeastern slopes of the Kenai Mountains, Montague Island, and the nearby regions extending into the Gulf of Alaska. Some resurveys made in 1967 across Shelikof Strait show that Ushagat Island, Afognak Island, and Kodiak Island have been displaced to the east and south with a direction that is fully related to the displacement of the Kenai Mountains. The data for these 1967 surveys are not included in the analyses by Parkin or by Pope.

In evaluating and interpreting the computed horizontal displacements over the entire region, the first area of inspection is the Matanuska Valley and the extension of the survey between Anchorage and Glennallen. In Parkin's investigation the western end of this scheme was held fixed, or treated as the stable point. The eastern end was permitted to seek its most probable position. A comparison of the positions indicates a movement of 4 m in a southeasterly direction. The length of the survey is approximately 250 km. The indicated movement, then, is roughly one part in 60,000 of the length of the survey. This ratio is about the same as the expected proportional accuracy of the survey, and if the two surveys were considered as a folded loop, the closure would be 4 m in 500 km or one part in 125,000. If, at some future date, resources are available for additional studies, consideration should be given to treating each end of the north side of this valley as stable or fixed in position.

The comparison of the positions on the south side of the valley shows a definite elongation of the survey lines crossing the valley. These changes in length range from 0.5 to 1.0 m. This deformation is of the order of one part in 10,000. The strain components calculated by Pope show very clearly that these values are well determined and are not subject to any uncertainty because of errors of triangulation.

If we assume that, basically, there was no displacement in the vicinity of Glennallen, the effect on the other vectors throughout the entire region would be merely a matter of subtraction, with some slight change for a secondary scale effect. A similar review of the data for the extension along the Richardson Highway to Valdez permits a comparable conclusion. Within the arc of triangulation itself, there were differential changes that are reflected in the strain calculations; but, if one considers the broad regional aspects, the vectors representing displacement show a slow accumulative change from Glennallen to Valdez, with a ratio of displacement to length of arc that is comparable to that previously identified

along the Matanuska Valley. The indicated 8-m displacement, as calculated between Anchorage and Valdez, could be evaluated as being well within the probable limit of the surveys. However, one cannot disregard the fact that the shifts in position are consistent in direction with the general shift determined over the entire region. If the vectors were merely representing survey uncertainties, the direction of the vectors could have been in any other direction.

An inspection of the surveys in the vicinity of Anchorage and those extending to the south shows very conclusively that the mountain masses shifted southward. These surveys extend along Turnagain Arm toward Whittier and south to Seward. The strain data (Pope), vector displacement data (Parkin), and the raw observational data show conclusively that the mountain masses moved southward, with the amount of the movement increasing for the surveys extending to the east and to the south. Differences in observed angles of the triangulation net were 10–20 times larger than any possible error. Thus, the data in this section indicate that the magnitudes and directions of the displacements are well determined.

In reviewing the survey data westward across the Kenai Peninsula and thence southward along the eastern shore of Cook Inlet toward Homer Spit, one would conclude that, if there was any movement, it was negligible. The striking point in this region is the large relative shift between points near Homer Spit and the south side of the Kenai Mountains. This relative shift of more than 15 m in a distance of 75 km cannot be attributed to weakness or to looseness in the geodetic measurements. This ratio of one part in 5,000 is much larger than any indicated closure of preearthquake or postearthquake survey. The pattern of movement also agreed with the 1967 resurvey involving Ushagat Island.

The closure of the electronic survey across Prince William Sound, from the Kenai Peninsula on the west to the vicinity of Valdez on the east, was so small that the relation of the vectors and the values of strain for the region of Prince William Sound itself should be accepted with confidence.

In summary, then, for the horizontal movement, the most direct evaluation is that the major regional effect was a broad southward movement, with a gradual elongation accumulating to as much as 15 m for the region south of Montague Island. There are some indications of local disturbances or faulting contrary to this broad regional effect. Many of these have been identified within the triangulation, but the broad tectonic effect should be studied in relation to this maximum displacement.

The extent of the area affected by uplift or subsidence was so great and of such varied terrain that Small and Wharton used different methods for determining the magnitude of the disturbance. For the islands and shorelines adjacent to the Prince William Sound, the level of the sea provided an immediate reference. Tidal bench marks, referred to the postearthquake condition, were used to control the network of precise leveling extending from Seward to Anchorage to Glennallen to Valdez. A northern loop of precise leveling was closed on preearthquake elevations in the vicinity of Fairbanks. The differences on this northern loop indicated that the northern edge of the disturbance was probably along the Matanuska Valley. A comparison of the leveling along this valley showed a rather uniform subsidence of about 0.5 m. The comparison of the leveling line from Anchorage to Seward showed subsidence of 1–2 m, with a maximum in the vicinity of Portage. A review and comparison of the trigonometric leveling indicates that the mountain masses south of Portage subsided 3 m.

New tidal references on the islands in Prince William Sound, inspection of the shorelines for uplift, and other related studies, including the hydrographic surveys of the region south of Montague Island, have all rather clearly defined the pattern of uplift with a maximum amount of approximately 15 m for the sea floor south of Montague Island. The area of maximum uplift, in general, is the same as the area of maximum horizontal movement. Radial profiles from the point of maximum disturbance, extended to the west, northwest, and north, are similar in character, showing subsidence in the outer areas where the horizontal movement showed the initial elongation. These radial profiles, which cross the mountain masses and then converge in the region of maximum horizontal movement, show a striking uniformity with respect to uplift.

This three-dimensional model of crustal disturbance conforms almost exactly to the gravity model as reported by Rice and by Barnes. The extreme positive gravity anomaly in the region of maximum uplift, circled by the arc of negative anomalies extending along Cook Inlet and Matanuska Valley, which had subsided, would suggest a massive intrusion of magma. The magnitude of the earthquake, the tremendous number of aftershocks, and the evidence of crustal disturbance all contribute to the conclusion that the earth's crust was fractured in many different ways throughout the entire region. However, one can determine the broad regional pattern changes described from the basic geodetic survey data.

In addition to the regional studies, a detailed geodetic and photogrammetric study was made of the Anchorage area, primarily to provide the postearthquake monitoring that was thought essential for the future economic development of that city. Analytical aerotriangulation, controlled with a network of closely spaced geodetic points, provides this essential source of information. The photogrammetric technique described by Cravat and Sobieralski will be used to measure any additional slippage that occurs in those sections of the city where stabilization techniques were used after the earthquake. The significant value of this combined geodetic-photogrammetric technique is the availability of accurate information about movement for almost an infinite number of reference points. Most of all, it provides the type of information needed to determine shifts of the manmade structures—buildings, homes, streets, or any other structure that can be seen on aerial photographs. By using low-altitude photography, shifts as slight as 2 or 3 cm can be detected. A comparison of the 1965 geodetic control with the 1964 postearthquake survey indicates movement of about 3 cm for three control points along the shore of Knik Arm. This displacement is larger than can be attributed to observational uncertainties, and Meade suggests that there has been some minor postearthquake slippage. These reports by Cravat and Sobieralski, and by Meade emphasize the need for postearthquake monitoring at Anchorage.

The total extent of the geodetic and photogrammetric surveys made after the earthquake seems, in some respects, to be a mere reconnaissance. However, a more detailed study of the entire region is hardly practical. Though additional resurveys might be made in Prince William Sound between many of the points that were not included in the 1964 and 1965 work, the results could not change the broad regional pattern—they would only further document the extent of the fracturing of the earth's crust during one of the largest earthquakes ever recorded.

CHARLES A. WHITTEN
Office of National Geodetic Survey,
National Ocean Survey, NOAA

ERNEST J. PARKIN
U.S. COAST AND GEODETIC SURVEY*

Reprinted with minor changes from
U.S. Coast and Geodetic Survey Volume III: Geodesy and Photogrammetry,
"Horizontal Crustal Movements Determined from
Surveys After the Alaskan Earthquake of 1964"

Horizontal Crustal Movements

ABSTRACT: In 1964 and 1965, a major part of the triangulation in the vicinity of Prince William Sound was reobserved for the purpose of determining the horizontal displacement which occurred at the time of the earthquake. The preearthquake surveys over the islands consisted of many lower-order surveys established primarily for the control of nautical charting. The combination of triangulation and trilateration was used in the postearthquake surveys to span this portion of the disturbed area. A comparison of the pre- and postearthquake geographic positions indicates displacements of the order of 50 ft or more. Comparisons of pre- and postearthquake observations at adjacent common points verify the magnitude of this crustal movement.

INTRODUCTION

Volume I of this series of reports on the Prince William Sound Earthquake of 1964 contains an account of the crustal movement in Alaska [pages 121–122]. This movement was revealed by a comparison of the results of surveys made before the disastrous earthquake of March 27, 1964, with those made during the 1964 field season, immediately following the earthquake. During the 1965 field season additional triangulation was accomplished which, together with the work of 1964, formed a network spanning the damage area. This paper describes the amount and direction of horizontal crustal movement determined by comparing the results of the triangulation surveys made before the earthquake and those of the combined 1964–65 surveys.

The general area of interest is shown in figure 1. The epicenter of the main shock was on the north shore of Prince William Sound, roughly midway between Anchorage and Valdez.

PREEARTHQUAKE TRIANGULATION
(1900–1961)

The area studied extends from about latitude 59° to 62° N., and longitude 145° to 154° W. The preearthquake triangulation network in this area was begun in 1900 and was developed over a period of about 60 years. This network, shown in figure 2, consists of:

(1) A primary arc extending from Anchorage northeastward via Palmer to Glennallen, and from that point south and west via Thompson Pass to Valdez, was surveyed in 1941 and 1944.

---

*Now in part the Office of National Geodetic Survey, National Ocean Survey, NOAA.

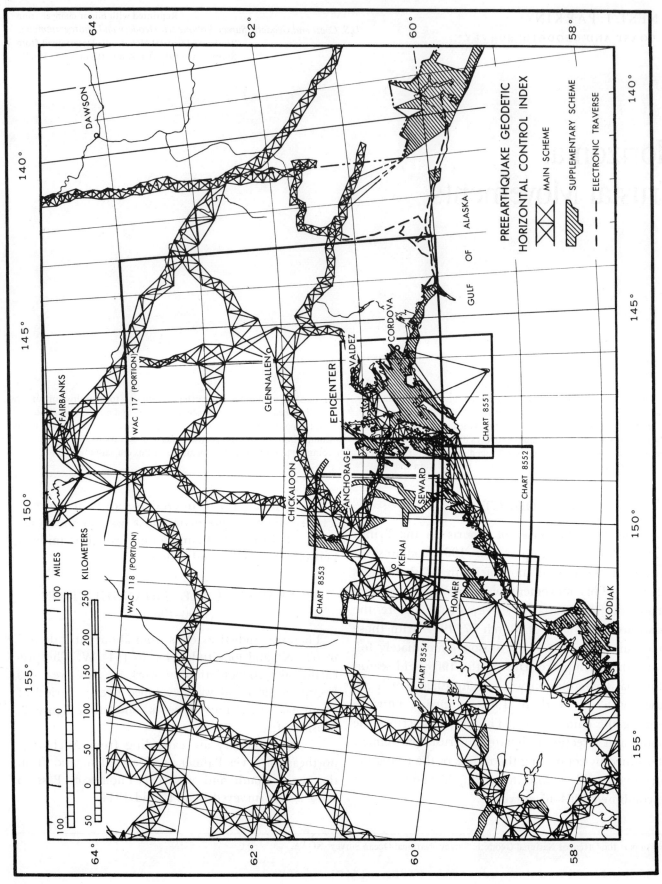

PREEARTHQUAKE GEODETIC
HORIZONTAL CONTROL INDEX

MAIN SCHEME

SUPPLEMENTARY SCHEME

ELECTRONIC TRAVERSE

FIGURE 1

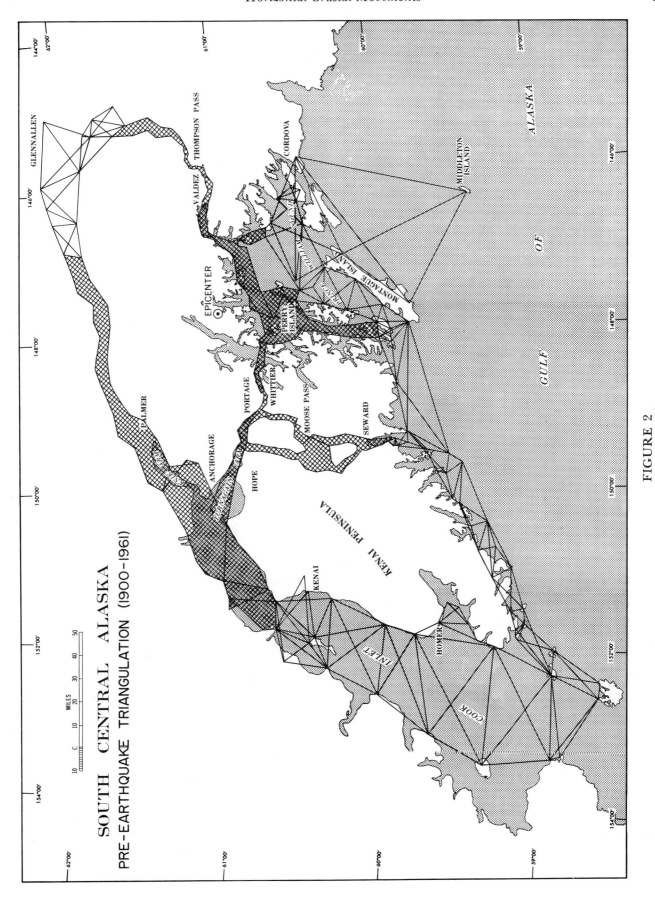

SOUTH CENTRAL ALASKA
PRE-EARTHQUAKE TRIANGULATION (1900–1961)

FIGURE 2

(2) A second-order arc extending across northern Prince William Sound from Valdez to Perry Island. This arc was surveyed in 1947–1948.

(3) A third-order arc extending from Perry Island to Anchorage. It was observed between 1910 and 1914 and closes this northern loop.

(4) The southern half of the network—spanning Prince William Sound, the Kenai Peninsula, and Cook Inlet—is all third-order triangulation. The double arc from Seward north to connections at Turnagain Arm was surveyed by the Corps of Engineers, U. S. Army, in 1941 and 1942. The rest of the triangulation was made mainly for chart control between 1900 and 1961.

The above surveys were made by the U. S. Coast and Geodetic Survey except for those made by the Corps of Engineers. All of the observations made were combined into a single composite network, and a free adjustment was made by the variation-of-coordinates method. (Free adjustment means the network was not constrained to fit previously adjusted geographic positions.) Only one position was held fixed, station 139, Fishhook 1944, (fig. 4) about 9 miles north of Palmer. In the area under study, the section where this station is located was believed by the seismologists to be the most stable.

There were 440 stations and a total of about 2,350 directions included in the adjustment. The average and maximum triangle closures were 2.88 and 15.69 seconds, respectively. In considering these figures, one should bear in mind that the net consists largely of third-order surveys made principally for charting purposes. At the time these surveys were planned, no thought was ever given to using them for crustal movement studies. The stations of the network are listed in table 1 by station code number and alphabetically.

The position closures of the large loops in the net were computed prior to the adjustment. The closure

TABLE 1.—*List of triangulation stations used in the determination of crustal movement*

Station code	Numerical index — Station name	Alphabetical index — Station name	Station code	Station code	Numerical index — Station name	Alphabetical index — Station name	Station code
1	Saw 1901	Agnes	576	40	Stuart North Base 1941	Ermi (USE)	405
2	Held 1901	Anchor	521	41	Tiekel 1941	Ernestine	46
4	Valdez North Base 1901	Anchor Point	186	42	Stuart 1941	Evans	591
5	Power 1941	Audry	180	43	Rice 1941	Fall	44
6	Sugar 1941	Axis (USE)	424	44	Fall 1941	Falls (USE)	487
7	Knife 1941	Baker	223	45	Summit 1941	Fire	106
8	Crombie 1941	Bear (USE)	486	46	Ernestine 1941	Fishhook	139*
9	Lowe 1941	Bench	21	47	Little Tonsina 1941	Fishlake	147
11	Sponge 1941	Bernard	49	49	Bernard 1941	Foot	32
13	Hogback 1941	Bird Point	312	50	Scarp 1950	Forks	39
15	Snow 1941	Bluff	480	51	Kenny 1941	Fossil	150
16	Key 1941	Bone	425	52	Tonsina 1941	Giant	580
17	Stone 1941	Bou	117	53	Stuck 1941	Glacier	118
18	Wortmann SW Base 1941	Boulder	344	54	Willow Creek S Base 1941	Glen E. Base	113
19	Wortmann NE Base 1941	Bruin	27	55	Klawasi 1941	Held	2
20	Divide 1941	Bunch	504	56	Hudson 1941	Hicks	121
21	Bench 1941	CAA	119	57	Shepard 1941	Hogback	13
22	Thompson Pass 1941	Cape (USE)	306	101	Tolsona 1944	Homer E. Base	188
23	Rock Spur 1941	Cape Cleare	553	102	Taz 1944	Horn	104
24	Odessey 1941	Cascade	124	104	Horn 1944	Hudson	56
25	Worthington SW Base 1941	Castle	130	105	Lina 1944	Ione	429
26	Worthington NE Base 1941	Central	325	106	Fire 1944	Isle	305
27	Bruin 1941	Chiswell	218	107	Tahneta 1944	John	419
28	Drop 1941	Chugach	36	108	Nel 1944	Kenny	51
29	Ptarmigan 1941	Cleo (USE)	439	109	Squaw 1944	Key	16
30	Tsina W. Base 1941	Cordova	555	110	Leila 1944	King	129
31	Tsina E. Base 1941	Crag (USE)	135	111	Sight 1944	Kinik	526
32	Foot 1941	Crombie	8	112	Nuska 1944	Klawasi	55
33	Rim 1941	Cub (USE)	403	113	Glen E. Base 1944	Knife	7
34	Square 1941	Dark	304	115	Sheep Astro 1943	Knob	609
35	Elbow 1941	Divide	20	116	Sheep Astro Azimuth 1943	Knowles	38
36	Chugach 1941	Divide (USE)	432	117	Bou 1944	Law (USE)	428
37	Tsina 1941	Drop	28	118	Glacier 1944	Lazy (USE)	138
38	Knowles 1941	Eklutna	142	119	CAA 1944	Lean (USE)	420
39	Forks 1941	Elbow	35	120	Red 1944	Leila	110
				121	Hicks 1944	Lina	105
				122	O'Brien 1944	Little Tonsina	47

* Station held fixed in the adjustment.

TABLE 1.—*List of triangulation stations used in the determination of crustal movement*—Continued

Numerical index		Alphabetical index		Numerical index		Alphabetical index	
Station code	Station name	Station name	Station code	Station code	Station name	Station name	Station code
123	Purin 1944	Long	149	346	Vista 1914	Slide	352
124	Cascade 1944	Loon	128	347	Shakespeare 1914	Snow	15
125	Rush 1944	Lowe	9	352	Slide 1914	Snow (USE)	433
126	Mat 1944	Mac RM 3	157	403	Cub (USE) 1942	Sponge	11
127	Pudd 1944	Mat	126	404	Walker (USE) 1942	Square	34
128	Loon 1944	Middle 2	478	405	Ermi (USE) 1942	Squaw	109
129	King 1944	Middleton	552	408	Nelson (USE) 1942	Stair	610
130	Castle 1944	Moose	137	409	Mouse (USE) 1942	Stetson (USE)	422
131	Park 1944	Mouse (USE)	409	410	Trib (USE) 1942	Stone	17
132	Young 1944	Nel	108	416	Summit (USE) 1942	Stuart	42
133	Ram (USE) 1941 1944	Nelson (USE)	408	419	John (USE) 1942	Stuart North Base	40
135	Crag (USE) 1941 1944	Ninilchik	184	420	Lean (USE) 1942	Stuck	53
136	Wish (USE) 1941 1944	Nuska	112	422	Stetson (USE) 1942	Sugar	6
137	Moose 1944	O'Brien	122	424	Axis (USE) 1942	Summit	45
138	Lazy (USE) 1941 1944	Odessey	24	425	Bone (USE) 1942	Summit (USE)	416
139*	Fishhook 1944	Park	131	428	Law (USE) 1942	Tahneta	107
140	Wasilla 1922	Pellew	501	429	Ione (USE) 1942	Taz	102
142	Eklutna 1922	Perry	536	432	Divide (USE) 1942	Thompson Pass	22
144	Peters E. Base 1922	Peters E. Base	144	433	Snow (USE) 1942	Tiekel	41
145	Peters W. Base 1922	Peters W. Base	145	435	Sew (USE) 1942	Tolsona	101
146	Rose 1914	Point	310	436	Trout (USE) 1942	Tonsina	52
147	Fishlake 1922	Power	5	437	Tune (USE) 1942	Trib (USE)	410
148	Whitney 1922	Ptarmigan	29	438	Ward (USE) 1942	Triple	321
149	Long 1944	Pudd	127	439	Cleo (USE) 1942	Trout (USE)	436
150	Fossil 1944	Purin	123	478	Middle 2 1927	Tsina	37
152	Ship 1944	Ram (USE)	133	479	Turn 1905	Tsina E. Base	31
157	Mac RM 3 1947 1961	Red	120	480	Bluff 1905	Tsina W. Base	30
180	Audry 1961	Red Head	558	486	Bear (USE) 1942	Tune (USE)	437
184	Ninilchik 1908	Reef	519	487	Falls (USE) 1942	Turn	479
186	Anchor Point 1908	Rice	43	501	Pellew 1947	Valdez North Base	4
188	Homer E. Base 1910	Rim	33	504	Bunch 1901	Visit	602
218	Chiswell 1905	Rock Spur	23	519	Reef 1942	Vista	346
223	Baker 1905	Rose	146	521	Anchor 1947	Walker (USE)	404
304	Dark 1912	Rush	125	526	Kinik 1947	Ward (USE)	438
305	Isle 1912	Salmon	341	528	Waver 1947	Wasilla	140
306	Cape (USE) 1912	Saw	1	536	Perry 1912	Waver	528
308	Windy 1912	Scarp	50	552	Middleton 1933	Whitney	148
310	Point 1912	Second	313	553	Cape Cleare 1933	Willow Creek S. Base	54
312	Bird Point 1912	Sew (USE)	435	554	Zaikof 1933	Windy	308
313	Second 1912	Shakespeare	347	555	Cordova 1933	Wish (USE)	136
318	Wood (USE) 1941	Sheep Astro	115	558	Red Head 1900	Wood (USE)	318
321	Triple 1912	Sheep Astro Azimuth	116	576	Agnes 1949	Worthington NE Base	26
325	Central 1912	Shepard	57	580	Giant 1949	Worthington SW Base	25
341	Salmon 1914	Ship	152	591	Evans 1905	Wortmann NE Base	19
344	Boulder 1914	Sight	111	602	Visit 1947	Wortmann SW Base	18
				609	Knob 1928	Young	132
				610	Stair 1905	Zaikof	554

* Station held fixed in the adjustment.

of the north loop (Anchorage–Glennallen–Valdez) was about 75 feet, or 1 part in 25,000. The closure of the southwest loop (Anchorage–Seward–Homer) was almost identical; 80 feet, or 1 part in 26,000. These two closures may be due to an error in the third-order work along Turnagain Arm, which is common to the two loops. There does not appear to be an anomalous change in the shifts of the stations in the area. The south-central loop (Whittier–Perry Island–Seward), the only other loop of any size, had a position closure of 12 feet, or 1 part in 92,000.

To furnish orientation and scale for the net, 5 Laplace azimuths, 15 taped base lines, and 1 Tel-lurometer length were included in the adjustment as observation equations. The azimuths and the base lines were each given a weight of unity. This means that a correction of 1 part in 200,000 to the length of a base is equivalent to an azimuth correction of 1 second. The direction observations were weighted as follows: First-order, 1.0; second-order, 0.5; and third-order, 0.25.

The adjustment yielded the following results. The average corrections to the directions (v's) and the maximum corrections to the angles in the various orders of work are as follows:

Order	Average v	Maximum correction to an angle
First	0."43	3."56
Second	0."96	5."26
Third	1."22	10."76

The average correction to a Laplace azimuth was 0.97 second. The average correction to a base line was one part in 270,000, and the correction to the Tellurometer length was 1 part in 63,000.

The probable errors of the resulting geographic positions of stations in Prince William Sound, relative to the fixed station near Palmer, considering the size of the residuals, are estimated to be 15 to 20 feet.

POSTEARTHQUAKE TRIANGULATION AND TRAVERSE (1964–1965)

The surveys made after the earthquake are shown in figure 3. The following first-order triangulation was accomplished from June to October 1964: Anchorage via Palmer to Glennallen, Anchorage to Whittier, Hope to Seward, and Valdez to Thompson Pass. During the same season, a Tellurometer traverse was run on the Kenai Peninsula from Moose Pass via Kenai to Homer. The rest of the network shown in figure 3 was observed during the summer of 1965. This 1965 work consisted (1) of first-order triangulation in Prince William Sound, in the vicinity of Seward, and from Thompson Pass to Glennallen; and (2) Tellurometer traverse from Perry Island to Whittier and from Seward via Resurrection Bay to Homer. Since the small schemes bridging Montague Strait and Unakwik Inlet, mentioned in Volume I [pages 122, 171, 174–176], were not connected to this large network, they could not be included in this study.

A free adjustment was made of all of this work by the same method as was used to adjust the earlier work. Also, the same station (Fishhook 1944) was held fixed. The adjustment included 292 stations and 1,476 observed directions. The average triangle closure was 0.91 second, the maximum being 4.13 seconds. The loop closures in this net ranged from 10 to 25 feet.

The orientation for this network was supplied by 5 Laplace azimuths observed after the earthquake, and the scale was furnished by 8 Geodimeter lengths and 146 Tellurometer lengths. Weights for the various types of work were assigned as follows: Directions were all first-order, 1.0; Laplace azimuths, 1.0; Geodimeter lengths, 1.0; the Tellurometer lengths, 0.1.

The following corrections to the various types of work resulted from the adjustment:

(1) Directions: average v = 0.34 second. maximum correction to an angle = 2.86 seconds.
(2) Laplace azimuths: average correction = 0.6 second.
(3) Geodimeter lengths: average correction = 1 part per 1,000,000. maximum = 1 part in 290,000.
(4) Tellurometer lengths: average correction = 1 part in 170,000. maximum = 1 part in 40,000.

The probable errors of the geographic positions of the stations in Prince William Sound area, resulting from this adjustment and estimated from the residuals, are 6 to 8 feet. These are again relative to the fixed station north of Palmer.

RESULTS

The approximate geographic positions of all of the stations common to the two adjustments are given in table 2. The code numbers, used to identify the stations for computer operations and also in figures 4 to 7, are listed in the first column of the table; their names are given in the second column; and their latitudes and longitudes to the nearest tenth of a minute in the last column.

Plane coordinates, based on the Alaska Plane Coordinate System, were computed from the geographic positions resulting from the two adjustments. [See *Plane Coordinate Intersection Tables, Alaska, Zones 2–9,* U. S. Department of Commerce, Coast and Geodetic Survey Publication 65–1, Part 50, 1960.] Stations east of the 148th meridian were computed on Zone 3; those west of 148° on Zone 4. Table 3 contains the differences between the plane coordinates resulting from the two adjustments of all common stations. The columns in table 3 contain the following information: first column, station code number; second and third, the differences in the X- and Y-coordinates in feet; fourth and fifth, the length in feet and azimuth of the resultant vector. The X- and Y-shifts are computed in the sense "new minus old"; hence, plus signs indicate east and north shifts, respectively. The vector length is the hypotenuse of the right triangle formed by ΔX and ΔY, and the azimuth is reckoned clockwise from the south. These vectors are shown graphically in figures 4 to 7. They show much more

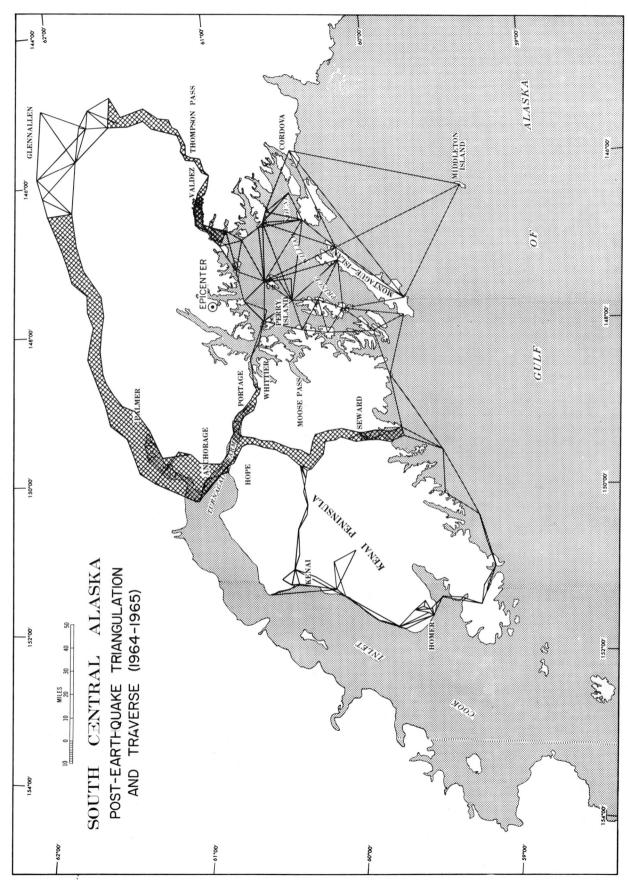

SOUTH CENTRAL ALASKA

POST-EARTHQUAKE TRIANGULATION
AND TRAVERSE (1964-1965)

FIGURE 3

TABLE 2.—*Approximate positions of the stations*

Station Code	Station name	Latitude ° ′	Longitude ° ′	Station Code	Station name	Latitude ° ′	Longitude ° ′
1	Saw 1901	61 05.4	146 24.5	121	Hicks 1944	61 48.9	147 54.6
2	Held 1901	61 07.7	146 22.7	122	O'Brien 1944	61 45.8	148 00.0
4	Valdez North Base 1901	61 07.4	146 16.8	123	Purin 1944	61 48.3	148 05.2
5	Power 1941	61 05.1	146 18.2	124	Cascade 1944	61 49.8	148 02.6
6	Sugar 1941	61 05.0	146 17.0	125	Rush 1944	61 50.9	148 11.4
7	Knife 1941	61 06.5	146 11.9	126	Mat 1944	61 46.5	148 13.3
8	Crombie 1941	61 04.4	146 12.9	127	Pudd 1944	61 51.2	148 19.7
9	Lowe 1941	61 03.1	146 08.1	128	Loon 1944	61 47.5	148 24.4
11	Sponge 1941	61 04.4	146 04.1	129	King 1944	61 45.6	148 30.5
13	Hogback 1941	61 02.4	145 58.9	130	Castle 1944	61 49.3	148 31.5
15	Snow 1941	61 04.9	145 56.6	131	Park 1944	61 45.6	148 34.9
16	Key 1941	61 04.3	145 51.7	132	Young 1944	61 46.7	148 44.5
17	Stone 1941	61 05.0	145 49.3	133	Ram (USE) 1941 1944	61 43.5	148 39.4
18	Wortmann SW Base 1941	61 06.0	145 51.9	135	Crag (USE) 1941 1944	61 40.3	148 50.3
19	Wortmann NE Base 1941	61 06.4	145 50.0	136	Wish (USE) 1941 1944	61 44.2	148 57.0
20	Divide 1941	61 07.8	145 46.4	137	Moose 1944	61 40.6	149 03.2
21	Bench 1941	61 05.3	145 45.3	138	Lazy (USE) 1941 1944	61 37.4	148 57.9
22	Thompson Pass 1941	61 07.7	145 43.8	139*	Fishhook 1944	61 43.0	149 14.0
23	Rock Spur 1941	61 09.5	145 44.3	140	Wasilla 1922	61 36.6	149 24.5
24	Odessey 1941	61 08.5	145 41.7	142	Eklutna 1922	61 27.5	149 19.0
25	Worthington SW Base 1941	61 09.8	145 42.4	144	Peters E. Base 1922	61 28.2	149 22.5
26	Worthington NE Base 1941	61 10.6	145 41.2	145	Peters W. Base 1922	61 25.7	149 29.3
27	Bruin 1941	61 10.8	145 43.8	146	Rose 1914	61 28.4	149 40.8
28	Drop 1941	61 10.9	145 39.8	147	Fishlake 1922	61 31.5	149 52.8
29	Ptarmigan 1941	61 12.5	145 37.6	148	Whitney 1922	61 23.3	149 40.0
30	Tsina W. Base 1941	61 12.1	145 33.0	149	Long 1944	61 25.9	149 59.8
31	Tsina E. Base 1941	61 12.2	145 31.6	150	Fossil 1944	61 16.8	149 36.6
32	Foot 1941	61 10.9	145 32.3	152	Ship 1944	61 12.5	149 37.6
33	Rim 1941	61 12.7	145 29.7	157	Mac RM 3 1947 1961	61 14.3	149 59.1
34	Square 1941	61 11.3	145 28.5	180	Audry 1961	60 30.8	151 16.6
35	Elbow 1941	61 12.5	145 25.7	184	Ninilchik 1908	60 00.6	151 42.8
36	Chugach 1941	61 13.7	145 24.8	186	Anchor Point 1908	59 48.8	151 49.7
37	Tsina 1941	61 13.2	145 20.4	188	Homer E. Base 1910	59 36.1	151 24.9
38	Knowles 1941	61 15.3	145 18.0	218	Chiswell 1905	59 36.1	149 33.9
39	Forks 1941	61 15.4	145 16.1	223	Baker 1905	59 51.7	149 23.3
40	Stuart North Base 1941	61 16.4	145 16.7	304	Dark 1912	61 02.4	149 46.7
41	Tiekel 1941	61 17.0	145 18.0	305	Isle 1912	61 01.0	149 44.1
42	Stuart 1941	61 16.8	145 12.1	306	Cape (USE) 1912	60 58.1	149 46.0
43	Rice 1941	61 22.8	145 18.4	308	Windy 1912	60 56.2	149 33.8
44	Fall 1941	61 20.5	145 11.2	310	Point 1912	60 57.1	149 24.6
45	Summit 1941	61 26.0	145 12.7	312	Bird Point 1912	60 55.6	149 21.7
46	Ernestine 1941	61 26.0	145 03.1	313	Second 1912	60 55.6	149 21.2
47	Little Tonsina 1941	61 31.6	145 16.8	318	Wood (USE) 1941	60 56.4	149 10.6
49	Bernard 1941	61 34.3	145 08.4	321	Triple 1912	60 53.4	149 11.2
50	Scarp 1950	61 38.2	144 52.4	325	Central 1912	60 51.9	149 01.4
51	Kenny 1941	61 46.6	145 02.1	341	Salmon 1914	60 47.6	148 54.2
52	Tonsina 1941	61 39.7	145 15.7	344	Boulder 1914	60 46.4	148 50.3
53	Stuck 1941	61 47.5	145 15.2	346	Vista 1914	60 46.7	148 45.9
54	Willow Creek S Base 1941	61 50.3	145 13.5	347	Shakespeare 1914	60 45.0	148 45.1
55	Klawasi 1941	62 04.9	145 00.4	352	Slide 1914	60 46.1	148 43.0
56	Hudson 1941	61 52.1	145 40.3	403	Cub (USE) 1942	60 51.0	149 29.1
57	Shepard 1941	62 06.7	145 54.4	404	Walker (USE) 1942	60 51.5	149 23.2
101	Tolsona 1944	62 06.3	146 10.3	405	Ermi (USE) 1942	60 49.8	149 28.9
102	Taz 1944	61 55.0	146 21.7	408	Nelson (USE) 1942	60 48.3	149 23.8
104	Horn 1944	62 01.0	146 47.1	409	Mouse (USE) 1942	60 45.0	149 25.7
105	Lina 1944	61 54.2	146 51.1	410	Trib (USE) 1942	60 44.1	149 30.5
106	Fire 1944	61 58.9	146 51.4	416	Summit (USE) 1942	60 38.2	149 35.3
107	Tahneta 1944	61 58.3	147 06.0	419	John (USE) 1942	60 34.2	149 31.6
108	Nel 1944	61 51.4	147 09.3	420	Lean (USE) 1942	60 30.8	149 44.8
109	Squaw 1944	61 56.4	147 18.2	422	Stetson (USE) 1942	60 26.8	149 47.8
110	Leila 1944	61 48.8	147 16.7	424	Axis (USE) 1942	60 27.1	149 36.6
111	Sight 1944	61 50.6	147 27.9	425	Bone (USE) 1942	60 22.1	149 37.9
112	Nuska 1944	61 45.6	147 30.5	428	Law (USE) 1942	60 23.2	149 24.2
113	Glen E. Base 1944	61 49.0	147 28.0	429	Ione (USE) 1942	60 21.4	149 27.9
115	Sheep Astro 1943	61 48.0	147 34.4	432	Divide (USE) 1942	60 14.9	149 24.0
116	Sheep Astro Azimuth 1943	61 47.1	147 34.5	433	Snow (USE) 1942	60 15.3	149 17.4
117	Bou 1944	61 50.8	147 43.5	435	Sew (USE) 1942	60 12.2	149 24.9
118	Glacier 1944	61 44.6	147 45.7	436	Trout (USE) 1942	60 11.4	149 19.2
119	CAA 1944	61 47.3	147 40.3	437	Tune (USE) 1942	60 09.1	149 27.6
120	Red 1944	61 48.2	147 51.9	438	Ward (USE) 1942	60 07.7	149 19.8

* Station held fixed in the adjustment.

TABLE 2.—*Approximate positions of the stations*—Continued

Station Code	Station name	Latitude		Longitude		Station Code	Station name	Latitude		Longitude	
		°	′	°	′			°	′	°	′
439	Cleo (USE) 1942	60	48.1	149	02.6	536	Perry 1912	60	43.1	147	53.9
478	Middle 2 1927	60	03.4	149	20.4	552	Middleton 1933	59	26.1	146	19.9
479	Turn 1905	59	59.7	149	23.1	553	Cape Cleare 1933	59	49.1	147	41.0
480	Bluff 1905	60	00.5	149	20.0	554	Zaikof 1933	60	14.9	147	00.8
486	Bear (USE) 1942	60	52.9	149	29.7	555	Cordova 1933	60	30.5	145	44.1
487	Falls (USE) 1942	60	52.9	149	22.3	558	Red Head 1900	60	40.2	146	29.5
501	Pellew 1947	61	05.1	146	36.5	576	Agnes 1949	60	36.8	147	23.4
504	Bunch 1901	61	04.9	146	39.9	580	Giant 1949	60	31.7	147	23.1
519	Reef 1942	60	50.7	146	50.6	591	Evans 1905	60	02.2	148	04.7
521	Anchor 1947	60	53.1	147	15.1	602	Visit 1947	61	05.0	146	31.7
526	Kinik 1947	60	50.3	147	37.6	609	Knob 1928	59	56.0	148	37.1
528	Waver 1947	60	41.9	147	44.9	610	Stair 1905	59	50.0	147	53.1

vividly than any column of numbers the relative changes in the positions of the stations. Figure 4 is a general picture of the entire area. Since the arcs of preearthquake triangulation from Anchorage via Palmer and Glennallen to Valdez and from Hope to Seward were done fairly recently, nearly all of the stations were recovered and included in the postearthquake surveys. Therefore to avoid confusion, only about 20 percent of the recovered stations are plotted in figure 4. However, all of the recovered stations on the first-mentioned arc are shown in figures 5 and 6 and all recovered stations on the second arc are shown in figure 7.

Referring to table 3 and to figures 4, 5, and 6, it is seen that beginning at station 139, Fishhook 1944, the station held fixed in both adjustments—the vector difference in the plane coordinates is necessarily zero. Proceeding clockwise around the loop, the divergences increase to 15 feet in the vicinity of Glennallen and to about 25 feet near Valdez. Continuing west along the north shore of Prince William Sound, the divergence increases to 48 feet at Perry Island (station 536, Perry 1912), which is just south of the epicenter. It then decreases to 25 feet near Whittier, to 12 feet at Hope on Turnagain Arm, and back to zero at station 139. It will be noted that the direction of these vectors is generally southeast, varying in azimuth from about 300° to 350°.

If the divergences from Palmer northeastward along the Glenn Highway, which parallels the Matanuska River almost to Eureka Roadhouse, are examined closely, it will be noted that the stations south of the highway show slightly larger divergences (on the order of 2 feet) than those to the north, as though some slight dilation has taken place there. Also, upon examining the vector divergences of the stations on either side of Knik Arm southwestward from Palmer, it will be noted that the stations northwest of Knik Arm have moved about 3 feet northwestward while those southeast of Knik Arm have moved 2 to 5 feet southward, all relative to the fixed station 139 (Fishhook) near Palmer.

Stations along the east shore of Cook Inlet show discrepancies up to about 10 feet at Homer, but this can probably be attributed to weakness in the triangulation and not to any crustal movement. Proceeding eastward to the station 218 on Chiswell Island the vector difference is 58 feet south; then, proceeding north through Seward to Hope (fig. 7), there is a gradual decrease to 12 feet. Although all of these vectors are generally southerly, closer examination of the divergences from Seward northward shows that those at stations on the east side of the arc are greater than those at stations on the west side. The difference is a maximum of 5 feet at Seward tapering off to zero at Hope. This is in keeping with the right lateral movement found across the San Andreas fault in California.

In Prince William Sound (fig. 4), a general increase in the divergence is from about 50 feet near Perry Island to 70 feet on islands in the southwest part of the sound. The discrepancy between the shifts of 67 feet at station 610 (Stair 1905) on the southwest tip of Montague Island and 29 feet at station 553 (Cape Cleare 1933) across the island is difficult to explain, as is also the small size of the vector, 31 feet, on Middleton Island. However, this shortening of the distance between stations on Latouche and Knight Islands and stations to the southeast is consistent with the results of reobserving a small isolated scheme spanning Montague Strait between Latouche and

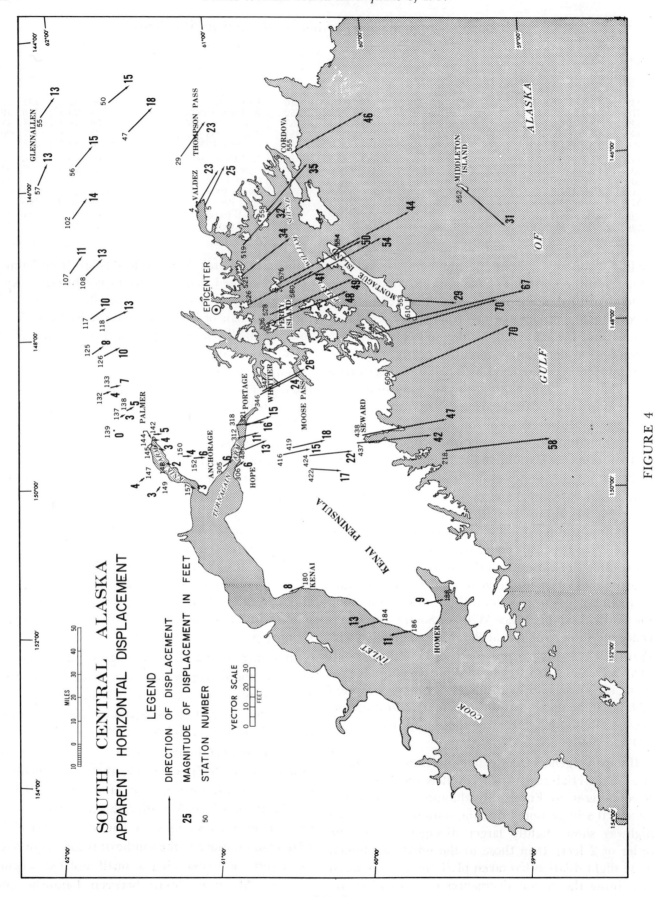

FIGURE 4

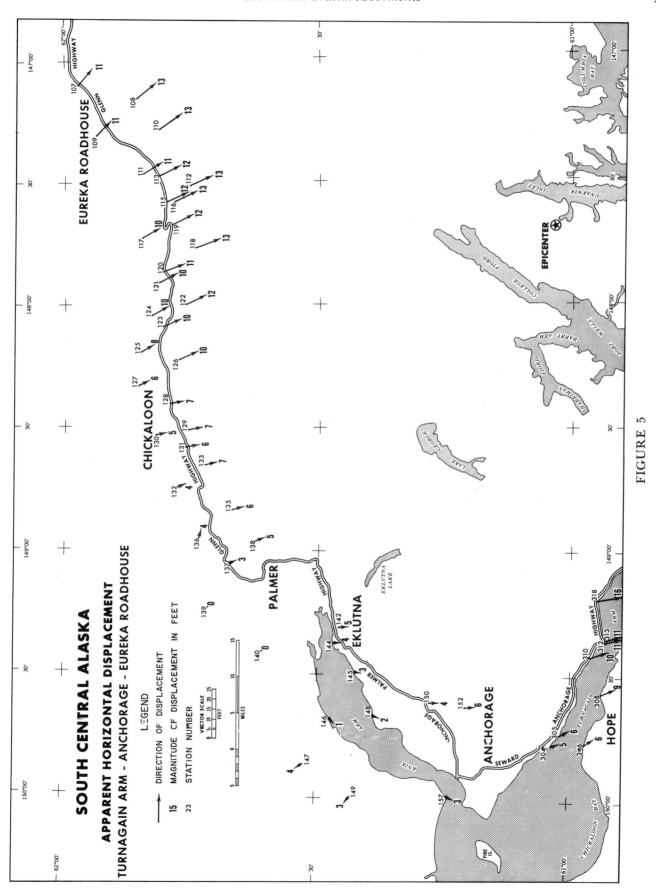

FIGURE 5

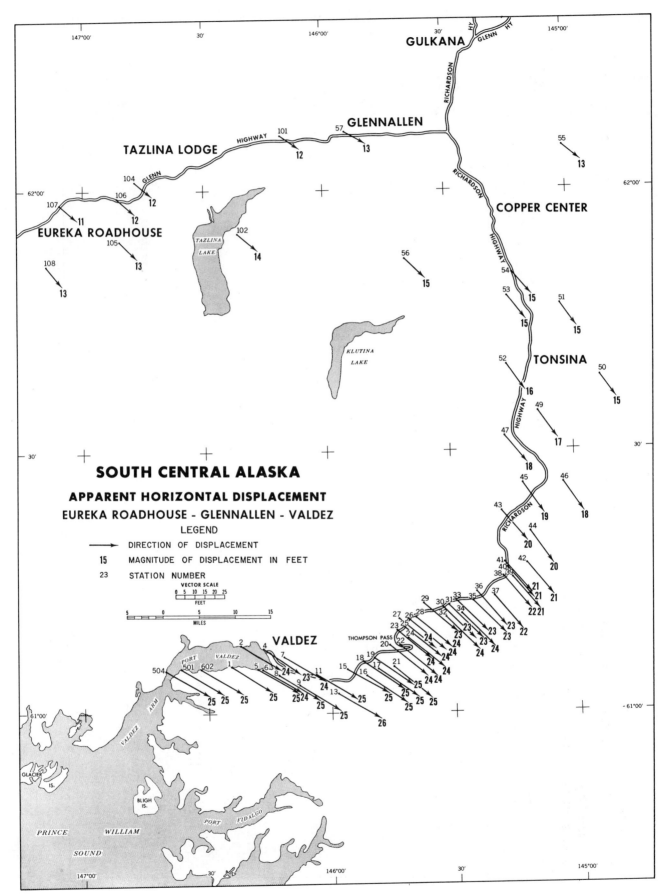

FIGURE 6

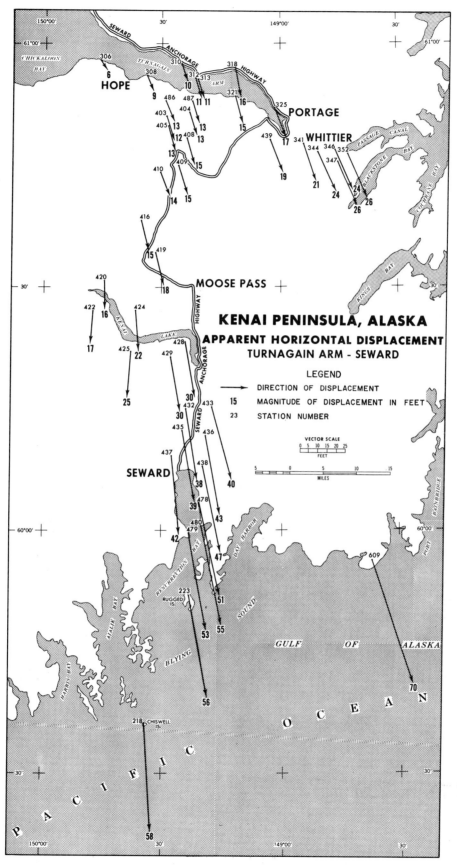

FIGURE 7

[431]

TABLE 3.—*Differences in plane coordinates*

A. North Loop
Palmer—Glennallen—Valdez—Whittier—Anchorage—Palmer

Station code	Position shifts ΔX (Feet)	Position shifts ΔY (Feet)	Resultant vector Length (Feet)	Resultant vector Azimuth (Degrees)
139*	0	0	0	
138	+1.55	−4.74	4.99	340
137	+0.83	−2.37	2.51	340
136	+3.45	−0.79	3.54	285
135	+1.70	−5.61	5.86	345
133	+1.45	−6.61	6.77	350
132	+1.46	−3.91	4.17	340
131	+0.93	−6.31	6.38	350
130	+1.01	−5.22	5.32	350
129	+1.60	−7.26	7.43	350
128	+1.17	−6.95	7.05	350
127	+2.74	−5.81	6.42	335
126	+3.88	−9.23	10.01	335
125	+3.83	−7.09	8.06	330
124	+4.55	−8.43	9.58	330
123	+4.27	−8.70	9.69	335
122	+4.66	−10.57	11.55	335
121	+4.28	−9.34	10.27	335
120	+4.13	−10.19	11.00	340
119	+5.27	−10.75	11.97	335
118	+4.64	−12.48	13.31	340
117	+5.26	−8.88	10.32	330
116	+5.23	−11.59	12.72	335
115	+5.27	−11.00	12.20	335
113	+5.31	−10.72	11.96	335
112	+5.16	−12.17	13.22	335
111	+5.93	−9.78	11.44	330
110	+7.28	−11.23	13.38	325
109	+7.72	−7.50	10.76	315
108	+8.01	−10.23	12.99	320
107	+8.47	−7.73	11.47	310
106	+8.90	−7.85	11.87	310
105	+9.18	−9.36	13.11	315
104	+8.84	−7.46	11.57	310
102	+10.05	−9.03	13.51	310
101	+9.52	−7.13	11.89	305
57	+10.74	−6.82	12.72	300
56	+10.08	−10.47	14.53	315
55	+10.06	−7.82	12.74	310
54	+9.50	−11.39	14.83	320
53	+9.28	−11.69	14.93	320
52	+9.77	−13.06	16.31	325
51	+8.80	−11.62	14.58	325
50	+8.45	−11.84	14.55	325
49	+9.93	−13.87	17.06	325
47	+11.17	−14.32	18.16	320
46	+10.09	−15.24	18.28	325
45	+11.31	−14.95	18.75	325
44	+11.96	−16.12	20.07	325
43	+12.52	−15.63	20.03	320
42	+12.79	−16.26	20.69	320
41	+13.49	−16.26	21.13	320
40	+13.53	−16.23	21.13	320
39	+13.59	−16.60	21.45	320
38	+13.93	−16.53	21.62	320
37	+14.79	−16.73	22.33	320
36	+15.64	−17.24	23.28	320
35	+16.13	−16.26	22.90	315
34	+16.86	−16.46	23.56	315
33	+16.63	−16.06	23.12	315
32	+17.56	−16.38	24.01	315
31	+17.09	−15.97	23.39	315
30	+17.20	−15.91	23.43	315
29	+17.32	−15.39	23.17	310
28	+17.79	−15.81	23.80	310
27	+18.12	−15.38	23.77	310
26	+18.11	−15.68	23.95	310
25	+18.21	−15.67	24.02	310
24	+18.42	−15.79	24.26	310
23	+18.50	−15.54	24.16	310
22	+18.89	−15.45	24.40	310
21	+19.71	−15.18	24.88	310
20	+19.35	−14.99	24.48	310
19	+20.34	−14.45	24.95	305
18	+20.48	−14.17	24.90	305
17	+20.44	−14.50	25.06	305
16	+21.05	−13.87	25.21	305
15	+21.51	−13.12	25.20	300
13	+21.93	−13.07	25.53	300
11	+21.65	−12.38	24.94	300
9	+21.66	−12.09	24.81	300
8	+21.70	−11.74	24.67	300
7	+21.39	−11.57	24.32	300
6	+21.66	−10.76	24.19	295
5	+21.66	−11.50	24.52	300
4	+18.74	−13.73	23.23	305
2	+21.45	−11.23	24.21	300
1	+21.83	−11.51	24.68	300
602	+22.08	−12.02	25.14	300
501	+22.00	−12.50	25.30	300
504	+21.64	−13.08	25.29	300
519	+22.13	−22.78	31.76	315
521	+19.46	−28.40	34.43	325
526	+18.01	−37.17	41.30	335
528	+18.19	−45.85	49.33	340
536	+16.68	−44.77	47.78	340
352	+11.32	−23.18	25.80	335
347	+10.72	−24.23	26.50	335
346	+9.68	−21.89	23.93	335
344	+9.44	−21.63	23.60	335
341	+7.58	−19.87	21.27	340
325	+5.56	−16.13	17.06	340
321	+3.94	−14.22	14.76	345
318	+3.26	−15.58	15.92	350
313	+2.86	−10.82	11.19	345
312	+2.96	−10.69	11.09	345
310	+2.43	−9.52	9.83	345
308	+2.90	−8.16	8.66	340
306	+3.29	−5.50	6.41	330
305	+2.77	−4.83	5.57	330
304	+2.56	−4.17	4.89	330
157	−1.54	−2.43	2.88	30
152	+0.58	−5.56	5.59	355
150	−0.07	−4.38	4.38	0
149	−2.46	+2.06	3.21	130
148	−0.51	−2.04	2.10	15
147	−1.84	+3.15	3.65	150
146	−0.92	−0.39	1.00	65
145	−0.49	−3.41	3.45	10
144	+0.40	−3.68	3.70	355
142	+0.58	−4.71	4.75	355
140	+0.10	−0.40	0.41	345
139*	0	0	0	

B. West Loop
Hope—Seward—Chiswell Island—Homer—Kenai

Station code	Position shifts ΔX (Feet)	Position shifts ΔY (Feet)	Resultant vector Length (Feet)	Resultant vector Azimuth (Degrees)
486	+4.09	−11.98	12.66	340
487	+3.28	−12.19	12.62	345
403	+2.98	−11.86	12.23	345
404	+3.52	−12.28	12.77	345
405	+3.34	−12.40	12.84	345
408	+3.72	−14.18	14.66	345

* Held fixed in the adjustment.

TABLE 3.—*Differences in plane coordinates*—Continued

Station code	Position shifts		Resultant vector		Station code	Position shifts		Resultant vector	
	$\triangle X$	$\triangle Y$	Length	Azimuth		$\triangle X$	$\triangle Y$	Length	Azimuth
	Feet	*Feet*	*Feet*	*Degrees*		*Feet*	*Feet*	*Feet*	*Degrees*
409	+3.37	−14.83	15.21	345	480	+8.67	−54.15	54.84	350
410	+4.33	−13.71	14.38	340	218	+5.08	−58.20	58.42	355
416	+2.63	−14.85	15.08	350	223	+8.15	−55.46	56.06	350
419	+2.64	−18.23	18.42	350	188	−1.95	+9.03	9.24	170
420	−0.04	−15.58	15.58	0	186	−2.26	+11.06	11.29	170
422	−1.08	−17.25	17.28	5	184	−2.78	+12.23	12.54	165
424	+1.85	−21.59	21.67	355	180	−2.57	+7.45	7.88	160
425	−1.30	−25.31	25.34	5					
428	+5.37	−29.67	30.15	350		C. Prince William Sound			
429	+4.60	−29.53	29.89	350	576	+22.24	−45.30	50.46	335
432	+6.18	−37.26	37.77	350	580	+23.59	−48.63	54.05	335
433	+8.72	−39.23	40.19	345	558	+25.94	−23.87	35.25	315
435	+5.78	−38.67	39.10	350	555	+20.85	−41.30	46.26	335
436	+8.60	−41.89	42.76	350	554	+18.63	−39.50	43.67	335
437	+5.34	−41.20	41.54	355	591	+18.60	−67.40	69.92	345
438	+8.84	−46.34	47.18	350	609	+22.06	−66.56	70.12	340
439	+6.27	−17.75	18.82	340	610	+11.30	−66.35	67.30	350
478	+8.19	−50.80	51.46	350	553	−3.14	−28.77	28.94	5
479	+7.63	−52.71	53.26	350	552	−21.56	−22.61	31.24	45

Knight Islands to the northwest and Montague Island to the southeast.

A comparison of distances measured by Tellurometer in 1964 with a 1933 survey indicates that the distance across Montague Strait is now 15 to 20 feet shorter. Another possible explanation, for at least a part of this discrepancy, is the fact that there is no direct tie between the two stations. They were originally established in separate schemes which were not connected except at the northern part of Prince William Sound. In the 1965 triangulation, the tie is somewhat closer but still not direct.

CONCLUSION

Most of the stations in the Prince William Sound area occupied during the summer of 1965 were located on the higher points of the islands, and the divergences discussed here, therefore, represent the shifts of stations at elevations of 1,500 to 3,000 feet above sea level. It is hoped that additional triangulation can be accomplished in the near future, observing stations at sea level to determine what changes have taken place at that level. For example, a tilt of 1 degree in a block of the earth's crust containing a 3,000-foot peak would result in a differential horizontal movement of 50 feet between sea level and the peak.

A resurvey of the triangulation network bridging Cook Inlet and extending south to Shelikof Strait and

Kodiak Island would furnish valuable information concerning crustal deformation in that area. At least one observer reported that an apparent widening of Cook Inlet was revealed by an electronic distance measurement of lines across Cook Inlet. Also, it would be desirable to extend the retriangulation at the northwest and northeast corners of this network farther northward to determine whether the station selected as the fixed station is really as stable as it is believed to be.

In the report published by the U. S. Coast and Geodetic Survey (1969), complete numerical data are listed from which the pre- and postearthquake observations may be computed: lists of 7 directions, measured baselines, and Laplace azimuths.

REFERENCES

U. S. Coast and Geodetic Survey, 1960. Plane coordinate intersection tables, Alaska, zones 2-9, U. S. Coast and Geodetic Survey Publication 65-1, part 50. Washington: Government Printing Office.

U. S. Coast and Geodetic Survey, 1966. The Prince William Sound, Alaska, earthquake of 1964 and aftershocks. Fergus J. Wood, editor. Volume I: Operational phases of the Coast and Geodetic Survey program in Alaska for the period March 27 to December 31, 1964. Washington: Government Printing Office. 263 p.

U. S. Coast and Geodetic Survey, 1969. The Prince William Sound, Alaska, earthquake of 1964 and aftershocks. Louis E. Leipold, editor. Volume III: Research studies and interpretive results—geodesy and photogrammetry. Washington: Government Printing Office. 161 p.

ALLEN J. POPE
U.S. COAST AND GEODETIC SURVEY *

Reprinted with minor changes from
U.S. Coast and Geodetic Survey Volume III: Geodesy and Photogrammetry,
"Strain Analysis of Horizontal Crustal Movements in Alaska Based on Triangulation Surveys
before and after the Prince William Sound Earthquake of March 27, 1964"

Strain Analysis of Horizontal Crustal Movements in Alaska Based on Triangulation Surveys before and after the Earthquake

ABSTRACT: Components of strain are computed to facilitate interpretation of displacements indicated by repeated triangulation in the Anchorage, Seward, and Valdez areas. The method of computation is described and the components are presented in tabular and graphic form. Various factors that limit or enhance the usefulness of this strain computation in interpreting crustal movements are discussed. Widespread elongation along a north-northwest to south-southeast axis and a reversal to shear in the Prince William Sound area are predominant features of the strain pattern.

INTRODUCTION

Horizontal crustal movements associated with the Prince William Sound, Alaska, Earthquake of March 27, 1964, have been determined by comparing pre-earthquake triangulation surveys with postearthquake surveys done in 1964 and 1965. For a detailed description of these surveys, and tables and diagrams of the horizontal earth movement indicated by them, see E. J. Parkin, HORIZONTAL CRUSTAL MOVEMENTS DETERMINED FROM SURVEYS AFTER THE ALASKAN EARTHQUAKE OF 1964, in this volume. To further aid in interpreting this movement, vectors (showing the differences between adjusted postearthquake positions of triangulation stations and their adjusted preearthquake positions) have been used to compute strain components.

This report describes the method of computation used, summarizes factors that limit or enhance the usefulness of the strain components in interpreting crustal movement, and presents the strain components in tabular and graphic form.

METHOD OF COMPUTING STRAIN

The strain components were computed on the assumption that the horizontal displacements in areas containing three or more neighboring points (resur-

---

*Now in part the Office of National Geodetic Survey, National Ocean Survey, NOAA.

veyed triangulation stations) can be expressed as a linear function of the station coordinates. That is, the strain is assumed to be locally homogeneous [Terada and Miyabe, 1929; Pope, 1966]. Specifically, for each selected group of n neighboring points with coordinates x_i, y_i and corresponding displacements

$$\Delta x_i, \Delta y_i, \ i = 1, \ \cdots, \ n$$

coefficients ε_{11}, ε_{12}, ε_{21}, ε_{22}, a, b are determined such that

$$\Delta x_i + v_i = \varepsilon_{11}\, x_i + \varepsilon_{12}\, y_i + a$$
$$\Delta y_i + u_i = \varepsilon_{21}\, x_i + \varepsilon_{22}\, y_i + b$$
$$\text{for } i = 1, \ \cdots, \ n.$$

If $n = 3$, the residuals v_i, u_i, are all zero and the coefficients are exactly determined. For $n > 3$, the coefficients ε_{ij}, a, and b are determined by minimizing the sum of squares of residuals,

$$\sum_{i=1}^{n} (v_i^2 + u_i^2).$$

The computations can be summarized as follows: Given x_i, y_i, Δx_i, Δy_i at each point (in feet, Alaska State Plane Coordinates, zone 4), for each specified group of n points, compute

the coordinates of the centroid of the n points,

$$\bar{x} = \frac{1}{n} \sum_{i=1}^{n} x_i$$

$$\bar{y} = \frac{1}{n} \sum_{i=1}^{n} y_i$$

the coordinates of the n points referred to this centroid as an origin,

$$\hat{x}_i = x_i - \bar{x}$$
$$\hat{y}_i = y_i - \bar{y}$$

the (nonsymmetric) strain tensor,

$$\mathbf{E} = \begin{vmatrix} \varepsilon_{11} & \varepsilon_{21} \\ \varepsilon_{12} & \varepsilon_{22} \end{vmatrix} = \begin{vmatrix} \sum_{i=1}^{n} \hat{x}_i^2 & \sum_{i=1}^{n} \hat{x}_i \hat{y}_i \\ \sum_{i=1}^{n} \hat{x}_i \hat{y}_i & \sum_{i=1}^{n} \hat{y}_i^2 \end{vmatrix}^{-1}$$

$$\times \begin{vmatrix} \sum_{i=1}^{n} \hat{x}_i \Delta x_i & \sum_{i=1}^{n} \hat{x}_i \Delta y_i \\ \sum_{i=1}^{n} \hat{y}_i \Delta x_i & \sum_{i=1}^{n} \hat{y}_i \Delta y_i \end{vmatrix}$$

and the strain components (see Jaeger, 1956, for a detailed explanation of the significance of each quantity),

shear components, $\quad \gamma_1 = \varepsilon_{11} - \varepsilon_{22}$

$$\gamma_2 = \varepsilon_{12} + \varepsilon_{21}$$

rotation, $\quad \omega = \frac{1}{2} (\varepsilon_{12} - \varepsilon_{21})$
(positive clockwise)

dilation, $\quad \rho = \frac{1}{2} (\varepsilon_{11} + \varepsilon_{22})$
(average extension over 360° or $.5\Delta$ where Δ, "dilatation" or "divergence," is the area change per unit area)

maximum shear, $\quad \gamma_m = (\gamma_1^2 + \gamma_2^2)^{\frac{1}{2}}$

principal axes
of strain,

maximum extension, $\mathrm{E}_1 = \rho + \dfrac{\gamma_m}{2}$

minimum extension, $\mathrm{E}_2 = \rho - \dfrac{\gamma_m}{2}$

orientation of principal
axes of strain (azimuth of E_1, measured clockwise from North),

$$\theta = \frac{1}{2} \operatorname{Arctan} \left(-\frac{\gamma_2}{\gamma_1} \right)$$

All of the above quantities, particularly E_1, E_2, θ, ω, and γ_m are referred to in this report as "strain components," although the term strictly denotes only the components of the symmetric part of the strain tensor; that is $\varepsilon_{11} = \mathrm{E}_x$, $\varepsilon_{22} = \mathrm{E}_y$ and $\gamma_2 = \gamma_{xy}$. Note that first-order formulas are used. This is certainly justified since the ε_{ij}'s are of the order of magnitude of 10^{-5}.

In addition, the root-mean-square residual was computed by the formula

$$s = \left[\frac{\sum_{i=1}^{n} (v_i^2 + u_i^2)}{n - 3} \right]^{\frac{1}{2}}$$

s is not an indication of the accuracy of the strain components but gives an idea of the adequacy of the linear model when $n > 3$. The average group consisted of five points from an area roughly corresponding to that covered by a single quadrilateral figure of the triangulation, of the order of 10 miles on a side. Many groups containing fewer or more than five points were included to provide computational checks. These also provide, along with s, a partial check on the assumption of homogeneous strain.

Use of the least-squares linear model and the presence of overlap between adjacent groups of more than three points has the effect of smoothing the strain components to some extent. A more detailed spacing, such as every three neighboring points, or a displacement model containing quadratic terms, is contraindicated by the configuration of the triangulation net, the accuracy of older surveys, and the above-mentioned checks.

Nonlinear strain on a scale smaller than the spacing between triangulation stations can not be detected. A representation of any large-scale nonlinear features is approximated by the simultaneous presentation of the piece-wise linear segments, just as one might approximate a three-dimensional surface with many small, linear "facets."

Altogether, 155 sets of strain values were computed. Of these 77 were selected for coverage without undue repetition or gaps. Figure 1 shows the location of the centroids of the 77 groups, numbered 1 through 77. Table 2 lists the stations in each group (station numbers are those used by E. J. Parkin in this volume). Table 1 lists the strain components for each group. These have been computed to five decimals and rounded off to units of 10^{-5} proportional parts

(or radians). Figures 2, 3, 4, and 5 present, respectively, the principal axes of strain, directions and magnitude of maximum shear, dilations, and rotations. Each diagram or value is depicted at the centroid of the group of points used to compute it.

INTERPRETATION OF THE STRAIN VALUES

The strain components must be interpreted in the light of considerations of the form and quality of the triangulation on which they are based. Therefore, some implications of the placement, configuration, and accuracy of the surveys are discussed before examining the computed values.

LOCALIZATION OF THE STRAIN VALUES

Displacements can be determined only at those points that were part of a preearthquake survey. Stations in these early surveys were placed for their accessibility, intervisibility, and the achievement of a quadrilateral arc configuration. For this reason the

TABLE 1.—*Strain values computed from each of the groups identified in table 2*

Group	$E_1 \times 10^5$	$E_2 \times 10^5$	θ	$\gamma_m \times 10^5$	$\rho \times 10^5$	$\omega \times 10^5$	Group	$E_1 \times 10^5$	$E_2 \times 10^5$	θ	$\gamma_m \times 10^5$	$\rho \times 10^5$	$\omega \times 10^5$
1	+8	0	−37°	7	+4	+1	40	+3	−4	−31°	7	0	0
2	+8	+1	−34°	6	+4	+2	41	+2	−9	−32°	11	−3	0
3	+8	+1	−32°	7	+4	+3	42	+2	−7	−31°	9	−2	+2
4	+8	0	−32°	7	+4	+3	43	+1	−9	−39°	10	−4	+1
5	+8	0	−30°	8	+4	+2	44	+3	−4	−35°	7	0	+1
6	+13	+4	+13°	9	+9	+7	45	+3	−2	−40°	5	0	+1
7	+11	+2	−13°	9	+6	+7	46	+2	−12	−53°	14	−5	−3
8	+11	−6	−18°	16	+2	+6	47	+2	−10	−55°	12	−4	−4
9	+10	−2	−22°	12	+4	+3	48	0	−2	+77°	2	−1	−4
10	+10	+3	−30°	7	+7	+2	49	+9	+2	+23°	7	+6	−5
11	+10	+2	−20°	7	+6	+1	50	+7	+1	+14°	6	+4	+2
12	+9	+2	−13°	7	+5	+1	51	+15	+2	+15°	13	+9	−7
13	+9	−1	−15°	10	+4	+1	52	+15	+2	+17°	14	+9	−7
14	+10	+4	+3°	6	+7	+1	53	+9	+1	+16°	9	+5	−2
15	+7	−1	−13°	8	+3	+2	54	+9	−3	+20°	12	+3	0
16	+8	+1	−3°	8	+5	+2	55	+6	−12	+40°	18	−3	0
17	+8	0	+6°	7	+4	+1	56	+15	+3	+14°	12	+9	−6
18	+8	+4	−3°	4	+6	+1	57	+13	+5	+9°	8	+9	−4
19	+8	+4	−1°	4	+6	+2	58	+11	−2	−43°	12	+5	+3
20	+6	+2	−5°	4	+4	+1	59	+23	+6	−20°	18	+14	0
21	+5	+1	−7°	4	+3	0	60	+14	+1	−42°	12	+8	+2
22	+4	+1	−12°	3	+3	0	61	+8	−1	−52°	9	+3	+1
23	+4	+1	−18°	3	+2	0	62	+9	−5	−44°	15	+2	+4
24	+4	0	−5°	3	+2	0	63	+13	−3	−18°	16	+5	0
25	+4	0	0	5	+2	+1	64	+7	−3	−25°	11	+2	+2
26	+4	−1	0	5	+2	+1	65	+6	−3	−45°	9	+1	+1
27	+2	−1	+16°	3	0	+1	66	+6	−1	−13°	7	+3	+2
28	+2	−2	+7°	4	0	−1	67	+8	−2	−28°	10	+3	+3
29	+2	−2	+5°	4	0	−1	68	+8	−5	−29°	13	+2	+4
30	+4	−2	0	6	+1	−2	69	+10	−3	−23°	13	+4	+7
31	+4	−3	−1°	6	0	−2	70	+15	+2	−36°	13	+9	+7
32	+3	−4	−11°	7	−1	−1	71	+15	+6	−29°	9	+11	+10
33	+3	−5	−12°	8	−1	−1	72	+18	+11	−54°	7	+14	+9
34	+2	−5	−18°	7	−1	−1	73	+21	+6	−39°	15	+13	+6
35	+4	−5	−15°	9	0	−2	74	+21	+6	−47°	15	+14	+6
36	−1	−7	0	6	−4	−3	75	+26	+8	−36°	18	+17	+6
37	−2	−8	−33°	6	−5	−2	76	+24	+6	−40°	18	+15	+9
38	+7	−5	−25°	11	+1	−1	77	+13	+3	−58°	10	+8	+4
39	+6	−3	−27°	10	+2	−1							

TABLE 2.—*Group identification numbers; stations in each group; number of stations in each group; and* s

[Defined in the text]

Group	Points used						Number	s (Ft.)	Group	Points used						Number	s (Ft.)
1	157	152	150				3	—	41	24	23	22	21	20	19	6	.1
2	157	152	149	148			4	.5	42	21	19	18	17	16	15 13	7	.2
3	149	148	147	146			4	.3	43	21	19	18	17	16	15	6	.1
4	148	147	146	145	144	142 140	7	.3	44	16	15	13	11			4	.3
5	142	140	139	138	137		5	.3	45	15	13	11	9	8	7	6	.1
6	139	137	136	135			4	1.2	46	9	8	7	6	5	4 2	7	1.4
7	138	137	136	135			4	1.4	47	8	7	6	5	4	2 1	7	1.4
8	136	135	133	132			4	1.0	48	2	1	602	501	504		5	.2
9	133	132	131	130	129		5	.4	49	1	602	501	504	519	521 558	7	1.0
10	130	129	128	127	126		5	.7	50	519	521	554	555	558		5	7.9
11	127	126	125	124	123		5	.3	51	519	521	526	558	576	580	6	.7
12	126	125	124	123	122		5	.2	52	519	521	558	576			4	.5
13	124	122	121	120	118		5	.3	53	519	521	526	528	536	554 555 558 576 580	10	8.1
14	120	119	118	117			4	.2	54	554	555	558	576	580	591 609 610	8	8.6
15	119	117	116	115	112		5	.2	55	554	555	558	576	580	552 553 591 609 610	10	14.6
16	119	117	116	115	113	112 111	7	.3	56	519	521	526	528	536	558 576 580	8	1.7
17	116	115	113	112	111		5	.3	57	526	528	536	576	580		5	.9
18	115	113	112	111	110		5	.4	58	526	528	536	576	580	352 347 346 344	9	3.9
19	111	110	109	108			4	.3	59	352	347	346	344			4	.6
20	109	108	107	105			4	.5	60	344	341	439	325			4	.6
21	108	107	106	105	104		5	.4	61	439	325	321	318			4	1.5
22	108	107	106	105	104	102 101	7	.5	62	321	318	313	312	487		5	1.1
23	105	104	102	101			4	.5	63	313	312	487	486	310	308	6	.5
24	102	101	57	56			4	.9	64	310	308	306	305			4	.1
25	57	56	55	54			4	.2	65	308	306	305	304	157	152	6	1.1
26	56	55	54				3	—	66	487	486	403	404	405	408	6	.7
27	54	53	51				3	—	67	403	404	405	408	409	410	6	.6
28	54	53	52	51	50		5	.3	68	405	408	409	410			4	.6
29	53	52	51	50			4	.4	69	409	410	416	419			4	.9
30	52	50	49				3	—	70	416	419	420	424			4	.7
31	52	50	49	47	46		5	.5	71	420	422	424	425			4	1.1
32	49	47	46	45			4	.2	72	424	425	428	429			4	1.3
33	47	46	45	44	43		5	.2	73	428	429	432	433			4	.5
34	44	43	42	41			4	.1	74	432	433	435	436			4	.4
35	42	41	40	39	38		5	.1	75	435	436	437	438			4	.3
36	39	38	37	36			4	.2	76	437	438	478	480			5	.5
37	37	36	35	34	33		5	.5	77	479	480	218	223	609		5	.5
38	34	33	32	31	30	29	6	.1									
39	32	29	28	27	26	25	6	.1									
40	27	26	25	24	23		5	.1									

surveys, with few exceptions, follow a geographic feature such as an inlet, valley, or pass.

From the triangulation alone, it is impossible to differentiate between area-wide crustal distortion and movement localized at these features. Consequently, extrapolation of the strain pattern beyond the areas covered by repeated triangulation, for example, into the interior of the north loop (fig. 1) is not justified.

Localization of the movement in time also presents some problems. The periods of preearthquake surveys were: 1941–1944 from Anchorage via Glennallen to Valdez (fig. 1); 1947–1948 in the northern part of Prince William Sound; 1910–1914 from Prince William Sound via Turnagain Arm to Anchorage; 1941–1942 from Turnagain Arm southward to Seward (see report of E. J. Parkin in this volume). Proceed-

ing southward from Anchorage to Seward, the 30-year variation in dates of old surveys, from 1912 to 1942 is not mirrored by correspondingly significant changes in the strain components. On the other hand, large changes in the pattern of shear do occur at the western and eastern sides of Prince William Sound corresponding respectively to approximately 35 and 5 years' changes in the dates of old surveys.

However, the Prince William Sound area also shows evidence of having sustained greater disturbances during the earthquake. There appears to be no reason to reject the hypothesis that all, or most, of the indicated displacements are associated with the earthquake rather than the result of a gradual accumulation. Future repetitions of surveys will help resolve this point.

IMPLICATIONS OF THE CONFIGURATION OF THE TRIANGULATION

Any error whose effect is systematic in the sense of being the same in both surveys does not affect the displacement vectors.

However, the predominant quadrilateral arc configuration of the triangulation introduces the possibility of errors of position in one year's survey (and therefore in the displacement vectors) due to the unfavorable error propagation in arcs of triangula-

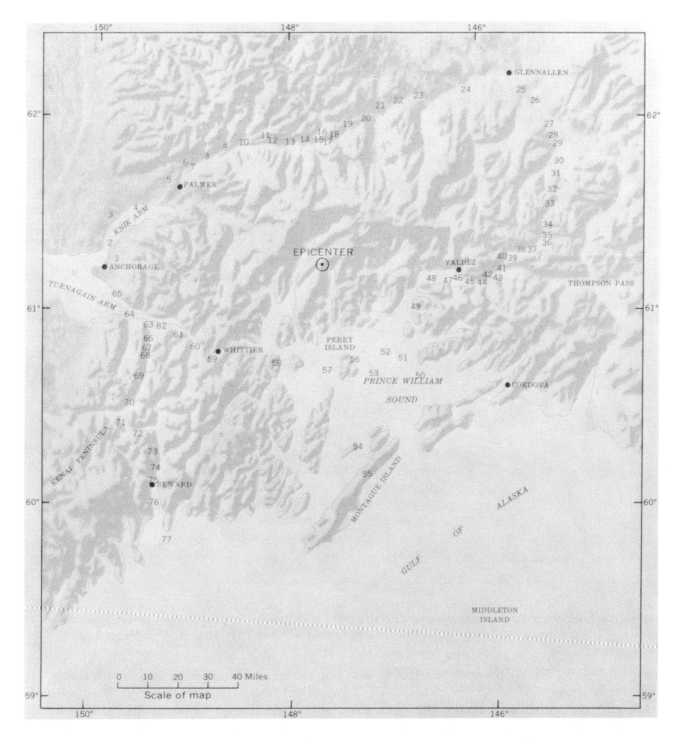

FIGURE 1.—Locations of the centroids of the 77 groups of neighboring triangulation stations whose displacements were used to compute strain values.

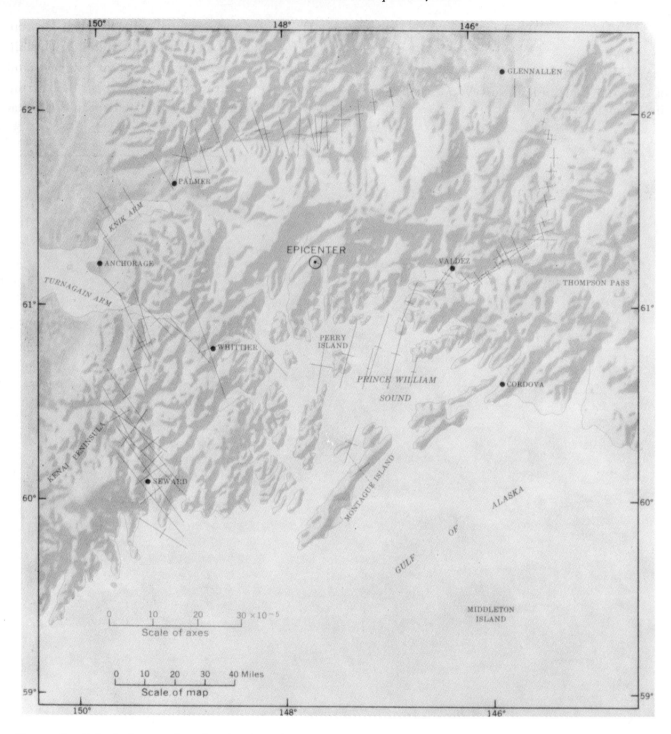

FIGURE 2.—Principal axes of strain, showing directions and magnitudes (in proportional parts) of maximum and minimum elongation (solid line) or contraction (dashed line). Measure total length.

tion compared to that in triangulation having uniform area coverage.

The problem is that the combined effect of a particular set of random errors of observation on derived quantities, such as the displacement vectors, may appear as a systematic function of position. (This sort of systematic distortion arising from random errors is called "quasi-systematic error" in the geodetic literature.) Because of the importance of the distinction for the following discussion, the term "error" will be reserved for errors in observed quantities, whereas errors induced in derived quantities (not directly observed) by these observational errors will be designated "effects." Such effects can increase nonlinearly or oscillate as one moves along the arc. Corresponding effects can appear in the strain components. However, strain components are less sensitive to some types of error than are the earth movement vectors.

Effects of Errors in Control

Strain components are simple functions of partial derivatives of displacement with respect to x or y. (In fact, these derivatives must be estimated from discrete samples of the displacement function; that is,

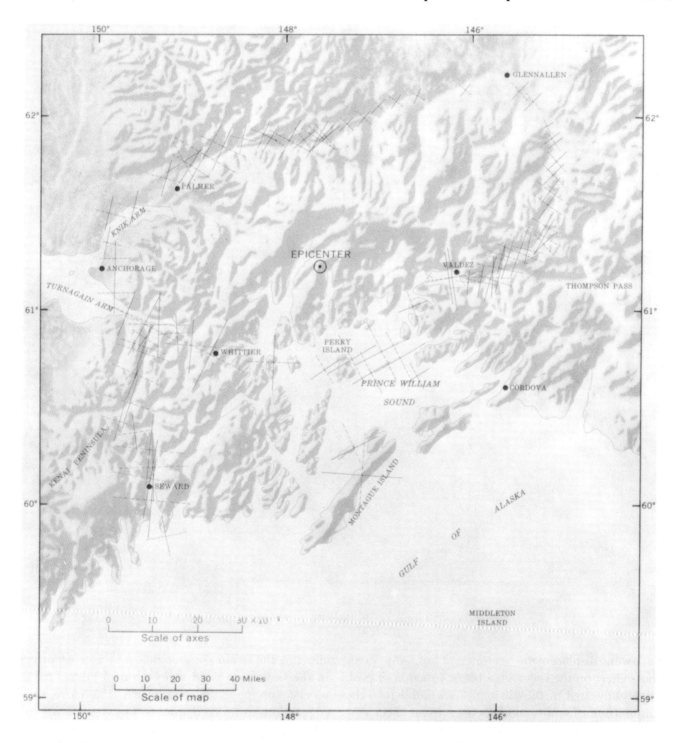

FIGURE 3.—Maximum shear (γ_m), showing directions and magnitude (in radians) of maximum positive simple shear (solid line) and maximum negative simple shear (dashed line). Measure total length.

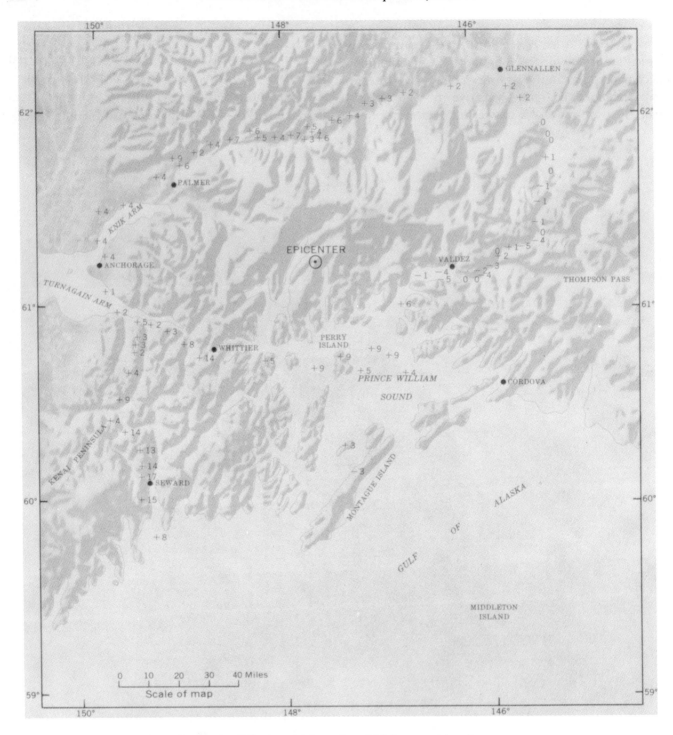

FIGURE 4.—Dilation (ρ) in units of 10^{-5} proportional parts.

the given displacement vectors.) Thus, any error whose effect on the vectors is a linear function of position is converted by the differentiation implicit in the computation of strain components into an effect that is constant, that is, independent of position. Correspondingly, an effect on the vectors that is a quadratic function of position is converted into a linear effect in the strain components, and a constant error in the vectors (a rigid translation of all points) has no effect on the strain components. Therefore, knowledge of the strain components does not require absolute displacements, but only displacements relative to an arbitrary local origin. For example, in the adjustments on which the earth movement vectors in Alaska were based, station number 139 (in group 6) was held fixed. An error in this choice of translational control, that is, any actual movement of point 139, contributes nothing to the strain components.

In addition to angle measurements and translational control, every triangulation must contain the equivalent of one or more measured (or fixed) lengths and azimuths to supply scale and orientation control.

As a step toward understanding the effect of any errors in control on the strain components, first consider the case of minimal control, that is, one (the same) measured base, azimuth, and fixed point in each survey. In this situation the effects can be simply and rigorously characterized.

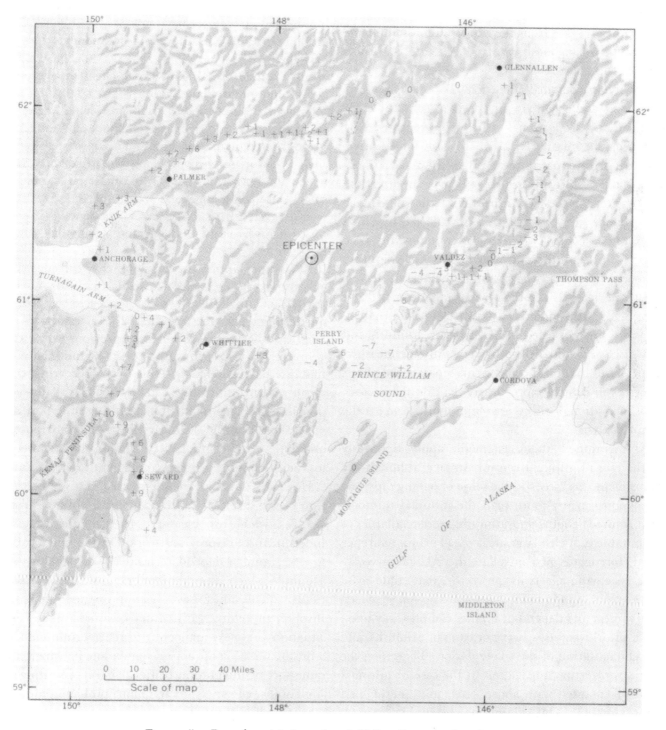

FIGURE 5.—Rotation (ω) in units of 10^{-5} radians ($= 2''$ of arc).

An error in scale or orientation control contributes an erroneous component to the apparent displacement vector at each point that is respectively parallel, or perpendicular, to the line joining the point in question to the arbitrarily chosen fixed origin. The length of the erroneous component is proportional to the length of this line. In other words, the effects on the vectors of errors in either scale or orientation control is a linear function of position. Therefore, we see from the above discussion that a constant error, at most, is introduced into the strain components.

A still more detailed discussion [Pope, 1966] shows that E_1, E_2 and ρ contain an additive, constant error equal to any proportional error in the repeated base measurement. Similarly, ω can contain an additive, constant error equal to the error in the repeated, observed azimuth (expressed in radians). In effect, the zero datum for these quantities is unknown. On the other hand, γ_1, γ_2, γ_m and θ are not affected by errors in minimal control. (Strictly, θ contains the same error from azimuth control as does ω but the effect on θ, which need only be known to the nearest degree, can be neglected since the error in question will not exceed 3×10^{-5} radians at most.) Also note that E_1, E_2 and ρ are not affected by errors in azimuth and conversely ω is not affected by errors in base measurement. Thus the strain components separate the effects of errors in control more clearly than do the vectors. This separation of effects is a major motivation for the strain analysis.

As mentioned, these statements apply rigorously in the case of minimal control. In fact, although the adjustment was "free" in the sense of having only one fixed point, many more than the minimal numbers of measured lengths and azimuths were available, as is desirable in such a large area. (See Parkin, reference cited, for details of control in the Alaska surveys.) The systematic effects in the vectors that could arise from errors in redundant control are no longer necessarily linear and depend in a rather complex way upon the a priori weights, spacing of bases or azimuths, and the configuration of the triangulation. Therefore, the features of error propagation in the case of minimal control, pointed out above, are only useful first approximations which should not be applied to areas larger than a quandrant of the north loop at most.

Other Effects Related to Configuration

As well as errors whose effects on the vectors are constant or linear functions of position, it is possible that other systematic effects may manifest themselves in the vectors as quadratic functions of positions (even in the case of minimal control), and therefore contribute spurious linear "drifts" to some of the strain components. Quadratic or higher order effects are more difficult to formulate precisely, but some general implications for the strain components can be described.

An example of a higher order effect that is especially relevant to triangulation is any conformal distortion of the net (a distortion preserving angles in small areas). While rigorously precluded by the finite size of the triangulation figures, an approximation to such a distortion becomes possible in long arcs in which the length of a single line between stations is small relative to the total extent of the arc. This would result in quadratic error components in vectors, linear errors in E_1, E_2, θ, and ρ, but little or no error in θ or γ_m.

As another approach, for simplicity, consider first a "cantilevered" or "free" quadrilateral arc of triangulation. In effect, control for each succeeding quadrilateral is reestablished by propagation of lengths and azimuths through the previous work. The above results concerning the effects of minimal control can be reapplied in each quad, observing that errors in "current control" in any quad carry forward into all succeeding quads. The resulting superposition (or "convolution") of linear effects can contribute a quadratic error component to the displacement vectors and therefore, a linear component to E_1, E_2, ω and ρ. However, θ and γ_m are not affected. This is a reflection of the fact that θ and γ_m depend only on angle changes, which are measured in each quadrilateral independently of previous work. On the other hand, E_1, E_2, ρ, and ω depend respectively on lengths and azimuths which, if not directly measured in a particular quad, must have been propagated forward through preceding works from measured lines. The situation is closely analogous to that encountered in adjustments of strip aerotriangulation in which the same sort of integration of linear effects resulting in high-order effects is a common problem. Similar effects remain even if the arc is not strictly "cantilevered" but forms a closed loop.

From still another point of view, one can see that E_1, E_2, and ρ possess a high degree of autocorrelation as a function of distance along an arc, whereas θ and γ_m do not. High autocorrelation characteristically means that the variable in question exhibits spurious variations that appear nonrandom or even oscillatory over short intervals but are in fact the result of random errors.

Other potentially misleading effects would show up in the form of correlations with either the spacing of stations or the direction of the arc. The absence of any correlation with the spacing of stations would suggest the presence of a unform areal distortion (that is, accumulative rather than localized at a fault). On the other hand, movement that is sharply localized, for instance along the center lines of the features spanned by the triangulation, would result in strain strongly, but negatively, correlated with the spacing of stations. For example, a 1-foot displacement on a fault spanned by a 5-mile line produces a strain of 4×10^{-5} proportional parts, whereas the same fault spanned by a 20-mile line would yield strain values of 1×10^{-5}. Correlation with the direction of the arc could arise from differences in the differential error propagation characteristics of arcs along their transverse and longitudinal directions. In fact, strain values from groups of points with average spacings of from less than 5 to more than 30 miles (see Parkin, figs. 4, 5, and 6) are generally consistent and θ remains relatively constant even though the arc turns through 180° in the north loop, suggesting the presence of uniform, areal distortion.

Magnitude and Propagation of Random Error

Up to this point, qualitative features of some possible systematic effects arising from various errors or their combination have been examined. Attention has been centered on possible differential effects of errors in a single crustal movement solution (that is, the comparison of two surveys). It is also of interest to know something about the dispersion (as measured, for example, by the standard error) that would result if the surveys could be repeated many times under identical conditions. The distinction between the types of errors and effects thus far considered and standard errors is basically that between propagation of first moments (means) and second moments (variances and covariances) of a probability density function. The latter provides an "envelope" (in probabil-

ity measure) for the first, but may not reveal relevant details of the distortion pattern that could arise from a particular set of errors in one earth movement analysis. The size of this "envelope" places a fundamental limit on the magnitude of earth movement that can be reliably detected.

By arguments which are a slight extension of those used to deduce some of the features of the propagation of differential errors, the following can be shown to hold in the case of minimal control [Pope, 1966; Frank, 1966]. (All statements are unchanged if probable error is used.)

Standard errors of E_1, E_2, ρ, and ω contain constant contributions from the standard errors of measured bases (E_1, E_2, ρ) and azimuths (ω). In addition, the standard errors of E_1, E_2, ρ, and ω contain a component that is proportional to the distance from control. On the other hand, the standard errors of θ and γ_m are of the same order of magnitude as the standard error (expressed in radians) of adjusted angle changes in the vicinity of the particular group of points used to compute them. Standard errors of angle changes are not a function of the position or accuracy (that is, weight given to) control. Evidence from the adjustment suggests 1×10^{-5} as a conservative estimate of the standard error of an adjusted angle (in radians). Thus, with the usual 3-σ rule, strain values greater than 3×10^{-5} (6" of arc) will be regarded as certainly significant. The resulting "signal to noise ratio", ranging from less than one to ten, is admittedly not favorable. A more complete error analysis could supply a confidence interval for each and every component; however, the above figure is a mean for the net as a whole.

Review of Capabilities of the Strain Analysis

A strong argument for the effectiveness of strain analysis of triangulation resurveys in detecting earth movement has always been the remarkable agreement between the strain components so obtained and independent lines of evidence such as known fault displacements and fault-plane solutions [Tsuboi, 1932, and Kasahara and Sugimura, 1964]. The determination of least-squares linear strain from successive overlapping groups of vectors obtained from adjusted triangulation was chosen as a straightforward approach to the problem of extracting the mean trend from noisy data and of building up a piecewise linear picture of the total, nonlinear pattern of strain. Any single strain value, taken in isolation, is a somewhat unreliable guide to the details of earth movement in the immediate area. However, shared features or patterns exhibited by many sets of strain values over large areas are reliable synoptic indications of distortion.

The purpose of the above discussion has been to outline the effects of the known sources of systematic and quasi-systematic distortions in surveys like those in Alaska which could produce spurious indications of movement. It is clear by implication that many sources can be eliminated in surveys designed for the specific purpose of earth movement detection.

Features which cannot be accounted for by such known sources of distortion must be attributed to earth movement. The residue of this "process of elimination" is considerable. Specifically, θ and γ_m emerge relatively unscathed by all sources of distortion. For this reason, a separate plot of γ_m and its directions ($\theta + 45°$ for γ_m, $\theta - 45°$ for $-\gamma_m$, angles measured clockwise) has been provided (fig. 3), even though this information is implicitly contained in the principal axis diagrams (fig. 2). The remaining strain components, E_1, E_2, ρ, and ω frequently exceed the 3×10^{-5} significance level and therefore are also given but must be interpreted with due caution in the light of the foregoing points.

RESULTS OF STRAIN ANALYSIS

Figures 2, 3, 4, and 5 can now be examined in more detail.

Principal Axes of Strain

Predominant features are the general elongation along approximately a NNW. to SSE. line and the increase in the magnitude of all strain components as one goes from NE. to SW. (fig. 2). Areas of greatest disturbance (as measured by the nonlinearity of the strain) are Prince William Sound and Turnagain Arm. Strain components characteristically bring out features of the displacement pattern that are not obvious in vector diagrams. An example of this is the contraction along the southeast side of the north loop (fig. 2). The anomalous orientation of the principal axes of group 55 (fig. 2, vicinity of Montague Island) can be attributed to the fact that the displacement vector of the station on Middleton Island was included in this group. This station showed movement whose

sense was considerably different from the general trend in the area (fig. 4 of Parkin in this volume).

Maximum Shear

The directions and magnitude of maximum shear are the strain components least affected by many types of errors in triangulation. Values of maximum shear (fig. 3) range from 2×10^{-5} to 18×10^{-5} radians (or 4″ to 36″ of arc). The mean value is 8×10^{-5} (16″); well above the 3-σ level of 3×10^{-5}. Shear of this magnitude cannot be explained by known sources of systematic or quasi-systematic error in triangulation. Its presence lends credence to the reality of the widespread distortion pattern indicated by the triangulation.

Figure 3 is of special interest because the direction of maximum shear should agree approximately with the orientations of any fractures. In fact, the average orientation of ground cracks in the Kenai lowlands [Foster and Karlstrom, 1967, p. F4] agree well with the orientation of shear from the closest triangulation (in the vicinity of Turnagain Arm and southward). If the displacements are the result of strike-slip faulting, then the strike of the fault will be the direction of maximum positive simple shear (solid line) if right lateral, and the direction of maximum negative shear (dashed line) if left lateral. The ambiguity can be resolved by the sense of the associated rotation. Positive (clockwise) rotation (ω) indicates right-lateral movement while negative rotation indicates left-lateral movement. The evidence of rotation (fig. 4) suggests right-lateral throughout the western and northern extent of the net (clockwise from Seward to Glennallen) and left-lateral in Prince William Sound. The evidence of rotation is inconclusive in the Glennallen to Valdez arc.

Rotation and Dilation

Dilation (ρ) and rotation (ω) are plotted (fig. 4 and 5) for reference. As mentioned above, both small- and large-scale variations in these quantities are not reliable indications of corresponding earth movement because of the high autocorrelation and the spacing between scale and azimuth control. For this reason the slight oscillation in magnitude about a mean value seen in ρ and ω (and E_2) along the north loop cannot be attributed to earth movement with any confidence.

A comparison of the dilations with independently deduced elevation changes in the area yields only a slight negative correlation, if any.

GEOPHYSICAL IMPLICATIONS

The area covered by triangulation represents only a small part of the total area affected by the earthquake. Nevertheless, it is remarkable that significant shear, the most reliable measure of distortion from the triangulation, is wide spread and relatively uniform throughout this area. The general trend of the principal axes is in excellent agreement with the trend of geological features in the area.

It should be noted that the strain computed here can only be regarded as an alternate and advantageous method of describing displacements that have taken place, not as elastic strain reflecting a corresponding state of stress. Because of the "poor resolution" in time and the absence of continuous independent checks on possible movements at surface features (put another way, determination of details of the time history of strain on a scale smaller and shorter than that of the present spacing between stations and epochs), discrimination of the elastic and nonelastic components is not possible.

One of the most interesting features is the reversal of the sense of shear in the Prince William Sound area. Discontinuous changes in the axes of strain occur on the two sides of Prince William Sound, roughly in the Whittier and Valdez areas. Unfortunately, the interpretation is again clouded by the fact that these changes also correspond to discontinuities in the configuration, quality, and time of the preearthquake surveys.

No single, simple fault mechanism seems capable of accounting for all the computed strain. However, recent studies show that the strain patterns near the ends of even simple faults can be quite complex.

All lines of evidence from seismology and geodesy agree in demonstrating that the Alaskan earthquake of 1964 was indeed a large-scale and complex phenomena involving an extremely large area. (See Volumes I and II in this series.) Beyond this point, however, agreement is less than perfect.

Fault-plane solutions of the initial shock involve an essential ambiguity between planes of faulting, roughly characterized as thrust or normal. The strain analysis supports the existence of significant horizontal components favorable to the thrust hypothesis. One of the most emphatic features of the strain components is the general elongation along a NNW. to SSE. axis. This can be made compatible with the fault-plane data by invoking rebound or by appeal to still more complex mechanisms such as a magma intrusion like that suggested by Inoue [1960] as an explanation of several earthquakes in Japan. This last hypothesis is attractive in several respects. It could explain known patterns of gravity anomalies as well as both the horizontal and vertical (deduced from seashore changes) movements.

Future repetitions of geodetic surveys and the large scale, "long time constant," strain along with the small scale, "short time constant" information provided by continued monitoring of seismic events in the area, will undoubtedly contribute to the eventual resolution of these questions.

REFERENCES

Foster, Helen L. and Karlstrom, Thor N. V., "The Alaska Earthquake, March 27: Regional Effects—Ground Breakage and Associated Effects in the Cook Inlet Area, Alaska, Resulting From the March 27, 1964, Earthquake," *U. S. Geological Survey Professional Paper 543–F*, 28 pp., 1967.

Frank, F. C., "On the Deduction of Earth Strains From Survey Data," *Bulletin of the Seismological Society of America*, vol. 56, no. 1, pp. 35–42, 1966.

Inoue, E., "Land Deformation in Japan," *Bulletin of the Geographical Survey Institute*, vol. VI, part 2–3, Ministry of Construction, Japan, pp. 73–134, November 1960.

Jaeger, J. C., *Elasticity Fracture and Flow, With Engineering and Geological Applications*, John Wiley and Sons, N. Y., 1st edition, 1956.

Kasahara, K. and Sugimura, Arata, "Horizontal Secular Deformation of Land Deduced From Retriangulation Data. 1. Land Deformation in Central Japan," *Bulletin of the Earthquake Research Institute*, University of Tokyo, vol. 42, pp. 479–490, 1964.

Pope, Allen J., *Strain Analysis of Repeated Triangulation for the Investigation of Crustal Movement*, Thesis, The Ohio State Univerity, 1966.

Terada, T. and Miyabe, Naomi, "Deformation of the Earth Crust in Kwansai Districts and Its Relation to the Orographic Feature," *Bulletin of the Earthquake Research Institute*, University of Tokyo, vol. 7, part 2, pp. 223-239, 1929.

Tsuboi, Chûji, "Investigation on the Deformation of the Earth's Crust in the Tango District Connected With the Tango Earthquake of 1927 (Part 4)," *Bulletin of the Earthquake Research Institute*, University of Tokyo, vol. 10, part 2, pp. 411–434, 1932.

JAMES B. SMALL
LAWRENCE C. WHARTON
U.S. COAST AND GEODETIC SURVEY*

Reprinted with minor changes from
U.S. Coast and Geodetic Survey Volume III: Geodesy and Photogrammetry,
"Vertical Displacements Determined by Surveys after the Alaskan Earthquake of March 1964"

Vertical Displacements

ABSTRACT: Extensive vertical-control surveys, made after the Alaska earthquake, established up-to-date elevations of bench marks for engineering and mapping purposes and determined the changes of bench-mark elevations since the previous levelings. Releveling and gravity observations were made simultaneously. Releveling included 1,191 mi of first-order lines. Gravity anomalies gave some indication of large crustal movement.

Tide observations were made at localities where previous observations had been made and where the bench marks had not been destroyed by the earthquake. The differences in the values of the tidal datum planes, when referred to common bench marks, indicated the amount of land movement.

PART I: Vertical Bench Mark Displacement

During the period from April to October 1964, first-order leveling, totaling 956 miles, was undertaken by the Coast and Geodetic Survey in Alaska to establish up-to-date elevations of bench marks for engineering and mapping purposes, and also to determine the changes of bench-mark elevations since the previous levelings. Of this total, 722 miles was releveling of previously established first-order leveling by the Coast and Geodetic Survey, and 234 miles was new leveling on the Kenai Peninsula. From May to August 1965, first-order leveling totaled 623 miles. Of this amount, 469 miles was releveling and 154 miles, original leveling. Therefore, in 1964 and 1965,

there was a total of 1,579 miles of leveling—1,191 miles of releveling and 388 miles of original leveling. A preliminary report including the procedures, instrumentation, and some tentative evaluations is in Volume I, of this series of reports.

When comparing the results of the original leveling and the relevelings of 1964 and 1965, one should not assume that all of the divergences between the levelings represent vertical movement caused by the earthquake of 1964, but no doubt most of the changes took place at that time. It is believed appropriate to first review a history of the precise leveling in Alaska and in the nearby Yukon Territory, along with the verti-

---

*Now in part the National Ocean Survey, National Oceanic and Atmospheric Administration.

cal changes noted by a small amount of releveling undertaken prior to 1964 (fig. 1).

HISTORY OF PRECISE LEVELING IN ALASKA

The first precise leveling established in Alaska was in 1910 between Skagway and White Pass by the Alaska Boundary Commission. All marks were set in solid rock. Between 1908 and 1910, the Geodetic Survey of Canada conducted and extended leveling from White Pass via Whitehorse to Takhini in the Yukon Territory in connection with the Boundary Survey along the 141st meridian. Some of the marks were in solid rock and others in iron pipes.

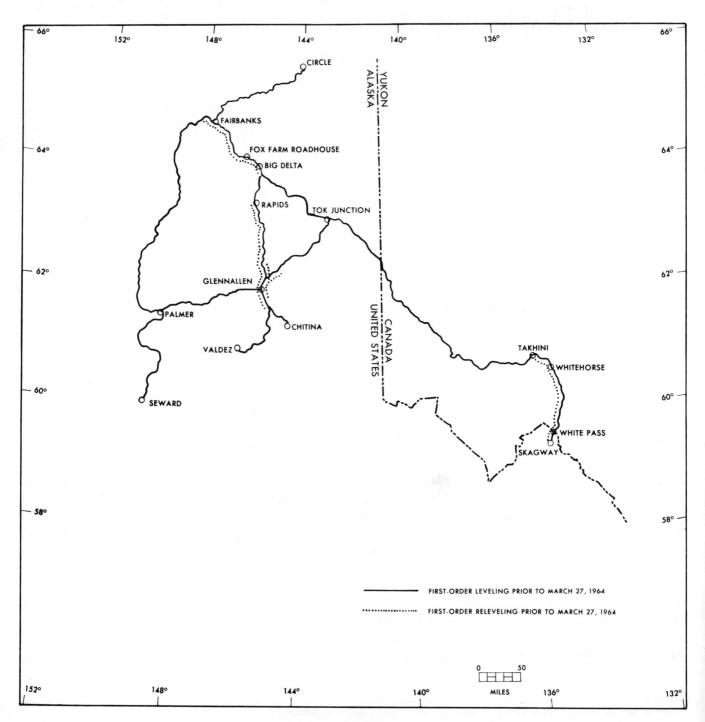

FIGURE 1.—Level net of Alaska. Original leveling and releveling prior to March 27, 1964. (For the 1964–1965 leveling, see fig. 6.)

First-order leveling was established in 1922 from Anchorage along the Alaska Railroad to Fairbanks and southeast along the Richardson Highway to Fox Farm Roadhouse (50 miles SE. of Fairbanks). In 1923, leveling was continued from Fox Farm Roadhouse to Valdez, with a spur from Willow Creek to Chitina, and leveling was established along the Alaska Railroad from Seward to Anchorage.

To establish leveling along the Alaska Highway in 1943, it was planned to start at Whitehorse with a tie to the leveling by the Geodetic Survey of Canada, but since the field party failed to obtain an agreement with the original leveling at Whitehorse, releveling was continued to White Pass before a check was obtained. Since the divergence between the releveling and the original leveling was so large, releveling was undertaken in 1944 from Skagway to White Pass to determine what changes had taken place on that portion. The total divergence between the original leveling and releveling from Skagway via Whitehorse to Takhini was 163.6 centimeters or 5.367 feet (fig. 2). Notice that this is practically a straight-line divergence from Skagway to Takhini. This was the first indication of regional tilt in this area, as shown through precise leveling activities.

The rise of Tidal 3 of 68 centimeters or 2.2 feet at Skagway from 1910 to 1944 was determined by tidal observations. Based on this, the rate of land rise at Skagway is about 2 centimeters per year.

In 1944, the leveling from Matanuska to Tok Junction (fig. 6) indicated some sizable changes in elevation along the Richardson Highway in the vicinity of Glennallen and Gulkana, where 41 miles of the 1923 leveling was releveled from Copper Center to bench mark Q 8, 7 miles south of Sourdough, to obtain a tie. A tie was obtained in the vicinity of Copper Center at bench marks D 9, C 9, and Z 8, but at the northern extremity subsidence at bench mark Q 8 was 1.296 meters or 4.252 feet, based on observed differences in elevation. The divergences between the two levelings were as follows:

Copper Center to 7 Miles South of Sourdough, Alaska

Bench mark	Distance	1923 Obs. elev.	1944 Obs. elev.	New minus old
	Kilometers	*Meters*	*Meters*	*Milli-meters*
D 9 (Astronomic Station)	0.0	313.0915	313 0915	0.0
C 9	2.6	314.4291	314.4288	−0.3
Z 8	16.7	363.8527	363.8525	+0.2
W 8	34.1	487.2277	487.1678	−59.9
V 8	38.0	486.3245	486.0912	−233.3
U 8	42.0	420.0926	419.8914	−201.2
R 8	60.0	541.9255	540.6284	−1297.1
Q 8	64.7	577.9082	576.6120	−1296.2

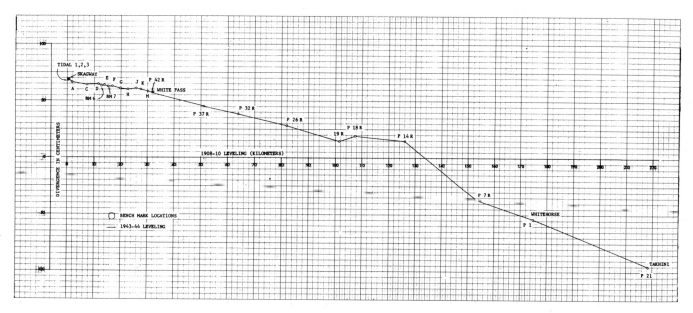

FIGURE 2.—Divergence between levelings: Skagway, Alaska, via White Pass to Takhini, Canada (1943–1944 minus 1908–1910).

RELEVELING IN 1951–1952

Because of the large divergences between the 1944 and 1923 levelings, releveling was undertaken in 1952 from bench mark B 10 Reset (11 miles south of Copper Center) to bench mark Rapids Airport (at Rapids) to determine the extent of the changes. The 1952 releveling showed that bench marks W 27 to Q 8 in the vicinity of 7 and 11 miles S. of Sourdough had continued to subside. Based on observed differences the maximum was at bench mark Q 8 which subsided 37.7 centimeters or 1.237 feet additionally from 1944 to 1952, or a total of 5.492 feet since 1923, assuming stability at Copper Center where an agreement be-

tween levelings was obtained on four marks—H 9, K 9, B 61, and L 9. A comparison of the 1944 and 1952 leveling shows a maximum heaving of 16.2 centimeters or 0.531 foot at J 27, about 3 miles south of Gulkana (fig. 3).

A fair agreement of the original 1923 leveling and 1952 releveling was obtained between the extremities, with a maximum subsidence using adjusted values of Q 8 = 5.213 feet and R 8 = 4.708 feet from 1923 to 1952 (fig. 4).

Releveling of 1951–1952 from Fairbanks to Big Delta again shows good overall agreement between the extremities, with a maximum subsidence of 82.4 centimeters or 2.703 feet (fig. 5).

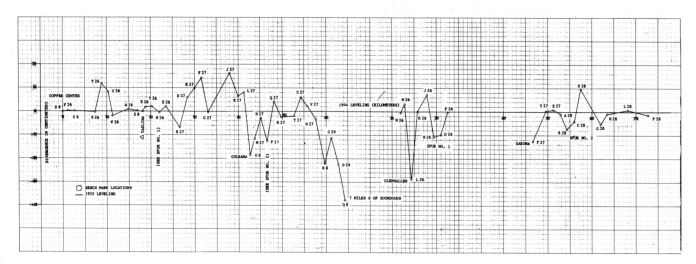

FIGURE 3.—Divergence between levelings: Copper Center to 7 miles south of Sourdough, Alaska (1952 minus 1944).

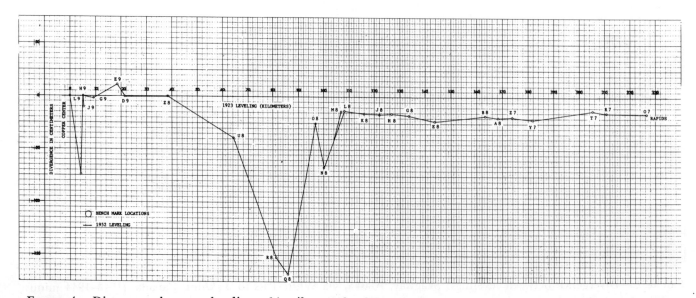

FIGURE 4.—Divergence between levelings: 14 miles south of Copper Center to Rapids, Alaska (1952 minus 1923).

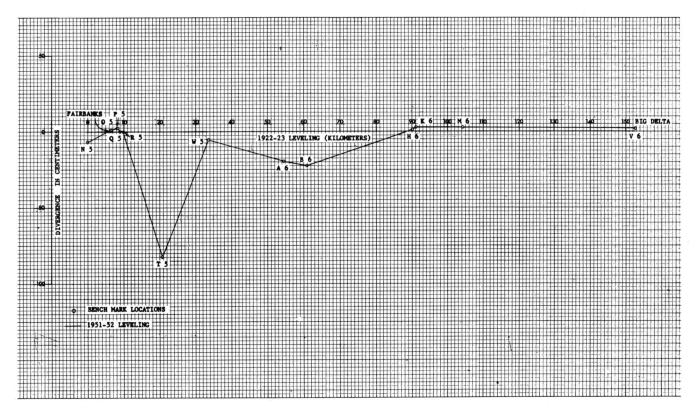

FIGURE 5.—Divergence between levelings: Fairbanks to Big Delta, Alaska (1951–1952 minus 1922–1923).

LEVELING IN 1964–1965

The leveling undertaken in 1964 and 1965 is shown in figure 6. Three levelings were undertaken in the vicinity of Valdez in 1964, as this area was believed to be continuing to move. Leveling in April was undertaken from Valdez to 20 miles NE. of Valdez along Richardson Highway when the field party first arrived in Alaska. A second leveling was made in July on the main line from Glennallen to 5 miles NW. of Valdez, and a third in September from 5 miles SE. of Valdez to 5 miles NW. of Valdez. Changes in bench-mark elevations were of small magnitude, with a maximum subsidence of 2 centimeters. A second releveling was undertaken in October 1964 from Portage to 22 miles NW. of Portage and showed an additional subsidence at Portage of about 4 centimeters (fig. 7).

The adjustment of the 1964 leveling was made holding new mean-sea-level determinations at Homer, Seward, Whittier, and Valdez (fig. 8). The pier on which the gage was located at Valdez was settling; this accounts for the shorter series at that location. There is a slope in the mean tide level in the Cook Inlet; therefore, tidal observations at Anchorage were not held because this location does not represent open coast conditions. The previous adjusted elevation of bench mark A 11 (USE) about 27 miles SE. of Fairbanks was also held in the adjustment.

There were 23 bench marks for the 11-mile stretch from 15 miles SE. of Fairbanks to 27 miles SE. of Fairbanks where the previously adjusted elevations were not changed by the adjustment of the 1964 leveling. The 1965 releveling was fitted to the 1964 adjustment by distributing the closing error from bench marks D 87 and F 20 near Matanuska to N 5 about 5 miles SE. of Fairbanks (fig. 9).

The bar graph shown on figure 9 indicates the magnitude of bench-mark changes for the portions as follows: Seward to Matanuska from 1922–23 to 1964; Matanuska via Glennallen to 9 miles N. of Gulkana from 1944 to 1964; Glennallen to Valdez from 1923 to 1964; 9 miles N. of Gulkana to Fairbanks from 1923 to 1964; and Matanuska to Fairbanks from 1922 to 1965. In general, the subsidence on the entire portion from Seward to Anchorage ranged from a minimum of 2.342 feet to a maximum of 6.243 feet. For the portion from Anchorage to Matanuska to Glennallen, the average subsidence was from 1 to 2½ feet, with a maximum of 5.151 feet and the minimum of

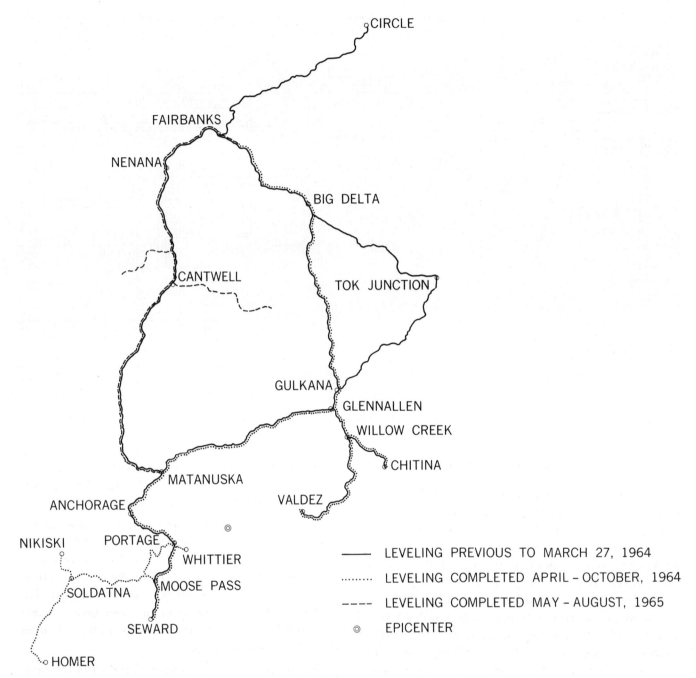

FIGURE 6.—Level net of Alaska and releveling of 1964–1965.

0.167 foot. The only evidence of upheaval along the releveling from Seward via Anchorage and Glennallen to Valdez was for bench marks D 11 and E 11, located 5 and 10 miles E. of Valdez. These heaved 0.55 and 0.35 foot, respectively (see pages 122–130 of Volume I of this report series). From Glennallen toward Fairbanks, the maximum subsidence was 7.028 feet at Q 8 with an upheaval of 0.3 to 0.8 foot in the Alaska Range along the Richardson Highway (see

table 11, pages 127–128, Volume I of this publication series, bench marks M 8 through V 6).

Since a fair agreement between the 1923 and 1952 levelings was obtained from the vicinity of 4 miles south of Sourdough to Rapids, it is believed the uplift shown by the 1964 releveling in the Alaska Range along the Richardson Highway resulted from the earthquake of 1964. From Matanuska to 15 miles SE. of Fairbanks, there was a maximum subsidence of 1.9

feet (bench marks P 20 and S 20) near Matanuska, and a 0.4-foot upheaval of C 4 in the higher elevations of the Alaska Range.

Types of bench marks are described on pages 104 and 105 of Volume I of this publication series. Elevation changes of bench marks are fully significant in a study of vertical displacement only if they properly represent crustal or local ground changes. The first choice for the location of the installation of bench-mark disks is in bedrock, with second choice in a substantial structure, such as a building or bridge. Where such locations were not readily available, bench marks on the leveling prior to 1964 were placed in concrete posts which were 5 feet in length with a belled-out portion at the base. Because the Alaskan climate is so severe and the terrain so varied, there is danger that particular elevation changes of concrete posts may represent upheaval due to frost action or settlement in boggy ground. Rather than install concrete posts for new marks on the 1964 and 1965 leveling, copper-coated steel rods driven to refusal were used as bench marks. It is believed that these marks would better cope with changes caused by frost action.

The rods are procured in 8-foot lengths, threaded at each end, and driven with a gasoline hammer. The hammer is placed on an 8-foot section which is driven to the ground surface. A second section is attached to the first section with a brass coupling and also driven to the ground surface. This procedure is continued until refusal is reached, at which time the rod is cut off slightly above the ground and a disk fastened to the top of the rod. There were 742 rod-type marks established during the 1964 and 1965 leveling. These marks were driven to an average depth of 22 feet. The minimum depth was 5 feet, and the maximum depth, 96 feet.

On the 1910 leveling from Skagway to White Pass, photographs of all bench-mark locations were taken, including a closeup and a distant view with some mountain terrain in the background, where possible. In 1944, the field party reported that when releveling this line the photos were invaluable, since many of the old marks would have not been found without the 1910 photography. The practice of taking photographs of bench-mark locations was continued on the 1964 and 1965 leveling.

In 1965, releveling was undertaken from Anchorage to Portage, following the route of the 1964 releveling. This releveling was undertaken because it was believed that Anchorage and Portage were still subsiding. In comparing the 1964 and 1965 relevelings, there was a check between 13 bench marks that indicated a stability about halfway between these two locations, with a subsidence of 0.32 foot at Anchorage, and 0.51 foot at Portage (table 1). Gravity observations of 1964 and 1965 also showed rather closely this same indication (see GRAVITY OBSERVATIONS IN

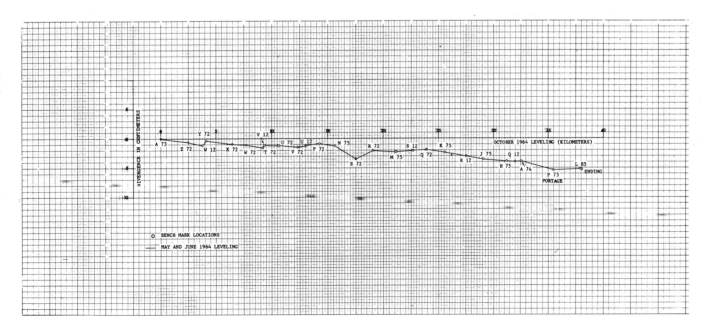

FIGURE 7.—Divergence between levelings: 22 miles northwest of Portage to 2 miles southwest of Portage, Alaska (October 1964 minus May and June 1964).

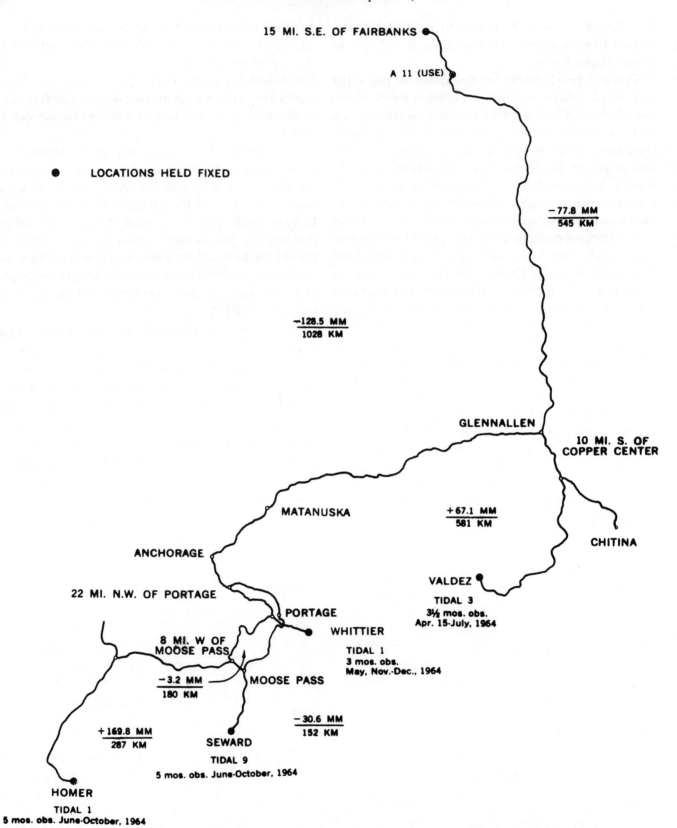

FIGURE 8.—Adjustment sketch of 1964 leveling in Alaska. Closures shown in millimeters, distances in kilometers.

ALASKA, 1964–1965, INCLUDING SOME REPEAT OBSER-
VATIONS, this volume). Admittedly, the gravity anomalies are not a precise measurement of vertical changes,
but they do give some indication of large crustal

movement. Since gravimeter observations can be obtained at relative low cost, it is considered desirable in
areas of movement to have the releveling and gravity
observations accomplished simultaneously.

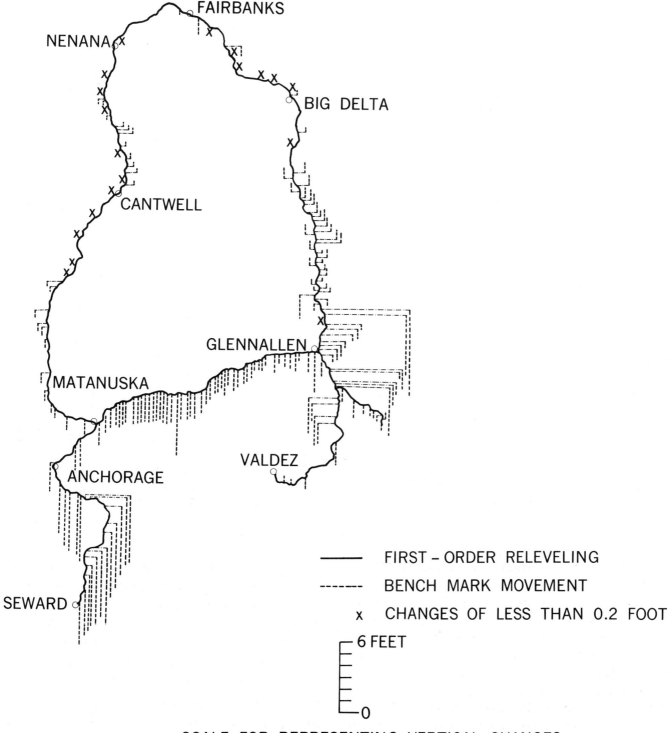

FIRST – ORDER RELEVELING

------- BENCH MARK MOVEMENT

x CHANGES OF LESS THAN 0.2 FOOT

6 FEET

0

SCALE FOR REPRESENTING VERTICAL CHANGES

FIGURE 9.—Movement of bench marks as shown by releveling of 1964 and 1965.

TABLE 1.—*Changes in elevations of bench marks from Anchorage to Portage, Alaska*
(*May–June 1964 to May 1965*)

Bench mark	Distance	May–June 1964 elevation	May 1965 elevation	May 1965 minus May–June 1964	Bench mark	Distance	May–June 1964 elevation	May 1965 elevation	May 1965 minus May–June 1964
	Miles	*Feet*	*Feet*	*Feet*		*Miles*	*Feet*	*Feet*	*Feet*
Anchorage					V 73	11	155.794	155.685	−0.109
Tide Staff	0	19.298	18.976	−0.322	U 73	12	148.789	148.674	−0.115
Tidal 15	0	20.732	20.410	−0.322	T 73	13	134.626	134.550	−0.076
B 75	0	20.423	20.112	−0.311	S 73	14	112.060	112.024	−0.036
Tidal 13	1	20.194	19.872	−0.322	R 73	15	16.243	16.224	−0.019
Tidal 14	1	21.975	21.713	−0.262	N 73	16	21.699	21.683	−0.016
Tidal 9	1	24.528	24.268	−0.260	P 11	17	35.006	34.990	−0.016
A 75	2	19.006	18.730	−0.276	M 73	18	43.904	43.904	0.000
Tidal 12	2	22.815	22.549	−0.266	L 73	18	39.134	39.134	0.000
					K 73	19	37.693	37.693	0.000
Spur Line					Isle	20	24.147	24.147	0.000
Tidal 1 (ARR)	2	25.630	25.371	−0.259	J 73	21	39.012	39.012	0.000
Tidal 2 (ARR)	2	25.728	25.469	−0.259	H 73	22	43.734	43.734	0.000
No. 1 WR	2	103.038	102.772	−0.266	R 11	23	55.774	55.774	0.000
(USGS)					G 73	24	52.890	52.890	0.000
B 1	3	108.330	108.054	−0.276	F 73	25	66.424	66.424	0.000
104.89 (C. of A.)	3	102.657	102.392	−0.265	S 11	26	44.961	44.961	0.000
B 74	3	111.830	111.588	−0.242	E 73	27	37.392	37.392	0.000
Merrill RM 1	4	128.428	128.199	−0.229	D 73	27	56.850	56.850	0.000
D 74	4	127.775	127.539	−0.236	C 73	29	30.262	30.262	0.000
C 74	4	132.260	132.024	−0.236	B 73	30	27.543	27.516	−0.027
					T 11	30	27.424	27.398	−0.026
End of the Spur Line					A 73	30	33.031	33.005	−0.026
C 75	3	17.664	17.385	−0.279	Z 72	32	22.444	22.408	−0.036
D 75	4	54.593	54.321	−0.272	Y 72	33	19.180	19.131	−0.049
G 75	5	60.935	60.672	−0.263	X 72	34	27.037	26.952	−0.085
F 75	6	94.449	94.216	−0.233	W 72	35	25.262	25.177	−0.085
L 75	6	100.128	99.931	−0.197	V 12	36	27.169	27.080	−0.089
					U 72	37	28.576	28.474	−0.102
Spur Line					V 72	38	25.666	25.548	−0.118
					U 12	38	26.529	26.421	−0.108
Q 73	7	88.018	87.795	−0.223	P 72	39	29.977	29.882	−0.095
E 75	8	73.507	73.264	−0.243	N 75	40	28.304	28.205	−0.099
CAA Hangar	9	82.103	81.840	−0.263	S 72	41	18.428	18.202	−0.226
(USE)					R 72	42	24.462	24.301	−0.161
CAA Terminal	9	87.021	86.752	−0.269	M 75	43	30.403	30.213	−0.190
(USE)					S 12	44	46.358	46.145	−0.213
					Q 72	45	54.153	53.930	−0.223
End of the Spur Line					K 75	46	45.859	45.604	−0.255
					R 12	47	32.237	31.952	−0.285
Z 73	7	112.221	112.034	−0.187	J 75	48	27.293	26.968	−0.325
Y 73	8	79.819	79.685	−0.134	H 75	50	26.204	25.843	−0.361
X 73	9	103.258	103.126	−0.132	Q 12	50	24.747	24.373	−0.374
W 73	10	136.233	136.125	−0.108	A 74	50	26.014	25.640	−0.374
					P 73	52	21.945	21.437	−0.508

Repeat gravity observations at stations G 884 and G 885 in Middleton Island show (1) a gravity decrease of about 0.17 milligal from 1964 to 1965, which is an indication of about a 2-foot upheaval (see GRAVITY OBSERVATIONS IN ALASKA, 1964–1965, INCLUDING SOME REPEAT OBSERVATIONS, this volume), and (2) that changes and warping are still going on.

In determining vertical changes in Alaska, other data are available in Parkin's HORIZONTAL CRUSTAL MOVEMENTS DETERMINED FROM SURVEYS AFTER THE ALASKAN EARTHQUAKE OF 1964, this volume.

Barnacle studies have been undertaken by the U. S. Department of Interior, Geological Survey. It is interesting to note how the results from one type of survey support the data from another. For example, the U. S. Coast and Geodetic Survey tidal observations showed an upheaval of 31.5 feet at Macleod Harbor, Montague Island, and a U. S. Geological Survey barnacle study reported an upheaval of 33 feet. A repeat of hydrographic surveys off Montague Island showed an underwater upheaval of from 42 to 50 feet.

PART II: Tidal Datum Plane Changes Resulting From the Earthquake of March 27, 1964

To verify the amount of land change and to revise tidal datum planes and charts, it is necessary to make tide observations at locations where previous tide observations have been obtained (fig. 10). All of the tide observations upon which this report is based were made at localities where previous observations were made, tidal bench marks established, or where bench marks had not been destroyed by the earthquake.

In 1964, five additional control tide stations were established in southwestern Alaska for the study of sea level and for future use as reference stations, bringing the total to eight control tide stations operating in this area. In addition, tide observations also were made at 11 other locations where tides had been observed prior to the earthquake.

During the 1965 field season, the operation was expanded to include the establishment of tide gages at 26 locations where tides had previously been observed. Six were locations which had been reoccupied in 1964. The eight control tide stations were also kept operating during the 1965 season.

The results of the tide observations obtained at the various locations were reduced to mean values by simultaneous comparison with our control tide station at Sitka. Sitka, the nearest location at which the C&GS has been operating a control tide station for a number of years, apparently was not affected by the earthquake. The amount of land movement was then determined by taking the difference in the elevations of the common bench marks at each location that

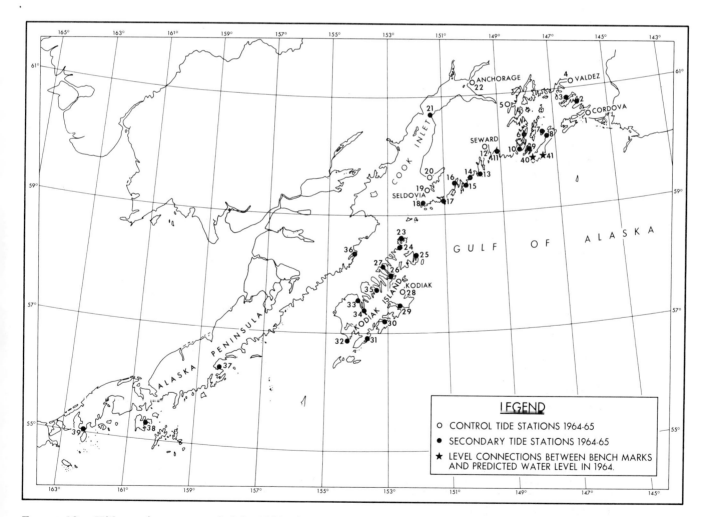

FIGURE 10.—Tide stations reoccupied in 1964–1965 for the study of vertical land movement resulting from the earthquake of 1964.

had been connected by levels to the series of tide observations prior to and following the earthquake.

Figure 10 shows the location of the numbered tide stations as listed in table 2 which were established in 1964 and 1965, along with the length of tide observations and the amount of land movement relative to

sea level for each location. Since some of the gages at C&GS Alaskan control tide stations did not operate continuously in 1964 and 1965, comparable periods of tide observations were used from each year to show the amount of land movement between the two periods.

TABLE 2.—*Tidal datum plane changes at Alaska tide stations*

Station nos. (See fig. 10)	Location	Type of gage [1]	Period of tide observations 1964	Land movement	Type of gage [1]	Period of tide observations 1965	Land movement
				Feet			*Feet*
1	Cordova, Prince William Sound	SA	May–Nov.	+6.2	SA	May–Nov.	+6.2
2	Port Gravina, Prince William Sound	PA	July 3–31	+4.5	B	May 16–June 16	+4.2
3	Port Fidalgo, Prince William Sound	——	——	——	PA&B	June 18–July 17	+2.4
4	Valdez, Prince William Sound	B	May–July	−0.9	B	July–Nov.	−3.5
5	Whittier, Prince William Sound	SA	May–June, Oct.–Dec.	−5.4	SA	July–Nov.	−5.7
6	Chenega Island (SW. end), Prince William Sound	PA	July 7–Aug. 4	+4.8	——		——
7	Green Island, Prince William Sound	——	——	——	B	August	+6.6
8	Port Chalmers, Montague Island, Prince William Sound	PA	May 19–30 July 7–Aug. 6	+10.6	B	July 19–Aug. 23	+10.5
9	Sawmill Bay, Evans Island, Prince William Sound	PA	May 20–June 1	+7.2	B	June 14–July 7	+7.2
10	Hogg Bay, Bainbridge Island, Prince William Sound	——	——	——	B	July 20–Aug. 16	+5.8
11	Day Harbor, Kenai Peninsula	——	——	——	ADR	May 7–June 30	−0.5
12	Seward, Kenai Peninsula	B	June–Dec.	−3.6	B	Jan.–Sept.	−3.6
13	Aialik Bay, Kenai Peninsula	——	——	——	ADR	May–June	−4.5
14	Two Arm Bay, Kenai Peninsula	——	——	——	ADR	May 14–June 30	−5.4
15	Chance Cove, Kenai Peninsula	——	——	——	ADR	May 15–June 30	−6.6
16	Shelter Cove, Nuka Bay, Kenai Peninsula	——	——	——	ADR	July	−5.4
17	Port Dick, Kenai Peninsula	——	——	——	ADR	May 21–June 30	−6.2
18	Port Chatham, Kenai Peninsula	——	——	——	ADR	May 22–June 4	−4.6
19	Seldovia, Cook Inlet	SA	June–Oct.	−3.9	SA	April–July	−3.8
20	Homer, Cook Inlet	B	June–Dec.	−5.4	B	Sept.–Nov.	−5.8
21	Nikiski, Cook Inlet	B	June 18–July 31	−0.9	——		——
22	Anchorage, Cook Inlet	B	May–Oct.	−2.6	B	April–Oct.	−2.3
23	Carry Inlet, Shuyak Island	——	——	——	B	July 8–Aug. 7	−3.2
24	Red Fox Bay, Afognak Island	——	——	——	PA	July 1–Aug. 8	−3.4
25	Tonki Bay, Afognak Island	——	——	——	ADR	July 10–Aug. 7	−5.2
26	Nachalni Island, Kupreanof Strait	——	——	——	B	June 14–July 10	−3.9
27	Dolphin Point, Afognak Island	——	——	——	B	June 7–July 8	−2.9
28	Saint Paul Harbor, Kodiak Island	B	June–Oct.	−5.5	B	May–Nov.	−5.0
29	Ugak Bay Kodiak Island	——	——	——	B	June 12–July 10	−4.2
30	Port Hobron, Sitkalidak Island	——	——	——	ADR	July 26–Aug. 27	−0.7
31	Jap Bay, Kodiak Island	——	——	——	ADR	July 28–Aug. 24	0.0
32	Lazy Bay, Kodiak Island	PA	June 11–Aug. 14	−0.4	ADR	July 28–Aug. 15 Aug. 20–24	−0.2
33	Larsen Bay, Kodiak Island	PA	June 13–Aug. 31	−2.5	PA	July 18–Aug. 17	−2.4
34	Uyak Bay (Eastern Passage), Kodiak Island	——	——	——	PA	July 22–Aug. 17	−1.9
35	Port O'Brien, Uganik Bay	PA	July–Aug.	−3.6	PA	June 8–July 19	−3.6
36	Kukak Bay, Alaska Peninsula	——	——	——	B	July 17–Aug. 16	−0.5
37	Chignik, Chignik Bay, Alaska Peninsula	PA	June 19–Aug. 17	−0.3	——	——	——
38	Humboldt Harbor, Shumagin Islands	PA	June 19–Aug. 18	+0.2	——	——	——
39	King Cove, Alaska Peninsula	PA	June 21–Aug. 18	+0.2			

Listed below are two additional locations giving the amount of land movement relative to sea level which was obtained during 1964 by leveling from the existing bench marks to the predicted water level. No tide observations were obtained which could be referred to the original bench marks.

| 40 | Macleod Harbor, Montague Island | | | +31.5 | | | |
| 41 | Patton Bay, Montague Island | | | +14.9 | | | |

[1] SA =standard automatic tide gage; PA =portable automatic tide gage; B =bubbler-type tide gage; ADR =analog to digital recorder.

In obtaining the tide observations, the pressure-recording tide gage and the analog-to-digital recorder were used as well as portable and standard tide gages. The newer type of gage was found to be quite useful in making installations where the terrain was difficult or there was considerable waterfront damage.

In conclusion, it should be stated that not all the sites in the earthquake area where tides had previously been observed were reoccupied in 1964–1965. However, tide observations were made at a sufficient number of locations to give an indication of the amount of land change for the particular areas and to approximate the line of demarcation between them. In the years ahead, the U. S. Coast and Geodetic Survey will attempt to reoccupy the balance of the sites, so that much of the published information, which is now obsolete, will be superseded by up-to-date tidal datum information reflecting earthquake conditions.

DONALD A. RICE
U.S. COAST AND GEODETIC SURVEY *

Reprinted with changes from
U.S. Coast and Geodetic Survey Volume III: Geodesy and Photogrammetry,
"Gravity Observations in Alaska, 1964–1965, Including Some Repeat Observations"

Gravity Observations in Alaska

INTRODUCTION

As a part of the damage surveys following the Prince William Sound earthquake of March 1964, special gravity observations were made by the U.S. Coast and Geodetic Survey (USC&GS) in the summer of 1964 in southeastern Alaska near Juneau, in Prince William Sound near the epicentral area, and along new level lines on the Kenai Peninsula. Also, accurate connections were made by air transport between previously established gravity base stations in Anchorage, Juneau, and Fairbanks. In 1965, observations were repeated in the Prince William Sound area, over the 1964 level lines on the Kenai Peninsula, and on the Anchorage–Juneau–Fairbanks base-station triangle. Also, new gravity traverses were observed over the 1964 level lines west of Prince William Sound and on the loop from Anchorage to Valdez by way of Palmer and Glennallen. In 1967, certain gravity differences were remeasured from the primary base in Anchorage to examine further the postearthquake gravity change on Middleton Island, made evident by the 1964–1965 series of measurements.

For additional details of the measurements, tables of gravity data, and analysis of results of these surveys, see *The Prince William Sound, Alaska, Earthquake of 1964 and Aftershocks,* Volume III, "Research Studies and Interpretive Results, Geodesy and Photogrammetry," U.S. Coast and Geodetic Survey (1969).

For the analysis of results of gravity reobservations, it is important to be able to distinguish between vertical ground movements and possible changes of gravity anomaly in a disturbed region. Accordingly, in conducting these surveys extra care was taken to obtain the most accurate possible elevations above sea level at the time gravity observations were made.

The major objective of the 1964–1967 program was to lay a foundation for future studies of abrupt and secular gravity changes. A better understanding of these changes may ultimately aid in predicting earthquake activity. In addition, the gravity-anomaly patterns, brought out in several areas,

ABSTRACT: The U.S. Coast and Geodetic Survey of the Environmental Science Services Administration conducted a gravity measurement program in Alaska from 1964 to 1967, to provide a basis for study of postearthquake changes in the epicentral region of the 1964 Alaska earthquake. In addition to an area survey in Prince William Sound near the epicenter, observations were made on several traverses along lines of spirit levels in regions affected by the earthquake and in southeast Alaska. Also, direct gravity-meter connections were made between Anchorage and distant locations of stability to detect possible general uplift in the Anchorage region. The postearthquake gravity changes generally did not exceed a few hundredths of a mgal during the 1964–1967 period. An exception is the apparent uplift of about 0.5 m that occurred at Middleton Island, about 160 km south of the epicenter, during the year following the earthquake.

---

*Now in part the Office of National Geodetic Survey, National Ocean Survey, NOAA.

afford improved knowledge of the regional geology and crustal structure.

All gravity observations were made with LaCoste & Romberg Meter Number G-6, a well-seasoned instrument that has been in regular use since its manufacture in 1960. It is capable of measuring gravity differences consistently with a mean-square error of less than ±0.05 mgal, and its average short-term drift rate is essentially zero. The observations were corrected for theoretical earth-tide effect, and all gravity values were referred to the 1952 USC&GS pendulum station at Anchorage.

BASE CONNECTIONS

Unfortunately, only a few preearthquake measurements are sufficiently accurate for the evaluation of gravity changes directly associated with the March 1964 earthquake. However, the Anchorage-Juneau-Fairbanks base-station triangle did provide a basis for determining whether or not the Anchorage location had undergone a significant gravity change relative to the other two locations.

Combined pendulum and gravity-meter operations of the USC&GS in 1952 provided a gravity difference between Anchorage and Fairbanks with an estimated mean-square error of about ±0.2 mgal. During gravity calibration operations by the U.S. Air Force (USAF) and other agencies in 1963, the Anchorage–Fairbanks gravity difference was measured with a mean-square error of ±0.04 mgal. The USC&GS Meter Number G-6 was included in the 1963 calibration operations for part of the project, and sufficient observations were made with the instrument so that its calibration could be adjusted to the mean of the other seven meters within one part in 10^4. Thus, calibration uncertainties would be unlikely to exceed ±0.05 mgal when comparing the Anchorage–Fairbanks gravity difference of 1963 with the differences obtained in 1964 and 1965.

The Anchorage–Juneau gravity differences, as observed in 1964 and 1965, were compared with the differences observed by the group under G. P. Woollard in 1950–1956 with Worden meters (Thiel and others, 1958). The earlier observations, undertaken primarily to develop regional gravity coverage, have a mean-square error of about ±0.2 mgal.

The measured gravity differences are compared in Table 1. Within the limits of observational error, there seems to be no evidence of appreciable gravity change in the Anchorage-Juneau-Fairbanks base-station triangle as a result of the March 1964 earthquake. Because Fairbanks is considered a relatively stable location, it is significant that the four connections with Anchorage have a range of less than 0.1 mgal between 1952 and 1965. Indications from the 1964 and 1965 measurements, which are probably the most reliable for purposes of comparison, set a limit of about 0.1 mgal to the

TABLE 1 Comparison of Gravity Differences on Base Connections

Instrument	Differences Δg (mgals)
Anchorage to Fairbanks	
USC&GS pendulum measurements, 1952	+325.2
USAF adjusted gravity meter, 1963	+325.25
USC&GS gravity meter, 1964	+325.21
USC&GS gravity meter, 1965	+325.25
Anchorage to Juneau	
Worden gravity meter, 1950–56	−170.3
USC&GS gravity meter, 1964	−170.08
USC&GS gravity meter, 1965	−169.98

changes during the postearthquake period ending August 1965.

In analyzing the present results in connection with future remeasurements, any changes in elevation of the measurement sites should be duly considered. It should also be noted that existing data for connections involving Anchorage actually determine long-term stability for only the 1952 USC&GS pendulum site at Elmendorf Air Force Base, the common point occupied in 1952, 1963, 1964, and 1965.

OBSERVATIONS IN SOUTHEASTERN ALASKA

Field measurements were accomplished at 36 stations in southeastern Alaska, July 20-30, 1964, with logistic support from the USC&GS ship *Lester Jones*. Except for recoveries of some of the previous gravity stations, observations were taken at well-marked and accessible points that could be occupied in future surveys. Most of the new points were USC&GS triangulation marks embedded in rock near the water level. In general, elevations were not available for these triangulation stations, but in each case a careful estimate was made of the height of the mark above the water at the time of the gravity observation. The elevation of the mark above mean sea level was later calculated from marine-tide information with a mean-square error of ±1.0 ft. Because the measurement of gravity changes by resurveys was a major objective, attention was given to the effect of time-varying attraction of the water mass at the various occupied points. The rise and fall of the tide can change the measured gravity by a few hundredths of a mgal at a point near the water, the amount depending on the shore configuration and the average slope of the foreshore. For a straight shore line, a slope of 45°, and a 10-ft tide, the change in attraction is about 0.05 mgal, or slightly more than the operating accuracy of the gravity meter under ideal conditions. For the 1964 survey in southeastern Alaska, the maximum marine-tide effect was

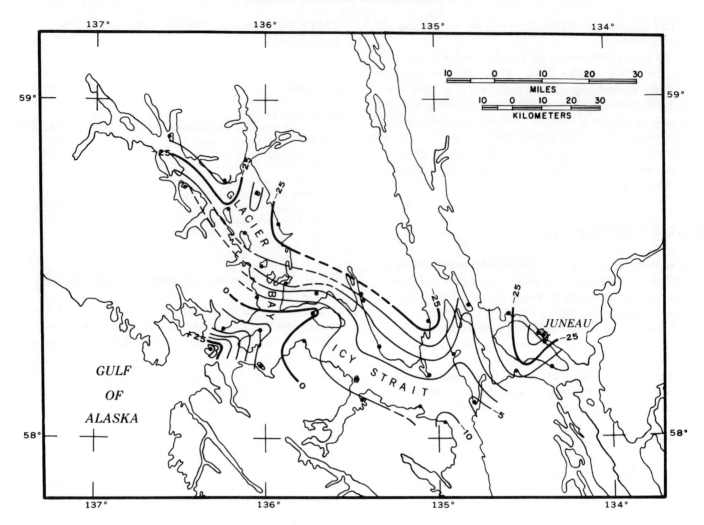

FIGURE 1   Free-air gravity anomalies, southeastern Alaska, 1964.

estimated to be minus 0.02 mgal, corresponding to a tide of −8.1 ft at the time of the gravity observation. Accordingly, the marine-tide effects were neglected.

The free-air anomaly contours in Figure 1 confirm the trends of previous regional gravity maps (Woollard and others, 1960), although near the intersection of Glacier Bay and Icy Strait there is a well-defined positive gravity anomaly that needs further development.

TRAVERSES OVER LEVEL LINES

In conjunction with the 1964 spirit-level operations on the Kenai Peninsula, gravity traverses of about 260 mi were run in August 1964 (Figures 2, 3). In all, 270 bench marks were occupied, with primary stations established at 5-mi intervals. The observations were carried from Anchorage to Portage via highway and railroad, thence via highway to Soldotna. A spur

line was measured to a tidal bench mark at Kenai, and the traverse was continued southward from Soldotna to the vicinity of Anchor Point. The gravity traverses were resumed in May 1965, repeating all of the 1964 observations and extending the traverse southward to Homer. Traverses were then run from the Sterling Highway to Seward via Moose Pass in June 1965. Observations were also made over the newly-established level line from Anchorage to Valdez via Palmer and Glennallen. Work on the traverses was completed with measurements from Portage to Whittier and Moose Pass via the Alaska Railroad. The 1965 traverses covered about 650 mi.

Taken as a whole, the 1964–1965 gravity differences are remarkably small. For the 40 primary stations on the traverses between Anchorage and Homer, the maximum difference is +0.10 mgal. The root-mean-square difference is ±0.047 mgal, corresponding to a mean-square error of observation of ±0.033 mgal for each year, assuming no change in

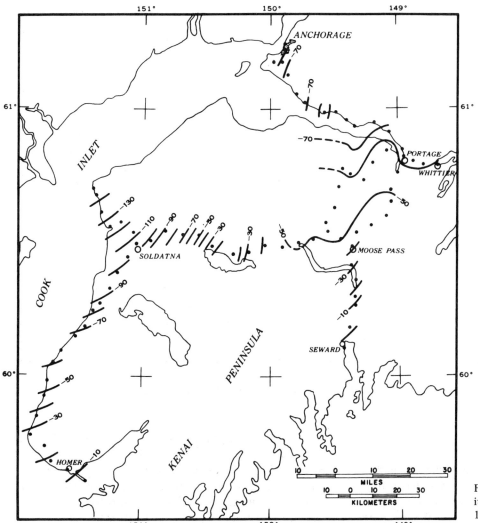

FIGURE 2 Bouguer anomalies on gravity traverses, Kenai Peninsula, 1964 and 1965.

the actual gravity values during the 1-year interval. Because an error of ±0.033 mgal is close to the ultimate accuracy obtainable with a gravity meter under good field conditions, it seems likely that the postearthquake gravity changes on the Kenai Peninsula were essentially zero.

The 1964 spirit leveling from Anchorage to Portage was repeated in 1965 because of suspected subsidence. This releveling provided an opportunity to compare the 1964-1965 differences in both elevation and gravity at 14 stations. In relative terms, the Anchorage and Portage ends of the releveled section dropped about 0.4 ft with respect to the center of the section. The corresponding measured gravity change was about +0.15 mgal for the two ends with respect to the center. Although the elevation and gravity changes agree as to algebraic sign, the gravity change is 4 or 5 times larger than would be expected from bench-mark displacement alone.

However, because this discordance is close to the accuracy tolerance of the gravity measurements, it is of limited significance.

The Bouguer gravity anomalies shown in Figures 2 and 3 are in good agreement with previous regional maps (Woollard and others, 1960). The gravity minimum on the Kenai Peninsula indicates sedimentation of several kilometers thickness, the Bouguer anomaly reaching −142 mgals at the narrow part of Cook Inlet just east of Redoubt Bay. On the Anchorage-Glennallen traverse, the Bouguer anomaly reaches a maximum at the highest point near Sheep Mountain, reflecting a lack of isostatic compensation or excess rock density. Postearthquake changes on the level line between Tonsina and Valdez may be studied by comparing results of the 1964 U.S. Geological Survey gravity survey (Barnes, 1966, and this volume) with the 1965 USC&GS results on that line.

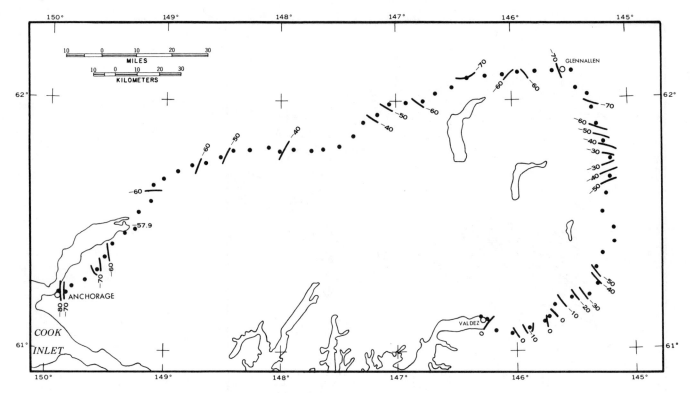

FIGURE 3   Bouguer anomalies on gravity traverse, Anchorage to Valdez via Palmer and Glennallen, 1965.

PRINCE WILLIAM SOUND

Gravity observations were made in Prince William Sound during September and October, 1964, and repeated in July and August, 1965. The three stations on Middleton Island were again occupied in August 1967. Most of the transportation was by float plane based at Anchorage, a helicopter was used for a few stations, and a twin-engine Piper Aztec was used in the connections to Middleton Island.

There were 92 stations established in 1964, and 70 of these were positively recovered in 1965. The stations were either triangulation marks, tidal bench marks, or chiseled squares in rock outcrops or boulders and were established as near as possible to mean-tide level to ensure accuracy of the measured elevations. The stations were photographed from the incoming direction of flight and also from the ground.

In view of the scattered pattern of the gravity stations occupied, a special observing sequence was employed to obtain maximum accuracy in the 1964–1965 gravity comparisons. Several stations were observed in a single day's drift loop, each loop originating at the primary gravity base in Anchorage. The various drift loops were interconnected by observing a common station from day to day, providing an estimate of the station accuracy obtained. The indicated mean-square errors were ±0.055 mgal in 11 comparisons in 1964, and ±0.060 mgal in 9 comparisons in 1965.

In studying the year-to-year comparisons, special attention was given to eight groups that involved five or more common stations. These groups were sufficiently well distributed throughout the entire area to disclose any appreciable localized changes in gravity intensity. A t distribution test was applied to each group to determine whether the calculated mean-gravity difference was significant in terms of its own precision. At the 5 percent level, probable significance is contraindicated for all groups except one. Because the stations in this group overlap other groups where the significance is below the 5 percent level, it is thought that the 1964–1965 differences, if they exist, are below the accuracy capability of the survey. As further evidence, the mean of individual 1964–1965 differences was +0.003 mgal, and the overall root-mean-square difference corresponds to a measurement accuracy of ±0.062 mgal, an accuracy figure close to that derived from the day-to-day station recoveries.

There is one exception to the negative indications of post-earthquake changes in the Prince William Sound region. Measurements at two stations on Middleton Island showed a mean change of –0.17 mgal for the period September 1964 to August 1965. In the repeat observations taken in August 1967, three measurements taken on Middleton Island indicated that the Anchorage–Middleton Island gravity difference, which changed significantly between 1964 and 1965, has since stabilized (Table 2). The apparent increase of 0.03 mgal between 1965 and 1967 is within the uncertainty range of the measurements.

The free-air anomalies are shown in Figure 4. A predominant feature is the very strong positive anomaly that reaches a maximum over Knight Island and extends northeastward to Glacier Island and Valdez Arm.

CONCLUSIONS

The 1964–1967 gravity observations in Alaska provide a basis for future study of tectonic changes in the epicentral region of the March 1964 earthquake. The attained measurement accuracies ranged from ±0.03 to ±0.06 mgal (mean-square error), de-

TABLE 2 Gravity Changes Observed on Middleton Island

	Gravity Differences (mgals)		
	1964	1965	1967
Vicinity of Anchorage			
CAA Terminal	00.00	00.00	00.00
K 73	+10.92	+10.91	+10.92
Middleton Island			
G 884	+47.40	+47.21	+47.24
G 885	+47.30	+47.15	+47.18
G 886	+50.78	a	+50.62

aNot observed in 1965.

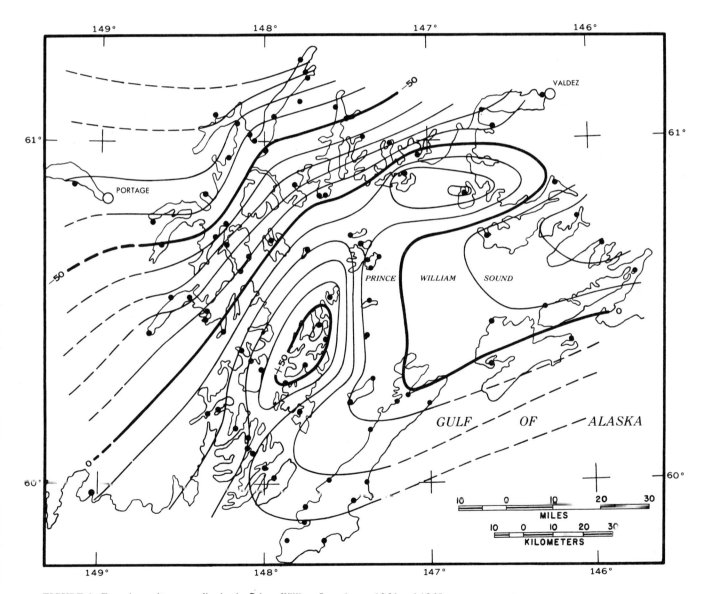

FIGURE 4   Free-air gravity anomalies in the Prince William Sound area, 1964 and 1965.

[467]

pending on transport facilities and length of drift loops. This kind of accuracy can detect elevation changes of 0.5 ft if applied to a carefully executed resurvey program.

Of perhaps more fundamental importance, gravity changes, when correlated with elevation changes determined by spirit leveling, may disclose internal-mass changes portending a destructive earthquake. Accordingly, future gravity resurveys should be made concurrently with releveling in an earthquake-region.

The gravity differences observed in the first postearthquake year indicate that anomaly changes attributable to geophysical causes do not exceed a few hundredths of a milligal in the investigated areas. An exception to this is the apparent upheaval on Middleton Island. Gravity changes occurring at the time of the earthquake are difficult to evaluate because of the small number of suitable preearthquake observations. However, the available data indicate no gross effects of this nature.

REFERENCES

Barnes, David F., 1966. Gravity changes during the Alaska earthquake. *Journal of Geophysical Research,* 71 (January 15), 451–456. Also *in* The Great Alaska Earthquake of 1964: Seismology and Geodesy. NAS Pub.1602. Washington: National Academy of Sciences, 1972.

Thiel, Edward, W. E. Bonini, Ned A. Ostenso, and G. P. Woollard, 1958. Gravity measurements in Alaska *in* Woods Hole Oceanographic Institution Reference No. 58-54. Woods Hole: Woods Hole Oceanographic Institution. p. 105.

U.S. Coast and Geodetic Survey, 1969. The Prince William Sound, Alaska, earthquake of 1964 and aftershocks. Louis E. Leipold, editor. Volume III: Research studies and interpretive results—geodesy and photogrammetry. Washington: Government Printing Office. 161 p.

Woollard, George P., Ned A. Ostenso, E. C. Thiel, and W. E. Bonini, 1960. Gravity anomalies, crustal structure, and geology in Alaska. *Journal of Geophysical Research*, 65 (March), 1021–1037.

DAVID F. BARNES

U.S. GEOLOGICAL SURVEY

Reprinted from
Journal of Geophysical Research, Vol. 71, No. 2,
"Gravity Changes during the Alaska Earthquake" 1

Gravity Changes

Abstract. A gravity traverse made in 1962 along the Richardson Highway between Valdez and Tonsina, Alaska, with a LaCoste and Romberg geodetic meter having a reading sensitivity of 0.01 mgal, was repeated in September 1964 with the same instrument. The observed gravity changes were used in computing elevation changes produced by the March 27, 1964, earthquake. Elevation changes determined by this method are in general agreement with changes determined by post-earthquake releveling of a 1923 Coast and Geodetic Survey first-order geodetic line coincident with the traverse. The conversion factor could not be precisely determined because the maximum elevation change at any station amounted to only about 0.6 meters. Gravity changes observed in other parts of the earthquake area, where greater elevation changes occurred (up to 3 meters), indicate that the conversion factor is closer to the normal Bouguer gravity gradient (0.2 mgal/m) than to a free-air gradient (0.3 mgal/m). This suggests that the elevation changes were accompanied by a net change of the total mass affecting the gravity readings, rather than by purely chemical or elastic changes. The data are preliminary and indicate the need for more pre- and post-earthquake comparisons.

The sensitivity of gravity measurements to small changes in elevation and rock density has long been recognized, but recent improvements in the sensitivity, calibration, and stability of gravimeters have increased the possibilities of using gravimetric techniques for detecting changes in elevation and changes in composition of the earth's crust. *Iida et al.* [1952] have already recorded changes in gravity during an eruption of Mihara volcano, Japan, and *Matuzawa* [1964, p. 41] has investigated changes in gravity during the Nankaido earthquake with results he considered inconclusive. However, the large-scale elevation changes during the March 27, 1964, Alaska earthquake provided an even better opportunity to test the applicability of measurements of gravity changes to tectonic studies. There were few published pre-earthquake gravity surveys for the areas where the earthquake elevation changes occurred, and many of these surveys were made with insensitive or poorly calibrated instruments or involved readings at stations which were not described in sufficient detail to make accurate reoccupation possible. Several pre-earthquake measurements justified repetition in 1964, however, and the results suggest that gravimetric techniques show the elevation changes and also provide some limitations on the tectonic processes that caused them. Other areas that were surveyed before the earthquake were resurveyed during the 1965 field season.

Perhaps the easiest to resurvey of the pre-earthquake gravity surveys within the earthquake area was a profile along the Richardson Highway between Valdez and a bench mark 3 miles south of Tonsina, which was surveyed by R. V. Allen and R. C. Jachens in August 1962. They used LaCoste and Romberg geodetic gravimeter G-17 which has a reading sensitivity of approximately 0.0104 mgal scale division, and I repeated their profile in September 1964 using the same meter. The calibration of gravimeter G-17 has been established by several ties between the North American standardization stations [*Woollard and Rose*, 1963] and is repeatedly checked on mountain calibration loops used by the Geological Survey [*Oliver*, 1965; *Barnes*, 1965]. Checks on such a loop near Fairbanks, Alaska, one week after the initial 1962 survey and one week before the 1964 repeat survey differed by less than 0.04 mgal over a 143-mgal range, which is approximately the reproducibility of measurements with this instrument.

Most of the gravity stations were located on the paved road shoulder opposite mileposts or other features that showed on the Alaska Highway Department plans, which provided the

1 Publication authorized by the Director, U. S. Geological Survey.

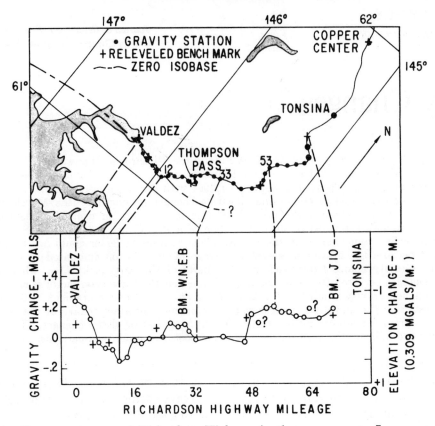

Fig. 1. Upper part, map of Richardson Highway in the survey area. Lower part, differences between 1962 and 1964 gravity measurements plotted as a function of mileage from Valdez.

elevations for the 1962 survey (see Figure 1).

The U. S. Coast and Geodetic Survey ran a first-order level line along the roadway in 1922 [*Rappleye*, 1930] and repeated the line during the summer of 1964 [*Small*, 1965]. Preliminary elevation differences obtained at six bench marks on this line are also plotted in Figure 1. The bench mark elevation changes include earthquake-induced changes and possibly the effects of 40 years of frost action and other natural processes on the bench marks. The elevation scale in Figure 1 was determined by dividing the gravity scale by 0.309 mgal/m, which is the free-air gradient of gravity at the earth's surface and which is correct if there is no change in the total mass of the underlying rock nor significant curvature in the local gravity field. Data presented later in this paper suggest that a lower conversion factor should be used in other parts of the earthquake area, but this factor seems to give a reasonable comparison on the Richardson Highway. Comparisons between the elevation and gravity changes

are seriously influenced by the choice of datum levels and gravity base-station values, the pre- and post-quake accuracy of which are hard to evaluate.

Figure 1 shows both gravity increases and land-surface sinking along most of the Richardson Highway between Valdez and Copper Center, however. The only pronounced gravity decrease occurred between mile 5 and mile 20 along the most southerly part of the highway. This is also the part of the highway where leveling indicated a rising land surface, although the gravity near mile 12 suggests a significantly greater upward movement where no bench mark elevation changes were measured. Extrapolation of level change data from shoreline studies in Prince William Sound [*Plafker*, 1965] suggests that the zero isobase or line of no elevation change is a few miles south of Valdez and may extend east-northeast toward a point north of milepost 12 and also somewhat closer to the other area of slightly negative gravity changes between mileposts 31 and 46, although actual elevation increase in this area is doubtful. The leveling indications of elevation change differ most from the gravity changes within the town of Valdez, where both the gravity and elevation changes are complicated by both subsidence of sediments and frost action on bench mark H11 where the gravity was measured.

The Richardson Highway data show that gravity changes are capable of showing the earthquake elevation changes and that they have approximately the correct magnitude to be used as a measure of the elevation changes. However, the quantitative relationship between gravity change and elevation change may have more important geologic significance than surveying significance. The force of gravity at a station on the earth's surface is a function of both the distance of the station from the center of the earth and of the rock masses close enough to influence the gravity measurements. If the earth's surface is locally deformed so that the masses influencing the measurement are not changed, the gravity change would be related to the elevation change by approximately 0.309 mgal/m, the normal free-air gradient of gravity above the earth's surface. If the earth's surface is deformed so that masses are added or subtracted at places where they would influence the measurement, however, the gravity changes should be related to the elevation changes by a factor closer to 0.197 mgal/m. The Bouguer modification of this gradient is based on the assumption that the elevation change has been caused by the addition or subtraction of an infinite layer of uniform thickness and density of 2.67 g/cm³.

Figure 2 illustrates diagramatically the types of processes that would cause a gravity change related to an elevation change by either the free-air or Bouguer gradients. The columns represent the masses influencing the gravity observation, even though in the earth such masses may not be directly below the station. The first two columns represent uplift processes without gravitationally detectable mass changes such as the elevation of the earth's crust by addition of mass at an infinite (or at least gravimetrically remote) depth in column A and the elevation of crustal sections by equal-mass expansion processes at shallower depths in column B. The latter processes could include phase change, chemical reaction, or thermal or elastic

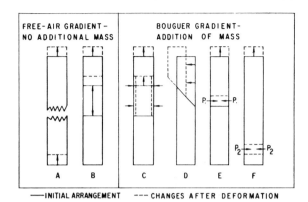

Fig. 2. Diagrams illustrating possible processes that can cause different changes in gravity during crustal elevation.

expansion without horizontal displacement, a condition that would eliminate the elastic deformation implied by Poisson's ratio for an elongating column contracting in its transverse dimensions.

The last four columns represent uplift processes that are accompanied by gravitationally detectable mass changes. Column C represents deformational processes that involve vertical expansion combined with horizontal compression and addition of mass from the side; such processes might be elastic or plastic and could involve either a net volumetric expansion or compression of the deformed layer. Column D represents the vertical movements that could be caused by faulting such as the simple 45° thrust shown, and column E represents the filling of a crustal layer by material from an adjacent area, such as injection of an igneous sill. It is perhaps worth mentioning that both columns C and D suggest horizontal compression of the crust, but the corollary for subsidence of the ground surface would suggest horizontal extension. Also the injection of an igneous sill (column E) probably would not occur suddenly over a broad area but might cause accumulated stresses which could be relased by an earthquake. However, gravity data would not show such a process unless the pre-earthquake measurement were made before the injection of the sill. Column F is essentially the same as Column E and is included only as a reminder that if the new mass were added at a greater depth, such as at the base of the crust, either greater, equal, or smaller effects might be expected. Material added at depth might have a higher density and thus a greater effect; however, the gravitational effect of material of limited extent decreases with its depth. If the distribution of the gravity changes on the earth's surface could be measured, it might be possible to estimate the depth. There are obviously many possible combinations and variations of the mechanisms shown in Figure 2, but this discussion has already provided sufficient background for interpretation of the limited data.

The Richardson Highway data, although perhaps the most accurate comparison of pre- and post-earthquake gravity data, do not include large enough elevation changes to permit us to determine the relationship between gravity and elevation change accurately. However, during the summer of 1964 gravity ties were made to a few other stations that had been established before the earthquake with meters which were owned by the Geological Survey or the University of Wisconsin [*Thiel et al.*, 1958] and which presumably had well-established calibrations. These reoccupied stations are shown on the map in Figure 3 and cover a wide part of both the uplifted and depressed portions of the earthquake zone. The accuracy of both the pre- and post-earthquake measurements in this series was probably inferior to the accuracy of

measurements made along the southern Richardson Highway, but this second group of comparisons includes a wider range of elevation changes and provides a better chance to determine the relationship between elevation change and gravity change.

The gravity changes obtained from these comparisons are plotted in Figure 4 versus the elevation changes obtained from leveling or shoreline studies near these stations. The two inclined lines represent the theoretical gradients normally used for the reduction of gravity data. The steepest slope is the free-air gravity gradient that implies no change in underlying mass, and the less steep slope is the simple Bouguer modification of this gradient, which is based on the assumption that the elevation change has been accompanied by the addition or subtraction of an infinite layer of uniform thickness and density (usually considered to be 2.67 g/cm³ as used in Figure 4).

The fact that the larger observed gravity differences seem to fall closer to the Bouguer gradient than to the free-air gradient suggests that the earth's crust has been so deformed that the total mass influencing the gravity observation has been changed. However, the positions of the three points suggesting the Bouguer gradient

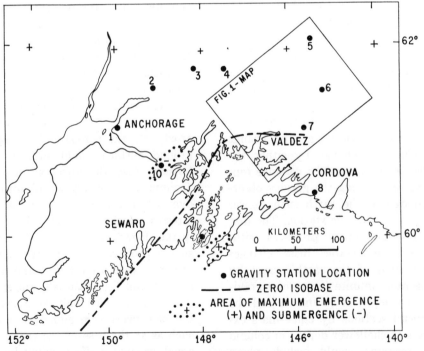

Fig. 3. Location of additional gravity stations that were reoccupied in 1964.

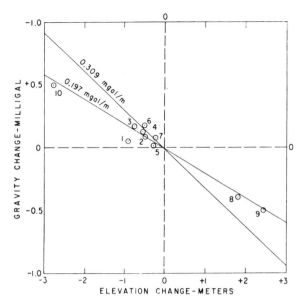

Fig. 4. Observed gravity changes versus elevation changes determined by leveling.

are subject to some uncertainties. The elevation change at Cordova (point 8) was determined at the town, but the gravity change was measured at the airport. The location of the pre-earthquake gravity station at Port Ashton (point 9) may not have been accurately re-covered, and the elevation change may be 0.6 m lower. Likewise the elevation change at Portage bench mark 'Salmon' (point 10) could be 0.6 m smaller. Additional data obtained during the summer of 1965 (and to be published later) support the conclusion that at least in the uplift area the gravity changes indicate a Bouguer relationship and the addition of mass. It should also be emphasized that the elevation changes during the Alaska earthquake extended over distances of hundreds of kilometers, so there is some justification for assuming the added masses also covered a broad area. Thus mass changes within or just beneath the crust, which is probably 20 to 50 km thick in the earthquake area [Shor, 1962, Tatel and Tuve, 1956], are the most probable cause of the gravity changes.

Figure 4 also shows that the difference between the Bouguer and free-air gradients is determined by gravity-change differences of approximately 0.3 mgal for the larger elevation changes. The maximum elevation changes during the earthquake occurred at Montague Island, where there were no pre-earthquake measurements but where the total gravity change would

have been more than 2 mgal and where the difference between gravity changes determining either the free-air or Bouguer gradients would have exceeded a milligal. These change differences are significant in relation to the accuracy of modern gravity measurements (probably about 0.05 mgal, according to Woollard [1964]), even though the pre-earthquake data for Alaska are not that accurate.

Because of the uncertainties in the limited data now available, perhaps only two conclusions should be drawn from this comparison of pre- and post-earthquake data: (1) The gravity changes do indicate the elevation changes. (2) They provide some information about the mass changes that produced the elevation changes.

A greater number of accurate pre-earthquake data would have provided more valuable results. For example, the level changes that occurred in the earthquake can only be measured along the sea coast and on two first-order level lines into the interior. These data alone [Plafker, 1965] show that the elevation changes were complex. If good gravity coverage had been established before the earthquake, the form and extent of these elevation changes could have been much more accurately determined within the interior, where only vertical-angle triangulation control was available. Accurate gravity measurements might be a good addition to all triangulation surveys. Certainly all gravity measurements in earthquake belts should be made with well-calibrated instruments and should include good base-station control and a reasonable number of reoccupiable stations.

REFERENCES

Barnes, D. F., The U. S. Geological Survey's program of Alaskan gravity observation, Trans. Am. Geophys. Union, 46(1), 231–233, 1965.
Iida, K., M. Kayakawa, and K. Katayose, Gravity survey of Mihara volcano, Oooshima Island, and changes in gravity caused by eruption, Geol. Surv. Japan, Rept. 152, pp. 1–23, 1952.
Matuzawa, T., A Study of Earthquakes, 41, Uno Shoten, Tokyo, 1904.
Oliver, H. W., The U. S. Geological Survey's gravity program in California, Hawaii, Nevada, and Oregon, Trans. Am. Geophys. Union, 46(1), 218–222, 1965.
Plafker, G. L., Tectonic deformation associated with Alaska's Good Friday earthquake of March 27, 1964, Science, 148(3678), 1675–1687, 1965.
Rappleye, H. S., First-order leveling in Alaska,

U. S. Coast & Geodetic Surv. Spec. Publ. 169, pp. 1–28, 1930.

Shor, G. G., Seismic refraction studies off the coast of Alaska, 1956–57, *Bull. Seismol. Soc. Am., 52*(1), 37–57, 1962.

Small, J. B., Report on releveling undertaken subsequent to Alaska earthquake of March 27, 1964 (abstract), *Trans. Am. Geophys. Union, 46*(1), 45, 1965.

Tatel, H. E., and M. A. Tuve, The earth's crust, seismic studies, *Carnegie Inst. Wash. Year Book 55,* pp. 81–84, 1956.

Thiel, E., W. E. Bonini, N. Ostenso, and G. P. Woollard, Gravity measurements in Alaska, *Woods Hole Oceanog. Inst. Ref. 58–54,* pp. 1–103, 1958.

Woollard, G. P., An analysis of the reliability of gravimeter measurements, *Hawaii Inst. Geophys., Univ. Hawaii, Sci. Rept. 3,* pp. 15–18, June 1964.

Woollard, G. P., and J. C. Rose, *International Gravity Measurements,* 39–41, Society of Exploration Geophysicists, Tulsa, Okla., 1963.

BUFORD K. MEADE
U.S. COAST AND GEODETIC SURVEY*

Abridged with minor changes from
U.S. Coast and Geodetic Survey Volume III: Geodesy and Photogrammetry,
"Precise Surveys of the Anchorage Monitoring System"

Precise Surveys of the Anchorage Monitoring System

ABSTRACT: A program for reobserving the primary triangulation networks in the Anchorage–Prince William Sound area of Alaska was started shortly after the severe Prince William Sound earthquake of March 1964. Resurveys accomplished from June to October 1964 were Anchorage to Palmer to Glennallen, Anchorage to Whittier, Hope to Seward, and Valdez to Thompson Pass. During the 1965 season, resurveys were extended over Prince William Sound, from Thompson Pass to Glennallen, and from Seward via Resurrection Bay to Homer. The results obtained from these resurveys are related to those of pre-earthquake surveys in a paper by Ernest J. Parkin (1969).

In the vicinity of Anchorage the resurveys disclosed relative horizontal movements of 7 to 9 ft between points on opposite sides of Knik Arm during the interval 1942 to 1964, but what part of this movement occurred during the earthquake is not certain. No appreciable movement occurred during the time between the two resurveys in September 1964 and June 1965.

*Now in part the Office of National Geodetic Survey, National Ocean Survey, NOAA.

OBSERVATIONS

In order to monitor any systematic crustal changes occurring in the Anchorage area after 1964, plans were made soon after the earthquake to establish a primary network of closely spaced stations and to reobserve this network at yearly (or greater) intervals. A network of stations extending approximately 13 mi in an east–west direction and 9 mi in a north–south direction was established over the Anchorage area. This network of 30 stations with lines ranging in length from 1 to 5 mi was observed first in the fall of 1964. Precise measurements with a Model 4D Geodimeter were made over 35 lines in the triangulation network. The second survey of the net was accomplished in 1965. Observations at three additional stations, Numbers 17, 18, and 19, were included in the scheme as well as the measurement of three geodimeter lines, 17–18, 17–19, and 18–19. These stations were added because first-order astronomic observations for azimuth and position had been observed from station 18 to station 17 to furnish independent orientation for the new surveys.

A sketch of the 33-station network is shown in Figure 1. The names identifying the station numbers in the Anchorage Monitoring System are indexed in Table 1, both numerically and alphabetically.

ADJUSTMENTS

Independent adjustments were made of the 1964 and 1965 sets of observations using the method of variation of coordinates. In order to have the same number of observation equations in each adjustment, observations involving the three stations added to the 1965 net (17, 18, and 19) were also included in the adjustment of the 1964 survey. To furnish orientation and scale for the adjustments, the 1965 Laplace azimuth, 18 to 17, and the Geodimeter lengths were used as azimuth and length observation equations. The azimuth, length, and direction observation equations were given equal

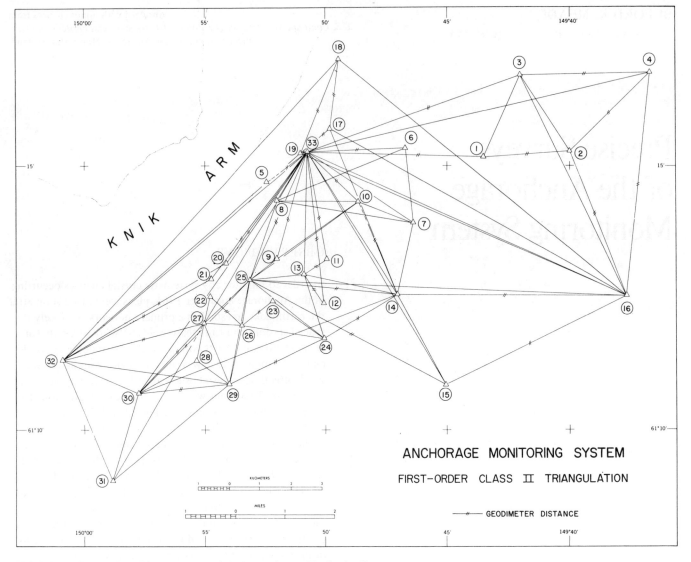

FIGURE 1   Sketch of the 33-station network in the Anchorage Monitoring System.

weight in the adjustments. The position held fixed in each adjustment, station 16, was determined from a free adjustment of the 1964–1965 surveys in the Anchorage–Prince William Sound area. This free adjustment is discussed in Parkin (1969, and this volume).

RESULTS

The final results from the adjustments indicate the observations in the 1964 and 1965 surveys were well within the requirements for first-order triangulation. Corrections obtained from the adjustments are

	1964	1965
	Seconds	Seconds
Average correction to observed direction	0.32	0.36
Maximum correction to observed direction	1.21	1.40
Maximum correction to observed angle	2.00	1.92
	Millimeters	Millimeters
Average correction to geodimeter length	6.5	7.8
Maximum correction to geodimeter length	24.0	21.0

TABLE 1   Stations in the Anchorage Monitoring System

Numerical Index		Alphabetical Index	
Number	Station	Number	Station
1	Aircom, 1964	1	Aircom
2	Richard, 1964	30	Airport
3	Circle, 1964	20	Anchor
4	Fossil, 1944	25	Anchorage
5	Sandbag, 1960	8	Cherry
6	Whit, 1964	23	Chet
7	Ranger, 1964	3	Circle
8	Cherry, 1964	13	Control RM 3
9	Gamb, 1964	29	Crest
10	Elmen, 1964	14	Debarr
11	Norm, 1964	12	Don
12	Don, 1964	17	Dorf
13	Control RM 3, 1964	10	Elmen
14	Debarr, 1964	4	Fossil
15	Tudor, 1964	9	Gamb
16	Ship, 1944	18	Globe Bie (USE)
17	Dorf, 1961	33	Loop 2 (USE) RM 3
18	Globe Bie (USE), 1961	11	Norm
19	Sawyer 2 (USE), 1964	21	Rage
20	Anchor, 1964	7	Ranger
21	Rage, 1964	2	Richard
22	Slope, 1964	5	Sandbag
23	Chet, 1964	31	Sand Lake
24	Wendler, 1964	26	Sarto
25	Anchorage, 1964	19	Sawyer 2 (USE)
26	Sarto, 1964	16	Ship
27	Spenard, 1964	22	Slope
28	Woodland, 1964	27	Spenard
29	Crest, 1964	15	Tudor
30	Airport, 1964	32	Vance
31	Sand Lake, 1964	24	Wendler
32	Vance, 1964	6	Whit
33	Loop 2 (USE) RM 3, 1964	28	Woodland

The adjusted geographic positions determined from each set of observations are given in Table 2 and the state plane coordinates, Alaska Zone 4, are given in Table 3. Differences between the two sets of coordinates, 1965 minus 1964, are also tabulated in Table 3.

SUMMARY

The results of these surveys show that no appreciable movement occurred in this area during the period between the surveys, September 1964 to June 1965. This fact is significant in evaluating the stabilization efforts. It should be noted that the differences in x in Table 3 are all negative but the differences in y are either positive or negative. If the fixed control

TABLE 2   Adjusted Geographic Positions

Station	Latitude Longitude 1964 °	′	″	1965 ″
1	61	15	12.29091	12.29068
	149	43	27.33806	27.34078
2	61	15	18.35933	18.35884
	149	39	55.87903	55.88113
3	61	16	43.69921	43.69874
	149	41	55.22951	55.23170
4	61	16	46.71855	46.71823
	149	36	35.80752	35.80986
5	61	14	40.49061	40.48976
	149	52	21.19315	21.19459
6	61	15	19.98330	19.98309
	149	46	38.31925	38.32188
7	61	13	55.76094	55.76123
	149	46	21.39499	21.39823
8	61	14	19.68113	19.68150
	149	51	59.87478	59.87785
9	61	13	12.50856	12.50825
	149	51	59.69210	59.69575
10	61	14	20.12759	20.12790
	149	48	37.35679	37.35875
11	61	13	14.00044	14.00047
	149	49	57.09180	57.09402
12	61	12	23.43865	23.43839
	149	50	08.46684	08.46945
13	61	12	54.96098	54.96120
	149	50	52.09616	52.09880
14	61	12	32.19657	32.19616
	149	47	00.76483	00.76728
15	61	10	50.95977	50.95864
	149	45	04.69584	04.69687
16	61	12	31.14968	31.14968
	149	37	35.70838	35.70838
17	61	15	40.61005	40.61010
	149	49	44.72823	44.73098
18	61	17	01.97326	01.97335
	149	49	22.60454	22.60727
19	61	15	13.76591	13.76597
	149	50	56.05081	56.05351
20	61	13	12.28377	12.28409
	149	54	03.69782	03.70233
21	61	12	52.16617	52.16794
	149	54	43.79869	43.80518
22	61	12	31.37476	31.37505
	149	54	48.92461	48.92719
23	61	12	25.54445	25.54431
	149	52	11.31970	11.32102

TABLE 2 (Continued)

Station	Latitude Longitude 1964				1965
	°	′	″		″
24	61	11	44.17951		44.17970
	149	50	04.59856		04.60131
25	61	12	50.47225		50.47244
	149	53	05.36847		05.37069
26	61	11	57.68809		57.68822
	149	53	26.47260		26.47507
27	61	12	00.31809		00.31832
	149	55	06.64721		06.65016
28	61	11	18.04444		18.04398
	149	55	19.87601		19.87920
29	61	10	50.69553		50.69543
	149	53	59.03480		59.03745
30	61	10	42.85599		42.85579
	149	57	41.78799		41.79021
31	61	09	05.64247		05.64134
	149	58	49.99923		50.00072
32	61	11	16.89021		16.89090
	150	00	52.37188		52.37648
33	61	15	13.41044		13.41051
	149	50	44.79571		44.79867

station is shifted from station 16 to 17, the x differences would sum to zero and the changes having any significance would be at the following stations:

Station	Δx ft
16	+0.13
20	−0.10
21	−0.18
32	−0.09

These changes are larger than would be expected when one considers the accuracy of the surveys. Stations 20, 21, and 32 are on the eastern shore of Knik Arm and the changes at these stations could be due to slippage. At each station the direction of indicated movement is toward the west.

Stations in this network were used as control in the photogrammetric analysis for the study of crustal-movement changes (Cravat and Sobieralski, 1969, and this volume). Definite plans have not been made for another resurvey of the Anchorage Monitoring System (Figure 1), but a resurvey should be undertaken in 1970 or soon after.

TABLE 3 State Plane Coordinates Alaska Zone 4

Station	1964 x and y Feet	1965 x and y Feet	1965–1964 Δx Feet	Δy Feet
1	548,555.14	548,555.00	−0.14	
	2,650,188.42	2,650,188.40		−0.02
2	558,895.25	558,895.15	−0.10	
	2,650,852.93	2,650,852.88		−0.05
3	553,017.72	553,017.61	−0.11	
	2,659,490.41	2,659,490.36		−0.05
4	568,627.39	568,627.28	−0.11	
	2,659,879.61	2,659,879.58		−0.03
5	522,448.45	522,448.37	−0.08	
	2,646,878.68	2,646,878.59		−0.09
6	539,210.84	539,210.71	−0.13	
	2,650,933.92	2,650,933.90		−0.02
7	540,068.37	540,068.21	−0.16	
	2,642,384.38	2,642,384.41		+0.03
8	523,495.82	523,495.67	−0.15	
	2,644,767.65	2,644,767.68		+0.03
9	523,518.68	523,518.50	−0.18	
	2,637,946.59	2,637,946.56		−0.03
10	533,406.26	533,406.17	−0.09	
	2,644,837.47	2,644,837.50		+0.03
11	529,521.51	529,521.40	−0.11	
	2,638,111.90	2,638,111.90		0.00
12	528,977.44	528,977.31	−0.13	
	2,632,976.18	2,632,976.15		−0.03
13	526,832.72	526,832.59	−0.13	
	2,636,171.95	2,636,171.97		+0.02
14	538,169.43	538,169.31	−0.12	
	2,633,892.28	2,633,892.24		−0.04
15	543,893.94	543,893.89	−0.05	
	2,623,632.45	2,623,632.34		−0.11
16	565,848.14	565,848.14	0.00	
	2,633,910.84	2,633,910.84		0.00
17	530,087.96	530,087.83	−0.13	
	2,653,001.03	2,653,001.03		0.00
18	531,147.46	531,147.33	−0.13	
	2,661,266.02	2,661,266.03		+0.01
19	526,606.46	526,606.33	−0.13	
	2,650,266.52	2,650,266.53		+0.01
20	517,446.68	517,446.45	−0.23	
	2,637,912.97	2,637,913.00		+0.03
21	515,485.84	515,485.53	−0.31	
	2,635,867.32	2,635,867.50		+0.18
22	515,237.59	515,237.47	−0.12	
	2,633,755.71	2,633,755.74		+0.03
23	522,958.82	522,958.76	−0.06	
	2,633,176.46	2,633,176.45		−0.01
24	529,177.02	529,176.88	−0.14	
	2,628,990.09	2,628,990.11		+0.02

TABLE 3 (Continued)

Station	1964 x and y Feet	1965 x and y Feet	1965–1964 Δx Feet	Δy Feet
25	520,306.73	520,306.62	−0.11	
	2,635,702.79	2,635,702.81		+0.02
26	519,282.11	519,281.99	−0.12	
	2,630,341.04	2,630,341.05		+0.01
27	514,373.41	514,373.26	−0.15	
	2,630,600.94	2,630,600.96		+0.02
28	513,730.35	513,730.19	−0.16	
	2,626,307.47	2,626,307.42		−0.05
29	517,697.05	517,696.92	−0.13	
	2,623,535.72	2,623,535.71		−0.01
30	506,776.59	506,776.48	−0.11	
	2,622,728.08	2,622,728.06		−0.02
31	503,435.10	503,435.03	−0.07	
	2,612,855.09	2,612,854.97		−0.12
32	497,432.95	497,432.73	−0.22	
	2,626,182.38	2,626,182.45		+0.07
33	527,157.07	527,156.93	−0.14	
	2,650,231.71	2,650,231.72		+0.01

REFERENCES

Cravat, H. R., and V. Ralph Sobieralski, 1969. 1965 and 1966 photogrammetric operations in Volume III: The Prince William Sound, Alaska, earthquake of 1964 and aftershocks. Environmental Science Services Administration, U.S. Coast and Geodetic Survey. Washington: Government Printing Office. p. 121–155. Also in The Great Alaska Earthquake of 1964: Seismology and Geodesy. NAS Pub. 1602. Washington: National Academy of Sciences, 1972.

Parkin, Ernest J., 1969. Horizontal crustal movements determined from surveys after the Alaskan earthquake of 1964 in Volume III: The Prince William Sound, Alaska, earthquake of 1964 and aftershocks. Environmental Science Services Administration, U.S. Coast and Geodetic Survey. Washington: Government Printing Office. p. 35–98. Also in The Great Alaska Earthquake of 1964: Seismology and Geodesy. NAS Pub. 1602. Washington: National Academy of Sciences, 1972.

H. R. CRAVAT
V. RALPH SOBIERALSKI
U.S. COAST AND GEODETIC SURVEY*

Abridged with minor changes from
U.S. Coast and Geodetic Survey Volume III: Geodesy and Photogrammetry,
"1965 and 1966 Photogrammetric Operations".

Aerial Photogrammetric Crustal-Movement Study at Anchorage

INTRODUCTION

The report, *Anchorage Area Soil Studies, Alaska* (Shannon & Wilson, Inc., 1964) indicated that considerable crustal movement had occurred in the Bootlegger Cove area and between West 3rd and West 15th Avenues. This report of crustal movement was confirmed by the U.S. Geological Survey and later described in USGS Professional Paper 542-A (Hansen, 1965, and Geology volume). To detect further sliding, settling, and long-term postearthquake adjustments, it was considered desirable to monitor crustal movements, particularly in the heavily populated areas of Anchorage where numerous fractures and grabenlike depressions (Figure 1) were evident. Woodcock and Lampton (1964) had demonstrated this could be done. The Photogrammetric Analytical Aerotriangulation System, developed by the Coast and Geodetic Survey (Harris, Tewinkel, and Whitten, 1962), had sufficient accuracy and flexibility to measure crustal movements to within 3 to 4 in. (8 to 10 cm) with ground-control spacing up to nearly 2 mi. The system was ideally suited to the study of crustal movements at Anchorage because an aerial photographic record of the position of all ground details could be obtained and repeated as needed, making it possible to measure new points and to compile topographic maps incorporating observed changes at any time. The method also provided an economical means of locating an infinite number of points in an urban area, in contrast to the limited number of points that could be located by ground surveys.

The crustal-movement survey involves repeat photogrammetric measurements of the positions of more than 50 points. These points were rather uniformly distributed throughout a rectangular area of approximately 6 mi². The initial aerial photography for the crustal movement survey was flown in the 1965 field season in conjunction with the reobservation of the precise triangulation network established in 1964, which provided the basic geodetic control for the photogrammetric crustal-movement survey (Meade, 1969, and this volume).

ABSTRACT: To monitor future crustal movement in the Anchorage area, control points were established in the city for a photogrammetric analytical triangulation system.

*Now in part the Office of Marine Surveys and Maps, National Ocean Survey, NOAA.

FIGURE 1 Graben areas, formed by Prince William Sound earthquake of March 27, 1964, delineated on an aerial photograph of Anchorage, Alaska.

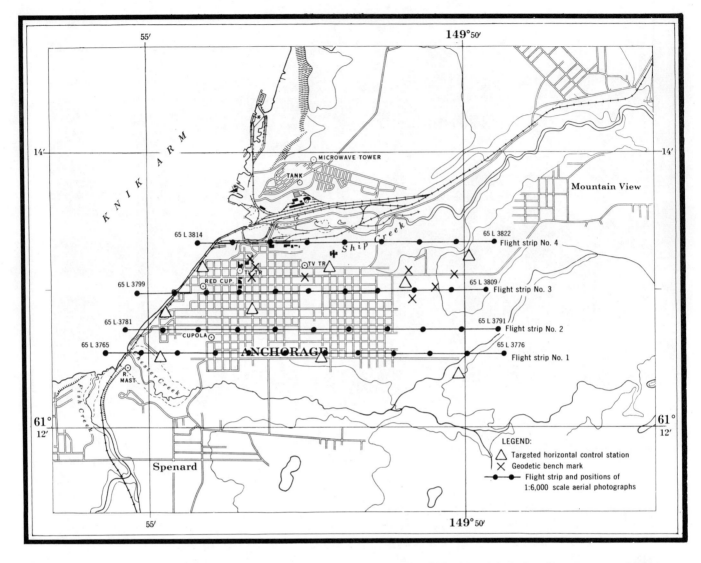

FIGURE 2 Planning diagram for Anchorage Crustal Movement Study showing location of 9 horizontal control stations, placement of 4 flight strips, and spacing of aerial photographs.

FIELD OPERATIONS

Nine horizontal control stations, 7 vertical control points, and 34 recoverable photogrammetric points were paneled. Seventeen statute miles of second-order leveling were required to connect the 9 horizontal control stations (Figure 2) to the Alaska postearthquake vertical datum. The premarked points were targeted on the ground with 12-in. (30 cm)-diameter white disks centered on 4-ft (120 cm)-square black panels (Figure 3). Some panels were made of plywood, others were painted on the street.

AERIAL PHOTOGRAPHY

The project area was photographed on June 14, 1965, by USC&GS Air Photo Mission 375, using a Wild RC-8 aerial camera. The camera was equipped with an Aviogon wide-angle lens of 6-in. (153 mm) focal length and with 8 fiducial marks spaced at 45° (50 grads) around the periphery of its 9 X 9-in. (23 X 23 cm) focal plane. The scale of photography was 1:6,000 [a minimum flight altitude of 3,000 ft (900 m) was imposed by local regulations] . Figure 2 shows the placement of flight lines and spacing of photographs along each

FIGURE 3 Enlarged section of aerial photograph showing paneled photogrammetric point No. 16 near 15th Avenue and P Street, Anchorage. Photograph enlarged 10× to 1:600 scale.

line to obtain about 60 percent endlap between adjacent photographs. Thirty-nine photographs in four flight strips were used: 10 photographs each from strips 1, 2, and 3; and 9 photographs from strip 4. Side lap was 80 percent between strips 1 and 2; 60 percent between strips 2 and 3; and 50 percent between strips 3 and 4.

PHOTOGRAPH MEASUREMENT

All laboratory and data-reduction operations for the 1965 aerial photography were completed at the U.S. Coast and Geodetic Survey's headquarters at Rockville. Glass-plate diapositives were used to measure the photograph image coordinates of a selected set of premarked ground-control stations and other ground-control stations located by aerotriangulation. These stations consisted of premarked horizontal and vertical control (9 horizontal control stations, numbers 1 through 9, which also served as vertical control points, and 7 additional vertical control points, letters A, B, D, E, F, H, and J); 34 premarked photogrammetric points, numbers 11 through 44; and 18 additional office-identified photogram-

metric points, numbers 45 through 62 (Figure 4 and Tables 1 and 2).

Passpoints in the common overlap area of adjacent photographs were measured, but not diagrammed. The white circular targets of premarked points were recorded as 35-micron images on the 1:6,000-scale aerial photographs. All photogrammetric points were marked on the glass-plate diapositives, using a Wild PUG point-transfer device to drill a 50- to 60-micron-diameter hole in the photographic emulsion. Coordinate measurements were made using a Wild STK Stereocomparator having a standard error of coordinate measurement of approximately 1 micron after compensation for known systematic errors. The principal sources of error in aerotriangulation are (1) optical distortion of the camera lens and (2) plastic deformation of the aerial film. Both sources of error were compensated for by correcting the comparator coordinates.

ANALYTIC AEROTRIANGULATION

Strip aerotriangulation of the four Anchorage strips was completed using the three-dimensional geometric coupling of succeeding stereotriplets. The first step was coordinate refinement. Preliminary horizontal and vertical coordinates of each strip were adjusted to ground control in the area of the strip and, when possible, to other points located by the adjacent strip of photography. A final simultaneous solution of the entire block of photographs was made to fix the orientation of each photograph and to determine the three-dimensional coordinates of all points. The observational errors (photograph coordinate errors) and residuals of adjustments to ground control were minimized by the method of least squares.

For the analytic aerotriangulation, seven of the nine targeted geodetic points—peripheral stations Anchor, Gamb, Norm, Rage, Slope, Chet, and Don—were selected as control points; the other two stations, Anchorage and Control, were not used as control points in the adjustment, but were treated as new points to check the accuracy of the fit (Figure 4).

The accuracy of the analytic aerotriangulation is indicated by the difference between the adjusted and fixed coordinates and elevations for the 7 peripheral geodetic control points and the 2 withheld geodetic control points and by the difference between the adjusted and fixed elevations of the 7 additional withheld points (A, B, D, E, F, H, and J) of known elevation as illustrated in Figure 5. The horizontal coordinate standard error for all 9 horizontal control points was 1.1 in. (2.8 cm) and the standard error of elevation for all 16 vertical control points was 1.1 in. (2.8 cm). Stated in terms of the 3,000-ft height of the aerial photography, the accuracy of the analytic aerotriangulation was 1 part in 33,000 for both the horizontal and vertical fit.

[483]

FIGURE 4   Location of horizontal control stations numbers 1 through 9 (open triangles), vertical control points A, B, D, E, F, H, and J (cross marks), premarked photogrammetric points numbers 11 through 44 (open squares), and office-identified photogrammetric points numbers 45 through 62 (open circles). The 9 horizontal control stations also served as vertical control points. Approximate scale 1:10,000.

[484]

TABLE 1 Geographic Positions and Elevations of Stations Used To Control the Anchorage Crustal-Movement Study

Designation on Figure 4	Station	Latitude °	′	″	Longitude °	′	″	Elevation, Feet
Horizontal and vertical control points[1]	ANCHOR, 1964	61	13	12.28409	149	54	03.70233	
1	Targeted Sub. Pt. for ANCHOR, 1964	61	13	12.19359	149	54	03.48809	96.207
	GAMB, 1964	61	13	12.50825	149	51	59.69575	
2	Target on GAMB, RM #2, 1964	61	13	12.67644	149	52	07.30209	113.989
	NORM, 1964	61	13	14.00047	149	49	57.09402	
3	Targeted Sub. Pt. for NORM, 1964	61	13	14.13577	149	49	56.86616	138.143
	RAGE, 1964	61	12	52.16794	149	54	43.80518	
4	Target on RAGE, RM #1, 1964	61	12	52.44365	149	54	43.32933	41.978
5	Target on ANCHORAGE, 1964	61	12	50.47244	149	53	05.37069	105.305
6	Target on CONTROL, 1964	61	12	56.69620	149	50	53.30901	125.229
	SLOPE, 1964	61	12	31.37505	149	54	48.92719	
7	Targeted Sub. Pt. for SLOPE, 1964	61	12	31.18459	149	54	48.93632	24.829
	CHET, 1964	61	12	25.54431	149	52	11.32102	
	CHET, RM #3, 1964	61	12	24.24579	149	52	11.49839	
8	Targeted Sub. Pt. for CHET, RM #3, 1964	61	12	24.57994	149	52	12.75335	67.034
	DON, 1964	61	12	23.43839	149	50	08.46945	
9	Targeted Sub. Pt. for DON, 1964	61	12	23.18988	149	50	08.17796	123.638
Additional vertical control points[2]								
A	Level Point A	61	13	02.1208	149	54	24.2648	32.188
B	Level Point B	61	12	47.9431	149	53	43.3004	98.996
D	Level Point D	61	12	24.2711	149	53	06.3152	41.079
E	Level Point E	61	13	12.9687	149	53	13.8822	67.254
F	Level Point F	61	12	51.0261	149	51	53.0441	107.188
H	Level Point H	61	13	12.5026	149	51	03.3893	99.383
J	Level Point J	61	12	30.0068	149	50	59.1418	88.136

[1]Shown on Figure 4 by open triangles.
[2]Shown on Figure 4 by cross marks.

Table 1 gives the geographic positions and elevations of the 9 horizontal and vertical control stations and the 7 additional vertical control stations that were used for the basic control of the Anchorage Crustal-Movement Study. Table 2 gives the photogrammetrically determined positions and elevations of the 52 recoverable ground points. All data are filed in the USC&GS Photogrammetry Division at Rockville, Maryland, for comparison with values obtained from future geodetic and photogrammetric surveys. It is anticipated that surveys will be repeated at intervals of 3 to 5 years or after crustal movements in excess of 3 in. are reported within the area of the Anchorage Crustal-Movement Study.

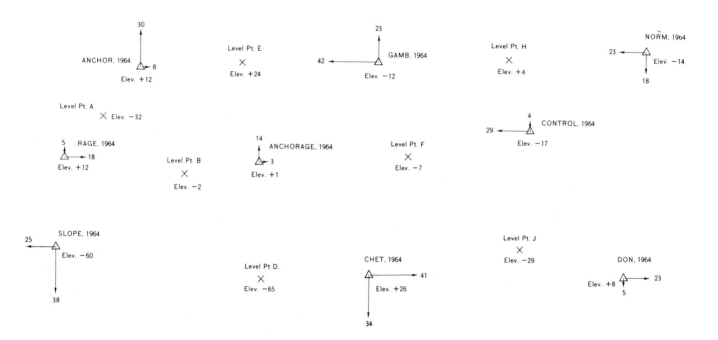

FIGURE 5   Accuracy of analytic aerotriangulation; vectors and elevations (in millimeters) indicate lack of fit of photogrammetrically determined positions and elevations at ground-control points.

TABLE 2 Photogrammetrically Determined Positions and Elevations of Auxiliary Points

Designation on Figure 4	Latitude			Longitude			Elevation, Feet
	°	'	"	°	'	"	
Premarked points[1]							
11	61	13	00.9181	149	54	27.3147	31.43
12	61	12	47.2427	149	54	35.0755	88.92
13	61	12	40.4310	149	54	49.4730	88.15
14	61	12	51.0651	149	54	20.0696	88.40
15	61	12	36.8821	149	54	20.0701	61.31
16	61	12	29.7180	149	54	27.1032	34.95
17	61	12	20.8262	149	54	02.2201	20.61
18	61	12	29.7123	149	53	54.3482	95.52
19	61	12	47.8121	149	54	05.3551	93.78
20	61	13	02.1208	149	54	24.2648	32.19
21	61	13	05.2667	149	54	05.5006	97.22
22	61	12	54.6044	149	53	58.0093	96.66
23	61	13	08.7838	149	53	50.6491	98.10
24	61	13	01.6940	149	53	50.6516	98.71
25	61	12	29.7827	149	53	43.3158	96.65
26	61	12	20.1899	149	53	45.1371	24.55
27	61	12	58.1466	149	53	35.9528	100.79
28	61	13	08.7822	149	53	35.9410	100.51
29	61	13	13.9917	149	53	28.4661	75.67
30	61	13	01.6891	149	53	21.2394	102.22
31	61	13	01.6833	149	53	06.5352	105.01
32	61	13	08.7796	149	53	06.5280	105.25
33	61	13	12.9687	149	53	13.8822	67.25
34	61	13	15.4556	149	52	51.7592	83.37
35	61	13	12.3126	149	52	37.1125	94.60

36	61	13	01.6786	149	52	44.4776	107.18
37	61	12	29.7637	149	52	37.1638	99.92
38	61	12	24.4213	149	52	33.9426	55.40
39	61	13	08.7610	149	52	22.4153	112.39
40	61	13	01.6663	149	52	15.0735	111.78
41	61	12	23.7693	149	52	08.2216	74.45
42	61	13	05.2022	149	51	45.6657	116.18
43	61	13	12.2936	149	51	38.0322	72.70
44	61	13	12.5026	149	51	03.3893	99.38
Office-identified points[2]							
45	61	13	08.5656	149	54	07.7834	95.94
46	61	13	12.0522	149	53	42.6715	95.27
47	61	12	58.4258	149	54	06.1334	95.65
48	61	12	44.7670	149	54	19.5957	92.06
49	61	12	38.9885	149	54	18.5938	66.86
50	61	12	36.6868	149	54	35.4227	54.33
51	61	12	40.2054	149	54	35.4047	88.92
52	61	12	30.0335	149	54	13.9037	57.77
53	61	12	38.6518	149	53	51.0618	97.60
54	61	12	51.4183	149	53	28.0309	101.07
55	61	12	42.2649	149	53	21.7177	102.13
56	61	12	35.8443	149	53	35.4900	98.88
57	61	12	32.4886	149	53	20.7901	85.23
58	61	12	42.1762	149	52	58.9638	87.18
59	61	12	54.1456	149	52	32.1913	109.17
60	61	12	58.0706	149	51	38.2612	112.88
61	61	12	39.2033	149	51	16.7684	115.96
62	61	12	33.4654	149	52	03.8712	109.12

[1] Field-targeted recoverable photogrammetric points shown on Figure 4 by open square symbols.
[2] Office-identified recoverable photogrammetric points shown on Figure 4 by open circles.

REFERENCES

Hansen, Wallace R., 1965. Effects of the earthquake of March 27, 1964, at Anchorage, Alaska. U.S. Geological Survey Professional Paper 542-A. Washington: Government Printing Office. 68 p. Also *in* The Great Alaska Earthquake of 1964: Geology. NAS Pub. 1601. Washington: National Academy of Sciences, 1971.

Harris, W. D., G. C. Tewinkel, and C. A. Whitten, 1962. Analytic aerotriangulation. U.S. Coast and Geodetic Survey Technical Bulletin 21. Washington: Government Printing Office. 39 p.

Meade, Buford K., 1969. Precise surveys of the Anchorage monitoring system *in* Volume III: The Prince William Sound, Alaska, earthquake of 1964 and aftershocks. Environmental Science Services Administration, U.S. Coast and Geodetic Survey. Washington: Government Printing Office. p.113–118. Also *in* The Great Alaska Earthquake of 1964: Seismology and Geodesy. NAS Pub. 1602. Washington: National Academy of Sciences, 1972.

Shannon & Wilson, Inc., 1964. Report on Anchorage area soil studies, Alaska, to U.S. Army Engineer District, Anchorage, Alaska, August 28. Seattle: Shannon & Wilson, Inc. 300 p.

Woodcock, Lorin F., and B. Frank Lampton, 1964. Measurement of crustal movements by photogrammetric methods. *Photogrammetric Engineering*, 30 (November), 912–916.

IV
RELATED
GEOPHYSICAL
EFFECTS

Introduction

A catastrophic natural event such as a large earthquake is often accompanied by other unusual phenomena that appear to be related but for which no immediate physical explanation is available. In many instances these unusual occurrences may be only coincidental and have no other relation to the earthquake; however, there are so many uncertainties in our knowledge of the mechanism of a great earthquake, and the opportunities to observe such events are so rare, that it becomes most important to thoroughly document these occurrences whenever the opportunity exists. The great Alaska earthquake provides one such unique opportunity.

This section includes papers that review such geophysical phenomena related to the event as ionospheric disturbances, groundwater fluctuations, changes in the earth's rotation, long-period vibrations of the earth, and local geomagnetic effects. In addition, several previously published papers are reprinted here to help ensure the availability of selected data or records at a later date for checking new hypotheses, particularly about those phenomena that are not now understood.

For example, excitation of elastic oscillations of the earth and gravitational oscillations of the atmosphere, as discussed in this section, are clearly predictable effects for a great earthquake that displaces a large section of the earth's crust, and, as such, do not raise fundamental questions about the physical mechanism involved. Rather, they add one more constraint to the possible mechanism that could have been acting during the earthquake. The papers on geomagnetic effects, however, for which the mechanism is much less well understood, do not add directly to our knowledge of the earthquake mechanism, but they pose important questions that will undoubtedly be explored and more fully explained in subsequent work.

STEWART W. SMITH
University of Washington

RONALD V. ROW[*]

SYLVANIA ELECTRIC PRODUCTS, INC.

Reprinted with minor changes from
Sylvania Electronic Systems Research Report No. 525 (Project No. 603-01),
"Atmospheric Waves Related to the Alaskan Earthquake of 28 March 1964 (U.T.)"

Atmospheric Waves

ABSTRACT: Observational data concerning atmospheric and
ionospheric disturbances following the Prince William Sound earthquake are reviewed and classified into early- and late-arriving phenomena. The early-arriving ground-level pressure disturbances are associated with atmospheric coupling to seismic waves in the earth. The
late-arriving phases are consistent with the theory of ducted acoustic
waves propagating in the lower atmosphere (at velocities of about
300 m/sec) that have been excited by tectonic deformation over a region consistent with the pre- and postearthquake elevation data. The
ionospheric disturbances also show an early-arriving phase attributable
to local passage of seismic waves, which in turn excited acoustic waves
that propagated up to the ionosphere. A later-arriving long-period disturbance has the character of an acoustic-gravity wave propagating obliquely from the epicentral region to F-region heights of a few hundred kilometers. It resembles disturbances seen after some large yield
low-altitude nuclear detonations. In the ionospheric records, the evidence for an even later-arriving disturbance corresponding to the one
seen (propagating at about 300 m/sec) on ground-based microbarographs is inconclusive, in spite of the fact that this type of ionospheric
disturbance is commonly observed following nuclear detonations.

[*]Now with Symbionics Consultants, Inc., Waltham, Massachusetts.

This paper is concerned with atmospheric and ionospheric
disturbances associated with the main shock of the Prince
William Sound earthquake that were recorded on instruments
such as barographs, microbarographs, and ionospheric high-
frequency radio sounders. Audible atmospheric effects that
accompanied the earthquake are not discussed but resembled
subjective observations during other large earthquakes
(Richter, 1958). Because of the magnitude of the tectonic
displacements, as well as ground motion at teleseismic distances, and because of the relative abundance of microbarographs, the associated atmospheric disturbances were registered on a larger number of these instruments than for any
previous earthquake. The general nature of these observations
and their relation to past studies will be mentioned briefly.
Samples of the data and more detailed discussions of their
interpretation are found in succeeding papers.

The early-arriving disturbances seen on many microbarographs, and described as air waves, coupled to Rayleigh waves
in the ground are consistent with similar effects accompanying other earthquakes reported at least as far back as 1951
(Benioff, Ewing, and Press). The microbarograph records
from the 1964 Alaska earthquake provided data, however,
that have permitted additional qualitative and quantitative
confirmation of the ground-coupled nature of the early-
arriving air-pressure disturbances.

A later-arriving disturbance of much larger amplitude,
which looked like a highly damped sine wave of period
14 minutes with superposed shorter-period structure, was
seen on several widely separated microbarographs and has
been identified by Bolt (1964) as well as other investigators
as a seismic air wave traveling in the atmosphere from the vicinity of the epicenter of the main shock. Some thirty years

ago, Benioff and Gutenberg (1939) tentatively identified a group of relatively short-period waves (3 seconds or less) as being air waves launched from near the epicenter of an earthquake about 670 km from their microbarograph. The microbarograph records taken at the time of the 1964 Alaska earthquake seem to be the first evidence of a clear, long-duration, propagating pulse-type air wave associated with an earthquake. The records are good enough to permit qualitative speculation, and Mikumo (1968) has carried out a quantitative study of the nature of the ground motion producing the seismic air wave. Such waves are commonly associated with volcanic eruptions and with large nuclear detonations, a fact that has stimulated much theoretical study concerning their generation and propagation.

If the seismic air wave described by Bolt (1964) and other investigators was indeed generated by ground motion near the epicenter, then one might have expected to see some ground-level pressure changes in Alaska. A microbarograph located at the Geophysical Institute, College, Alaska (about 416 km from the epicenter of the main shock) registered very large oscillatory pressure fluctuations of period 30 seconds or less, and peak-to-peak amplitude at least 0.54 mb (millibars). These very large pressure swings lasted for only a few minutes and then persisted at much smaller and diminishing amplitude for about 1.5 hours. Many, but by no means all, standard barographs maintained by the U.S. Weather Bureau throughout Alaska at the time recorded some more-or-less abrupt pen deflections identifiable with the occurrence of the main shock. These abrupt pen deflections probably are due to mechanical response of these instruments to local ground motion, rather than to real atmospheric pressure variations.

The Alaska earthquake seems to be the first for which noticeable ionospheric disturbances were recorded. Early-arriving short-period disturbances were seen on high-frequency, pulsed or continuous-wave, phase-coherent (Doppler) vertical sounders as well as on stable-frequency long-distance (oblique) paths. At least one set of such data (Davies and Baker, 1965) has been identified as arising from propagation into the ionosphere of air-coupled Rayleigh waves (Cook and Baker, 1965). Variations of virtual height and critical frequencies on a few standard swept-frequency ionograms (Leonard and Barnes, 1965; Row, 1966) as well as on a few Doppler sounders (Row, 1966) demonstrate the existence of a long-period traveling disturbance moving outward at a velocity much higher than that of a sound wave in the lower atmosphere. This disturbance has been tentatively identified as an acoustic-gravity wave pulse propagating in the neutral atmosphere, and its kinship to similar traveling ionospheric disturbances associated with nuclear detonations has been pointed out (Row, 1966, 1967). Further theoretical work is necessary to determine the transient response of an ionospheric observable to various idealized models of large-scale ground motion near the epicenter.

PRESSURE DISTURBANCES AT GROUND LEVEL

EARLY-ARRIVING DISTURBANCE (FROM GROUND-COUPLED AIR WAVES)

Distant Observations

Figure 1 from Bolt (1964) is typical of microbarograph records of atmospheric pressure obtained at large distances from the epicenter. In this case, the instrument (a Davey–Marion barovariograph) was located at Berkeley, California, 3133 km from the epicenter of the main shock. The deflection on the chart record is proportional to the rate of flow of air from the atmosphere into a 40-liter reservoir. The response of the instrument to abrupt change in atmospheric pressure is a deflection of the output recorder stylus with a rise time somewhat less than 10 seconds followed by an exponential decay with a time constant of the order of 10 minutes. Consequently, the chart record is a faithful reproduction of differential atmospheric pressure for short-duration pressure fluctuations (short compared to the time constant of the instrument), but requires correction to determine the pressure for slow changes.

On the record, the first sign of a seismically related event is the sudden increase in pressure of about 21 μbars commencing at 0350 GMT on March 28. This pressure increase is the beginning of a train of oscillations of maximum peak-to-peak swing of 43 μbars and period that decreases from about 1 minute to 15 seconds in a time of 5 minutes and persists at this short-period limit for many hours. Based on a time of occurrence of the main shock of 0336 GMT, the group velocity of the first arrival is about 3.7 km/sec. Bolt (1964) identifies this early-arriving group of oscillations with coupling between the atmosphere and Rayleigh waves in the ground, a conclusion supported by Donn and Posmentier (1964) who have performed a dispersion analysis of the barogram from the Lamont Instrument at Berkeley and of others from Honolulu, Hawaii, and Palisades, New York. Figure 2 is a plot of group velocity against period for the Berkeley barogram obtained by using the peak-and-trough method of Ewing and Press (1954). The solid curves and cross-hatching indicate observed dispersion for first-mode continental and oceanic Rayleigh waves. In addition, Donn and Posmentier (1964) have carried out a Fourier spectrum analysis on a sound spectrograph of 12 minutes of the Berkeley microbarograph record, which confirms the data shown in Figure 2.

Among other reports on the occurrence of the early-arriving pressure wave, that of Young and others (1965) on observations at Boulder, Colorado; Washington, D.C.; and Boston, Massachusetts, is especially interesting. The observing sites at Boulder and Washington were equipped with an array of 4 pressure sensors from which the direction of arrival of the incoming waves could be determined. Some part of the

[495]

UNIVERSAL TIME, MARCH 28, 1964

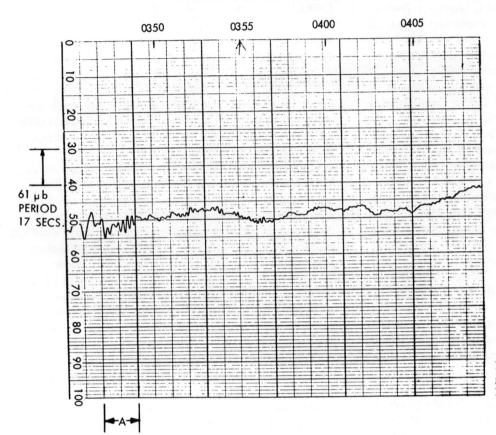

FIGURE 1 March 28, 1964, microbaro-gram from Berkeley, California; after Bolt (1964).

observed wave trains was thus estimated to come from the Rocky Mountains, indicating that some especially efficient atmospheric coupling mechanism was operating in the mountains. T. Madden (personal communication, 1967) has micro-barograph records from La Jolla and Point Loma, California, and T. Taylor (personal communication, 1966) those from Golden, Colorado. Cook (1965) has commented on the nature of the radiation of "sound" from earthquakes, more particularly with reference to resonant coupled waves and their effect on the ionosphere rather than at the surface of the earth.

The maximum amplitudes of the short-period vertical ground motion and the short-period air-pressure oscillations observed at the same location appear to be consistent with local coupling between ground and air. Thus, Donn and Posmentier (1964) use the observations at Palisades, New York, of a maximum pressure-swing of 40 μbars at a period of 23 seconds to infer a peak-to-peak ground motion of 3.72 cm. The actual peak-to-peak vertical ground motion estimated from seismic records was 4.2 cm. Their estimate is based on the formula

$$p = \rho c v$$

connecting (local) vertical ground velocity, v, with the (local) perturbation pressure p, and ambient density ρ. This formula

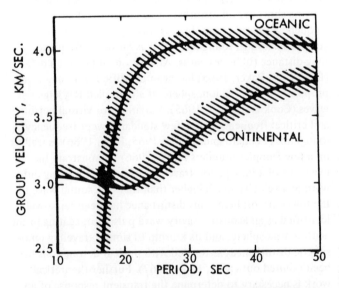

FIGURE 2 Air pressure wave dispersion for Berkeley (See Figure 1) and the empirical curve for first-mode, continental and oceanic Rayleigh waves. From Donn and Posmentier (1964).

[496]

is an approximation valid at distances from the ground that are small compared to the wavelength and at periods short compared to the local Brunt-Väisälä period and in the absence of resonant ground-to-air-wave coupling of the type discussed by Ewing and others (1957). Bolt (1964) indicates that the maximum ground displacement measured at the Berkeley seismograph station was 1 cm, corresponding to passage of a group of waves of period 17 seconds. From the above formula, a peak-to-peak vertical ground displacement of 2 cm of this period would correspond to a peak-to-peak pressure swing of 29 μbars. The microbarograph record shows a group of oscillations (labeled A) in Figure 1 of approximate period 18–16 seconds with a maximum peak-to-peak amplitude of 35–40 μbars.

Nearby Observations

Figure 3 shows a portion of a microbarograph recording obtained by E. Berg (personal communication, 1966) at the Geophysical Institute, University of Alaska at College on March 28 (GMT), 1964. This instrument was approximately

416 km from the epicenter of the main shock and was located on the second floor of a building and connected to the outside atmosphere by a hose. As far as is known, it was the only microbarograph with such sensitivity and time resolution in Alaska and the closest to the epicenter of any such instruments. This instrument operates on the same principle as the one used by Bolt (1964). A step increase of differential pressure Δp microbars between the atmosphere and reservoir produces a chart deflection given approximately by

$$d = \frac{\Delta p}{6} \exp(-t/6) \text{ divisions,}$$

where t is the elapsed time in minutes. According to Berg, the initial positive-pressure jump (about 10 chart divisions at 0337.5 in Figure 3) corresponds to the first seismic *P*-wave arrival. This jump is followed immediately by a very large short-period oscillatory deflection of the stylus lasting approximately 2½ minutes and corresponding to the seismic *S* waves. The maximum peak-to-peak pressure swing is at least 540 μbars and the period is remarkably constant at about

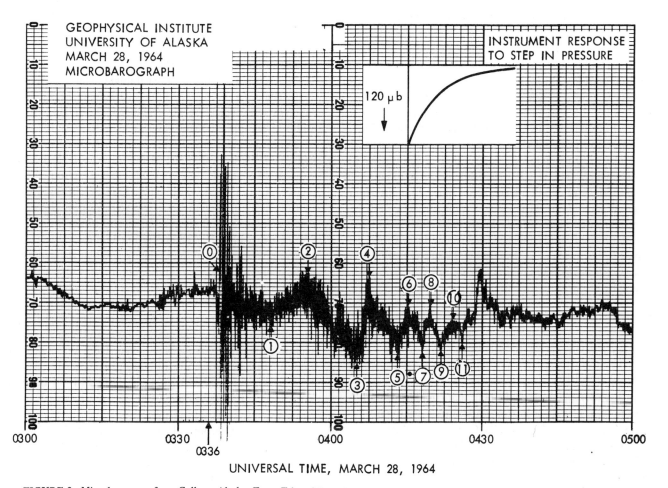

FIGURE 3 Microbarogram from College, Alaska. From Eduard Berg (personal communication, 1966).

[497]

26 seconds. A vertical ground displacement of 57 cm peak-to-peak would produce such pressure swings. The stylus evidently hit the stops on the chart recorder on two swings between 0338 and 0340 GMT, so that the apparent pressure-swings may have been larger.

A second group of much smaller pressure oscillations of the same period commences at 0341 GMT, builds up over a minute to a peak-to-peak maximum of about 192 μbars, and decays rapidly to a peak-to-peak amplitude of approximately 60 μbars that persists for at least 30 minutes superimposed on much slower pressure changes. These short-period pressure oscillations must be due to atmospheric coupling to local ground and building motion because they commence long before any air wave launched from the vicinity of the epicenter could have arrived. They cannot represent resonant coupling to the ground, because the period of the oscillations is much too long to permit a Rayleigh mode in the ground to have a horizontal phase velocity as low as the speed of sound in air. This same remark applies to the pressure observations at distant points discussed previously.

I have examined barograph records from some 21 U.S. Weather Bureau locations in Alaska to see whether they give any useful indication of atmospheric pressure changes at the time of the main shock. These instruments were at distances between 118 and 810 km from the epicenter. As a rule, those barographs within 300 km of the epicenter (9 in number) show a more-or-less abrupt and momentary pen deflection, and those beyond 300 km (11 in number) do not. One exception is the U.S. Navy barograph at Kodiak that is about 455 km from the epicenter and shows an abrupt pen deflection. These abrupt momentary deflections probably result from shaking of the instruments rather than real atmospheric pressure changes. The U.S. Weather Bureau barograph at Fairbanks, only a few kilometers from College (416 km from the epicenter), did not show a large abrupt pen deflection. There is, however, a discernible wiggle in the trace starting at about 0338 GMT and lasting less than 5 minutes, with an estimated peak swing of 200–300 μbar. Perhaps fortuitously, this is consistent with the pressure swings seen on the microbarograph at College.

LATE-ARRIVING SEISMIC AIR WAVES

Distant Observations

Figure 4 is a later section of the microbarograph record obtained by Bolt (1964) at Berkeley, California. Microbarograph records obtained at La Jolla, California, and Point Loma, California (T. Madden, personal communication, 1967)—both points about 800 km south of Berkeley—show this same wave form, though with less time resolution. The large-amplitude disturbance, having a compression maximum at about 0619 GMT and a rarefaction maximum at 0626 GMT followed by shorter-period small oscillations, has been discussed briefly by Bolt (1964) and Donn and Posmentier (1964). Using the first rarefaction maximum at 0626 GMT as the group arrival time, Bolt infers a group velocity of 317 m/sec and an apparent period of 3 minutes assuming the wave was initiated at the epicenter at 0336 GMT. Donn and Posmentier quote a velocity of 329 m/sec at a period of 3–5 minutes based on the arrival time of 0615 GMT.

Actually it is difficult to attach any precision to the idea of a period as pertaining to this part of the record without carrying through a Fourier spectrum analysis. There is a group of oscillations, with period somewhat less than a minute, that reaches a peak amplitude at about 0631 GMT (this same group appears, although less clearly, on the La Jolla and Point Loma records). Bolt (1964) gives a group velocity of 298 m/sec for this part of the record, and Donn and Posmentier (1964) quote 292 m/sec. It is apparent then that a dispersive wave phenomenon can be associated with the Berkeley record between about 0615 and 0635 GMT. The group velocity based on a source at the epicenter thus ranges from something like 320 m/sec at periods in excess of 3 minutes to 290–300 m/sec for periods somewhat less than a minute. This dispersion of group velocity is consistent with observations of ground-level pressure disturbances following nuclear detonations as discussed by Donn and Ewing (1962).

Apparently no evidence of earthquake-related pressure disturbances has been seen in microbarograph records of the Japan Meteorological Agency (Mikumo, 1968). However, Mikumo has applied digital filtering techniques to the microbarograms from College, Berkeley, and San Diego with three-band pass filters covering the period intervals 1.75–3.5, 3.5–7.0, 7.0–14.0 minutes and concludes that the group- and phase-velocity dispersion obtained from these filtered records by time-delay measurements agrees well with the theoretical dispersion curves of Press and Harkrider (1962) and Pfeffer and Zarichny (1963). Apparently the amplitude spectra obtained in this way from the Berkeley and San Diego records show peaks at 13, 4.3–5.2, and 2.9 minutes. Furthermore, the phase spectra show phase shifts corresponding to the difference in distance between the two observing sites.

Bowman and Shrestha (1965) have reported an earthquake that gave rise to seismic air waves similar to the late-arriving components of the Alaska earthquake. They report observations at Brisbane, Australia, of atmospheric pressure waves from a large Japanese earthquake at 0401:44 GMT on June 16, 1964, with its epicenter 7,400 km from Brisbane. In this case, the earliest arrival is a group of oscillations of period 168 seconds with group velocity approximately 300 m/sec followed by other prominent groups of period 60 and 70 seconds and velocity between 260 and 275 m/sec. The dispersion of these waves seems to be consistent with Press and Harkrider's (1962) ducted modes.

UNIVERSAL TIME, MARCH 28, 1964

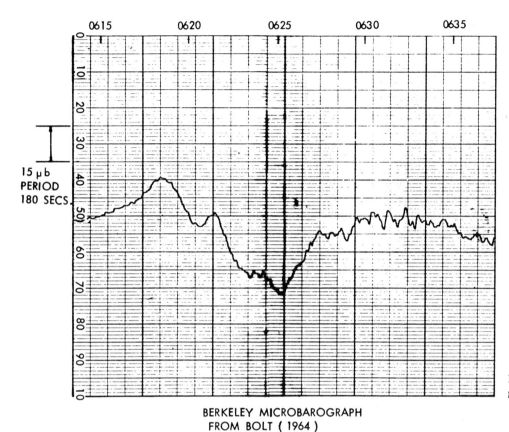

15 µb
PERIOD
180 SECS.

BERKELEY MICROBAROGRAPH
FROM BOLT (1964)

FIGURE 4   Later section of microbarogram. From Berkeley after Bolt (1964).

Nearby Observations at College, Alaska

As mentioned previously, the microbarograph record (Figure 3) obtained by E. Berg (personal communication, 1966), at College is the only one in Alaska that shows any great detail of pressure disturbances at a point relatively close (416 km) to the epicenter of the main shock. The short-period structure commented on earlier is superimposed on some longer-period changes that may have some relation to earthquake-launched air waves. As shown in Figure 3, the major peaks and troughs in the chart record have been numbered in sequence starting with zero at 0337.5 GMT. In Figure 5, these numbers are plotted against their corresponding time. When the record is viewed in this way, it is apparent that there are two groups of points forming periodic sequences distinguished by widely differing periods. Points 0–3 form one set, with a period of about 18 minutes; and 5 through 11 form another, with a period of about 4.5 minutes. Point number 4, which does not lie within either sequence, is close to the transition between them. From these observations and from the magnitude of the corresponding deflections on the record, it is tempting to speculate that these ef-

fects were produced by propagating air-pressure waves. The long period of approximately 18 minutes associated with points 0–3 is within the range of periods of oscillatory pressure fluctuations commonly associated with gravity waves in the lower troposphere, which sometimes are of high amplitude in this location during the wintertime (E. Berg, personal communication, 1967). Indeed the sequence 0–2 appears to fit in with the appearance of the record previous to point 0. However, the magnitude of the pressure increase between 2 and 3 is sufficiently unusual that points 1-2-3 may signal the presence of an earthquake-related long-period wave. If one assumes for the moment that it was launched at the epicenter 416 km away, a group velocity of 360 m/sec is indicated based on the arrival time of the peak numbered 2. Based on a period of 18 minutes, this velocity is too high to fit the empirical dispersion curves deduced by Donn and Ewing (1962) from several nuclear detonations. At the same time, it is too low to fit the theoretical dispersion calculated by Pfeffer and Zarichny (1963) for the fundamental acoustic mode. Some allowance for prevailing upper atmospheric winds and uncertainty regarding the location of the source of the postulated and earthquake-related air wave can cause the

[499]

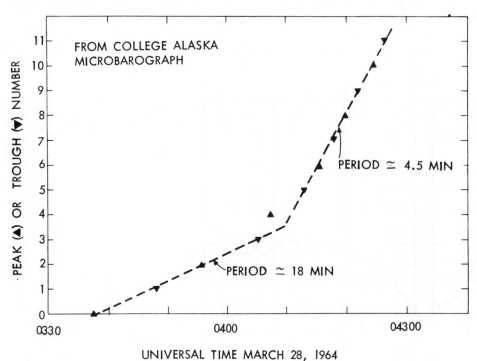

FIGURE 5 Time sequence of major peaks and troughs in microbarogram from College, Alaska.

estimates of velocity to vary within wide limits. With these endless possibilities in mind, it does not seem profitable to push any further the question of an earthquake source of the disturbance seen on the College microbarograph between points 0 and 3.

Between points 3 and 4 there is a very sharp drop in pressure followed by a decaying oscillatory sequence up through point 11. According to E. Berg (personal communication, 1967), this is a unique event on the College microbarograph. A component with about this period (4.5 minutes) is prominent in the microbarograph records from many nuclear detonations (Donn and Ewing, 1962; Pfeffer and Zarichny, 1963). A certain dispersion is implicit in the transition from point 3 to the almost perfectly periodic sequence 5 through 11. This dispersion is consistent with the first ducted gravity mode as in the theoretical models of Pfeffer and Zarichny (1963), who deduce a maximum group velocity of 303 m/sec for this mode in their model Arctic-winter atmosphere. If the first arrival is taken to be point number 3 at 0405 GMT and it is assumed the source acted (briefly) at 0336 GMT, then the source of this disturbance is inferred to be at a range of 526 km. It so happens that Montague Island, which according to Plafker (1965) is at the center of the zone of maximum tectonic uplift (of about 10 m), is about this distance south of College. It is difficult to see how raising the ground at a distance would produce an initial decrease in pressure as implied by the change from point 3 to 4 in the College microbarograph record. Again according to Plafker, the center of the zone of maximum subsidence is only about

400 km south of College. Some reduction in apparent mode velocity by upper-atmosphere winds could permit a plausible explanation of the sequence 3 through 11, based on the zone of subsidence as the effective source. One other prominent event on the College microbarograph record appears as a rapid drop in pressure starting about one minute before 0430 GMT and followed by a slower decay. In appearance, this part of the record looks very similar to the record between points 3 and 5. It is a matter of conjecture as to what relation, if any, this event bears to the earthquake. The lack of microbarograph data from other locations in Alaska makes it impossible to separate out purely local meteorological effects so that earthquake-caused long-period air waves can be identified with certainty.

Source Mechanism for the Late-Arriving Air Waves

Some speculations have appeared in print concerning possible source mechanisms of the late-arriving seismic air waves. Thus Bolt (1964) suggests that the air wave may have been caused by a sudden vertical displacement or tilting of the ground in the vicinity of the epicenter, such as caused the major tsunami. He comments that a computation of the approximate amplitude of the recorded air wave with a period of 3 minutes is about 0.75 m (based on the relation $p = \rho cv$), which is the order of magnitude of the ground displacements noted.

Bolt also comments that the extended nature of the source will complicate the waveform. Van Dorn (1965, and Oceanography and Coastal Engineering volume) has used the air-wave disturbance obtained on a microbarograph at La

Jolla as additional evidence for inferring a sudden vertical motion (uplift) under the sea as the principal source of the tsunami recorded at large distances from Prince William Sound.

Donn and Posmentier (1964) note the difference between the appearance of the first portion of the late-arriving air wave after the Alaska earthquake and those seen following nuclear detonations. They speculate that this difference and the lack of very obvious dispersion in the earthquake record are probably due to the extended area of the source that caused the air wave observed after the earthquake. Mikumo (1968), however, finds from the results of digital Fourier spectrum analysis that dispersion in these air-pressure records is consistent with the theoretical models of Press and Harkrider (1962) and Pfeffer and Zarichny (1963).

The centers of the zones of maximum uplift and maximum subsidence as delineated by Plafker (1965) are separated by about 110 km. These zones lie parallel to the tectonic hinge line, which in turn is almost perpendicular to the great circle from the epicenter to Berkeley, with the zone of maximum uplift being closer to Berkeley. An air wave propagating at a speed of 310 m/sec would take about 6 minutes to cross from the center of the zone of maximum subsidence to that of maximum uplift. It just so happens that the maximum-compression and maximum-rarefaction peaks on the Berkeley and La Jolla records are separated by 7 minutes. This time difference may have some bearing on the nature of the source. In addition to the major uplift and smaller amount of subsidence identified by Plafker, there was a very extensive horizontal movement of a large area of terrain (Parkin, 1969, and this volume). This displacement, as much as 70 ft in places, was generally toward the southeast, and largest near the tectonic hinge line identified by Plafker (1965). This horizontal motion, believed to have been completed within a few minutes after the main shock, could launch air waves.

Mikumo (1968) has made progress in interpreting the records of late-arriving air waves on the basis of various source mechanisms. This study does not encourage the view that much can be inferred about the nature of gross tectonic displacements from microbarograph records.

IONOSPHERIC EFFECTS

Ionospheric effects attributed to the March 28 Alaska earthquake may be put into early-arriving and late-arriving groups also. Figure 5 shows distance plotted against time for various ionospheric observations and illustrates the grouping.

EARLY-ARRIVING DISTURBANCES

Leonard and Barnes (1965) in their report of the earthquake-related ionospheric disturbances as seen on swept-frequency

vertical-incidence ionosondes show a disturbance arriving at Adak, Alaska, much earlier than could be accounted for by a pressure wave in the neutral atmosphere. These instruments measure the apparent height of reflection of a pulsed radio wave from the ionosphere.

The Davies and Baker (1965) report of an early-arriving disturbance seen at Boulder, Colorado, is based on the records from three fixed-frequency phase-coherent (Doppler) sounders. These sounders measure the time-rate of change of phase between a radio signal transmitted from the ground via the ionosphere to a ground-based receiver. Two of these are near vertical-incidence sounders located near Boulder and operate on frequencies of 4.000 and 5.054 MHz. The third receives signals at 10.000 MHz from station WWV, Washington, and station WWVH, Hawaii. All three records shown in Figure 6 exhibit a large-amplitude oscillatory frequency shift commencing more or less abruptly at about 0355 GMT and building up within a few minutes to exceed the maximum indication of the records (about 6 Hz). Based on a travel time of 24 minutes from the epicenter (3690-km distant), this wave phenomenon can be assigned a group velocity of 2.56 km/sec.

Cook and Baker (1965) have interpreted the ionospheric motion as due to acoustic waves launched almost vertically upward from the ground in an area below the reflection point in the ionosphere. According to linearized hydrodynamic theory for a nonviscous fluid, a vertically propagating sound wave with a vertical fluid velocity at the ground estimated to be about 0.5 cm/sec would grow with height to about 10^4 cm/sec at an altitude of 160 km, by which point the wave phenomenon has become nonlinear. Somewhat below this altitude (Cook and Baker estimate 138 km) some form of shock wave will be formed. A mirror with a vertical velocity of 10^4 cm/sec would produce a Doppler shift of 2.67 Hz on a vertical sounder operating at 4 MHz. Actually, larger Doppler shifts were seen. An examination of the Boulder Doppler records, with increased time resolution, indicates periods of 30 seconds or more for this group of large-amplitude oscillations. Allowing 8 minutes for propagation at an average sound velocity of 520 m/sec (U.S. Standard Atmosphere) from the ground to the reflection level in the ionosphere (estimated to be 250 km from the Boulder 0400-GMT ionogram) gives a group velocity of the initiating ground wave of 3.84 km/sec, which is reasonable for a continental Rayleigh wave of this period.

The Boulder records show a more gradual buildup of the disturbance on 10 MHz than on 4 MHz. Furthermore, the peak of this large-amplitude short-period Doppler disturbance occurs a few minutes earlier on the 10-MHz record than on the 4-MHz record. This behavior is consistent with the fact that the great-circle path from Hawaii to Boulder passes within 3130 km of the epicenter and thus the continental (or oceanic) Rayleigh wave would reach some point on this path

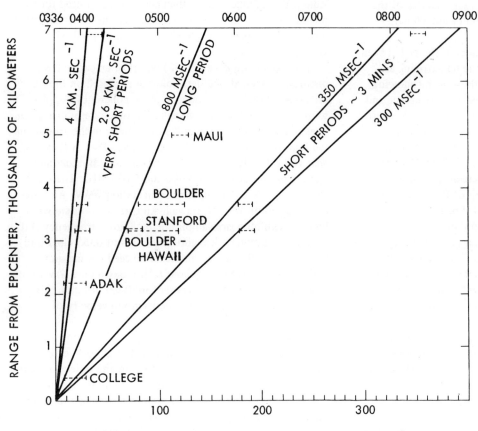

FIGURE 6 Ionospheric event range time diagram for Alaska earthquake of March 28, 1964.

a few minutes before it reached Boulder. Doppler records obtained by L. Edwards (personal communication, 1966) from a number of frequency-stable transmitters over a path passing within 6900 km of the epicenter exhibit high-amplitude short-period large oscillatory Doppler shifts starting with a period of a few minutes about 0405 GMT, building a maximum at 0417 GMT at much shorter periods, and persisting with decaying amplitude for about 30 minutes. The first arrival in this disturbance has an apparent velocity of about 4 km/sec and the maximum-amplitude section an apparent velocity of 2.8 km/sec. This spread of group velocity is consistent with the dispersion of first-mode oceanic Rayleigh waves as discussed by Donn and Posmentier (1964). Because most of the path between the epicenter and the great-circle route between transmitter and receiver is over the ocean, it seems reasonable to identify these disturbances with ground-coupled atmospheric waves. Although no detailed theoretical analysis has been done to connect the transient ground motion to an ionospheric observable such as the apparent frequency (Doppler) shift on a vertical or oblique high-frequency sounder, the mechanism proposed by Cook and Baker (1965)

seems a reasonable one to explain the early-arriving high-amplitude Doppler shifts.

The effect of vertically-propagating acoustic waves from a ground-level detonation on a phase-coherent high-frequency sounder has been studied by Barry and others (1966). Their theoretical model (based on linearized equations of hydrodynamics) includes viscous damping, which for an altitude of 220 km is shown to effectively damp out motions with periods shorter than about 20 sec. It seems then that viscous effects should be examined in further analytical studies of ionospheric effects of ground-coupled air waves. A more detailed dispersion analysis of the Doppler records of the type made by Donn and Posmentier (1964) on the microbarograph records might add to the evidence that the early-arriving Doppler disturbance is a result of atmospheric coupling to the Rayleigh waves from the earthquake.

LATE ARRIVAL

Leonard and Barnes (1965) and Row (1966) have drawn attention to a late-arriving wave-like ionospheric disturbance

[502]

associated with the earthquake. Figure 6 shows the arrival time of the disturbance as seen at different ranges. The observations of Leonard and Barnes (1965) are based on swept-frequency vertical-incidence ionograms obtained at 15-minute intervals at College and Adak, Alaska; Stanford, California; and Maui, Hawaii. The parameter f_oF_2 obtained from the Maui and Stanford ionograms shows an increase within 15 minutes of approximately 0.5 MHz corresponding to the arrival of the disturbance. This increase comes during a period when f_oF_2 is normally decreasing (as at Maui) or near its minimum nighttime value (as at Stanford). The increase is followed by a slight decrease and, in the case of the Maui record at least, a slight oscillation in f_oF_2. The Doppler sounder records at Boulder (Figure 7a, b) show this disturbance in much greater detail and have been discussed by Row (1966, 1967). The solid curves in Figure 8a, b are tracings of the slowly varying part of the 4-MHz and 10-MHz Doppler records as shown in Figure 7a, b. Figure 9a, b show the extraordinary mode virtual-height at 2 MHz and 4 MHz as scaled from the swept-frequency ionograms obtained at

Boulder on the day of the earthquake and on adjacent days. The disturbance on these plots shows up as a distinct and unusually abrupt reduction in virtual-height starting about 0500 GMT. In the case of the 4-MHz virtual-height, this drop amounts to about 65 km. Figure 9c is a plot of the vertical displacement of a mirror required to give the observed Doppler shift on 4 MHz as plotted in Figure 7. The displacement computed in this way gives a maximum downward displacement of 57 km, which agrees well in magnitude and shape with the height change scaled from the ionograms.

An especially interesting feature of both the Doppler shift and the 4-Hz virtual-height scaled from the ionograms at Boulder, is the very-long-period (90 minutes) oscillatory behavior of these quantities. This same behavior is evident in the behavior of f_oF_2 scaled from the ionograms at Maui by Leonard and Barnes (1965). Row (1967) has shown that this type of behavior, which has been seen in ionospheric records following atmospheric nuclear detonations, is characteristic of transient propagation of acoustic-gravity waves in a planar isothermal, gravitationally stratified, unbounded neutral at-

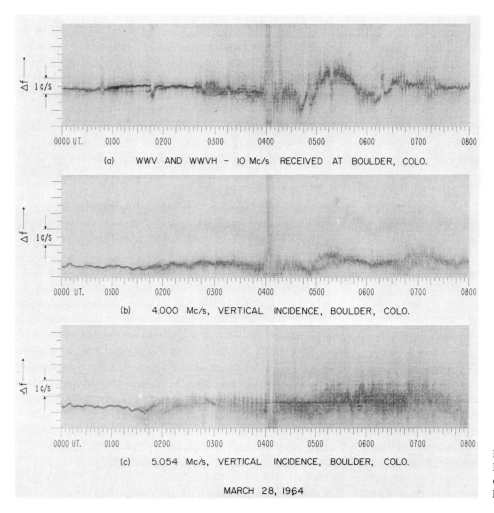

(a)   WWV AND WWVH – 10 Mc/s RECEIVED AT BOULDER, COLO.

(b)   4.000 Mc/s, VERTICAL INCIDENCE, BOULDER, COLO.

(c)   5.054 Mc/s, VERTICAL INCIDENCE, BOULDER, COLO.

MARCH 28, 1964

FIGURE 7 Doppler spectrum at Boulder, Colorado, for Alaska earthquake of March 28, 1964. From Davies and Baker (1965).

[503]

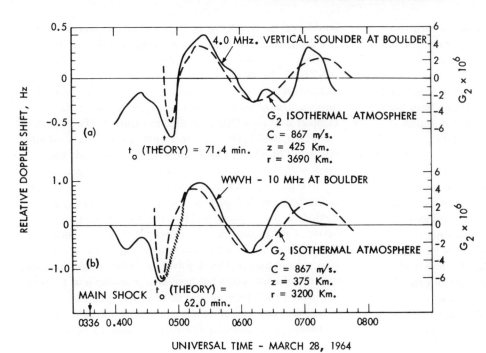

FIGURE 8 High-frequency Doppler records at Boulder, Colorado, following the great Alaska earthquake. From Davies and Baker (1965); best fit from the isothermal atmosphere theory (Row, 1967).

mosphere. The phenomenon comes about by virtue of the fact that, in such an atmosphere, propagation at a particular period can take place only in directions, making an angle θ with the horizontal, that satisfy the inequality

$$\sin \theta < \tau_B/\tau$$

where τ_B is the Brunt period of the atmosphere, and equals

$$2\pi C/(\gamma-1)^{\frac{1}{2}}g$$

for an isothermal atmosphere with adiabatic sound speed C, ratio of specific heats γ, and gravitation acceleration g. Thus for an impulse-type source near the ground, the period of the longest-period component (ringing period) that will propagate to a distant observer will become greater as the angle θ becomes smaller. Hence in the case of the Alaska earthquake, from the effects observed in the ionosphere over Boulder at a height of 300–700 km (a height roughly equal to one tenth the distance to the epicenter), the ringing period of the neutral atmosphere would be about ten times the Brunt period.

The dashed curves shown in Figure 8 are two examples of the theoretically computed characteristic response of a planar isothermal, gravitationally stratified, unbounded neutral atmosphere to a point-source impulse disturbance located a distance z below, and r radially outward from, an observer. In these cases, the sound speed C and altitude z were chosen to provide the best qualitative fit to the smoothed Doppler data obtained at Boulder after the Alaska earthquake. There is no

particular significance to the absolute magnitude of the ordinate of these curves, which was scaled to permit qualitative comparison with the Doppler data. It is interesting to note that, according to this theoretical model, a rather high velocity, 867 m/sec, is necessary to produce the match between theoretical and observed waveforms shown in Figure 8, whereas velocities in the range 275–320 m/sec appeared in the ground-based pressure observations discussed in the section on late-arriving seismic air waves. An acoustic velocity this large is found only at altitudes above 250 km in the atmosphere. This model is, of course, a great simplification of the real atmosphere, the temperature (and local Brunt period) of which varies with the height and which is in contact with the rigid ground.

Press and Harkrider (1962) and Pfeffer and Zarichny (1963) have discussed time-harmonic wave propagation in more realistic atmospheres with a view to explaining ground-based pressure disturbances from nuclear detonations. Their computations predict a mode, termed the fundamental (acoustic) mode by the latter two authors, whose phase and group velocities for long periods approaches the speed of sound in the upper half-space with which they terminate their layered atmosphere. No evidence of a pressure wave arriving with this speed is seen in any microbarograph records taken at the time of nuclear detonations (Donn and Ewing, 1962) or the Alaska earthquake. However, high-velocity components similar to those described for the Alaska earthquake have been seen on some ionospheric records obtained at the time of atmospheric nuclear detonations (Row, 1967;

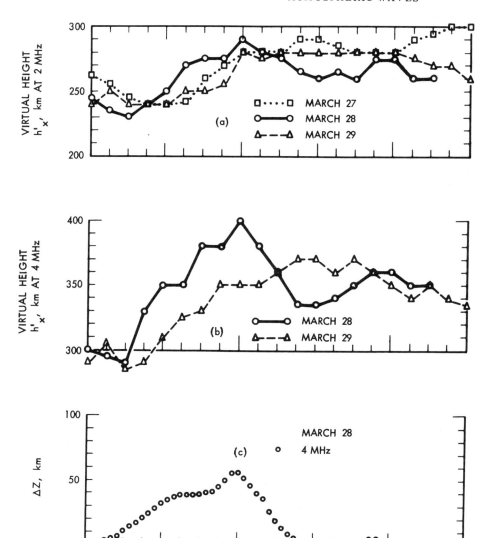

FIGURE 9 (a) and (b) Extraordinary mode virtual-heights from Boulder ionograms (scaled to nearest 5 km). (c) $\Delta z = -(c/2f)\,\Delta f\,dt$, evaluated from Doppler records of Figure 8(a).

Kanellakos, 1967; Albee and Kanellakos, 1968). The ability to detect the high-velocity branch of this mode may be enhanced by observing conditions in the ionosphere.

No detailed quantitative study has yet been made relating the magnitude of the ionospheric effects at long distances to a particular source mechanism such as a detonation or displacement of the ground. Displacement as a source mechanism is of special interest to the study of effects on the atmosphere of ground motion near the epicenter of the Alaska earthquake. As mentioned earlier, Barry and others (1966) have examined ionospheric perturbations directly over a ground-level detonation. These authors assume that the ions and electrons are moved along the earth's magnetic-field lines in the E-region by collisional coupling with the neutral gas.

The authors then compute the perturbation of the ionospheric ion (electron) density through use of the continuity equation for ions, neglecting diffusion and recombination. This latter assumption is apparently justified for coupling to a neutral gas motion whose period is short compared to the characteristic diffusion and recombination times at the ionospheric height under observation (D. Cunnold, personal communication, 1966). This same assumption is made in the analysis of ionospheric disturbances induced by nuclear detonation as reported by Kanellakos (1967).

A search through the stable-frequency transmission records obtained by L. Edwards (personal communication, 1966) fails to show any clear evidence of a long-period, damped, oscillatory Doppler shift, similar to that seen on the

Doppler records and ionograms at Boulder. Edwards' records, however, do show a short-period oscillatory phase disturbance (period approximately 3 minutes) starting at 0611 GMT and persisting for about 15 minutes. The apparent velocity of first arrival in this group is 740 m/sec, based on an assumed earthquake-epicenter launching. The Boulder Doppler records show similar short-period disturbances at some times both pre- and postearthquake. It is not possible to say whether any of these has a positive association with the earthquake. In any case, none of them appears to propagate with a velocity of 740 m/sec from the epicenter. However, there is a pronounced short-period oscillation, commencing at 0633 GMT on the 10-MHz Doppler record and about 1 minute earlier on the 4-MHz record and lasting about 15 minutes. This oscillation is remarkably similar in appearance to the disturbance seen on Edwards' records at 0611 GMT.

Inasmuch as such disturbances occur rather commonly on Doppler records, it is entirely possible that the event occurring at 0611 GMT on Edwards' record is not assignable to the class of ionospheric disturbances caused by the Alaska earthquake. There is a possibility that the short-period oscillations occurring at 0633 GMT on the Boulder Doppler records and at 0920 GMT on Edwards' records are earthquake-associated. The apparent propagation velocity of the first arrival is 300 m/sec on the WWVH–Boulder great-circle path; 350 m/sec on the 4-MHz vertical Doppler sounder at Boulder; and 334 m/sec on the great-circle path used by Edwards. These velocities are appropriate to atmospheric acoustic modes of period less than about 4 minutes, according to Press and Harkrider (1962) and Pfeffer and Zarichny (1963); and, as discussed previously, waves in this range of periods were seen in the microbarograph records following the earthquake. D. M. Baker (personal communication, 1966) has found similar oscillatory signatures in the Boulder Doppler records taken at the time of several nuclear detonations. O. G. Villard (personal communication, 1964) noted some quasi-periodic frequency fluctuations on a high-frequency propagation path from Okinawa to Guam between the hours of 0400–0500 GMT and 0600–0800 GMT. These variations are unusual and may be earthquake related, possibly through backscatter from the sea surface to the east of Guam. No further attempts to explain them have been reported.

H. Kohl (personal communication, 1966) at Lindau-Harz, Germany, and G. Bowman (personal communication, 1966) at Brisbane, Australia, saw no evidence of an ionospheric disturbance on ionograms from those locations. European ionospheric sounders were experiencing the usual, rapid daily increase in $f_o F_2$ and corresponding drop in reflecting height, which could have obscured any earthquake-related disturbance of the size seen at Boulder and other U.S. stations, including Maui. The sounder at Brisbane is so much farther from the epicenter (at a distance of 11,200 km) than any of the U.S. stations that the magnitude of the effect could have been too small to detect on an ionogram.

No systematic search for ionospheric effects attributed to the Alaska earthquake has been made among ionograms for other locations than those already discussed.

SUMMARY

The main shock of the Prince William Sound, Alaska, earthquake of March 1964 produced detectable atmospheric and ionospheric disturbances of an oscillatory wave nature at large distances. The first of these to arrive at any location are relatively short-period (a few minutes down to a few tens of seconds). Analysis of the frequency dispersion of the microbarograph records and comparison of pressure amplitude and estimated ground displacement in the vicinity of the microbarograph, show that these waves are caused by more-or-less local ground motion. In a few instances, these waves were observed to be coming from locations that, for some reason, couple more effectively to the atmosphere. In general, the mechanism of resonant coupling between Rayleigh waves in the ground and acoustic waves in the atmosphere has not been identified. Coupling of more-or-less vertical ground motion to the atmosphere and subsequent upward propagation of the resulting acoustic waves to ionospheric altitudes is also a plausible mechanism for explaining the early-arriving disturbances seen on several phase-coherent high-frequency ionospheric propagation paths. No detailed dispersion analysis of these ionospheric records has been made comparable to that carried out on the microbarograph records. An interesting feature of the records is that the Doppler shifts observed are consistent with particle velocities comparable to the speed of sound at E- and F-region heights. Particle velocities this large are predicted by linearized hydrodynamic theory.

The next arrival in the sequence of events is a long-period ionospheric disturbance, which appears to propagate with a velocity approximately equal to that of a sound wave in the neutral atmosphere at F-region heights. No evidence of this wave is seen in the pressure records at ground level. In general, the microbarographs reporting any disturbance from the Alaska earthquake have a long-period cutoff of a few tens of minutes at most. The long-period oscillatory character of this portion of the ionospheric disturbance was seen most clearly on phase-coherent sounders and is similar to that seen after several nuclear detonations in the atmosphere. This type of response is predicted for a simple unbounded isothermal atmosphere excited by a point source. Additional theoretical work is required to determine whether more realistic models of the atmosphere and source, assumed to be ground motion near the epicenter, will provide a means of extracting useful estimates of this ground motion from a study of ionospheric records.

[506]

The next arrival in the sequence of disturbances is a dispersive wave train seen on microbarograph records (possibly the same mode or one closely related to the one seen on the ionospheric Doppler records). It is a pressure pulse approximately five times as large as the early-arriving ground-coupled air wave. The longest-period components (period greater than 3 minutes) have an apparent velocity of about 320 m/sec, whereas the shorter-period components have a somewhat smaller velocity consistent with the detailed mode analyses that have been made on air waves from nuclear detonations. The nature of the ground motion near the epicentral region required to produce the observed pressure has been studied but the results are not definitive.

REFERENCES

Albee, P. R., and D. P. Kanellakos, 1968. A spatial model of the F-Region ionospheric traveling disturbance following a low-altitude nuclear explosion. *Journal of Geophysical Research, 73* (February 1), 1039–1053.

Barry, G. H., L. J. Griffiths, and J. C. Taenzer, 1966. HF radio measurement of high-altitude acoustic waves from a ground level explosion. *Journal of Geophysical Research, 71* (September 1), 4178–4182.

Benioff, Hugo, and B. Gutenberg, 1939. Waves and currents recorded by electromagnetic barographs. *Bulletin of the American Meteorological Society, 20* (December), 421–426.

Benioff, Hugo, Maurice Ewing, and Frank Press, 1951. Sound waves in the atmosphere generated by a small earthquake. *Proceedings of the National Academy of Sciences, 37* (July), 600–603.

Bolt, Bruce A., 1964. Seismic air waves from the great 1964 Alaskan earthquake. *Nature, 202* (June 13), 1095–1096.

Bowman, G. G., and K. L. Shrestha, 1965. Atmospheric pressure waves from the Japanese earthquake of 16 June 1964. *Quarterly Journal of the Royal Meteorological Society, 91* (April), 223–224.

Cook, Richard K., 1965. Radiation of sound by earthquakes. Paper delivered before the 5th Congrés International d'Acoustique, Liège, Belgium, 7–14 September 1965.

Cook, Richard K., and Donald M. Baker, 1965. Ionospheric motions caused by Rayleigh waves (Abstract). *Transactions, American Geophysical Union, 46* (March), 55.

Davies, Kenneth, and Donald M. Baker, 1965. Ionospheric effects observed around the time of the Alaskan earthquake of March 28, 1964. *Journal of Geophysical Research, 70* (May 1), 2251–2253.

Donn, William L., and Maurice Ewing, 1962. Atmospheric waves from nuclear explosions. Part I, *Journal of Geophysical Research, 67* (May), 1855–1866. Part II, *Atmospheric Sciences, 19* (May), 264–273.

Donn, William L., and Eric S. Posmentier, 1964. Ground-coupled air waves from the great Alaskan earthquake. *Journal of Geophysical Research, 69* (December 15), 5357–5361.

Ewing, W. M., and F. Press, 1954. An investigation of mantle Rayleigh waves. *Bulletin of the Seismological Society of America, 44* (January), 127–147.

Ewing, W. M., W. S. Jardetzky, and F. Press, 1957. Elastic waves in layered media. New York: McGraw-Hill. p.230.

Kanellakos, D. P., 1967. Response of the ionosphere to the passage of acoustic-gravity waves generated by low-altitude nuclear explosions. *Journal of Geophysical Research, 72* (September 1), 4559–4576.

Leonard, Robert S., and R. A. Barnes, Jr., 1965. Observation of ionospheric disturbances following the Alaskan earthquake. *Journal of Geophysical Research, 70* (March 1), 1250–1253.

Mikumo, Takeshi, 1968. Atmospheric pressure waves and tectonic deformation associated with the Alaskan earthquake of March 28, 1964. *Journal of Geophysical Research, 73* (March 15), 2009–2025.

Parkin, Ernest J., 1969. Horizontal crustal movements determined from surveys after the Alaskan earthquake of 1964 *in* Volume III: The Prince William Sound, Alaska, earthquake of 1964 and aftershocks. Environmental Science Services Administration, U.S. Coast and Geodetic Survey. Washington: Government Printing Office. p.35–98. Also *in* The Great Alaska Earthquake of 1964: Seismology and Geodesy, NAS Pub.1602. Washington: National Academy of Sciences, 1972.

Pfeffer, R. L., and J. Zarichny, 1963. Acoustic-gravity wave propagation in an atmosphere with two sound channels. *Geofisica pura e applicata* (Milano), *55* (May–August), 175–199.

Plafker, George, 1965. Tectonic deformation associated with the 1964 Alaska earthquake. *Science, 148* (June 25), 1675–1687.

Press, Frank, and David Harkrider, 1962. Propagation of acoustic-gravity waves in the atmosphere. *Journal of Geophysical Research, 67* (September), 3889–3908.

Richter, Charles F., 1958. Elementary seismology. San Francisco: W. H. Freeman and Company. 768 p.

Row, Ronald V., 1966. Evidence of long-period acoustic-gravity waves launched into the *F* region by the Alaskan earthquake of March 28, 1964. *Journal of Geophysical Research, 71* (January 1), 343–345.

Row, Ronald V., 1967. Acoustic-gravity waves in the upper atmosphere due to a nuclear detonation and an earthquake. *Journal of Geophysical Research, 72* (March 1), 1599–1610.

Van Dorn, William G., 1965. Source mechanism of the tsunami of March 28, 1964 in Alaska. Proceedings of the Ninth Conference (1964) on Coastal Engineering (Chapter 10). New York: American Society of Civil Engineers. p.166–190. Also *in* The Great Alaska Earthquake of 1964: Oceanography and Coastal Engineering. NAS Pub.1605. Washington: National Academy of Sciences, in press.

Young, Jessie M., Gary E. Greene, and Vernon H. Goerke, 1965. Air waves from the Alaskan earthquake of 28 March 1964 (Abstract). *Acoustical Society of America Journal, 37* (June), 1208. Also *Transactions, American Geophysical Union, 46* (March), 55.

D. E. SMYLIE*
L. MANSINHA
UNIVERSITY OF WESTERN ONTARIO

Draws heavily on
Mansinha, L., and D. E. Smylie, *Journal of Geophysical Research*, Vol. 72, No. 18,
"Effect of Earthquakes on the Chandler Wobble and the Secular Polar Shift"

Chandler Wobble and Secular Motion of the Pole

ABSTRACT: With the fault parameters deduced from the near-field displacements for the Alaska earthquake of March 27, 1964 (AST), the far-field displacements are found from the elasticity theory of dislocations to be remarkably extensive. The reality of the extent of the displacement field is indicated by the significant permanent strain observed in Hawaii, some 4,500 km away. Contributions to the Chandler wobble excitation and the secular polar shift caused by these displacements are found to be several orders of magnitude larger than previously estimated. We consider here both vertical faults and faults with a range of dip angles, using the parameters of Press for a vertical fault and those of Savage and Hastie for a shallow dipping fault. A statistical estimate of the cumulative effect of all earthquakes is made, based on calculations for the several faults for which parameters are available in the literature. The conclusion is that earthquakes must be considered as serious contenders in attempts to explain the Chandler wobble excitation and the secular polar shift.

*Now with the University of British Columbia.

In applying the elasticity theory of dislocations to the study of faulting (Rochester, 1956; Kasahara, 1957; Chinnery, 1961), the fault parameters are determined from the near-field displacements. A significant advance in the subject was made by Press (1965, and this volume) when he used the theory to compute the far-field displacements, strains and tilts. He found these fields to be very extensive and argued that the several observations that had been made of permanent strains and tilts at great distances from major earthquakes were probably real. A striking example of such an observation was recorded for the Alaska earthquake of March 27, 1964, on a strain seismograph located in Hawaii (Press, 1965, and this volume): A permanent strain change of 10^{-8} was recorded at a distance close to 4,500 km. These results indicate that the scale of the redistribution of mass in the earth accompanying an earthquake has been grossly underestimated in the past (Munk and MacDonald, 1960, p. 163) and that the effect of earthquakes on the motion of the earth's pole of rotation must be reexamined.

The motion of the pole of rotation is usually decomposed into its periodic and aperiodic parts. The periodic part is called wobble and the aperiodic part secular polar motion. The wobble consists of two principal components: an annual line, which has been satisfactorily explained as resulting from the annual rearrangement of mass in the atmosphere; and a broadened spectral peak, centered at a period of about 14 months and named for Chandler, who first isolated it in 1891. The Chandler wobble represents the free or Eulerian nutation familiar in the dynamics of rigid bodies, corrected for the elastic and anelastic deformations of which the real earth is capable. The elastic deformations lengthen the period from 10 to 14 months, while the anelastic deformations probably account for the observed broadening of the spectral peak. Analysis of the data, with the Chandler wobble assumed to be the result of applying a random excitation to a linear damped oscillator, gives a root-mean-square amplitude of 0.14-second angular displacement of the rotation axis relative to the reference axis (0.01-second angular displacement of the axes is roughly equivalent to 1-ft polar displacement), a resonant period of 1.19 year, and a damping time between 10 and 30 years (Munk and MacDonald, 1960, Chap. 10). The secular polar motion amounts to about 0.003 sec/year (Markowitz and others, 1964).

The problem of identifying the source of the Chandler wobble excitation has been one of the more challenging problems of geophysics. It was most often ascribed to the seasonal redistribution of mass in the atmosphere until the power available at the Chandler frequency was shown to fall short of the observed excitation by one or two orders of magnitude (Munk and Hassan, 1961). Because of their lower velocities and smaller relative density changes, the effect of the oceans must be even smaller than that of the atmosphere (Munk and MacDonald, 1960, p. 127). The core is left as the only remaining fluid part of the earth. The small time scale suggests the fluid parts are prime suspects. Accordingly, the exchange of angular momentum between the shell and the core was examined (Rochester and Smylie, 1965). Electromagnetic coupling is dominant but fails by a factor of several hundred to explain the observed excitation.

This paper is an abbreviated account of a general study (Mansinha and Smylie, 1967) of the contribution of earthquakes to both the Chandler wobble excitation and the secular polar motion, with special reference to the Alaska earthquake of 1964. In the general study, Press' fault parameters for the Alaska earthquake were used. The fault was taken as a vertical dip-slip fault. Observational support of these theoretical calculations has since been found (Smylie and Mansinha, 1968; Mansinha and Smylie, 1970; Smylie and others, 1970). Savage and Hastie (1966, and this volume) have given an alternative interpretation, that of a shallow dipping dip-slip fault. We present, here, the displacement fields for dipping dip-slip faults as given by the elasticity theory of dislocations and use them to compute the effect of the Alaska earthquake in terms of Savage and Hastie's parameters.

DISPLACEMENT FIELDS

We require descriptions of entire displacement fields, whereas in most seismological applications only the surface fields are of interest. The fields for vertical strike-slip and dip-slip faults were given in Mansinha and Smylie (1967). Those for dip-slip faults of arbitrary dip can be obtained from the appropriate form of Volterra's theorem (Maruyama, 1964). The surface fields have already been derived by Savage and Hastie (personal communication). Volterra's theorem is conveniently expressed in terms of the displacement fields for a point force in a half-space listed by Press (1965, and this volume).

Figure 1 illustrates the fault orientation with respect to the fault coordinate system (z_1, z_2, z_3). The z_3 axis of this

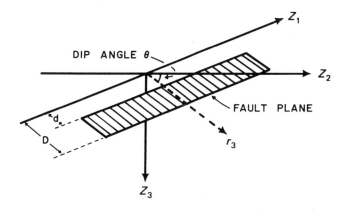

FIGURE 1 Orientation of the fault with respect to the fault coordinate system.

right-handed coordinate system is positive downward. The fault is taken to be rectangular, extending laterally over the range $-L \leqslant z_1 \leqslant L$. It strikes along the z_1 axis and the dip angle θ is measured from the positive z_2 axis. The coordinate r_3 lies in the fault plane and is positive down the dip. Thus, the surface of the fault extends over $d \leqslant r_3 \leqslant D$. It represents a uniform dislocation surface in the elastic half-space $z_3 \geqslant 0$.

Volterra's theorem gives the displacement field (u_1, u_2, u_3) as an integral over the fault surface. If U is the uniform dip-slip dislocation and if equal Lamé constants are assumed, the integral is

$$u_i = \frac{U}{12\pi} \iint \left[\left(\frac{\delta u_i^2}{\delta \zeta_2} - \frac{\delta u_i^3}{\delta \zeta_3} \right) \sin 2\theta - \left(\frac{\delta u_i^2}{\delta \zeta_3} + \frac{\delta u_i^3}{\delta \zeta_2} \right) \cos 2\theta \right] dS$$

where the quantities (u_1^j, u_2^j, u_3^j) are the displacement components produced by a single force in the half-space located at $(\zeta_1, \zeta_2, \zeta_3)$ and acting in the z_j direction. Writing

$$\zeta_2 = \zeta \cos \theta \qquad \zeta_3 = \zeta \sin \theta$$

and using the chain rule for partial derivatives, we obtain

$$u_i = \frac{U}{12\pi} \int_d^D \int_{-L}^L \left[2 \left(\sin \theta \frac{\delta u_i^2}{\delta \zeta} - \cos \theta \frac{\delta u_i^3}{\delta \zeta} \right) + \left(\frac{\delta u_i^3}{\delta \zeta_2} - \frac{\delta u_i^2}{\delta \zeta_3} \right) \right] d\zeta_1 d\zeta$$

When the integrations are carried out, we find

$$12\pi\,\frac{u_1}{U} = (z_2 - \zeta_2)\sin\theta\left[\frac{2}{R} + \frac{4}{Q} - \frac{4\zeta_3 z_3}{Q^3}\right.$$

$$\left. - \frac{3}{Q + z_3 + \zeta_3}\right] - \cos\theta\left[3\ln(Q + z_3 + \zeta_3)\right.$$

$$+ \frac{2(z_3 - \zeta_3)}{R} + \frac{4(z_3 - \zeta_3)}{Q} + \frac{4\zeta_3 z_3(z_3 + \zeta_3)}{Q^3}$$

$$+ \frac{3}{\cos\theta}\left[\ln(Q + z_3 + \zeta_3) - \sin\theta\,\ln(Q + q_3 + \zeta)\right]$$

$$\left. + 6z_3\left[\frac{\cos\theta}{Q} - \frac{q_2\sin\theta}{Q(Q + q_3 + \zeta)}\right]\right] \bigg\|\bigg\| \qquad (1)$$

$$12\pi\,\frac{u_2}{U} = \sin\theta\left[-\ln(R + z_1 - \zeta_1) + \ln(Q + z_1 - \zeta_1)\right.$$

$$+ \frac{4\zeta_3 z_3}{Q(Q + z_1 - \zeta_1)} + \frac{3(z_1 - \zeta_1)}{Q + z_3 + \zeta_3}$$

$$+ (z_2 - \zeta_2)^2\left\{\frac{2}{R(R + z_1 - \zeta_1)} + \frac{4}{Q(Q + z_1 - \zeta_1)}\right.$$

$$\left.\left. - 4\zeta_3 z_3\left(\frac{2Q + z_1 - \zeta_1}{Q^3(Q + z_1 - \zeta_1)^2}\right)\right\}\right]$$

$$- \cos\theta\left[(z_2 - \zeta_2)\left\{\frac{2(z_3 - \zeta_3)}{R(R + z_1 - \zeta_1)} + \frac{4(z_3 - \zeta_3)}{Q(Q + z_1 - \zeta_1)}\right.\right.$$

$$\left.\left. + 4\zeta_3 z_3(z_3 + \zeta_3)\left(\frac{2Q + z_1 - \zeta_1}{Q^3(Q + z_1 - \zeta_1)^2}\right)\right\}\right.$$

$$+ 6\tan^{-1}\left\{\frac{(z_1 - \zeta_1)(z_2 - \zeta_2)}{(h + z_3 + \zeta_3)(Q + h)}\right\}$$

$$- 3\tan^{-1}\left\{\frac{(z_1 - \zeta_1)(r_3 - \zeta)}{r_2 R}\right\}$$

$$\left. + 6\tan^{-1}\left\{\frac{(z_1 - \zeta_1)(q_3 + \zeta)}{q_2 Q}\right\}\right]$$

$$+ 6\left[\frac{1}{\cos\theta}\tan^{-1}\left\{\frac{(k - q_2\cos\theta)(Q - k) + (q_3 + \zeta)k\sin\theta}{(z_1 - \zeta_1)(q_3 + \zeta)\cos\theta}\right\}\right.$$

$$+ z_3\left\{\frac{(\sin^2\theta - \cos^2\theta)(q_3 + \zeta) + 2q_2\cos\theta\sin\theta}{Q(Q + z_1 - \zeta_1)}\right.$$

$$\left.\left. + \frac{(z_1 - \zeta_1)\sin^2\theta}{Q(Q + q_3 + \zeta)}\right\}\right] \bigg\|\bigg\| \qquad (2)$$

$$12\pi\,\frac{u_3}{U} = \sin\theta\left[(z_2 - \zeta_2)\left\{\frac{2(z_3 - \zeta_3)}{R(R + z_1 - \zeta_1)}\right.\right.$$

$$\left. + \frac{4(z_3 - \zeta_3)}{Q(Q + z_1 - \zeta_1)} - 4\zeta_3 z_3(z_3 + \zeta_3)\left(\frac{2Q + z_1 - \zeta_1}{Q^3(Q + z_1 - \zeta_1)^2}\right)\right\}$$

$$- 6\tan^{-1}\left\{\frac{(z_1 - \zeta_1)(z_2 - \zeta_2)}{(h + z_3 + \zeta_3)(Q + h)}\right\}$$

$$+ 3\tan^{-1}\left\{\frac{(z_1 - \zeta_1)(r_3 - \zeta)}{r_2 R}\right\}$$

$$\left. - 6\tan^{-1}\left\{\frac{(z_1 - \zeta_1)(q_3 + \zeta)}{q_2 Q}\right\}\right]$$

$$+ \cos\theta \left[\ln(R + z_1 - \zeta_1) - \ln(Q + z_1 - \zeta_1) \right.$$

$$- \frac{2(z_3 - \zeta_3)^2}{R(R + z_1 - \zeta_1)} - \frac{4\{(z_3 + \zeta_3)^2 - \zeta_3 z_3\}}{Q(Q + z_1 - \zeta_1)}$$

$$\left. - 4\zeta_3 z_3 (z_3 + \zeta_3)^2 \left(\frac{2Q + z_1 - \zeta_1}{Q^3(Q + z_1 - \zeta_1)^2} \right) \right]$$

$$+ 6 z_3 \left[\cos\theta \sin\theta \left\{ \frac{2(q_3 + \zeta)}{Q(Q + z_1 - \zeta_1)} + \frac{z_1 - \zeta_1}{Q(Q + q_3 + \zeta)} \right\} \right.$$

$$\left. \left. - q_2 \frac{(\sin^2\theta - \cos^2\theta)}{Q(Q + z_1 - \zeta_1)} \right] \right\| \qquad (3)$$

where

$$r_2 = z_2 \sin\theta - z_3 \cos\theta \qquad q_2 = z_2 \sin\theta + z_3 \cos\theta$$

$$r_3 = z_2 \cos\theta + z_3 \sin\theta \qquad q_3 = -z_2 \cos\theta + z_3 \sin\theta$$

$$R^2 = (z_1 - \zeta_1)^2 + (z_2 - \zeta_2)^2 + (z_3 - \zeta_3)^2$$

$$= (z_1 - \zeta_1)^2 + r_2^2 + (r_3 - \zeta)^2$$

$$Q^2 = (z_1 - \zeta_1)^2 + (z_2 - \zeta_2)^2 + (z_3 + \zeta_3)^2 = (z_1 - \zeta_1)^2 + h^2$$

$$= (z_1 - \zeta_1)^2 + q_2^2 + (q_3 + \zeta)^2 = k^2 + (q_3 + \zeta)^2$$

The symbol $\Big\|$ indicates that the limits of the double integration are to be substituted.

Examples of cross sections of these displacement fields are shown in Figures 2, 3 and 4.

POLAR MOTION DUE TO THE ALASKA EARTHQUAKE

Measurements of the position of the instantaneous pole of rotation are made in the geographic coordinate system (Munk

and MacDonald, 1960, p. 11-12). This system moves with the mean motion of the observatories. Taking the x_1 axis through the Greenwich meridian, the x_2 axis through long. 90°E, and the x_3 axis through the reference pole of rotation, with the origin at the center of mass of the earth, the geographic system rotates in space with angular velocity

$$\Omega(\vec{m} + \hat{e}_3)$$

where $\hat{e}_3$ is the unit vector in the x_3 direction and Ω (7.29 × 10⁻⁵ rad/sec) is the mean diurnal rotation rate of the earth. The components m_1, m_2 of the vector $\vec{m}$ represent the angular displacement of the instantaneous axis of rotation from the reference axis. Alternatively, when the proper conversion of units is made, they can be thought of as the Cartesian coordinates of the pole. Hence, it is often convenient to use the complex plane in describing polar motion, the position of the pole being described by the single complex function of time (t)

$$m(t) = m_1(t) + i\, m_2(t)$$

Under the assumption that the mass redistribution due to the jth earthquake of a sequence is completed in a time that is short compared to the Chandler wobble period, it is shown by Mansinha and Smylie (1967) that the resulting motion of the pole is given closely by

$$m(t) = \left(1 - e^{i\sigma_o(t - t_j)}\right) s_j \qquad (4)$$

$$s_j = \frac{\Omega}{A\sigma_o}(\Delta C_{13j} + i\,\Delta C_{23j}) \qquad (5)$$

where A is the equatorial moment of inertia of the earth (8.05 × 10³⁷ kg m²), and σ_o represents the Chandler angular frequency with real part ω (1.68 × 10⁻⁷ rad/sec). ΔC_{13j}, ΔC_{23j} are the changes in the products of inertia of the earth, while t_j is the time of occurrence of the quake. Damping of the wobble can be taken into account by giving σ_o the imaginary part $1/\tau$ where τ is the damping time ($\sim$ 20 years). The first term on the RHS (right-hand side) of Equation (4) represents a change in the position of the secular pole, whereas the second term gives the contribution to the Chandler wobble. Thus, there is negligible immediate change in the position of the pole of rotation, only a change in the path it follows with time. The effect of an earthquake on the polar path is illustrated in Figure 5.

The procedure used in calculating ΔC_{13j}, ΔC_{23j} from the displacement fields is described in detail in Mansinha and Smylie (1967). It consists of calculating the changes in the components of the inertia tensor of the earth in an epicentral coordinate system. This coordinate system is a geographic

[511]

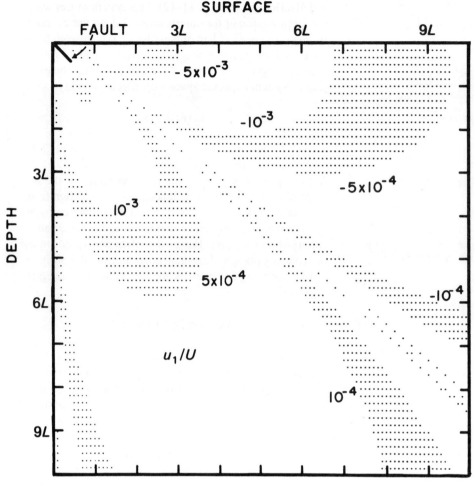

FIGURE 2 u_1 displacement component on a vertical plane. The fault dips at 135° and intersects the surface. Fault width is 0.5 L. The section shown is in the plane

$$z_1 = -z_2 \text{ for } 0 \leqslant z_1 \leqslant \frac{10 L}{\sqrt{2}}, \ 0 \geqslant z_2 \geqslant$$

$$-\frac{10 L}{\sqrt{2}}, \ 0 \leqslant z_3 \leqslant 10 L.$$

system that has been rotated so that the x_3 axis passes through the origin of the fault system, and the fault strikes in the x_1 direction. ΔC_{13j}, ΔC_{23j} can then be calculated from the changes in the components of the inertia tensor in the epicentral system by performing the appropriate similarity transformation.

The displacement fields, Equations (1) to (3), are those for a half-space and cannot be used directly. We have used the mapping

$$u_r = -u_3 \qquad\qquad z_1 = r\,\theta\,\cos\phi$$

$$u_\theta = u_1 \cos\phi - u_2 \sin\phi \qquad z_2 = -r\,\theta\,\sin\phi$$

$$u_\phi = -u_1 \sin\phi - u_2 \cos\phi \qquad z_3 = a - r$$

where r, θ, ϕ are spherical polar coordinates in the epicentral system and u_r, u_θ, u_ϕ are the corresponding components of the displacement field. a represents the radius of the earth. We believe this mapping underestimates the displacement

fields and, hence, we are developing a full spherical theory that takes into account the variation of density and elastic properties in the mantle and crust (Smylie and Mansinha, 1971).

Once the values of ΔC_{13j}, ΔC_{23j} are found, the polar shift s_j can be calculated from Equation (5). Table 1 shows the magnitude and direction obtained for the polar shift due to the Alaska earthquake of 1964, using the parameters of Press (1965, and this volume) for a vertical fault and those of Savage and Hastie (1966, and this volume) for a shallow dipping fault. Also shown are the results found using Savage and Hastie's parameters with a range of dip angles. The depth to the top of the fault surface is held constant. A mass density of 5,000 kg/m^3 was used throughout.

CUMULATIVE EFFECTS

At present, it does not seem that enough information is available to calculate the effect of individual earthquakes on the polar motion or to perform an addition to deduce the cumulative effect of them all. Therefore, we can only make a statistical estimate of their cumulative effect.

We have averaged the magnitude of the polar shift due to individual earthquakes over fault azimuth and epicentral latitude. Because of axial symmetry, variations in epicentral longitude have no effect on the magnitude of the polar shift (Mansinha and Smylie, 1967). The average polar shift S, for the several earthquakes for which fault parameters are available, is shown plotted against magnitude M in Figure 6. Curves for hypothetical strike-slip and dip-slip faults are also shown. The connection between fault length and magnitude (Tocher, 1958; Press and Brace, 1966) permits a similar relation to be made between average polar shift and magnitude. Fault widths of 0.5 L and slips of 5 m are assumed. Vertical faults intersecting the surface and with depth of burial $d = 0.1 L$ were studied. The results for the two cases do not differ sufficiently to show them as separate curves.

The motion of the pole due to all earthquakes is the summation of the RHS of Equation (4) over j. In making a statistical estimate of this sum, we observe that because of the time-varying phase of the Chandler wobble component and the assumed random time of occurrence of earthquakes, making an estimate of this part of the sum is equivalent to finding the result of a two-dimensional random-walk. All step directions will be equally probable and step lengths will be drawn from the appropriate distribution function. The part of the sum giving the motion of the secular pole is treated as a random-walk as well, in the knowledge that not all step directions are likely to be equally probable and we may obtain an underestimate.

The distribution function from which the step lengths are to be drawn can be found by combining the frequency-magnitude relation

$$\log_{10} N = A - b M$$

(where N is the number of earthquakes per year, with magnitude M and greater and A and b are constants) with a similar approximation to the information displayed in Figure 6

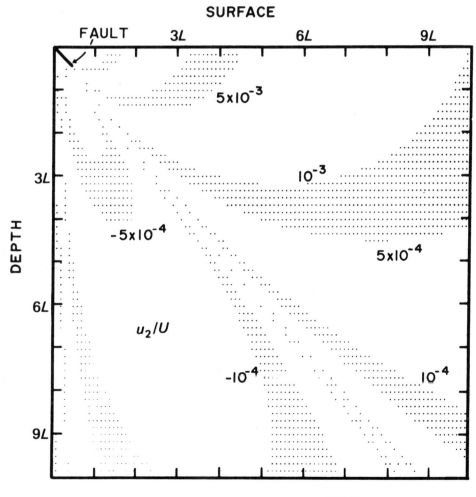

FIGURE 3 u_2 displacement component on a vertical plane. The fault dips at 135° and intersects the surface. Fault width is 0.5 L. The section shown is in the plane

$$z_1 = -z_2 \text{ for } 0 \leqslant z_1 \leqslant \frac{10 L}{\sqrt{2}}, 0 \geqslant z_2 \geqslant$$

$$\frac{-10 L}{\sqrt{2}}, 0 \leqslant z_3 \leqslant 10 L.$$

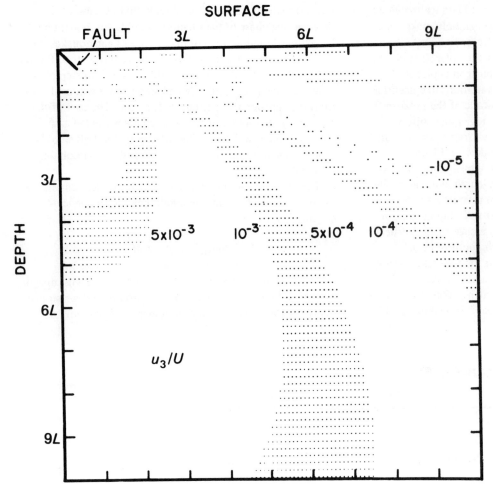

FIGURE 4 u_3 displacement component on a vertical plane. The fault dips at $135°$ and intersects the surface. Fault width is $0.5\ L$. The section shown is in the plane

$$z_1 = -z_2 \text{ for } 0 \leqslant z_1 \leqslant \frac{10\ L}{\sqrt{2}}, 0 \geqslant z_2 \geqslant$$

$$\frac{-10\ L}{\sqrt{2}}, 0 \leqslant z_3 \leqslant 10\ L.$$

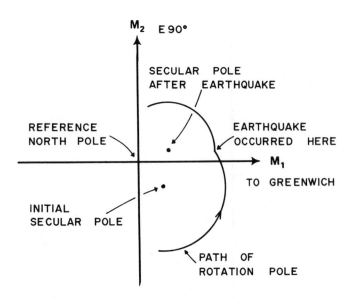

FIGURE 5 The effect of an earthquake on the polar motion.

$$\log_{10}\left(\frac{S}{S_1}\right) = c\ (M - M_1)$$

where S_1 is the average polar shift at magnitude M_1 and c is a constant. The curves shown in Figure 6 for the hypothetical strike-slip and dip-slip faults, for example, are closely approximated for $M_1 = 8.5$, by $c = 2.03$, $S_1 = 0.0069$ sec and $c = 3.04$, $S_1 = 0.0015$ sec, respectively.

If S_m is the average polar shift at the maximum magnitude considered, M_m, and S_o is that at the minimum, M_o, it is shown in Mansinha and Smylie (1967) that the root-mean-square estimate of Chandler wobble excitation is

$$S_m \qquad \sqrt{\frac{b}{2\,c - b}\left(\frac{S_o}{S_m}\right)^{b/c}\frac{N_o\,\tau}{2}} \qquad (6)$$

where N_o is the total number of earthquakes per year with

[514]

TABLE 1 Polar Shift Due to the Alaska Earthquake of March 27, 1964

Analysis by	Depth to Fault Top (km)	Fault Width (km)	Fault Half-Length (km)	Dip-Slip (m)	Fault Dip[a] (degrees)	Polar Shift (0.01 sec)	Longitude of Shift (degrees E)	Average Shift[b] (0.01 sec)
Press[c]	16	184	400	9	90	0.21	94	0.19
	16	117	400	6	90	0.06	94	0.05
Savage and Hastie[d]	20	200	300	10	171	0.32	43	0.34
	20	200	300	10	165	0.19	−90	0.55
	20	200	300	10	150	0.44	−90	0.96
	20	200	300	10	135	0.63	−90	1.11
	20	200	300	10	120	0.69	−90	0.97
	20	200	300	10	105	0.81	−90	0.58
	20	200	300	10	90	0.21	94	0.19

[a] Fault dip is varied over the quadrant in which that of Savage and Hastie (1966, and this volume) lies.
[b] Averaged over fault azimuth and epicentral latitude.
[c] 1965, and this volume.
[d] 1966, and this volume.

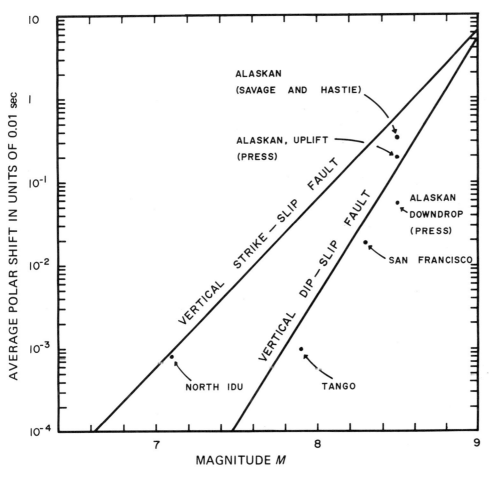

FIGURE 6 The dependence of the average polar shift on magnitude. The fault parameters used for the San Francisco, Tango, and North Idu earthquakes were those of Chinnery (1961).

magnitude greater than M_o. The most probable annual secular polar shift in the random-walk approximation is found to be $\sqrt{1/\tau}$ times the root-mean-square Chandler wobble excitation. Over a period of T years the most probable secular polar shift would be $\sqrt{T/\tau}$ times the Chandler wobble excitation.

Figure 7 shows the root-mean-square Chandler wobble excitation, computed from Equation (6), as a function of the parameters c and S_1. M_1 is taken as 8.5, τ as 20 years, b equal to unity, M_o as 7.0, M_m as 8.9, and N_o equal to 23.5/years. N_o was determined from a count of large shallow and intermediate depth shocks for the period 1918–1955 tabulated by Richter (1958).

DISCUSSION

It is evident that values of the parameters c and S_1 can be chosen that are both representative of the data in Figure 6 and in agreement with the hypothesis that earthquakes excite the Chandler wobble.

From Table 1, it appears that the average polar shift for dipping dip-slip faults can vary by a factor of five with dip angle, the maximum occurring at a dip of 45° with minima for shallow dipping and vertical faults. This variation could result in a larger estimate of Chandler wobble excitation if the true dips of faults were to be considered.

For the 44-year period 1903–1947, the most probable annual secular polar shift is found to be 0.005 sec/year, providing we assume the full excitation of the Chandler wobble to be due to earthquakes. This figure compares with the observed value of 0.003 sec/year. No account is taken of the relaxation with time of the displacement fields.

Our conclusion is that both the Chandler wobble excitation and the secular polar shift could be caused by earthquakes. A search of the observational data for correlations is under way. [*Editorial Note:* A correlation was subsequently found and reported in Smylie and Mansinha (1968).]

ACKNOWLEDGMENT

We are both grateful to the National Research Council of Canada for financial support of our research and computations.

REFERENCES

Chinnery, M. A., 1961. The deformation of the ground around surface faults. *Bulletin of the Seismological Society of America*, 51 (July), 355–372.

Kasahara, K., 1957. The nature of seismic origins as inferred from seismological and geodetic observations. *Bulletin of the Earthquake Research Institute*, University of Tokyo, 35 (September), 473–532.

Mansinha, L., and D. E. Smylie, 1967. Effect of earthquakes on the Chandler wobble and the secular polar shift. *Journal of Geophysical Research*, 72 (September 15), 4731–4743.

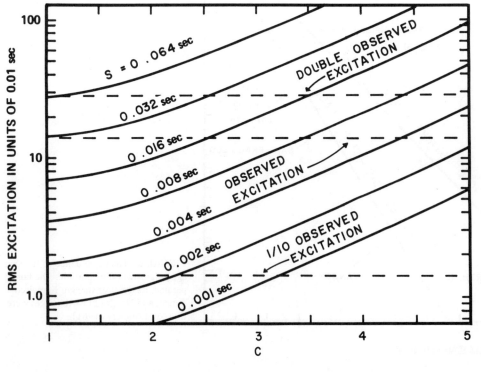

FIGURE 7   The dependence of the root-mean-square Chandler wobble excitation on the parameters c and S_1.

Mansinha, L., and D. E. Smylie, 1970. Seismic contribution to the excitation of the Chandler wobble *in* Earthquake displacement fields and the rotation of the earth. Mansinha, L., D. E. Smylie, and A. E. Beck, editors. Dordrecht [Netherlands]: D. Reidel. p. 122-135.

Markowitz, W., N. Stoyko, and E. Fedorov, 1964. Longitude and latitude *in* Research in geophysics. H. Odishaw, Editor. Volume 2. Cambridge [Massachusetts]: MIT Press. p. 149-162.

Maruyama, T., 1964. Statical elastic dislocations in an infinite and semi-infinite medium. *Bulletin of the Earthquake Research Institute*, University of Tokyo, 42 (June), 289-368.

Munk, W. H., and E. S. M. Hassan, 1961. Atmospheric excitation of the earth's wobble. *Geophysical Journal of the Royal Astronomical Society of London*, 4 (No. 1), 339-358.

Munk, W. H., and G. J. F. MacDonald, 1960. The rotation of the earth. London: Cambridge University Press. 323 p.

Press, Frank, 1965. Displacements, strains, and tilts at teleseismic distances. *Journal of Geophysical Research*, 70 (May 15), 2395-2412. Also *in* The Great Alaska Earthquake of 1964: Seismology and Geodesy. NAS Pub. 1602. Washington: National Academy of Sciences, 1972.

Press, Frank, and W. F. Brace, 1966. Earthquake prediction: Recent developments reopen the question of the predictability of earthquakes. *Science*, 152 (June 17), 1575-1584.

Richter, Charles F., 1958. Elementary seismology. San Francisco: W. H. Freeman and Company. 768 p.

Rochester, M. G., 1956. The application of dislocation theory to fracture of the earth's crust (M.A. thesis). Toronto [Canada]: University of Toronto.

Rochester, M. G., and D. E. Smylie, 1965. Geomagnetic core-mantle coupling and the Chandler wobble. *Geophysical Journal of the Royal Astronomical Society of London*, 10 (No. 2 and 3), 289-315.

Savage, J. C., and L. M. Hastie, 1966. Surface deformation associated with dip-slip faulting. *Journal of Geophysical Research*, 71 (October 15), 4897-4904. Also *in* The Great Alaska Earthquake of 1964: Seismology and Geodesy. NAS Pub. 1602. Washington: National Academy of Sciences, 1972.

Smylie, D. E., G. K. C. Clarke, and L. Mansinha, 1970. Deconvolution of the pole path *in* Earthquake displacement fields and the rotation of the earth. L. Mansinha, D. E. Smylie, and A. E. Beck, editors. Dordrecht [Netherlands]: D. Reidel. p. 99-112.

Smylie, D. E., and L. Mansinha, 1968. Earthquakes and the observed motion of the rotation pole. *Journal of Geophysical Research*, 73 (December 15), 7661-7673.

Smylie, D. E., and L. Mansinha, 1971. The elasticity theory of dislocations in real earth models and changes in the rotation of the earth. *The Geophysical Journal of the Royal Astronomical Society*, 23 (August), 329-354.

Tocher, Don, 1958. Earthquake energy and ground breakage. *Bulletin of the Seismological Society of America*, 48 (April), 147-153.

GEORGE W. MOORE

U.S. GEOLOGICAL SURVEY

Reprinted with minor changes from
Nature, Vol. 203, No. 4944, "Magnetic Disturbances Preceding the
1964 Alaska Earthquake"

Magnetic Disturbances Preceding the Earthquake

MAGNETIC DISTURBANCES PRECEDING THE 1964 ALASKA EARTHQUAKE

Through a fortunate circumstance, a recording magnetometer was operating in the city of Kodiak, 30 km northwest of the surface of a fault zone along which movement occurred at the time when the earthquake occurred in Alaska on March 27, 1964. Fortunately, too, the instrument was on such high ground that it was not reached by the subsequent seismic sea wave which virtually destroyed the city. The magnetometer recorded the fact that the largest of several magnetic disturbances briefly increased the intensity of the Earth's magnetic field by 100 γ at Kodiak, 1 h 6 min before the earthquake (Fig. 1).

The magnetometer had been installed for the Superior Oil Co. and the Pan American Petroleum Corp. by Fairchild Aerial Surveys to serve as a ground monitor for an airborne magnetic survey being made of the region. The instrument is a Gulf flux-gate magnetometer, which records the total magnetic field intensity on an Esterline Angus recorder. The sensing element had been installed on the grounds of the Bay Shore Motel in Kodiak.

The record was stopped at the beginning of the earthquake by a massive short circuit in the city power system. Automatic equipment in the Kodiak power plant made four unsuccessful attempts, in a period of about 3 sec, to reclose the circuits, and then cut off the power indefinitely.[1] Because Fairchild lost their aeroplane and one member of their team in the disaster, the magnetometer was disconnected and put in storage before the city power was turned on again. The trace that follows the record of the power failure on Fig. 1 was made approximately a month later, when the survey was resumed.

An electric clock which ran on city power in the room with the recorder stopped at 1739 Alaska Standard Time,

ABSTRACT: Positive magnetic disturbances recorded on a megnetometer in Kodiak just over an hour before the 1964 Alaska earthquake suggest that magnetic monitoring may provide a means of predicting major earthquakes in time to save lives and property.

[518]

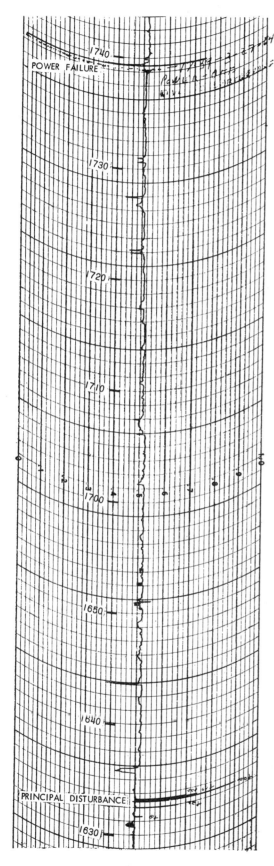

March 27, 1964. This time reference has an estimated precision of ± 1 min (ref. 2), and according to it, the principal magnetic event occurred at 1633 A.S.T. The official time for the earthquake at its focus, 440 km to the northeast, was 1736.2 A.S.T. (0336.2 G.M.T., March 28).

The chart shows many small negative magnetic disturbances that were caused by automobiles passing on a road about 15 m south-east of the sensing element. The positive disturbances, however, which are believed to have been associated with the earthquake, began at 1632 A.S.T. with three sharp events extending over a period of about a minute, and culminated in a positive disturbance equal to 100 γ. This was immediately followed by two somewhat smaller events, and a still smaller one occurred 18 min later. No other sharp positive disturbances were found on about a month of record.

One possibility is that the magnetic events which preceded the Alaska earthquake resulted from piezomagnetic effects of rocks undergoing a change in stress.[3] Why such abrupt disturbances occurred in advance of the earthquake is not known; but a causal relation is indicated by the fact that Breiner[4] has recently reported similar positive magnetic disturbances prior to minor earthquakes in Nevada and California. These observations, taken together, suggest that magnetic monitoring may provide a means of predicting a major earthquake in time to save lives and property.

John W. Davidson, of the Superior Oil Co., contributed to this report in helpful discussions. I thank the Superior Oil Co. for its co-operation, the Pan American Petroleum Corp., and the Fairchild Aerial Surveys in permitting the release of the information. Publication was authorized by the Director, U.S. Geological Survey.[5]

[1] Alexander, H., Kodiak Electric Assoc. (personal communication, 1964).

[2] Ashby, W. O. Fairchild Aerial Surveys (personal communication, 1964).

[3] Stacey, F. D., *Nature,* 200, 1083 (1963).

[4] Breiner, S., *Nature,* 202, 790 (1964).

[5] See also Grantz, A., Plafker, G., and Kachadoorian, R., *Alaska's Good Friday Earthquake, March 27, 1964: a Preliminary Geologic Evaluation* (U.S. Geol. Survey, Circ. 491, Washington, D.C., 1964).

Fig. 1   Record of the positive magnetic disturbances which preceded the Alaska earthquake. Heavy time divisions equal 7.6 min. Time is Alaska Standard Time, March 27, 1964. Full scale for the magnetic intensity, which increases toward the right, is 250 gammas.

JOAN HIRSHBERG
STANFORD UNIVERSITY
ROBERT G. CURRIE*
VARIAN ASSOCIATES
SHELDON BREINER†
STANFORD UNIVERSITY

Reprinted with minor changes from
Earth and Planetary Science Letters 3,
"Long Period Geomagnetic Fluctuations after the 1964 Alaskan Earthquake"

Long-Period Geomagnetic Fluctuations after the Earthquake

After the 1960 Chilean earthquake, Winch, Bolt and Slaucitjs reported [1] that periodic magnetic variations were observed having the same frequencies as the two lowest frequency torsional modes of the earth's free oscillations. The suggestion was made that the earth's oscillations might have induced the magnetic variations. The Alaskan earthquake of 28 March 1964 also excited the earth's eigenvibrations. However, the only power spectrum of the magnetic field reported for the period after the Alaskan earthquake failed to show any significant peaks [2]. In this note, we present power spectra of the post-quake geomagnetic field that do show lines having frequencies of several of the gravest torsional eigenmodes of the earth.

At the time of the Alaskan earthquake, a Varian Associate rubidium vapor magnetometer was recording the total magnetic field intensity at the Lamont Geological Observatory's magnetic station in Lebanon, New Jersey. Power spectra of this field were calculated in the following manner. The analogue record was digitized to within an accuracy of 0.1 gamma at 2.5 minute intervals, and an $N = 50$ weight high-pass or trend elimination filter [3] was then applied to 32-hour segments of the record. This filter attenuates diurnal period amplitudes by 99%. This prevents power leaking [4] from the intense diurnal variation and contaminating the higher frequency continuum. The amplitude response of the filter is within 0.5% of unity for the periods reported in this note. After filtering, high resolution power spectra were computed [4] with 200 lags (6.7 degrees of freedom). Decreasing

the number of lags merely broadened the line spectra; hence, although the degrees of freedom for the spectra presented are relatively low, the line spectra are stable.

In order to compare the immediate postquake spectra with spectra that were not influenced by the earth's oscillations, 8 non-quake records were analyzed. These records were chosen to have the same magnetic character as the postquake period, i.e., quiet magnetic conditions. The period immediately preceding the earthquake is typical of many of these non-quake spectra and is shown in fig. 1. Note that it contains lines of dubious statistical significance and bands centered at 20 and 28 minutes. Other non-quake spectra exhibited bands and lines of greater statistical significance. Hence we find that in the absence of any great seismic activity it is not unusual to find significant power in the geomagnetic field at these frequencies. This agrees with the observations of Horton and Hoffman [5] and Herron [6].

Fig. 2 shows the spectrum of the 32-hour record immediately following the earthquake. Note the low

---

*Now with the University of California, Berkeley.
†Now with GeoMetrics.

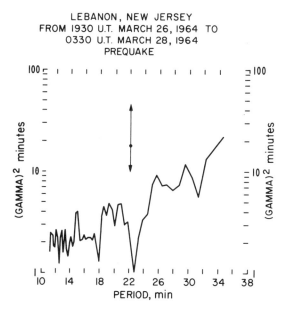

Fig. 1. Power spectrum of the total geomagnetic field for the 32 hours immediately preceding the Alaskan earthquake. An arrow indicating the 80% confidence level is shown in this and the other figures.

power levels relative to fig. 1. The periods of the free oscillations of the earth [7] are given for comparison. Torsional modes, labeled $_nT_l$, are modes in which the particle motions are tangential to the earth's surface The spheroidal modes, $_nS_l$, involve both tangential and radial motion. The integer n denotes the number of modes along a radius of the earth while l describes the number of lines of modal latitude on the surface of the earth. The period range of the $_0T_2$ (lowest frequency torsional) mode is not shown in any of our figures because no line appeared above the continuum spectrum at that period. The $_0T_2$ mode was not reported on the seismic records after the Alaskan earthquake either [8].

Fig. 3 shows the spectrum for the record beginning approximately 20.5 hours after the quake. The power levels have increased relative to fig. 2. In fig. 3, the lower spectrum is compared to the spheroidal modes alone and there is no statistically significant agreement. The upper line shows this same spectrum compared to the torsional modes of the earth. In this case the agree-

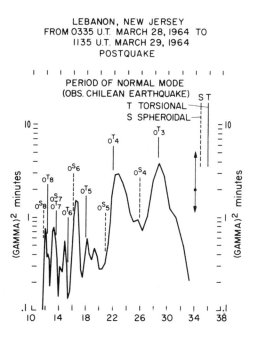

Fig. 2. Power spectrum of the geomagnetic field for the 32 hours immediately after the Alaskan earthquake. When the heavy dotted centroid of the 80% confidence level is placed on the peaks of the two lowest frequency lines they are above the continuum. The frequencies of oscillation of the earth are shown for comparison.

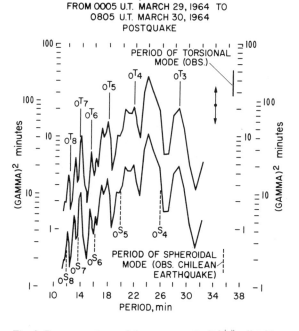

Fig. 3. Power spectrum of the geomagnetic field for the 32 hour record beginning 20.5 hours after the quake. The lower curve is the spectrum compared with the frequencies of the spheroidal modes of the earth's vibration. There is no significant agreement. The upper curve shows the same spectrum compared to the torsional modes of the earth. In this case the correspondence is suggestive of a relationship.

[521]

ment is better than would be expected if there were no relationship. The strong line near 25 minutes, not corresponding to an eigenoscillation, may be accounted for by noting again that it is not unusual for spectra to display lines even during non-quake times.

The above results are in contrast to the spectra of Alaskan post-quake data previously given by Stacey and Westcott [2] which they interpreted as showing no significant peaks. This lack of lines and bands may be due to severe 'leakage' problems where power associated with the intense low frequency diurnal variation (which they state [2] was not removed prior to their spectrum analysis) leaked across the spectrum and covered up any lines that might have been present [9] *.

It has been found then, that after both the 1960 Chilean [1] and 1964 Alaskan earthquakes, spectra of magnetic records show peaks of the same periods as grave torsional oscillations. Several possible mechanisms that might cause such variations to be induced by the earth's oscillations have been reviewed [2] and none appeared promising. Of course the results reported here may be fortuitous owing to the occurrence of magnetic variations in this frequency range even during non-quake periods. However, the results suggest that further studies of mechanisms may be fruitful and that magnetic spectra should continue to be computed at times when the earth is in oscillation.

---

* The fact that Stacey and Westcott's [2] 65 lag spectrum was systematically higher than their 130 lag spectrum for the same record supports the 'leakage' viewpoint. If the power in the first few lowest frequency estimates of an unsmoothed spectrum is sufficiently high relative to the rest of the spectrum, and if the unsmoothed spectrum is computed for m and $2m$ lags, then, when the estimates are convolved with the Tukey-Hanning window weights (0.25, 0.5, 0.25) as in ref. [2], the m lag spectrum will be systematically higher than the $2m$ lag spectrum. In a different context, examples of severe 'leakage' problems from both geophysical and artificially generated times series have been published [9, 10].

ACKNOWLEDGEMENTS

We wish to thank T. J. Herron of Lamont Geological Observatory for supplying the data. One of us (J.H.) was at Lamont when this work began and another (R.G.C.) is a NAS-NRC Research Associate with Ames Research Center. This work was partially supported at Lamont under NSG 445-63.

REFERENCES

[1] D. E. Winch, B. A. Bolt and L. Slaucitjs, Geomagnetic fluctuations with the frequencies of the torsional oscillations of the earth, J. Geophys. Res. 68 (1963) 2685.

[2] F. D. Stacey and P. Westcott, The record of a vector proton magnetometer after the March 1964 Alaskan earthquake, J. Geophys. Res. 70 (1965) 3321.

[3] R. G. Currie, Magnetic shielding properties of the earth's mantle, J. Geophys. Res. 72 (1967) 2623.

[4] R. B. Blackman and J. W. Tukey, The Measurement of Power Spectra (Dover, New York, 1959).

[5] C. W. Horton and A. A. J. Hoffman, Power spectrum analysis of the telluric field at Tbilisi, USSR for periods from 2.4 to 60 minutes, J. Geophys. Res. 67 (1962) 3369.

[6] T. J. Herron, An average geomagnetic power spectrum for the period range 4.5 to 12,900 seconds, J. Geophys. Res. 72 (1967) 759.

[7] B. A. Bolt, Recent information of the earth's interior from studies of mantle waves and eigenvibrations, Phys. Chem. Earth 5 (1964) 55.

[8] S. W. Smith, Free oscillations excited by the Alaskan earthquake, J. Geophys. Res. 71 (1966) 1183.

[9] C. W. F. Granger and M. Hatanaka, Spectral Analysis of Economic Time Series (Princeton University Press, Princeton, 1964).

[10] R. G. Currie, The geomagnetic spectrum – 40 days to 5.5 years, J. Geophys. Res. 71 (1966) 4579.

F. D. STACEY*
P. WESTCOTT

METEOROLOGICAL OFFICE RESEARCH UNIT

CAMBRIDGE, ENGLAND

Reprinted with minor changes from
Journal of Geophysical Research, Vol. 70, No. 14,
"The Record of a Vector Proton Magnetometer
after the March 1964 Alaskan Earthquake"

The Record of a Vector Proton Magnetometer after the Earthquake

Abstract. Power spectrums of the data from a digitally recording, vector proton-precession magnetometer, which was operating at the time of the March 1964 Alaskan earthquake, give no evidence of magnetic fluctuations with frequencies of torsional modes in the earth's free oscillation spectrum. The absence of spectral peaks and the low spectral levels make it evident that if magnetic oscillations were present their amplitudes could not have exceeded 0.02 γ in total field or 0.05 γ in horizontal field. This is in conflict with an earlier analysis of conventional magnetic data after the 1960 Chilean earthquake. It seems possible that the earlier observations were purely fortuitous, but the analysis of digital magnetometer data after the next large earthquake is necessary to confirm our conclusion. The proton magnetometer data are more precise and more suitable for digital processing than variometer records, as reflected by the fact that our general spectral levels are ten times smaller than those of the earlier work. A survey of mechanisms by which such oscillations could have been induced shows them to be quite inadequate.

Introduction. The first of three digitally recording, vector proton-precession magnetometers, now in use by the Meteorological Office, was set up at Cardington, Bedfordshire (52°6′N, 0°25′W), for an experimental period early in 1964 and was operating at the time of the March 28 earthquake in Alaska. The data obtained from it allowed us to make an objective appraisal of the possibility that magnetic fluctuations accompany torsional oscillations of the earth. Evidence of magnetic fluctuations with periods of torsional oscillations was obtained by *Winch et al.* [1963] from magnetic variometer records after the 1960 Chilean earthquake. Unlike variometers, proton magnetometers are unaffected by slight mechanical movements, and this we believe to be essential to a satisfactory search for free oscillation periods. A further advantage is that the data output of our proton magnetometers is in the form of punched paper tape, which is fed directly into a digital computer for processing, making an analysis of this kind both convenient and objective.

The instrumental details are very similar to the proposal by *Alldredge* [1960] for a station magnetometer. We favored a proton detector rather than rubidium, as now in use by *Alldredge and Saldukas* [1964], but the principle is otherwise the same. Readings are taken in cycles of six every 36 seconds; in each cycle the total field F is recorded twice, at an interval of 18 seconds, and the four additional readings are of F plus biasing fields in the plane normal to F. Conventional components of the earth's field (H, D, Z) are computed at intervals of 36 seconds from these readings. For this purpose readings taken with biased fields are interpolated between cycles to approximate the ideal requirement that all the readings in a particular cycle be taken simultaneously instead of in sequence.

Power spectrums. In all our data processing we use a preliminary numerical 'comb' to eliminate the occasional spurious reading which can be produced by a proton magnetometer. Individual readings which depart grossly from the ones (with the same bias) before and after it are eliminated and a zero value substituted. For the purpose of the power spectrum analyses reported here 3-minute (5-value) averages were taken of total field F and horizontal field H, giving 480 data points for each in 24 hours. The computer was programmed to take an average of the four valid readings when a zero value appeared, so that the averaged data points were

* Now at the Physics Department, University of Queensland, Brisbane, Australia.

unaffected by occasional spurious readings. Since the primary values of F are accurate to about 0.5 γ and the derived values of H to about 1 γ, the 3-minute averages are at least as good as this.

The data interval which we have used was 1000 UT March 28 to 1000 UT on March 29, which was, fortunately, a magnetically quiet time. (The earthquake occurred at 0336 UT on March 28.) It was not possible to improve the analyses by extending the record because a period of increasing magnetic disturbance followed on March 29. We preferred not to use the data before 1000 UT because an accident in tape-changing at that time caused some loss of data and spoiled the sequence. No attempt was made to pre-whiten the data or to remove the diurnal variation.

The power spectrums shown in Figure 1 were obtained by the method of *Blackman and Tukey* [1959]. All three spectrums are very much smoother than those reported by *Winch et al.* [1963], and their general spectral levels in the frequency range of interest (0.02 to 0.05 cpm) are lower by a factor 10 to 100. The 65-lag analyses were applied first and were chosen to give a frequency spacing similar to that of Winch et al. When they were plotted, we were suspicious that spectral peaks did correspond roughly to the $_0T_2$, $_0T_3$, and $_0T_4$ modes, although similar peaks occurred at all points in the spectrums and no statistical significance could be claimed for them. The 130-lag total field analysis halved the spacing of spectral points and showed clearly that no significant spectral peaks are present. It is conceivable that mechanical tilting of the biasing coils could have introduced an apparent oscillation in the horizontal field data, but the analysis shows no evidence of such an oscillation. The total field data could not have been influenced by mechanical effects.

Our negative result does not constitute conclusive proof that free oscillation periods are absent in all magnetic data, because the position of our station could conceivably have been unfavorable to the observation of them. However, D. E. Winch (private communication) reports that free oscillation periods did not appear in variometer records at Port Moresby or Witteveen after the Alaskan earthquake. The most plausible explanation for their appearance after the Chilean earthquake is that there happened

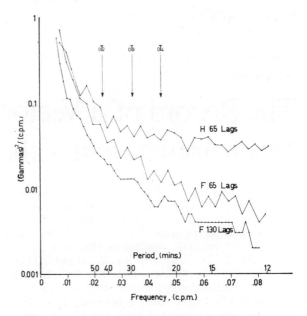

Fig. 1. Power spectrums of total field (F) and horizontal field (H) at Cardington for 24 hours after the Alaska earthquake. Values of the field (480 data points) are averaged over 3-minute periods.

to be a magnetic fluctuation with this form, purely fortuitously.

Mechanisms for the generation of magnetic oscillations. The electrical conductivity of the lower mantle precludes the possibility of magnetic fluctuations with periods less than an hour reaching the surface from depths greater than 1000 km [*McDonald*, 1957; *Tozer*, 1959]. On this time scale the surface field can be regarded as anchored in the mantle at a depth not greater than about 700 km. Torsional oscillations must involve a relative movement between the earth's surface and the mantle at this depth, thus causing the surface to move through the field. The maximum magnitude of the consequent magnetic field change at any point on the surface can be estimated from the maximum field gradient apparent on a large-scale map of the geomagnetic field (about 1 γ per 100 m). Only the broad features of the field are relevant to this consideration because local features arise in the crust and therefore move with it. Reports of observations of free oscillations contain very little information on amplitudes, but from the noise figure quoted by *Ness et al.* [1961] for their tidal gravimeter data it appears improbable that movements of the earth's surface with respect to the mantle at about 700 km could exceed 10^{-5} cm as a result of any mode of free oscillation. The corresponding magnetic fluctuation would be 10^{-9} γ. This cannot be so gross an underestimate that the fluctuation would actually be observable. The maximum magnetic oscillation generated by the earth tide would be about 10^{-4} γ.

Irregularities in upper mantle conductivity would modify the magnetic disturbance pattern by oscillating in the main field and thereby generating circulating currents within themselves. However, with the assumed amplitude of oscillation, the oscillatory fields so generated could not exceed 10^{-8} to 10^{-9} γ

Piezomagnetic effects in the crust are similarly too small by a large factor. A stress of σ kg/cm^2 changes the magnetization I of rocks by about $\Delta I = 10^{-4}$ σ I [$Stacey$, 1963a, b] and the corresponding field change at the surface can only exceed $\Delta H = 10^{-3}$ σ I at the corners of a highly angular ore body. Rocks in which $I > 0.1$ emu are very rare, so that the maximum allowable piezomagnetically induced fluctuation in H is $\Delta H = 10^{-4}$ σ oe. For the solid tide, $\sigma \approx 10^{-2}$ kg/cm^2 and the corresponding ΔH which could be observed close to a highly magnetic body of rock is 0.1 γ. Since the stress accompanying free oscillations is smaller by a factor of the order 10^5, its piezomagnetic effect is negligible.

The viscous coupling of the atmosphere to the earth is problematical, but even supposing that the ionosphere followed free oscillations with full amplitude its peak velocity relative to the field lines would be less than 10^{-7} cm/sec, and, according to the dynamo theory of geomagnetic diurnal variation, this would induce a field of strength less than 10^{-9} γ at the surface.

Acknowledgment. This paper is submitted for publication by permission of the Director-General of the Meteorological Office.

References

Alldredge, L. R., A proposed automatic standard magnetic observatory, *J. Geophys. Res., 65,* 3777–3786, 1960.

Alldredge, L. R., and I. Saldukas, An automated standard magnetic observatory, *J. Geophys. Res., 69,* 1963–1970, 1964.

Blackman, R. B., and J. W. Tukey, *The Measurement of Power Spectra from the Point of View of Communications Engineering,* Dover, New York, 1959.

McDonald, K. L., Penetration of the geomagnetic secular field through a mantle with variable conductivity, *J. Geophys. Res., 62,* 117–141, 1957.

Ness, N. F., J. C. Harrison, and L. B. Slichter, Observations of the free oscillations of the earth, *J. Geophys. Res., 66,* 621–629, 1961.

Stacey, F. D., The physical theory of rock magnetism, *Advan. Phys., 12,* 45–133, 1963a.

Stacey, F. D., Seismomagnetic effect and the possibility of forecasting earthquakes, *Nature, 200,* 1083–1085, 1963b.

Tozer, D. C., The electrical properties of the earth's interior, *Phys. Chem. Earth, 3,* 414–436, 1959.

Winch, D. E., B. A., Bolt, and L. Slaucitajs, Geomagnetic fluctuations with the frequencies of torsional oscillations of the earth, *J. Geophys. Res., 68,* 2685–2693, 1963.

(Manuscript received January 25, 1965; revised March 10, 1965.)

ALI A. NOWROOZI*

UNIVERSITY OF CALIFORNIA, BERKELEY

Reprinted from
Journal of Geophysical Research, Vol. 70, No. 20,
"Eigenvibrations of the Earth after the Alaskan Earthquake"

Eigenvibrations of the Earth after the Earthquake

Abstract. Spectrums of the free oscillations of the earth were computed from long-period pendulum seismograph recordings obtained at the Berkeley and Oroville seismographic stations after the Alaskan earthquake of March 28, 1964. Resolution was obtained for modal orders between $l = 2$ and $l = 29$. Longitudinal and transverse components of the ground motion at Oroville were synthesized by appropriate vector addition of the horizontal-component seismograms. Harmonic analysis of the separated components yielded spectrums of the torsional and spheroidal oscillations. A striking result was the appearance of the $_0S_{12}$ mode in the spectrum of the longitudinal motion and its absence in the spectrum of the vertical motion. The Oroville station was therefore near a nodal line for the vertical component of the $_0S_{12}$ mode. The variations of the spherical amplitudes at both the Berkeley and Oroville stations indicated an azimuthal order number $m = 0$. The average vertical ground amplitudes of several modes were estimated. Between 15 and 20 peaks on each spectrum were significant at the 95% confidence level. The measured eigenfrequencies are in close agreement with similar measurements from other earthquakes. Comparison with computed periods for four earth models showed that the Gutenberg–Bullen A model gives the most satisfactory agreement with the observations.

Introduction. An important series of eigenvibrations of the earth was measured after the Chilean earthquake of May 1960 [*Benioff et al.*, 1961; *Ness et al.*, 1961; *Connes et al.*, 1962; *Alsop et al.*, 1961; *Bogert*, 1961; *Bolt*, 1963a; *Alsop*, 1964]. Additional series of observations were reported after the Kurile Islands earthquake of October 1963 [*Alsop*, 1964; *Blum et al.*, 1964]. *Bolt* [1963b] and *Press* [1964] have surveyed the available observational data of the Chilean earthquake and critically reviewed the inferences drawn from them.

Measurements of the free oscillations of the earth after the Alaskan earthquake of 03h 36m 13s UT, March 28, 1964, are discussed in this paper. Novel features of these measurements include the determination of an azimuthal order number m and the amplitude variations of the spectrums in terms of the pattern of nodal lines.

Materials used. Seismograms from the long-period instruments located at the Berkeley and Oroville seismographic stations in northern California were used in the analysis. The instruments, the free period of the galvanometers T_g, and the free period of the seismometers T_0, are listed in Table 1. The horizontal-component seismograph, called 'ultra-long period,' has a

Press-Ewing seismometer coupled to a 300-sec galvanometer designed by F. Lehner. Berkeley and Oroville have distances of 28.1° and 26.8°, respectively, from the preliminary USCGS location of 61.1°N, 147.6°W, for the Alaskan earthquake epicenter. The azimuths of Berkeley and Oroville to this epicenter are 333.8° and 331.9°, respectively.

The amplitude at each sampling point on the seismogram was measured on an electronic digitizer to the nearest 50 μ. The sampling point interval Δt was 30 sec for all the seismograms. The measured amplitudes were directly punched on cards in a preset format, and the digitized seismograms were then plotted by an automatic plotter and compared with the original seismograms to check for digitization errors. Table 2 gives the initial time and the length of the digitized seismograms used in the analysis.

TABLE 1. Recording Instruments

Stations	Instruments	T_0, sec	T_g, sec
Berkeley	Sprengnether (Z, N-S, E-W)	30	100
Berkeley	Ultra-long period (N-S)	40	300
Oroville	Geotech (Z, N-S, E-W)	20	100

*Now with Lamont-Doherty Geological Observatory.

TABLE 2. Data Used for Analysis

Stations	Components	Initial Points h	m	s	Date	Length, min	Number of Sample Points
Berkeley	Z	05	40	00	March 29	731.5	1463
	N-S	08	41	00	March 29	597.0	1194
	E-W	01	40	30	March 29	626.0	1252
Berkeley (ULP)	N-S	15	53	00	March 28	1491.5	2983
Oroville	Z	06	37	00	March 29	921.5	1843
	N-S	06	37	00	March 29	921.5	1843
	E-W	06	37	00	March 29	920.5	1841
Transverse (synthesized)		06	37	00	March 29	920.5	1841
Longitudinal (synthesized)		06	37	00	March 29	920.5	1841

Method of analysis. Any time series consisting of a finite number of equally spaced data points can be completely represented by a finite number of Fourier sine and cosine terms in the following way.

Let $f(I)$, $I = 1, 2, \ldots, N$, represent the digitized seismograms; then the decomposition of $f(I)$ into its Fourier components is expressed by

$$f(I) = \frac{a_0}{2} + \sum_{k=1}^{M} \left\{ a_k \cos \frac{2\pi kI}{N} + b_k \sin \frac{2\pi kI}{N} \right\} \quad (1)$$

where

$$a_k = \frac{2}{N} \sum_{I=1}^{N-1} f(I) \cos \frac{2\pi kI}{N} \quad a_0 = \frac{2}{N} \sum_{I=1}^{N-1} f(I) \quad (2)$$

$$b_k = \frac{2}{N} \sum_{I=1}^{N-1} f(I) \sin \frac{2\pi kI}{N} \quad N = 2M + 1 \quad (3)$$

Each pair of sines and cosines in (1) can also be written as

$$a_k \cos \frac{2\pi kI}{N} + b_k \sin \frac{2\pi kI}{N}$$
$$= c_k \cos \left(\frac{2\pi kI}{N} - \psi_k \right) \quad (4)$$

where

$$c_k = (a_k^2 + b_k^2)^{1/2} \quad \psi_k = \tan^{-1}(b_k/a_k) \quad (5)$$

The period T_k of the kth harmonic is calculated from

$$T_k = N\Delta T/k \quad (6)$$

where N is the number of data points and T is the sample interval. The quantities c_k and ψ_k are the amplitude and phase factors associated with each period T_k. The half-width period of the kth harmonic is a measure of precision in the estimation of a period T close to T_k and is defined by

$$dT_k = (T_{k-1} - T_{k+1})/4 \quad (7)$$

In addition to the harmonic analysis of each seismogram, certain joint properties of pairs of seismograms were computed. Let $f_j(I)$, $j = 1$, 2, be the amplitude variation of each seismogram. Let C_{k1} and ψ_{k1} be the amplitude and phase factors associated with the first seismogram and C_{k2} and ψ_{k2} be the amplitude and phase factors of the second seismogram, respectively. Equations 8 to 10 defining the quantities 'in-phase energy,' 'out-phase energy,' and 'common-energy' are, respectively,

$$INE_k = C_{k1}C_{k2} \cos (\psi_{k1} - \psi_{k2}) \quad (8)$$

$$OUE_k = C_{k1}C_{k2} \sin (\psi_{k1} - \psi_{k2}) \quad (9)$$

and

$$CME_k = (INE_k^2 + OUE_k^2) = C_{k1}C_{k2} \quad (10)$$

Equations 1 to 10 were used in the period analysis given in the following sections. A computer program was written, yielding errors of less than 1% in the calculation of amplitudes and phases.

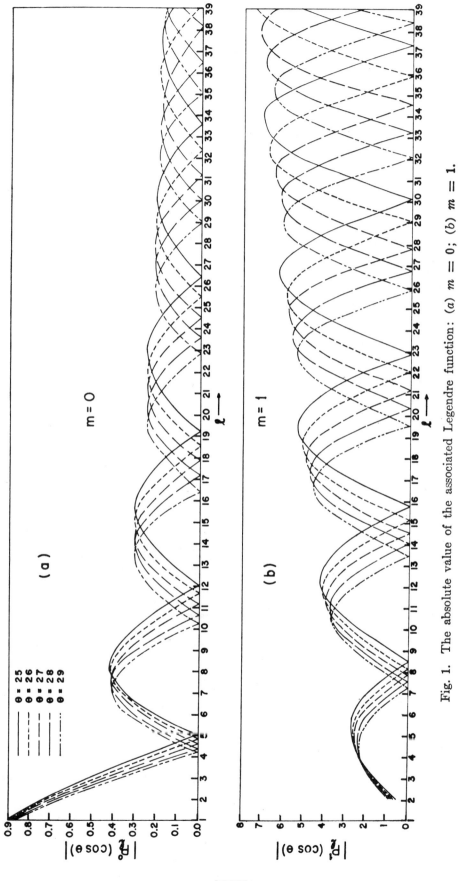

Fig. 1. The absolute value of the associated Legendre function: (a) $m = 0$; (b) $m = 1$.

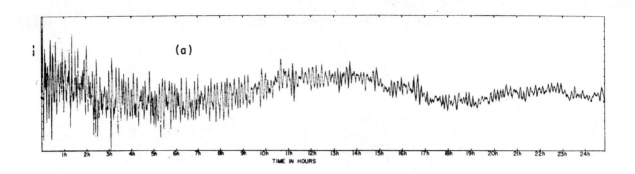

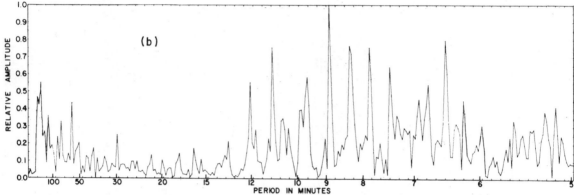

Fig. 2. (a) The seismogram of the ultra-long period instrument at Berkeley before the tidal effect was removed. (b) The spectrum of the seismogram after the tidal effect was removed.

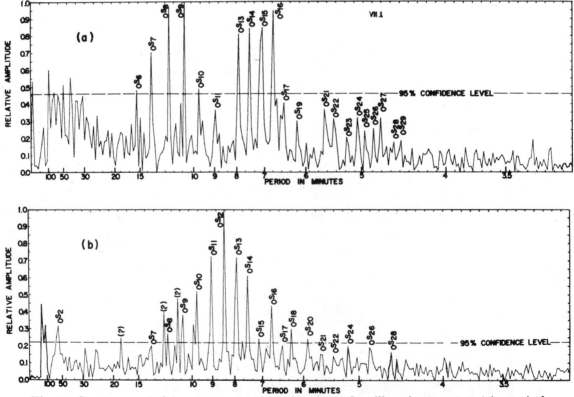

Fig. 3. Spectrums of the components of motion from Oroville seismograms: (a) vertical; (b) longitudinal.

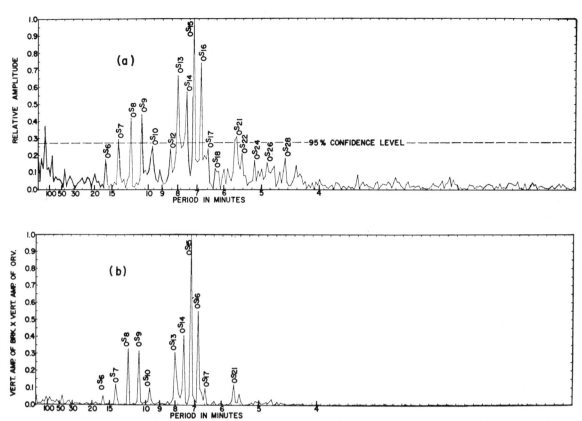

Fig. 4. Spectrum of (a) the vertical component of motion from Berkeley and (b) the product of the harmonic amplitudes of the vertical components from Berkeley and Oroville.

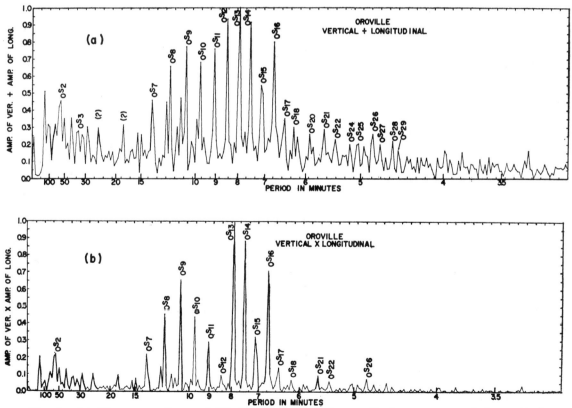

Fig. 5. (a) The summation and (b) the product of the amplitude spectrums of the vertical and longitudinal components from Oroville.

Power and cross-spectrum analyses were also used in estimating the eigenfrequencies in the same cases. In general, however, the methods were found to lack the precision of the harmonic analysis given by (1) to (10).

Theoretical amplitude variations. At the surface of a sphere, the vertical amplitude of a spheroidal oscillation is proportional to the tesseral harmonic $P_l{}^m(\cos\theta)e^{im\phi}$, where θ is the colatitude and ϕ is the azimuthal angle. The horizontal amplitude of both the spheroidal and torsional oscillations contains a term which is the derivative of the tesseral harmonic with respect to either θ or ϕ. The integers l and m determine the pattern of nodal lines associated with zero surface displacements, and the number of nodal lines related to the coordinates θ and ϕ are $l - |m|$ and $2m$, respectively. Nodal surfaces within the sphere associated with overtones of the fundamental oscillations are specified by an index n. In terms of l, m, and n, the patterns of displacement on a spherical surface are denoted by $_nS_l{}^m$, and $_nT_l{}^m$ for spheroidal and torsional oscillation, respectively.

The absolute values of the associated Legendre function $P_l{}^m(\cos\theta)$ for values of $m = 0$ and $m = 1$ are plotted in Figure 1 versus order number l for $25° \leqq \theta \leqq 29°$. If the adopted epicenter is assumed to be the pole of the spherical coordinate system, θ corresponds to the epicentral distance between the Alaskan earthquake and Oroville or Berkeley. A range of θ is needed to allow for the uncertainty in epicentral distances arising from the spatial extent of the earthquake source.

For $l \leqq 7$ and $m = 0$, the values of the associated Legendre function were found in a published table [*Byerly*, 1959]. For $l > 7$ and

TABLE 3. The Mean Vertical-Component Ground Displacement in Microns

Order No.	R(I)		R(I, θ)	
	Berkeley	Oroville	Berkeley	Oroville
6		351		1223
7	303	301	747	767
8	283	278	707	671
9	220	206	745	613
10	92	77	701	392
11		45		160
12	56		295	
13	136	68	474	272
14	97	61	312	198
15	147	52	560	175
16	95	51	483	226
17		19		172
21	22		90	

$m = 0$, the values of the functions were calculated using the asymptotic expansion,

$$P_l{}^m(\cos\theta) = (-1)^m l^m \left(\frac{2}{l\pi \sin\theta}\right)^{1/2}$$

$$\cdot \cos\left\{\left(l + \frac{1}{2}\right)\theta + \frac{m\pi}{2} - \frac{\pi}{4}\right\} \quad (11)$$

For $m = 1$, all the calculations are based on (11). This approximation introduces an error, decreasing with increasing l, which is not important in our discussion. Figure 1a predicts that, in particular for $m = 0$, the vibrations corresponding to order numbers $l = 4, 5, 10–12, 16–19$, and $23–26$ will have small amplitudes that depend on the values of θ. By contrast, if $m = 1$, Figure 1b, predicts that the amplitude of vibrations corresponding to $l = 2, 7–9, 13–16$, and $19–23$ will be small. Those vibrations

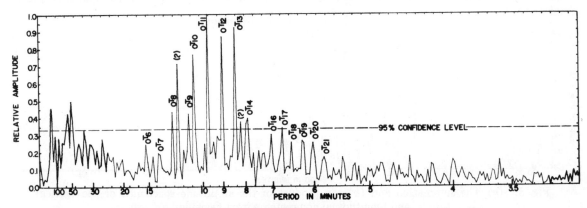

Fig. 6. Spectrums of the transverse component of motion at Oroville.

having small amplitude in the case $m = 0$ have large amplitude in the case $m = 1$. Therefore, a comparison of the observed amplitude of the vertical motion with Figure 1 makes it possible to discriminate between two values of m.

Results of harmonic analysis. The digitized seismogram from the Berkeley ultra-long-period seismograph is plotted in Figure 2a. The visible long-period wave, with an approximate period of 12 hours, corresponds to the semidiurnal body tide of the earth. The harmonic amplitude of this seismogram, after the tidal effect is removed, is plotted in Figure 2b. Individual spectral peaks, although significant, cannot be assigned uniquely to spheroidal or torsional oscillations because, at an azimuth to the epicenter of 333.8°, the horizontal-component seismometer responds to both spheroidal and torsional oscillations.

A solution to this problem was attempted by resolving vectorially the mutually orthogonal horizontal components of motion at Oroville into their longitudinal and transverse components of motion. The magnification curves for the horizontal component seismometers at Oro-

ville were in agreement to within 2%. For $m = 0$ the longitudinal and transverse components of motion correspond to the spheroidal and torsional oscillations, respectively. A check on the spheroidal oscillations can be made by comparing the spectrum of the vertical component of motion with the spectrum of the longitudinal component of motion.

Figure 3a shows the spectrum of the vertical-component seismogram obtained at Oroville. The horizontal line across the figure is the 95% confidence level calculated from the *Fisher* [1929] test of significance in harmonic analysis. The spectral peaks above the horizontal line have only 1 chance in 20 of being due to random fluctuations. The spectral peaks marked $_0S_6$ to $_0S_{16}$, with the exception of those marked $_0S_{11}$ and $_0S_{12}$, are above this level. The $_0S_{12}$ peak is missing. If the uncertainty in the determination of the epicentral distance θ is considered, the agreement between the amplitudes in Figure 3a and the theoretical dependence of the amplitudes on the Legendre function for $m = 0$ given in Figure 1a is excellent. The curve for $P_l^0(\cos 26°)$ also agrees well with the observed large ampli-

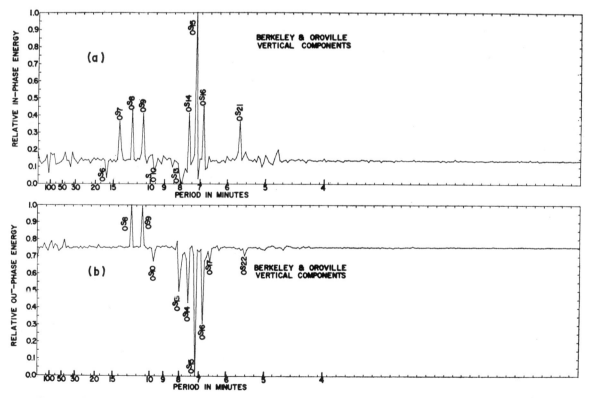

Fig. 7. Spectrums of (a) the relative in-phase energy and (b) the relative out-phase energy for the vertical components of motion at Berkeley and Oroville.

[533]

tudes for the orders $l = 7, 8,$ and 9 and $l = 13,$ $14, 15$ and 16. The absence of $_0S_{12}$ indicates that Oroville is near the nodal line for the vertical component of this mode.

On a rotating earth the nodal line of the tesseral harmonics will drift westward at a rate of $\beta\Omega$, where $\beta = 1/l(l + 1)$ for torsional oscillation [*Backus and Gilbert*, 1961] and Ω is the frequency of the rotation of the earth, 0.7272×10^{-4} sec^{-1}. The rate of drift approaches zero as l becomes large. For torsional oscillation, $l = 12$, the period of precession of the nodal line is about 3744 hours; and for spheroidal oscillation of the same mode, the nodal line drifts at about the same rate. Compared with the duration of recording, 15h 20m, the effect of this drift is therefore negligible. Figure 3b shows the spec-

trum of the longitudinal motion at Oroville. The peak marked $_0S_{12}$—missing in the spectrum of the vertical component—now has the maximum relative amplitude. The peaks marked $_0S_{10}$ and $_0S_{11}$, previously under the 95% confidence level, are now prominent.

From theory, the amplitude of the longitudinal component over a sphere is proportional to the derivative of the associated Legendre function with respect to θ. Therefore, for a given m, the relative maximum amplitude of the harmonics of the vertical motion corresponds to the relative minimum amplitude of the harmonics of the longitudinal motion.

Figure 4a shows the spectrum from the vertical-component seismogram obtained at Berkeley. The general form of this spectrum resembles

TABLE 4. Periods of Observed and Theoretical Spheroidal Modes in Minutes

| Mode | Observed Periods | | | Theoretical Periods | | | |
	1964 Alaskan Quake	Half-Width	Mean of Chilean Data (after *Press* [1964])	Jeffreys–Bullen A	Jeffreys–Bullen B	Gutenberg–Bullen A	Gutenberg–Bullen B
2*	54.14	±1.59	53.95	53.43	53.72	53.50	53.78
3	35.40	±0.68	35.62	35.25	35.52	35.32	35.58
4			25.82	25.50	25.75	25.53	25.78
5			19.86	19.62	19.85	19.65	19.88
6*	16.15	±0.14	16.07	15.90	16.17	15.92	16.15†
7*	13.53	±0.10	13.52	13.42	13.65	13.43†	13.67
8*	11.80	±0.07	11.76	11.73†	11.97	11.73†	11.97
9*	10.58	±0.06	10.57	10.53†	10.77	10.53†	10.77
10*	9.659	±0.051	9.629	9.650†	9.883	9.650†	9.883
11*	8.937	±0.043	8.917	8.950†	9.183	8.950†	9.183
12*	8.368	±0.038	8.362	8.383†	8.617	8.383†	8.617
13*	7.867	±0.033	7.875	7.887†	8.105	7.887†	8.108
14*	7.484	±0.030	7.465	7.473	7.680	7.475†	7.683
15*	7.136	±0.027	7.102	7.107	7.300	7.108†	7.305
16*	6.768	±0.025	6.778	6.780†	6.962	6.782	6.967
17	6.482	±0.023	6.492	6.488†	6.658	6.492	6.663
18*	6.262	±0.021	6.231	6.227	6.383	6.230†	6.390
19	6.178	±0.020	5.998	5.988	6.133	5.993	6.142†
20*	5.901	±0.019	5.778	5.772	5.907†	5.778	5.915
21*	5.613	±0.017	5.595	5.575	5.698†	5.582	5.708
22	5.415	±0.016	5.410	5.392	5.505	5.402†	5.515
23	5.230	±0.015	5.256	5.225†	5.327	5.235†	5.338
24	5.171	±0.014	5.105	5.068	5.162	5.080	5.175†
25	4.949	±0.013	4.959	4.923	5.007	4.937†	5.022
26	4.819	±0.012	4.827	4.787	4.862	4.802†	4.878
27	4.720	±0.012	4.694	4.660	4.727†	4.675	4.743
28	4.557	±0.011	4.588	4.540	4.600	4.557†	4.617
29	4.490	±0.011	4.469	4.427	4.478	4.445	4.478†

* Above 95% confidence level.
† Best fit to observations of Alaskan earthquake.

the spectrum of the vertical component of motion at Oroville, except that in this spectrum the peak corresponding to $l = 11$ is missing. Again, the curve for P_l^0 (cos 28°) in Figure 1a predicts this fact.

The variations of the spectral amplitudes at both the Berkeley and Oroville stations therefore indicate that $m = 0$. Although some of the higher-order spectral peaks have amplitudes under the 95% confidence level, those marked give periods agreeing within 1% with the mean of previous observations estimated by *Press* [1964] (see Table 4). The smaller amplitudes of the higher-order oscillations are caused by a higher dissipation function and by the variation of the Legendre function for these modes.

The effect of the nodal line has been removed from the spheroidal spectrum in Figure 5a by summing the amplitude spectrums of the longitudinal and vertical components. The sum should reveal all the spectral peaks of the spheroidal oscillations; however, in the long-period part of the spectrum, significant peaks corresponding to $_0S_4$, $_0S_5$, and $_0S_6$ do not appear.

The marked $_0S_2$ with a period of 54.1 min is above the 95% confidence level in Figure 3b, and it is of interest. However, as Table 4 indicates, the half-width period for this mode is large, and this observation is not as precise as the previous

observations, which were based on a longer time duration of the record [*Benioff et al.,* 1961; *Ness et al.,* 1961; *Alsop et al.,* 1961]. It should be noted that $_0S_2$ is clearly resolved in both spectrums of Figure 5. From the spectrum of the longitudinal component the average ground displacement for $_0S_2$ is calculated to be 1.8 mm.

The instrument response curves from Oroville and Berkeley allow the measured amplitude of the significant Fourier harmonics to be reduced to the ground motion in microns. The average vertical ground displacements at Berkeley and Oroville for order numbers $l = 6$–17 and $l = 21$ are listed in Table 3; in each case the average is taken over 731.5 and 921.5 min, respectively. $R(I)$ denotes correction for the response of the instruments only; $R(I, \theta)$ denotes correction for the response of the instrument and the associated Legendre function.

A plot of the amplitude for the transverse motion at Oroville is given in Figure 6. All the spectral peaks marked from $_0T_8$ to $_0T_{14}$ are above the 95% confidence level, and those identified spectral peaks under the 95% confidence level have periods that are close to values measured by other observers. The spectral peak corresponding to $_0T_{15}$ is missing.

Three peaks in the spectrum of the longitudinal component and two peaks in the spec-

TABLE 5. Periods of Observed and Theoretical Torsional Modes in Minutes

Mode	Observed Periods			Theoretical Periods		
	1964 Alaskan Quake	Half-Width	Mean of Chilean Data (after *Press* [1964])	Jeffreys–Bullen A	Jeffreys–Bullen B	Gutenberg–Bullen A
6	15.34	±0.13	15.36	15.28	15.54	15.36†
7	13.73	±0.10	13.53	13.37	13.72	13.57†
8*	12.27	±0.08	12.25	12.13	12.33	12.22†
9*	10.96	±0.07	11.14	11.05†	11.23	11.15
10*	10.58	±0.06	10.32	10.20	10.34†	10.28
11*	9.689	±0.051	9.614	9.50	9.59†	9.55
12*	8.937	±0.043	8.975	8.86	8.95	8.93†
13*	8.368	±0.038	8.379	8.33	8.40†	8.39
14*	7.867	±0.033	7.942	7.86†	7.92	7.93
15			7.527	7.43	7.50†	7.51
16	7.081	±0.027	7.161	7.07†	7.12	7.15
17*	6.768	±0.025	6.819	6.73	6.78†	6.81
18	6.528	±0.023	6.502	6.45	6.48	6.52†
19	6.262	±0.021	6.246	6.18	6.20	6.24†
20	6.016	±0.019	6.006	5.93	5.95	5.99†
21	5.796	±0.018	5.769	5.70	5.72	5.77†

* Above 95% confidence level.
† Best fit to observations of Alaska earthquake.

trum of the transverse component—all above the 95% confidence level—are designated by question marks in Figures 3b and 6. The periods of the spectral peaks of the longitudinal component in minutes are 17.70 ± 0.17, 12.11 ± 0.08, and 10.96 ± 0.06, where uncertainties denote the half-width period. These spectral peaks may be attributed to the $_1S_3$, $_1S_5$, and $_1S_6$ oscillations, respectively. The periods of the two spectral peaks from the transverse component of motion are 11.80 ± 0.07 and 8.146 ± 0.036 min. The first of these (11.80 min) peaks may be attributed to $_1T_3$, but the lack of theoretical periods for overtones of higher-order torsional oscillations does not permit similar identification of the second spectral peak (8.146 min).

A further complication enters if coupling between spheroidal and torsional oscillation occurs, as *MacDonald and Ness* [1961] have suggested. An order of magnitude value based on their equation, the equation preceding equation 15, was calculated using the periods in question. These calculations, however, showed that the amplitude of the vertical oscillation caused by the gyroscopic forces is unlikely to reach 5% of the amplitude of the horizontal oscillation.

Figure 4b emphasizes the common spectrum amplitudes at the two stations for the vertical component. In agreement, with theory, for $m = 0$ the spectral peaks of $_0S_{11}$, $_0S_{12}$, $_0S_{18}$, and $_0S_{19}$ are missing and the spectral peaks of $_0S_{17}$ and $_0S_{21}$ have rather small amplitude. On the average,

the periods of corresponding spheroidal modes measured at Berkeley and Oroville for spectral peaks above the 95% confidence level (i.e, $l = 7, 8, 9, 13, 14, 15$, and 16) differ by only 1.8 sec, which is below the resolution of the harmonic analysis. It is not possible, therefore, to make any inferences about the earth structure below Berkeley and Oroville from these differences.

The numerical values of the phase angle ψ_k for each significant mode from Berkeley and Oroville data were studied, but no clear pattern emerged. The relative in-phase energy and out-phase energy as defined in (8) and (9) are plotted in Figure 7 for the vertical components of motion at Berkeley and Oroville. The in-phase and out-phase energy plots give information about phase differences and spectral amplitudes for each harmonic between the two stations. The distance between Oroville and Berkeley is small in comparison with the wavelength of these oscillations; it is therefore expected that most of the energy is in phase, and it is confirmed in Figure 7.

Periods of spheroidal oscillations. A summary of the theoretical and observational results of spheroidal oscillations is given in Table 4. The mean of previous observation as reported by *Press* [1964] is also included for comparison. The theoretical periods were calculated by *Alsop* [1963] for four earth models using the Jeffreys and Gutenberg velocity distributions, each taken with a Bullen A and a Bullen B density model.

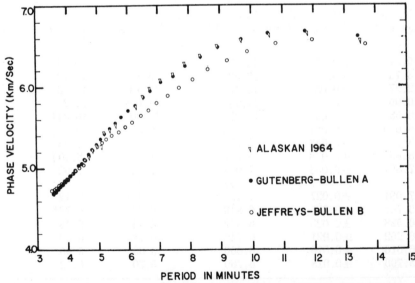

Fig. 8. Comparison of fundamental Rayleigh wave phase velocities obtained from observed free periods of oscillations with two earth models.

The model among the four theoretical models having a period closest to the observed period from the Alaskan earthquake is designated by a dagger †. The modes having amplitudes above the 95% confidence level are shown by an asterisk *.

For the spheroidal modes $_0S_2$ to $_0S_6$, the half-width periods defined by (6) are not fine enough to permit us to discriminate clearly between either velocity distribution or density models. The half-width periods of the $_0S_6$ to $_0S_{24}$ modes are smaller than the differences between the corresponding theoretical periods of these modes when they have the same velocity distribution. That is, the measurements of these modes differentiate effectively only density models. Comparing the periods of these modes with the theoretical periods indicates that the Bullen model A is preferable to the Bullen model B. Beyond the $_0S_{24}$ mode the half-width periods are smaller than the differences between periods of corresponding modes for modes with the same density distribution; therefore, differentiation is between velocity distributions. The observations agree most closely with the Gutenberg velocity distribution.

Periods of torsional oscillations. The measurements for the torsional modes are given in Table 5. The theoretical periods of two earth models with (1) the velocity distribution of Jeffreys and the density of model B of Bullen and (2) the velocity distribution of Gutenberg and the density of model A of Bullen are from

Pekeris and Jarosch [1961]. The theoretical periods of an earth model with the Jeffreys velocity distribution and the Bullen model A densities are from *Satô et al.* [1960]. Since the measured half-width periods of the $_0T_6$ to $_0T_{13}$ modes are smaller than the differences between the corresponding theoretical periods for models with the same velocity distribution, the measurements discriminate between density models and again show the superiority of the Bullen A density model. Similarly, the measured periods of modes beyond $_0S_{13}$ allow inferences to be drawn about the preferred velocity distribution for a given density model, and the measurements support the velocity distribution of Gutenberg.

Phase velocity. The normal mode oscillation of a sphere is represented by standing waves generated by the superposition of two waves traveling in opposite directions. It can be shown [*Jeans*, 1923; *Alterman et al.*, 1961] that the phase velocity C of the traveling wave is related to the period T of the corresponding normal mode l and to the radius of the earth R by

$$C = 2\pi R/(l + \tfrac{1}{2})T_l \qquad (12)$$

The measured periods from the Oroville data and the theoretical periods corresponding to the Gutenberg–Bullen A and Jeffreys–Bullen B models, which are given in Tables 4 and 5, and equation 12 were used in calculating the phase velocity C. The results are phase velocities of fundamental Rayleigh and Love waves and are plotted in Figures 8 and 9.

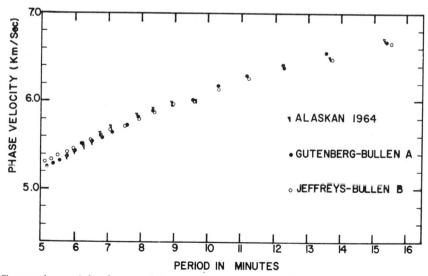

Fig. 9. Comparison of fundamental Love wave phase velocities obtained from observed free periods of oscillations with two earth models.

[537]

The great-circle path of the traveling wave is about 70% oceanic with a continental section through parts of Alaska and Asia. It is possible that slight deviations between observed and theoretical velocities would arise from the difference in structure of the crust and upper mantle of the models and of the actual great-circle path, since all theoretical models have a continental crust.

The theoretical phase velocities of the fundamental Rayleigh wave (Figure 8) are not significantly different for periods smaller than 5 min, but the lower velocity of the Jeffreys–Bullen B model for periods greater than 5 min is a remarkable feature of this model and permits an unequivocal differentiation to be made. The velocities for modes $l = 19$ and 20 are not plotted in Figure 8. The amplitudes of these modes are small and their identification is not certain. The observations of the Rayleigh wave favor the Gutenberg–Bullen A model over the Jeffreys–Bullen B model.

Although for periods shorter than 6 min the theoretical phase velocities of the fundamental Love wave (Figure 9) differ significantly, the two models are very close between 6 and 12 min. The measurements in this case do not differentiate clearly between these models. For periods greater than 13 min, two observations are available, one favoring each model.

Acknowledgments. This research was undertaken at the suggestion of Professor B. A. Bolt. I wish to express my appreciation for many suggestions received from him during this work. I am also grateful to Professor T. V. McEvilly and Dr. C. Lomnitz for helpful discussions.

REFERENCES

Alsop, L. E., Free vibrations of the earth at very long period, *Bull. Seismol. Soc. Am., 53,* 483–502, 1963.

Alsop, L. E., Free periods of the earth observed at eight stations around the world, *Bull. Seismol. Soc. Am., 54,* 755–776, 1964a.

Alsop, L. E., Excitation of free oscillation of the earth by the Kurile Islands earthquake of 13 October, 1963, *Bull. Seismol. Soc. Am., 54,* 1341–1348, 1964b.

Alsop, L. E., G. H. Sutton, and M. Ewing, Free oscillations of the earth observed on strain and pendulum seismograph, *J. Geophys. Res., 66,* 631–641, 1961.

Alterman, Z., H. Jarosch, and C. L. Pekeris, Propagation of the Rayleigh waves in the earth, *Geophys. J., 4,* 219–241, 1961.

Backus, G., and F. Gilbert, The rotation splitting of the free oscillations of the earth, *Proc. Natl. Acad. Sci., U. S., 47,* 362–371, 1961.

Benioff, H., F. Press, and S. Smith, Excitation of the free oscillation of the earth by earthquakes, *J Geophys. Res., 66,* 605–615, 1961.

Blum, P., R. Gaulon, G. Jobert, and N. Jobert, Résultats obtenus à l'aide d'un inclinamètre fonctionnant sous vide, *Compt. Rend.,* 283–285, 1964.

Bogert, B. P., An observation of the free oscillations of the earth, *J. Geophys. Res., 66,* 643–646, 1961.

Bolt, B. A., Revised torsional eigenperiods from 1960 Trieste data, *Geophys. J., 7,* 510–512, 1963a.

Bolt, B. A., Recent information on the earth's interior from studies of mantle waves and eigenvibrations, *Phys. Chem. Earth, 5,* 55–115, 1963b.

Byerly, W. E., *An Elementary Treatise on Fourier's Series,* Dover Publications, New York, 1959.

Connes, J., P. A. Blum, G. Jobert, and N. Jobert, Observations des oscillations propres de la terre, *Ann. Geophys., 18,* 260–268, 1962.

Fisher, R. A., Test of significance in harmonic analysis, *Proc. Roy. Soc., London, A, 125,* 54–59, 1929.

Jeans, J. H., The propagation of earthquake waves, *Proc. Roy. Soc., London, A, 102,* 554–574, 1923.

MacDonald, G. J. F., and N. F. Ness, A study of the free oscillations of the earth, *J. Geophys. Res., 66,* 1865–1912, 1961.

Ness, N. F., J. C. Harrison, and L. B. Slichter, Observations of the free oscillations of the earth, *J. Geophys. Res., 66,* 621–629, 1961.

Press, F., Long-period waves and free oscillations of the earth, in *Research in Geophysics,* vol. 2, M.I.T. Press, 1964.

Satô, Y., M. Landisman, and M. Ewing, Love waves in a heterogeneous, spherical earth, *J. Geophys. Res., 65,* 2395–2404, 1960.

(Manuscript received June 28, 1965.)

STEWART W. SMITH*

CALIFORNIA INSTITUTE OF TECHNOLOGY

Reprinted from
Journal of Geophysical Research, Vol. 71, No. 4,
"Free Oscillations Excited by the Alaskan Earthquake"

Free Oscillations Excited by the Earthquake

Abstract. Periods of spheroidal and toroidal modes are determined from strain and pendulum recordings of the Alaskan earthquake of March 28, 1964. Combinations of orthogonal strains provide a means for separation and identification of mode types. Results in general confirm the measurements made after the Chilean earthquake of 1960, with a few minor differences attributed to misidentification in the earlier data. A comparison of the mode excitation of the Alaskan and Chilean earthquakes at a single station yields only the estimate that the temporal and spatial extent of these two sources were comparable even though the force systems may well have been quite different.

Introduction. The earth's free oscillations have been observed with varying degrees of precision for earthquakes in Kamchatka (1954), Chile (1960), the Kurile Islands (1963), and Alaska (1964). The evolution of both instrumental techniques and analytical methods during this time makes it appear quite likely that within a few years it will be possible to observe the excitation of free oscillations due to earthquakes with magnitude as small as 6 and due to sources other than earthquakes. We do not necessarily expect that the accuracy of free oscillation periods will be improved with each new observation. As the data increase, however, errors due to misidentification of modes should decrease. Neither do we expect that the average of a large number of observations will be necessarily closer to the true value; however, since the relative excitation of the various modes is different for each earthquake, we may expect to improve the accuracy of a few well-recorded modes with each new earthquake. Such is the case for the Alaskan earthquake. A few of the previous errors have been corrected and some small changes in observed periods are noted. For example, the mode T_7 reported by *Bolt* [1963] is shown to be S_7 by mode identification techniques developed here. The largest gap in data on free oscillations of the earth remains the period of the fundamental toroidal mode of order 2. It is not clear that this mode has

ever been observed and adequately measured.

In the observations of high-order oscillations, lateral inhomogeneities of the earth may become significant. This effect will manifest itself by the observation of different apparent free oscillation periods for different stations. One can think of the period of oscillation as being determined by the interference of surface waves traveling along the great-circle path through the epicenter and the station. The order number or wavelength at which inhomogeneities begin to have a significant effect has a direct bearing on the depth to which the earth is laterally inhomogeneous. This effect can best be understood in terms of the relative excitation of the various split lines that would be present for an inhomogeneous earth.

Instrumentation. A number of different instruments were used in the observations of the Alaskan earthquake. A brief summary of the types of instruments used follows.

1. *Isabella, California.* A number of changes were made in this station after the Chilean earthquake. An additional component of strain was installed at right angles to the existing one, and the outputs of each instrument were recorded at two levels of sensitivity with a 20-db separation. A passive network with a maximum response at a period of 1 hour was used [*Benioff*, 1963]. As a result of this dual recording, the entire signal from the Alaskan earthquake was on scale and available for analysis. The additional strain component made possible a better separation of mode types.

2. *Dalton, California.* An experimental liq-

*Now with the University of Washington.

uid pendulum [*Benioff*, 1965] had just been put into operation at this site when the earthquake occurred. The drift rate due to its recent installation was quite high; however, it provided an interesting long-period record of horizontal motion. The free period was 72 sec, and it was recorded directly without low-pass filtering.

3. *Kipapa, Hawaii.* A strain seismograph was installed here early in 1964 [*Blayney and Gilman*, 1966]. It was recording at the time of the earthquake and had a long-period response identical to those of the strain instruments at Ñaña, Peru (inoperational during the Alaskan earthquake), and Isabella, California.

4. *Pasadena, California.* An experimental vertical-component instrument consisting of a standard long-period pendulum modified to include a displacement transducer and feedback stabilization was operating during the earthquake. A time constant of 12,000 sec was achieved in the feedback loop by the use of partially charged nickel-cadmium batteries in place of capacitors. The output of this instrument, along with outputs of a similar horizontal pendulum and a microbarograph, was recorded by means of a multiplexor, a digitizer, and an incremental-drive magnetic tape recorder. The word size was 14 bits, which was large enough to provide an on-scale recording of all but the early part of the Rayleigh waves. A summary of the instruments used, the recording mediums, and the sample rates are shown in Table 1.

Analysis. Data were sampled at rates between 20 per minute and 2 per minute, depending upon the instrument response and the recording medium. In places where data on the high-sensitivity recordings was clipped, it was patched by means of the low-sensitivity recordings. With some experimental instruments that had large drift rates, linear trends were removed from intervals of lengths between 2 and 6 hours as required. The next step was low-pass filtering and decimation to reduce the sample rate and produce two sets of data with sample intervals of 1 minute and 3 minutes for analysis of high-order and low-order modes, respectively. A recursive scheme of digital filtering was used rather than the usual convolution with sets of filter coefficients [*Smith*, 1965]. The two orthogonal strain instruments at Isabella were corrected for their different sensitivities and

TABLE 1. Data Sources

Station	Instrument	Recorder Speed	Sample Rate
Isabella	NW strain	6 inch/hour	2/min
Isabella	NE strain	6 inch/hour	2/min
Dalton	NW mercury pendulum	3 inch/hour	1/min
Pasadena	NS pendulum	Magnetic tape	20/min
Pasadena	Vertical pendulum	Magnetic tape	20/min

length, and the sum and difference of the resulting signals were formed. The various sets of data from individual instruments and combinations of components were subjected to power-spectrum analysis as described by *Blackman and Tukey* [1958]. The least-squares amplitudes of the tidal constituents M_2, S_2, K_1, and O_1 were estimated, and these harmonic components were then subtracted with proper phase.

Mode separation. One of the principle uncertainties in some of the free oscillation data results from the misidentification of a mode by the assignment of either an incorrect order number or an incorrect mode type. Spheroidal and toroidal modes have thus far been distinguished only by the presence or absence of a vertical component of motion. Separation of these modes cannot be made with horizontal instruments only because both mode types have significant longitudinal and transverse motion, particularly at low order number. The primary method for assignment of order numbers has been to use the observed period to calculate an equivalent phase velocity and then to select order numbers that produce a smooth variation in phase velocity with period. Because the earth's elastic structure is already known to first order from seismic travel-time observations, no real difficulties have been encountered in assigning order numbers to observed free oscillations. The obvious way to determine order numbers unambiguously for both fundamental and higher-mode oscillations would be by spatial filtering, or equivalently by spatial harmonic analysis. Unfortunately, the number and distribution of long-period stations are not adequate for this type of analysis. One way of improving mode identification without the use of many stations will be described here.

The surface displacement of spheroidal and toroidal modes can be written as

$$\xi_s = \mathbf{r} r^{-1} U(r) P_l{}^m(\cos \theta)$$
$$+ r V(r) \nabla (P_l{}^m(\cos \theta) e^{im\phi}) \quad (1)$$

$$\xi_T = - W(r) \mathbf{r} \times \nabla (P_l{}^m(\cos \theta) e^{im\phi}) \quad (2)$$

where U, V, and W are functions of depth that depend upon the distribution of elastic parameters, θ is the colatitude, ϕ is the longitude, l is the polar order number, and m is the azimuthal order number of the associated Legendre function. Strains corresponding to these displacements are:

Spheroidal

$$e_{\theta\theta} = \frac{1}{r} [V(r) P_l{}^m(\cos \theta)''$$
$$+ U(r) P_l{}^m(\cos \theta)] \cos m\phi$$

$$e_{\phi\phi} = \frac{1}{r} \left[V(r) P_l{}^m(\cos \theta)' \cot \theta - \frac{m^2}{\sin^2 \theta} V(r) \right.$$
$$\left. \cdot P_l{}^m(\cos \theta) + U(r) P_l{}^m(\cos \theta) \right] \cos m\phi$$

$$e_{\theta\phi} = \frac{1}{r} \frac{2m}{\sin \theta} V(r) [P_l{}^m(\cos \theta)'$$
$$- \cot \theta P_l{}^m(\cos \theta)] \sin m\phi \quad (3)$$

Toroidal

$$e_{\theta\theta} = \frac{1}{r} \frac{m W(r)}{\sin \theta} [(1 - m) \cot \theta P_l{}^m(\cos \theta)$$
$$+ P_l{}^{m+1}(\cos \theta)] \sin m\phi$$

$$e_{\phi\phi} = - e_{\theta\theta} \quad (4)$$

$$e_{\theta\phi} = W(r) \left[-P_l{}^m(\cos \theta)'' + P_l{}^m(\cos \theta)' \right.$$
$$\left. \cdot \cot \theta - \frac{m^2}{\sin^2 \theta} P_l{}^m(\cos \theta) \right] \cos m\phi$$

where the prime indicates differentiation with respect to θ.

If two horizontal extensometers or strain gages are installed at right angles and they make an angle ψ with the geographic coordinates, the displacement in the direction of each instrument will be given by

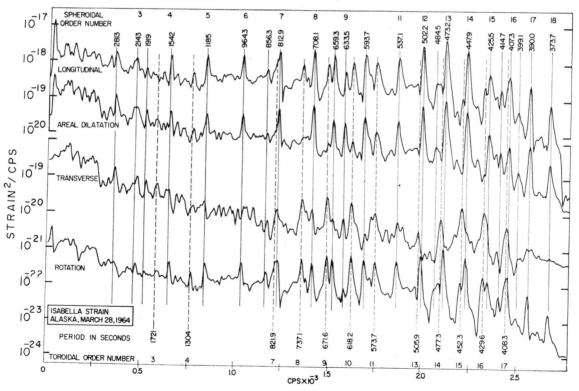

Fig. 1. Spectrum of Alaskan earthquake recorded on Isabella strain seismometer. Record length, 8340 min; sample interval, 3 min; bandwidth, 180,000⁻¹ cps. Fundamental spheroidal and toroidal modes indicated by solid and dashed lines, respectively.

$$X = e_{\theta\theta} \cos^2 \psi + e_{\theta\phi} \cos \psi \sin \psi$$
$$+ e_{\phi\phi} \sin^2 \psi \qquad (5)$$

$$Y = e_{\theta\theta} \sin^2 \psi - e_{\theta\phi} \cos \psi \sin \psi$$
$$+ e_{\phi\phi} \cos^2 \psi$$

The sum of the outputs from these two instruments is

$$\Delta = e_{\theta\theta} + e_{\phi\phi} \qquad (6)$$

and the difference is

$$\Omega = (e_{\theta\theta} - e_{\phi\phi}) \cos 2\psi + e_{\theta\phi} \sin 2\psi$$

Substituting (3) and (4) into (6) leads to $\Delta = 0$ for all toroidal modes independent of n, m, or l, whereas $\Omega \approx 0$ for spheroidal modes only if $U/V \gg l^2$, a condition that holds for only a few low order modes. For example, when $l = 2$, $U/V \approx 50$, if the elastic properties of the earth are assumed to be those given by Gutenberg.

Thus the sum Δ will contain only spheroidal modes and the difference Ω will contain only toroidal modes at low order number. This is to be compared with horizontal-component seismometers oriented in directions longitudinal and transverse to the great-circle path through the epicenter and the station. Expanding (1) and (2) to find the longitudinal U_θ and transverse U_ϕ components of motion, we get:

Spheroidal motion

$$U_\theta = V(r)[m \cot \theta P_l{}^m(\cos \theta)$$
$$- P_l{}^{m+1}(\cos \theta)]e^{im\phi} \qquad (7)$$
$$U_\phi = im V(r) \csc \theta P_l{}^m(\cos \theta)e^{im\phi}$$

Toroidal motion

$$U_\theta = im W(r) \csc \theta P_l{}^m(\cos \theta)e^{im\phi}$$
$$U_\phi = W(r)[m \cot \theta P_l{}^m(\cos \theta)$$
$$- P_l{}^{m+1}(\cos \theta)]e^{im\phi} \qquad (8)$$

There is an exact separation of spheroidal and toroidal modes into longitudinal and transverse motion as in the case of Love and Rayleigh waves only when the azimuthal order number $m = 0$. Sources that would excite modes for which $m = 0$ would be an isolated vertical force, a point compressional source, or a horizontal torque, all applied at the surface. Since realistic earthquake sources do not produce an azimuthal order number $m = 0$ only, horizontal-component seismometers alone can provide only an approximate means of mode separation. For large l and $l \gg m$, (7) and (8) can be expanded using the asymptotic value for the Legendre function. With this approximation the ratios of longitudinal and transverse motion become

$$\frac{U_\theta}{U_\phi} \approx \frac{l}{im \sin \theta} \quad \text{spheroidal}$$

$$\frac{U_\theta}{U_\phi} \approx \frac{im}{l \sin \theta} \quad \text{toroidal}$$

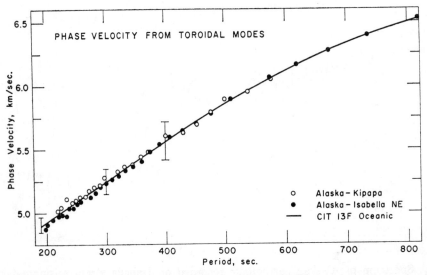

Fig. 2. Equivalent phase velocity from fundamental toroidal modes compared with theoretical results for oceanic crust and mantle.

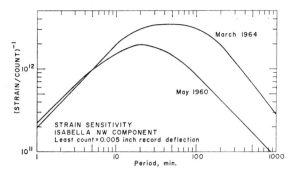

Fig. 3. Experimentally determined strain response curves valid for recordings of Chilean (1960) and Alaskan (1964) earthquakes.

Thus the separation of modes using horizontal-component seismometers is effective when $l \gg m$. For low orders, separation is a problem for only a few special cases such as the near co-

dal; if it is on the transverse T alone, it is toroidal. If it appears both on L and T and also on Δ, it is spheroidal; if it is on both L and T and also on Ω, it is toroidal. A good illustration of this can be seen by comparing T_9 and S_9, both of which show peaks on the longitudinal and transverse components. T_9, however, also appears on the rotation; S_9 appears on the dilatation, thus confirming the identification.

The fact that at low-order number Ω responds only to toroidal motion leads us to believe that the mode at 2813 sec is spheroidal and not toroidal, since it is not present in the combination Ω. This mode might be $_0S_1$ or $_1S_1$, which have been described by Pekeris et al. [1963], and Alsop [1963], although the period is far from the 2500 sec predicted for these modes. Since the Alaskan earthquake was not

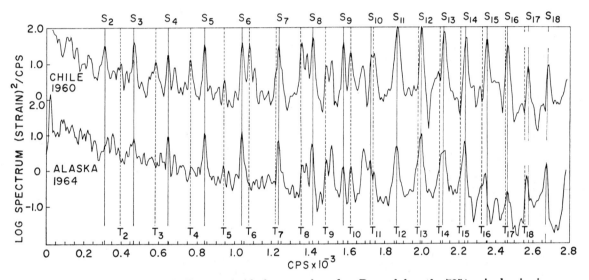

Fig. 4. Comparison of Chilean and Alaskan earthquake. Record length, 7854 min beginning 285 min after origin time for both events; sample interval, 3 min; bandwidth, $180,000^{-1}$ cps.

incidence of $_0T_2$ and $_1S_1$ or $_0T_5$ and $_1S_3$, for example. For a real earthquake the azimuthal order number m probably runs from 0 to at least 2, with a distribution depending upon the details of the source mechanism. Since the distribution of energy among the modes with different azimuthal order numbers is not known, we cannot calculate theoretically the functions Δ and Ω to compare with the experimental observations. The experimentally determined functions Δ and Ω are shown in Figure 1 and were used in the following way to separate spheroidal and toroidal modes. If a mode is present on the longitudinal component L alone, it is spheroi-

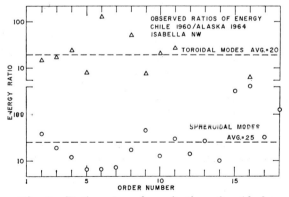

Fig. 5. Ratios of mode excitations for Alaskan and Chilean earthquakes. Corrected for all effects except geometry of source.

TABLE 2. Toroidal Modes, Alaskan Earthquake

Order No.	Kipapa Strain		Isabella Strain		Dalton Mercury Pendulum	
	Period, sec	Phase Velocity, km/sec	Period, sec	Phase Velocity, km/sec	Period, sec	Phase Velocity, km/sec
2					2692.?	5.946
3			1721.	6.644	1690.	6.766
4			1304.	6.820		
5					1078.	6.750
6						
7			821.9	6.492*		
8			737.1	6.387*	740.0	6.362
9			671.6	6.272*		
10			618.2	6.165†	614.4	6.203
11	575.8	6.053†	573.7	6.065†		
12	537.8	5.955†				
13	502.9	5.896†	505.9	5.895*	505.6	5.862
14	476.6	5.792†	477.3	5.781*		
15	453.2	5.699†	452.3	5.707*	456.2	5.689
16	430.4	5.636†	429.6	5.646*	431.0	5.627
17	407.6	5.612†	408.3	5.600*		
18	390.1	5.547*	390.4	5.541†		
19	374.5	5.482*	374.5	5.480*		
20	358.6	5.446*	361.1	5.405*		
21	345.6	5.386*	346.7	5.367*		
22	331.5	5.366	333.6	5.331*		
23	319.7	5.328†	321.9	5.290*		
24	309.9	5.272	310.3	5.264		
25	297.4	5.279*	300.0	5.231		
26	289.5	5.218*	290.1	5.205*		
27	279.8	5.202	282.2	5.156*		
28	271.3	5.177	274.0	5.124		
29	264.4	5.131				
30	255.9	5.129*	257.7	5.090†		
31	249.1	5.101*	250.6	5.068†		
32	242.3	5.084	244.4	5.038†		
33	233.7	5.113	237.3	5.034		
34			233.2	4.974		
35	223.6	5.004†	226.1	4.984		
36	218.5	5.020†	220.3	4.976		
37	213.3	5.005†				
38	208.5	4.986	210.0	4.949		
39	203.2	4.988				
40	198.7	4.975†	201.3	4.909		
41	194.8	4.951†	197.7	4.877		
42	190.7	4.938†				
43	186.2	4.941				
44	182.6	4.925				

* Mode believed to be better recorded for Alaskan earthquake than for Chilean earthquake.
† Mode equally well recorded for Alaskan and Chilean earthquakes.

TABLE 3. Spheroidal Modes, Alaskan Earthquake

Order No.	Isabella Strain		Pasadena Vertical		Dalton Mercury Pendulum	
	Period, sec	Phase Velocity, km/sec	Period, sec	Phase Velocity, km/sec	Period, sec	Phase Velocity, km/sec
2						
3	2152.	5.312				
4	1542.	5.768 †				
5	1185.	6.139 †				
6	964.3	6.384 *				
7	812.9	6.563 *			810.0	6.587
8	708.1	6.648 †				
9	633.5	6.649 †			633.4	6.650
10					580.8	6.562
11	537.1	6.478 †	536.4	6.487 †	536.2	6.489
12	502.2	6.374 †	502.8	6.367 †		
13	473.2	6.264	473.5	6.260 †	473.5	6.260
14	447.9	6.161 †	451.8	6.108	448.8	6.149
15	425.5	6.068			426.5	6.053
16	407.3	5.954	404.5	5.995		
17	390.0	5.863	390.0	5.864 †		
18	373.7	5.788 †	371.9	5.816		
19	359.9	5.701	360.2	5.697		
20	345.1	5.656	349.6	5.583		
21						
22	324.3	5.483 †	326.2	5.452 †		
23	315.6	5.396 †	315.1	5.405 †		
24	306.5	5.329 †	307.3	5.315 †		
25	298.4	5.259 †	296.8	5.286		
26	290.9	5.190				
27			282.9	5.144 †		
28	275.0	5.105 †	275.4	5.098 †		
29	268.7	5.048 †	268.8	5.045 †		
30	262.1	5.006 †				
31	256.9	4.944	257.6	4.931		
32	250.5	4.915	250.4	4.917 †		
33			244.8	4.879		
34	239.9	4.835 †	240.5	4.823 †		
35	234.5	4.806 †	234.3	4.811		
36	230.3	4.761 †	231.4	4.738		
37			225.7	4.728 †		
38			220.5	4.714 †		
39	216.8	4.673 †	217.5	4.658 †		
40	213.0	4.639 †	212.5	4.650 †		
41	208.5	4.625	209.5	4.603		
42	205.1	4.591 †	204.9	4.595 †		
43			200.8	4.581 †		
44	197.5	4.553 †	107.8	4.546		
45			194.0	4.534 †		
46	191.1	4.503 †	191.2	4.501 †		
47			187.4	4.496 †		
48	184.8	4.465	183.8	4.489		

* Mode believed to be better recorded for Alaskan earthquake than for Chilean earthquake.
† Mode equally well recorded for Alaskan and Chilean earthquakes.

very efficient in exciting the lower-order modes, there is little to be gained from a discussion of the data for order numbers less than 4 or 5.

Lateral inhomogeneities. Observations of toroidal modes for the path through Kipapa, Hawaii, and for the path through Isabella, California, appear to be significantly different for periods shorter than 350 sec. This can be interpreted in the following manner: For a spherically symmetric earth the modes of vibration have a $(2n + 1)$-fold degeneracy. Lateral inhomogeneities of any kind will remove this degeneracy and produce a multiplet in the spectrum, [*Backus and Gilbert*, 1961]. For high-order modes the spacing between individual lines in the multiplets is smaller than the broadening of the lines due to attenuation [*Gilbert and Backus*, 1965], so that one observes only the envelope of the multiplet. The apparently different frequencies for different paths are thus simply due to the fact that the relative amplitude of the individual lines in the multiplet is a function of the position of the recording instrument, and changes in these amplitudes will shift the apparent frequency of the center of the envelope. The divergence of observed frequencies is best displayed by calculating the phase velocity as a function of frequency and is shown in Figure 2 for the two paths through Hawaii and California. Only toroidal modes are shown because the orientation of the strain seismograph at Kipapa was unfavorable for the detection of spheroidal modes. The divergence becomes significant for periods shorter than about 350 sec. This period

can be interpreted as a depth to which inhomogeneities extend if we make use of the partial derivative tables of phase velocities published by *Anderson* [1964]. Subject to the usual uncertainties and lack of uniqueness in the interpretation of dispersion data, reasonable variations in the rigidity of materials would have to extend to depths of several hundred kilometers to produce the observed divergence at periods of 350 sec [*Toksöz and Anderson*, 1965]. For comparison, the dispersion curve for a standard oceanic model given by *Anderson* [1964] is also shown in the figure. The oceanic structure gives a result that is very close to the average of the data over the two paths considered. It is interesting that both of these paths consist of about 50% continent and 50% oceanic structures. The particular continents and oceans traversed by these two paths are quite different, however. The path through Hawaii includes almost all of the major shield areas of the world's continents. Almost 50% of the continental part of this path is through shield areas. The continental regions traversed by the path through Isabella consist of most of the earth's major tectonic regions. Thus the differences in phase velocity between these two paths may be attributed to the major differences between the types of continental structures traversed and not simply to the difference between oceanic and continental structures. The tectonic regions are characterized by a lower velocity than the shield areas, which could be accounted for by a more pronounced low-velocity layer under the tectonic regions. *Brune*

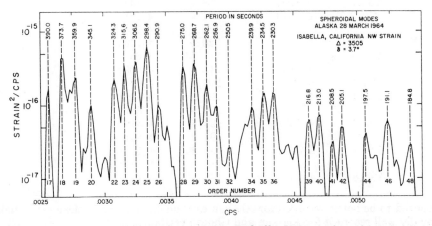

Fig. 6. Spheroidal modes, order numbers 17–48; Isabella NW strain oriented 3.7° to great-circle path. Record length, 1980 min; sample interval, 1 min; bandwidth, 60,000⁻¹ cps.

and Dorman [1963] have shown that the mantle low-velocity layer under the Canadian shield is less pronounced than that under typical oceanic areas. *Toksöz and Anderson* [1965] have also shown a distinction in mantle structure under oceans, shields, and high mountain regions.

The depth to which significant lateral variations occur is an important factor in understanding the evolution of the earth. It has a direct bearing on the mechanism of differentiation of continental materials from the mantle.

Comparison of mode excitation by the Chilean and the Alaskan earthquakes. To compare the excitation of various modes it is first necessary to know the station location in terms of the source coordinates for the two earthquakes. Using the aftershock distribution to determine roughly the extent and direction of the two sources, we find that the azimuth of the strike of the fault in Chile is 10°, and that in Alaska is 315°. The azimuth from the source to Isabella is 325° for Chile and 130° for Alaska. If θ and ϕ are the coordinates of the station referred to the source and δ is the angle between the strain instrument and the great-circle paths, we get the following relationships for the NW Isabella strain:

Source	ϕ	θ	δ
Alaska	90°	31°	2°
Chile	45°	84°	4°

Since the extension along the axis of the strain seismograph is given by

$$e_{NW} = e_{\theta\theta} \cos^2 \delta + \cos \delta \sin \delta e_{\theta\phi}$$
$$+ e_{\phi\phi} \sin^2 \delta$$

with δ as given above, the observations represent almost a pure $e_{\theta\theta}$ strain for both earthquakes.

The instrument sensitivity was changed somewhat in the interval between 1960 and 1964 in order to move the peak response to a period of 1 hour and to increase the attenuation of the tidal components at 12 hours period. The strain sensitivity was obtained by spectrum analysis of the response to 1-min calibration pulses. The strain sensitivity curves are shown in Figure 3. The spectrum of an identical time sample of these two earthquakes is shown in Figure 4. All fundamental spheroidal and toroidal modes are indicated. Significant peaks present for both earthquakes but not labeled are higher-mode oscillations. Order numbers are difficult to assign to these modes without additional information. It can be seen by referring to Figure 1 that all of these unidentified higher modes are of the spheroidal type. There are several means of determining order numbers for higher modes without resorting to a large number of stations. They depend on the differences in horizontal and vertical motion at the surface and on apparent rates of amplitude decay. The data from vertical instruments used in this study, however, were not adequate for this type of analysis. Stable, precisely matched vertical- and horizontal-component instruments are now in operation and will pro-

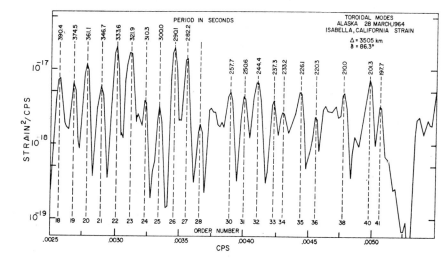

Fig. 7. Toroidal modes, order numbers 18–41; Isabella NE strain oriented 86.3° to great-circle path. Record length, 1980 min; sample interval, 1 min; bandwidth, 60,000⁻¹ cps.

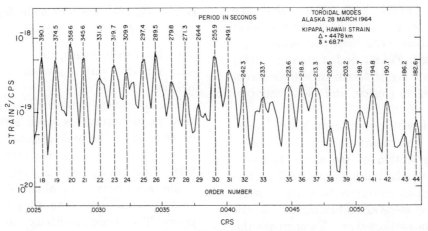

Fig. 8. Toroidal modes, order numbers 18–44; Kipapa NW strain oriented 68.7° to great-circle path. Record length, 1890 min; sample interval, 1 min; bandwidth, 60,000⁻¹ cps.

vide better information on higher modes for the next large earthquake. The corrected ratios of fundamental mode excitation are shown in Figure 5. It is not possible to use these numbers to compare the energy released by the two earthquakes without knowing some of the details of the fault dimensions associated with each earthquake. Making use of a result of *Ben-Menahem* [1964], we can relate the mode excitation to the fault parameters. Equation 57 of Ben-Menahem's paper gives the longitudinal motion for a double-couple source as a function

of fault plane orientation. Using this, we can determine that if the Alaskan earthquake had been produced by a horizontal strike-slip fault at the azimuth given previously there should have been zero response at the Isabella station. The strike-slip component of the Chilean earthquake, however, would have produced a maximum effect at Isabella. Roughly speaking, the energy ratios in Figure 5 can be considered as the comparison of the excitation due to the dip-slip component of the Alaskan earthquake and the strike-slip component of the Chilean

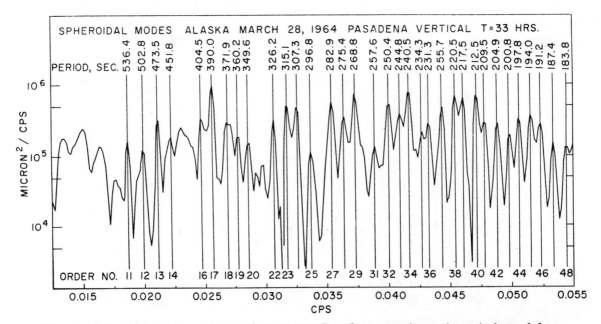

Fig. 9. Spheroidal modes, order numbers 11–48; Pasadena experimental vertical pendulum. Record length, 1012 min; sample interval, 1 min; bandwidth, 60,000⁻¹ cps.

earthquake. It is interesting that the observed ratios are almost independent of frequency, which means that, in spite of the difference in geometry of the sources, the time duration and spatial extent of the sources must have been comparable. When estimates of the fault parameters from surface wave studies become available, the ratios of mode excitation given in Figure 5 can be converted to a direct total-energy ratio for the two events.

Observed free periods. Tables 2 and 3 summarize the results of the spectrum analysis of the various recordings of the Alaskan earthquake. The individual spectrums are shown in Figures 6, 7, 8, and 9. As pointed out earlier, the signal-to-noise ratio for low-order modes was not as good as in the case of the Chilean earthquake; the numbers therefore do not necessarily represent improvements in the existing data. As was also mentioned earlier, averaging of these numbers with existing data will not necessarily produce a better result. On the basis of a comparison of the signal-to-noise ratios of the Alaskan and Chilean data recorded at Isabella, those modes which we believe were better recorded during the Alaskan earthquake are indicated with asterisks. Those modes which were equally well recorded and which might well be averaged with previous data are denoted by daggers.

Acknowledgment. I am indebted to Dr. Hugo Benioff for devising, perfecting, and installing the first generation of ultra-long-period instruments that made this study possible.

This research was supported by the Advanced Research Projects Agency and was monitored by the Air Force Office of Scientific Research under contract AF 49(638)-1337 and by grant AF-AFOSR-62-421 and NSF GP 3640.

REFERENCES

Alsop, L. E., Free spheroidal oscillations of the earth at very long periods, 2, Effect of rigidity of the inner core, *Bull. Seismol. Soc. Am., 53,* 503–515, 1963.

Anderson, D. L., Universal dispersion tables. 1, Love waves across oceans and continents on a spherical earth, *Bull. Seismol. Soc. Am., 54,* 681–726, 1964.

Backus, G., and F. Gilbert, The rotational splitting of the free oscillations of the earth, *Proc. Natl. Acad. Sci. U.S., 47,* 362–371, 1961.

Benioff, Hugo, Source wave forms of three earthquakes, *Bull. Seismol. Soc. Am., 53,* 893–903, 1963.

Benioff, Hugo, A liquid mercury pendulum seismograph (abstract), *Trans. Am. Geophys. Union, 46*(1), 149, 1965.

Ben-Menahem, Ari, Spectral response of an elastic sphere to dipolar point sources, *Bull. Seismol. Soc. Am., 54,* 1323–1340, 1964.

Blackman, R. B., and J. W. Tukey, *The Measurement of Power Spectra,* Dover Publications, New York, 1958.

Blayney, J. L., and R. Gilman, A semi-portable strain meter with continuous interferometric calibration, *Bull. Seismol. Soc. Am.,* in press, 1966.

Bolt, B., Revised torsional eigenperiods from the 1960 Trieste data, *Geophys. J., 7,* 510–512, 1963.

Brune, J., and J. Dorman, Seismic waves and earth structure in the Canadian shield, *Bull. Seismol. Soc. Am., 53,* 167–209, 1963.

Gilbert, F., and G. Backus, The rotational splitting of the free oscillations of the earth, 2, *Rev. Geophys., 3,* 1–9, 1965.

Pekeris, C. L., Z. Alterman, and H. Jarosch, Studies in terrestrial spectroscopy, *J. Geophys. Res., 68,* 2887–2908, 1963.

Smith, S. W., Seismic digital data acquisition systems, *Rev. Geophys., 3,* 151–156, 1965.

Toksöz, M. N., and D. Anderson, Velocities of long-period surface waves and structure of the upper mantle (abstract), *Trans. Am. Geophys. Union, 46,* 157, 1965.

(Manuscript received June 15, 1965; revised October 31, 1965.)

V
SUMMARY
AND
CONCLUSIONS

S. T. ALGERMISSEN
U.S. COAST AND GEODETIC SURVEY*

Seismic Hazards Reduction in Alaska

In 1964, Alaska experienced the entire spectrum of damage that a major earthquake is capable of inflicting (Hansen and others, 1966). Tectonic subsidence and uplift (Plafker, 1965) altered many shorelines and rendered many harbors useless. The resulting tsunami, seiches, and slide-induced waves caused great damage and loss of life to coastal communities. The 10 tsunami waves that struck Kodiak destroyed all but one of the docking facilities and more than 215 structures (Kachadoorian and Plafker, 1967, and Geology volume). Landslides and soil failures of various kinds altered shorelines and caused severe damage in Anchorage (Hansen, 1965, and Geology volume). Vibration damage was common in Anchorage and other cities. It was proportionately greater in large multistory buildings than in smaller structures (Steinbrugge and others, 1967). The period of strong shaking is believed to have been greater than half a second, and the duration of shaking at levels above 2 percent gravity was at least 3 minutes in duration (Cloud, 1967).

No strong-motion seismographs were in operation in Alaska prior to the 1964 earthquake, and only two seismograph stations—College and Sitka—were operated in the state on a routine basis before that time. Thus, we have no record of strong motion during the 1964 earthquake, nor do we have much knowledge of the seismicity of Alaska for earthquakes of magnitude less than 5 or 6 before 1964. The lack of strong-motion recordings of the 1964 earthquake has been a severe handicap in the study of damage to buildings and other effects of this shock; the small number of seismograph stations before 1964 precluded any detailed study of local seismicity and its relation to the geologic structure in the area.

According to plan, the Seismic Sea Wave Warning System for the Pacific area, operated by the U.S. Coast and Geodetic Survey, issued warnings, which were effectively disseminated at points along the western coast of the United States and the islands of the Pacific, but it was, in general, not capable of warning areas within a few hundred miles of the epicenter of the 1964 shock. According to Spaeth and Berkman (1969),

ABSTRACT: This paper briefly describes the efforts made in seismology since 1964 to reduce the hazards associated with earthquakes in Alaska. Reconstruction after the earthquake, including engineering and geological work aimed at earthquake-hazard reduction, has been discussed in several referenced publications.

*Now in part Earth Sciences Laboratories, NOAA.

[553]

The City of Kodiak and the Kodiak Naval Station were the only places in Alaska which received advance warning of the tsunami. The U.S. Fleet Weather Central at the Kodiak Naval Station, which participates in the Seismic Sea Wave Warning System by maintaining a tide station and by serving as a disseminating agency, provided this local warning.

The earthquake was not located by the warning system (Honolulu Observatory) until 0452 (GMT). By 0435, the first wave had crested at 22 ft above the tide staff zero at Kodiak, giving a rise of about 16 ft on the first wave. The highest crest at Kodiak was about 30 ft above the tide staff zero (Spaeth and Berkman, 1969).

After the 1964 earthquake, funds became available for the design, installation, and operation of an Alaska Regional Tsunami Warning System. This system, operated by the Environmental Science Services Administration (ESSA), U.S. Coast and Geodetic Survey, was established in September 1967. The primary function of the warning system is to detect and locate major earthquakes in the Alaska area and to provide timely information on tsunamis and warnings to residents of that state.

The Alaska Regional System is directed from an observatory at Palmer, Alaska. A tripartite seismic array, approximately 25 mi on a side, is operated at Palmer. In addition, seismic and tide data are telemetered in real time to Palmer from a number of locations throughout Alaska. Figure 1 indicates the extent of the system. Seismic observatories manned by Coast and Geodetic Survey personnel are maintained at Adak Island, College, and Sitka, in addition to the warning system headquarters at Palmer. Details of the instrumentation and telemetry methods used by the system are given by Tilgner and Peterson (1969). Subsidiary warning systems operated at the Sitka and Adak observatories have a limited warning responsibility in their immediate areas. The warning center at Palmer may extend or cancel any watch or warning issued by Sitka or Adak. For tsunamis generated outside the Alaska region, the Palmer Observatory (Alaska Regional Tsunami Warning System) has no warning responsibilities; warnings for these tsunamis are issued from the Honolulu Observatory.

It is important to note that warnings issued by the Alaska Regional Tsunami Warning System are normally based on

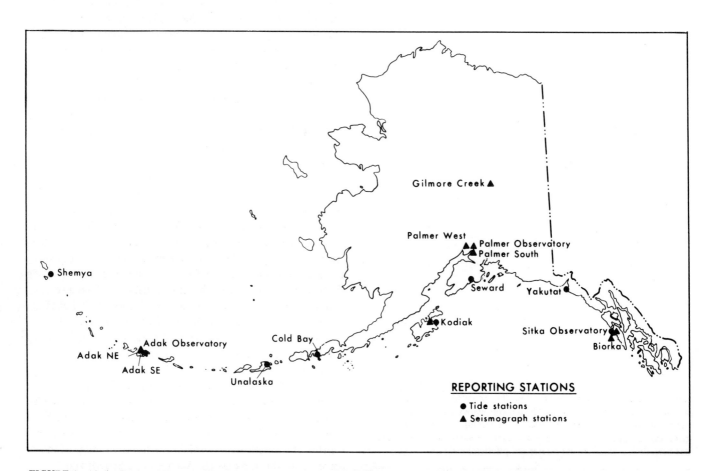

FIGURE 1   Alaska Regional Tsunami Warning System, showing reporting stations. U.S. Coast and Geodetic Survey.

seismic data, even though tide-gage data are telemetered to the center of the warning system at Palmer. Because of the need for rapid warning and because of the time required to detect a tsunami from tide data telemetered to Palmer, it is essential that preliminary warnings be issued on the basis of earthquake magnitude and hypocentral location as soon as a large earthquake is known to have occurred. At present, warnings are disseminated by the Palmer Observatory through the Alaska Disaster Office, the Office of Civil Defense, the Office of Emergency Preparedness (Region 8), the Alaska Command (Military), and the Federal Aviation Administration.

It is inevitable that warnings will at times be issued for earthquakes that will not produce damaging tsunamis. Only a small fraction of the many earthquakes of magnitude 6 or more occurring in Alaska produce tsunamis with appreciable wave heights. This creates a difficulty for the warning system since it is not possible, with the present state of knowledge, to discriminate, on the basis of the seismic signal, between tsunamigenic and nontsunamigenic earthquakes. Refinement of the warning system will involve the telemetry of data from a number of newly installed tide gages; the development of some new technique to identify tsunamigenic earthquakes uniquely from their seismic signal, or the emergence, through research, of a presently unforeseen method of tsunami detection. One of the latter two developments seems to be the more attractive alternative for refinement of the warning system because of the high cost of installation, maintenance, and telemetry of tide-gage data.

In addition to seismograph stations either installed specifically as part of the Alaska Regional Tsunami Warning System or absorbed into the system, other seismographs and associated instrumentation have been installed since 1964 and are currently in operation in Alaska. A seismograph station originally placed on Middleton Island in 1964 by the U.S. Coast and Geodetic Survey as a temporary station for aftershock studies has been kept in continuous operation since that time. A station at Barrow became operational in 1964. A tripartite three-component mercury tube tiltmeter with a base length of 100 ft, installed by ESSA on Kodiak Island in September 1967, has operated more or less continuously since that time. The Geophysical Institute of the University of Alaska greatly expanded its seismic measurement program after 1964. Since that time, it has conducted seismic research programs in the Katmai area and in south central Alaska and has installed seismograph stations at as many as 12 locations

throughout Alaska. At the present time, data from eight stations in central and south central Alaska, located at Tanana, Pedro Dome, Black Rapids, Sheep Creek Mountain, Big Mountain, McKinley, Sparrevohn, and Paxson, are telemetered into the Geophysical Institute at College. The Geophysical Institute is currently installing three complete seismometer borehole packages for the purpose of monitoring crustal tilt. Installations are planned for Paxson and McKinley Park. A unit has already been installed and is operational at Gilmore Creek, north of Fairbanks (University of Alaska, 1970).

Lack of strong-motion data, as pointed out previously, is a severe deficiency in our knowledge of the 1964 earthquake. With funds that became available in the aftermath of the 1964 earthquake, ESSA installed 15 three-component accelerographs and 98 seismoscopes in Alaska during 1964 and 1965. These instruments have already yielded a number of useful records of earthquake strong motion. Figure 2 shows the distribution of strong-motion accelerographs in Alaska at the present time. The 98 seismoscopes are installed in clusters in the vicinity of each accelerograph.

Seismographs were installed by ESSA on Semisopochnoi and Little Sitkin islands; five were installed on Amchitka Island for the purpose of recording the nuclear shot MILROW detonated on October 2, 1969. Strain extensometers were also installed on Amchitka to monitor the shot. To monitor regional seismicity, some of the seismograph systems were installed 3 months before the shot. The five units on Amchitka remain in operation on a continuous basis at present.

The great amount of various kinds of seismic instrumentation installed in Alaska since 1964 has already appreciably reduced earthquake hazards to life and property through the implementation of a regional tsunami warning service and through strong-motions records, which will prove useful in the earthquake-resistant design of buildings. The research papers on every phase of the earthquake phenomenon in Alaska are only now beginning to appear in the literature. They are, for the most part, based on geophysical data recorded, collected, and analyzed since the 1964 earthquake. This greatly expanded base of data and the analysis of these data will undoubtedly lead to a more thorough understanding of seismic hazards in Alaska and will result in the development of techniques to further reduce the hazards to life and property in the future.

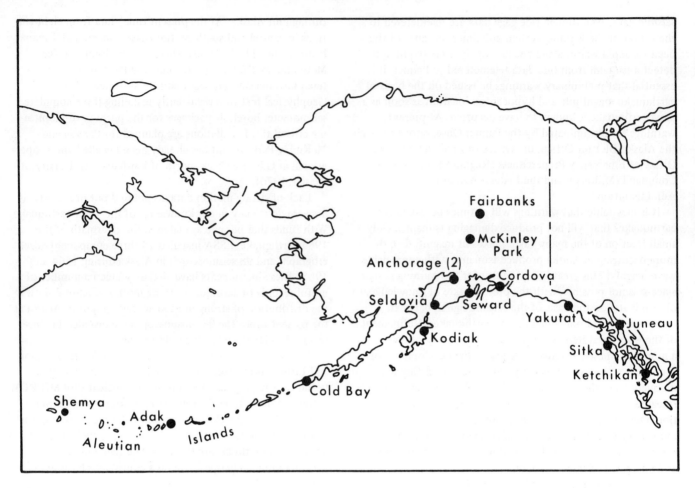

FIGURE 2   Three-component strong-motion accelerograph installations in Alaska.

REFERENCES

Cloud, William K., 1967. Strong-motion and building-period measurements *in* Volume II-A: The Prince William Sound, Alaska, earthquake of 1964 and aftershocks. Environmental Science Services Administration, U.S. Coast and Geodetic Survey. Washington: Government Printing Office. p. 319–331.

Hansen, Wallace R., 1965. Effects of the earthquake of March 27, 1964, at Anchorage, Alaska. U.S. Geological Survey Professional Paper 542-A. Washington: Government Printing Office. 68p. Also *in* The Great Alaska Earthquake of 1964: Geology. NAS Pub. 1601. Washington: National Academy of Sciences, 1971.

Hansen, Wallace R., Edwin B. Eckel, William E. Schaem, Robert E. Lyle, Warren George, and Genie Chance, 1966. The Alaska earthquake, March 27, 1964: Field investigations and reconstruction effort. U.S. Geological Survey Professional Paper 541. Washington: Government Printing Office. 111 p.

Kachadoorian, Reuben, and George Plafker, 1967. Effects of the earthquake of March 27, 1964 on the communities of Kodiak and nearby islands. U.S. Geological Survey Professional Paper 542-F. Washington; Government Printing Office. 41 p. Abstract *in* The Great Alaska Earthquake of 1964:Geology. NAS Pub.1601.

Washington: National Academy of Sciences, 1971.

Plafker, George, 1965. Tectonic deformation associated with the 1964 Alaska earthquake. *Science,* 148 (June 25), 1675–1687.

Spaeth, Mark G., and Saul C. Berkman, 1969. The tsunami of March 28, 1964, as recorded at tide stations *in* Volume II-B,C: The Prince William Sound, Alaska, earthquake of 1964 and aftershocks. Environmental Science Services Administration, U.S. Coast and Geodetic Survey. Washington:Government Printing Office, p. 223–307.

Steinbrugge, Karl V., John H. Manning, and Henry J. Degenkolb, 1967. Building damage in Anchorage *in* Volume II-A: The Prince William Sound, Alaska, earthquake of 1964 and aftershocks. Environmental Science Services Administration, U.S. Coast and Geodetic Survey. Washington: Government Printing Office. p. 7–217.

Tilgner, Edward E., and Jon R. Peterson, 1969. The Alaska Tsunami Warning System *in* Volume II-B,C: The Prince William Sound, Alaska, earthquake of 1964 and aftershocks. Environmental Science Services Administration, U.S. Coast and Geodetic Survey. Washington: Government Printing Office. p. 309–324.

University of Alaska, 1970. Geophysical Institute Annual Report, 1968–69. College: University of Alaska. 111 p.

[556]

DON TOCHER

NATIONAL OCEANIC AND ATMOSPHERIC ADMINISTRATION

The 1964 Alaska Earthquake: Seismologic Conclusions

The Alaska earthquake of March 28, 1964, felt over an estimated area of 1,800,000 km², was sufficiently strong to produce damage over an area of approximately 200,000 km² (Cloud and Scott, 1969, and this volume). These estimates do not include distant areas affected by the action of seiches and by the tsunami that originated in the coastal waters of south central Alaska and spread over the entire Pacific Basin. The shock was accompanied by regional displacements, both vertical and horizontal, which were detectable over an area probably greater than 280,000 km² (Plafker, 1969, and this volume).

The epicenter most satisfactorily derivable from available seismographic data is at lat. 61.04 ±0.05°N, long. 147.73 ±0.07°W, a point just north of Prince William Sound (Sherburne and others, 1969, and this volume).

Pertinent data from seismic stations at teleseismic distances allow us to conclude that the depth of the hypocenter was normal, or less than 60 km beneath the earth's surface. The sparseness of seismic instrumentation in Alaska at the time of the shock makes a more precise determination of the depth impossible. Sherburne and others therefore arbitrarily restricted the focal depth at 33 km (the depth of the base of the earth's crust in the Jeffreys–Bullen earth model) and thence derived an origin time of 03^h 36^m 14.0^s Greenwich Mean Time (GMT). The magnitude M_s (derived from 37 observations of surface waves recorded at distant stations) was found to be 8.3 ± 0.3 (Sherburne and others, 1969, and this volume). This value of M_s places the 1964 Alaska earthquake in the same rank as the San Francisco earthquake of April 18, 1906.

Several of the seismologic studies in this volume lead to the conclusion that the present instrumentation in most seismic stations is not suitable for adequately recording major earthquakes. The lessons learned from the 1964 Alaska earthquake have led to the installation of a great deal of new instrumentation, designed to give improved tsunami warnings in Alaska and to provide additional strong-ground-motion recordings, particularly those needed by architects and structural engineers for earthquake-resistant design. Although these augmentations of existing instrumentation networks were clearly necessary, they are far from sufficient to remove all the deficiencies in our capability to record adequately the seismic disturbances from a future major earthquake in Alaska.

Despite such limitations, studies of this shock have already led to fundamentally important conclusions regarding the mechanism operative in the hypocentral region and the earthquake's effect on the permanent strain field at great distances from the hypocenter. Wyss and Brune (1967, and this volume) have carefully documented the complexities of the source failure mechanism and conclude that the short-period records of the earthquake indicate a multiple-event mechanism whereby a propagating rupture triggered a succession of distinct events.

An interesting topic of fundamental significance concerns the orientation of the fault plane and the direction of the relative movement of the rock on either side of it. The ambiguity of interpretation inherent in studies of the direction of first motions of P waves led to an early difference of opinion on the focal mechanism of the Alaska earthquake. The

P-wave data are consistent with either of two mechanisms: reverse faulting on a fault with strike N 062°–072°E and a steep dip to the southeast; or thrust faulting on a fault with nearly the same strike, but dipping northwestward at a gentle angle under Alaska. The section of this volume that deals with the focal mechanism of the earthquake includes early postearthquake papers favoring both interpretations. These are followed by other more recently completed studies that add, bit by bit, to the preponderance of evidence favoring the interpretation that, in the Alaska earthquake, movement took place on a low-angle thrust fault dipping to the north or northwest. This fault movement lends support to the theory of plate tectonics (Isacks and others, 1968), because the movement represents thrusting of an oceanic plate under the continental margin.

CONCLUSIONS

The investigations reported in this volume and the deliberations of the Panel on Seismology have led to the broad conclusion that basic research in all aspects of seismology and geodesy and the general application of modern technological developments to seismic instrumentation and geodetic surveying can and will contribute to the overall goal of reducing earthquake hazards. In selecting the following five conclusions for discussion from a much longer list that might have been discussed, the Panel has chosen to emphasize those areas of seismologic and geodetic effort that seem to hold the most immediate promise of a reasonably quick return on the required investment.

1. *More extensive seismological and geodetic research should be undertaken on the physical mechanisms involved in the buildup, storage, and release of elastic-strain energy in the earth. Particularly important are geodetic studies of areal strain, faulting-movement studies in regions of fault creep and earthquake activity, studies of local earthquake strains and tilts in association with microearthquake investigations, and teleseismic studies of failure-plane orientations. Theoretical and experimental investigations of mechanisms of rock failure are also of great importance.*

A thorough understanding of the mechanisms involved in the sudden conversion of elastic-strain energy into elastic-wave energy is a vital prerequisite to any program of earthquake prediction, modification, or control. The tools with which to investigate directly the changes in the strain field of the earth's crust were developed many years ago, but have not been deployed in numbers sufficient to provide more than a glimpse into the pattern of strain changes in seismically active regions. Indirect techniques for detecting strain changes, such as those involving measurements of telluric currents, subsurface resistivity, or magnetic fields, eventually

may provide even more useful information on strain changes at depth.

It is now well established that segments of some faults in highly seismic regions may undergo aseismic offset, or fault creep. Studies of the distribution of fault creep in space and time, coupled with concurrent studies of strain changes and microearthquake activity, should provide additional insight into the understanding of earthquake mechanisms.

Even the failure mechanism or mechanisms involved in earthquakes are not definitely identified. Laboratory and *in situ* investigations of fracture propagation, the effects of confining pressure, temperature, pore pressure, and other variables on rock failure, and a variety of related investigations hold considerable promise of enhancing our understanding of the failure mechanism that results in the release of earthquake energy.

2. *Support should be provided for the continued operation and improvement of the World-Wide Network of Standard Seismographs, and for seismological station coverage in Alaska, the most seismically active area in North America.*

Observational seismology has a long tradition of international cooperation. The destructive forces of earthquakes know no national boundaries, and seismologists generally have been willing to exchange seismograms, bulletins, and other seismic data freely with investigators of all nations.

A milestone in the history of international cooperation was reached with the establishment in the early 1960's of the World-Wide Network of Standard Seismographs. The network consists of 115 stations located in 61 different countries; each station is equipped with three long-period and three short-period seismographs and precision calibration and timing systems. In only a decade of operation, this network has contributed data from standardized, well-calibrated equipment on a scale unprecedented in the science of seismology. These data, freely available to scientific investigators of all nations, have contributed to a burgeoning increase in our understanding of the tectonic processes that lead to earthquakes, as well as of the mechanics of the earthquakes themselves.

The Alaska earthquake of March 28, 1964, not only underscored the importance of the World-Wide Network of Standard Seismographs, but it also emphasized some important deficiencies in the facilities in existence at the time of the shock. Despite Alaska's well-documented history of major earthquakes, only two seismographic stations were operating in this vast region on March 28, 1964. Even though a number of new stations have commenced operation in Alaska since 1964, the density of coverage is far below that considered desirable in other seismically less active areas in the United States.

Furthermore, most of the first-class seismographic stations around the world had insufficient dynamic recording range to record properly the maximum ground motions from this major Alaska earthquake, so that a great deal of potentially useful information was lost. Extension of the useful range of recordable ground motions at a selected subset of stations in the World-Wide Network of Standard Seismographs would go far toward correcting this obvious deficiency in global seismographic coverage. A minimum of 30 of the existing stations, well distributed geographically, should be equipped with three-component low-magnification seismographs to provide on-scale recordings of major earthquakes. Additionally, a minimum of 10 stations, well distributed geographically, should be equipped to record seismic waves in the period range of 100–500 seconds.

3. *Recordings of ground motions at the structural-damage level are urgently needed. The existing incomplete network of strong-motion recording instruments should be improved and extended to all regions in which earthquakes are a potential hazard. Some instruments should be placed in important structures like high-rise buildings, dams, and nuclear-power plants; others should be installed on different kinds of foundation material remote from large structures.*

Strong-motion seismographs designed to provide the basic data on which the earthquake engineers can base their designs have been operated in the United States since 1932 by the Seismological Field Survey, now of the National Oceanic and Atmospheric Administration. In addition, a large number of strong-motion seismographs have been installed in large Los Angeles buildings under recently adopted provisions of the Los Angeles building code. Other large cities on the Pacific Coast are considering the adoption of similar code provisions. Nevertheless, the existing set of strong-motion data is still limited in scope and does not provide earthquake engineers with an adequate basis for proper design of structures on all types of foundation materials.

There is a chance, however, that the proliferation of strong-motion seismographs in buildings over six stories tall will mask the need for instruments at locations remote from large buildings, which would record differences in ground motion on a variety of rock and soil types and on different thicknesses of near-surface materials of relatively low strength. Additional instruments are particularly needed near active faults.

An effort should be made to encourage the installation of strong-motion seismographs in other countries that are subject to strong earthquakes and thus to increase the worldwide accumulation of useful strong-motion data.

4. *Research should be directed toward improving the tsunami-warning system. Delay in confirming a tsunami's existence can be lessened by further improvement in communications. A continuation of present efforts to find in the seismic signal itself criteria of the generation of a tsunami is particularly important. Success of such efforts would obviate the need to wait for data from tide gages to confirm the existence of a potentially dangerous wave.*

As a general rule, tsunamigenic earthquakes originate in regions some distance away from the coastal population centers of California, Oregon, Washington, and Hawaii. The existing Pacific Seismic Sea Wave Warning System in Honolulu has, with few exceptions, been able to give an adequate warning of an impending tsunami in the interval between the occurrence of the earthquake and the time of arrival of the tsunami at the population centers.

In the case of tsunamis generated locally, such as in southern Alaska, it is difficult, if not impossible, to issue a warning fast enough to be effective. There appears to be no substitute for a continuing program of education of the public in coastal regions subject to strong earthquakes. In some parts of Japan frequently subject to tsunami effects, the rule is that "If you feel an earthquake, move to high ground." In southern Alaska, where tsunamis are less frequent, it will be necessary to remind the public continually of the tsunami hazard associated with strong earthquakes.

Within the next few years, the transmission of water-level data from numerous tide gages around the edge of the Pacific Ocean via satellite telemetry to the Honolulu Tsunami Warning Center should make possible the more timely issuance of tsunami warnings and should contribute to a sharp reduction in the number of false alarms.

Expanded research to establish methods of predicting wave-runup height variations can contribute greatly to the issuance of more detailed, and therefore more useful, tsunami warnings.

The greatest promise for longer-term improvements in the tsunami-warning process seems to lie in efforts to extract from the seismic signals some information on the amount and areal extent of vertical dislocation of the ocean floor in the epicentral region, thus permitting a seismometrically based estimate of tsunami magnitude to be made even before specific wave-height data are available.

5. *Precise first-order triangulation and level surveys should be made in areas in which earthquakes are likely to occur, to provide a base for the study of actual surface deformation in an earthquake. Periodic measurement of the national first-order network and other regional networks would give information on slow tectonic movement and hence would lead to further identification of earthquake-prone regions.*

From precise, first-order triangulation surveys in California made before and immediately after the major earthquake of April 18, 1906, Professor Harry Fielding Reid deduced the elastic rebound theory of earthquake generation. If of sufficient precision and accuracy, geodetic surveys (triangulation, trilateration, and level surveys) repeated periodically in the more seismic land areas may yield a much more comprehensive picture than we now possess of the nature of changes in the strain field of the earth's crust before and after large earthquakes. If extended to other regions of lower seismicity, the periodic repetition of precise geodetic surveys will probably permit the identification of regions where a future major shock is likely to occur. In the entire recorded history of the United States, only one series of major shocks has occurred near New Madrid, Missouri (1811–1812), and only one destructive earthquake has struck Charleston, South Carolina (1886). It seems not unlikely that one or more future shocks of similar size and destructiveness may occur in other regions of low seismicity that have not yet, in recorded history, been visited by a major earthquake. If extended to areas of relatively low seismicity, precise, periodically repeated geodetic surveys may well serve to identify regions where a major shock is likely to occur in the future.

REFERENCES

Cloud, William K., and Nina H. Scott, 1969. Distribution of intensity, Prince William Sound earthquake of 1964 in Volume II-B,C: The Prince William Sound, Alaska, earthquake of 1964 and aftershocks. Environmental Science Services Administration, U.S. Coast and Geodetic Survey. Washington: Government Printing Office. p. 5–48. Also in The Great Alaska Earthquake of 1964: Seismology and Geodesy. NAS Pub. 1602. Washington: National Academy of Sciences, 1972.

Isacks, Bryan, Jack Oliver, and Lynn R. Sykes, 1968. Seismology and the new global tectonics. Journal of Geophysical Research, 73 (September 15), 5855–5899.

Plafker, George, 1969. Tectonics of the March 27, 1964, Alaska earthquake. U.S. Geological Survey Professional Paper 543-I. Washington: Government Printing Office. 74 p. Also in The Great Alaska Earthquake of 1964: Seismology and Geodesy. NAS Pub. 1602. Washington: National Academy of Sciences, 1972.

Sherburne, R. W., S. T. Algermissen, and Samuel T. Harding, 1969. The hypocenter, origin time, and magnitude of the Prince William Sound earthquake of March 28, 1964 in Volume II-B,C: The Prince William Sound, Alaska, earthquake of 1964 and aftershocks. Environmental Science Services Administration, U.S. Coast and Geodetic Survey. Washington: Government Printing Office. p. 49–69. Also in The Great Alaska Earthquake of 1964: Seismology and Geodesy. NAS Pub. 1602. Washington: National Academy of Sciences, 1972.

Wyss, Max, and James N. Brune, 1967. The Alaska earthquake of 28 March 1964: A complex multiple rupture. Bulletin of the Seismological Society of America, 57 (October), 1017–1023. Also in The Great Alaska Earthquake of 1964: Seismology and Geodesy. NAS Pub. 1602. Washington: National Academy of Sciences, 1972.

Annotated
Bibliography

Aki, Keiiti, Minoru Hori, and Hideteru Matumoto. Micro-aftershocks observed at a Temporary Array Station on the Kenai Peninsula from May 19 to June 7, 1964 *in* Volume II-B, C: The Prince William Sound, Alaska, earthquake of 1964 and aftershocks. Environmental Science Services Administration, U.S. Coast and Geodetic Survey. Washington: Government Printing Office, 1969. p. 131–156. Also *in* The Great Alaska Earthquake of 1964: Seismology and Geodesy. NAS Pub. 1602. Washington: National Academy of Sciences, 1972.
Describes the method used to study microaftershocks associated with the Alaska earthquake of March 28, 1964 (GMT), and the conclusions reached.

Algermissen, S. T. Energy and depth of foci of the aftershocks of the Prince William Sound earthquake of March 28, 1964 (Abstract) *in* Science in Alaska, 1964: Proceedings Fifteenth Alaskan Science Conference, College, Alaska, August 31 to September 4, 1964. George Dahlgren, editor. College: Alaska Division American Association for the Advancement of Science, March 15, 1965. p. 169.
Explains the energy distribution of the aftershocks of the Prince William Sound earthquakes of March 28. Compares depth of foci of aftershocks computed using the temporary USC&GS network with the depth established by using *pP* and other depth-phased recordings on seismograms at teleseismic distances.

Algermissen, S. T. Introduction: Foreshocks and aftershocks *in* The Great Alaska Earthquake of 1964: Seismology and Geodesy. NAS Pub. 1602. Washington: National Academy of Sciences, 1972.
Describes seismic setting of the Prince William Sound–Kodiak region and Alaska as a whole before 1964. Briefly analyzes aftershock data. Expresses hope that volume will stimulate further research.

Algermissen, S. T. Introduction to seismological and marine geological studies of the 1964 Prince William Sound, Alaska, earthquake *in* Volume II-B, C: The Prince William Sound, Alaska, earthquake of 1964 and aftershocks. Environmental Science Services Administration, U.S. Coast and Geodetic Survey. Washington: Government Printing Office, 1969.
Introduces the volume on the seismological aspects of the earthquake and explains some of the difficulties that limited the collection of data.

Algermissen, S. T. Mechanism of the Prince William Sound earthquake *in* ESSA Symposium on Earthquake Prediction. Washington: Government Printing Office, 1966. p. 20–25.
Suggests that a study of first-motion directions for all earthquakes in a region might reveal some significant pattern useful for prediction.

Algermissen, S. T. Seismic hazards reduction in Alaska *in* The Great Alaska Earthquake of 1964: Seismology and Geodesy. NAS Pub. 1602. Washington: National Academy of Sciences, 1972.
New and expanded seismological research and operational programs in Alaska are directed toward the reduction of earthquake hazards. Programs include instrumentation and analysis designed to obtain earthquake strong-motion and building-response data, new tsunami warning facilities, and study of crustal structure and local seismicity.

Algermissen, S. T. Seismic studies in Alaska *in* ESSA Symposium on Earthquake Prediction. Washington: Government Printing Office, 1966. p. 48–52.
Reports that south central Alaska has been selected as a desirable area for monitoring all indicators that might foretell the occurrence of an earthquake. Seismic instrumentation was installed after the 1964 earthquake. Gives some results from data already available.

Algermissen, S. T. The program in engineering seismology of the Coast and Geodetic Survey *in* Earthquake and Geologic Hazards Conference, 1964. San Francisco: California Resources Agency [1965]. p. 54–60.
Summarizes development of USC&GS engineering seismology program, which has involved primarily the development of a strong-motion seismograph network. Future work in engineering seismology will include more digital-computer methods of analysis.

Algermissen, S. T., W. A. Rinehart, R. W. Sherburne, and W. H. Dillinger, Jr. Preshocks and aftershocks of the Prince William Sound earthquake of March 28, 1964 *in* Volume II-B,C: The Prince William Sound, Alaska, earthquake of 1964 and aftershocks. Environmental Science Services Administration, U.S. Coast and Geodetic Survey. Washington: Government Printing Office, 1969. p. 79–130. Also *in* The Great Alaska Earthquake of 1964: Seismology and Geodesy. NAS Pub. 1602. Washington: National Academy of Sciences, 1972.

Presents data on 2,210 aftershocks and preshocks. Finds that nearly all energy released in the aftershock sequence was confined to the shelf area adjacent to Kodiak Island, the Kenai Peninsula, and Prince William Sound.

Alsop, L. E., and J. N. Brune. Observation of free oscillations excited by a deep earthquake. *Journal of Geophysical Research*, 70 (December 15, 1965), 6165–6174.
Finds that results of Fourier analysis of a seismogram of horizontal motion obtained after the August 15, 1963, earthquake on the Peru-Bolivia border make it possible to limit the source of the mechanism to several possibilities, one of which–dip-slip normal motion along a plane with an angle of dip nearly equal to 45°–agrees with a fault-plane solution based on long-period *P* waves.

Anderson, William A. Tsunami warning in Crescent City, California, and Hilo, Hawaii *in* The Great Alaska Earthquake of 1964: Human Ecology. NAS Pub. 1607. Washington: National Academy of Sciences, 1970. p. 116–124.
Finds the tsunami warning system better organized in Hilo than in Crescent City because public officials in Hilo had acted on information received and had improved warning and evacuation procedures in the community.

Balakrishna, S., and S. Ramakrishna. Alaskan earthquake and gravity time-curve. *Current Science*, 33 (December 5, 1964), 714–715.
The record obtained by the gravimeter in Hyderabad during the Alaska earthquake on March 28–29 shows four large aftershocks in addition to the main shock, over a period of about 5 hours.

Barnes, David F. Gravity changes during the Alaska earthquake. *Journal of Geophysical Research*, 71 (January 15, 1966), 451–456. Also *in* The Great Alaska Earthquake of 1964: Seismology and Geodesy. NAS Pub. 1602. Washington: National Academy of Sciences, 1972.
Reports on gravity changes observed by comparison of gravity traverse made in 1962 with one made in 1964 along Richardson Highway, Alaska. These gravity changes were used to compute elevation changes produced by the earthquake and to provide information about the mass changes that brought about the elevation changes.

Berg, Eduard. Crustal structure in Alaska *in* The Great Alaska Earthquake of 1964: Seismology and Geodesy. NAS Pub. 1602. Washington: National Academy of Sciences, 1972.
Presents seismic-refraction profiles and gravity and magnetic surveys in Alaska. These provide knowledge of crustal structure in interior Alaska.

Berg, Eduard. Fundamental and applied research in seismology in Alaska. Final Report UAG R-179. College: University of Alaska, Geophysical Institute, May 1966. 44 p.
Lists the seismic stations that had been established and the results registered. Mentions that a catalog of earthquakes that had occurred before 1965 had been compiled. Outlines the technical improvements planned and the new fields of research–tectonic movement and deformation release–that were to be developed.

Berg, Eduard. The Alaskan earthquake, its location and seismic setting *in* Science in Alaska, 1964: Proceedings Fifteenth Alaskan Science Conference, College, Alaska, August 31 to September 4, 1964. George Dahlgren, editor. College: Alaska Division American Association for the Advancement of Science, March 15, 1965. p. 218–232.

Presents a study of the seismicity and energy release for Alaska from 1904 to 1964, including the March 28 earthquake. Fault-plane solutions for the main shock and a major aftershock are presented and discussed.

Berg, Eduard. The Alaskan earthquake of March, 1964. University of Alaska Geophysical Institute's Annual Report 1963–64. College: University of Alaska, Geophysical Institute, 1964. p. 69–82.
Presents a seismologist's review, based on the work of several investigating institutions, of the nature and effects of the great Alaska earthquake.

Berg, Eduard. Triggering of the Alaskan earthquake and major aftershocks *in* University of Alaska Geophysical Institute's Annual Report 1965–66. College: University of Alaska, Geophysical Institute, 1966. p. 62.
Suggests that the unloading of the crust in the Continental Shelf area of the Gulf of Alaska by the large ocean tides may be considered as a triggering mechanism for the great Alaska earthquake and for major aftershocks.

Berg, Eduard. Triggering of the Alaskan earthquake of March 28, 1964, and major aftershocks by low ocean tide loads. *Nature*, 210 (May 28, 1966), 893–896. Also *in* The Great Alaska Earthquake of 1964: Seismology and Geodesy. NAS Pub. 1602. Washington: National Academy of Sciences, 1972.
Because the Alaska earthquake occurred during low tide levels, the tsunami did not cause as much damage as if it had occurred at high tide level. The unloading of the crust by large ocean tides may be considered as a triggering mechanism for the earthquake and major aftershocks.

Berg, Eduard, Susumu Kubota, and Jurgen Kienle. Preliminary determination of crustal structure in the Katmai National Monument, Alaska. *Bulletin of the Seismological Society of America*, 57 (December 1967), 1367–1392.
Gives the results of seismic and gravity observations made in the active volcanic area of Katmai in the summer of 1965. These show a correlation between the earthquakes and the tectonics and volcanoes of the area; the presence of material with low rigidity at a depth below the Moho; weak agreement between the gravity data and seismic data on the depth of the Moho; an uplift along a very steep Bouguer anomaly associated tectonically with the volcanoes and a possible magma reservoir at its southwestern tip.

Berg, Eduard, Norbert Sperlich, and William Feetham. Large aperture seismic telemetering system for central Alaska. Scientific Report UAG R-188. College: University of Alaska, Geophysical Institute, May 1967. 43 p.
Describes technical details of the large-aperture seismic telemeter network in Alaska. The sensitivity of the seismic stations allows recording of earthquakes down to magnitude 4 in the 80°-distant range.

Blum, P. A., R. Gaulow, Georges Jobert, and Nelly Jobert. On ultralong period seismometers operating under vacuum. Royal Society [London] Proceedings. Ser. A, 290, No. 1422, 1966, 318–322.
Announces that a new ultralong-period seismometer, operating in a vacuum, was in operation at various stations for the purpose of studying the free and forced oscillations of the earth. Gives results concerning the free periods from the Alaska earthquake, March 28, 1964.

Blume, John A. A structural-dynamic analysis of an earthquake damaged 14-story building *in* Volume II-A: The Prince William

Sound, Alaska, earthquake of 1964 and aftershocks. Environmental Science Services Administration, U.S. Coast and Geodetic Survey. Washington: Government Printing Office, 1967. p. 357–382.
Examines the effects of forced-vibration tests performed by the USC&GS on the Mt. McKinley apartment building, Anchorage, that had been damaged during the earthquake. Discusses the damage, the structure, and its calculated preearthquake dynamic properties.

Blume, John A., and Associates Research Division. Report on structural damage in Anchorage, Alaska, caused by the earthquake of March 27, 1964. Report prepared for Structural Response Program, Operational Safety Division, Nevada Operations Office, U.S. Atomic Energy Commission. San Francisco: John A. Blume and Associates Research Division, 1966. 91 p.
Observes and evaluates the response of typical structures to the ground motion caused by the earthquake. Analyzes the structural damage from the point of view of the causative mechanisms.

Bolt, Bruce A. Seismic air waves from the great 1964 Alaskan earthquake. Nature, 202 (June 13, 1964), 1095–1096.
Relates that exceptional atmospheric waves, resembling those from large nuclear explosions, were recorded at Berkeley after the great Alaska earthquake. Apparently no such intense dispersive seismic air wave has previously been reported, and the observation suggests the possibility of an additional method of predicting a tsunami.

Branch, D. D. Effect at Rabaul of seismic sea waves generated by the great Alaskan earthquake of 28 March 1964 in Short papers from the Vulcanological Observatory, Rabaul, New Britain. Australia Bureau of Mineral Resources, Geology and Geophysics Report No. 107, 1967. p. 17–19.
A tsunami with an initial wave height of 4 in. arrived at Rabaul on March 29, 1964, from the Alaska earthquake. The third wave was 16 in. in height; a maximum double amplitude of 24 in. was later recorded. Calculates the velocity of the first wave to be 480 mph, and the average ocean depth between Alaska and Rabaul to be 15,500 ft.

Bredehoeft, John D., Hilton H. Cooper, Jr., Istavros S. Papadopulos, and Robert R. Bennett. Seismic fluctuations in an open artesian water well in Geological Survey Research 1965: Chapter C. U.S. Geological Survey Professional Paper 525-C. Washington: Government Printing Office, 1965. p. 51–57.
Analysis of the fluctuations caused by the Alaska earthquake of March 27, 1964, in an artesian well in northern Florida illustrates the theory that the degree to which the water level in an open well responds to a seismic wave is determined by (a) the dimensions of the well, (b) the transmissibility, storage coefficient, and porosity of the aquifer, and (c) the period and amplitude of the seismic wave.

Brown, Delmer L. Tsunamic activity accompanying the Alaskan earthquake of 27 March 1964. Anchorage: U.S. Army Corps of Engineers, 1964. 31 p.
Investigates the probable cause of the tsunamis and studies their nature. Concludes that the movement of the earthquake occurred along a fault zone extending from a point near Valdez Arm, through southwestern Prince William Sound, to Kodiak Island. Considers that movement along this fault was responsible for the tsunamis.

Bureau of Land Management. Anatomy of an earthquake–based on reports by U.S. Geological Survey. Our Public Lands, 14 (July 1964), 10–11.
Describes very vividly the mechanics and disastrous effects of the great Alaska earthquake.

California Division of Mines and Geology. Geologic hazards: Land level changes in Alaskan earthquake. Mineral Information Service, 18 (October 1965), 184.
Discusses the tremendous area affected by the earthquake and the enormous land-level changes that resulted.

California Division of Mines and Geology. Getting nearer to earthquake prediction. Mineral Information Service, 22 (April 1969), 68–69.
Presents the views of L. C. Pakiser of the U.S. Geological Survey who shows cautious optimism on the possibilities of earthquake prediction and potential methods of earthquake modification and control. He estimates that a 10-year intensified research program leading to earthquake prediction would be necessary.

California Division of Mines and Geology. Table top disasters: Seismic sea waves to be studied. Mineral Information Service, 22 (February 1969), 18.
Announces that experimental and theoretical studies at California Institute of Technology will deal with the generation, travel, and effects of tsunamis on coastlines. Describes the undersea earth motion associated with the earthquake as "like a giant wave paddle, producing a tsunami that traveled across the open sea to damage portions of our coast."

Case, J. E., D. F. Barnes, George Plafker, and S. L. Robbins. Gravity survey and regional geology of the Prince William Sound epicentral region, Alaska. U.S. Geological Survey Professional Paper 543-C. Washington: Government Printing Office, 1966. 12 p. Also in The Great Alaska Earthquake of 1964: Geology. NAS Pub. 1601. Washington: National Academy of Sciences, 1971.
Gives the results of the studies of regional geology, changes of land level, faulting, and effects of waves on shorelines, that were conducted by the U.S. Geological Survey after the great Alaska earthquake. Discusses also the gravity survey that was conducted to establish the regional geologic and tectonic setting of the earthquake.

Chouhan, R. K. S. Aftershock sequence of Alaskan earthquake of 28th March 1964. Pure and Applied Geophysics, 64, No. II (1966), 43–48.
Finds that the aftershock sequence of the Alaska earthquake consisted of two linear segments of compressional elastic creep; the duration of activity was about 24 days. Calculates that 2 percent of total strain energy stored in the elastic-creep element was used as tsunamis and the rest lost as heat. Most of the tsunami energy resulted from the shear type of recovery.

Christensen, Mark N., and Bruce A. Bolt. Earth movements: Alaskan earthquake, 1964. Science, 145 (September 11, 1964), 1207–1216.
Symposium finds that the earthquake revealed an unexpected pattern of regional crustal movement. Obtains valuable information on problems of design and execution of buildings that must withstand shaking. Finds grave problems exist for expanding metropolitan areas in seismic zones.

Cloud, William K. Forced vibration of the Mt. McKinley Building (field measurements) in Volume II-A: The Prince William Sound, Alaska, earthquake of 1964 and aftershocks. Environmental Science Services Administration, U.S. Coast and Geodetic Survey. Washington: Government Printing Office, 1967. p. 333–355.
Explains the results of a series of exploratory forced-vibration tests run by the USC&GS on the 14-story reinforced-concrete Mt. McKinley apartment building in Anchorage. Information obtained on six of the

structure's natural modes of vibration showed that the building had a softening spring system.

Cloud, William K. Strong-motion and building-period measurements *in* Volume II-A: The Prince William Sound, Alaska, earthquake of 1964 and aftershocks. Environmental Science Services Administration, U.S. Coast and Geodetic Survey. Washington: Government Printing Office, 1967. p. 319–331.
Presents the only strong-motion seismogram obtained of the earthquake's (M = 8.4) shock from nearest strong-motion USC&GS seismograph station located at Tacoma, Washington, 1,300 mi from the epicenter. Provides records from two strong-motion seismographs flown to Anchorage immediately after the earthquake. These recorded several aftershocks. Records of the natural periods of seven multistory buildings in the Anchorage area reflect response of damaged buildings to forces generated by light breezes and traffic. As a result of the earthquake, 15 strong-motion seismographs and 12 other seismographs were installed in Alaska as part of a permanent network.

Cloud, William K., and Nina H. Scott. Distribution of intensity, Prince William Sound earthquake of 1964 *in* Volume II-B,C: The Prince William Sound, Alaska, earthquake of 1964 and aftershocks. Environmental Science Services Administration, U.S. Coast and Geodetic Survey. Washington: Government Printing Office, 1969. p. 5–48. Also *in* The Great Alaska Earthquake of 1964: Seismology and Geodesy. NAS Pub. 1602. Washington: National Academy of Sciences, 1972.
Gives eye-witness reports of the effects of the Prince William Sound earthquake of 1964. Summarizes these effects on an intensity map. The area over which the earthquake was felt is estimated at approximately 700,000 mi^2; damage area, exclusive of distant areas affected by tsunami and seiche action, is estimated at about 80,000 mi^2.

Coble, R. W. Alaska earthquake effects on ground water in Iowa *in* Hydrologic effects of the earthquake of March 27, 1964, outside Alaska. U.S. Geological Survey Professional Paper 544-C. Washington: Government Printing Office, 1967. p. 23–27. Also *in* The Great Alaska Earthquake of 1964: Hydrology. NAS Pub. 1603. Washington: National Academy of Sciences, 1968. p. 157–161.
Relates that the earthquake caused the water levels to fluctuate in many wells in Iowa. Gives location of reported ground-water disturbances and summarizes ground-water disturbances caused by the earthquake.

Committee on Seismology. Seismology: Responsibilities and requirements of a growing science. Part I, Summary and recommendations. A report of the Committee on Seismology of the Division of Earth Sciences. Washington: National Academy of Sciences, 1969. 38 p.
Reviews the status and role of seismology in the modern world, forecasts seismology's role in the future, and makes six general recommendations for developing the technical capability in seismology for current and future needs.

Committee on Seismology. Seismology: Responsibilities and requirements of a growing science. Part II, Problems and prospects. A report of the Committee on Seismology of the Division of Earth Sciences. Washington: National Academy of Sciences, 1969. 59 p.
Reviews and illustrates the history of seismology, particularly in the United States. Discusses the main areas of research and applications of seismologic methods. Provides insights into new or insufficiently exploited areas that can benefit the nation. Gives planners, administrators, educators, and students a reasonably comprehensive overview of the science.

Committee on the Alaska Earthquake. Toward reduction of losses from earthquakes: Conclusions from the great Alaska earthquake of 1964. Washington: National Academy of Sciences, 1969. 34 p.
Summarizes comprehensive study on the 1964 earthquake, gives committee, as well as panel, recommendations, and advocates loss-reduction programs designed not only for earthquakes but also for other sudden-impact environmental hazards.

Cook, Richard K. Radiation of sound by earthquake. Paper delivered before the 5e Congrès International d'Acoustique, Liège, Belgium, 7–14 Septembre 1965. 4 p. (Copy on file, Library, National Academy of Sciences–National Academy of Engineering, Washington, D.C.)
Discusses the manner in which, after a strong earthquake, traveling waves from the earthquake spread over the earth's surface and radiate sound into the atmosphere. The vertical component of the earth's surface motions gives rise to the sound radiation.

Cook, Richard K., and Donald M. Baker. Ionospheric motions caused by Rayleigh waves (Abstract). *Transactions, American Geophysical Union,* 46 (March 1965), 55.
Estimates the particle velocity of a ground-motion-launched, vertically propagating air wave. Shows that the velocity becomes large enough to develop into a shock wave at ionospheric heights.

Cooper, Hilton H., Jr., John D. Bredehoeft, Istavros S. Papadopulos, and Robert R. Bennett. The response of well-aquifer systems to seismic waves. *Journal of Geophysical Research,* 70 (August 15, 1965), 3915–3926. Also *in* The Great Alaska Earthquake of 1964: Hydrology. NAS Pub. 1603. Washington. National Academy of Sciences, 1968. p. 122–132.
Discusses parameters of seismic water-level fluctuations in wells. The theory developed is applied to a hydroseism of the Alaska earthquake recorded in a Florida well.

Cox, Doak C. Performance of the Seismic Sea-Wave Warning System, 1948–1967. Report HIG-68-2. Honolulu: University of Hawaii, Institute of Geophysics, March 25, 1968. 79 p.
Outlines the establishment of the SSWWS, its development, and performance during 14 warnings. Recommends improvements in the system that include avoiding unnecessary warnings and minimizing the inconveniences of necessary warning periods. Considers that a regional policy of hazard evaluation is necessary.

Cox, Doak C., Masashi Hom-ma, Masatsugu Suzuki, Ryutaro Takahasi, and Robert L. Wiegel. Physically feasible means for protecting Hilo from tsunamis. Third Report of the Hilo Technical Tsunami Advisory Council to the Board of Supervisors, Hawaii County, through its Tsunami Advisory Committee. Hilo [Hawaii] : Hilo Technical Tsunami Advisory Council, 1965. 38 p.
Comments on the physical feasibility of various possible protective schemes for Hilo.

Cravat, H. R., and Capt. V. Ralph Sobieralski. 1965 and 1966 photogrammetric operations *in* Volume III: The Prince William Sound, Alaska, earthquake of 1964 and aftershocks. Environmental Science Services Administration, U.S. Coast and Geodetic Survey. Washington: Government Printing Office, 1969. p. 121–155. Also, Anchorage portion *in* The Great Alaska Earthquake of 1964: Seismology and Geodesy. NAS Pub. 1602. Washington: National Academy of Sciences, 1972.
Describes the priorities assigned for 1965 field operations that made the photogrammetric program more productive. Outlines photogram-

metric activities in the Prince William Sound area during 1965 and 1966.

Crimmin, Eileen. One year later—What happened in Alaska. *Science Digest*, 57 (March 1965), 42–46.
Reviews facts that were known about the earthquake one year later. Business already was almost as usual, despite 9,200 additional tremors recorded in Alaska since the great earthquake.

Crumlish, Joseph D., and George F. Wirth. A preliminary study of engineering seismology benefits. Environmental Science Services Administration, U.S. Coast and Geodetic Survey. Washington: Government Printing Office, 1967. 46 p.
Examines the manner in which engineering seismology and the use of USC&GS data have affected building codes. Investigates benefits derived from the incorporation of earthquake-resistant features into the construction of public buildings, particularly schools. Recommends an increase in the effectiveness of strong-motion instrumentation. Stresses also the need for collection and analysis of relevant economic data and a study of the method used to incorporate engineering–seismology advances into building codes and practices.

Davies, Kenneth, and Donald M. Baker. Ionospheric effects observed around the time of the Alaskan earthquake of March 28, 1964. *Journal of Geophysical Research*, 70 (May 1, 1965), 2251–2253.
Draws attention to ionospheric disturbances observed near Boulder, Colorado, around the time of the Alaska earthquake. Considers it possible that infrasonic waves and ionospheric disturbances observed may have been caused by pressure waves generated by the movement of the earth.

Dillinger, William H., Jr., and S. T. Algermissen. Magnitude studies of Alaska earthquakes *in* Volume II-B,C: The Prince William Sound, Alaska, earthquake of 1964 and aftershocks. Environmental Science Services Administration, U.S. Coast and Geodetic Survey. Washington: Government Printing Office, 1969. p. 175–183. Also *in* The Great Alaska Earthquake of 1964: Seismology and Geodesy. NAS Pub. 1602. Washington: National Academy of Sciences, 1972.
Compares M_L, M_s, and m_b for the main shock and aftershocks of the Prince William Sound earthquake of March 28, 1964 (GMT), and for other south central Alaska and Aleutian Islands earthquakes.

Donn, William L. Alaskan earthquake of 27 March 1964: Remote seiche stimulation. *Science*, 145 (July 17, 1964), 261–262.
Considers that water waves of up to 6 ft along the coasts of Louisiana and Texas that arrived at the time of the seismic waves, but disconnected geographically from any possible tsunami, were probably seiches generated in resonance with the seismic waves.

Donn, William L., and Eric S. Posmentier. Ground-coupled air waves from the great Alaskan earthquake. *Journal of Geophysical Research*, 69 (December 15, 1964), 5357–5361.
Shows that micropressure fluctuations that occurred at the same time as the arrival of seismic waves at various locations were produced by vertical ground motion associated with local Rayleigh waves arriving from the epicenter.

Engineering News-Record. New findings shake seismic data. *Engineering News-Record*, 175 (November 18, 1965), 138, 141.
Computer analyses of buildings that failed in Anchorage during the March 1964 earthquake reveal structural behavior that does not agree with some conventional engineering-design assumptions.

Engineering News-Record. Quake took time to move land. *Engineering News-Record*, 173 (October 8, 1964), 56.
Shannon & Wilson, Inc., Seattle, conclude that it took 1½–2 minutes of shaking to break loose the earth surface and move it around in the Alaska earthquake of March 27, 1964. Failure occurred 60 ft below the surface; most major land movements took the form of block slippage of about 15–20 ft.

Environmental Science Services Administration. ESSA Science and Engineering, July 13, 1965, to June 30, 1967. Washington: Government Printing Office, 1968. 150 p.
The first consolidated overview of ESSA. Outlines the mission, organization, and resources of ESSA and its products and services. Summarizes their 3-volume Alaska earthquake report.

Environmental Science Services Administration. ESSA Symposium on Earthquake Prediction, Rockville, Maryland, February 7, 8, 9, 1966. Washington: Government Printing Office, 1966. 167 p.
At the request of the President's Office of Science and Technology, ESSA assesses and clarifies its technical capability to manage a program for research on earthquake prediction.

Farengol'ts, I. V. Upheaval of Montague Island after the earthquake [in translation]. *Okeanologiya* (Moscow, USSR), 5, No. 6 (1965), 1124.
An investigation of Montague Island and the ocean bottom surrounding it reveals the formation of a fault in the sea bottom 7 mi southwest of Cape Clear and a fault, 35-mi long, in the region of the north slope of Montague Island.

Furumoto, Augustine S. Analysis of Rayleigh wave, Part II *in* Source mechanism study of the Alaska earthquake and tsunami of 27 March 1964. Report HIG-65-17. Honolulu: University of Hawaii, Institute of Geophysics, 1965. p. 31–42. See also *Pacific Science*, 21 (July 1967), 311–316. Also *in* The Great Alaska Earthquake of 1964: Seismology and Geodesy. NAS Pub. 1602. Washington: National Academy of Sciences, 1972.
Investigates the source mechanism of the earthquake by analyzing the Rayleigh wave recorded on the strain seismograph at Kipapa Station, Hawaii. Results compare favorably with field data on the earthquake.

Ganopole, Gerald. The great Alaskan earthquake *in* Guidebook: Field Trip Routes—Anchorage to Sutton, 1963; Sutton to Caribou Creek, 1964. Anchorage: Alaska Geological Society, 1964. p. 23–24.
Surveys the effects of the great Alaska earthquake and concludes that the tremendous amount of data on the earthquake being gathered and studied will lead to a better understanding of the earth and its dramatic releases of energy. Geological sciences must be extended into active areas of everyday living, and into city and land-use planning.

George, Warren. Earthquake induced slides in the Anchorage area. Paper presented at Fifteenth Alaskan Science Conference, College, Alaska, August 31 to September 4, 1964. 11 p. (Copy on file, Library, National Academy of Sciences-National Academy of Engineering, Washington, D. C.)
An engineer describes the investigation, testing, and analysis of five major slides and a number of minor slides in the Anchorage area. Explains the nature of the slides, the methods by which they were studied, measurement of ground movement, and possible treatments to stabilize the slides.

Geotimes. Alaska earthquake study. *Geotimes*, 12 (March 1967), 22.
Gives details of the 10- (now 8-) volume Alaska earthquake study planned by the National Research Council.

Gouin, Pierre. Coincidence of magnetic disturbances with local earthquakes recorded from the Ethiopian rift system. *Nature*, 208 (November 6, 1965), 541–543.
Findings at the geophysical observatory, Addis Ababa, on magnetic effects related to local earthquakes. An astonishingly sudden increase in the intensity of the total field was recorded on a flux-gate magnetometer at Kodiak, 66 minutes before the Alaska earthquake of March 27, 1964.

Gruening, Ernest. Earthquake research is needed—it should prove a valuable investment. *Congressional Record* (February 4, 1965), 1974–1977.
Announces that an earthquake of 7.5–8 magnitude on the Richter scale was registered on Amchitka Island that day. Quotes an article by Lawrence Lessing, "Solving the Riddle of the Shuddering Earth," *Fortune*, February 1965.

Hansen, Wallace R. The Alaska earthquake of 1964. *Nature*, 215 (July 22, 1967), 348–351.
Geophysical observations include discussion of the magnitude of the main shock and of the numerous aftershocks. The area affected, the intensity of the earthquake, the deformation caused, the effects on the flora and fauna are also discussed, together with the tsunamis, and the effects on the fishing industry.

Hansen, Wallace R., Edwin B. Eckel, William E. Schaem, Robert E. Lyle, Warren George, and Genie Chance. The Alaska earthquake, March 27, 1964: Field investigations and reconstruction effort. U.S. Geological Survey Professional Paper 541. Washington: Government Printing Office, 1966. 111 p.
Bases a summary description of the great Alaska earthquake on the work of numerous investigators. Deals with the geologic setting and effects, the field investigations, and the public and private reconstruction efforts.

Harding, Samuel T., and S. T. Algermissen. The focal mechanism of the Prince William Sound earthquake of March 28, 1964, and related earthquakes *in* Volume II-B,C: The Prince William Sound, Alaska, earthquake of 1964 and aftershocks. Environmental Science Services Administration, U.S. Coast and Geodetic Survey. Washington: Government Printing Office, 1969. p. 185–221. Also *in* The Great Alaska Earthquake of 1964: Seismology and Geodesy. NAS Pub. 1602. Washington: National Academy of Sciences, 1972.
Presents focal mechanism solutions for the main shock, two preshocks, and six aftershocks of the great Alaska earthquake. Gives also composite focal mechanisms, based on an analysis of the first motions recorded from aftershocks at seven temporary seismograph stations installed after the March 28 earthquake, and on readings from the College Observatory.

Harkrider, David G., and Ralph A. Alewine. The excitation of tsunamis and associated atmospheric pressure disturbances (Abstract). *EOS Transactions, American Geophysical Union*, 51 (April 1970), 362.
Approximates the tectonic displacement and source motion of the 1964 Alaska earthquake as a comparison to the actual water wave and the atmospheric pressure disturbance associated with tsunamis, and calculates the theoretical pressure and water displacements at distance.

Hatori, Tokutaro. On the Alaska tsunami of March 28, 1964, as observed along the coast of Japan. *Bulletin of the Earthquake Research Institute*, University of Tokyo, 43 (June 1965), 399–408.
Dispersion curves obtained from the 1964 Alaska tsunami record at Miyagi-Enoshima coincide well with the calculation for the case of a continental shelf 40-km wide and with a mean depth of 500 m, bordering an ocean 5,000-m deep. Estimates the decay coefficient of the tsunami waves to be approximately 0.010 per hour.

Heroy, William B., Jr. Earthquakes, explosions . . . research, and prediction. *Geotimes*, 10 (December 1965–January 1966), 14–15.
Shows record of an underground nuclear explosion on Amchitka as recorded by seismographic network in California. Outlines the proposed 10-year program for research in earthquake prediction proposed by the Office of Science and Technology.

Hirshberg, Joan, Robert G. Currie, and Sheldon Breiner. Long period geomagnetic fluctuations after the 1964 Alaskan earthquake. *Earth and Planetary Science Letters* (Amsterdam), 3 (February 1968), 426–428. Also *in* The Great Alaska Earthquake of 1964: Seismology and Geodesy. NAS Pub. 1602. Washington: National Academy of Sciences, 1972.
Presents power spectra of the geomagnetic field (after the 1964 earthquake) that show lines with frequencies of several of the gravest torsional eigenmodes of the earth.

Hori, Minoru, Hideteru Matumoto, and Keiiti Aki. Observation of microaftershocks of the Alaska earthquake of March 28, 1964. *Zisin* (Journal of the Seismological Society of Japan), 19 (September 1966), 187–199.
Presents observations made from a temporary-array station set up about 125 km southwest of the epicenter of the main shock of the 1964 earthquake. Determines epicenters and focal depths for 797 aftershocks.

Housner, George W. Engineering for earthquakes. *Engineering and Science*, 32 (January 1969), 7–13.
Discusses prospects and methods for building-in earthquake protection in seismic regions.

Hudson, Donald E., and William K. Cloud. Seismological background for engineering studies of the earthquake *in* The Great Alaska Earthquake of 1964: Engineering. NAS Pub. 1606. Washington: National Academy of Sciences, in press.
Uncertainty about the location of the main source of energy release of the Alaska earthquake complicates interpretation of damage patterns described by the isoseismal map of earthquake intensities. However, for the first time it was possible to relate the generation of a tsunami to measurable patterns of tectonic displacements.

Iacopi, Robert. Earthquake country: How, why and where earthquakes strike in California. Menlo Park: Lane Books, 1964. 192 p.
Explains the reasons for California's earthquakes, explores the faults, and discusses the prospects of future earthquakes in the area. Because the great Alaska earthquake occurred while this book was in press, the author added a page of comment to show similarities between that earthquake and those that strike California.

Kanamori, Hiroo. The Alaska earthquake of 1964: Radiation of long-period surface waves and source mechanism. *Journal of Geophysical Research*, 75 (September 10, 1970), 5029–5040. Also *in* The Great Alaska Earthquake of 1964: Seismology and Geodesy. NAS Pub. 1602. Washington: National Academy of Sciences, 1972.

Compares the seismograms recorded by WWNSS stations with synthetic seismograms for radiation pattern and amplitude to estimate source parameters. The moment and width of the fault plane of the 1964 Alaska earthquake are found to be much larger than those of any other earthquakes reported.

Kawasumi, Hirosi, and Etsuzo Shima. Spectra of microtremors observed in the city of Anchorage and their relation to soils *in* Volume II-A: The Prince William Sound, Alaska, earthquake of 1964 and aftershocks. Environmental Science Services Administration, U.S. Coast and Geodetic Survey. Washington: Government Printing Office, 1967. p. 299–331.
Microtremor measurements made in Anchorage provided data for the study of frequency characteristics of the ground surface and their relationships to subsoil structures. Predominant period tended to become longer near the shoreline—an indication that the subsoil layers at the shoreline are thicker than inland.

Kovach, Robert L., and Don L. Anderson. Study of the energy of the free oscillations of the earth. *Journal of Geophysical Research*, 72 (April 15, 1967), 2155–2168.
Provides tables that allow estimates to be made of the energy contained in long-period surface waves and free oscillations. An estimate of the energy in the low-order spheroidal oscillations excited by the great Alaska earthquake suggests a value of 10^{23} ergs over the period range from 450 to 830 seconds.

LaChapelle, Edward R. The character of snow avalanching induced by the Alaska earthquake *in* The Great Alaska Earthquake of 1964: Hydrology. NAS Pub. 1603. Washington: National Academy of Sciences, 1968. p. 355–361.
The Alaska earthquake occurred at a time of natural avalanche hazard in the Chugach Mountains. It generated two separate avalanche cycles; because of the powerful triggering action, most of the avalanche danger zones have been identified.

Landen, David. Alaska earthquake, 27 March 1964. *Science*, 145 (July 3, 1964), 74–76.
Cause and effect of the Alaska earthquake disaster are discussed at a meeting sponsored by the American Society of Photogrammetry, the American Congress on Surveying and Mapping, and the Eastern Section of the Seismological Society of America.

Lazareva, A. P. Long-period Rayleigh waves of the Alaska earthquake on Pulkovo seismograms. *English Edition of Izvestiya*, Academy of Sciences, USSR, Physics of the Solid Earth, No. 7 (July 1966), 457–460.
Gives information obtained at the Pulkovo seismic station on the traces of the long surface waves generated by the earthquake from which the structure of the earth's mantle can be assessed.

Leonard, Robert S., and R. A. Barnes, Jr. Observations of ionospheric disturbances following the Alaska earthquake. *Journal of Geophysical Research*, 70 (March 1, 1965), 1250–1253.
Analyzes ionospheric disturbances after the Alaska earthquake. Data show indications of the perturbation in two different forms; the form depends on the distance between the observing station and the epicenter of the earthquake.

Lessing, Lawrence. Solving the riddle of the shuddering earth. *Fortune*, 71 (February 1965), 164–168, 170, 172, 174.
Shows that undersea exploration, nuclear testing, and observation of the orbits of space satellites are providing new clues to the causes of

earthquakes. Thinks that the new knowledge may provide ways to warn against these disasters and to minimize their damage.

Lindemuth, I. W. Earthquakes and Cape Hinchinbrook Light Station, Alaska. *The Engineer's Digest* (U.S. Coast Guard), 133 (October–November–December 1965), 37–42.
Gives a brief history of the earthquake-caused trials and tribulations at Cape Hinchinbrook Light Station, Alaska.

Lomnitz, Cinna, and Arnoldo Hax. Clustering in aftershock sequences *in* The Earth Beneath the Continents. American Geophysical Union Monograph 10, NAS Pub. 1467. Washington: National Academy of Sciences, 1966. p. 502–508.
Reports that clustering obtains when individual aftershocks tend to develop smaller aftershock sequences of their own. When the decay trend of aftershock sequences was removed, it was found that the Alaska aftershock sequences were uncorrelated.

Long, Erwin, and Warren George. Turnagain slide stabilization, Anchorage, Alaska. *Journal of the Soil Mechanics and Foundations Division* (American Society of Civil Engineers), 93 (September 1967), 611–627.
Tests conducted in early 1966 show that soil strength under the seaward toe of the Turnagain slide would not fail in an equivalent future earthquake. Recommends protection of the slide toe against future erosion believed to be caused primarily by ice rafting of soil.

Loomis, Harold G. Spectral analysis of tsunami records from stations in the Hawaiian Islands. *Bulletin of the Seismological Society of America*, 56 (June 1966), 697–713.
A compilation of intermediate results in a program of analyzing tsunami wave records by digital techniques. An effort to gain more quantitative information on the behavior of tsunamis in the Hawaiian Islands.

McGarr, Arthur. Excitation of seiches in channels by seismic waves. *Journal of Geophysical Research*, 70 (February 15, 1965), 847–854. Also *in* The Great Alaska Earthquake of 1964: Hydrology. NAS Pub. 1603. Washington: National Academy of Sciences, 1968. p. 133–139.
Reviews seiches that occurred along the Gulf Coast of the United States and in Norway at the times of the Alaska earthquake of 1964 and the Assam earthquake of 1950. Finds that the seismic surface waves from the Alaska earthquake provided enough energy to produce all the observed seiches in the Gulf Coast area.

McGarr, Arthur, and Robert C. Vorhis. Seismic seiches from the March 1964 Alaska earthquake. U.S. Geological Survey Professional Paper 544-E. Washington: Government Printing Office, 1968. 43 p. Also *in* The Great Alaska Earthquake of 1964: Hydrology. NAS Pub. 1603. Washington: National Academy of Sciences, 1968. p. 196–236.
Recording of seiches caused by the 1964 earthquake shows that their distribution is related to the distribution of short-period seismic surface waves. The most important factor in controlling seiche distribution is variation of thickness of low-rigidity sediments; this distribution may be used to map seismic intensity that can be expected from future local earthquakes.

McKenzie, D. P., and R. L. Parker. The North Pacific: An example of tectonics on a sphere. *Nature*, 216 (December 30, 1967), 1276–1280.
This study indicates that individual aseismic areas move as rigid plates

on the surface of a sphere. Application of the Mercator projection to slip vectors shows that the paving-stone theory of world tectonics is correct and applies to about a quarter of the earth's surface. Refers to 1964 Alaska earthquake work of Stauder and Bollinger, 1966.

Major, M. W., and J. H. Healy. Spheroidal and torsional oscillations recorded on the strain seismometers at Bergen Park, Colorado (Abstract). *Transactions, American Geophysical Union*, 45 (December 1964), 634–635.
Usable records were obtained between 2 and 100 hours after the time of the first arrivals. Prominent spectral peaks were found from 275 seconds to beyond 600 seconds. Good separation between torsional and spheroidal modes was achieved.

Malloy, Richard J. Gulf of Alaska: Seafloor upheaval. *Geo-Marine Technology*, 1 (May–June 1965), 22–26.
Describes reconnaissance investigations of USC&GS ships after the Alaska earthquake. These included bottom soundings, tide-gage inspection and repair, gravity, magnetics, continuous seismic profiling, coring, and bottom photography.

Malloy, Richard J. Marine geological reconnaissance of epicentral and aftershock regions 1964 Alaska earthquake (unpublished manuscript). Rockville [Maryland]: Environmental Science Services Administration, Institute for Oceanography, 1967. 45 p. (Copy on file, Library, National Academy of Sciences–National Academy of Engineering, Washington, D.C.)
Investigations, which included depth soundings, seismic-reflection profiling, and side-look sonar, revealed that only a portion of the sea floor in the regions of the 1964 earthquake exhibited measurable open-water submarine tectonic deformation. The Aleutian Trench appears to be in a period of active submergence.

Malloy, Richard J., and George F. Merrill. Vertical crustal movement of the sea floor associated with the Prince William Sound, Alaska, earthquake *in* Volume II-B,C: The Prince William Sound, Alaska, earthquake of 1964 and aftershocks. Environmental Science Services Administration, U.S. Coast and Geodetic Survey. Washington: Government Printing Office, 1969. p. 327–338. Also *in* The Great Alaska Earthquake of 1964: Oceanography and Coastal Engineering. NAS Pub. 1605. Washington: National Academy of Sciences, in press.
A survey conducted in 1965 on the USC&GS ship *Surveyor* reveals sea-floor uplift of more than 15 m southwest of Montague Island. Fresh fault scarps were traced seaward for a distance of 19 km.

Mansinha, L., and D. E. Smylie. Effect of earthquakes on the Chandler wobble and the secular polar shift. *Journal of Geophysical Research*, 72 (September 15, 1967), 4731–4743.
Concludes that both the Chandler wobble excitation and the secular polar shift could be caused by earthquakes. With the use of fault parameters deduced from the near-field displacements for the 1964 Alaska earthquake, the far-field displacements are found to be remarkably extensive, according to the elasticity theory of dislocations.

Matumoto, Tosimatu, and Robert A. Page, Jr. Microaftershocks following the Alaska earthquake of March 28, 1964: Determination of hypocenters and crustal velocities in the Kenai Peninsula–Prince William Sound area *in* Volume II-B,C: The Prince William Sound, Alaska, earthquake of 1964 and aftershocks. Environmental Science Services Administration, U.S. Coast and Geodetic Survey. Washington: Government Printing Office, 1969. p. 157–173. Also *in* The Great Alaska Earthquake of 1964: Seismology and Geodesy. NAS Pub. 1602. Washington: National Academy of Sciences , 1972.

Describes the program carried out by seismologists from the Lamont-Doherty Geological Observatory to record microaftershocks following the great Alaska earthquake. Most of the 249 microshocks for which hypocenters were determined are interpreted as microaftershocks that occurred in the uplifted tectonic block–Prince William Sound and eastern Kenai Peninsula.

Meade, Buford K. Precise surveys of the Anchorage monitoring system *in* Volume III: The Prince William Sound, Alaska, earthquake of 1964 and aftershocks. Environmental Science Services Administration, U.S. Coast and Geodetic Survey. Washington: Government Printing Office, 1969. p. 113–118. Also *in* The Great Alaska Earthquake of 1964: Seismology and Geodesy. NAS Pub. 1602. Washington: National Academy of Sciences, 1972.
Gives the observations, adjustments, and results of the program for reobserving the primary triangulation networks in the Anchorage–Prince William Sound area.

Meehan, John F. The response of several public school buildings in Anchorage, Alaska, to the March 27, 1964, earthquake *in* Volume II-A: The Prince William Sound, Alaska, earthquake of 1964 and aftershocks. Environmental Science Services Administration, U.S. Coast and Geodetic Survey. Washington: Government Printing Office, 1967. p. 219–243.
Describes the earthquake's effects on school buildings in Anchorage. The response of the low one- and two-story buildings was, in general, good; no school buildings collapsed, but damage would have been more extensive if the schools had been built on more rigid foundations.

Mikumo, Takeshi. Atmospheric pressure waves and tectonic deformation associated with the Alaskan earthquake of March 28, 1964. *Journal of Geophysical Research*, 73 (March 15, 1968), 2009–2025.
Concludes that large-scale ground deformations, such as those that accompanied the great Alaska earthquake, could generate atmospheric pressure waves observable at long distances. A possible time rate of the surface deformations could be estimated from observations made under favorable circumstances.

Miller, Maynard M. Our restless earth. *National Geographic Magazine*, 126 (July 1964), 140–141.
Examines briefly various theories of the causes of earthquakes.

Mogi, Kiyoo. Development of aftershock areas of great earthquakes [with Japanese abstracts]. *Bulletin of the Earthquake Research Institute*, University of Tokyo, 46, Part 2 (1968), 175–203.
Reports that a rapid systematic propagation of aftershock activity during several hours after the 1964 Alaska earthquake is attributed to brittle fracture.

Mohammadioun, Bagher. Structure de la croûte et spectres d'énergie des ondes longitudinales [Crustal structure and energy spectrums of longitudinal waves] (Abstract) *in* Geophysical Abstracts 232: May 1966 (U.S. Department of the Interior Geological Survey). Washington: Government Printing Office, 1966. p. 445.
Finds that the sources of the Alaska earthquakes occur in a band that plunges beneath the continent, within the confines of the continental and oceanic structures. A relation appears to exist between the structures and the energy spectra. (Original in French.)

Moore, George W. Magnetic disturbances preceding the 1964 Alaska earthquake. *Nature*, 203 (August 1, 1964), 508–509. Also *in* The Great Alaska Earthquake of 1964: Seismology and Geodesy. NAS Pub. 1602. Washington: National Academy of Sciences, 1972.
Large positive magnetic disturbances recorded before earthquakes in

Alaska, Nevada, and California suggest that magnetic monitoring may provide a means of predicting a major earthquake.

New Scientist. Predicting earthquakes by changes in rock magnetism. *New Scientist*, 36 (October 19, 1967), 176.
Discusses a paper by S. Breiner and R. L. Kovach of Stanford University that claims to be the first report of observations of a magnetic change without simultaneous creep, strain, or seismic activity. Supports the idea that a continual monitoring of the earth's magnetic field around earthquake-prone zones may lead to a viable method of earthquake prediction.

Northrop, John. T phases from 80 Alaskan earthquakes, March 28–31, 1964. *Bulletin of the Seismological Society of America*, 55 (February 1965), 59–63.
Discusses a large T-phase signal from the great Alaska earthquake received at Pt. Sur, California, and additional T phases received from 90 percent of the 80 aftershocks studied in the Kodiak Island area. Finds that the largest T phases were received from hypocenters beneath the upper portion of the Continental Shelf.

Nowroozi, Ali A. Eigenvibrations of the earth after the Alaskan earthquake. *Journal of Geophysical Research*, 70 (October 15, 1965), 5145–5156. Also *in* The Great Alaska Earthquake of 1964: Seismology and Geodesy. NAS Pub. 1602. Washington: National Academy of Sciences, 1972.
Finds that eigenfrequencies of the earth measured at Berkeley and Oroville after the Alaska earthquake were in close agreement with similar measurements from other earthquakes.

Nowroozi, Ali A. Measurements of Q values from the free oscillations of the earth. *Journal of Geophysical Research*, 73 (February 15, 1968), 1407–1415.
Estimates the Q values for spheroidal and torsional oscillations of the earth from the time decay of spectral amplitudes for each mode, using data from the Alaska earthquake of March 1964 and the Aleutian earthquake of February 1965.

Oakeshott, Gordon B. The Alaskan earthquake. *Mineral Information Service* (Publication of the California Division of Mines and Geology), 17 (July 1964), 119–121, 124–125.
The most interesting geological event of the Alaska earthquake was the downward movement of a large north-northeast-trending block of the surface crust of the earth. Focus was at a maximum depth of about 37 mi—perhaps too deep to cause surface faulting.

Office of Science and Technology. Earthquake prediction: A proposal for a ten year program of research. A report prepared by the *Ad Hoc* Panel on Earthquake Prediction. Washington: Office of Science and Technology, 1965. 136 p.
Recommends programs for a 10-year research effort to accomplish the prediction of earthquakes. These include geophysical and geological surveys of earthquake fault zones, research on the physical basis of earthquakes, earthquake engineering, and other projects.

Office of Science and Technology. Proposal for a ten-year national earthquake hazards program: A partnership of science and the community. Prepared by the *Ad Hoc* Interagency Working Group for Earthquake Research of the Federal Council for Science and Technology. Washington: Office of Science and Technology, December 1968. 81 p.
Recommends implementation of a 10-year national earthquake hazards research program, including establishment of a *permanent* coordinating and guidance group, to provide adequate protective measurements and guidelines for future construction before the next great earthquake occurs. Cooperation with foreign programs is suggested.

Office of Science and Technology. Recommendations concerning Alaska. A report prepared by the *Ad Hoc* Panel on Seismological Research. Washington: Office of Science and Technology, April 19, 1964. 3 p.
Recommends action to be taken to gain useful knowledge from the great Alaska earthquake and its aftermath. Suggests that a commission be established to coordinate the investigation and preparation of a comprehensive report on the earthquake and its effects.

Oliver, Jack. Earthquake prediction. *Science*, 153 (August 26, 1966), 1024–1026.
An increasing interest in earthquake mechanisms and earthquake prediction is shown at the Conference on Research Related to Earthquake Prediction. George Plafker gives the geological setting of the Alaska earthquake and some data on the resulting uplift and subsidence.

Orlin, Hyman. Gravity surveys *in* ESSA Symposium on Earthquake Prediction. Washington: Government Printing Office, 1966. p. 128–130.
Stresses the need for geophysical surveys. The 1964 Alaska earthquake provided an ideal opportunity to determine gravity variations over a short time period.

Ozawa, Izuo, and Tsuneo Eto. On the observations of the long period's oscillations of the earth by means of the extensometers and the water-tube tiltmeter. *Bulletin of the Disaster Prevention Research Institute*, Kyoto University [Japan], 15 (November 1965), 43–58.
Analyzes records of the long-period oscillations of the earth by means of autocorrelation.

Page, Robert. Aftershocks and microaftershocks of the great Alaska earthquake of 1964. *Bulletin of the Seismological Society of America*, 58 (June 1968), 1131–1168.
Results of a field program to record microaftershocks after the great Alaska earthquake. The microaftershock data, together with the data for the teleseismically recorded aftershocks, furnish new information on the aftershock process.

Pararas-Carayannis, George. Water waves, Part I *in* Source mechanism study of the Alaska earthquake and tsunami of 27 March 1964. Report HIG-65-17. Honolulu: University of Hawaii, Institute of Geophysics, 1965. p. 1–30. See also *Pacific Science*, 21 (July 1967), 301–310. Also *in* The Great Alaska Earthquake of 1964: Seismology and Geodesy. NAS Pub. 1602. Washington: National Academy of Sciences, 1972.
Determines the tsunami-generating area and discusses the extent of crustal displacement and the limits of the areas of subsidence and uplift revealed by geologic evidence.

Parkin, Ernest J. Alaskan surveys to determine crustal movement: Part II, Horizontal displacement. *Surveying and Mapping*, 27, No. 3 (1967), 423–430.
Discusses the horizontal displacement of the earth's crust shown by a comparison of the results of triangulation and traverse surveys made before and after the earthquake.

Parkin, Ernest J. Horizontal crustal movements determined from surveys after the Alaskan earthquake of 1964 *in* Volume III: The Prince William Sound, Alaska, earthquake of 1964 and aftershocks. Environmental Science Services Administration, U.S. Coast and

Geodetic Survey. Washington: Government Printing Office, 1969. p. 35–98. Also *in* The Great Alaska Earthquake of 1964: Seismology and Geodesy. NAS Pub. 1602. Washington: National Academy of Sciences, 1972.
Finds that a comparison of pre- and postearthquake geographic positions indicates displacements of 50 ft or more. Comparisons of pre- and postearthquake observations at adjacent common points verify the magnitude of this crustal movement.

Pecora, William T. National Center for Earthquake Research, USGS. *Geotimes*, 10 (December 1965–January 1966), 13.
Announces establishment (within the USGS) of a National Center for Earthquake Research at Menlo Park, California. This center is the result of a recommendation (by Dr. Hornig's panel, convened after the Alaska Earthquake) that studies in earthquake prediction be made by experts during a 10-year period.

Plafker, George. Surface faults on Montague Island associated with the 1964 Alaska earthquake. U.S. Geological Survey Professional Paper 543-G. Washington: Government Printing Office, 1967. 42 p. Also *in* The Great Alaska Earthquake of 1964: Geology. NAS Pub. 1601. Washington: National Academy of Sciences, 1971.
Contains description and tectonic analysis of ground breakage and surface warping along two reverse faults reactivated during the Alaska earthquake—the Patton Bay and Hanning Bay faults.

Plafker, George. Tectonics of the March 27, 1964, Alaska earthquake. U.S. Geological Survey Professional Paper 543-I. Washington: Government Printing Office, 1969. 74 p. Also *in* The Great Alaska Earthquake of 1964:Seismology and Geodesy. NAS Pub. 1602. Washington: National Academy of Sciences, 1972.
Presents available data on the distribution and nature of displacements and effects of tectonic movements that accompanied the Alaska earthquake.

Plafker, George, and Reuben Kachadoorian. Geologic effects of the March 1964 earthquake and associated seismic sea waves on Kodiak and nearby islands, Alaska. U.S. Geological Survey Professional Paper 543-D. Washington: Government Printing Office, 1966. 46 p. Also *in* The Great Alaska Earthquake of 1964: Geology. NAS Pub. 1601. Washington: National Academy of Sciences, 1971.
The most devastating effect of the earthquake on Kodiak Island resulted from tsunamis. This report was based on a reconnaissance study of the vast uninhabited parts of Kodiak and the nearby islands.

Plafker, George, Reuben Kachadoorian, Edwin B. Eckel, and Lawrence R. Mayo. Effects of the earthquake of March 27, 1964, on various communities. U.S. Geological Survey Professional Paper 542-G. Washington: Government Printing Office, 1969. 50 p. Also *in* The Great Alaska Earthquake of 1964: Geology. NAS Pub. 1601. Washington: National Academy of Sciences, 1971.
Describes damage to smaller communities in south central Alaska from the 1964 earthquake; this damage resulted primarily from sea waves, vertical tectonic movements, and seismic vibration.

Plafker, George, and L. R. Mayo. Tectonic deformation, subaqueous slides and destructive waves associated with the Alaskan March 27, 1964 earthquake: An interim geologic evaluation. U.S. Geological Survey Open-File Report. Menlo Park [California]: U.S. Geological Survey, 1965. 34 p.
Report on USGS field investigations, summarizing phenomena known by August 1964. Describes unprecedented tectonic warping in south

central Alaska, destructive long-period waves generated by uplift of the sea bottom, and numerous earthquake-triggered subaqueous slides in Prince William Sound and on the Kenai Peninsula.

Plafker, George, and Meyer Rubin. Vertical tectonic displacements in south-central Alaska during and prior to the great 1964 earthquake. *Journal of Geoscience*, 10 (March 1967), 53–66.
Examines vertical tectonic deformation accompanying the 1964 earthquake in relation to the geologic record of Holocene (Recent) movements along coasts of south central Alaska. Recent submergence may be related to earthquake strain buildup.

Pope, Allen J. Strain analysis of horizontal crustal movements in Alaska based on triangulation surveys before and after the Prince William Sound earthquake of March 27, 1964 *in* Volume III: The Prince William Sound, Alaska, earthquake of 1964 and aftershocks. Environmental Science Services Administration, U.S. Coast and Geodetic Survey. Washington: Government Printing Office, 1969. p. 99–111. Also *in* The Great Alaska Earthquake of 1964: Seismology and Geodesy. NAS Pub. 1602. Washington: National Academy of Sciences, 1972.
Reports on method of computation of strain components, summarizes factors limiting or increasing the usefulness of these components in interpreting crustal movements, and presents the components in tabular and graphic form.

Press, Frank. Displacements, strains, and tilts at teleseismic distances. *Journal of Geophysical Research*, 70 (May 15, 1965), 2395–2412. Also *in* The Great Alaska Earthquake of 1964: Seismology and Geodesy. NAS Pub. 1602. Washington: National Academy of Sciences, 1972.
The vertical displacement field from the Alaska earthquake indicates that the primary fault extended to a depth of 150–200 km and that it probably came to within 15 km of the surface. Examines observations of residual strains and tilts.

Press, Frank. Free oscillations, aftershocks, and Q *in* The Earth Beneath the Continents. American Geophysical Union Monograph 10, NAS Pub. 1467. Washington: National Academy of Sciences, 1966. p. 498–501.
Aftershock sequences for the 1964 Alaska earthquake were used to estimate energy decay for the entire sequence of main shocks and aftershocks. Aftershock energy cannot be used to explain large Q values reported for the radial mode $_0S_0$.

Press, Frank. Resonant vibrations of the earth. *Scientific American*, 213 (November 1965), 28–37.
The earth vibrates when it is disturbed; a major earthquake sets the entire globe to oscillating like a bell for weeks or months. These free oscillations provide information on structure of earth's crust and mantle. Gives power spectra of seismic waves and strain change for the Alaska earthquake.

Press, Frank, and W. F. Brace. Earthquake prediction: Recent developments reopen the question of the predictability of earthquakes. *Science*, 152 (June 17, 1966), 1575–1584.
Forewarning of a large earthquake might come from tilts and strains in the epicentral region, general increase in number of small seismic events, and changes in physical properties of rocks near the fault as they are strained. Gives vertical extent of faulting in the Alaska earthquake.

Press, Frank, and David Jackson. Alaskan earthquake, 27 March 1964:

Vertical extent of faulting and elastic strain energy release. *Science*, 147 (February 19, 1965), 867–868. Also *in* The Great Alaska Earthquake of 1964: Seismology and Geodesy. NAS Pub. 1602. Washington: National Academy of Sciences, 1972.
Reports that the vertical extent of the Alaska earthquake is an order of magnitude greater than that reported for all other earthquakes. Elastic strain energy of 10^{25} ergs was released. About 12,000 aftershocks probably occurred in a 69-day period after the main shock.

Ragle, Richard. Letter to Dr. Troy Péwé, Department of Geology, University of Alaska, 17 April 1964, Relating Personal Observations of Wavelength, Amplitude, Velocity of the Earthquake in Anchorage. 2 p. (Copy on file, Library, National Academy of Sciences–National Academy of Engineering, Washington, D.C.)
Data from observation of two cars parked at Elmendorf Air Force Base during Alaska earthquake: slow and massive waves observed. Frequency: 70 pulses/min; velocity: more than 5 fps.

Rasmussen, Norman H. Earthquakes and related activity. *Alaska Sportsman*, 30 (June 1964), 29–30, 32, 34.
Data on earthquakes in general and the Alaska earthquake in particular. Discussion of seismic belts, tsunamis, and magnitude versus intensity.

Rexin, Elmer, and Robert C. Vorhis. Hydroseismograms from the Nunn-Bush Shoe Co. well, Wisconsin *in* Hydrologic effects of the earthquake of March 27, 1964, outside Alaska. U.S. Geological Survey Professional Paper 544-C. Washington: Government Printing Office, 1967. p. 10–13. Also *in* The Great Alaska Earthquake of 1964: Hydrology. NAS Pub. 1603. Washington: National Academy of Sciences, 1968. p. 146–148.
Gives the most detailed of all hydroseismic records of the Alaska Earthquake in the form of a chronological list of hydroseismic data from the Nunn-Bush Shoe Co. well at Milwaukee, Wisconsin, March 28–30, 1964.

Rice, Donald A. Gravity observations in Alaska, 1964–1965, including some repeat observations *in* Volume III: The Prince William Sound, Alaska, earthquake of 1964 and aftershocks. Environmental Science Services Administration, U.S. Coast and Geodetic Survey. Washington: Government Printing Office, 1969. p. 5–20. Updated version *in* The Great Alaska Earthquake of 1964: Seismology and Geodesy. NAS Pub. 1602. Washington: National Academy of Sciences, 1972.
The 1964–1965 gravity observations made by USC&GS provide a sound basis for future study of tectonic changes in the Prince William Sound area. Future repeat gravity observations will be most useful if made concurrently with releveling in an earthquake region.

Richardson, Jacques. Earthquakes: Man cannot eliminate, but he may mitigate. *International Science & Technology* (August 1964), 86–87.
UNESCO-backed research on earthquakes is paying off. UNESCO plans (a) to send earthquake reconnaissance missions to be on the site within 72 hours (as was the case in Alaska), (b) to send study missions (to stay for periods up to 3 months), and (c) to establish a 24-hour earthquake watch.

Richter, C. F. Caltech's Seismological Laboratory goes to work on the Alaskan earthquake. *Engineering and Science*, 27 (April 1964), 7–11.
From the seismograph installed in his living room, the author saw the initial recording of the Alaska earthquake and was able to set the minimum magnitude; he then made further studies at the Seismologi-cal Laboratory. The aftershocks seemed not to be as large as would have been expected. The spectacular breaks in the ground represented lateral lurching, rather than faulting.

Rinehart, John, and Anabeth Murphy. Observations on pre- and post-earthquake performance of Old Faithful geyser. *Journal of Geophysical Research,* 74 (January 15, 1969), 574–575.
Mean interval between eruptions of Old Faithful appears to be correlated with major earthquake activity: 2–3 years before the earthquake, the interval begins to decrease uniformly (from 67.0–65.5 minutes before 1964 Alaska earthquake) and then suddenly increases at the time of the earthquake (to 67.1 min after the Alaska earthquake).

Rinehart, Wilbur. A digital computer program for the location of local earthquakes *in* Volume II-B,C: The Prince William Sound, Alaska, earthquake of 1964 and aftershocks. Environmental Science Services Administration, U.S. Coast and Geodetic Survey. Washington: Government Printing Office, 1969. p. 71–77.
Discusses a digital computer program used to calculate hypocenters of earthquakes within range of a local network of seismic stations. Such a network was established in Alaska after the 1964 earthquake.

Rinne, John E. Oil storage tanks *in* Volume II-A: The Prince William Sound, Alaska, earthquake of 1964 and aftershocks. Environmental Science Services Administration, U.S. Coast and Geodetic Survey. Washington: Government Printing Office, 1967. p. 245–252.
Records the nature of earthquake damage to oil-storage tanks in Alaska and analyzes the importance of this damage to the fundamental earthquake-resistant design criteria for tanks.

Rosenfeld, Albert. What causes earthquakes, hopes for predicting them. *Life,* 56 (April 10, 1964), 37–38.
Considers the cause of havoc in Alaska earthquake to be the slippage of rock masses against one another along geologic faults. Tsunamis are recognized by the first motion along a shoreline as a withdrawal of the water similar to a very low tide.

Row, Ronald V. Acoustic-gravity waves in the upper atmosphere due to a nuclear detonation and an earthquake. *Journal of Geophysical Research,* 72 (March 1, 1967), 1599–1610.
Theory for pulse propagation in neutral atmosphere is developed by comparison of a large ionospheric disturbance with a similar but weaker disturbance noted after the great Alaska earthquake of 1964.

Row, Ronald V. Atmospheric waves related to the Alaskan earthquake of 28 March 1964 (U.T.). Research Report 525. Waltham [Massachusetts]: Sylvania Electronic Systems [1967]. 34 p. Also *in* The Great Alaska Earthquake of 1964: Seismology and Geodesy. NAS Pub.1602. Washington: National Academy of Sciences, 1972.
Reports on instrumental records of atmospheric disturbances associated with the 1964 Alaska earthquake. This earthquake appears to have produced the first ionospheric disturbances noticed. The first disturbances to arrive are short-period waves, followed by a long-period ionospheric disturbance, and then a dispersive wave train.

Row, Ronald V. Evidence of long-period acoustic-gravity waves launched into the *F* region by the Alaskan earthquake of March 28, 1964. *Journal of Geophysical Research,* 71 (January 1, 1966). 343–345.
Data suggest that long-period disturbances are a manifestation of

acoustic-gravity waves launched into the ionosphere near the epicenter of the Alaska earthquake.

Savage, James C. The stopping phase on seismograms. *Bulletin of the Seismological Society of America,* 55 (February 1965), 47–58.
The stopping phase is associated with the termination of fracture; the breakout phase is recorded from shallow-focus earthquakes that produce surface faulting (*P* wave of Alaska earthquake studied).

Savage, J. C., and L. M. Hastie. Surface deformation associated with dip-slip faulting. *Journal of Geophysical Research,* 71 (October 15, 1966), 4897–4904. Also *in* The Great Alaska Earthquake of 1964: Seismology and Geodesy. NAS Pub. 1602. Washington: National Academy of Sciences, 1972.
Deals with fault surfaces with reasonable values of dip. The preferred fault modes for the Alaska earthquake are: $2L$ = 600 km, W = 200 km, δ = 9°, h = 20 km, and Δu = 10 m (horizontal length $2L$, width W, dip δ, depth h, dip-slip motion Δu).

Savarenskiy, Ye. F., and G. L. Kosarev. Digital filtering of long-period vibrations of the Alaska earthquake of 1964. *Akademiya Nauk SSSR Izvestiya, Fizika Zemli* [Academy of Sciences of the U.S.S.R. Bulletin, Physics of the Earth], No. 12 (December 1967), 57–59.
Shows how digital filtering can be accomplished with the aid of a computer to suppress the comparatively short-period waves and amplify those with periods of more than 100 seconds. This filtering was applied to data of the Alaska earthquake of 1964.

Savarenskiy, Ye. F., O. E. Starovoyt, and S. A. Fedorov. Long-period Rayleigh waves of the Alaskan earthquake on March 28, 1964. *Akademiya Nauk SSSR Izvestiya, Seriya Geofizicheskaya* [Academy of Sciences of the U.S.S.R. Bulletin, Geophysics Series], No. 12 (December 1964), 1103–1106.
Analyzes dispersion of group and phase velocities of the Rayleigh waves of the Alaska earthquake registered in the central seismic station in Moscow. In Alaska, movement of the fault to the south explains the great intensity of the Rayleigh waves with even indices.

Schatz, C. E., and Peter Dehlinger. Oregon State University Seismological Bulletin No. 3, January 1 to March 31, 1964. Corvallis: Oregon State University, Department of Oceanography, Geophysics Research Group, October 1964. 8 p.
Seismological records of 32 earthquakes of varying intensities, March 28–31, 1964, in Alaska; recorded by the World-Wide Network of Standard Seismographs station at Corvallis and the seismic stations at Klamath Falls (both operated by Oregon State University).

Science Journal. Seiche excitation—new theory explains water movement. *Science Journal,* 1 (August 1965), 12–14.
Theory connecting seismic motion with seiches used in calculating amplitude in Texas water channel after recording of seiches due to Alaska earthquake waves. For surface-wave periods less than 600 seconds, seiches are set up by horizontal component of motion.

Sham, P. Earthquakes recorded in April, 1964. Royal Observatory, Hong Kong, Monthly Seismological Bulletin, R. O. 43, April 1964. Hong Kong: Royal Observatory, 1964. 15 p.
Analysis of seismograms from Royal Observatory Sprengnether instruments. Presents aftershocks of Alaska earthquake beginning March 31, 1964.

Sherburne, R. W., S. T. Algermissen, and Samuel T. Harding. The hypocenter, origin time, and magnitude of the Prince William Sound earthquake of March 28. 1964 *in* Volume II-B,C: The Prince William Sound, Alaska, earthquake of 1964 and aftershocks. Environmental Science Services Administration, U.S. Coast and Geodetic Survey. Washington: Government Printing Office, 1969. p. 49–69. Also *in* The Great Alaska Earthquake of 1964: Seismology and Geodesy. NAS Pub. 1602. Washington: National Academy of Sciences, 1972.
Ten separate epicenter computations were made with various data sets, computer programs, and traveltime curves. The preferred epicenter is latitude 61.04 N, longitude 147.73 W. Origin time was 03:36:14.0; with 37 observations the surface-wave magnitude was found to be 8.3 ± .33.

Shreve, Ronald L. Sherman landslide, Alaska. *Science,* 154 (December 30, 1966), 1639–1643. Also *in* The Great Alaska Earthquake of 1964: Hydrology. NAS Pub. 1603. Washington: National Academy of Sciences, 1968. p. 395–401.
As a result of the 1964 Alaska earthquake, rock (3×10^7 m^3) fell 600 m and then slid at high speed 5 km across the nearly level Sherman glacier near Cordova. Landslide differs from others in its large content of snow, pattern of longitudinal grooves, and air-layer lubrication.

Slichter, Louis B. Earth's free modes and a new gravimeter. *Geophysics,* 30 (June 1965), 339–347.
Comparison of gravitational observations of free vibrations of the earth due to Alaska earthquake with those for Chilean earthquake. Improved drill-hole sites are required; Havens' drill-hole gravimeter shows encouraging capabilities.

Slichter, Louis B. Spherical oscillations of the earth *in* International Upper Mantle Committee Symposium on non-elastic processes in the mantle. Proceedings of the Royal Astronomical Society, 1966, Newcastle-upon-Tyne. *Geophysical Journal,* 14, Nos. 1–4 (1967), 171–177.
For the lower-degree modes in the spheroidal free oscillations observed at Los Angeles due to the Alaska earthquake, the values are generally an order of magnitude more precise than those customarily reported.

Small, James B., and Ernest J. Parkin. Alaskan surveys to determine crustal movement: Part I, Vertical bench mark displacement. *Surveying and Mapping,* 27, No. 3 (1967), 413–422.
In 1964 and 1965, the USC&GS undertook 1,579 mi of first-order leveling. Subsidence of bench marks is given, along with evidence of upheaval.

Small, James B., and Lawrence C. Wharton. Vertical displacements determined by surveys after the Alaskan earthquake of March 1964 *in* Volume III: The Prince William Sound, Alaska, earthquake of 1964 and aftershocks. Environmental Science Services Administration, U.S. Coast and Geodetic Survey. Washington: Government Printing Office, 1969. p. 21–33. Also *in* The Great Alaska Earthquake of 1964: Seismology and Geodesy. NAS Pub. 1602. Washington: National Academy of Sciences, 1972.
Describes vertical-control surveys after the earthquake; 1,191 mi of first-order lines were releveled for engineering and mapping purposes. Gives a brief history of previous leveling and compares elevations before and after the earthquake.

Smith, Stewart W. Free oscillations excited by the Alaskan earthquake. *Journal of Geophysical Research,* 71 (February 15, 1966), 1183–1193. Also *in* The Great Alaska Earthquake of 1964: Seismology and Geodesy. NAS Pub. 1602. Washington: National Academy of Sciences, 1972.

Determines periods of spheroidal and toroidal modes for the Alaska earthquake and generally confirms measurements made after the Chilean earthquake.

Smith, Stewart W. Introduction: Related geophysical effects *in* The Great Alaska Earthquake of 1964: Seismology and Geodesy. NAS Pub. 1602. Washington: National Academy of Sciences, 1972.
It is important to thoroughly document geophysical phenomena related to the 1964 Alaska earthquake so that data and records will be available later for checking new hypotheses.

Smylie, D. E., and L. Mansinha. Chandler wobble and secular motion of the pole *in* The Great Alaska Earthquake of 1964: Seismology and Geodesy. NAS Pub. 1602. Washington: National Academy of Sciences, 1972.
Concludes that earthquakes must be considered as possible causes in attempts to explain the Chandler wobble excitation and the secular polar shift. This is a revised and updated version of the Mansinha and Smylie paper listed earlier.

Spaeth, Mark G., and Saul C. Berkman. The tsunami of March 28, 1964, as recorded at tide stations. ESSA [Environmental Science Services Administration] Technical Report C&GS 33. Washington: Government Printing Office, 1967. 86 p. Also *in* The Great Alaska Earthquake of 1964: Oceanography and Coastal Engineering. NAS Pub. 1605. Washington: National Academy of Sciences, in press.
Report contains reproductions of (1) tidal curves showing the tsunami and (2) curves showing oscillations induced by the long-period seismic waves. Also contains brief history of Tsunami Warning System.

Spaeth, Mark G., and Saul C. Berkman. The tsunami of March 28, 1964, as recorded at tide stations *in* Volume II-B,C: The Prince William Sound, Alaska, earthquake of 1964 and aftershocks. Environmental Science Services Administration, U.S. Coast and Geodetic Survey. Washington: Government Printing Office, 1969. p. 223–307.
Contains 107 reproductions of tide curves showing the tsunami and 12 curves showing oscillations induced by long-period seismic waves. Gives also a brief history of the Seismic Sea-Wave Warning System (called Tsunami Warning System since March 15, 1967) and a report of its operation during the tsunami warning action.

Srinivasan, P. K. Record of Alaskan earthquake of 1964 on Annamalainagar magnetograms. *Indian Journal of Meteorology and Geophysics*, 17 (April 1966), 287–288.
Magnetic impulse recorded at Kodiak 66 minutes before Alaska earthquake and also recorded at Annamalainagar indicates that magnetic instruments may become useful tools in earthquake prediction.

Stacey, F. D., and P. Westcott. The record of a vector proton magnetometer after the March 1964 Alaskan earthquake. *Journal of Geophysical Research*, 70 (July 15, 1965), 3321–3323. Also *in* The Great Alaska Earthquake of 1964: Seismology and Geodesy. NAS Pub. 1602. Washington: National Academy of Sciences, 1972.
Power spectra of data from a digitally recording, vector proton precession magnetometer (operating during the 1964 Alaska earthquake) give no evidence of magnetic fluctuation with frequencies of torsional modes in the earth's free-oscillation spectrum.

Stauder, William. Introduction: Parameters of the main shock *in* The Great Alaska Earthquake of 1964: Seismology and Geodesy. NAS Pub. 1602. Washington: National Academy of Sciences, 1972.
Describes the efforts to determine the different parameters of an earthquake, the collection of information on the source, and the evidence afforded by the data that have been collected.

Stauder, William. Tensional character of earthquake foci beneath the Aleutian Trench with relation to sea-floor spreading. *Journal of Geophysical Research*, 73 (December 15, 1968), 7693–7701.
Study of tensional character of foci under the Aleutian Trench supports the hypothesis of sea-floor spreading and underthrusting of the island arcs.

Stauder, William, and G. A. Bollinger. The focal mechanism of the Alaska earthquake of March 28, 1964, and of its aftershock sequence. *Journal of Geophysical Research*, 71 (November 15, 1966), 5283–5296. Also *in* The Great Alaska Earthquake of 1964: Seismology and Geodesy. NAS Pub. 1602. Washington: National Academy of Sciences, 1972.
Uniformity of motion in the entire Alaska earthquake sequence is illustrated by consideration of one preshock, the main shock, and more than 25 aftershocks. Criteria favor the hypothesis of thrust faulting.

Stauder, William, and G. A. Bollinger. The S-wave project for focal mechanism studies, the Alaska earthquake sequence of 1964. Air Force Cambridge Research Laboratories Scientific Report 1 (AFCRL-66-572). Bedford [Massachusetts]: Office of Aerospace Research, United States Air Force, 1966. 125 p.
Focal mechanisms of the Alaska earthquakes related to the main shock bear remarkable similarity to one another and to the main shock. In all but three cases, there is a single, steeply dipping nodal plane of *P*.

Steinbrugge, Karl V. Introduction to the earthquake engineering of the 1964 Prince William Sound, Alaska, earthquake *in* Volume II-A: The Prince William Sound, Alaska, earthquake of 1964 and aftershocks. Environmental Science Services Administration, U.S. Coast and Geodetic Survey. Washington: Government Printing Office, 1967. p. 1–6.
As a background for the papers on earthquake engineering, the author reviews briefly some of the seismological data that have been developed on the earthquake.

Steinbrugge, Karl V., John H. Manning, and Henry J. Degenkolb. Building damage in Anchorage *in* Volume II-A: The Prince William Sound, Alaska, earthquake of 1964 and aftershocks. Environmental Science Services Administration, U.S. Coast and Geodetic Survey. Washington: Government Printing Office, 1967. p. 7–217.
Studies vibrational damage and its related effects on buildings in Anchorage and vicinity and on the 14-story Hodge Building in Whittier. Develops useful information for the evaluation of design methods and practices and is the basis for a review of earthquake building-code provisions.

Stepp, J. C., W. A. Rinehart, and S. T. Algermissen. Earthquakes in the United States 1963-1964 and an evaluation of the detection capability of the United States seismograph stations. Final Report. [Rockville: U.S. Coast and Geodetic Survey], November 16, 1965. 235 p.
Gives probability of detecting an earthquake, with known hypocenter and magnitude, by at least five stations of the total network of seismograph stations. Seismicity based on earthquakes in the United States during 1963 and 1964 is presented.

Stimson, Thomas. They're bracing for California's overdue earthquake. *Popular Mechanics*, 122 (July 1964), 75–79, 184.
Because California is crisscrossed by a maze of earthquake faults, scientists have studied Alaska earthquake damage and are trying to make the state as earthquake-resistant as possible. Intensity of shaking of structures depends more on the kind of ground that a structure rests on than on its distance from the epicenter.

Tandon, A. N., and H. M. Chaudhury. Records of mantle Rayleigh waves at Delhi. *Indian Journal of Meteorology and Geophysics*, 16, No. 3 (1965), 395–410.
Long-period seismographs at Delhi recorded mantle Rayleigh waves from the great Alaska earthquake; periods as long as 600 seconds were clearly recorded for waves that had made 21 complete revolutions of the earth.

Tilgner, Edward E., and Jon R. Peterson. The Alaska Tsunami Warning System *in* Volume II-B,C: The Prince William Sound, Alaska, earthquake of 1964 and aftershocks. Environmental Science Services Administration, U.S. Coast and Geodetic Survey. Washington: Government Printing Office, 1969. p. 309–324.
Outlines the basic system concepts and describes instrumentation used in the initial installation of a tsunami warning system to provide adequate warning information to coastal communities in Alaska and to input data to the warning center at the Honolulu Observatory.

Tillotson, Ernest. The Alaska earthquake of March 28–30, 1964. *Nature*, 202 (April 25, 1964), 336.
Alaska must be considered a major seismic and volcanic zone of the earth (40 earthquakes were felt and recorded in Alaska in 1959). Depth of focus in the 1964 shock is considered shallow, and Richter magnitude shows it to be one of world's greatest earthquakes.

Tobin, Don G., and Lynn R. Sykes. Relationship of hypocenters of earthquakes to the geology of Alaska. *Journal of Geophysical Research*, 71 (March 15, 1966), 1659–1667.
Reports renewed interest in seismicity of Alaska since 1964 earthquake and contains results of 10-year study (before 1965) of relation of epicenters to geologic and tectonic features, such as island arcs, deep-sea trenches, and faults.

Tocher, Don. General introduction: Tectonics and seismic effects of the Alaska earthquake and the seismicity of Alaska *in* The Great Alaska Earthquake of 1964: Seismology and Geodesy. NAS Pub. 1602. Washington: National Academy of Sciences, 1972.
Discusses tectonics and the nature and the manner of assessing the seismic effects of the Alaska earthquake. Concludes that 17 percent of worldwide seismic energy release between 1953 and 1965 took place in the Aleutian–Alaskan arc and in interior Alaska.

Tocher, Don. The 1964 Alaska earthquake: Seismologic conclusions *in* The Great Alaska Earthquake of 1964: Seismology and Geodesy. NAS Pub. 1602. Washington: National Academy of Sciences, 1972.
Summarizes the lessons learned and presents the Panel's conclusions.

Toksöz, M. Nafi, and Don L. Anderson. Phase velocities of long-period surface waves and structure of the upper mantle [Part] 1: Great-circle Love and Rayleigh wave data. *Journal of Geophysical Research*, 71 (March 15, 1966), 1649–1658.
Measures phase velocities of mantle Love and Rayleigh waves from the Alaska earthquake and determines a structure for the upper mantle which satisfies the composite-path data.

Toksöz, M. Nafi, Ari Ben-Menahem, and David G. Harkrider. Source mechanism of Alaska earthquake from long-period seismic surface waves (Abstract). *Transactions, American Geophysical Union*, 46 (March 1965), 154.
Study of mantle Love and Rayleigh waves in 1964 earthquake reveal that rupture propagated with a velocity of 3 km/sec for 600 km in direction of S50° W. Preliminary results indicate double couple-type sources, a steeply dipping fault plane, and a motion with strike–slip and dip–slip components.

Townshend, John B., and William K. Cloud. Preliminary intensity evaluations of the Prince William Sound earthquake of March 28, 1964 *in* Science in Alaska: Proceedings Fifteenth Alaskan Science Conference, College, Alaska, August 31 to September 4, 1964. George Dahlgren, editor. College: Alaska Division American Association for the Advancement of Science, March 15, 1965. p. 233–238.
Explains the Modified Mercalli Intensity Scale, assigning an intensity of VII to the earthquake in Anchorage and Valdez (with a few exceptions).

Trainer, Frank W., and Roger M. Waller. Subsurface stratigraphy of glacial drift at Anchorage, Alaska *in* Geological Survey Research 1965: Short Papers in the Geological Sciences. U.S. Geological Survey Professional Paper 525-D. Washington: Government Printing Office, 1965. p. 167–174.
Glacial drift at Anchorage reaches a thickness greater than 500 ft. Disastrous slides during Alaska earthquake were caused by failure of a thick clay unit exposed in bluffs at Anchorage.

Tufty, Barbara. Our trembling earth. *Science News*, 90 (September 10, 1966), 178–179.
Describes stresses slowly built up in earth's crust until strain becomes enormous and rocks snap, as in Alaska earthquake. Gives statistics on other earthquakes and points out need for constant earthquake check.

Die Umschau über die Fortschritte in Wissenschaft und Technik. Die pazifische Erdbebenzone und das Beben von Alaska [The Pacific earthquake zone and the Alaska quake]. *Die Umschau über die Fortschritte in Wissenschaft und Technik*, 65 (October 15, 1965), 649–650.
Finds that the great Alaska earthquake shed further light on fault planes of the northeast Pacific earthquake belt. In the 2 months after the main shock, 12,000 additional small shocks were recorded. The tsunami reached Antarctica 22 hours after the main shock.

U.S. Coast and Geodetic Survey. Assistance and recovery, Alaska/1964: a report covering the activities of the U.S. Coast and Geodetic Survey in conjunction with the Prince William Sound, Alaska, earthquake of 1964 for the period March 27–December 31, 1964. Washington: U.S. Department of Commerce, 1965. 45 p.
Outlines progress made by the USC&GS in restoring technical foundation for reconstruction of Alaska during the 9 months after 1964 earthquake. Details the horizontal and vertical control surveys, gives the results of geodetic, gravity, and field surveys, and summarizes USC&GS ship reconnaissance.

U.S. Coast and Geodetic Survey. Coast and Geodetic Survey activities pertinent to the Alaska earthquake study. Washington: U.S. Coast and Geodetic Survey [1964]. 12 p.
Five portable seismograph stations were installed in Alaska less than 3 days after the March 1964 earthquake. Outlines photogrammetric, oceanographic, cartographic, and geodetic programs of the USC&GS.

U.S. Coast and Geodetic Survey. Report on tsunami warning system in operation during the Alaskan earthquake of March 27, 1964, and how it should be improved and recommendations for research in tsunami and earthquake forecasting. Washington: U.S. Coast and Geodetic Survey, 1964. 23 p.
Tsunami warning system functioned satisfactorily during the Alaska earthquake. Weather Bureau's warning service should also be used. System could be improved by conducting an extensive public education program, adding seismic equipment, and installing a separate warning system for Alaska.

U.S. Coast and Geodetic Survey. The Prince William Sound, Alaska, earthquake of 1964 and aftershocks. Fergus J. Wood, editor. Volume I: Operational phases of the Coast and Geodetic Survey program in Alaska for the period March 27 to December 31, 1964. Washington: Government Printing Office, 1966. 263 p.
Summarizes USC&GS operations in Alaska between March 27 and December 31, 1964. Contains an account of the seismic history and setting of the area, mobilization efforts to meet the disaster, summary of the 1964 field work in Alaska, and future plans.

U.S. Coast and Geodetic Survey. The Prince William Sound, Alaska, earthquake of 1964 and aftershocks. Fergus J. Wood, editor. Volume II-A: Research studies–Engineering seismology. Washington: Government Printing Office, 1967. 392 p.
Introduces engineering seismology or earthquake engineering of the earthquake and presents 8 other papers on building damage and landslides in Anchorage, oil storage tanks, the relation of microtremors to soils, strong-motion and building-period measurements, forced vibration measurements, and a structural-dynamic analysis of a 14-story building damaged by the earthquake.

U.S. Coast and Geodetic Survey. The Prince William Sound, Alaska earthquake of 1964 and aftershocks. Louis E. Leipold, editor-in-chief. Volume II-B,C: Research studies–Seismology and marine geology. Washington: Government Printing Office, 1969. 350 p.
Introduces seismological and marine geological studies of the earthquake. Part B on seismology contains 10 other papers on parameters of the main shock, foreshocks and aftershocks, focal mechanism, and tsunami and warning system studies. Part C on marine geology describes vertical crustal movements of the sea floor associated with the earthquake.

U.S. Coast and Geodetic Survey. The Prince William Sound, Alaska, earthquake of 1964 and aftershocks. Louis E. Leipold, editor-in-chief. Volume III: Research studies and interpretive results–Geodesy and photogrammetry. Washington: Government Printing Office, 1969. 161 p.
Contains an evaluation of the geodetic and photogrammetric surveys conducted after the earthquake. The topics of the 5 geodetic papers include gravity observations, vertical and horizontal displacements, strain analysis, and precise surveys in Anchorage. The photogrammetric paper reports 1965 and 1966 operations.

U.S. Coast and Geodetic Survey. Tsunami! The story of the Seismic Sea-Wave Warning System. U.S. Coast and Geodetic Survey Publication. Washington: Government Printing Office [1965]. 46 p.
Tsunami speed is determined solely by water depth; this makes it possible to forecast tsunami arrival times. Seismic Sea-Wave Warning System, started in 1948, gives early warning to all Pacific nations and thereby reduces tsunami casualties; however, a local warning network is still needed.

U.S. Coast Guard. [70 official incoming and outgoing messages between Coast Guard Light Station Cape Hinchinbrook and Coast Guard District 17, 28 March 1964 to 5 April 1964]. [Juneau: U.S. Coast Guard District 17, 1964]. 70 p. (Copy on file, Library, National Academy of Sciences–National Academy of Engineering, Washington, D.C.)
Messages reveal tremors felt at Cape Hinchinbrook Light Station during the week after the 1964 Alaska earthquake. These persistent tremors did only small damage to station buildings, but caused some consternation among personnel.

Utsu, Tokuji. Variations in spectra of P waves recorded at Canadian Arctic seismograph stations. *Canadian Journal of Earth Sciences*, 3 (October 1966), 597–621.
Analysis of *P* waves from seismograms of the Alaska earthquake recorded at four Canadian Arctic stations shows that the crust thins toward the Arctic.

Van Dorn, William G. Source mechanism of the tsunami of March 28, 1964 in Alaska. Proceedings of the Ninth Conference (1964) on Coastal Engineering (Chapter 10). New York: American Society of Civil Engineers, 1965. p. 166–190. Also *in* The Great Alaska Earthquake of 1964: Oceanography and Coastal Engineering. NAS Pub. 1605. Washington: National Academy of Sciences, 1972.
Tsunami from the Alaska earthquake was produced by a dipolar movement of the earth's crust. Preliminary calculations indicate that the initial positive phase contained about 2.3×10^{21} ergs of energy.

Varian Associates. Varian Associates reports...[report of microbarograph (Berkeley, California) recording of Alaska earthquake]. *Geotimes*, 10 (December 1965), 38.
Microbarograph located at Berkeley detected a drop in atmospheric pressure due to a ¼-in. rise in elevation.

Von Hake, Carl A., and William K. Cloud. United States earthquakes, 1964. Environmental Science Services Administration, U.S. Coast and Geodetic Survey. Washington: Government Printing Office, 1966. 91 p.
Report contains summary of earthquake activity in the United States for 1964. Maximum intensity of Alaska earthquake is given as IX–X. Through April 30, 19 aftershocks with magnitude of 6 or more were reported. Gives extensive eyewitness accounts, including those on direction of motion and duration of shock.

von Huene, Roland. Geologic structure of the continental margin *in* The Great Alaska Earthquake of 1964: Seismology and Geodesy. NAS Pub.1602. Washington: National Academy of Sciences, 1972.
Suggests that the 1964 earthquake may have occurred along the fault off Montague and Kodiak islands. The absence of an active large thrust fault in the Aleutian Trench strengthens the possibility that a near-vertical fault slipped during the Alaska earthquake.

von Huene, Roland. Seaquakes *in* The Great Alaska Earthquake of 1964: Oceanography and Coastal Engineering. NAS Pub. 1605. Washington: National Academy of Sciences, in press.
Seaquake is a shaking or other phenomenon related to an earthquake that is felt on vessels at sea. No rise of sea surface or submarine volcanic events were reported during Alaska earthquake; many aftershocks occurred seaward of Hinchinbrook Island, and the initial shock intensity off Kodiak Island was greater than in Prince William Sound.

von Huene, Roland. [Untitled notes of consulting geologist to U.S.

Coast Guard regarding his reconnaissance of Cape Hinchinbrook Light after the Alaska earthquake]. [China Lake, California: U.S. Naval Ordnance Test Station, 1966]. 14 p. (Copy on file, Library, National Academy of Sciences–National Academy of Engineering, Washington, D.C.)

Notes on the effects of the earthquake on Cape Hinchinbrook reveal that the men at the lighthouse had used binoculars for their observations and had not left the immediate lighthouse area to make inspections. The consultant decided that slides or fault slippage would not immediately endanger the station and personnel.

von Huene, Roland, Richard J. Malloy, George G. Shor, Jr., and Pierre St.-Amand. Geologic structures in the aftershock region of the 1964 Alaskan earthquake. *Journal of Geophysical Research, 72* (July 15, 1967), 3649–3660.

Seismic and echo sounder profiles in the aftershock region of the 1964 earthquake define a preexisting zone of discontinuous faults in the area of maximum aftershock strain release. An anticline at the continental margin with local large structural relief was also uplifted during this earthquake.

von Huene, Roland, and George G. Shor, Jr. The structure and tectonic history of the eastern Aleutian Trench. *Geological Society of America Bulletin,* 80 (October 1969), 1889–1902.

A sequence of pretrench deep oceanic sediments rests on the downwarped crust that forms the eastern Aleutian Trench. This trench appears to be younger than the central Aleutian Trench—a relation that helps explain the distribution of sediment along the two trench segments.

von Huene, Roland, George G. Shor, Jr., and Erk Reimnitz. Geological interpretation of seismic profiles in Prince William Sound, Alaska. *Geological Society of America Bulletin,* 78 (February 1967), 259–268.

Three rock units recognized in the seismic reflection profiles (Alaska, 1964) are ice-sculptured metamorphic basement, overlain by probable glacial drift, and Holocene marine sediments. The Holocene strata have been faulted, but only one fault has expression on the sea floor.

Vorhis, Robert C. Hydrologic effects of the earthquake of March 27, 1964, outside Alaska (*with sections on* Hydroseismograms from the Nunn-Bush Shoe Co. well, Wisconsin, by Elmer E. Rexin and Robert C. Vorhis *and* Alaska earthquake effects on groundwater in Iowa, by R. W. Coble). U.S. Geological Survey Professional Paper 544-C. Washington: Government Printing Office, 1967. 54 p. Also *in* The Great Alaska Earthquake of 1964: Hydrology. NAS Pub. 1603. Washington: National Academy of Sciences, 1968. p. 140–189.

Presents hydroseismic data obtained throughout most of the United States after the 1964 Alaska earthquake. The largest recorded seiche outside Alaska was 1.83 ft on a reservoir in Michigan; the largest fluctuation in a well was 23 ft, registered by a pressure recorder near Belle Fourche, South Dakota.

Walsh, John. Earthquake prediction: OST [Office of Science and Technology] panel recommends 10-year program. *Science,* 150 (October 15, 1965), 321–323.

Office of Science and Technology panel recommended a 10-year program (costing $137 million) of research to develop warning methods and minimize loss of life and property damage. The program is to emphasize improved instrumentation.

Whitten, Charles A. An evaluation of the geodetic and photogram-

metric surveys *in* Volume III: The Prince William Sound, Alaska, earthquake of 1964 and aftershocks. Environmental Science Services Administration, U.S. Coast and Geodetic Survey. Washington: Government Printing Office, 1969. p. 1–4. Also *in* The Great Alaska Earthquake of 1964: Seismology and Geodesy. NAS Pub. 1602. Washington: National Academy of Sciences, 1972.

Evaluates surveys made after the Prince William Sound earthquake and concludes that some postearthquake monitoring is essential for the future economic development of Anchorage.

Wiegel, Robert L. Earthquake engineering. Englewood Cliffs [New Jersey]: Prentice-Hall, Inc., 1970. 518 p.

Discusses man's knowledge of earthquakes, the causes and characteristics of elastic waves, ground motion, and tectonic displacement. Presents extensive material on damage, the structural performance of buildings, soil problems and behavior during an earthquake, and tsunamis. Applies modern methods of analysis to the design and construction of earthquake-resistant structures.

Willis, David E. Short-period teleseismic energy generated by Longshot (Abstract). *Transactions, American Geophysical Union,* 47 (March 1966), 165.

Three short-period seismograph stations in Michigan recorded Longshot (an underground nuclear device detonated at Amchitka in the Aleutians). Spectral comparisons are presented for aftershocks of the Alaska earthquake.

Wilson, Stanley D. Landslides in the city of Anchorage *in* Volume II-A: The Prince William Sound, Alaska, earthquake of 1964 and aftershocks. Environmental Science Services Administration, U.S. Coast and Geodetic Survey. Washington: Government Printing Office, 1967. p. 253–297.

Analyzes the five major landslides in the downtown and residential areas of Anchorage that accounted for a large part of the total earthquake damage in the area. Studies the landslides by field and laboratory investigations, and explains the results of the soil stability studies.

Wirth, Hans, and Lumir Skalský. Freie Schwingungen des Erdkörpers [Free oscillations of the earth (with English summary)]. *Gerlands Beiträge zur Geophysik* [Gerland's Contributions to Geophysics], 74, No. 3 (1965), 230–232.

Free oscillations of the earth after the Alaska earthquake were recorded by two horizontal pendulums in Břzové Hory station. Spectral analysis gave the periods of spheroidal and torsional modes $_nS_l$, $_nT_l$, where l goes from 1 to 25.

Wu, Francis T. The lower limit of total energy and partitioning of energy for three earthquakes (Abstract). *Transactions, American Geophysical Union,* 47 (March 1966), 163.

The free oscillation energy of the Alaska earthquake was calculated by using Isabella strain-seismometer data to estimate energy content at the low-frequency end of the spectrum.

Wyss, Max, and James N. Brune. The Alaska earthquake of 28 March 1964: A complex multiple rupture. *Bulletin of the Seismological Society of America,* 57 (October 1967), 1017–1023. Also *in* The Great Alaska Earthquake of 1964: Seismology and Geodesy. NAS Pub. 1602. Washington: National Academy of Sciences, 1972.

Seismograms of the Alaska earthquake are characterized by multiple *P*-phases not predicted by the travel-time curves. There is an average rupture velocity of 3.5 km/sec.

Young, Jessie M., Gary E. Greene, and Vernon H. Goerke. Air waves from the Alaskan earthquake of March 28, 1964 (Abstract). *Transactions, American Geophysical Union,* 46 (March 1965), 55. Traveling atmospheric pressure waves recorded at Washington, D.C., Boulder, and Boston were produced by ground motion at the epicentral region, surface-wave excitation at regions remote from epicenter, and surface-wave radiation near the receivers.

Zietz, Isidore. The mystery of earthquakes – where . . . when . . . what to do. *U.S. News & World Report,* 56 (April 13, 1964), 37–39. Building in earthquake areas requires special care and planning. Earthquakes also pose a danger to high dams. Energy in the Alaska earthquake was about a million times as great as that released by the Hiroshima and Nagasaki atomic bombs.

Contributors to
This Volume

KEIITI AKI, Massachusetts Institute of Technology, Cambridge, Massachusetts 02142

S. T. ALGERMISSEN, Environmental Research Laboratories, NOAA, Boulder, Colorado 80302

DAVID F. BARNES, U.S. Geological Survey, Menlo Park, California 94025

EDUARD BERG, University of Alaska, College, Alaska 99735

G. A. BOLLINGER, Virginia Polytechnic Institute, Blacksburg, Virginia 24061

SHELDON BREINER, GeoMetrics, 914 Industrial Avenue, Palo Alto, California 94303

JAMES N. BRUNE, University of California at San Diego, La Jolla, California 92037

WILLIAM K. CLOUD, University of California, Berkeley, California 94720

H. R. CRAVAT, National Ocean Survey, NOAA, Rockville, Maryland 20852

ROBERT G. CURRIE, University of California, Berkeley, California 94720

WILLIAM H. DILLINGER, Environmental Research Laboratories, NOAA, Boulder, Colorado 80302

AUGUSTINE S. FURUMOTO, University of Hawaii, Honolulu, Hawaii 96822

SAMUEL T. HARDING, Environmental Research Laboratories, NOAA, Boulder, Colorado 80302

L. M. HASTIE, Queensland Institute of Technology, Brisbane, Australia

JOAN HIRSHBERG, Stanford University, Stanford, California 94305

MINORU HORI, Earthquake Research Institute, University of Tokyo, Tokyo, Japan

DAVID JACKSON, University of California, Los Angeles, California 90024

HIROO KANAMORI, Earthquake Research Institute, University of Tokyo, Tokyo, Japan

LALATENDU MANSINHA, University of Western Ontario, London, Ontario, Canada

HIDETERU MATUMOTO, Earthquake Research Institute, University of Tokyo, Tokyo, Japan

TOSIMATU MATUMOTO, Lamont-Doherty Geological Observatory, Palisades, New York 10964

BUFORD K. MEADE, National Ocean Survey, NOAA, Rockville, Maryland 20852

GEORGE W. MOORE, U.S. Geological Survey, La Jolla, California 92037

ALI A. NOWROOZI, Lamont-Doherty Geological Observatory, Palisades, New York 10964

ROBERT A. PAGE, JR., U.S. Geological Survey, Menlo Park, California 94025

GEORGE PARARAS-CARAYANNIS, Coastal Engineering Research Center, Washington, D.C. 20016

ERNEST J. PARKIN, 1610 Palm Springs Drive, Vienna, Virginia 22180

GEORGE PLAFKER, U.S. Geological Survey, Menlo Park, California 94025

ALLEN J. POPE, National Ocean Survey, NOAA, Rockville, Maryland 20852

FRANK PRESS, Massachusetts Institute of Technology, Cambridge, Massachusetts 02142

DONALD A. RICE, National Ocean Survey, NOAA, Rockville, Maryland 20852

WILBUR A. RINEHART, Environmental Research Laboratories, NOAA, Boulder, Colorado 80302

RONALD V. ROW, Tower Road, Lincoln, Massachusetts 01773

JAMES C. SAVAGE, U.S. Geological Survey, Menlo Park, California 94025

NINA H. SCOTT, Seismological Field Survey, NOAA, San Francisco, California 94105

ROGER W. SHERBURNE, Pennsylvania State University, University Park, Pennsylvania 16802

JAMES B. SMALL, U.S. Coast and Geodetic Survey, Rockville, Maryland 20852 [deceased]

STEWART W. SMITH, University of Washington, Seattle, Washington 98105

DOUGLAS E. SMYLIE, University of British Columbia, Vancouver 8, British Columbia, Canada

V. RALPH SOBIERALSKI, 529 Lucerne Avenue, Tampa, Florida 33606

F. D. STACEY, University of Queensland, Brisbane, Australia

WILLIAM J. STAUDER, Saint Louis University, St. Louis, Missouri 63156

DON TOCHER, Earthquake Mechanism Laboratory, NOAA, San Francisco, California 94105

ROLAND E. VON HUENE, U.S. Geological Survey, Menlo Park, California 94025

P. WESTCOTT, Meteorological Office Research Unit, Cambridge, England

LAWRENCE C. WHARTON, 12918 Estelle Road, Silver Spring, Maryland 20906

CHARLES A. WHITTEN, National Ocean Survey, NOAA, Rockville, Maryland 20852

MAX WYSS, Lamont-Doherty Geological Observatory, Palisades, New York 10964

ENGLISH–METRIC CONVERSION TABLE

LENGTH

1 inch (in.)	=	2.54	centimeters (cm)
1 foot (ft) [12 in.]	=	30.48	cm
1 yard (yd) [3 ft]	=	91.44	cm
	=	0.914	meter (m)
1 mile (mi) [5280 ft]	=	1.610	kilometer (km)

AREA

1 square inch (in.^{2})	=	6.45	square centimeters (cm^2)
1 square foot (ft^2)	=	929.0	cm^2
	=	0.0929	square meter (m^2)
1 square yard (yd^2)	=	0.836	m^2
1 acre (a) [43560 ft^2]	=	0.4047	hectare (ha)
1 square mile (mi^2)	=	2.59	square kilometers (km^2)

VOLUME

1 cubic inch (in.^{3})	=	16.4	cubic centimeters (cm^3)
1 cubic foot (ft^3)	=	28.3	$\times 10^3$ cm^3
	=	0.0283	m^3
1 cubic yard (yd^3)	=	0.7646	cubic meter (m^3)
1 cubic mile (mi^3)	=	4.17	cubic kilometers (km^3)
1 quart (qt) [0.25 U.S. gallon (gal)]	=	0.95	liter
1 gal [4 qt]	=	3.79	liter
1 bushel (bu) [U.S. dry]	=	35.24	liter

MASS

1 pound (lb) [16 ounces (oz)]	=	453.6	grams (g)
	=	0.4536	kilogram (kg)
1 U.S. ton (tn) [2000 lb]	=	907.2	kg
	=	0.9072	metric ton (MT)
1 long ton (LT) [2240 lb]	=	1.016	MT

PRESSURE

1 pound per square inch (lb/in.^{2} or psi)	=	0.0704	kilogram per square centimeter (kg/cm^2)
1 pound per square foot (lb/ft^2)	=	4.8824	kilograms per square meter (kg/m^2)
1 bar [1000 millibars (mb)]	=	1.020	kg/cm^2

VELOCITY

1 foot per second (ft/s)	=	0.3048	meter per second (m/s)
	=	1.097	kilometer per hour (km/h)
	=	0.5925	international knot (kn)
1 mile per hour (mi/h)	=	1.609	km/h
	=	0.869	kn

METRIC–ENGLISH CONVERSION TABLE

LENGTH

1 millimeter (mm) [0.1 centimeter (cm)]	=	0.0394	inch (in.)
1 cm [10 mm]	=	0.3937	in.
1 meter (m) [100 cm]	=	39.37	in.
	=	3.28	feet (ft)
1 kilometer (km) [1000 m]	=	0.621	mile (mi)
1 international nautical mile [1852 m]	=	6076.1	ft

AREA

1 square centimeter (cm^2)	=	0.155	square inch ($in.^2$)
1 square meter (m^2)	=	10.76	square feet (ft^2)
	=	1.196	square yards (yd^2)
1 hectare (ha)	=	2.4710	acres (a)
1 square kilometer (km^2)	=	0.386	square mile (mi^2)

VOLUME

1 cubic centimeter (cm^3)	=	0.0610	cubic inch ($in.^3$)
1 cubic meter (m^3)	=	35.314	cubic feet (ft^3)
	=	1.31	cubic yards (yd^3)
1 cubic kilometer (km^3)	=	0.240	cubic mile (mi^3)
1 liter	=	1.06	quarts (qt)
	=	0.264	gallon (gal)

MASS

1 kilogram (kg) [1000 grams (g)]	=	2.20	pounds (lb)
	=	0.0011	ton
1 metric ton (MT) [1000 kg]	=	1.10	ton
	=	0.9842	long ton (LT)

PRESSURE

1 kilogram per square centimeter (kg/cm^2)	=	14.20	pounds per square inch ($lb/in.^2$)
	=	2048	pounds per square foot (lb/ft^2)

VELOCITY

1 meter per second (m/s)	=	3.281	feet per second (ft/s)
1 kilometer per hour (km/h)	=	0.9113	ft/s
	=	0.621	mile per hour (mi/h)
1 knot (kn) [1852 m/h]	=	1.6878	ft/s
	=	1.151	mi/h

Index

Figures in italic indicate major discussion of topic.